ANNUAL REVIEW OF PHYSIOLOGY

EDITORIAL COMMITTEE (1993)

Responsible for the organization of Volume 55
(Editorial Committee, 1991)

ANNUAL REVIEW OF PHYSIOLOGY

VOLUME 55, 1993

JOSEPH F. HOFFMAN, *Editor*

Yale University School of Medicine

PAUL De WEER, *Associate Editor*

University of Pennsylvania School of Medicine

ANNUAL REVIEW INC.   4139 EL CAMINO WAY,   P.O. BOX 10139   PALO ALTO, CALIFORNIA 94303-0897

ANNUAL REVIEWS INC.
Palo Alto, California, USA

International Standard Serial Number: 0066–4278
International Standard Book Number: 0–8243–0355-5
Library of Congress Catalog Card Number: 39-15404

♾ The paper used in this publication meets the minimum requirements of
American National Standard for Information Sciences—Permanence of Paper
for Printed Library Materials, ANSI Z39.48-1984.

Typesetting by Kachina Typesetting Inc., Tempe, Arizona; John Olson, President;
Jeannie Kaarle, Typesetting Coordinator; and by the Annual Reviews Inc. Editorial Staff

PRINTED AND BOUND IN THE UNITED STATES OF AMERICA

PREFACE

This preface begins with information about the current volume and ends with a brief discourse on the field called physiology. As with recent volumes of *Annual Review of Physiology*, the sections representing traditional subjects have been supplemented with special topics, which this year are Circadian Rhythms and Quantitative Light Microscopy. In both instances these sections bring advances in other fields to the attention of our readers, as well as complement material in the different sections. We again reaffirm to our readership that the ARP Editorial Committee welcomes comments and suggestions concerning its topics' coverage.

There is unrest in the community of physiologists because of the changing structure and content of its science. Those aspects that distinguish traditional disciplines (e.g. systems) are still in evidence, yet their borders are less distinct because of the rush and run of cellular and molecular biomedical science. Colleagues have expressed concern that the current pursuits of the reductionists veil if not obfuscate the importance and the interdisciplinary basis of the integrative biology that underlines whole animal physiology (see, for instance, References 1–3). As past prefaces have expressed, these anxieties while recurrent, are shared by the Editorial Committee of the ARP and are basic to their deliberation focused on the responsible coverage of our science. These notions are circumscribed within a recent definition of physiology (4) quoted below:

Physiology is the science of how living organisms function, from the smallest forms of life to multicellular organisms such as plants or animals. Since function is obligatorily coupled to structure, this interrelationship presents a principal focus at all levels of biological organization. Approaches that stem from physics and chemistry provide the format for analysis of cellular and subcellular processes in the service of function. Thus where general physiology may search for the "elemental condition for the phenomenon of life" for fundamental processes that may be common to all cells, comparative and mammalian physiology define the functioning of different systems and different organisms at varying levels of complexity.

Although Claude Bernard (1813–78) is known as the father of general physiology, Erasistratos (304–250?B.C.) is said to be the principal founder of physiological sciences and was evidently interested in applying physical laws to the study of functions in humans. Principles that apply at one level of organization have counterparts at another; for instance, understanding the mechanisms that govern the flow of ions, electricity, or fluid across cell membranes, that is, gradients in concentration, voltage, and pressure, underlie the basis, respectively, for water and electrolyte exchange between various body compartments, electrical signaling in the nervous system, and circulation through the heart and blood vascular system. Claude Bernard formulated the principle of the constancy of the internal environment (called homeostasis by Walter B. Cannon) that is illustrated by such integrated and controlled activities as in the adaptive responses of respiratory, contractile, and hormonal systems and in the set-points of blood pressure and body temperature. While it is clear that analysis of functional activity at the cellular and subcellular level is becoming increasingly more quantitative and molecular, it is also evident that there are functions that are only understandable at the integrated or whole animal level, such as preception, consciousness, exercise.

Physiology deals with the experimental analysis of normal processes in normal systems in contrast to pathophysiology that subserves medicine as attended by injury and disease. There is a clear reciprocity of fundamental insight that emerges from comparisons of normal and abnormal processes. The study of physiology lends understanding of life processes and provides us with profound opportunities to fulfill Paul's precept cited by William M. Bayliss, "Think of all, hold on to the beautiful."

JOSEPH F. HOFFMAN
EDITOR

1. Knobil, E., et al. 1990. What's past is prologue. *Physiologist* 33:161–80
2. Maddox, J. 1992. Is molecular biology yet a science? *Nature* 355:201
3. Hunt, C. 1992. Some issues of concern to physiologists. *Physiol. Soc. Mag.* (Oxford, U.K.) September Issue. pp. 20–21
4. Hoffman, J. F. 1992. Physiology. In *Academic Press Dictionary of Science and Technology,* ed. C. Morris, p. 1644. New York: Academic (Modified)

CONTENTS

viii   CONTENTS   (*Continued*)

OTHER REVIEWS OF INTEREST TO PHYSIOLOGISTS

From the *Annual Review of Biochemistry*, Volume 62 (1993):

Biochemistry of Nitric Oxide Formation, M. A. Marletta
Microtubule-Associated Motors, M. P. Sheetz
Endocytosis, I. Mellman
Biochemistry of Multidrug Resistance Mediated by the Multidrug Transporter,
   M. M. Gottesman
Control of Transcription by Cyclic AMP Receptor Protein, M. H. Buc, S. Adhya,
   S. Busby, S. Garges
Membrane-Anchored Growth Factors, J. Massagué, A. Pandiella
The Structure and Biosynthesis of Glycosyl Phosphatidylinositol Protein Anchors,
   P. T. Englund
Signalling by Receptor Tyrosine Kinases, W. J. Fantl, D. E. Johnson, L. Williams
Small G Proteins, D. Lowy
New Developments in Nerve Growth Factor Receptor, R. Bradshaw
Pathways of Protein Folding, C. R. Williams
Structural and Genetic Analysis of Protein Stability, B. W. Matthews

From the *Annual Review of Medicine*, Volume 44 (1993):

Physiologic Role of the Normal Pericardium, M. W. Watkins, M. M. LeWinter
*Role of Insulin Resistance in Human Disease (Syndrome X): An Expanded
   Definition*, G. M. Reaven
Serum Transferrin Receptor, J. D. Cook, B. S. Skikne, R. D. Baynes
Control of Brain Volume During Hyperosmolar and Hypoosmolar Conditions,
   S. R. Gullans, J. G. Verbalis
Cellular Mechanisms of Acute Ischemic Injury in the Kidney, M. Brezis,
   F. H. Epstein
Aging: Causes and Defenses, G. R. Martin, D. B. Danner, N. J. Holbrook
The Molecular Biology of Cystic Fibrosis, T. J. Sferra, F. S. Collins

From the *Annual Review of Neuroscience*, Volume 16 (1993):

Integrative Systems Research on the Brain: Resurgence and New Opportunities,
   T. Bullock
Genetic and Cellular Analysis of Behavior in C. elegans, C. Bargman
Neurotransmitter Transporters: Recent Progress, S. G. Amara, M. J. Kuhar
The Role of NMDA Receptors in Information Processing, N. W. Daw,
   P. S. G. Stein, K. Fox

Regulation of Ion Channel Distribution at Synapses, S. Froehner
Modeling of Neural Circuits: What Have We Learned? A. I. Selverston

From the *Annual Review of Nutrition,* Volume 12 (1992):

Vitamin A: Physiological and Biochemical Processing, R. Blomhoff, M. H. Green, K. R. Norum
Nutrient Transport Pathways Across the Epithelium of the Placenta, C. H. Smith, A. J. Moe, V. Ganapathy
Coordinated Multisite Regulation of Cellular Energy Metabolism, D. P. Jones, X. Shan, Y. Park
Iron-Dependent Regulation of Ferritin and Transferrin Receptor Expression by the Iron-Responsive Element Binding Protein, E. A. Leibold, B. Guo

From the *Annual Review of Pharmacology and Toxicology,* Volume 33 (1993):

Calmodulin in Neurotransmitter and Hormone Action, M. E. Gnegy
The Pharmacology of ATP-Sensitive Potassium Channels, A. H. Weston, G. Edwards
Covalent Modifications of G-Proteins, B. K. Fung

Silvio Weidmann

Annu. Rev. Physiol. 1993. 55:1–14

CARDIAC ACTION POTENTIALS, MEMBRANE CURRENTS, AND SOME PERSONAL REMINISCENCES

Silvio Weidmann

Physiological Institute, University of Berne, Buehlplatz 5, 3012 Berne, Switzerland

KEY WORDS: heart, electrophysiology, ions, sodium, potassium

INTRODUCTION

Newcomers tend to quote references of the past five years when publishing original work. Senior authors, on the other hand, have retained the work of 20 or 40 years ago, but often do not appreciate recent advances. While other articles in the Annual Reviews series are focused on recent developments, the prefatory chapters are written by people near the end of their careers. Depending on the wishes of the editors, a prefatory chapter may be for the most part biographical, featuring an interplay of the development of the author's field with personal involvement. Readers of this chapter must thus be aware that much emphasis is put on the past and that information becomes less and less complete as the year 1992 is approached.

The Change of Generations

Wilhelm Feldberg at Cambridge maintained that a change of generations proves beneficial to research: one generation accumulates money, and the next has a great deal of freedom in choosing where they will be trained and where they will accept appointments that are underpaid with respect to their value. Fortunately, my father belonged to the first generation. He exported the milk of Swiss, Dutch and Australian cows to the Far East and to Africa.

When entering the university in my home town I hesitated between studying physics and medicine and instead took a mixed course for one year. I never

1

0066–4278/93/0315-0001$02.00

felt at ease with mathematics and after a year of study, medicine seemed the best direction to take. I still belong to a group of individuals who have reasonably good intuition but are unable to describe results in terms of equations.

Alexander von Muralt was the director of Physiology from 1936 to 1968, and I did my undergraduate work with him. In the laboratory, I was fascinated by the spontaneous beat of the isolated frog's heart and often, instead of attending anatomy classes, kept one of the hearts and looked into all sorts of behavior that was not described in the laboratory manual. For example, I studied overdrive stimulation of the venous sinus, the post-stimulation rest, and the gradual resumption of activity. Knowing that emeritus Professor Leon Asher had once studied the "Electrosinogram" of the frog, I approached him to ask about writing a thesis under his guidance. His answer was convincing, "Everything has been done with the heart. Fundamental discoveries are now being made with nerves. Go and see Professor von Muralt." This I eventually did, with the result that I spent the better part of a year building a piece of equipment, an oscillographic polarograph. The method of synchronizing a sweep circuit by falling mercury drops eventually worked. But the biological investigation concerning the liberation of vitamin B1 from a nerve cross-section might as well have been carried out on the "slow" polarograph introduced by Heyrovsky (21). This is the typical outcome when people are enthusiastic about a new tool while a biological problem is their second concern.

Uppsala

One day in 1946 Torsten Teorell visited Berne. I was impressed by the interest he took in my work and by the questions he raised. Subsequently, I had a talk with my father. Fortunately, my parents had been conditioned by a friend of the family who had advised them, "The first years in a scientific career are the most decisive ones." I hoped to study with Teorell and to my joy he accepted me. After medical qualification and marriage to my wife Ruth, we set out in early 1947 for what became two summers and one winter in Sweden. We had a room in the attic of the Anatomy building and shared facilities and the scent of formaldehyde with three medical students working on their respective theses. This was the beginning of lasting friendships.

Physiology at Uppsala followed several directions. Teorell was interested in biological membranes and their selective permeabilities. Ernst Bárány studied the exchange of vitreous humor in the rabbit's eye. Karl-Johan Öbrink and Sven Linde looked at gastric secretion in Heidenhain and Pavlov pouches. Torbjörn Edlund and Håkan Linderholm studied transport across the synovial membrane of the rabbit's knee joint. Börje Löfgren measured electrical impedence of rabbit kidneys under various conditions of perfusion. I became familiar with the methods of measuring membrane potential, resistance, and reactance in *Nitella flexilis*, an excitable alga collected from a pond near Uppsala. Of my contributions as a plant physiologist, the one I like best, is the suggestion that the inductive element in membranes, as formally described by a coil (4), can more plausibly be explained as delayed rectification (48).

Cambridge

In my undergraduate days, on the suggestion of my teacher Alex von Muralt, I had read the original paper by Hodgkin (22) that contained strong evidence in favor of the electrical nature of impulse conduction (as against some sort of chemically mediated propagation). In 1947 at the first post-war IUPS Congress at Oxford, von Muralt listened to a preliminary account by Alan Hodgkin describing the Na-hypothesis of nerve activity. Since von Muralt hoped that one day I would come back to his laboratory, he enthusiastically recommended me to the Cambridge group. More effective, I suspect, was the support I received from Robert Stämpfli from Berne, who had started to work with Andrew Huxley on saltatory conduction in 1947.

In October 1948, upon my arrival at Cambridge, Alan Hodgkin handed over to me the first account (24) providing evidence for Na^+ as the carrier for inward-activating current in squid axons. I devoured this information in one weekend. Earlier in 1948, Hodgkin had visited the University of Chicago, where he had been introduced to the art of pulling and filling glass microelectrodes by Gilbert Ling. Ling & Gerard had penetrated single skeletal muscle fibers and directly measured resting potentials by means of a pH-meter (28). Hodgkin adapted the technique for the recording of fast events: (*a*) by filling the capillaries with 3 molar KCl, and (*b*) by making use of the cathode-follower principle to reduce input capacity. By Christmas 1948, Nastuk & Hodgkin had finished a paper that confirmed the correctness of the sodium hypothesis for frog skeletal muscle (31).

Hodgkin & Huxley were busy with the preparation of the 1949 squid season, and this gave me access to the microelectrode equipment. Hodgkin put me on the road by saying "Here is a powerful tool. Prod around in nature, but keep skeletal muscle reserved for me." The field was wide open. The chances for stable impalements seemed best with large cells that would not move. I recalled a description by Arvanitaki & Cardot (1) of *Aplysia* nerve cell bodies that reach several 100 μm in diameter. A number of animals arrived from the

Marine Biological Laboratory, Plymouth. The struggle lasted for two months, many electrode tips were broken, and there had been no successful penetration. If I had thought of removing the outer connective tissue sheath, my path into neurophysiology of the central nervous system would have opened.

Fate led me to a different organ. On July 19th, 1949, Wilhelm Feldberg demonstrated a Starling heart-lung preparation to a class of advanced physiology students. Subsequently, he allowed me to remove the dog's heart. The right ventricular wall was cut open and clamped to a microscope stage. A microelectrode was ready to be pushed against the inside of the wall. Before this heart had time to die, I could see a regular sequence of three or four action potentials. Hodgkin was enthusiastic about this possibility and remarked, "research grants will never be a problem for you in the future." How right he was! Edouard Coraboeuf, from the Sorbonne, had joined me for the summer of 1949. It was clear that we should select a cardiac preparation that would survive without the necessity of vascular perfusion (8), so we approached Inspector Turner of the Royal Society for the Prevention of Cruelty to Animals (RSPCA) for the use of dogs. He allowed us to put dogs to sleep by intraperitoneal Nembutal and made a sign to go ahead when he decided that the animal had died. Nobody yet has criticized the fact that all the data published in 1951 by Draper & Weidmann (12) are from old dogs, close to their natural death.

Robert Comline and his associates in veterinary physiology at Cambridge used new-born goats to study intestinal absorption. As soon as Comline had collected the various juices he needed, we took over the hearts. My teacher in pathology, when examining human hearts, had made a point in distinguishing between true tendons and false tendons. The latter appear more grayish and contain elements of the conductive system. However, the false tendons of kid hearts hardly move. They contain single fibers (strands of cells) that can be outlined easily under the microscope. Microelectrode tips meet little resistance when pushed through connective tissue, much less so than when penetrating the tougher false tendons of adult animals. Again, we could depend on a regular supply of biological material without having to worry about maintaining animal quarters.

If ever I discovered something accidentally, it was the phenomenon of all-or-nothing (and propagated) repolarization. With no thought of what to expect, I injected square pulses of constant current into kid Purkinje fibers by means of a second micro-pipette. When the strength of the repolarizing current was increased in a stepwise manner, a threshold was revealed. With small hyperpolarizations, the break of the pulse was followed by a return of the potential to the plateau; with increasing repolarization the membrane potential took an unexpected course towards its resting level; activity was in some manner interrupted and the interruption was propagated (49). This finding fits in with the general concept that the cardiac action potential can be accounted for by voltage- and time-dependent changes of ionic permeabilities.

While at Cambridge working with kid Purkinje fibers, I put Engelmann's concept of cardiac muscle as a functional syncytium (16) on a quantitative basis. The arguments are (50) that, with a cell length of about 80 μm and with five to eight cells on a cross-section of a fiber, the space constant (2 mm) and the resistivity of the internal conductor calculated from cable analysis (two to four times that of Tyrode solution) are compatible with a low cell-to-cell resistance, but incompatible with cells isolated from one another. This issue has remained under friendly discussion for more than twenty years, with Nick Sperelakis in the role of my major opponent. The question has recently been re-assessed in a two-volume book (44), for which I had the honor of writing a Foreword.

To follow Hodgkin & Huxley while getting ready for their expeditions to Plymouth, to look over their shoulders while working there, and to listen to their discussions on how far they should stick out their necks in attaching a physical meaning to their formalism (23) were invaluable lessons for me.

Cardiac Electrophysiology in the 1950s

A meeting held at the New York Academy of Sciences in 1956 and a Symposium held at the IUPS Congress at Leiden in 1962 provide a clue to major advances of the 1950s. The immediate goal of a number of groups was to characterize the cardiac action potential in terms of conductivity changes to various ions, by drawing on the experience gained by the Cambridge group with squid axon. Depolarization in analogy to squid nerve was explained by the influx of Na ions down their electrochemical gradient (12). The long-lasting plateau in the heart could not easily be accounted for by manipulating parameters of the squid axon membrane. Part of the solution was reached independently in 1960 by three groups (3, 5, 25). The level of the plateau between the K^+- and the Na^+-equilibrium potential, together with the high membrane resistance during the long-lasting plateau, required a K^+ conductance to drop during depolarization rather than to rise (as in the squid axon). Denis Noble presented a model in which only Na^+- and K^+-conductance were manipulated in a voltage- and time-dependent way (34). The model action potential resembled a recorded Purkinje fiber action potential in many details. In fact the successful modeling must have prevented many of us from thinking of additional ionic currents.

The 1960s and 1970s

Early hints pointing to a second inward current (besides Na^+) came from splitting the monophasic action potential, under special conditions, into a spike followed by a second elevation (dome). Moreover, in a perfusate containing less than 10% of the normal sodium, mammalian ventricular muscle showed an action potential of a practically normal length (7, 10). Also, it had been known since 1906 that a heart in a Ca-free solution does not contract, but is still active electrically (29). In 1966, Reuter (40) applied depolarizing pulses of direct current to Purkinje fibers in a Na-free solution and found a Ca_o-sensitive upswing of membrane potential beyond the range of 30–40 mV, inside negative. Independently, Niedergerke & Orkand (33), working with frog hearts driven at a very slow rate, found a quantitative correlation between $[Ca^{2+}]_o$ and action potential overshoot. A reasonable way to account for cardiac depolarization was suggested in 1969 (42): inward current with rapid activation/inactivation kinetics (Na^+) brings the membrane to its plateau level and turns on a second inward current with slower kinetics, which is normally carried by Ca ions but may, in the absence of calcium, be carried by Na ions.

A new method, which came into general use in the 1960s, was voltage clamping (9). Instead of allowing a cardiac action potential to take its free course, the potential difference of the membrane is stepped to pre-determined values and current is recorded as a function of time. An attempt is then made to look at the effect of ionic substitutions in order to "dissect" the total membrane current into its components. When used with multicellular preparations, this clamp method has several disadvantages (19, 26): (a) a temporal resolution of strong currents (Na^+) is impossible, (b) spatial uniformity of the clamp potential is never ideal, (c) accumulation/depletion of ions in the interspace may seriously affect interpretations, and (d) too often it would be difficult to distinguish between an inward current decreasing and an outward current increasing with time. Yet this now old-fashioned method gave results and raised new questions. Beeler & Reuter used the method to establish the time course of the Ca^{2+} inward current and in 1977 (2) proposed a quantitative description of the ventricular action potential in terms of Na^+-, Ca^{2+}- and K^+-currents.

Brooklyn, New York, 1954/55

Upon my return from Cambridge to Berne, I was fortunate to be given a relatively small teaching load. However, von Muralt insisted that a physiologist should be ready, on short notice, to give lectures on any subject in the field. Thus it was not too complicated for the Institute in Berne when I accepted an invitation to join the Downstate Medical College of New York State University for the academic year 1954/55. The chairman, Chandler Brooks, was the prototype of the father of a department. The dynamic figures were Brian Hoffman & Paul Cranefield. The former was bursting with energy to explore the heart. The latter was more inclined to criticism. During an exploratory visit (1953), I had seen that there would be practically no equipment for me to work with. Consequently, I had two racks of equipment shipped across the Atlantic, and I was able to begin work exactly one week after arrival.

The strength of Na^+ inward current as a function of resting (holding) potential was one of my concerns. Inward current was measured as upstroke velocity (v'_{max}) in the course of a propagating action potential. When plotted against the holding potential, this produced the so-called availability curve (h_∞ curve). There has been much discussion (and there still is) on the question of whether v'_{max} closely reflects Na inward current. I knew quite well in 1955 (51) that proportionality between v'_{max} and maximal inward current cannot be expected. Thus I wrote that "dv/dt_{max} can be taken as a measure for Na influx." But I now regret that I was not more outspoken at the time. Voltage clamps record the time course of activation/inactivation of Na^+ current when the membrane is depolarized, e.g. to -20 mV, from different holding levels. Inward current is then plotted against the holding level. With a free-running action potential, there is no way to know to what degree the channels have been activated at the moment of maximal dv/dt. Furthermore, in the case of propagated action potentials, sodium current is still rising beyond the inflection point in the upstroke of the action potential (see Figure 18 in Reference 23), and there is no theoretical reason to assume direct proportionality between V_{max} and maximal inward clamp current, both as functions of holding potential.

Since I used the technique of taking h_∞ curves, and since the physiology course in Brooklyn included pharmacology, I felt obliged to look at the effect of two anti-arrhythmic agents, quinidine and procaine amide. Both shifted the Na^+ availability curve to more negative values of membrane potential, an effect that would account for the decrease of excitability (52). Another so-called stabilizing agent, calcium ions, brought about a shift to less negative membrane potentials. This shift was uncomfortably small (6 mV with four times the normal Ca^{2+}), and I felt much relieved when Frankenhäuser & Hodgkin found a similar shift of the h_∞ curve for the squid axon (17).

In the spring of 1955 Hans Hecht and his colleagues at the University of Utah showed me how to use flexibly mounted tips of microelectrodes that would record from strongly moving preparations. Walter Wilde at Tulane University taught me to cannulate the (single) coronary artery of a turtle's heart. Using these methods, I could show that, when KCl in the perfusate is increased for a short while during the early part of the action potential, the result is a premature repolarization, contrary to expectations based on an estimate of the reduced outward driving force on K^+ (53). Since during undisturbed activity K ions were supposed to leave the fibers, K^+ accumulation within the interspace would, in principle, assist repolarization. Quantitative reasoning, however, seemed to exclude this as the main mechanism for repolarization.

The Cloister

When I reached 65, the retirement age at Berne University, Wolfgang Trautwein very frankly remarked to my wife, "Silvio had a rapid and excellent start, but he never learned to interact with colleagues, and this slowed him down in later years." André Kléber came out with an expression ("the cloister") that characterized our Institute rather well, "The monks use to meet for discussions in the cross-walks, and subsequently disappear, every one of them into his own cell." According to Harald Reuter, I left junior members of the Institute to struggle largely on their own. Although this was somewhat cruel and costly, it was, after all, a safe method of finding out who would succeed in the long run. Every beginner, I believe, got a worthwhile problem, often one I had looked at before in a preliminary way. It was part of my policy not to add my own name to papers unless I had contributed with my own hands at the micromanipulators. (This had been the case in the work by Earl Wood and by Gerhard Giebisch, 57, 19). Before about 1970 there was practically no hope, even for excellent people, to get a stable position in Swiss academic physiology departments. I therefore recruited MDs, who would promise that they saw their future in a clinical discipline. Alternatively, I filled positions with foreigners on a time-limited basis. Looking back on the 1960s and 1970s, I believe most of the worthwhile research was done by the numerous people from abroad.

Starting in about 1960, the number of medical students steadily grew. By reducing the admission of foreign students, we had the means to keep the total student population within limits. By 1970 the faculty brought the admission of foreigners to a complete stop, but the number of Swiss applicants continued to rise, and the political authorities throughout the country were faced with two alternatives— either to introduce a numerus clausus or to increase, in a massive way, the number of permanent teaching positions. Thanks to various factors including a promise of financial aid by the central government, the entrance door stayed open. We had no further inhibitions in recommending physiology as a career. Before being promoted to a tenured position, a colleague had to spend one or two years abroad. In this way, we were either reassured in our predictions, or we were warned in time. Among those who stayed are Paul Müller, Robert Weingart, André Kléber, Jürg Streit, and Ernst Niggli.

Becoming an Administrator

Alex von Muralt had been greatly involved in creating (1952) the Swiss National Science Foundation, an ever-growing enterprise that he presided over until 1968. By 1958 he wished to share teaching obligations. We took turns lecturing, each of us still covering the whole field of physiology. While I did not dislike this, it took away much of the time needed to devote to my experiments. On evening walks with my dog, instead of wondering why the membrane resistance is high during the plateau phase, I figured out how to re-organize the Department. Between 1957 and 1970 my entire output consisted of two original papers (54, 55). After 1970 (I was approaching 50 years of age then), there was practically no original work. Of course there was a sufficient amount of "after-discharge" in the way of reviews, symposium contributions, and obituaries to keep my bibliography growing. However, one only gets good ideas to be handed on to colleagues as long as one does experiments with one's own hands. Fortunately, this function of recognizing problems was taken over by the more experienced people in the Institute.

The medical faculty spared me a midlife crisis by nominating me for the rectorship of the University for the year 1974/75, which meant that I had administrative tasks between 1973 and 1976. Student unrest, which had surfaced elsewhere by 1968, reached Berne with a typical time-lag. My predecessors had wishfully thought that problems between the official Students' Union and the establishment would take care of themselves as time elapsed. This was not so, and my competence was strained to the limit by having to sign several expulsions in an attempt to avoid further damage. Most painful were the discussions with a minority of my own colleagues, who sought the salvation of their university on the side of leaders of the student opposition.

Puerto Rico

After the storms in the "Rektorat", I was granted a sabbatical leave for the winter term 1976/77, which I took in Puerto Rico. During that time my wife and our youngest son went to school to learn Spanish, while I shuttled between Centro Medico at Rio Piedras and San Juan, attempting to do some electrophysiology on the highly toxic Palytoxin in the laboratory of Walmor Carlos DeMello. That stay was a lesson in the importance of a well-staffed workshop. There was apparently much money in Puerto Rico to import ready-made equipment, but there was nobody able to drill a hole into a piece of Perspex. The newly elected Associate Dean of Medical Sciences, Sven Ebbesson, went around the corridors and discovered much of equipment in its original packaging. Those who had placed the orders had disappeared in the meantime.

From Heart to Myocytes and Membrane Channels

In the late 1970s methods were elaborated to isolate single cells by mild enymatic digestion, and to record from their inside by patch electrodes (20, 27, 37). Methods were also found to record current through single channels (32) or through patches of surface membrane isolated from the rest of the cell (20). With membrane patches in intimate contact with the glass of the electrode tip, there is practically no leak between the inside of the electrode and the bath, and the only pathway for current is through protein channels spanning the lipid bilayer (20). The ionic composition of solutions both inside the pipette and within the bath can be chosen, and channels are characterized by their ion specificity, their unitary conductance, their open-probability at various membrane potentials, and their lateral spacing. Harald Reuter, who had made a quick move towards single cells, one day invited me to stop by his Institute (Pharmacology) and be taught the technique, which he assured me, would be much easier than the previous methods of voltage clamping. I was hesitant, figuring that many groups of competent people had turned to single channels and decided to abstain. At that point I had clearly missed the boat and was left to follow a truly exciting development in cell physiology in a passive role; on the editorial board of the *Journal of Physiology* (1985–1992).

A Look at the Inside of Cardiac Cells

In the early days we had the means to measure the membrane potential, to estimate intracellular ionic concentrations, and to measure unidirectional ionic flux by means of isotopes. Ion-specific electrodes were designed that translated the activity of certain intracellular ions into potential difference and allowed concentration changes to be followed in the course of an intervention. In the case of H^+, Na^+, Cl^-, and Mg^{2+}, the results obtained are satisfactory, although the methods are cumbersome and the temporal resolution is not good enough to follow changes during a single action potential. In the case of calcium, luminescence of intracellular aequorin allowed the course of intracellular Ca^{2+} activity to be established and correlated with the action potential and with contraction (56).

With single cells and patch electrodes, the composition of the intracellular fluid can be controlled. The volume of a pipette is much larger than that of a cell, and diffusion is a rapid process at those dimensions. Some skillful Japanese investigators (27, 36, 47) have even achieved a change of intracellular test solutions by perfusion of the patch pipette with different solutions, a method of high promise for the investigation of cell biochemistry and its effect on ionic channels.

How Far Have We Come?

Over the years, one of our main aims has been to account for the time course of the cardiac action potential in terms of ionic currents. The early view that any change of membrane potential depends on the displacement of charge (capacity current, membrane current) has retained its validity. The notion that passive membrane current is a function of driving forces and permeabilities for the various participants still seems to hold. Ionic gradients can be looked upon as a form of stored energy. If in the long run the gradients have to be kept, it becomes inevitable that downhill movements have to be reversed. There is good reason to assume an energy-consuming outward movement of Na^+ coupled to an inward movement of K^+ with a coupling ratio of about $3Na^+$ to $2K^+$ (18). Being electrogenic, this pump would deliver outward current, and thus assist repolarization.

Extrusion of Ca^{2+} has long been a puzzle. Inward Ca^{2+} current necessary for the plateau is remarkably strong, and much Ca^{2+} will consequently have to leave the fibers before the beginning of the next cycle of activity. In 1968, Reuter & Seitz (41) recognized the significance of extracellular Na concentration for driving the efflux of labeled Ca^{2+}. Mullins, in 1979, assumed this coupled exchanger to be electrogenic in the sense that Ca^{2+} efflux would require the influx of an excess of charge carried by Na^+ (30). After the first part of a ventricular action potential, at a high level of intracellular Ca^{2+} activity, the exchanger would extrude Ca^{2+}, thereby contributing inward current and tending to hold the plateau. At the same time, it would provide for a decreasing Ca^{2+} activity and thereby assist repolarization (14, 15, 35). Contrary to traditional thinking, Ca^{2+} activity seems to be back to very low levels at the end of repolarization (14, 46).

Continued research—as is usual—has led to a picture of increasing complexity. Instead of one channel type per participating ion species, there are now several that are distinguishable by their behavior: at least two for Na+ (see 6), two for Ca2+ (13), and two for K+ (43, 45, 58). Additional components are known, some of them with less ion specificity, others appearing under non-physiological conditions. There is, indeed, a choice of downhill currents, exchange processes, and pumps from which to construct a cardiac action potential of almost any shape (11, 38, 39).

To end this chapter, let me ask "what is typical in the life of a physiologist?" Physiologists have an intimate relationship to what they are doing. We often have periods of no progress. Sometimes we have to abandon a road that we have been following for months or years. But we also have moments of success, however small and partial. When we approach retirement, we still see a variety of things to be done and, provided we are well-behaved towards our colleagues, there will be some degree of affiliation or contact as long as we feel the need.

Literature Cited

1. Arvanitaki, A., Cardot, H. 1941. Observations sur la constitution des ganglions et conducteurs nerveux et sur l'isolement du soma neuronique vivant chez les mollusques gastropodes. *Bull. Histol. Techn. Micro.* 18:133–44

2. Beeler, G. W., Reuter, H. 1977. Reconstruction of the action potential of ventricular myocardial fibres. *J. Physiol.* 268:177–210

3. Brady, A. J., Woodbury, J. W. 1960. The sodium-potassium hypothesis as the basis of electrical activity in frog ventricle. *J. Physiol.* 154:385–407

4. Cole, K. S. 1941. Rectification and inductance in the squid giant axon. *J. Gen. Physiol.* 25:29–51

5. Coraboeuf, E. 1960. Aspects cellulaires de l'électrogenèse cardiaque chez les vertébrés. *J. Physiol. (Paris)* 52:323–414

6. Coraboeuf, E., Deroubaix, E., Coulombe, A. 1979. Effect of tetrodotoxin on action potentials of the conducting system in the dog heart. *Am. J. Physiol.* 236:H561–67

7. Coraboeuf, E., Otsuka, M. 1956. L'action des solutions hyposodiques sur les potentiels cellulaires de tissu cardiaque de mammifères. *C. R. Acad. Sci. Paris* 243:441–44

8. Coraboeuf, E., Weidmann, S. 1949. Potentiels d'action du muscle cardiaque obtenus à l'aide de microélectrodes intracellulaires. Présence d'une inversion de potentiel. *C. R. Soc. Biol. Paris* 143:1360–61

9. Deck, K. A., Kern, R., Trautwein, W. 1964. Voltage clamp technique in mammalian cardiac fibres. *Pflügers Arch.* 280:50–62

10. Délèze, J. 1959. Perfusion of a strip of mammalian ventricle. Effects of K-rich and Na-deficient solutions on transmembrane potentials. *Circ. Res.* 7:461–65

11. DiFrancesco, D., Noble, D. 1985. A model of cardiac electrical activity incorporating ionic pumps and concentration changes. *Philos. Trans. R. Soc. London Ser. B* 307:353–98

12. Draper, M. H., Weidmann, S. 1951. Cardiac resting and action potentials recorded with an intracellular electrode. *J. Physiol.* 115:74–94

13. Droogmans, G., Nilius, B. 1989. Kinetic properties of the cardiac T-type calcium channel in the guinea-pig. *J. Physiol.* 419:627–50

14. Egan, T. M., Noble, D., Noble, S. J., Powell, T., Spindler, A. J., Twist, V. W. 1989. Sodium-calcium exchange during the action potential in guinea-pig ventricular cells. *J. Physiol.* 411:639–61

15. Ehara, T., Matsuoka, S., Noma, A. 1989. Measurement of reversal potential of Na^+-Ca^{2+} exchange current in single guinea-pig ventricular cells. *J. Physiol.* 410:227–49

16. Engelmann, T. W. 1875. Über die Leitung der Erregung im Herzmuskel. *Pflügers Arch.* 11:465–80

17. Frankenhäuser, B., Hodgkin, A. L. 1957. The action of calcium on the electrical properties of squid axons. *J. Physiol.* 137:218–44

18. Gadsby, D. C., Nakao, M. 1989. Steady-state current-voltage relationship of the Na/K pump in guinea pig ventricular myocytes. *J. Gen. Physiol.* 94:511–37

19. Giebisch, G., Weidmann, S. 1971. Membrane currents in mammalian ventricular heart muscle fibers using a voltage-clamp technique. *J. Gen. Physiol.* 57:290–96

20. Hamill, O. P., Marty, A., Neher, E., Sakmann, B., Sigworth, F. J. 1981. Improved patch-clamp techniques for high-resolution current recording from cells and cell-free membrane patches. *Pflügers Arch.* 391:85–100

21. Heyrovsky, J. 1941. Polarographie. *Theoretische Grundlagen, praktische Ausführungen und Anwendungen der*

Elektrolyse mit der tropfenden Queck-silberelektrode. Wien: Springer-Verlag. 541 pp.

22. Hodgkin, A. L. 1939. Evidence for electrical transmission in nerve. Parts 1 and 2. *J. Physiol.* 90:183–210

23. Hodgkin, A. L., Huxley, A. F. 1952. A quantitative description of membrane current and its application to conduction and excitation in nerve. *J. Physiol.* 117:500–44

24. Hodgkin, A. L., Katz, B. 1949. The effects of sodium ions on the electrical activity of the giant axon of the squid. *J. Physiol.* 108:37–77

25. Hutter, O. F., Noble, D. 1960. Rectifying properties of heart muscle. *Nature* 188:495

26. Johnson, E. A., Lieberman, M. 1971. Heart: Excitation and contraction. *Annu. Rev. Physiol.* 33:479–532

27. Lee, K. S., Weeks, T. A., Kao, R. L., Akaike, N., Brown, A. M. 1979. Sodium current in single heart muscle cells. *Nature* 278:269–71

28. Ling, G., Gerard, R. W. 1949. The normal membrane potential of frog sartorius fibers. *J. Cell. Comp. Physiol.* 34:383–96

29. Locke, F. S., Rosenheim, O. 1907. Contribution to the physiology of the isolated heart. The consumption of dextrose by mammalian cardiac muscle. *J. Physiol.* 36:205–20

30. Mullins, L. J. 1979. The generation of electric currents in cardiac fibers by Na/Ca exchange. *Am. J. Physiol.* 236: C103–10

31. Nastuk, W. L., Hodgkin, A. L. 1950. The electrical activity of single muscle fibers. *J. Cell. Comp. Physiol.* 35:39–73

32. Neher, E., Sakmann, B. 1976. Single-channel currents recorded from membrane of denervated frog muscle fibres. *Nature* 260:799–803

33. Niedergerke, R., Orkand, R. K. 1966. The dual effect of calcium on the action potential of the frog's heart. *J. Physiol.* 184:291–311

34. Noble, D. 1962. A modification of the Hodgkin-Huxley equations applicable to Purkinje fibre action and pacemaker potentials. *J. Physiol.* 160: 317–52

35. Noble, D. 1984. The surprising heart: a review of recent progress in cardiac electrophysiology. *J. Physiol.* 353:1–50

36. Ono, K., Trautwein, W. 1991. Potentiation by cyclic GMP of β-adrenergic effect on Ca^{2+} current in guinea-pig

ventricular cells. *J. Physiol.* 443:387–404

37. Powell, T., Terrar, D. A. Twist, V. W. 1980. Electrical properties of individual cells isolated from adult rat ventricular myocardium. *J. Physiol.* 302:131–53

38. Rasmusson, R. L., Clark, J. W., Giles, W. R., Robinson, K., Clark, R. B., et al. 1990. A mathematical model of electrophysiological activity in a bull-frog atrial cell. *Am. J. Physiol.* 259: H370–89

39. Rasmusson, R. L., Clark, J. W., Giles, W. R., Shibata, E. F., Campbell, D. L. 1990. A mathematical model of a bullfrog cardiac pacemaker cell. *Am. J. Physiol.* 259:H352–69

40. Reuter, H. 1966. Strom-Spannuns-beziehungen von Purkinje-Fasern bei verschiedenen extracellulären Calcium-Konzentrationen und unter Adrenalineinwirkung. *Pflügers Arch.* 287: 357–67

41. Reuter, H., Seitz, N. 1968. The dependence of calcium efflux from cardiac muscle on temperature and external ion composition. *J. Physiol.* 195:451–70

42. Rougier, O., Vassort, G., Garnier, D., Gargouïl, Y.-M., Coraboeuf, E. 1969. Existence and role of a slow muscle inward current during the frog atrial action potential. *Pflügers Arch.* 308: 91–110

43. Sakmann B., Noma, A., Trautwein, W. 1983. Acetylcholine activation of single muscarinic K^+ channels in isolated pacemaker cells of the mammalian heart. *Nature* 303:250–53

44. Sperelakis, N., Cole, W. C. 1989. *Cell Interactions and Gap Junctions,* Boca Raton, FL: CRC Press. Vol.I:247 pp.; Vol.II:283 pp.

45. Shimoni, Y., Clark, R. B., Giles, W. R. 1992. Role of inwardly rectifying potassium current in rabbit ventricular action potential. *J. Physiol.* 448:709–27

46. Simurda, J., Simurdová, M., Braveny, P., Sumbera, J. 1992. Contraction-related component of slow inward current in dog ventricular muscle. Relation to Na/Ca exchange. *J. Physiol.* In press

47. Soejima, M., Noma, A. 1984. Mode of regulation of ACh-sensitive K-channel by muscarinic receptor in rabbit atrial cells. *Pflügers Arch.* 400: 424–31

48. Weidmann, S. 1950. Die Natur des induktiven Elements in biologischen Membranen. *Experientia* 6:53–54

49. Weidmann, S. 1951. Effect of current

flow on the membrane potential of cardiac muscle. *J. Physiol.* 115:227–36

50. Weidmann, S. 1952. The electrical constants of Purkinje fibres. *J. Physiol.* 118:348–60

51. Weidmann, S. 1955. The effect of the cardiac membrane potential on the rapid availability of the sodium-carrying system. *J. Physiol.* 127:213–24

52. Weidmann, S. 1955b. Effects of calcium ions and local anaesthetics on electrical properties of Purkinje fibres. *J. Physiol.* 129:568–82

53. Weidmann, S. 1956. Shortening of the cardiac action potential due to a brief injection of KCl following the onset of activity. *J. Physiol.* 132:157–63

54. Weidmann, S. 1966. The diffusion of radiopotassium across intercalated disks of mammalian cardiac muscle. *J. Physiol.* 187:323–42

55. Weidmann, S. 1970. Electrical constants of trabecular muscle from mammalian heart. *J. Physiol.* 210:1041–54

56. Wier, W. G., Hess, P. 1984. Excitation-contraction coupling in cardiac Purkinje fibers. Effects of cardiotonic steroids on the intracellular $[Ca^{2+}]$ transient, membrane potential, and contraction. *J. Gen. Physiol.* 83:395–415

57. Wood, E. H., Heppner, R. L., Weidmann, S. 1969. Inotropic effects of electric currents. I. Positive and negative effects of constant electric currents or current pulses applied during cardiac action potentials. II. Hypotheses: Calcium movements, excitation-contraction coupling and inotropic effects. *Circ. Res.* 24:409–45

58. Yazawa, K., Kameyama, M. 1990. Mechanism of receptor-mediated modulation of the delayed outward potassium current in guinea-pig ventricular myocytes. *J. Physiol.* 421:135–50

Colin S. Pittendrigh

Annu. Rev. Physiol. 1993. 55:17–54

TEMPORAL ORGANIZATION:
Reflections of a Darwinian
Clock-Watcher

Colin S. Pittendrigh

Harold A. Miller Professor of Biology, Emeritus, Director of the Hopkins Marine Station, Emeritus, Stanford University, Stanford, California 94305

DARWINIAN SPECTACLES

A Broken Window Leads to Darwin

This essay was prompted by the Editor's invitation to illustrate the excitement and adventure inherent in scientific work while reflecting on my own preoccupation, as an evolutionary biologist, with biological clocks. In considering the challenge, the first adventure that came to mind occurred one evening 30 years ago when a drunken graduate student, frustrated by an unwanted experimental result, attempted to throw me out of a second story window in Princeton. He didn't succeed. That seemed a good Indiana Jones start, but nothing as exciting occurred in later years, and all the adventures I can recount are less spectacular—the excitement of experiment and the hazardous fate of observation and ideas in the pursuit of understanding.

While circadian periodicities have been the immediate object of my research for 40 years, that "view of life," which Darwin so eloquently summarized in the last paragraph of "The Origin of Species," has so dominated and guided my approach that it gets substantial attention in these reflections and hopefully ties together much of what I have to say about biological clocks. This Darwinian approach to behavioral and physiological interests traces to the accidental way I became a biologist.

At 15 I kicked a soccer ball through a very large window in the Town Hall where I lived in the north of England. The only foreseeable source of the 13 shillings needed to replace it was a prize offered to local Boy Scouts for the best wild flower collection. In winning that prize, I got more money than was needed for the window and was seduced into a lasting love affair with plant

17

systematics (see 1, 2, 3). The reading that followed in my high school library began with Sir John Arthur Thomson's "The Great Biologists," where I discovered the previously unheard of Charles Darwin. "The Origin of Species" (a formidable task never finished in high school) gave new and exciting meaning to the affinities encountered in classifying plants. Then on to F. O. Bower's "The Origin of a Land Flora" that had an even greater impact in making the historical process, as such, a mandatory element in my understanding of anything alive.

This was reinforced when, shortly after College, I found a primitive terrestrial bromeliad (*B. humilis*) on a dry rocky island between Trinidad and Venezuela; its remarkable root system and associated epidermal trichomes (4) immediately suggested a desert origin for those epiphytic relatives, the bulk of the *Bromeliaceae*, that exploit and adorn the canopy of rain forests elsewhere in the New World. That discovery was an instructive experience: attention to possible origins, to early selection pressures, can enhance our understanding of contemporary organization.

My high-school interest in Darwinian evolution survived an undergraduate exposure to J. W. Heslop-Harrison's Lamarckian convictions (King's College, University of Durham), flourished during graduate school (Columbia) with Dobzhansky, and matured during several later years of friendship and collaboration on a book with G. G. Simpson.

The Origin Of Organization

A whimsical analogy I enjoy and find useful sees the living world as a vast literature comprising millions of volumes, many still available but even more out of print. All are vignettes written in the universal language of nucleotide sequences. All have the same happy ending (reproduction) which, when reached, assures the volume stays in print. That ending is reached, however, in an incredible diversity of ways: in daisies, Pitcher plants, and *Sequoias*; in African butterflies whose pupae are miniature death-masks of nearby monkeys; in fish that enjoy home-delivered food while living in the cloaca of sea cucumbers; in orchids that seduce innocent wasps in illicit copulation—a little soft porn in the literature here, and outright sadism in the behavior of female mantids devouring their lovers as copulation ends—and then humans, some raising corn and cows, some writing string quartets, and others contemplating the origin of black holes as well as themselves. I once described this diversity of vignettes as a baroque variation on a common theme only to be interrupted by Margaret Mead insisting, "No! more than baroque, it's rococo."

Unlike its (divine) Publisher, the author of this literature is both knowable and known, and some knowledge of his style is useful to the physiologist as well as to the naturalist. The historical process of natural selection has written all the vignettes under several pen-names: according to Dawkins (5) he is "The Blind Watchmaker," but for some time (6) I have known him as "Darwin's Demon," a physically respectable cousin of Maxwell's. Maxwell's Demon, it is recalled, stood at a closable aperture separating two gas chambers at equal pressure. By opening the door only for molecules moving in one direction he extracted work from the initial equilibrium creating negentropy in violation of the Second Law of Thermodynamics. The fallacy in this fantasy was pointed out by Szilard: the energy gained from the Demon's discriminations is wholly offset by the energy spent in acquiring information on which way the molecules are moving. Szilard's version of the Demon can indeed create negentropy locally, but only by increasing entropy in a larger context.

And so it is with Darwin's Demon, who stands on the threshold of each new generation granting favored entree to the offspring of those members of the previous generation that were the better reproducers. This single, mindless discrimination is an inevitable consequence of the reproductive process that alone assures perpetuation of the vignette, keeps it in print. The inexorable consequence of its relentless application is a local and expensive increase in negentropy within the world of life that has troubled and misled not only Alexis Carrel but Wolfgang Pauli[1]: there is no violation of the Second Law while the Demon continuously enhances the script that ensures reproductive success; in brief, as he generates and keeps improving the organization of living things.

---

[1]Sometime in the early 1960s Wolfgang Pauli, a visitor to The Institute for Advanced Studies in Princeton, asked our mutual humanist friend, Erich Kahler, to find a biologist with whom he could discuss evolution. Kahler steered him to me and insisted that when Pauli came to my home I was to provide him with "a hard-backed chair (to accommodate his corpus) and a bottle of good claret." The beginning of the evening was awkward. Pauli opened with a pronouncement that, "Evolution, of course, never occurred." After some moments of silence I asked if he could tell me how he reached that conclusion, uncommon in the scientific world. His answer was brief. "Were the passage of time to witness an increase in negentropy the Second Law would be violated; and that's not possible." The rest of the evening, with the help of the (good) claret, went more smoothly. I gave the great physicist, as humbly as I could, a brief introduction to population genetics and a sketch of how selection worked as an historical process. I also pointed out that the increase of information it engendered over time was limited to that small enclave of nature we say is living, and that Darwin's Demon is as physically respectable as Szilard's version of Maxwell's. The evening ended with a one-liner as arresting as the opener, "Well," he said, "I'm going to see Max Delbruck in New York tomorrow and I'll find out!" I was, to be sure, a little dismayed, having heard that Pauli was strong on put-downs such as, " Prof X ? He isn't even wrong!" As it turned out he was equally strong on disarming apologies. Two weeks later, after his return to Zurich, I got a letter thanking me for the discussion, which he had evidently enjoyed. He added that he had seen Delbruck in New York as planned, and had yet (two weeks later) to fully recover: Delbruck had told him that he (Pauli) and Bohr were unemployed physicists who should stick to what they knew something about. And he had the grace to tell me that.

I once asked von Neumann, given the opportunity of cocktail conversation, what he saw as the difference between order and organization, both non-random. His answer was short and to Darwinian ears sweet, "Organization has purpose; order does not." The one is information-dependent, the other is not. The primary purpose of biological organization is self-perpetuation by self-copying, and as such is the handiwork of Darwin's Demon. My choice of the von Neumann comment is deliberate: the computer revolution for which he was so largely responsible had a major impact on the climate of biological thought at mid-century. The mere title of a book by Wiener & Bigelow, "Purposeful Machines," makes the essential point (see also, 7). The apparent inseparability of purpose and consciousness was previously responsible for a major embarrassment and impediment to the biologist that Haldane put in a characteristically pithy way, "Teleology is like a mistress to the biologist; he dare not be seen with her in public but cannot live without her." It was my intention in 1957 (8) to help get Haldane's mistress out of the closet by describing her merits as teleonomic rather than teleological. Whether or not that did help (Monod & Davis found it useful!), the commonplace nature of programmable machines at midcentury gave teleology (as teleonomy) complete respectability in the society of biological ideas. The genome was the program of a Turing machine and Darwin's Demon was the programmer.

Many of my reflections are those of a naturalist, critic of the Demon's literature: how he has coped with the challenges of recurrent adversity and opportunity in the cyclic nature of the physical environment; and how, on the other hand, he has exploited the sheer predictability of those cycles as an opportunity to serve a great diversity of other very different ends, all subservient to his ultimate purpose, which is keeping his vignettes in print.

But I also maintain that as physiologist one can turn with profit to Darwin as well as to Loeb. The Loebian insistence on reduction to physical law, fundamental in its own right, is an insufficient arsenal for explanation in biology. The literature written by the Demon is no more deducible from a complete command of the nucleotide language, let alone physical law, than the works of Shakespeare or Alfred North Whitehead are deducible from a complete command of the English language. In all cases, the author's wholly unpredictable artifacts have to be addressed and understood in their own right, and with what Erich von Holst somewhere referred to as *eine niveau adequate terminologie*. And in that address a persisting concern with function and historical origin will yield valuable guide-posts in the challenging task of understanding what the Demon has written.

For my own part I would have been happier had "The Origin of Species" been called "The Origin of Organization": the non-theological explanation of biological organization (of Paley's "design") was the real Darwinian revolution, much more profound than the origin of diversity, which it incidentally entails.

TEMPORAL PROGRAMMING: Some Personal Previews

Circadian Rhythmicity

Figure 1 gives two modern examples of an observation that was first made by the French scientist, Jacques de Mairan, in 1729. Biological activities that characteristically occur once per day in nature continue in laboratory conditions of constant darkness and temperature as a persistent rhythm with a period (τ) that is close to but not exactly 24 hr: the period is said to be circadian (L. *circa, dies*). Such circadian rhythmicity has been observed at all levels of

DROSOPHILA PSEUDOOBSCURA: Eclosion activity

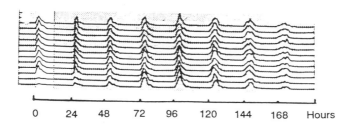

```
0    24   48   72   96   120  144  168   Hours
```

MUS MUSCULUS: Running wheel activity

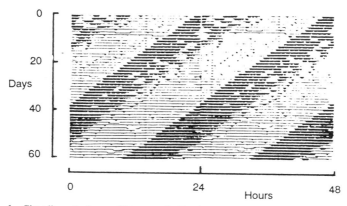

Figure 1 Circadian rhythms. (*Top panel*) Twelve replicate populations of *Drosophila pseudoobscura* pupae transferred from a 24 hr light/dark cycle into constant darkness and constant temperature 20°C. The emergence of adult flies (eclosion of pupae) occurs as a single peak of activity once per day. The period between peak medians is a few minutes longer than 24 hr (circadian). (*Lower panel*) Running-wheel utilization by a house-mouse (*Mus musculus*) kept in continuous darkness for 60 days. The heavy bars mark wheel utilization. The period (circadian) between onsets of activity is less than 24 hr.

organization, from the behavior of mammals, flies, and single cells, to the specific activity of enzymes, the activity of ribosomes, and the transcription of identified genes.

The endogenous nature of the rhythm is attested not only by its circadian period, but by the fact that (in suitable systems) its motion stops as soon as oxygen is withheld and promptly resumes as soon as oxygen is returned (9): and its innateness is attested in a variety of ways including many recent isolations of single gene mutations that alter its period. Circadian rhythms reflect extensive programming of biological activity that meets and exploits the challenges and opportunities offered by the periodic nature of the environment.

One of the truly remarkable features of these rhythms is their essentially indefinite persistence (>2 years in some rodents): they are driven by some self-sustaining cellular oscillation as pacemaker of the system. The stability and precision of the pacemaking oscillation are equally remarkable: the standard deviation on the average period (τ) of a mouse rhythm is about 1 minute, or 1/1000. A combination of this precision and the time constants involved constitute a formidable challenge to the cell physiologist.

Bananas, Mosquitoes, and Drosophila

My own introduction to biological timing came in wartime (1940s) Trinidad where, as a botanist with an undergraduate training in genetics, I had been sent to breed vegetables for the North African campaign that was, of course, already in progress! The Imperial College of Tropical Agriculture in Trinidad had a firmer grasp than the Colonial Office in London on the time-constants of such an undertaking and set me a task that lacked any redeeming relevance to the war, but was at least tractable: why were all the offspring of an interspecific banana hybrid pentaploid? Both parents were diploid. This entailed collecting banana ovaries while fending off a cloud of wasps at the top of a tall unstable ladder (adventure here!) and doing so at dawn when, I had been told, meiosis occurred. In fact it did, with the great majority of mother cells producing haploid (but sterile) embryo-sacs as one expected of an interspecific hybrid. However, in a small minority of mother cells that began meiosis much earlier than the norm, both meiotic spindles failed yielding, as a consequence, tetraploid embryo-sacs that were fully viable. The origin of pentaploids was explained (10), but I was perplexed at the restriction of meiosis to a limited time of day and even more perplexed by the spindle failures in atypically timed cells.

As soon as the banana work was finished (less than a year), I became involved, initially as a botanist, with the control of malaria on both the Naval and Airforce bases on the island. Both anopheline vectors bred in the "tanks" of water impounded by the overlapping leaves of epiphytic bromeliads, the plants that Cladimiro Picado (11) happily described as the "overhead ponds" of tropical rain-forests, and whose historical origin I came to think was in desert conditions. Of the two anophelines breeding in bromeliads, one (*A. homunculus*) was largely limited to the extremely wet north-eastern end of the island. It was gradually replaced by its close sibling, *A. bellator*, as one moved south-west into drier rainfall zones. That clear interspecific difference in moisture requirements was again encountered in the center of the island where the species overlapped; here *A. homunculus* always occupied lower (wetter) strata of the forest than *A. bellator* (Figure 2), and equally clearly delayed its evening peak of activity to a later (moister) time. This pattern of species-specific timing persisted day after day in spite of variation in overall humidity conditions (12). If no fixed moisture level determined the timing of these evening peaks, were they dictated from within?

The same vaguely formulated proposition arose soon after the war (1946) when, as a Dobzhansky student, I worked on the daily activity cycle of *Drosophila pseudoobscura* and *D. persimilis* in the ponderosa forest near Yosemite: day after day, rain or shine, *D. persimilis* dominated the (moister)

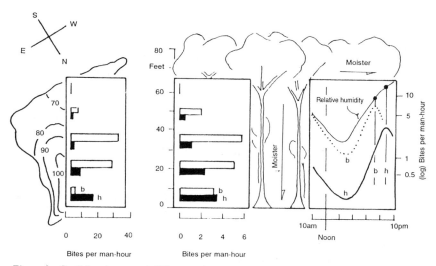

Figure 2   Spatial and temporal differences in the distribution of two anopheline mosquitoes on moisture gradients in Trinidad, West Indies (based on data in 12). (*Left panel*) The abundance of *A. homunculus* (h) is high in the wet NE of the island, and declines towards the SW as rainfall levels fall. Its sister species, *A. bellator*, (b) gradually replaces it in the drier areas. (*Middle panel*) In mid-island, where the species overlap, the interspecific difference in moisture requirement is reflected in the vertical distribution of the insects: *A. homunculus* is restricted to the lower, moister levels of the forest. (*Right panel*) The interspecific difference is again seen in the daily cycle of biting activity: the peak of *A. homunculus* activity occurs, day after day, at a later, cooler, moister time than that of *A. bellator*.

morning peak of activity and *D. pseudoobscura* that in the (drier) evening hours.

Bunning and Kalmus

All of this led me, with pointers from my friend Marston Bates, to the papers on endogenous daily rhythms that Hans Kalmus (13) and Erwin Bunning (14) had published in the 1930s. One of the main points of their papers was to dismiss the suggestion from Rosa Stoppel (15) that those daily rhythms, which persisted in conditions of constant light and temperature, were under exogenous not endogenous control, that they were driven by some unidentified geophysical cycle (factor-x) caused by the earth's rotation. In dismissing that suggestion, both Kalmus & Bunning reported that the period of the persisting rhythm was temperature-dependent: factor-x, whose period must clearly be independent of local temperature fluctuation, could not be the driver.

Interesting as those papers were, they failed to distract me from behavioral studies (8), which I hoped would explain the difference between *D. pseudo-obscura* and *D. persimilis* in their daily activity cycles. What did change my work was listening to a lecture by Gustav Kramer in what I think was 1951.

GUSTAV KRAMER: A Biological Clock

Listening to Kramer lecture on the sun-compass behavior (16) of starlings was one of the most exciting and esthetically rewarding experiences I have enjoyed. In his most telling experiment, Kramer used a bird he had trained outdoors to go in a particular compass direction for its food reward, evidently using the sun's azimuth as a compass. It was challenged to do so inside a laboratory where an electric light replaced the real sun as direction-giver. In hour after hour, as the bird sought its target direction (where the food should be) it added 15° of arc (counter-clockwise) to the angle it made relative to the artificial sun. Three strong conclusions emerged: (*a*) the bird knew that the angular velocity of the sun's azimuth is, on average, 15°/hr; (*b*) it had access to some reliable clock to compensate for its constantly shifting (azimuth) compass; and (*c*) it knew it was in the northern hemisphere. Klaus Hoffmann had not then completed his crucial and beautiful experiments (17) showing the clock was indeed internal to the bird and not some external "Stoppel-dinger"; but Kramer and everyone else listening to him in 1952 was assuming that to be true, so the question was, "What is the clock?"

I cannot recall now how many days it was after hearing him before the thought occurred to me, in fully explicit form, that Kramer's clock was based on or related to the endogenous daily rhythmicity of the Bunning & Kalmus papers of the 1930s. Didn't the expression of essentially the same period in their persistent daily rhythms itself imply that garden beans and fruit flies could measure time—that they had a "clock" measuring the duration of the cycle? That inference, only framed in such language after hearing Kramer, was as memorable and exhilarating as his lecture.

However, there was trouble. Bunning's initial basis for dismissing Stoppel's factor-x was his claim that temperature changed the period of the *Drosophila* rhythm. If the clock in Kramer's starlings were indeed the same as (even related to) the biological oscillation responsible for the flies' rhythm, its temperature-dependence would inevitably cause the birds to misjudge the position of the sun on warmer or colder days: a clock function for the oscillation demanded its angular velocity not vary with inevitable daily variation in temperature.

TEMPERATURE COMPENSATION: Functional Prerequisite

An Outhouse Experiment in the Rockies

Bunning's report was based on a very simple experiment I resolved to repeat. Abruptly dropping the temperature from 26 to 16°C when the flies were transferred to constant darkness, he found the first peak of the free-running rhythm was delayed almost 12 hr. My hope was to repeat that clearly crucial observation at Wood's Hole where several of the Princeton Department's senior members spent the summer and the facilities were excellent. However, Wood's Hole rentals in 1952 drove the family to the Rocky Mountain Biological Laboratory near Crested Butte in Colorado, where the rent was reasonable, but the facilities non-existent until I found a well-preserved outhouse (one-holer) near an abandoned mine shaft at approximately 10,000 feet. It was still erect and by now totally odorless. The walls and door were sufficiently intact that some tar paper and nails procured from Crested Butte made it a useful darkroom. Plyboard transformed the seat into an acceptable workbench. The presence of a small crystal-clear creek a few feet away provided a very stable source of low temperature—and a fine opportunity to fly-fish for trout. None of this would have been useful, however, without the pressure cooker that my wife had brought to ease the task of cooking at high altitudes. When emergence activity within them had begun, some vials of *D. pseudoobscura* were placed in the outhouse-darkroom and others in the pressure cooker-darkroom, which was then anchored in the creek to assure a constant low temperature. Its ventilation was effected by attaching, as a snorkel, a black rubber tube to the lid's steam outlet. To minimize distraction from trout, I limited observation to the emergence peak in both darkrooms after two days in darkness. To my surprise, because I was pessimistically expecting to confirm Bunning, the peak in the very much colder pressure cooker was only a couple of hours later than that in the outhouse: no more than an hour or so's delay in each of the two cycles at low temperature! Crude as the experiment was, its outcome was clearly in conflict with Bunning's report of significant temperature dependence. I well remember the excitement of that afternoon in 1952; one had a bear by the tail; the angular velocity of at least one endogenous daily rhythm was, indeed, sufficiently unaffected by temperature to render it a useful clock. But what about the Bunning data?

The Follow-up in Princeton

That question was answered a few months later in Princeton where I built better facilities than the Emerald Lake outhouse offered and had the help of two able undergraduates, Lincoln Brower and Lynn Parry. This time when the culture vials were transferred from a light cycle (at 26°C) to constant darkness (at 16°C) emergence activity was assayed hourly. The initial finding showed Bunning was indeed correct: the first emergence peak at 16°C, due approximately 27 hr after entry into darkness, was 12 hr overdue. Late at night I went home disconsolate: how to explain the Colorado data? My undergraduate friends did not give up, however, and greeted me the following day with apparently perplexing data. The second peak in darkness at 16°C was only 2 hr later than that at 26°C, the same as in Colorado! Moreover, as the following days showed, the interval between all subsequent peaks at 16°C was only trivially longer than that at 26°C. Bunning had been misled by a step-induced transient that does not reflect the steady-state behavior of the pacemaking oscillation that drives the rhythm; and the Princeton data left no doubt that the oscillation was sufficiently temperature-compensated to serve as a useful clock.

Hazards in the Fate of Observations

As early as 1948, Frank A. Brown found the period of a daily rhythm of melanophore expansion in the crab *Uca* to be invariant over a wide range of temperatures. His paper (18), unknown to me until we met in 1955, was clear on the importance of the observation, but in overlooking the plausability of temperature-independence as a functional prerequisite, Brown sought its explanation entirely in terms of external physical causation. In fact he invoked what amounted to factor-x as the cause and retained that position for many years thereafter.

In an ironically similar way, failure to anticipate temperature compensation as a functional prerequisite is what led Bunning to accept a transient as sufficient evidence of the period's temperature-dependence, which is clearly what he was looking for in his disbelief of Stoppel.

The von Frisch school's important contributions to this field illustrate a different hazard that observations face, i.e. the language used in reporting them. One of von Frisch's students, Ingeborg Beling, reported (19) a beautiful series of experiments in which she showed that honeybees, having found an experimental food source at, say, 3 PM, returned to that site at essentially 3 PM on several successive days without reinforcement. Beling spoke of the hour at which the food was found as the "dressaurzeit" (training time) and the bee's subsequent return at the same hour as evidence of its "zeitgedachtnis" (time memory). While in Munich in 1959, I asked Martin Lindauer why they (the von Frisch laboratory) had still not reset the bee's clock with a Hoffman-like shift of the light/dark cycle. "Because," he replied, "bees don't have clocks, they have zeitgedachtnis." The impact of Beling's original (1929) language in discussing her beautiful experiments has never really been shed by the Munich workers. The use of "memory" and "training" (zeitgedachtnis and dressaurzeit) seriously distracts attention from the innate components in the overall behavior. And unlike "clock," the word "memory" fails to raise the issue of phase or local time. Why was it necessary, when the von Frisch school did eventually address the issue of local time, to fly bees from Munich to New York via Pan Am instead of the easier, and much cheaper, procedure of shifting the light cycle in the Luisenstrasse basement? It is as though the tradition of the school finds it easier to attribute memory to the "bienenvolk" than envisage a clock (something too concrete?) inside them. Their resistance to an internal clock has persisted into the 1980s, when they (20) attribute the bees' timing behaviors to control by daily variations in the earth's magnetic field. John Brady (21) has given an excellent critique of this recent resort to Stoppel's factor-x.

AN UBIQUITOUS CELLULAR CLOCK

Shortly after the *Drosophila* results appeared, temperature compensation was reported in several plant rhythms and, surprisingly, in mammals. The first of Michael Menaker's many contributions to the circadian physiology of mammals and birds was made in the Princeton laboratory (1959), where he found that the period of a rhythm in hibernating bats remained circadian even when their body temperature was as low as 3°C (22). In 1960, Rawson reported the equally surprising finding that the temperature compensation of a very different mammalian rhythm remained essentially unimpaired when its homeothermy was suppressed by drugs (23).

This functional prerequisite for time-measurement has since been shown to be ubiquitous in circadian systems; it is, indeed, one of their defining properties.

In one of the more rewarding adventures of that period, Victor Bruce and I (24) looked for and found temperature compensation in a unicellular system (*Euglena*). Shortly thereafter, Sweeney & Hastings (25) found it in another unicell, (*Gonyaulax*), and Ehret (26) discovered it in (*Paramecium*). Bruce and I (27) deliberately sought and found it in *Neurospora*, as a simple eukaryote in which the genetics of the clock could be pursued. One of Bruce's students, Jerry Feldman, has done just that with great profit. And in the hands of Jay Dunlap, one of Feldman's students, *Neurospora* is proving a valuable tool for molecular work on the clock. While with us in Princeton, Feldman (28) also made the pioneering observation that slowing protein synthesis with cycloheximide slowed the clock, which opened up a new and major line of inquiry that has blossomed (the Feldman effect is widespread) and is returned to in the closing section of this essay.

TEMPORAL ORGANIZATION:
Handiwork of Darwin's Demon

Programs Coping with the Day Outside

Much of the discussion of circadian rhythmicity at the 1960 Cold Spring Harbor Symposium was structured by a general evolutionary perspective. From life's outset, the major environmental cycles of day, tide, month, and year have confronted natural selection with windows of opportunity and hazard that recur with precisely predictable frequency; and the Demon has exploited that predictability by elaborating innate temporal programs that phase many undertakings in the life of cell or organism, metabolic or behavioral, to an appropriate time in the outside day (29). Such programs offer the clear advantage of anticipatory preparation for predictably recurrent conditions.

Filarial parasites spend most of the day in deeper tissues of their host and come into the peripheral blood stream only during the few and predictable hours when their mosquito vectors are active. That time is different in the Philippines and India (30) and the innate daily program of the two filarial populations is appropriately different.

The activity of day-active insects is very commonly restricted to the hours near dawn and sunset when the saturation deficit is lower and the hazard of water loss thereby lessened. That activity pattern persists as a circadian program in laboratory conditions of constant temperature and darkness, and there is little doubt that the timing differences I had observed between *A. bellator* and *A. homunculus* in Trinidad were genetically programmed.

The photosynthetic activity of green plants placed in constant temperature and low intensity light similarly persists as a circadian rhythm, with activity occurring only during that half-cycle when natural light is anticipated. Most spectacular is the way components of the photosynthetic process in the Caryophyllacae, Bromeliaceae (31), and other xerophytic plants are temporally programmed. The uptake of CO_2 through open stomata, which entails the hazard of water loss, is limited to nighttime when saturation deficits are low, but there is no light to drive the photosystems; the CO_2 is initially stored in malate and released later at dawn when the now active photosystems can reduce it. Root-pressure pumping is similarly programmed in relation to the pattern of photosynthetic activity and transpiration.

The biological rhythmicity engendered by the environmental cycles becomes, itself, both challenge and opportunity for the Demon. Beling's demonstration of time-memory in honeybees is a classical case in point: a reliably phased rhythm of nectar secretion has set a premium on the insect's returning at the "right time," the day after initial discovery (32). The circadian timing of anthesis, in general, surely accounts for the circadian timing of banana meiosis that perplexed me in Trinidad.

In 1960 most of the programs coping with environmental periodicity were circadian. The years since then have produced abundant documentation of tidal, lunar, and annual programs. Stages in the development of Dietrich Neumann's intertidal midge *Clunio* are rigorously gated by a temperature-compensated 14-day clock that assures emergence of the tiny adult at low tide (33). Figure 3 from Gwinner (34) illustrates the extent to which the changing activity of a small passerine bird is programmed through the year, including the onset and duration of its migratory activity, as well as the sequence of its molts and gonadal growth. In species headed from Central Europe to South Africa, the programmed duration of nighttime flying ("zugunruhe") lasts many more days (in the Munich Laboratory) than it does in those species that (were they free) would only go to the south coast of the Mediterranean. Perhaps the most remarkable feature of these programs is their control of the bird's changing orientation to the earth's magnetic field, which it uses as reference in circumnavigating the Mediterranean. In some birds this circannual program has been read and reread for as many as 10 years in the basement of the Munich laboratory.

Programs Exploiting the Day Outside

Anticipation of a favorable time in the day outside has clearly been the Demon's goal in elaborating many circadian programs, but he has created at least as many, or more, with no such obvious function. The first such riddle in our own laboratory arose when Leland Edmunds (see 35) found DNA replication and mitosis in *Euglena* restricted to the darkness of night. Why? Why is meiosis in bananas restricted to the hours following dawn—and why do the meiotic spindles fail in those cells that initiate meiosis much earlier than the norm? Why is pupariation subject to strict circadian timing in *Drosophila victoria* but not in other *Drosophila* species? Why is the initiation of new developmental steps subject to similar circadian control in the straw strain of *D. melanogaster*, but not in other strains or species?

This challenge is nowhere stronger that in the circadian phase maps for

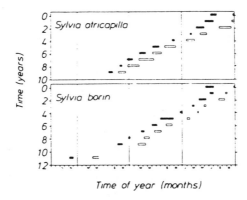

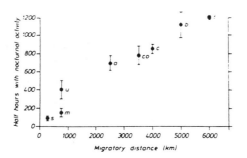

Figure 3 Circannual rhythms in small passerine birds (Warblers). (*Top panel*) The summer (*black bars*) and winter (*open bars*) molt in a Blackcap (*Sylvia atricapilla*) and a Garden Warbler (*S. borin*) kept for 8 and 10 years, respectively, under a constant short-day (10 light/14 dark) regime (from 34). (*Lower panel*) The total time spent in nocturnal migratory activity (zugenruhe) by 8 *Sylvia* species while in constant laboratory conditions is a function of the distance each would travel were they free to do so.

mice that Franz Halberg and his colleagues (36) have developed over the years. More than fifty physiological parameters have been assayed, each showing marked circadian periodicity with maxima at different times of day (Figure 4). For none is it clear why the particular activity is timed to its characteristic window in the outside day; what is the Demon up to?

The answer surely lies in his concern (inadvertant as usual) with temporal organization in its own right: organization that exploits the reliability of the external day as a time-reference and whose goal is an appropriate sequencing of diverse internal events rather than the concurrence of internal and external

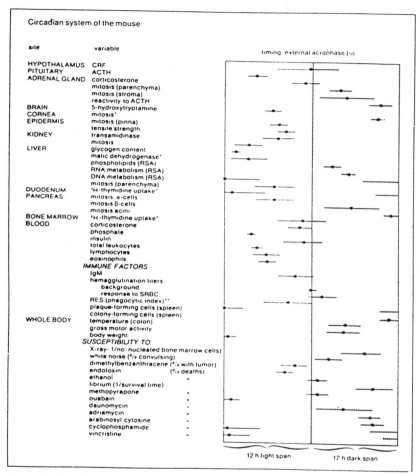

Figure 4 The circadian program of a house-mouse (*Mus musculus*). The timing of 50 physiological parameters in the house mouse (from 36).

events. We come back to this major role for circadian clocks in the closing section of this chapter.

Presence of such a circadian component in the organism's intrinsic temporal organization is also implied in the way abnormal entraining cycles often impair performance. The familiar stress imposed by rapid travel across time zones or shift work are examples. Both Aschoff's laboratory (37) and my own (38) have reported a negative impact on fly longevity when the insects are driven to day lengths other than 24 hr. But the classic and most impressive evidence is still that of Fritz Went (39) and his students at the Caltech Phytotron in the 1950s, which showed the impact of disrupted days on the growth of plants. Went himself provided the clearest evidence on the crucial issue; he exposed African violets (*Saintpaulia*) to light cycles whose period ranged from 20 to 28 hr. In spite of each offering equal time for photosynthesis (light on 50% of the time), the cycles differed markedly in the growth they fostered. Low on the longer and shorter periods; the growth was maximal on the 24 hr cycle, which suggested that the crucial issue was resonance of a circadian component with its entraining cycle.

It is recalled that the breakdown of meiosis in banana hybrids occurred in cells that initiated the process each day some hours ahead of the majority; it is tempting to see this as a breakdown in circadian timing–the ovarian environment not yet congenial.

It was this aspect of circadian physiology that Wilhelm Hufeland (40) had in mind long ago (1798) in referring to the 24 hr period as "... die Einheit unserer naturlichen Chronologie," and what Kalmus (41) was sketching in 1935 as the "autochronie" of organisms.

SYNCHRONIZING THE PROGRAM TO LOCAL TIME

Pacemaker Entrainment: An Empirical Model

My first paper (42) reporting the *Drosophila* results included brief notice of their bearing on sun-compass clocks. That brought an enthusiastic response from Kramer himself who told me his Institute was pursuing the same proposition: they not only saw a functional role for endogenous daily rhythmicity as the clock in sun-compass behavior, but were already testing the idea.

In a classic experiment, Klaus Hoffmann (17) showed that the starling clock could be reset 6 hr by a 6 hr shift in the light/dark cycle to which the bird was exposed. Following the shift, the bird made a 90° error (6 × 15°) in its pursuit of the compass direction where its food reward lay. Soon after that, Kenneth Rawson, working at Kramer's Institute, began an experiment that Schmidt-Koenig (43) completed: homing pigeons subjected to a 6 hr phase advance in their daily light cycle made a similar 90° (6 × 15°) counter-clockwise error in their initial headings for home: they set out from Giessen in Westphalia as if for Amsterdam instead of Wilhelmshaven. Clearly the daily cycle of light and darkness, which Aschoff calls the "zeitgeber," somehow synchronizes the clock (or program) to local time. But how?

Jurgen Aschoff (44) and I (45–47) independently introduced the oscillator language into the discussion of circadian rhythmicity in the middle 1950s. Aschoff's brother, a distinguished engineer, introduced my friend to the idea and to relevant literature; in my case, the start came from reading a paper by John Pringle (48), in which he uses the behavior of coupled oscillators to develop a model of learning. Reading that paper, which introduced me to the entrainment phenomena, was as seminal[2] as listening to Kramer: when one oscillator is coupled to and driven by another, it assumes the period of its driver and develops a unique phase-relation to it. Here was precisely the relationship of a circadian rhythm to the environmental cycle that synchronizes it to local time: first, their coupling ensures transformation of the organism's circadian (about a day) period to precisely 24 hr and, second, in so doing establishes a unique and functionally appropriate phase-relation between them.

It was clear from the outset (ca. 1956) that to lock on to the daily cycle of light and dark, the oscillator driving the rhythm must be differentially responsive to light at successive phases of its cycle. That led to experiments with *Drosophila*, which used a standard brief pulse of light (15 min 50 lux) to perturb the system, otherwise free-running in constant darkness, at successively later phases of the cycle.

The results are described by a phase-response-curve (PRC) that plots the phase-shifts caused by the light at successively later phases of the free-run. The major features of the *Drosophila* PRC (Figure 6), reporting the effects of 15 min pulses (50 lux), are nearly universal: the half-cycle of pacemaker motion that normally coincides with the darkness of night is designated the subjective night; it is very responsive to light, which causes phase-delays in the first half of the subjective night, and then advances later. The half-cycle

---

[2]On the first day we met (1956), Victor Bruce and I found we both thought temperature compensation of the clock's period was based on the mutual coupling of two temperature-dependent oscillators with complementary temperature coefficients. In my case that was entirely the result of reading Pringle. Bruce and I never had suitable experimental material to test that idea in Princeton, but when Ron Konopka came to my Stanford laboratory in the early 1970s with his now famous and invaluable clock mutants, the chance was at hand to do so. My specific proposition concerned the two alleles, per^s and per^l, that determined clocks with 19 and 29 hr periods, respectively; that they corresponded with the two oscillators Bruce and I had envisaged as the mutually coupled components of wild-type (which has an intermediate period of 24 hr). The testable feature of this proposition was that per^s and per^l would not only be more temperature-dependent than wild-type, but that they would have complementary temperature coefficients: the period of one would shorten while that of the other would lengthen as temperature changed. These predictions were promptly confirmed (Figure 5) in some very satisfactory experiments (49), but it is no longer clear that this confirmation makes the basis of prediction valid: molecular analysis traces both mutations to the same exon.

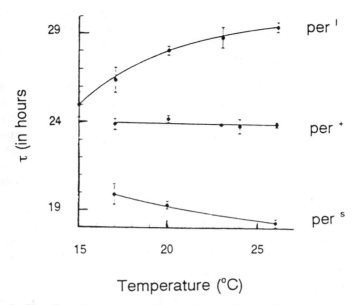

Figure 5   The effect of temperature on the period (τ) of the circadian rhythm of locomotory activity in *D. melanogaster*: in wild-type (*per*⁺) and in two mutants, *per*ˢ and *per*¹. The period of wild-type is essentially unaffected by an increase in temperature, but that of *per*ˢ shortens and that of *per*¹ lengthens as the temperature is increased (from 49).

designated subjective day is very unresponsive to light. All these features are rather obvious, indeed, they are analytic necessities (50).

What was not obvious is the way the phase-response-curve for a defined pulse (e.g. 15 min 50 lux) can be used to predict the phase relationship of the oscillator to an entraining cycle using that pulse. I discovered this initially by using a simple analogue device in which a circular version of the PRC was plotted on one sheet of transparent polar co-ordinate paper, and one or more light pulses were plotted on a second underlying sheet. Simulation of the oscillator's motion was effected by rotating its PRC (upper sheet) until interrupted by encounter with a light pulse on the lower sheet. The sign and amplitude of the PRC at encounter dictated a phase shift of the oscillator that I assumed occurred instantaneously. Implausible as that assumption was—a necessary oversimplification to get started—the simulations using it yielded essentially perfect predictions of the observed phase-relation between the oscillator and the light cycle that entrains it as Figure 7 attests. In steady state the light pulse in each cycle causes a discrete instantaneous phase-shift equal

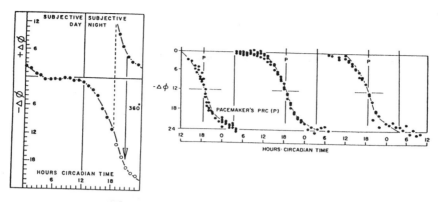

Figure 6 Drosophila pseudoobscure: phase-response-curves (PRCs) (for brief light pulses) of the pacemaker that drives the circadian rhythm of eclosion activity. (*Left*) The PRC for a pulse of white light (15 min 50 lux). See text for detail. By displacing the phase advances 360° one obtains a monotonic version of the PRC that is used in the right-hand panel. (*Right*) 72 replicate pupal populations are released into continuous darkness after entrainment by a 12 hr light/ 12 hr dark cycle. Each population receives the standard brief light pulse, but at successively later one hour intervals. The phase-shift elicited by the pulse identifies the phase of the pacemaker's cycle at which it was given. The pacemaker's time-course is tracked through three full cycles.

to the difference between τ and T, the periods of pacemaker and light-cycle, respectively.

The PRC is a footprint, as it were, of the pacemaker's time course: the shift elicited by a strong brief pulse reliably identifies the phase of the cycle at which it was given. The right-hand panel in Figure 6 gives such a footprint of the pacemaker's time-course through three full cycles of a free-run in darkness. The upper panels in Figure 7 also give the phase-shift response (solid points) at successive hourly intervals to document the pacemaker's time-course in the entrained steady states realized by 21 and 27 hr light cycles. The curves in Figure 7 (upper panels) are predictions based on the assumption that the light pulses responsible for entrainment do indeed cause an instantaneous $\Delta\phi$ response equal to the difference between τ and T. Observation (plotted points) amply confirms that prediction.[3]

[3]As Arthur Winfree's work as a graduate student at Princeton made clear, the pulse must be above some saturation strength for the explanation of discrete entrainment developed here to be valid. His landmark analysis (51) of the effects of varying signal strength, especially in the middle of the subjective night, explained the then perplexing difference between what he calls Type-1 and Type-O PRCs.

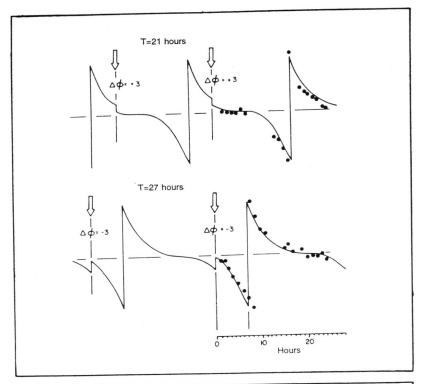

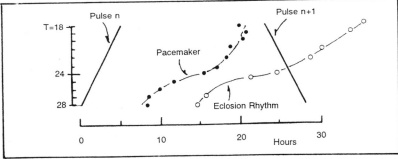

Figure 7   Entrainment of a circadian pacemaker (*Drosophila pseudoobscura*) by brief light pulses.
   Upper panels: The pacemaker of the pupal eclosion rhythm is entrained by cycles of brief (15 min. 50 lux) pulses of white light. The cycle length (T) in one is 21 hr and in the other is 27 hr. The solid curve represents (via its PRC) the time-course of the entrained pacemaker which undergoes a phase-shift equal to τ minus T at each light pulse. The solid points are measurements of the phase-shifts elicited by pulses at the times indicated, and match prediction closely.
   Lower panel: The entrained steady states effected by cycles of brief (15 min. 50 lux) light pulses, whose periods (T) range from 18 to 28 hr. The phase of the entrained pacemaker is given as solid points that mark the time at which (middle of the subjective night) the response to the light pulse is a 12 hr phase shift. The pacemaker's phase-lag on the entraining light pulse steadily increases as the period (T) of the light cycle is shortened; the curve is predicted from the entrainment model, and the points are observed. The open points are medians of the directly observed eclosion peaks; the rhythm's phase-lag on the pacemaker also increases as T is shortened (see text).

The assumption of an instantaneous phase-shift is clearly valid and loses its implausability if one thinks of the light causing a photochemical destruction of one of the oscillator's state variables.

These successes led me to predict what the so-called limits of entrainment were for the *Drosophila pseudoobscura* pacemaker Since both phase-advances and phase-delays of about 12 hr were possible, I inferred one could entrain the oscillator down to a ~12 hr or up to a ~36 hr cycle. Alas, while that confident assertion was in press (52) and irretrievable, we knew it was wrong. And thereby hangs a retellable tale.

Eric Ottesen, then a sophomore research assistant in my laboratory, had a computer science room-mate (Doug Sand) who laughed at the idea of our building a more complicated analogue device, and assured Eric and me that he could do better on the IBM 7090. He eventually did so, but not before his initial program (with 17 nested do-loops!) caused prolonged misery. Simplified and debugged, however, Sand's program opened up a entirely new world for us, although the first major dividend was an unwelcome bomb.

The limits of entrainment, according to the 7090, were 18 and 28 hr, not 12 and 36 hr as my paper (52), then in press, predicted. What was more, experiments promptly confirmed the IBM's prediction! Clearly something was missing from our model and that became the major concern of both of Ottesen and myself, who worked at it independently for some weeks without success until Eric alone, using high school algebra, found the answer. The slope of the PRC at the phase yielding the $\Delta\phi$ response necessary for entrainment (= τ-T) must lie between 0 and -2 for the steady state to be stable.

Delay in publishing his argument was prompted by the desire – principally mine – to have it stated in a more elegant mathematical form. This was a mistake that led to Ottesen being scooped in the open literature. Nevertheless, the excitement of discovery and the beauty of experimentally confirmed prediction (all of it an adventure) led Eric Ottensen to abandon Classics for a distinguished career in Biology and Medicine.

Challenge in Seasonal Change: Why is τ Circadian?

The difference between τ and 24 hr was, of course, a major piece of evidence in the rejection of factor-x during the 1950s. My own inclination at that time was to see τ as a tolerated approximation to the period of the outside day, sufficiently close to be entrainable by the light cycle. Remaining within the range of entrainment was all the Demon had demanded. The general idea of a tolerated approximation was made much more attractive by a delightful suggestion from Roger Revelle, whom I saw regularly at that time as a member of the NAS Oceanography Committee. Revelle's proposal was that τ was a living fossil. He had two premises. One was the chance, it so happens, that all the values of τ then known were less than 24 hr. The other was Wells' (53) now famous documentation from the growth rings of Paleozoic corals that the period of the earth's rotation was much shorter than 24 hr: there were more than 365 rings in the annual cycle. Since then, as the earth's rotation has slowed, and the length of the day/night cycle has increased, all the Demon has demanded is, again, that the perpetually short τ remain within the range of entrainment.

Attractive as it was to an evolutionist, Revelle's idea was short-lived. The death blow came from Jurgen Aschoff, who was the first to notice that all the early measurements of τ were made on night-active species and, as newer measurements came in, the day-active species all had τ longer than 24 hr. These diurnal creatures (plant, animal, and now *Homo sapiens*) are clearly not accommodated by Revelle's fossil hypothesis. On the other hand, Aschoff was quick to see the important ecological regularity that was emerging and elaborated on it, at Cold Spring Harbor in 1960 (54), as the Circadian Rule. At the same meeting I successfully renamed it Aschoff's Rule (55).

I spent much of a 1959 Guggenheim with Aschoff in Heidelberg trying to find functional significance for my host's Rule and had the beginning of an answer in my Cold Spring Harbor paper, but it was many years before Serge Daan and I (50, 56) published a more satisfactory interpretation of it based on computer simulations, which used the empirical model developed for *Drosophila*. We found that the known differences between day- and night-active species in τ and PRC shape were such that as daylength changed seasonally, the day-active program appropriately tracked dawn, while that of night-active species tracked sunset.

I recently (57) obtained the same general result much more easily using a family of curves that Peter Kaus, a physicist friend then at RCA in Princeton, introduced to Victor Bruce and myself as early as 1956. These curves, called Kaus-Curves (sometimes Kaus-Kurves) in our group, show how the phase-lag of an oscillator on its driving cycle (e.g. light/dark) increases as the oscillator's period (τ) is lengthened; and when the strength of the coupling (C) between oscillator and light cycle is increased, how the dependence of phase-lag on oscillator period (τ) decreases.

No matter what the coupling strength, however, the phase-lag is always $90°$ at resonance, i.e. when the oscillator's period (τ) is the same as that T of the light cycle. The consequence is a remarkable node in the family of Kaus-Kurves when $\tau = T$: to the left of that node, where $\tau < T$, an increase in coupling strength increases the phase-lag; but to the right of the node, where $\tau > T$ an increase in C decreases the phase-lag (Figure 8).

The coupling of circadian pacemakers to the light cycle is increased as daylength (photoperiod) increases in the spring, and consequently the phase-lag of those with $\tau < T$(night-active species) increases, tracking sundown, while those with $\tau > T$ (day-active species) track sun-up. τ variation around 24 hr is clearly a non-trivial issue, and much of it has strong functional significance.

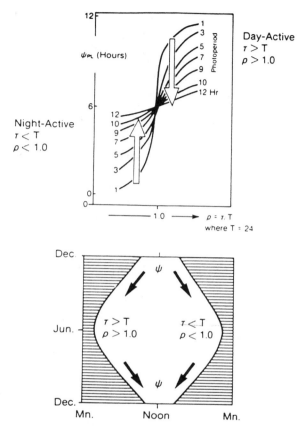

Figure 8   Aschoff's Rule (from 57). (*Upper panel*) A set of Kaus-Curves (see text) describes the phase-lag (ψPL) of a circadian pacemaker on the light cycle that entrains it, as a function of ρ, which is τ/T. As τ is increased, with T held constant at 24 hr, the phase-lag of the pacemaker is increased. The lag is also changed by increasing photoperiod, as shown for photoperiods of 1 to 12 hr. Increase of photoperiod reduces the phase-lag when ρ is greater than 1.0 but increases it when ρ is less than 1.0. (*Lower panel*) As photoperiod changes throughout the year, the long τ characteristic of day-active organisms ($\rho > 1$) assures their circadian program tracks sun-up; and the short τ characteristic of night-active animals ($\rho < 1$) assures their program tracks sun-down.

Higher Latitudes: "Subjective Light Intensity"

Seasonal change in the onset of the working day is not the only challenge incurred by the Demon's use of the daily light/dark cycle as the principal entraining agent for circadian programs. The increasing duration of light in high summer poses an entirely different challenge that is only heightened the farther north (or south) one goes towards the pole.

The Pavlidis pacemaker in Figure 9 illustrates the challenge: the action of light is to bleach one of the two state variables causing the amplitude of both to be steadily depressed as the photoperiod exceeds 12 hr. Were it not for some compensatory adjustment, the very long days of the far north would almost damp out the oscillation and certainly weaken whatever signal underlies the pacemaker's timing function. There is little doubt that this potential impairment of pacemaker function by the longer days at higher latitudes is responsible (via the Demon) for the south-north cline in PRC amplitude that Kuma Takamura and I (58) encountered among Japanese races of *Drosophila auraria*. The light pulse used to measure the PRC has a steadily weaker effect as one goes north; it is as though what we called "subjective light intensity" declines in the north, compensating for the increase in the light's duration (photoperiod).

An increase in the amplitude of the pacemaker's free-running motion is what we believe affects this reduction in the subjective light intensity and, hence, PRC amplitude. That increase has other advantages at higher latitudes that Kyner, Takamura, and I (59) have recently sketched in some detail.

THE CIRCADIAN COMPONENT IN PHOTOPERIODIC INDUCTION

Bunning's Hypothesis: A Chilly Reception

The most important element in Erwin Bunning's papers of the 1930s was his proposition that endogenous daily rhythms played a central role in the then

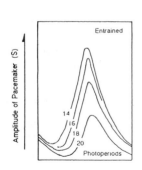 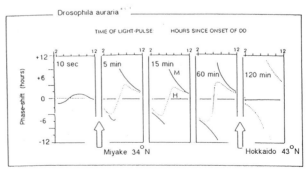

Figure 9   The effects of photoperiod and latitude on a circadian pacemaker (*Drosophila auraria*) (from 59). (*Left panel*) The amplitude of one of the state variables of the Pavlidis oscillator used to simulate the behavior of the *Drosophila* pacemaker (see 59) is steadily decreased as the daily photoperiod is increased beyond 12 hr. (*Right panel*) PRCs for pulses of increasing duration applied to a southern (M; Miyake at 34°N) and a northern (H; Hokkaido at 42°N) strain of *Drosophila auraria* in Japan. The northern strain's response to each pulse duration is weaker than that of the southern strain. The "subjective light intensity" is lower in the north.

recently discovered phenomenon of photoperiodic induction. This idea was especially appealing to me as an evolutionist: was measurement of daylength, as a signal of season, yet another function that Darwin's Demon had found for circadian oscillations, a function additional to general programming and sun-compass orientation? My attraction to the idea increased as the empirical model of entrainment promised to yield, as it eventually did, some especially valuable observations that not only added crucial support for Bunning's hypothesis, but helped define more sharply the issues involved.

Bunning divided what we now call the circadian cycle into "photophil" and "scotophil" halves that corresponded with what we now call the subjective day and subjective night. Induction of, e.g. flowering, by a long day was attributed by Bunning to the light invading the scotophil. Initially this idea was received with some sympathy in Europe, but almost none in the United States. That was especially true in the years (1950s) following the brilliant work of Hendricks and his colleagues at Beltsville, where they identifed the pigment, phytochrome, that mediates the photoperiodic responses of green plants. Given the clock paradigm, the central issue in the 1950s was seen as a time-measurement: how did the plant (or animal) measure the duration of the daily light, or was it the daily dark period? Hendricks invoked phytochrome not only as the receptor pigment, but the clock measuring the duration of the darkness at night: he saw the thermochemical reversion of phytochrome during the dark as an hourglass process that measured night-length. The attractiveness of this was clear: phytochrome was something very concrete, indeed a molecule, whereas rhythm, so Hendricks tells us (60), was seen by his colleague Borthwick as only a word; and a word, perhaps, with a vaguely dance-hall ambience?

Circadian Surfaces

A change in the attitude of American researchers to Bunning began in 1959 when Nanda & Hamner (61) reported their now classic experiments with soybeans. Holding a normally non-inductive photoperiod constant, they could induce flowering by greatly extending the duration of the associated dark period in their exotic light/dark cycles. The several inductive cycles created this way all had periods that were modulo 24 hr. One conclusion was that the duration of neither the light nor the dark was crucial; another was that there was indeed some circadian component in the reacting system, and in this sense Bunning was correct.

Much later (62), I extended this kind of Bunning support in a re-interpretation of Beck's data, which he had taken (63) as evidence that the photoperiodic clock was an hourglass, not an oscillator. I found his data yielded a surface the co-ordinates of which, in addition to response level, were the durations of light and dark in the exotic cycles to which Beck had exposed his moths. I plotted the responses as iso-induction contours (that connect all the cycles yielding a given response) which, to my surprise, defined a clear mountain peaking where the cycle length (combined durations of light and dark) was close to 24 hr, as though some circadian component in the insect were in resonance with the light cycle driving it (Figure 10, left).

I noticed that one transect (A) across this circadian surface yielded, as indeed it should, the standard photoperiodic response curve for diapause induction in *Ostrinia*. Another transect (B) corresponded with the experiments of Fritz Went, using African violets (*Saintpaulia*), in which he found that their growth rate was maximal when the light cycle's period was 24 hr and fell as it was either lengthened or shortened. Yet another transect (D) was the beginning of the protocol Nanda & Hamner had introduced in their ground-breaking experiments of 1959. The implication of this transect was obvious: if for every photoperiod that one used, the duration of the dark interval was extended out to, say, 72 hr, the single peak found in Beck's *Ostrinia* data would turn out to be only the first in a veritable range of circadian mountains.

David Saunders came to my laboratory at Stanford in 1972 just as I was about to test that proposition, using the parasitic wasp *Nasonia*, and he did the job using the blow-fly *Sarcophaga*, which he had brought with him from Edinburgh. The outcome (64) of the experiments in Palo Alto (Figure 10, right) was sufficiently rewarding to redeem the stench of *Sarcophaga* in our otherwise sweet-smelling *Drosophila* lab. I have given (62, 65) several plausible interpretations of such circadian surfaces and so has Watrus, a student of Peter Kaus, but I remain unconvinced we really understand them fully even in a formal sense.

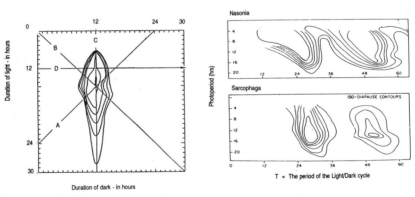

Figure 10 Circadian surfaces. (*Left panel*) Diapause induction in the European corn-borer (*Ostrinia nubilalis*) exposed to a wide range of exotic light/dark cycles. Iso-induction contours are plotted for response levels of 60, 70, 80, 90, 95, and 100%. The surface defined by these contours peaks near $T = 24$ hr, where T is the period of the light cycle (sum of the light and the dark periods) (from 62). (*Right panel*) Similar iso-induction contours for the blow fly *Sarcophaga* and the wasp *Nasonia* based on light cycles that included much longer dark periods, thus extending T, the period of the light/dark cycle, to almost 72 hr (from 64).

A Photo-Inducible Phase in the Circadian Cycle

The principal contribution of the Princeton and Stanford laboratories in developing Bunning's proposition emerged from the empirical model of entrainment. The model defined the experiments that show photoperiodic induction is not dependent on the duration of either the light or the dark in the daily cycle, but specifically on the coincidence, or non-coincidence, of light, with a very limited fraction of the subjective night. Long days are inductive not because the light lasts so long, but because, given the mechanism of entrainment, some light will coincide with the beginning or end of the subjective night. And the necessary coincidence may be very brief.

One of the experiments that established this point involved the skeleton photoperiods discussed earlier. The two brief pulses in each 24 hour cycle define two dark intervals, each of which may be taken as the night. When one of the two intervals is shorter than 10 hr, the oscillator's subjective night always falls in the longer, no matter what the initial conditions at the onset of entrainment. If, however, the two intervals in the skeleton regime both lie between 10 and 14 hr, the subjective night may fall in either the shorter or the longer interval depending on the initial conditions. In referring to all this as the bistability phenomena, one is emphasizing that for an experimental light cycle of this unusual kind, two very different stable steady states can be realized.

My late friend Bill Hillman heard me lecture on skeleton photoperiods at Brookhaven National Laboratory in the early 1960s, before the bistability complication had been clarified. He decided, as a Bunning skeptic, to see if his own experimental material (the duckweed *Lemna*) would accept two-pulse skeletons as a substitute for complete photoperiods. Specifically would his short-day plant distinguish between the skeletons of 11 and 13 hr photoperiods: a complete photoperiod of 11 hr induces flowering but one of 13 hr does not.

The experimental results, replotted and related to the bistability phenomena in (66), were spectacular and perplexing to Hillman, who nevertheless recognized their clear implication of a circadian component in the induction of flowering. His assumption had been that the two-pulse per cycle regime would be taken as the skeleton of an 11 hr photoperiod, merely by having the first dark interval be 11 hr. The initial results were unclear so he then varied the time of the first pulse. The result was (one wants to say, of course) precisely what the *Drosophila* bistability phenomenon would have predicted. The amount of flowering was high when the initial conditions (time of first pulse and duration of first interval) assured a steady state characteristic of an 11 hr photoperiod and low when the subjective day fell in the 13 hr interval (60).

Takamura and I (67) have since obtained the same results in assaying the effect of 11 and 13 hr skeletons on the induction of diapause in *Drosophila auraria*. (Figure 11). In this case, two groups of pupae from the same larval culture can be placed into the same experimental cabinet, where the two-pulse light cycle (with $T = 24$) offers the skeletons of 12 and 14 hr days, or 12 and 10 hr nights. Simply by varying the time when the two groups of pupae enter the cabinet, each of the two possible steady states can be realized: in one ($\psi 12$) the subjective night falls in the longer dark interval, and in the other ($\psi 14$) it falls in the shorter. When the incidence of diapause is assayed 10 days later, it is 27% higher in the insects on $\psi 12$ (short day) than those on $\psi 14$. The crucial issue is not the duration of either the light or the dark, but the phase of the circadian cycle that coincides with the brief light pulse; how far into the subjective night does the light penetrate?

This is also implied by the outcome of another exotic entrainment schedule that involves only one brief (15 min 50 lux) pulse per cycle. By making T increasingly different from τ, one can force the brief pulse further into the subjective night, and in doing so, one steadily reduces the incidence of diapause.

In 1964 Dorothy Minis and I (68) sketched a concrete version of this coincidence model: induction occurs when the maximum of a circadian rhythm in substrate concentration coincides with light that is necessary for activation of the relevant enzyme (40). This general approach, essentially pure Bunning, is now directly supported by the pioneering molecular observations of Kay & Miller (69), who find that the transcription of the *cab-2* gene in wheat is induced by photoactivated phytochrome, but the transcription is only success-

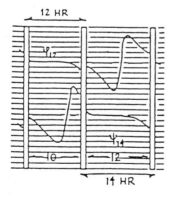
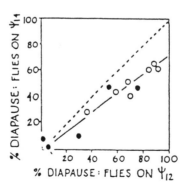

Figure 11 Photoperiodic induction and the bistability phenomena (from 67). (*Left*) The curves are PRCs tracing the time-course of the *D. auraria* pacemaker entrained by a skeleton photoperiod regime (two 1-hr light pulses per 24 hr cycle) in which the two dark intervals are 10 and 12 hr, and are separated by two 1-hr light pulses. Which of the two different steady states indicated in the figure is realized is determined by the initial conditions (see text). (*Right*) The overall level of diapause induction was varied from test to test by temperature, but in each test (a plotted point) the incidence of diapause was lower in those insects whose subjective night was compressed into the shorter dark period, as it would be on a long day.

ful when the activated phytochrome coincides with a limited phase of an ongoing circadian rhythm, the physical nature of which remains as obscure as it was when the Beltesville workers found it only a "word."

PACEMAKER AND PROGRAM : A Multi-Oscillator System

Association of Pacemaker and Photoreceptor

In the late 1950s, Janet Harker maintained that the oscillator driving the circadian rhythm of locomotory activity in the roach *Periplaneta* was housed in the insect's sub-esophageal ganglion. Enthusiastic attempts by Shephard Roberts in Princeton failed to confirm Harker (70). When Junko-Uwo came to us from Kyoto in the early 1960s, she was not only as skeptical as Roberts and myself about the Harker claim, but confident that the circadian clock of roaches would be found in their brain. In fact the experiments we did (71) indicated the optic lobes rather than the midbrain were the locus of the rhythm's bilaterally redundant pacemakers. Almost simultaneously, John Brady, a Harker student, came to the same conclusion. However, it was much later before Terry Page gave us rigorous proof based on transplantation experiments, whose serendipitous history began while he was still with us at Stanford (72).

Roaches, whose optic lobes have been surgically isolated from the midbrain, are always arrhythmic, but 30 such insects, whose utilization was inadvertently delayed a month while Page was in Europe, were found to have normal rhythms. Histological analysis showed that regeneration had indeed occurred, which permitted the pacemakers in the optic lobes to regain control. Page then found either or both native lobes could be completely removed and replaced by implants from other roaches. Using two strains with different circadian periods (one shorter, the other longer than 24 hr) he was able to make what Menaker has since happily called a "temporal chimaera." When one lobe of a long period host was replaced with an implanted lobe from a short period donor, both periods were expressed (Figure 12, lower panel), thus demonstrating pacemaker autonomy in the implanted lobe (72).

Pacemakers of many other individual circadian rhythms have now been localized, and in all of them— insect, mollusc, reptile, bird, and mammal— there is the same close association with a photoreceptor that we initially found in roaches, which emphasizes the dominant role of the light cycle in entraining the system.

Multi-Oscillator Structure of the Program

The first indication that control of a circadian program involves more than one oscillator came from observations Richard Swade and I (55) made on Arctic ground squirrels. Their daily band of activity was prone to break up

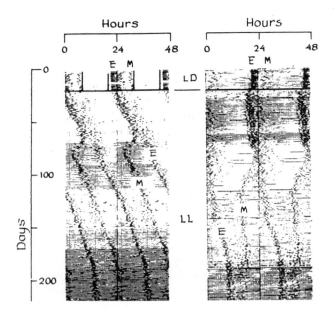

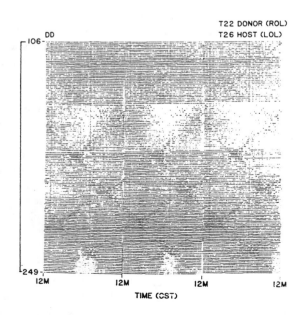

into two components that ran initially at two different circadian frequencies, but weeks later locked on to each other when their normal phase relation was re-established.

Such splitting of the day's activity into two oscillatory components was later encountered in more convincing detail when—once again serendipity!—the student who had tried to throw me out the window left hamsters in constant light for three months while he experimented with LSD instead of his animals. The prolonged exposure to light induced beautifully clear dissociation of morning and evening components in the daily program (9); those two components ran at very different frequencies until their original mutal phase relationship was regained or they reached 180° antiphase, which is an alternative stable steady state (Figure 12, upper panel).

Still more impressive evidence of many oscillators driving a program comes from experiments by Takahashi & Menaker (73) on house sparrows, in which the Menaker laboratory had already shown the principal pacemaker to be in the pineal gland, again the close association with photoreception. In an imaginative and elegant use of the bistability phenomenon we had found in *Drosophila*, Takahashi & Menaker showed that there is a host of other circadian oscillators in pinealectomised birds, each independently entrainable by the light cycle. In comparably important observations, Ishizaki and colleagues have shown that in addition to the pacemaker present in the forebrain of a *Saturnid* moth, there is another pacemaker, independently coupled to the light cycle, in its prothoracic glands.

In all these cases, each of the multiple oscillators is itself directly coupled to and entrained by light cycles. Control of the *Drosophila* eclosion rhythm, on the other hand, exemplifies multi-oscillator complexity of a different kind that has equally clear relevance to the structure of circadian programs in general. In this case, the signal that times eclosion does not come directly from the light-sensitive temperature-compensated pacemaker itself, but from a second slave oscillator that is coupled to and driven by the pacemaker. The slave oscillator differs from its pacemaker in two important respects: it is not light-sensitive, and its period is poorly temperature-compensated.

←——

Figure 12   Multiple pacemakers involved in a single circadian program. (*Upper panels*) Evening (*E*) and morning (*M*) components in the normal band of hamster activity (use of a running wheel) in each circadian cycle. They dissociate when the animal is exposed to prolonged constant light (*LL*). They continue running at different frequencies for many cycles but eventually lock on to each other again when they achieve 180° antiphase (*left*), or regain their original mutual phase-relationship (*right*) (from 9). (*Lower panel*) Two different circadian rhythms in one individual cockroach (*Leucophea madeirae*). An optic lobe from one individual whose pacemaker has a period less than 24 hr replaces the right optic lobe of a host insect whose own pacemaker has a period longer than 24 hr. When the implant has regenerated connections with the mid-brain, both periods are expressed. The animal is a "temporal chimaera" (from 72).

This is why the daily eclosion peak is advanced or delayed slightly by temperature change, although the phase of the pacemaker is not. It also explains the temperature-induced transient (a response of the slave) that misled Kalmus & Bunning into thinking the entire endogenous daily rhythm was temperature-dependent.

The lower panel in Figure 7 summarizes one of many otherwise surprising and interesting results that are explained, even predicted, by this two-oscillator structure of the system (65) and a Kaus-Curve, which in this case concerns (ψsp, the phase-lag of the slave oscillator on its pacemaker. That phase-lag is primarily a function of ρ, which is the ratio of the slave period over the pacemaker period, τs/τp. When entrainment by light shortens τp, the phase-lag of slave on pacemaker is predicted to lengthen (ρ has increased), but to shorten when entrainment lengthens τp. As the lower panel in Figure 7 shows, that is what one observes: the eclosion peak in each light/dark cycle coincides with an increasingly later phase of the pacemaker's cycle as its (pacemaker's) period is shortened by entrainment.

Collectively these observations on rodents, sparrows, moths, and flies suggest the many rhythmic components in a complex circadian program may well be timed by separate oscillators, some of them directly and others indirectly coupled to the light cycle, as the program's primary entraining agent. Even when current knowledge emphasizes the importance of a single program-pacemaker, like the supra-chiasmatic nucleus in mammals, it seems likely its control of the overall program reduces to entrainment of slave oscillations inherent in those systems it times.

While this multi-oscillator interpretation of an overall program has long seemed plausible and adequate for multicellular systems, the unicellular dinoflagellate *Gonyaulax* has eluded it. That single cell manifests five very different circadian rhythms whose maxima occur at different times of day. Phase-response-curves for the oscillation driving four of them are indistinguishable, which suggests that a common pacemaker drives all (75). While one cell/one pacemaker may have seemed plausible, it has always posed a major, if neglected, problem: how does a common pacemaker control such radically different processes as photosynthesis, bioluminescence, and mitosis? However, what is surely one of the most important developments in circadian physiology in many years appears to dispose of that problem: T. Roenneberg & D. Morse (personal communication) find that at least two of the *Gonyaulax* rhythms free-run with radically different periods, which implies that the program in this single cell clearly involves more than one pacemaker. While that disposes of the problem I thought *Gonyaulax* raised, it poses another equally challenging one: how is a light-sensitive, temperature-compensated oscillation incorporated into each of the separate components of a single cell's circadian program?

THE EVOLUTION OF CIRCADIAN ORGANIZATION

Order Precedes and Selects for Organization

The closing section of this essay, like its beginning, is Darwinian: it asks about possible origins of circadian organization as a guide to the concrete nature of its pacemaker. How did the Demon get started on programming a day within? What were the earliest selection pressures? Were they different from those prevailing today? Is their impact, given the Demon's lack of imagination, still detectable in the life of contemporary cells? Knowing his style, what can we expect?

Answers to most of these questions are necessarily conjectural, but one thing is sure: the daily cycles of temperature and light in the outside world must have imposed significant and predictable periodicity on the chemical milieu of early cells. Such order, not yet organization, would derive from inevitable variation in the temperature coefficients of the cell's constituent reactions, and the bottle-neck created by the cold at night. In a similar way the daily flood of UV and visible radiation must have created other day-night differences in the cell's photochemically reactive constituents. The resultant *temporal order* within the cell was probably as effective as the external cycles themselves in selecting for *temporal programming:* the predictable timing of one cellular event determined the optimum time for another. Such selection by temporal order internal to the cell ("The Day Within") is surely as old as that exerted more directly by the external cycles themselves ("The Day Outside").

Eukaryotic Generation Times

It seems equally clear, however, that such selection could only be effective after the cell's generation time had become as long or longer than a day because the Demon has elaborated no temporal programs whose duration exceeds the generation time of the individual organism: there are no circannual programs in organisms living less than a year; no lunar programs unless the individual lives more than a month. The nearly complete exclusion of circadian programming from prokaryotes is therefore more likely a function of their short generation time than evidence of an inadequate structural complexity. Strong support for this comes from the recent finding of a fully temperature-compensated circadian pacemaker in one prokaryote whose generation time matches that of eukaryotes (T. Kondo et al, personal communication).

In any case, the ubiquity of circadian programming in eukaryotes is a sharp reminder not just that their generation times are so much longer than those of prokaryotes, but that they cluster around the period of the earth's rotation. Lengthening its generation time must have evolved before the cell could respond to pressure for circadian organization as such. What was the Demon up to in lengthening the cell cycle? Was some crucial step in that cycle, such as copying or reading the genome, more successfully undertaken at one time of day than another? The gating of DNA replication and subsequent mitosis to the darkness of night in many flagellates certainly encourages that possibility. Whatever the pressure may have been, it is clear that the Demon has drawn out the cell cycle of eukaryotes and in so doing met a fundamental prerequisite for the subsequent (or concurrent?) evolution of circadian programs.

Escape from Light

The idea that the daily light/dark cycle has been a source of selection as well as an entraining agent in the history of our clocks was prompted by recalling a memorable exam question in graduate school: "Write an essay on the pre-requisites for organization in a chemical system." The answer that was looked for then (it was covered in lecture) was the necessity to avoid reactions that would proceed spontaneously at physiological temperatures; "relays" in the form of enzymes are essential for the necessary control. So much for the thermochemistry of the cell; it was much later before I saw the cell's daily bombardment by visible and UV radiation as a quite different, photochemical, threat to organization that specific protein relays cannot cope with. The Demon may have found, as usual, several ways around the problem including screening pigments, like flavins, at the cell level, as well as hair and colored skins at higher levels. A less obvious, but more intriguing, possibility was to select, whenever possible, for colorless alternatives among essential molecular devices; other, of course, than those exploited in energy-capture and vision. When colored components could not be replaced, was the last resort to restrict their involvement in the life of the cell to the darkness of night?

I think it likely (74) that such an escape from light has played a significant, indeed major, role in the evolution of circadian organization: that the entraining action of light will prove more complex than we have previously assumed (cf 78, 79) and reflect its earlier and overlapping role as an agent of selection.

Origin of the Photoperiodic Response

A especially appealing aspect of this possibility is its bearing on the circadian component in photoperiodic induction. In selecting primarily for temporal restriction to darkness did the Demon inevitably find some photo-sensitive reactions, still on the edge of the subjective night, were better left there? Photo-activated, but only on longer days, their temporal location in the cell's daily program provided a mechanism for sensing and responding to season. It would have been typical of the Demon to stumble on this role for daylength while responding to the different and more pervasive pressure posed by the daily bombardment of light.

Reading the Genome: Reading-Loop Oscillations

The photoperiodic phenomena themselves are most easily envisaged as the induction or suppression of a seasonally appropriate gene or genes. Is some aspect of protein synthesis impacted by light, thereby setting a premium on its relegation to darkness? Several recent developments leave no doubt that reading the genome is a central issue in circadian programming: the transcription of many genes, several in *Neurospora* (80) and *Drosophila* (R. van Gelder, personal communication) and one in wheat (69), is clock controlled. The *Drosophila* data from Russell van Gelder go further and encourage the idea that reading the genome has been part of the flight from light: the transcription of 19 out of 20 clock-controlled genes he has studied is restricted to the fly's subjective night. Why has the Demon left only 5% of these transcriptions exposed to light?

Other observations offer encouragement to the more radical proposition that the reading process is not just clock-controlled, but the fabric of the clock itself, as Ehret & Trucco (82) suggested years ago. The earliest of these was Jerry Feldman's pioneering finding, repeated and extended now with other drugs in a host of other organisms, that slowing protein synthesis slowed a circadian clock in *Euglena* (28). More recent and much more persuasive is the finding by T. Roenneberg & D. Morse (personal communication) that there are of at least two different pacemakers in the single *Gonyaulax* cell. But most impressive are the beautiful recent data from Hardin et al (83) on the circadian periodicity of transcript and gene product at Konopka's *per* locus in *Drosophila*. They strongly support the hypothesis that feedback of gene product on gene promoter is the core of the circadian oscillation. There is even evidence that light interferes with that loop in a way that would permit entrainment (48).

I am reminded here of two favorite lines from Eliot's "Little Gidding," "For last year's word belongs to last year's language/ And next year's word awaits another voice." Clearly our molecular colleagues have introduced "next year's words," giving us wholly new ways of framing questions and propositions one could state only vaguely in "last year's language." Russell van Gelder's data infuse new life into the escape from light adventure and my old suggestion that much circadian programming has a pacemaker-slave architecture. The new language would see it as cascading inhibition or stimulation of promoters at other oscillating (slave) loci by the gene product of a pacemaker locus itself directly entrained by light.

But strong as the promise of progress is here, it is also clear that the idea of a reading-loop oscillation has limited scope, even if valid. Tidal, lunar, and circannual clocks certainly elude such explanation and demand an entirely different fabric. On the other hand, such limitations, and there are others in the circadian domain itself, are no reason to reject the idea as valid within a limited scope. The Demon is notoriously prone to accept any solution that meets the prevailing challenge. So while there is good reason to think reading loop oscillations are involved in much circadian programming, either as pacemaker or slave, there is equally good reason to suspect there is much more to the story (84).

Stonehenge

One of my goals in these closing sections has been to illustrate—and enjoy!—what I take to be the real adventure in the scientific enterprise, which is, among other things, a search for pattern and meaning in what one observes. It is the necessarily conjectural nature of that search, at least at the outset, which entails hazard and makes the enterprise adventurous, not only for the observer himself, but for his observations and ideas. "Escape from light" is just such an adventure, which one enjoys for its own sake, and possibly will prove useful, perhaps even correct.

I have heard that at at the end of his Caltech lectures on "Mind from Matter," Max Delbruck admonished his very bright audience not to forget those people who, 4000 years ago, built Stonehenge. They, too, were very bright and probably knew it, but did they realize how much they didn't know? Understanding circadian and circannual programs has a long way to go.

Literature Cited

1. Pittendrigh, C. S. 1958. *J. Wash. Acad. Sci.* 48:315–16
2. Smith, L. B., Pittendrigh, C. S. 1953. *J. Wash. Acad. Sci.* 43:401–3
3. Smith, L. B., Pittendrigh, C. S. 1959. The Bromeliaceae. In *The Flora of Trinidad.* Port of Spain, Trinidad:The Government Printer
4. Pittendrigh, C. S. 1948. *Evolution* 2:58–89
5. Dawkins, R. 1986. *The Blind Watchmaker.* Longman's Scientific and Technical. pp. 1–332
6. Pittendrigh, C. S. 1961. *The Harvey Lectures.* 56:93–125
7. Rosenblith, W., Wiener, N., Bigelow, J. 1943. *J. Philos. Sci.* 10:18–34
8. Pittendrigh, C. S. 1957. In *Behavior and Evolution.* ed. A. Roe, G. G. Simpson. New Haven:Yale Univ. Press. pp. 390–416
9. Pittendrigh, C. S. 1974. In *The Neurosciences, Third Study Program.* ed. F. O. Schmitt, F. G. Worden. Cambridge, Mass:MIT Press. pp. 437–58
10. Dodds, K., Pittendrigh, C. S. 1946. *J. Genet.* 47:162–77
11. Picado, C. 1912. *Biologica* 11:110–15
12. Pittendrigh, C. S. 1950. *Evolution* 4:43–63
13. Kalmus, H. 1940. *Nature* 145:172; *Acta Med. Scand. Suppl.* 108:227–33
14. Bunning, E. 1935. *Ber. deutsch. bot. Gesell.* 53:594–623
15. Stoppel, R. 1916. *Z. Bot.* 8:609–84
16. Kramer, G. 1950. *Naturwiss* 37:188
17. Hoffmann, K. 1960. *Cold Spring Harbor Symp. Quant. Biol.* 25:370–88
18. Brown, F. A. Jr., Webb, H. M. 1948. *Physiol. Zool.* 21:371–81
19. Beling, I. 1929. *Z. fur vergl. Physiol.* 9:259–338
20. Martin, H., Lindauer, M., Martin, U. 1983. *Bay. Akad. Wiss. Math.-Nat. Klasse.* 1983:21–41
21. Brady, J. 1987. *J. Comp. Physiol. A.* 161:711–14
22. Menaker, M. 1959. *Nature* 184:1251–52

23. Rawson, K. 1960. *Cold Spring Harbor Symp. Quant. Biol.* 25:105–14
24. Bruce, V. G., Pittendrigh, C. S. 1956. *Proc. Natl. Acad. Sci. USA* 42:676–82
25. Sweeney, B., Hastings, J.-W. 1957. *J. Cell. Comp. Physiol.* 49:115–28
26. Ehret, C. 1960. *Cold Spring Harbor Symp. Quant. Biol.* 25:149–58
27. Pittendrigh, C. S., Bruce, V. G., Rosenzweig, N. S., Rubin. M. L. 1959. *Nature* 184:169–71
28. Feldman, J. F. 1967. *Proc. Natl. Acad. Sci. USA* 157:1080–87
29. Daan, S. 1981. In *Handbook of Behavioral Physiology, Vol.4 Biological Rhythms,* ed. J. Aschoff, New York:Plenum. pp. 275–98
30. Hawking, F. 1967. *Proc. R. Soc. London Ser. B* 169:59–76
31. Medina, E. 1974. *Evolution* 28:677–86
32. Kleber, E. 1935. *Z. vergl. Physiol.* 22:221–62
33. Neumann. D. 1981. See Ref. 29, pp. 351–80
34. Gwinner. E. 1986. *Circannual Rhythms.* Berlin:Springer
35. Edmunds, L. N. 1988. *Cellular and Molecular Bases of Biological Clocks.* New York: Springer-Verlag. pp. 1–497
36. Szabo, I., Kovats.T. G., Halberg. F. 1978. *Chronobiologica* 5:137–43
37. Aschoff, J., St. Paul, U., Wever, R. 1971. *Naturwiss.* 58:574
38. Pittendrigh, C. S., Minis, D. M. 1972. *Proc. Natl. Acad. Sci. USA* 69:1537–39
39. Went, F. 1960. *Cold Spring Harbor Symp. Quant. Biol.* 25:221–30
40. Hufeland, Chr. W. 1823. *Macrobiotik.* Berlin: G. Reimer. pp.1–616. (1st ed. 1798, Jena)
41. Kalmus, H. 1935. *Biol. Generalis* 11: 93–114
42. Pittendrigh, C. S., 1954. *Proc. Natl. Acad. Sci. USA* 40:1018-29
43. Schmidt-Koenig, K. 1961. *Naturwiss.* 48:110
44. Aschoff, J., Meyer-Lohmann, J. 1954. *Pflügers Arch.* 260:170–76
45. Pittendrigh, C. S. 1958. In *Perspectives in Marine Biology,* ed. A. Buzzatti-Trvaerso. Berkeley:Univ. Calif Press. pp. 239–68
46. Pittendrigh, C. S., Bruce, V. G. 1959. In *Photoperiodism and Related Phenomena in Plants and Animals,* ed. A. R. Withrow, R. Withrow. Am. Assoc. Adv. Sci. pp. 475–505
47. Pittendrigh, C. S., Bruce, V. G. 1957. In *Rhythmic and Synthetic Processes in Growth,* ed. D. Rudnick. Princeton: Princeton Univ. Press. pp. 75–109

48. Pringle, J. W. S. 1951. *Behavior* 3:274–315
49. Konopka, R., Pittendrigh, C. S., Orr, D. 1989. *J. Neurogenet.* 6:1–10
50. Pittendrigh. C. S., Daan, S. 1976. *J. Comp. Physiol.* 106:291–331
51. Winfree, A. T. 1970. *J. Theoret. Biol.* 28:327–74
52. Pittendrigh, C. S. 1965. In *Circadian Clocks,* ed. J. Aschoff. pp. 277–97. Netherlands:North-Holland
53. Wells, J. W. 1963. *Nature* 197:948–50
54. Aschoff, J. 1960. *Cold Spring Harbor Symp. Quant. Biol.* 25:11–28
55. Pittendrigh, C. S. 1960. *Cold Spring Harbor Symp. Quant. Biol.* 25:159–82
56. Pittendrigh, C. S. 1979. In *Biological Rhythms and their Central Mechanism,* ed. M. Suda, O. Hayaishi, H. Nakagawa. pp. 3–12. New York:Elsevier
57. Pittendrigh, C. S. 1988. *J. Biol. Rhythms* 3:173–88
58. Pittendrigh, C. S., Takamura, T. 1989. *J. Biol. Rhythms* 4:217–35
59. Pittendrigh, C. S., Kyner., W. T., Taka mura, T. 1989. *J. Biol. Rhythms* 6:299–313
60. Hendricks, S. B. 1976. In *Biographical Memoirs of the National Academy of Sciences.* Washington, DC:Natl. Acad. Sci. USA. pp. 105–22
61. Nanda, K. K., Hamner, K. C. 1959. *Planta* 53:45–52
62. Pittendrigh, C. S. 1972. *Proc. Natl. Acad. Sci. USA* 69:2734–37
63. Beck, S. D. 1962. *Biol. Bull.* 122:1–12
64. Saunders, D. S. 1973. *J. Insect Physiol.* 19:1941–45
65. Pittendrigh, C. S. 1981. In *Biological Clocks and Seasonal Reproductive Cycles,* ed. B. K. Follett. pp. 1–35. Bristol:John Wright
66. Pittendrigh, C. S., Minis, D. M. 1971. In *Biochronometry,* ed. M. Menaker. pp. 212–50. Washington, DC: Natl. Acad. Sci. USA
67. Pittendrigh, C. S., Takamura, T. 1987. *Proc. Natl. Acad. Sci. USA* 84:7169–73
68. Pittendrigh, C. S., Minis, D. M. 1964. *Am. Natl.* XCVIII:261–94
69. Kay, S., Miller, A. J. 1992. In *Molecular Genetics of Biological Rhythms,* ed. M. Young. pp. 73–89. New York:Decker
70. Roberts, S. K. 1960. *J. Cell. Comp. Physiol.* 55:99–110; *J. Cell. Comp. Physiol.* 59:175–86
71. Nishiitsutsuji-Uwo, J., Pittendrigh, C. S. 1968. *Z. vergl. Physiol.* 58:14–46
72. Page, T. L. 1983. *J. Comp. Physiol.* 153:353–63

73. Takahashi, J., Menaker, M. 1982. *J. Comp. Physiol. Ser. A* 146:245–53
74. Pittendrigh, C. S. 1965. In *Science and the Sixties, Proc. 1965 Cloudcroft Symp.* Air Force Office of Scientific Research, pp. 95–111
75. Sweeney, B. 1969. *Rhythmic Phenomena in Plants.* New York:Academic
76. Deleted in proof
77. Deleted in proof
78. Roenneberg, T., Hastings, J. W. 1991. *Photochem. Photobiol.* 53:525–33
79. Johnson, C. H., Kondo, T., Hastings, J. W. 1991. *Plant Physiol.* 97:1122–29
80. Loros, J. J., Denome, S. A., Dunlap, J. C. 1989. *Science* 243:385–88
81. Deleted in proof
82. Ehret, C., Trucco, E. 1967. *J. Theoret. Biol.* 15:240–62
83. Hardin, P. E., Hall, J. C., Rosbash, M. 1990. *Nature* 343:536–40
84. Pittendrigh, C. S. 1976. In *The Molecular Basis of Circadian Rhythms,* ed. J. W. Hastings, H.-G. Schwieger. pp. 11–48. Berlin:Dahlem Konferenzen

Annu. Rev. Physiol. 1993. 55:55–75

CONTROL OF CARDIAC GENE EXPRESSION BY MECHANICAL STRESS

Issei Komuro and Yoshio Yazaki

The Third Department of Internal Medicine, Faculty of Medicine, University of Tokyo, Tokyo 113, Japan

KEY WORDS: myocardium, gene expression, protein kinase C, stretch-sensitive channel, cAMP

INTRODUCTION

Cardiac growth can be divided into two categories: normal growth in the developmental process and cardiac hypertrophy induced by hemodynamic overload. Since cardiac myocytes are terminally differentiated and lose their ability to duplicate soon after birth, they respond to increased workload only by an increase in cell size (hypertrophy), not by an increase in cell number (hyperplasia). Moreover, the induction of specific gene expression is observed in cardiac hypertrophy. Cardiac hypertrophy induced by hemodynamic overload has two important aspects. The first is a medical issue. Cardiac hypertrophy and the resulting heart failure due to valvular disease and hypertension are one of the main causes of mortality and morbidity in humans. Although cardiac hypertrophy by a chronic overload per se is not a pathological but rather a physiological response of the heart to pathological states, heart failure as a final form of hypertrophy is an obvious disease. To know the mechanisms of cardiac hypertrophy by overload might pave the way to understand the mechanisms of heart failure.

The second aspect of cardiac hypertrophy is of biological interest. Cardiac myocytes respond to overload not only by an increase in cell volume, but also by altered expressions of specific genes. The myocardium has an extraordinary plasticity at the biochemical level as well as at the physiological level, and the regulation of gene expression is dynamic in the heart. There are many examples that show external physical (mechanical) stimuli to have significant effects on

55

the cell interior (e.g. sound, hair cells of the ear, shear stress, endothelial cells of the vasculature etc). Cardiac hypertrophy is one of the most important prototypes, and the myocardium is an excellent model system in which to address the broad biological questions. Therefore, we need to know how mechanical stimuli are converted into intracellular biochemical signals that lead to qualitative as well as quantitative changes in gene expressions in the heart. There should be receptors, transducers, and effectors for mechanical stress in the heart, and by understanding these signaling pathways, we should be able to elucidate the mechanisms of cardiac hypertrophy and failure.

CARDIAC GENE REGULATION BY MECHANICAL STRESS

Immediate Early Genes

The heart first responds to increased work load by altered function and next by an increase in muscle mass and by changes of gene expression. Much evidence indicates that the activation of a new program of gene expression in the overloaded heart is important to maintain cardiac function as an adaptation. Over the last several years, many genes that are responsive to increased workload have been identified in the heart. These genes can be divided into two classes: one is called immediate early genes (IEG), a group of genes whose transcription is activated rapidly and transiently within minutes of extracellular stimulation (35, 60, 77). This transcriptional induction is independent of new protein synthesis, but subsequent shut-off of transcription requires new protein synthesis (10, 16). The tightly controlled expression of IEG suggests a regulatory role in the cellular response to external stimuli. The second class is called the late response genes, whose expression is induced more slowly, over hours, and also needs new protein synthesis. Many IEGs were first isolated from fibroblasts as growth factor-responsive genes that might control the reentry of Go resting cells into the cell cycle. However, accumulating evidence suggests that IEGs not only play critical roles in the cell cycle, but also regulate the transcription of a variety of genes. At present, approximately 100 IEGs have been identified, and several genes such as the *fos* family (*c-fos, fra-1, fos-B*) (20, 34, 115), *jun* family (*c-jun, junB, junD*) (81, 92), *c-myc* (50), *Egr-1* (also termed *zif268, Krox24, NGFI-A*) (18, 68, 73, 104), and *nur/77* (also termed *NGFI-B*) (40, 74) have been well characterized.

The protein products of *c-fos* (Fos) and *c-jun* (Jun) interact with each other to form a heterodimeric transcription factor complex through a conserved dimerization motif, referred to as the leucine zipper (64). The leucine zipper domain is an α-helical structure composed of leucine residues spaced seven amino acids apart that promotes dimerization. The Fos/Jun heterodimer binds with high affinity and specificity to DNA elements of the consensus sequence, termed TRE, which was first identified as a phorbol ester-inducible promoter element and the binding site for a transcription factor, AP-1 (2, 67). Fos and Jun were recently shown to be the major constituents of AP-1 (11). There has been much evidence indicating that the expressions of *c-fos* and *c-jun* are induced rapidly by a number of external stimuli and that the Fos/Jun complex then turns on the expression of late response genes containing AP-1 sites (63). The regulatory specificity of the various combinations of the members of Fos and Jun family might be distinct. Whereas c-Fos/c-Jun complexes transactivate a number of genes containing AP-1 sites, c-Fos/JunB complexes repress them under some circumstances (17). Studies on *c-fos* induction in differentiated neuronal cells have provided evidence that IEGs also have a regulatory function in post-mitotic cells (35). The expression of *c-fos* was induced by specific neurotransmitters or depolarization in neuronal cells, and the transcription of neuronal genes such as the proenkephalin gene was activated because it contains an AP-1 binding site (100). The mechanism by which IEGs are induced is best characterized by studies of *c-fos*. *c-fos* is induced by multiple intracellular second messengers acting through distinct upstream regulating elements. Transcriptional activation by PKC is mediated by serum response element (SRE) located 300 bp upstream of the mRNA initiation site. The SRE consists of a 20 bp dyad symmetric sequence and is the specific binding site for dimeric serum response factor (SRF) and other associated factors such as SAP-1 (24, 108). Since SRF is abundantly expressed in a variety of cells before stimulation, PKC may activate SRF by modifying preexisting SRF or associated proteins; however, the precise mechanism is still unknown. *c-fos* stimulation by cAMP and Ca^{2+} is dependent on the Ca^{2+}/cAMP regulatory element (CRE) located 60 bp upstream of the mRNA start site. The Ca^{2+}/CRE is an 8 bp palindromic sequence and is the specific binding site for the dimeric transcription factor, CREB. The increase in intracellular cAMP and Ca^{2+} activate protein kinase A and Ca^{2+}/calmodulin kinase, respectively, and these kinases phosphorylate CREB at a specific residue (Ser-133) and activate it as a transcription factor (113).

 c-myc has been implicated in controlling both proliferation and differentiation in various cell types (71). Increased expression of *c-myc* results in an increase in the rate of proliferation and prevents differentiation (23, 89). Inhibition of *c-myc* expression by antisense strategy inhibits proliferation and initiates differentiation of a variety of cell types (36). Although *c-myc* is also a transcription factor and is able to induce a family of heat shock proteins (53), the transcriptional mechanism by which *c-myc* acts has not been clarified. Recently, *Max*, a partner of *c-myc* in forming a heterodimer complex, has been isolated, and the transcriptional functions of *c-myc* have been further elucidated (9). *Egr-1* was also isolated as an early response gene to growth factors. *Egr-1* is abundantly expressed in the brain and heart, and there is good correlation between the *Egr-1* expression and long-term potentiation (21). Taken together, IEGs might control the expression of late response genes as nuclear mediators that couple external stimuli to long-term changes in gene expression.

Immediate Early Genes in the Heart

As a model for the induction of IEGs by mechanical stress, expression of *c-fos* and *c-myc* was first reported in the rat heart in vivo (47, 59, 79). The expression of the same protooncogenes was reported in an isolated perfused rat heart (6). In a beating heart, but not an arrested one, the expression levels of protooncogenes paralleled coronary flow (and/or pressure). In another recent experiment, the induction of *c-fos* expression was observed in the cardiomyocytes of an isolated beating heart, and its level was proportional to the magnitude of peak LV systolic wall stress (94). These results suggest that mechanical stimuli such as coronary flow and systolic wall stress could directly induce the expression of IEGs in cardiomyocytes of the heart.

Since the heart consists of a syncytium of neural, vascular, endothelial, interstitial, and muscle cells, even in the perfused isolated heart, it is not possible to unequivocally evaluate the role of mechanical stress in controlling the gene expression in cardiomyocytes. Therefore, the authors have established an in vitro loading system that employs cultured quiescent cardiomyocytes. Since it is well known that stretching of the ventricular wall during hemodynamic overload is the most important mechanical factor for increased protein synthesis (112), neonatal rat cardiocytes were cultured in deformable silicone dishes, with defined serum-free media. A mechanical load was imposed by stretching the adherent cells (55, 56, 57, I. Komuro, unpublished data). Myocyte stretching stimulated expression of the IEGs such as *c-fos*, *c-myc*, *c-jun*, and *Egr-1*, in a stretch length-dependent manner, followed by an increase in amino acid incorporation into proteins. The induction of *c-fos* was most prominent (more than 20-fold) among these IEGs, and its expression levels were comparable to those found with the addition of 10^{-7}M– 10^{-8}M angiotensin II. The other three genes were slightly induced by stretching (three- to fivefold). *c-fos* mRNA induction was observed more abundantly in a myocyte-rich fraction than in a non-myocyte-rich fraction, which suggests that there might be heterogeneity in response to mechanical stress among cell types. The expression kinetics were similar to those of other cells stimulated by growth factors. Nuclear run-off experiments showed that *fos* expression was regulated at least in part at the transcriptional level. These results indicate that mechanical stress (stretch) directly regulates the expression of IEGs in cardiomyocytes. In other words, the initial response to the mechanical stimuli in the terminally differentiated cardiomyocytes might mimic early events of cell division induced by growth factors in a variety of cell types.

As mentioned above, Fos/Jun heterodimer complexes (AP-1) bind to TRE/AP-1 sequences in the 5′ flanking region and transactivate the expression of many genes. Actually atrial natriuretic factor (ANF) (61) and transforming growth factor β (TGFβ) (52) have TRE/AP-1 binding sites in the promoter regions and may become targets of these IEGs (ANF and AP-1 are discussed below). Recently, it was reported, using co-transfection assays, that *c-jun* or *c-jun/c-fos* transactivate human skeletal α-actin gene expression. The sequence between −153 and −36 of the 5′ flanking region is required for full transactivation and, interestingly, there are no consensus AP-1 sites in this sequence (7). These results suggest that skeletal α-actin may be regulated by the Fos/Jun complex and that there may be other transcriptional mechanisms activated by the Fos/Jun complex in addition to the AP-1/TRE mechanism.

c-myc is abundantly expressed in the heart during the fetal period; however, its expression becomes undetectable soon after birth (59). This observation suggests a relationship between *c-myc* expression and cardiocyte proliferation, and this notion was supported by findings in transgenic mice (45). The increased *c-myc* mRNA expression in cardiomyocytes of transgenic mice induced marked cardiac enlargement by myocyte hyperplasia during fetal development, but not by hypertrophy. The distribution of cardiac and skeletal α-actin isoforms was identical in the hearts of transgenic mice and nontransgenic mice. These results indicate that elevated *c-myc* mRNA expression stimulates hyperplastic myocyte growth, but does not induce cell hypertrophy, nor alter the terminal differentiation.

Egr-1 mRNA was induced by hemodynamic overload in vivo, and by α1-adrenergic agonists and stretch in vitro (42, I. Komuro, unpublished data). *Egr-1* has a zinc finger DNA-binding motif and has the ability to transactivate other genes, which have the target sequence, CGCCCCGC (104). In the cardiac genes, this sequence is not known as an important *cis* regulatory element, except as a serum response element of αMHC (38). However, since this sequence is relatively common and the sequence requirement of *Egr-1* seems to be relatively relaxed, there is a possibility that *Egr-1* may transactivate some cardiac genes after mechanical stress.

Other Early Load-Response Genes

In addition to these known genes, several other genes rapidly change their expression levels in the heart by hemodynamic overload (60). Using in vitro translation and two-dimensional gel electrophoresis, 10 out of over 400 translational products were recognized to rapidly change their mRNA levels. Although translatable mRNAs are quite different between adult and fetal hearts, most of pressure overload-response mRNAs exist in fetal hearts. These overload-response genes were isolated by a differential hybridization technique. One of these clones hybridized with two mRNAs of different size. Of interest is the fact that the larger transcript was not detectable before pressure overload, but it appeared soon after the imposition of load. Although the origin of these two transcripts remains unknown, the larger transcript was also induced by the inhibition of protein synthesis, and it was detected in the fetal and spontaneously hypertensive rat (SHR) heart. These results suggest that several genes rapidly respond to hemodynamic overload and that although there are significant differences in the growth rate between fetal hearts (hyperplasia with growth factors) and adult hearts (hypertrophy by mechanical stress), the hypertrophic response of adult cardiomyocytes to hemodynamic overload may mimic the mitogenic response of embryonic cells.

Reexpression of Fetal-Type Genes

The contraction unit of the myocardium is the sarcomere. The sarcomere has seven major proteins, myosin heavy chain (MHC), myosin light chain (MLC), tropomyosin (TM), troponin complex (TnT, TnI, TnC), and actin, and several minor ones. The major proteins have multiple isoforms generated by alternative pre-mRNA splicing (14) (α- and β-TM, TnT, and MLC) and by a multigene family (105) (MHC, MLC, actin, TM, TnT, TnI, and TnC). The expression of each member of these multigene families is regulated at the transcriptional level in a tissue-specific and developmentally regulated manner. In cardiac hypertrophy induced by increased afterload, some of these contractile protein genes are selectively activated, both at the alternative pre-mRNA splicing level (βTM) (44) and at the transcriptional level (βMHC, smooth and skeletal α-actin) (8, 43, 95). This response is characterized by the reexpression of the protein isoforms that are ordinarily expressed in the embryonic heart, but not in the adult heart. The reexpression of fetal isoforms in cardiac hypertrophy mimics the mitogenic response of many differentiated cell types, such as hepatocytes. During liver regeneration after hepatectomy or carbon tetrachloride infusion, fetal proteins such as alpha fetoprotein are upregulated (93). As a late response fetal gene, MHC is best studied both at the physiological and molecular levels (1, 69). In cardiac hypertrophy induced by hemodynamic overload, the Ca^{2+}-activated myosin ATPase is depressed and the change results from the shift from the V1 (homodimer of αMHC) to V3 (homodimer of βMHC) isoform. The transition from V1 to V3 decreases the initial speed of shortening, but improves the efficiency of contraction for an equivalent amount of work, which suggests that it might be the result of adaptation by the cardiac muscle. The physiological meanings of isoform transitions of other proteins have not been clarified.

This reprogramming of gene expression in the heart by hemodynamic overload is not limited to contractile proteins, but includes proteins involved in enzymes, such as creatine kinase (41), and hormones like ANF (25, 66). ANF is expressed in the ventricle as well as in the atrium during embryonic development, but after birth, the expression of ANF is restricted to the atrium and it is hardly detectable in the normal adult ventricle. In the overloaded ventricle, however, ANF is abundantly reexpressed. Since ANF has potent natriuretic, diuretic, and vasodilatory effects, the induction of ANF in the ventricle in response to hemodynamic overload might be interpreted as an adaptational response to reduce wall stress. Mechanical stretch induced the expressions of skeletal α-actin, βMHC, and ANF in the cultured cardiocytes (56, 57, I. Komuro & Y. Yazaki, unpublished data). This fetal gene induction by mechanical stress might be at least partially or, more likely, mainly at the pretranslational level. α1-adrenergic agonists have been known to stimulate protein synthesis and evoke reexpression of fetal genes in the cardiomyocytes in a manner that is similar to mechanical stress, and the α1-adrenergic response elements have been characterized in several genes. In skeletal α-actin 5' flanking sequence, a 67 bp fragment (-113–46) conferred myocyte specificity and inducible ability by α1-adrenergic stimulation (48). This fragment contains a CArG box, Sp1, and M-CAT consensus sequences. A 64 bp region $(-215/-152)$ of βMHC gene promoter mediates myocyte-specific and α1-adrenergic stimulated expression, and some protein binding was observed in $-215/-195$ elements (47). Several candidate cis-elements for mediating α-adrenergic expression were determined within the 315 bp sequence $(-638/-323)$ of ANF (CRE, AP-2, AP-1, Egr-1, CArG) and the 92 bp $(-92/+1)$ sequence of MLC-2 (AP-1, CArG, MEF-2, AP-2) fragments (54). Since α1-adrenergic stimulation and mechanical stress may share common signal transduction pathways, including PKC activation, response elements of the genes for mechanical stress may be the same as those for α1-adrenergic stimulation.

The induction of ANF gene expression during hypertrophy may be regulated by protooncogenes, c-fos and c-jun. ANF gene expression has been known to be regulated by a variety of stimuli such as hormones (25, 30) and physical stretch of myocardial tissue (66). As intracellular signals, activation of PKC induces secretion of ANF as well as expression of the ANF gene (65). PKC stimulates the expression of both the c-fos and c-jun genes and activates target gene expression through the AP-1 complex. In ANF 5' flanking region, there are three potential AP-1 binding sites. Recently, c-jun/c-fos complex was shown to interact with this region, and selective mutation of this site suppressed basal activity of the ANF promoter (61). Overexpression of c-fos had a biphasic effect on ANF gene promoter activity. At low levels, c-fos activated the ANF gene expression in concert with c-jun, while at higher levels, c-fos suppressed it via its carboxy-terminal domain. This is the first report showing that protooncogenes may code for potential second messengers that may link environmental stimuli with other forms of gene expression of later events in the cardiac hypertrophy.

In contrast to those upregulated genes, some genes are down-regulated by hemodynamic overload. One of these genes encodes the Ca^{2+}-ATPase of the sarcoplasmic reticulum. The mRNA level of Ca^{2+}-ATPase is gradually decreased by pressure overload in the animal model (58, 80), and the reduced expression of Ca^{2+}-ATPase was observed in the failing human heart (72). The down-regulation of Ca^{2+}-ATPase is not only induced by mechanical stress, but also by the addition of some growth factors (86), and the expression levels are greatly reduced during the fetal stage (58). This decrease in mRNA levels is accompanied by reduced protein levels, which may be, at least in part, the reason for the abnormal Ca^{2+} handling in the hypertropic, failing, and fetal hearts. Down-regulation of specific genes is also observed during liver regeneration, such as those that encode albumin, cytochrome P450 R-17, apoA-1 and apoE (93). Therefore, we can conclude that changes in pre-translational regulation of specific genes during cardiac hypertrophy reflect a return to an earlier state of cardiocyte differentiation. In addition, this phenomenon suggests the existence of common mechanisms of transcriptional regulation between fetal hearts and hypertrophic hearts.

MECHANISMS OF CARDIAC GENE REGULATION BY MECHANICAL STRESS

Acceleration of protein synthesis in the heart by mechanical stimulus was first reported by stretching quiescent papillary muscle in vitro (87). Elevation of aortic pressure in perfused hearts caused an increase in protein synthesis (106). Papillary muscle, whose tendon was cut to release the tension, did not show hypertrophy even during aortic constriction, whereas the neighboring uncut papillary muscle showed marked hypertrophy (22). As mentioned above, specific gene expression is also induced by mechanical stress during cardiac hypertrophy. How can the mechanical stress be converted into biochemical signals? Are the transduction mechanisms or second messenger systems different between protein synthesis and gene expression? The authors have examined these questions using the in vitro stretch model, where mechanical stimuli can be directly added and the possibility of the participation of humoral or neural factors can be excluded. Myocyte stretching stimulated expression of IEGs, followed by the expression of fetal genes, and by an increase in protein synthesis (55, 56, 57). These results suggest that this in vitro stretch model mimics the in vivo heart exposed to hemodynamic overload. Since c-fos expression by stretching was quite significant (more than a 20-fold increase) and rapid (detectable within 5 min), we used c-fos expression as a molecular marker to examine the signal transduction pathways from mechanical stress to gene expression.

Phospholipase C—PKC

GENE EXPRESSION   The load-response element of *c-fos* gene promoter was first examined in order to understand the mechanisms of *c-fos* induction by stretching. The transfected chloramphenicol acetyltransferase gene linked to upstream sequences of the *c-fos* gene indicated that the sequences containing an SRE were required for efficient transcription by stretching and that sequences containing a Ca^{2+}/CRE were not sufficient for *c-fos* response to stretching (57). This result suggests the involvement of PKC in *c-fos* expression by mechanical stress, which was supported by pharmacological studies. The *c-fos* induction was suppressed by the inhibitors for PKC and by down-regulation of PKC. *c-fos* gene expression was not inhibited by streptomycin and gadolinium, which are thought to block the stretch-activated ion channels (84, 114), amilorides (blocker of Na^+/H^+ pump), terazosin and yohimbine (α1- and α2-adrenergic antagonist, respectively), propranolol (β-adrenergic antagonist), tetrodotoxin (Na^+ channel blocker), nifedipine, diltiazem, and nicardipine (Ca^{2+} channel blocker), pertussis toxin (Gi protein inhibitor), or by short exposure to EDTA. The *c-fos* expression was observed even under Na^+-free (replaced by choline) or Ca^{2+}-free media (56, 57). These pharmacological data suggest that the *c-fos* induction by stretching in the cardiomyocytes depends on the PKC activation, but not on Ca^{2+} or Na^+ ions and that adrenergic receptors or Gi protein may not be involved in these signal transduction pathways. Inositol phosphate levels were measured in the cardiocytes, in the presence or absence of mechanical stress, as an index of increased formation of intracellular regulators of stress. Myocyte stretching slightly but significantly increased inositol phosphate levels, which suggests that PKC can be activated by an accompanying product, 1,2-diacylglycerol (DG). Activation of PKC by phorbol esters or DG stimulated the expression of protooncogenes and fetal genes. As mentioned above, activation of the α1-adrenergic receptor results in the selective upregulation of the protooncogene (*c-myc*) and fetal genes (skeletal α-actin and βMHC) (70). The expression of these genes is induced by the activation of α1a-receptor subtype that is responsible for phosphatidylinositol hydrolysis, but not by the activation of β1b-receptor that promotes Ca^{2+}influx. More directly, PKC was demonstrated to directly activate βMHC, MLC-2, and ANF transcription by co-transfection of constitutively activated PKC and reporter genes (36, 46). Taken together, these results strongly suggest that PKC might be a key component in the pathway between mechanical stress and gene regulation. Since PKC is a serine/threonine kinase, PKC might regulate gene expression through phosphorylation of transcription factors or other regulators. The activities of two nuclear enhancer-binding proteins, AP-1 and AP-2, were shown to be increased by phorbol esters, and PKC has been shown to phosphorylate a nuclear transcription factor CREB (113) and cytosolic regulator IkB (31), in vitro.

PROTEIN SYNTHESIS   Extensive evidence suggests that PKC activation stimulates protein synthesis in the cardiomyocytes. Since the mechanisms of general protein synthesis may be different from those of specific gene expression, the signal transduction pathway of protein synthesis that was activated by stretching was examined to define sites of phosphorylation using the same in vitro stretch model (T. Yamazaki & Y. Yazaki, unpublished data).

Increased protein synthesis in response to hormones and growth factors is generally associated with an increase in phosphorylation of S6 protein in the 40S ribosome (103). The increase in S6 phosphorylation is thought to be caused by increased S6 kinase activity. It has been recently reported that S6 kinase is phosphorylated and activated by a mitogen-activated protein (MAP) kinase (102), which is a serine/threonine protein kinase (33) that can be activated by a variety of stimuli such as growth factors and tumor promoters (12). Thus MAP kinase is proposed to play an important role in the increased efficiency of protein synthesis in 40S ribosome. The authors examined MAP kinase activity of cardiac myocytes before and after stretching, using MBP as an exogenous substrate. MBP kinase activity was increased after stretching, and this observation was confirmed by using a MAP kinase-specific antibody. The phosphorylation sites were phosphothreonine and phosphotyrosine residues. By using MBP-containing gels, increased MBP kinase activities migrating at 43 kd (MAP kinase) and 76 kd (PKC) were observed. Since activation of MAP kinase was partially dependent on PKC activity, PKC may be upstream of MAP kinase. Recently MAP kinase was shown to phosphorylate and activate the protooncogene, c-jun (88). Since some amount of c-jun is expressed in the heart before stretching, the induction of c-fos by PKC, and phosphorylation and activation of pre-existing c-jun by MAP kinase can synergistically activate the function of the AP-1 complex. A ras oncogene product $p21^{c-ras}$ recently was shown to mediate PKC modulation of MAP kinase and S6 kinase (111). Since ras family genes are abundantly expressed in the heart, it is of interest to know what roles $p21^{c-ras}$, including GTP-bound activated $p21^{c-ras}$, play in cardiac hypertrophy caused by stretching.

As discussed above, the signal transduction pathways of mechanical stress in the cardiocytes may be similar to those of growth factors and hormones. Considerable biochemical and pharmacological data in other cells indicate the existence of complex interactions among a number of signals, and this may be true in the cardiocytes as well. Several other second messenger systems for protein synthesis have been reported in the myocardium; however, the regulation of gene expression has not been well examined in many cases. Thus the mechanisms of hypertrophy, but not of gene regulation, are mainly discussed for other second messengers.

Adenylate Cyclase—cAMP

cAMP has been reported to induce cardiac hypertrophy from a variety of stimuli. The increase in cAMP by mechanical stretch was first observed in the isolated frog ventricle (99). When aortic perfusion pressure was raised in either beating or tetrodotoxin-arrested rat hearts, rates of protein synthesis and ribosome formation were accelerated, which were dependent on increases in cAMP content and cAMP-dependent protein kinase activity (19, 32, 112). Many genes are known to be regulated by cAMP, and the cAMP-regulated genes are divided into two groups (90). Group 1 genes are rapidly induced by cAMP and are insensitive to a protein synthesis inhibitor, while group 2 genes are induced slowly. Two *cis*-acting elements have been identified in the genes of group 1, cAMP regulatory elements (CRE) and activator protein 2 binding sites (AP-2). Since the activation of the protein kinase A by cAMP is necessary for the activation of gene transcription, and since cAMP does not alter the binding affinity of AP-2 or CREB for their respective regulatory elements, cAMP may regulate gene transcription by phosphorylating the transcriptional activation domains of the CREB or AP-2. Although AP-2 sequences are found in ANF, MLC-2, and MLC-1 5′ flanking regions (54, 62), it is not known whether these AP-2 elements are important for expression of these genes. The altered gene expression by mechanical stress might not be caused by cAMP for the following reasons. When the heart was subjected to pressure overload in vivo, or the cultured cardiocytes were stretched in vitro, the expression levels of *Egr-1*, βMHC, and ANF were increased. These genes are known to be induced in vitro through α1- but not β-adrenergic-mediated mechanisms (42, 54, 70). These results suggest that an α-adrenergic-mediated mechanism, possibly involving PKC activation, but not the β-adrenergic pathway, involving (cAMP), may be important for gene regulation by mechanical stress.

Mechanosensitive Channels—Ion Flux

Many cells respond to a variety of environmental stimuli by ion channels in the plasma membrane (78). Mechanosensitive ion channels are ideal candidates for the primary transduction event, i.e. the sensing of membrane tension. It is a question whether single-channel mechanosensitivity is an artifact of patch recording, however, mechanosensitive ion channels have been observed with single-channel recordings in more than 30 cell types of prokaryotes, plants, fungi, and all animals so far studied (78). Stretch-activated channels have been proposed as the transduction mechanism between load and protein synthesis in cardiac hypertrophy (15). The existence of ionic channels that opened, or increased their frequency of opening, was shown by applying patch-clamp techniques to cultured chicken embryo cardiac myocytes (37) and to isolated adult guinea pig cardiocytes (15). These stretch-sensitive channels allowed the passage of the major monovalent physiological cations, Na^+ and K^+. Using Ca^{2+}-binding fluorescent dye, mechanically induced Ca^{2+} changes, which suggest Ca^{2+}-induced Ca^{2+} release, were also reported (W. Sigurdson, unpublished). Na^+ influx through stretch-sensitive channels was also observed in adult ferret papillary muscle by increasing the mechanical load (51). Na^+ uptake and protein synthesis were increased by stretch in quiescent or contracting papillary muscle, and both increases were inhibited by streptomycin. With use of several regulating agents, Na^+ influx was shown to be sufficient and necessary for protein synthesis in the heart.

When the Na^+ ionophore, monensin or veratridine, was added to cultured cardiomyocytes, c-fos expression was observed, possibly because of increased Ca^{2+} uptake by the Na^+/Ca^{2+} exchange, but the expression of fetal-type genes was not induced (56, I. Komuro & Y. Yazaki, unpublished data). Although we cannot rule out the existence of gadolinium-insensitive stretch channels in cardiomyocytes, gadolinium could not inhibit the c-fos expression by stretching (I. Komuro, unpublished observation). Streptomycin, amiloride, or ouabain (Na^+-K^+ ATPase inhibitor) had no effect on c-fos induction by stretching (56). The hypothesis that cardiac deformation opens stretch-activated channels, induces Na^+ or Ca^{2+} influx, and then stimulates protein synthesis is straightforward; however, the mechanisms of gene expression by stretching may not involve Na^+ loading, at least in neonatal cardiomyocytes.

Paracrine and/or Autocrine Mechanisms

Many cells produce and secrete a variety of growth factors and cytokines. Cardiomyocytes or other cells in the heart such as endothelial cells, fibroblasts, and smooth muscle cells may secrete some hypertrophy-promoting factors following a stretch stimulus. Mechanical stress in myocardial cells has been reported to increase the synthesis of some growth-promoting factors (39). A cardiac hypertrophy-related factor has been purified recently (96). It is not known whether this factor is induced by mechanical stimuli. There are many known factors that promote cardiac hypertrophy. A number of growth factors, including acidic and basic fibroblast growth factor (FGF), TGFβ, insulin-like growth factor I and II, have been reported to exist in the heart, and some of them can induce cardiocyte hypertrophy and specific gene expression in vitro. When cardiocytes were stimulated with basic FGF or TGFβ, the reexpression of fetal genes was observed (for review, see Reference 86), but their role in cardiac hypertrophy caused by mechanical stress remains unknown. The precursor genes for the renin-angiotensin system, angiotensinogen and renin mRNA, have been detected in the heart, and the translatable products (renin, angiotensin I and II) have also been detected in the heart (28). Recently, angiotensin II was shown to be a potent stimulus for protein synthesis (4) and IEG expression (49). Of interest is the fact that the increase in left ventricular mass induced by constricting the abdominal aorta was completely prevented by the angiotensin-converting enzyme inhibitor without decreasing the arterial pressure (5). An increase in angiotensinogen mRNA was also demonstrated in the left ventricle without a change in plasma renin activity. These results suggest that a localized cardiac renin-angiotensin system may be involved in inducing cardiac hypertrophy by mechanical stress. However, the question remains as to how mechanical stress regulates the renin-angiotensin system? In smooth muscle and endothelial cells, cAMP is reported to induce the secretion of angiotensin II (82, 107). Does mechanical stress induce the secretion of angiotensin II through cAMP activation? To address these questions, the mechanisms of activation of the renin-angiotensin system and of secretion of angiotensin II should be elucidated. Endothelin is another candidate for a hypertrophy-promoting factor by paracrine mechanism. Endothelin has been shown to stimulate cardiocyte hypertrophy, sarcomere assembly, and the expression of IEG and ANF, with an increase in phosphoinositide hydrolysis and the accumulation of DG (98). Whether the production of endothelin is increased by mechanical stress remains unanswered. In skeletal muscle, the efflux of PGE_2 and F_2alpha increased with mechanical stimulation, and the long-term stretch induced elevation of PGF_2alpha efflux correlated with a long-term increase in total protein synthesis rates (109). Thus mechanical stimuli could evoke a variety of signals, and these signals may function in concert to induce cardiac hypertrophy.

OTHER MECHANICAL STRESSES AND THEIR TRANSDUCTION MECHANISMS

As discussed above, mechanical stress might evoke multiple second messenger systems and regulate gene expression. However, the mechanisms by which mechanical stimuli are converted into biochemical signals are still unknown. Since many fundamental cellular processes are conserved evolutionally, to know the transduction mechanisms of other species or other mechanical stimuli may help us to understand the signal transduction pathways in the heart.

Osmoregulation, Lymphocytes, and E. coli

In addition to cardiac hypertrophy, there have been numerous reports that mechanical stimuli modulate cAMP concentration in a variety of cells. There might be an intimate relationship between cell volume and cAMP. Hypoosmotic swelling of S49 mouse lymphoma cells induces cAMP accumulation (110), and the addition of cAMP analogues decreases cell volume in MDCK cells (75). The increased adenylate cyclase activity with swelling is not mediated either by Gs or Gi. Disruption of the actin membrane cytoskeleton blocked the increase in cAMP (110). Adenylate cyclase has been known to have multiple isoforms, and mechanoresponsiveness is different among members of the adenylate cyclase family. When calmodulin-sensitive Type I adenylate cyclase was expressed in 293 cells, which lack endogenous mechanoresponsive adenylate cyclase activity, cAMP accumulated in response to mechanical stimuli. In contrast, expression of the olfactory-specific Type III adenylate cyclase in 293 cells does not impart mechanoresponsive cAMP accumulation (P. A. Watson, unpublished). The mechanisms of osmoregulation have been well characterized in *Escherichia coli*. Four major membrane proteins, EnvZ, OmpR, OmpF, and OmpC, are regulated by medium osmolarity (76, 101). EnvZ protein is a transmembrane osmotic sensor that phosphorylates or dephosphorylates OmpR protein. When the medium osmolarity is low, OmpR protein is dephosphorylated by EnvZ, which transactivates OmpF gene expression. As the medium osmolarity increases, the relative amount of the phosphorylated form of the OmpR protein increases, which in turn results in activation of the OmpC gene. The osmotic change may induce structural change of EnvZ protein and may modulate the relative strength of its kinase/phosphatase activity, however, the primary osmotic signal remains unknown.

Shear Stress—Endothelial Cells

Mechanical forces associated with blood flow play important roles in the regulation of vascular tone, vascular remodeling, and the focal development of atherosclerotic lesions. Shear stress is the frictional force tangential to the surface of the endothelial cell in the direction of flow. Shear stress rapidly stimulates prostacyclin (29), tissue plasminogen activator (26), and endothelial-derived relaxing factor (EDRF) production (91), and it also activates the expressions of several genes. As fast events, the activation of K^+ channels (85), increase in intracellular Ca^{2+} (27) and IP_3 (83) have been reported, however, it is unknown how these events are transduced into gene regulation.

Sound—Hair Cells

Hair cells of the acousticolateralis are specialized to optimize the conversion of mechanical energy into neuronal signals (3). The current view favors a mechanical transducer channel in the stereocilial membrane that is similar to stretch-activated channels. Displacement of the hair bundle directly opens ionic channels and conducts cations into the cell. This phenomenon is not dependent either on enzymatic regulation of channel proteins, or on the effect of second messengers (84). The depolarization induces the influx of Ca^{2+} and increased Ca^{2+} then activates Ca^{2+}-activated K^+ channels in basolateral membranes. Many ion channels such as K^+ (outward and inward rectifier), Ca^{2+} and Na^+ channels (ATP- and acetylcholine-activated) have been reported in the basolateral membrane of hair cells, and complex interactions among these channels are thought to transduce mechanical energy into electrical signals.

Environmental Mechanical Stimuli—Plants

A variety of environmental stimuli cause alterations in plant growth patterns. Plants exposed to mechanical stimuli such as rain, wind, touch, and wounding tend to be less elongated with thicker stem diameters. Recently, five cDNAs, representing genes whose expression levels increase dramatically 30 min after mechanical stimuli, have been cloned and, interestingly, three have calmodulin or calmodulin-related sequences (13). The Ca^{2+}- calmodulin complex is known to activate some 20 different enzymes including phosphodiesterase, brain adenylate cyclases, protein kinases, phosphatases, and Ca^{2+}-ATPases. Although the mechanisms by which these calmodulin or calmodulin-related genes are induced by mechanical stress remain unknown, these observations imply that calcium and calmodulin may be key components in the signal transduction pathway of plants.

SUMMARY AND IMPLICATIONS

Mechanical stress directly induces gene expression in the cardiomyocytes. The response of the cardiomyocytes to mechanical stress is similar to that of other cells to growth factors. IEGs are first induced and then fetal-type genes are reinduced. IEGs may be involved in regulating the expression of late response genes. Mechanical stress can evoke a variety of signals, and PKC activation may be a key component for gene regulation by mechanical stress in the cardiomyocytes.

A number of intriguing questions remain unanswered. How is mechanical stress converted into biochemical signals? What is the mechanoreceptor in the cardiomyocytes? How are fetal genes induced? After conversion from mechanical stimuli to biochemical signals, the signal transduction pathway in the cardiomyocyte might be similar to that of other cell types. However, the mechanoreceptor is usually different among cell types and stimuli. Since we do not have well characterized cardiomyocyte cell lines, it is difficult, at present, to manipulate the cardiomyocytes using recombinant DNA technology. We can only do transient expression studies with primary cardiocytes, and we have to rely on pharmacological agents. The establishment of cardiomyocyte cell lines is necessary in order to examine the regulation of cardiac-specific genes. However, we may be able to use other cells such as cardiac fibroblasts to understand the cardiac mechanoreceptor. As mentioned above, there is heterogeneity among cell types in response to stretch. It is of interest to know whether fibroblasts would respond to stretch by transfecting candidate genes such as phospholipase C and adenylate cyclase. In skeletal muscle development, MyoD families have been demonstrated to function as master key genes, and the mechanisms of gene regulation specific to skeletal muscle have been elucidated. In contrast, no key genes have been found in the heart and the regulatory mechanisms of cardiac-specific genes remain unknown. Information about the genes that determine cardiac specificity during physiological development is still necessary to understand gene regulation during cardiac hypertrophy.

Literature Cited

1. Alpert, N. R., Mulieri, L. A. 1982. Increased myothermal economy of isometric force generation in compensated cardiac hypertrophy induced by pulmonary artery constriction in the rabbit. A characterization of heat liberation in normal and hypertrophied right ventricular papillary muscles. *Circ. Res.* 50:491–500

2. Angel, P., Imagawa, M., Chiu, R., Stein, B., Imbra, R. J., et al. 1987. Phorbol ester-inducible genes contain a common *cis* element recognized by a TPA-modulated *trans*-acting factor. *Cell* 49:729–39

3. Ashmore, J. F. 1991. The electrophysiology of hair cells. *Annu. Rev. Physiol.* 53:465–76

4. Baker, K. M., Aceto, J. F. 1990. Angiotensin II stimulation of protein synthesis and cell growth in chick heart cells. *Am. J. Physiol.* 259:H610–18

5. Baker, K. M., Chernin, M. I., Wixson, S. K., Aceto, J. F. 1990. Renin-angiotensin system involvement in pressure-overload cardiac hypertrophy in rats. *Am. J. Physiol.* 259:H324–32

6. Bauters, C., Moalic, J. M., Bercovici, J., Mouas, C., Emanoil-Ravier, R., et al. 1988. Coronary flow as a determinant of c-myc and c-fos proto-oncogene expression in an isolated adult rat heart. *J. Mol. Cell. Cardiol.* 20:97–101

7. Bishopric, N. H., Webster, K. A. 1991. Fos and Jun regulate preferential induction of the skeletal α-actin gene in neonatal rat heart cells. *Circulation* 84:11–87 (Abstr.)

8. Black, F. M., Packer, S. E., Parker, T. G., Michael, L. H., Roberts, R., et al. 1991. The vascular smooth muscle α-actin gene is reactivated during cardiac hypertrophy provoked by load. *J. Clin. Invest.* 88:1581–88

9. Blackwood, E. M., Eisenman, R. N. 1991. Max: a helix-loop-helix zipper protein that forms a sequence-specific DNA-binding complex with Myc. *Science* 251:1211–17

10. Boheler, K. R., Dillmann, W. H. 1988. Cardiac response to pressure overload in the rat: the selective alteration of in vitro directed RNA translation products. *Circ. Res.* 63:448–56

11. Bohmann, D., Bos, T. J., Admon, A., Nishimura, T., Vogt, P. K., Tjian, R. 1987. Human proto-oncogene c-jun encodes a DNA binding protein with structural and functional properties of transcription factor AP-1. *Science* 238:1386–92

12. Boulton, T. G., Nye, S. H., Robbins, D. J., Ip, N. Y., Radziejewskk, E., et al. 1991 ERKs: a family of protein-serine/threonine kinases that are activated and tyrosine phosphorylated in response to insulin and NGF. *Cell* 65: 663–75

13. Bream, J., Davis, R. W. 1990. Rain-, wind-, and touch-induced expression of calmodulin and calmodulin-related genes in Arabidopsis. *Cell* 60:357–64

14. Breitbart, R. E., Andreadis, A., Nadal-Ginard, B. 1987. Alternative splicing: a ubiquitous mechanism for the generation of multiple protein isoforms

from single genes. *Annu. Rev. Biochem.* 56:467–95

15. Bustamante, J. O., Ruknudin, A., Sachs, F. 1991. Stretch-activated channels in heart cells: relevance to cardiac hypertrophy. *J. Cardiovasc. Pharmacol.* 17 (Suppl. 2):S110–13

16. Castellucci, V. F., Kennedy, T. E., Kandel, E. R., Goelet, P.1988. A quantitative analysis of 2-D gels identifies proteins in which labeling is increased following long-term sensitization in *Aplysia. Neuron* 1:321–28

17. Chiu, R., Angel, P., Karin, M. 1989. jun-B differs in its biological properties from, and is a negative regulator of, c-Jun. *Cell* 59:979–86

18. Christy, B. A., Lau, L. F., Nathans, D. 1988. A gene activated in mouse 3T3 cells by serum growth factors encodes a protein with "zinc finger" sequences. *Proc. Natl. Acad. Sci. USA* 85:7857–61

19. Chua, B. H. L., Russo, L. A., Gordon, E. E., Kleinhans, B. J., Morgan, H. E. 1987. Faster ribosome synthesis induced by elevated aortic pressure in rat heart. *Am. J. Physiol.* 252:C323–27

20. Cohen, D., Curran, T. 1988. *fra-1*: a serum-inducible, cellular immediate-early gene that encodes a Fos-related antigen. *Mol. Cell. Biol.* 8:2063–69

21. Cole, A. J., Saffen, D. W., Baraban, J. M., Worley, P. F. 1989. Rapid increase of an immediate early gene messenger RNA in hippocampal neurons by synaptic NMDA receptor activation. *Nature* 340:474–76

22. Cooper, G., Kent, R. L., Uboh, C. E., Thompson, E. W., Marino, T. A. 1985. Hemodynamic versus adrenergic control of cat right ventricular hypertrophy. *J. Clin. Invest.* 75:1403–14

23. Coppola, J. A., Cole, M. D. 1986. Constitutive c-myc oncogene expression blocks mouse erythroleukemia cell differentiation but not commitment. *Nature* 320:760–63

24. Dalton, S., Treisman, R. 1992. Characterization of SAP-1, a protein recruited by serum response factor to the c-fos serum response element. *Cell* 68:597–612

25. Day, M. L., Schwartz, D., Wiegand, R. C., Stockman, P. T., Brunnert, S. R., et al. 1987. Ventricular atriopeptin: unmasking of messenger RNA and peptide synthesis by hypertrophy or dexamethasone. *Hypertension* 9:485–91

26. Diamond, S. L., Eskin, S. G., McIntyre, L. V. 1989. Fluid flow stimulates tissue plasminogen activator

27. Dull, R. O., Davies, P. F. 1991. Flow modulation of agonist(ATP)-response (Ca^{2+}) coupling in vascular endothelial cells. *Am. J. Physiol.*261:H149–54

28. Dzau, V. J. 1988. Cardiac renin-angiotensin system. *Am. J. Med.* 84 *(Suppl.* 3A):22–27

29. Frangos, J. A., Eskin, S. G., McIntyre, L. V., Ives, C. L. 1985. Flow effects on prostacyclin production by cultured human endothelial cells. *Science* 227:1477–79

30. Gardner, D. G., Gertz, B. J., Hane. S. 1987. Thyroid hormone increases rat atrial natriuretic peptide messenger ribonucleic acid accumulation in vivo and in vitro. *Mol. Endocrinol.* 1:260–65

31. Ghosh, S., Baltimore, D. 1990. Activation in vitro of NF-κB by phosphorylation of its inhibitor IκB. *Nature* 344:678–82

32. Gordon, E. E., Kira, Y., Demers, L. M., Morgan, H. E. 1986. Aortic pressure as a determinant of cardiac protein degradation. *Am. J. Physiol.*250:C932–38

33. Gotoh, Y., Nishida, E., Yamashita, T., Hoshi, M., Kawakami, M., et al. 1990. Microtubule-associated-protein (MAP) kinase activated by nerve growth factor and epidermal growth factor in P12 cells. Identity with the mitogen-activated MAP kinase of fibroblast cells. *Eur. J. Biochem.* 193:661–69

34. Greenberg, M. E., Ziff, E. B. 1984. Stimulation of 3T3 cells induces transcription of the c-fos proto-oncogene. *Nature* 311:433–38

35. Greenberg, M. E., Greene, L. A., Ziff, E. B. 1985. Nerve growth factor and epidermal growth factor induce rapid transient changes in proto-oncogene transcription in PC12 cells. *J. Biol. Chem.* 260:14101–10

36. Griep, A. E., Westphal, H. 1.988. Antisense myc sequences induce differentiation of F9 cells. *Proc. Natl. Acad. Sci. USA* 85:6806–10

37. Guharay, F., Sachs, F. 1984. Stretch-activated single ion channel currents in tissue-cultured embryonic chick skeletal muscle. *J. Physiol.* 352:685–701

38. Gupta, M. P., Gupta, M., Zak. R., Sukhatme, V. P.1991. Egr-1, a serum-inducible zinc finger protein, regulates transcription of the rat cardiac alpha-myosin heavy chain gene. *J. Biol. Chem.* 266:12813–16

39. Hammond, G. L., Wieben, E., Market, C. L. 1979. Molecular signals for initiating protein synthesis in organ

hypertrophy. *Proc. Natl. Acad. Sci. USA* 76:2455–59

40. Hazel, T. G., Nathans, D., Lau, L. F. 1988. A gene inducible by serum growth factors encodes a member of the steroid and thyroid hormone receptor superfamily. *Proc. Natl. Acad. Sci. USA* 85:8444–48

41. Ingwall, J. S., Kramer, M. F., Fifer, M. A., Grossman, W., Allen, P. 1985. The creatine kinase system in normal and diseased human myocardium. *N. Engl. J. Med.* 313:1050–54

42. Iwaki, K., Sukhatme, V. P., Shubeita, H. E., Chien, K. R. 1990. Alpha- and beta-adrenergic stimulation induces distinct patterns of immediate early gene expression in neonatal rat myocardial cells. fos/jun expression is associated with sarcomere assembly; Egr-1 induction is primarily an alpha 1-mediated response. *J. Biol. Chem.* 265:13809–17

43. Izumo, S., Lompre, A.-M., Matsuoka, R., Koren, G., Schwartz, K., et al. 1987. Myosin heavy chain messenger RNA and protein isoform transitions during cardiac hypertrophy. *J. Clin. Invest.* 79:70–77

44. Izumo, S., Nadal-Ginard, B., Mahdavi, V. 1988. Proto-oncogene induction and reprogramming of cardiac gene expression produced by pressure overload. *Proc. Natl. Acad. Sci. USA* 85:339–43

45. Jackson, T., Allard, M. F., Sreenan, C. M., Doss, L. K., Bishop, S. P., et al. 1990. The c-myc proto-oncogene regulates cardiac development in transgenic mice. *Mol. Cell. Biol.* 10:3709–16

46. Kariya, K., Karns, L. R., Simpson, P. C. 1991. Expression of a constitutively activated mutant of the β-isozyme of protein kinase C in cardiac myocytes stimulates the promoter of the b-myosin heavy chain isogene. *J. Biol. Chem.* 266:10023–26

47. Kariya, K., Karns, L. R., Simpson, P. C. 1991. A 64-bp region of the b-myosin heavy chain (MHC) gene promoter mediates myocyte-specific and α1-adrenergic- and protein kinase C (PKC)-stimulated expression in cardiac myocytes. *Circulation* 84:II–88 (Abstr.)

48. Karns, L. R., Kariya, K., Simpson, P. C. 1991. Activation of skeletal a-actin promoter in cardiac myocytes. *Circulation* 84:II–87 (Abstr.)

49. Katoh, Y., Komuro, I., Shibasaki, Y., Yamaguchi, H., Yazaki, Y. 1989. Angiotensin II induces hypertrophy and oncogene expression in cultured rat

heart myocytes. *Circulation* 80:II–450 (Abstr.)

50. Kelly, K., Cochran, B. H., Stiles, C. D., Leder, P. 1983. Cell-specific regulation of the c-myc gene by lymphocyte mitogens and platelet-derived growth factor. *Cell* 35:603–10

51. Kent R. L., Hoober, K., Cooper, C. 1989. Load responsiveness of protein synthesis in adult mammalian myocardium: role of cardiac deformation linked to sodium influx. *Circ. Res.* 64:74–85

52. Kim, S.-J., Angel, P., Lafyatis, R., Hattori, K., Kim, K. Y., et al. 1990. Autoinduction of transforming growth factor β1 is mediated by the AP-1 complex. *Mol. Cell. Biol.* 10:1492–97

53. Kingston, R. E., Baldwin, A. S. Jr., Sharp, P. A. 1984. Regulation of heat shock protein 70 gene expression by c-myc. *Nature* 312:280–82

54. Knowlton, K. U., Baracchini, E., Ross, R. S., Harris, A. N., Henderson, S. A., et al. 1991. Co-regulation of the atrial natriuretic factor and cardiac myosin light chain-2 genes during (α-adrenergic stimulation of neonatal rat ventricular cells. *J. Biol. Chem.* 266:7759–68

55. Komuro, I., Kaida, T., Shibazaki, Y., Kurabayashi, M., Katoh, Y., et al. 1990. Stretching cardiac myocytes stimulates proto-oncogene expression. *J. Biol. Chem.* 265:3591–98

56. Komuro, I., Katoh, Y., Hoh, E., Takaku, F., Yazaki, Y. 1991. Mechanisms of cardiac hypertrophy and injury:possible role of protein kinase C activation. *Jpn. Circ. J.* 55:1149–57

57. Komuro, I., Katoh, Y., Kaida, T., Shibazaki, Y., Kurabayashi, M., et al. 1991. Mechanical loading stimulates cell hypertrophy and specific gene expression in cultured rat cardiac myocytes. *J. Biol. Chem.* 266:1265–68

58. Komuro, I., Kurabayashi, M., Shibazaki, Y., Takaku, F., Yazaki, Y. 1989. Molecular cloning and characterization of a $Ca^{2+} + Mg^{2+}$-dependent adenosine triphosphatase from rat cardiac sarcoplasmic reticulum. *J. Clin. Invest.* 83: 1102–8

59. Komuro, I., Kurabayashi, M., Takaku, F., Yazaki, Y. 1988. Expression of cellular oncogenes in the myocardium during the developmental stage and pressure-overload hypertrophy of the rat heart. *Circ. Res.* 62:1075–79

60. Komuro, I., Shibazaki, Y., Kurabayashi, M., Takaku, F., Yazaki, Y. 1990. Molecular cloning of gene sequences from rat heart rapidly responsive to

pressure overload. *Circ. Res.* 66:979–85

61. Kovacic-Milivojevic, B., Gardner, D. G. 1992. Divergent regulation of the human atrial natriuretic peptide gene by c-jun and c-fos. *Mol. Cell. Biol.* 12:292–301

62. Kurabayashi, M., Komuro, I., Shibasaki, Y., Tsuchimochi, H., Takaku, F., et al. 1990. Functional identification of the transcriptional regulatory elements within the promoter region of the human ventricular myosin alkali light chain gene. *J. Biol. Chem.* 265:19271–78

63. Lamph, W. W., Wamsley, P., Sassone-Corsi, P., Verma, I. M. 1988. Induction of proto-oncogene JUN/AP-1 by serum and TPA. *Nature* 334:629–31

64. Landschulz, W. H., Johnson, P. F., McKnight, S. L. 1988. The leucine zipper:a hypothetical structure common to a new class of DNA binding proteins. *Science* 240:1759–64

65. La Pointe, M. C., Deschepper, C. F., Wu, J., Gardner, D. G. 1990. Extracellular calcium regulates expression of the gene for atrial natriuretic factor. *Hypertension* 15:20–28

66. Lattion, A. L., Michel, J. B., Arnauld, E., Corvol, P., Soubrier, F. 1986. Myocardial recruitment during ANF mRNA, increase with volume overload in the rat. *Am. J. Physiol.* 251:H890–96

67. Lee, W., Mitchell, P., Tjian, R. 1987. Purified transcription factor AP-1 interacts with TPA-inducible enhancer elements. *Cell* 49:741–52

68. Lemire, P., Revelant, O., Bravo, R., Charnay, P. 1988. Two mouse genes encoding potential transcription factors with identical DNA-binding domains are activated by growth factors in cultured cells. *Proc. Natl. Acad. Sci. USA* 85:4691–95

69. Lompre, A.-M., Schwartz, K., D'Albis, A., Lacombe, G., Thiem, N. V., et al. 1979. Myosin isoenzyme distribution in chronic heart overload. *Nature* 282: 105–7

70. Long, C. S., Kariya, K., Karns, L., Simpson, P. C. 1991. Sympathetic activity: Modulator of myocardial hypertrophy. *J. Cardiovasc. Pharmacol.* 17(Suppl.):S20–24

71. Marcu, K. B. 1987. Regulation of expression of the c-myc protooncogene. *Bioessays* 6:28–32

72. Mercadier, J.-J., Lompre, A.-M., Duc, P., Boheler, K. R., Fraysse, J.-B., et al. 1990. Altered sarcoplasmic reticulum Ca^{2+}-ATPase gene expression in

the human ventricle during end-stage heart failure. *J. Clin. Invest.* 85:305–9

73. Milbrandt, J. 1987. A nerve growth factor-induced gene encodes a possible transcriptional regulatory factor. *Science* 238:797–99

74. Milbrandt, J. 1988. Nerve growth factor induces a gene homologous to the glucocorticoid receptor gene. *Neuron* 1:183–88

75. Mills, J. W., Lubin, M. 1986. Effect of adenosine 3′,5′-cyclic monophosphate on volume and cytoskeleton of MDCK cells. *Am. J. Physiol.* 250: C319–24

76. Mizuno, T., Mizushima, S. 1990. Signal transduction and gene regulation through the phosphorylation of two regulatory components: the molecular basis for the osmotic regulation of the porin genes. *Mol. Microbiol.* 4:1077–82

77. Morgan, J. I., Curran, T. 1986. Role of ion flux in the control of c-fos expression. *Nature* 322:552–55

78. Morris, C. E. 1990. Mechanosensitive ion channels. *J. Membr. Biol.* 113:93–107

79. Mulvagh, S. L., Michael, L. H., Perryman, M. B., Roberts, R., Schneider, M. D. 1987. A hemodynamic load in vivo induces cardiac expression of the cellular oncogene, c-myc. *Biochem. Biophys. Res. Commun.* 147:627–36

80. Nagai, R., Zarain-Herzberg, A., Brandl, C. J., Fujii, J., Tada, M., et al. 1989. Regulation of myocardial Ca^{2+}-ATPase and phospholamban mRNA expression in response to pressure overload and thyroid hormone. *Proc. Natl. Acad. Sci. USA* 86:2966–70

81. Nakabeppu, Y., Ryder, K., Nathans, D. 1988. DNA binding activities of three murine Jun proteins: stimulation by Fos. *Cell* 55:907–15

82. Nakamaru, M., Jackson, E. K., Inagami, T. 1986. Beta-adrenoceptor-mediated release of angiotensin II from mesenteric arteries. *Am. J. Physiol.* 250: H144–48

83. Nollert, M. U., Eskin, S. G., McIntire, L. V. 1990. Shear stress increases inositol trisphosphate levels in human endothelial cells. *Biochem. Biophys. Res. Commun.* 170:281–87

84. Ohmori, H. 1985. Mechano-electrical transduction currents in isolated vestibular hair cells of the chick. *J. Physiol.* 359:189–217

85. Olesen, S. P., Clapham, D. E., Davies, P. F. 1988. Haemodynamic shear stress activates a K^+ current in vascular endothelial cells. *Nature* 331:168–70

86. Parker, T. G., Schneider, M. D. 1991.

Growth factors, proto-oncogenes, and plasticity of the cardiac phenotype. *Annu. Rev. Physiol.* 53:179–200

87. Peterson, M. B., Lesch, M. 1.972. Protein synthesis and amino acid transport in isolated rabbit right ventricular muscle. *Circ. Res.* 31:317–27

88. Pulverer, B. J., Kyriakis, J. M., Avruch, J., Nikolakaki, E., Woodgett, J. R. 1991. Phosphorylation of c-jun mediated by MAP kinases. *Nature* 353:670–74

89. Ramsey, G. M., Moscovici, G., Moscovici, C., Bisho, J. M. 1990. Neoplastic transformation and tumorigenesis by the human protooncogene MYC. *Proc. Natl. Acad. Sci. USA* 87:2102–6

90. Roesler, W. J., Vandenbark, G. R., Hanson, R. W. 1988. Cyclic AMP and the induction of eukaryotic gene transcription. *J. Biol. Chem.* 263: 9063–66

91. Rubanyi, G. M., Romero, J. C., Vanhoutte, P. M. 1986. Flow-induced release of endothelium-derived relaxing factor. *Am. J. Physiol.* 250: H1145–49

92. Ryder, K., Lau., L. F., Nathans, D. 1988. A gene activated by growth factors is related to the oncogene v-jun. *Proc. Natl. Acad. Sci. USA* 85:1487–91

93. Schafritz, D. A. 1988. Transcriptional and post-transcriptional control of liver gene expression during various physiologic and pathophysiologic states. *Semin. Liver Dis.* 8:285–92

94. Schunkert, H., Jahn, L., Izumo, S., Apstein, C. S., Lorell, B. H. 1992. Localization and regulation of c-fos and c-jun protooncogene induction by systolic wall stress in normal and hypertrophied rat hearts. *Proc. Natl. Acad. Sci. USA* 88:11480–84

95. Schwartz, K., de la Bastie, D., Bouveret, P., Oliviero, P., Alonso, S., et al. 1986. a-skeletal muscle actin mRNAs accumulate in hypertrophied adult rat hearts. *Circ. Res.* 59:551–55

96. Sen, S., Kundu, G., Mekhail, N., Castel, J., Misono, K., et al. 1990. Myotrophin: purification of a novel peptide from spontaneously hypertensive rat heart that influences myocardial growth. *J. Biol. Chem.* 265:16635–43

97. Deleted in proof

98. Shubeita, H. E., McDonogh, P. M., Harris, A. N., Knowlton, K. U., Glembotski, C. C., et al. 1990. Endothelin induction of inositol phospholipid hydrolysis, sarcomere assembly, and cardiac gene expression in ventricular myocytes. A paracrine mechanism for myocardial cell hypertrophy. *J. Biol. Chem.* 265:2055–62

99. Deleted in proof

100. Sonnenberg, J. L., Rauscher, F. J., Morgan, J. I., Curran, T. 1989. Regulation of proenkephalin by Fos and Jun. *Science* 246:1622–25

101. Stock, A. M., Ninfa, A. J., Stock, A. M. 1989. Protein phosphorylation and regulation of adaptive response in bacteria. *Microbiol. Rev.* 53:450–90

102. Sturgill, T. W., Ray, L. B., Erikson, E., Maller, J. L. 1988. Insulin-stimulated MAP-2 kinase phosphorylates and activates ribosomal protein S6 kinase II. *Nature* 334:715–18

103. Sturgill, T. W., Wu, J. 1991. Recent progress in characterization of protein kinase cascades for phosphorylation of ribosomal protein S6. *Biochim. Biophys. Acta* 1092:350–57

104. Sukhatme, V. P., Cao, X., Chang, L. C., Tsai-Morris, C.-H., Stamenkovich, D., et al. 1988. A zinc finger-encoding gene coregulated with c-fos during growth and differentiation, and after cellular depolarization. *Cell* 53:37–43

105. Swynghedauw, B. 1986. Developmental and functional adaptation of contractile proteins in cardiac and skeletal muscles. *Physiol. Rev.* 66:710–71

106. Takala, T. 1981. Protein synthesis in the isolated perfused rat heart:Effects of mechanical workload, diastolic ventricular pressure, and coronary flow on amino acid incorporation and its transmural distribution into left ventricular protein. *Basic Res. Cardiol.* 76:44–61

107. Tang, S.-S., Stevenson, L., Dzau, V. J. 1990. Endothelial renin-angiotensin pathway: adrenergic regulation of angiotensin secretion. *Circ. Res.* 66:103–8

108. Treisman, R. 1986. Identification of a protein-binding site that mediates transcriptional response of the c-fos gene to serum factors. *Cell* 46:567–74

109. Vandenburgh, H. H., Hatfaludy, S., Sohar, I., Shansky, J. 1990. Stretch-induced prostaglandins and protein turnover in cultured skeletal muscle. *Am. J. Physiol.*259:C232–40

110. Watson, P. A. 1990. Direct stimulation of adenylate cyclase by mechanical forces in S49 mouse lymphoma cells during hypoosmotic swelling. *J. Biol. Chem.* 265:6569–75

111. Wood, K. W., Sarnecki, C., Roberts, T. M., Blenis, J. 1992. ras mediates nerve growth factor receptor modulation of three signal-transducing protein kinases: MAP kinase, Raf-1, and RSK. *Cell* 68:1041–50

112. Xenophontos, X. P., Gordon, E. E.,

Morgan, H. E. 1986. Effects of intraventricular pressure on protein synthesis in arrested rat hearts. *Am. J. Physiol.* 251:C95–98

113. Yamamoto, K. K., Gonzalez, G. A., Biggs, W. H. III, Montminy, M. R. 1988. Phosphorylation-induced binding and transcriptional efficacy of nuclear factor CREB. *Nature* 334:494–98

114. Yang, X.-C., Sachs, F. 1989. Block of stretch-activated ion channels in *Xenopus* oocytes by gadolinium and calcium ions. *Science* 243:1068–71

115. Zerial, M., Toschi, L., Ryseck, R.-P., Schuermann, M., Muller, R., et al. 1989. The product of a novel growth factor activated gene, fos B, interacts with JUN proteins enhancing their DNA binding activity. *EMBO J.* 8:805–13

Annu. Rev. Physiol. 1993. 55:77–95

TRANSCRIPTIONAL REGULATION DURING CARDIAC GROWTH AND DEVELOPMENT

Kenneth R. Chien, Hong Zhu, Kirk U. Knowlton, Wanda Miller-Hance, Marc van-Bilsen, Terrence X. O'Brien, and Sylvia M. Evans

Department of Medicine, Center for Molecular Genetics, and the American Heart Association-Bugher Foundation Center for Molecular Biology, University of California, San Diego, School of Medicine, La Jolla, California 92093

KEY WORDS: cardiogenesis, muscle gene regulation, cardiac hypertrophy, signaling pathways, myosin

INTRODUCTION

During the last decade, a variety of morphological, physiological, and biochemical studies have provided an improved definition of the alterations in myocardial structure and function that herald the sequential stages of cardiac growth and development. Initially, there is a commitment of mesodermally derived progenitor cells to the cardiac muscle cell lineage that is followed by the formation of a primordial heart tube. Organogenesis proceeds through a series of involutions of the heart tube and the onset of septation, which results in distinct cardiac chambers and the acquisition of regional-specific properties of atrial, ventricular, and conduction system cells. The subsequent enlargement of the embryonic heart is largely dependent on an increase in myocyte number, which continues until shortly after birth, when cardiac myocytes lose their proliferative capacity and acquire the terminally differentiated phenotype of adult cardiac muscle cells. In response to hormonal, physiological, hemodynamic, and pathological stimuli, adult ventricular muscle cells can adapt to increased workloads through the activation of a hypertrophic process, characterized by an increase in the contractile protein content of individual

77

0066–4278/93/0315–0077$02.00

cardiac muscle cells with a lack of a concomitant proliferative response. The current challenge of modern cardiovascular research is to identify the factors that control these "multiple lives" of cardiac muscle cells during the various stages of myocardial growth and development, i.e. commitment, septation, regional specification, terminal differentiation, and adaptation. The elucidation of the precise molecular switches that control the normal growth and development of the heart continues to be one of the central questions in cardiovascular physiology and medicine, with far-reaching implications for understanding the pathogenesis of congenital heart disease and the transition of compensatory hypertrophy to overt heart failure.

One experimental approach to attack this complex problem has been to identify the mechanisms that regulate the expression of genetic markers that are closely linked to the onset of the developmental stage of interest. The inherent assumption is that the elucidation of the mechanisms that regulate the expression of these cardiac muscle genes will eventually lead to the identification of the molecular switches that control many aspects of the cardiac muscle cell phenotype at a certain stage of development. Thus the genetic marker could be viewed as the final step in the molecular pathway(s) that control the complex processes of commitment, specification, and adaptation. Initial work in this area has been hampered by the lack of continuous, differentiated cell lines that mimic various stages of cardiac growth and development. However, based on the availability of well-characterized cardiac muscle genes, and the recent development of transgenic, transfection, and microinjection approaches for studies in differentiated cardiac muscle cells, the unraveling of the pathways that control the complex physiology of cardiac growth and development appears to be experimentally feasible.

This brief review highlights recent advances in our understanding of the mechanisms that regulate the transcription of muscle genes during cardiogenesis and in the setting of myocardial cell hypertrophy. Since many of the major advances in muscle gene regulation have been made in the skeletal muscle context, potential parallels between the growth and development of cardiac and skeletal muscle are discussed throughout the review. Our hope is that this comparison will lead to an appreciation of the pathways that are shared by these striated muscle subtypes and will also serve to highlight the distinct nature of the cardiac muscle gene program.

TRANSCRIPTIONAL REGULATION DURING CARDIAC DEVELOPMENT

E-Box-Dependent Pathways

Recent studies of skeletal myogenesis have uncovered a number of master transcriptional factors that can dominantly specify the differentiated muscle cell phenotype following their expression in permissive cell types (9, 14, 55, 75, 92, 93). The identification of a host of myogenic determination genes (*myoD*; *myf-5*; myogenin; *myf-6*/MRF4/herculin), has led to a wealth of information on the mechanisms that regulate muscle genes during skeletal myogenesis. The activation of the skeletal muscle gene program first requires the formation of a heterodimer, consisting of a muscle-specific myogenic determination factor, like MyoD, and a ubiquitous helix-loop-helix partner, E12/E47 (6, 57, 58). These heterodimers subsequently bind to CANNTG sequences (E-box sites) found in many muscle-specific genes, thereby activating their expression (6, 10). Similar paradigms requiring CANNTG sites have been found in studies of the chymotrypsin gene in pancreatic exocrine cells (61), as well as of immunoglobulin gene expression in lymphoid cell lines (11). The ubiquitous expression of E12/E47 (58, 61), as well as its negative regulatory counterpart Id, (2), has also given rise to the concept that E-box-dependent pathways may represent a generalized paradigm for the control of tissue-specific gene expression in a wide variety of cell types, including those outside of the muscle cell lineage (65).

The overlapping expression of many contractile protein genes in skeletal and cardiac muscle cells raises the question as to whether similar transcription factors regulate muscle gene expression in these closely related, but distinct subtypes of striated muscle. There appear to be shared DNA recognition elements in several cardiac and skeletal muscle promoters (CARG (56), M-CAT (51), and MEF2 (13, 20); see Table 1). The pivotal role of E-box sites in the expression of several muscle genes raises the question as to the role of the E-box sites and cognate helix-loop-helix proteins in cardiac muscle. While the MyoD family is not expressed in mammalian cardiac muscle (81), the mRNAs for their helix-loop-helix partners, E12/E47 and Id, are expressed in the heart (15, 61). Co-transfection studies of *myoD* expression vectors with skeletal muscle promoter-reporter constructs in cardiac cells indicate that the cardiac context is permissive for *myoD* (15), which suggests that the appropriate co-factors are indeed functional in these cells. Furthermore, in transgenic mice, the anomalous expression of MyoD results in the activation of endogenous skeletal muscle markers in the embryonic myocardium (54). Several genes, including cardiac α actin (80), skeletal α actin (R. Schwartz, personal communication), and muscle creatine kinase (S. Hauschka, personal communication), whose expression in skeletal muscle is dependent on E-box promoter elements, are also expressed in cardiac cells (Table 2). Mutations in E-box sites within the control regions of these genes decrease their expression in both skeletal and cardiac muscle cells (80, R. Schwartz, personal communication; S. Hauschka, personal communication), which suggests that cardiac cells are utilizing E-box-dependent pathways for the expression of these muscle genes. The observation that both cardiac and α skeletal actin promoter-reporter constructs are down-regulated by co-transfection with Id

Table 1   Cardiac muscle regulatory elements

	E-box	CARG	MCAT	HF-1a	HF-1b/MEF2	AP5/GTII
Cardiac α actin (80)	+	+	—	—	—	—
Skeletal α actin (83)	+	+	—	—	—	—
β myosin heavy chain (89)	—	+	—	—	—	+
Creatine kinase (24)	+	—	—	—	+	—
Cardiac troponin T (28)	—	—	+	—	+	—
Myosin light chain-2 (60)	—	—	—	+	+	—

References are in parentheses.

Table 2   Molecular paradigms for the control of cardiac muscle specific expression

E-box-dependent	E-box-independent
Cardiac α actin (80)	MLC-2 (60)
Skeletal α actin (83)	Troponin T (28)
	Troponin C (71)

References are in parentheses.

expression vectors in either skeletal or cardiac muscle cells provides additional experimental support for this notion (15, 80). Id is thought to counteract the activation of skeletal muscle promoters by titrating out the available levels of MyoD (2). However, co-transfection of cardiac cells with Id and other cardiac promoter-reporter constructs (myosin light chain-2 and ANF luciferase fusion genes) does not result in the down-regulation of luciferase activity, which suggests that there may be E-box-independent pathways for gene expression in cardiac muscle (15). The precise molecular nature of the cardiac muscle factors that mediate E-box-dependent pathways for the activation of these muscle genes is still in question (64, 80). Whether these sites are occupied by conventional helix-loop-helix proteins, or by transcriptional factors with divergent DNA binding motifs, is still a matter of intense inquiry.

The potential role of helix-loop-helix proteins during cardiac development remains to be fully explored. A number of members of the MyoD family are expressed early during skeletal muscle development and are therefore thought to play an important role in skeletal myogenesis (67). In the developing chick heart, an antibody to the second helix of MyoD specifically recognizes an epitope that appears transiently in cardiac embryonic heart extracts (45), but the molecular nature of the factor is unknown. In situ analysis of Id mRNA expression during embryonic development of the mouse indicates a high level of Id expression in the developing endocardial cushion (16), which suggests the possibility that helix-loop-helix proteins might play a role in the ontogeny of this region of the embryonic heart.

E-Box-Independent Pathways

The presence of E-box-dependent pathways in cardiac and skeletal muscle might initially suggest that similar programs exist to control the expression of muscle genes in these two striated muscle subtypes. Consistent with this notion, studies of the creatine kinase (32) and troponin T genes (50) suggest that overlapping elements may mediate their expression in both cardiac and skeletal muscle. However, deletional analysis of the 5' flanking regions indicates the presence of elements that have selective effects on expression of these two muscle genes in either the cardiac or skeletal muscle context (50, 32). In addition, recent studies have provided clear evidence that distinct molecular paradigms control the expression of a single contractile protein gene (the rat cardiac/slow twitch muscle myosin light chain-2; *MLC-2*) in cardiac vs skeletal muscle through E-box-independent pathways (25, 44, 60, 94). Transgenic mice, which harbor a 250 bp promoter fragment of the rat cardiac *MLC-2* gene fused to a luciferase reporter cDNA, display reporter activity exclusively within the myocardium (44). Background levels are observed in other tissues, including slow skeletal muscle, which expresses the endogenous cardiac *MLC-2* gene as an abundant mRNA (25, 44). Presumably, the *cis* sequences required for expression in the skeletal muscle context are absent from the short *MLC-2* promoter fragment, which retains the ability to confer cardiac specificity. In a similar manner, transient assays have provided clear evidence of distinct enhancers for the control of the cardiac and skeletal muscle-specific expression of the cardiac/slow twitch muscle troponin C gene (70, 71).

Recent studies have led to the characterization of the *cis* regulatory elements and their corresponding factors, which are components of the E-box-independent pathway for cardiac muscle-specific expression of the *MLC-2* gene (60, 95, 96). A conserved 28 bp element (HF-1) confers cardiac-specific expression to a heterologous promoter (96), and two distinct cardiac factors have been identified that bind to this regulatory element (60). HF-1 is a ubiquitous factor that binds to a core region of the 28 bp HF-1 element, which corresponds to a half site for a retinoic acid receptor response element (Figure 1). A muscle factor, HF-1b, binds to a A+T-rich element in the 3' end of the 28 bp element (Figure 1), which conforms to a consensus binding site for MEF-2, a factor that appears to be important in the muscle-specific expression of the creatine kinase gene (13, 20). By a number of separate criteria, (gel shift, mutagenesis, and expression studies), HF-1b and MEF-2 appear to be indistinguishable (60). The HF-1a and HF-1b sites are both required for the maintenance of cardiac muscle specificity (60). Point mutations within the single E-box site of the 250 bp MLC-2 promoter fragment have no effect on the expression of the 250 bp *MLC-2* luciferase fusion gene in either transient assays in cultured myocardial cells (60), or in mice that harbor the construct as a transgene (43). However, point mutations within the MEF-2 sites significantly cripple the MLC-2 promoter activity in both transient analyses (60, 96) and transgenic studies (43). In a similar manner, recent studies of the creatine kinase gene have documented an important role of the MEF-2 site in the cardiac-specific expression of the creatine kinase gene, which is also co-expressed in cardiac and skeletal muscle (S. Hauschka, personal communication). With respect to the chick cardiac troponin T gene, an analogous role for an A+T-rich element, which conforms to a consensus MEF-2 site, has been found in transient assays in primary chick cardiac muscle cells (28). The A+T-rich cardiac-specific element within the chick troponin T gene effectively competes for binding to the HF-1b site in the *MLC-2* gene (60), which suggests that similar factors may mediate cardiac-specific expression of these two muscle genes (Table 2). Analogous to the requirement for HF-1a in the 250 bp MLC-2 promoter fragment, the chick cardiac troponin T promoter requires a ubiquitous factor (MCAT) for the maintenance of cardiac muscle specificity (50). Together these studies present evidence that factors that bind A+T-rich elements with homology to MEF-2, in concert with ubiquitously expressed factors, may play an important role in conferring cardiac muscle specificity. These elements provide one of the first molecular paradigms for the control of the cardiac muscle gene program through E-box-independent pathways.

Several laboratories have recently characterized the muscle factors that bind to the A+T-rich MEF-2 sites within the creatine kinase and *MLC-2* genes (13, 26, 27, 60, 95). At the present time, there appear to be ubiquitous factors that can bind to MEF-2 consensus sites. Earlier studies of the brain and muscle creatine kinase genes have documented the presence of MEF-2 binding factors in non-muscle cells (26, 27). Recent studies by Pollack & Treisman have identified a ubiquitously expressed gene, with homology to SRF (RSRFC-4), that encodes a factor that binds to the MEF-2 site in the creatine kinase enhancer region (74). RSRFC-4 antibodies can partially super-shift the MEF-2 complex in gel shift studies with skeletal muscle extracts, which suggests that RSRFC-4 is a component of the MEF-2 binding activity, but also indicates the presence of additional nuclear factors that can occupy this site (74). Recently it was seen that cardiac muscle cells may express factors distinct from RSRFC-4, which can bind to A+T-rich sequences in the rat cardiac *MLC-2* gene (95). A novel zinc finger gene (*HF-1b*), with homology to SP-1, has been isolated from a neonatal rat cardiac muscle cell cDNA library (95). The HF-1b gene product displays sequence-specific binding to HF-1b rather than to HF-1a target sequences, and antibodies directed against a HF-1b fusion protein and selectively remove the HF-1b/MEF-2 binding activity in cardiac nuclear extracts (95). Co-transfection of a HF-1b expression vector with a

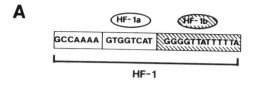

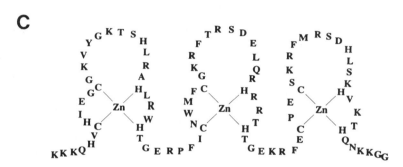

Figure 1 E-box independent pathways for cardiac muscle gene expression. (*A*) HF-1a and HF-1b target sites within the rat cardiac MLC-2 gene; (*B*) diagram of the serine- and glutamine-rich and zinc finger domains in the HF-1b binding factor; (*C*) primary structure of the three HF-1b zinc finger domains.

construct containing a minimal TK promoter-luciferase gene fused to a single copy of the HF-1 element results in up-regulation of the reporter activity that requires an intact HF-1b binding site (95). These results indicate that a novel zinc finger gene may also play a potential role in the cardiac-specific and inducible expression of the *MLC-2* gene during cardiac growth and development. Interestingly, a similar role for HF-1a and HF-1b regulatory elements has been found in the alpha myosin heavy chain gene (97). Recent studies that identified cardiac regulatory elements within the β-myosin heavy chain (89) and troponin C (71) genes should also lead to rapid progress in the isolation and characterization of additional nuclear factors that control the expression of the cardiac muscle gene program.

Regional Specification

Cardiogenesis not only requires the initial commitment of mesodermally derived progenitor cells to the cardiac muscle lineage, but also involves the development of distinct cardiac chambers and specialized conduction tissue (atrial, ventricular, nodal, Purkinje fiber, etc). The acquisition of the divergent morphological, electrophysiological, biochemical, and contractile properties of these specialized cardiac cell types is largely because of the activation of regional specific programs of gene expression, e.g. ANF expression in atrial muscle cells. Although relatively little is currently known concerning the mechanisms that govern regional expression of muscle genes within the heart, in situ hybridization studies of murine embryos by Buckingham and co-workers have provided initial insight into the events that lead to atrial and ventricular specification of a subset of cardiac muscle genes that are expressed in either the atrium or the ventricle in the adult myocardium (49). During the earliest stages of cardiac development, (day 8, murine embryonic development) these genes are co-expressed in the atrial and ventricular compartments of the embryonic myocardium, with regional specification occurring subsequent to the completion of cardiac septation and chamber development (49). For example, specification of the atrial *MLC-1* and ANF genes occurs shortly before birth, when the expression of these atrial markers is down-regulated in the ventricular compartment (79). With respect to these atrial genes, regional specificity is largely accomplished through their negative regulation in the non-expressing (ventricular) region (Figure 2). Further support for this notion is provided by studies of the ventricular *MLC-1* gene, which is co-expressed in all cardiac chambers in the early embryonic heart (day 10), and then is selectively down-regulated in the atrium during the later developmental stages (49) (Figure 2).

Recent studies of the developmental regulation of the *MLC-2* gene suggest that this view cannot be generalized to other ventricular-specific genes (63). In situ analyses of day 8 murine embryos show that this *MLC-2* gene is expressed exclusively in the ventricular region of the heart tube, with negligible expression in the atrial primordia, which suggests that ventricular specification can occur prior to septation and the development of distinct atrial and ventricular chambers (Figure 2) (63). Further analysis of the molecular regulation of the *MLC-2* gene should provide insight into the process of ventricular specification at the earliest stages of cardiogenesis, i.e. whether this pattern of restricted ventricular expression is related to the establishment of a morphogenetic field within the primordial heart tube, or is simply a reflection of early, direct commitment to the ventricular muscle cell lineage from pre-committed progenitor cells (53). It will be particularly interesting to determine whether this field of ventricular-specific expression is established

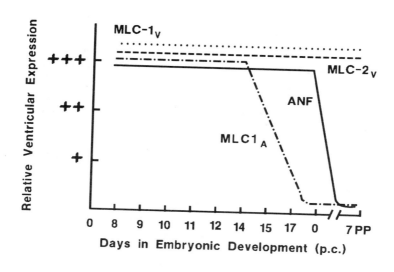

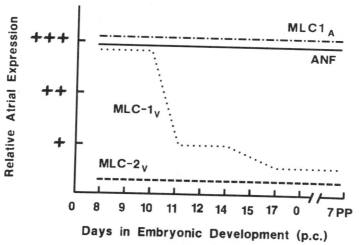

Figure 2 Developmental regulation of atrial- and ventricular-specific genes in the embryonic mouse heart.

by cardiac muscle homeotic genes, similar to the recently described *M-Hox* gene (66). Recently it was shown that a 250 bp MLC-2 promoter fragment can not only confer cardiac muscle specificity, but can restrict expression of the luciferase reporter genes specifically to the ventricular compartment at the earliest stages of cardiac development (day 9 of murine development) (63).

The question of the role for the HF-1 regulatory element and HF-1a/HF-1b factors in commitment to the cardiac lineage and in maintenance of ventricular-specific expression of the 250 bp *MLC-2* luciferase fusion gene in transgenic mice remains to be determined. Similarly, the demonstration that a 500 bp fragment of the human ANF promoter can confer atrial-specific expression in transgenic mice, coupled with recent advances in identifying regulatory regions in the ANF 5 flanking region (35, 40, 94), may provide information regarding the negative regulatory pathways that mediate regional specificity.

In addition to the development of atrial and ventricular chambers, cardiogenesis also requires the development of valvular structures derived from the endocardial cushions, as well as the ontogeny of the highly specialized pacemaker properties of the conduction system. Unfortunately, because of the lack of cell type-specific markers, relatively limited information is currently available regarding the pathways that regulate gene expression in these specific cardiac cell contexts. Within the endocardial cushion, TGFβ (72) and a specific isoform of the FGF receptor (73) are co-expressed. In addition, recent studies have documented the expression of the negative helix-loop-helix regulator, Id, in the developing endocardial cushion (16). Whether the expression of these genes reflects their critical role in the subsequent development of valvular structures and septation events remains a question. In the conduction system, the SA and AV nodal cells display the expression of neural genes, such as neurofilament-1 (91), which suggests that the conduction system may either be derived or influenced by neural crest derivatives during cardiogenesis (19). Whether the nodal cells represent modified muscle or neural cells, and what the precise role of the neural crest is in the initiation of conduction system development, is still to be determined. Obviously, one of the highest priorities is the development of a panel of regional-specific genetic markers for the endocardial cushion and conduction system that will allow implementation of molecular, cellular, and genetic approaches to identify the molecular pathways that activate their cell-specific programs during cardiogenesis.

PARADIGMS FOR INDUCIBLE EXPRESSION DURING CARDIAC GROWTH AND HYPERTROPHY

The acquisition of the hypertrophic phenotype is largely dependent upon the activation of a cardiac muscle gene program. The up-regulation of constitutively expressed contractile protein genes leads to the accumulation of contractile proteins, while the activation of a subset of embryonic marker genes results in the expression of fetal characteristics in the hypertrophied myocardium. Presumably, an improved understanding of the mechanisms that lead to the activation of genetic markers of the hypertrophic response will ultimately lead to the identification of the signaling pathways that orchestrate this important adaptive physiologic response. Utilizing a cultured myocardial cell model and genetic markers, which are closely linked to the hypertrophic phenotype, several important steps in the signaling pathway for cardiac growth and hypertrophy have recently been identified, including a pathway that extends from the membrane to the nucleus (see Table 3) (for detailed review, see 12; I. Komuro & Y. Yazaki, this volume). The question arises as to which of these signals represents the critical molecular switches for the activation of the hypertrophic response.

Ras and Immediate Early Genes

The development of high efficiency approaches for the cytoplasmic injection of neutralizing antibodies and purified recombinant proteins, as well as nuclear injection of expression vectors in living, contracting neonatal rat cardiac muscle cells, has provided a valuable system to distinguish between signaling molecules, which are simply required for the response, as opposed to those that can dominantly activate the hypertrophic phenotype (87). Using this approach, recent studies have documented an important role for *H-Ras* in the activation of cardiac muscle cell hypertrophy (90). The microinjection of purified, recombinant oncogenic *Ras* in single cardiac muscle cells results in the induction of *c-fos*, but does not lead to the activation of DNA synthesis or cell proliferation (90). However, the microinjected cells display several features of myocardial cell hypertrophy, including the activation of atrial natriuretic factor (ANF) gene expression, an increase in cell size, and an increase in the organization of an individual contractile protein, MLC-2, into organized sarcomeric units (90). Co-transfection studies document that activated *Ras* can lead to the transcriptional activation of an ANF-luciferase fusion gene, while the expression of the wild-type *Ras* is without significant effect. Co-transfection of a dominant negative ras vector, which interferes

Table 3 Signaling molecules that mediate the induction of genetic markers for the hypertrophic response

Agonists	Transduction	Kinases	Nuclear factors
α Adrenergic (4, 34, 35)			
Angiotensin II (1)	H-Ras (90)	Protein kinase C (33, 85)	Hf-1a/HF-1b (62, 96)
Endothelin-1 (86)	G_q (41)		
FGF (69)			
TGF-β (69)			
Stretch (38)			

References are in parentheses.

with *Ras*-dependent signaling pathways, significantly blocks phenylephrine induction of the ANF gene, thereby suggesting that *Ras* is not only sufficient for activating ANF gene expression, but is also required for the up-regulation of the gene during the onset of myocardial hypertrophy (90). Taken together, these studies provide compelling evidence for Ras-dependent signaling pathways for the activation of cardiac muscle genes during hypertrophy. The question arises as to the mechanisms by which a conventional G protein-coupled receptor, such as the α-1A adrenergic receptor (46), activates *Ras* and the subsequent induction of the ANF gene. Recent studies with neutralizing G_q antibodies have documented a role for this G_α subunit in transduction of α-1_A receptor-mediated hypertrophy (36) and the associated induction of the ANF gene (41). Accordingly, it will be of interest to explore the potential interactions between G_q and *Ras*-mediated signaling pathways for the activation of the embryonic gene program during cardiac muscle cell hypertrophy.

In other cell types, the activation of Ras-dependent signaling pathways results in the rapid induction of proto-oncogenes, such as *c-fos* (23). During the onset of myocardial hypertrophy, there is an analogous induction of a program of proto-oncogenes and immediate early gene expression that includes *c-fos, c-jun, jun B*, EGR-1, and nur-77 (29, 31, 38, 39, 77) (for further information, see I. Komuro & Y. Yazaki, this volume). A similar subset of immediate early genes is up-regulated during in vivo pressure overload hypertrophy and α-adrenergic-mediated hypertrophy of cultured myocardial cells, which suggests that conserved mechanisms might orchestrate the activation of cardiac muscle genes, independently of the hypertrophic stimulus (29, 77). The question remains as to whether immediate early gene induction is required for the subsequent activation of cardiac muscle target genes, whose induction lags behind by 4 to 6 hr (35). However, at the present time, there is no direct evidence for a role of any of the immediate early genes in the activation of the cardiac muscle target genes during the course of hypertrophy. Although co-transfection studies in primary cardiac muscle cells have suggested that the overexpression of *c-jun* may up-regulate an ANF promoter-reporter gene (40), it is currently unclear as to whether *c-jun* is necessary for induction of the ANF gene during myocardial cell hypertrophy. The role of putative AP-1 sites in the ANF promoter region, remains to be tested (35, 78).

Induction of an Embryonic Gene Program

Previous studies of pressure overload hypertrophy in rat model systems have documented a qualitative change in myosin composition from the V1 to V3 isoform (59). This alteration in myosin composition is largely the result of the down-regulation of the α myosin heavy chain (MHC) gene and the concomitant re-activation of βMHC gene expression (30), which is normally expressed in embryonic ventricular muscle cells. Accordingly, the reactivation of βMHC expression became one of the first well-characterized molecular markers for the activation of an embryonic gene program during myocardial cell hypertrophy (7). Interestingly, βMHC induction displays a perivascular distribution (82), which suggests the potential participation of vascular-derived factors for this response. In contrast, another marker of the embryonic gene program, the skeletal α-actin gene, is uniformly induced throughout the ventricular compartment (47, 82). The *cis* regulatory elements and corresponding *trans*-acting factors that mediate the up-regulation of the βMHC (7, 30), skeletal α-actin (3, 47, 48), and smooth muscle actin (5) genes during hypertrophy are not completely determined, but are currently under intense scrutiny (33, 69). Recent studies by Simpson and co-workers have localized a small fragment within the βMHC promoter region that mediates inducible expression during α-adrenergic stimulation of myocardial cell hypertrophy (33). The characterization of the factor(s) that recognize the βMHC element and further definition of its role in the activation of βMHC gene expression during hypertrophy, should be of interest; however, there may be limited relevance to clinical hypertrophy in man, since the hypertrophic induction of both the βMHC and skeletal α-actin genes is predominantly a feature of rodent species (8). Ventricular hypertrophy in larger animals (canine, pig, etc, including humans) is not associated with the induction of either the βMHC or skeletal α-actin genes, which are constitutively expressed in the larger species (8).

As a result, a number of studies have utilized the ANF gene as a marker for the induction of the embryonic gene program during hypertrophy (12). ANF gene induction is a conserved genetic feature of hypertrophied ventricular muscle cells from all species currently examined, and it occurs in response to a wide variety of hypertrophic stimuli (for a review, see 12). The level of induction (> than 20-fold) and the availability of well-characterized antibodies and promoter constructs has made it useful as a genetic marker of cardiac hypertrophy in a variety of species. While the precise pathways that lead to the induction of the ANF gene remain unclear, the mechanisms that dictate its regional-specific expression in the atrium (17) can be clearly segregated from those that are responsible for inducibility (77). While numerous candidate transcriptional factors have been proposed to potentially regulate the ANF gene, including CREB, Egr-1, *c-fos*, *c-jun*, SRF, etc, to date there has been no direct evidence for a role of any of these factors in the activation of the ANF gene during hypertrophy. In fact, recent studies have mapped the inducible regulatory elements in the rat ANF gene to a proximal region of the ANF promoter that lacks consensus Egr-1, CRE, AP-1, or CArG elements (22). The recent development of an in vivo murine model that can be applied to transgenic mice (43, 77) and the adaptation of microinjection approaches in cultured myocardial cell model systems (87) should lead to the rapid evaluation of the role of these candidate signaling molecules, as well as other novel factors, in this genetic marker.

Constitutive Contractile Protein Gene Program

In addition to qualitative alterations in the cardiac muscle gene program, there are also quantitative increases in the expression of constitutively expressed contractile protein genes that lead to the characteristic accumulation of contractile proteins and sarcomeric units in individual cardiac muscle cells. As a model for the up-regulation of constitutively expressed cardiac contractile protein genes, the rat cardiac *MLC-2* gene has been employed (35, 42, 62, 96). A 250 bp fragment, which confers cardiac-specific expression, is also sufficient for inducible expression, as revealed by studies in both cultured myocardial cell models (35), and during in vivo pressure overload in transgenic mice that harbor a 250 bp *MLC-2* luciferase fusion gene (43). Mapping studies employing point mutations in various regulatory regions of the *MLC-2* gene document an important role for HF-1, which confers both cardiac-specific and inducible expression to heterologous promoters (96). This result suggests that inducibility of a constitutively expressed cardiac contractile protein gene may be accomplished through the modulation of factors that control cardiac muscle specificity. It will necessary to determine if inducibility is mediated by either covalent modification of the HF-1a/HF-1b factors, which bind to HF-1, or whether induction is mediated through interactions with new partners via protein-protein interactions (62). The recent cloning of HF-1 binding factors (95) should facilitate these studies.

SUMMARY AND FUTURE DIRECTIONS

During the past few years, great progress has been made in identifying genetic markers to study cardiac growth and development. In a few cases, *cis* regulatory elements have been identified that control muscle gene expression during various stages of cardiac growth and development. The corresponding *trans*-acting factors have been characterized at an initial level in cardiac nuclear extracts. However, further progress will depend on the isolation and cloning of these various factors to allow a critical analysis of their relative role in the control of the cardiac muscle gene program. In the absence of continuous cardiac cell lines, these studies will increasingly rely on transient studies in cultured myocardial cells that utilize microinjection of antibodies to neutralize the effects of these factors, or of duplex competitor oligonucleotides to bind the *trans*-acting factors. In addition, genetic approaches in transgenic animals, in which the full repertoire of phenotypic responses during cardiac development and growth/hypertrophy can now be studied, should prove to be extremely valuable. The recent development of embryonic stem cell systems for the inactivation of specific target genes by homologous recombination holds great promise for the application of mouse genetics to the study of cardiac muscle gene regulation in these two settings. The establishment of in vitro models, in which totipotent embryonic stem cells will differentiate into cardiac muscle cells (76), may offer the possibility of developing in vitro models to study regional specification during the acquisition of atrial, ventricular, and conduction system-specific features (K. Chien & W. Miller-Hance, unpublished). With the availability of these in vitro systems, it will be feasible to examine the mechanisms by which mutant myosin heavy chain proteins activate a hypertrophic response in cardiac muscle cells (18, 88). This information should provide a groundwork for understanding the molecular switches that regulate the cardiac muscle gene program and eventually the mechanisms that control abnormal cardiac growth and development.

ACKNOWLEDGMENTS

This work is supported by grants to K.R.C. from National Institutes of Health (HL-36139, HL-45069, and HL-46345) and the American Heart Association (88-0235 and 91-022170), to S.M.E. from National Institutes of Health (HL4671-01A1) and the California Affiliate of the American Heart Association(90-112). H.Z. and M.V.B. are supported by fellowships from the California American Heart Association Affiliate. M K.U.K. and W.M.-H. are supported by the National Heart, Lung, and Blood Institute Clinical Investigator Awards (HL-02618-01 and HL-02712-01; respectively). T.X.O. is an Associate Investigator of the Veterans Administration, San Diego, California. K.R.C is an Established Investigator of the American Heart Association.

Literature Cited

1. Baker, K. M., Aceto, J. F. 1990. Angiotensin-II stimulation of protein synthesis and cell growth in chick heart cells. *Am. J. Physiol.* 259:H610–18
2. Benezra, R., Davis, R. L., Lockshon, D., Turner, D. L., Weintraub, H. 1990. The protein Id: a negative regulator of helix-loop-helix DNA binding proteins. *Cell* 61(1):49–59
3. Bishopric, N. H., Kedes, L. 1991. Adrenergic regulation of the skeletal alpha-actin gene promoter during myocardial cell hypertrophy. *Proc. Natl. Acad. Sci. USA* 88:2132–36
4. Bishopric, N. H., Simpson, P. C., Ordahl, C. P. 1987. Induction of the skeletal α actin gene in α1 adrenoceptor-mediated hypertopy of rat cardiac myocytes. *J. Clin. Invest.* 80:1194–99
5. Black, F. M., Packer, S. E., Parker, T. G., Michael, L. H., Roberts, R., et al. 1991. The vascular smooth muscle alpha-actin gene is reactivated during cardiac hypertrophy provoked by load. *J. Clin. Invest.* 88:1581–88
6. Blackwell, T. K., Weintraub, H. 1990. Differences and similarities in DNA-binding preferences of MyoD and E2A protein complexes revealed by binding site selection. *Science* 250:1104–10
7. Boeheler, K. R., Carrier, L., Chassagne, C., de la Bastie, D., Mercadier, J. J., et al. 1991. Regulation of myosin heavy chain and actin isogenes expression during cardiac growth. *Mol. Cell. Biochem.* 104:101–7
8. Boeheler, K. R., Carrier, L., de la Bastie, D., Allen, P. D., Komajda, M., et al. 1991. Skeletal actin mRNA increases in the human heart during

ontogenic development and is the major isoform of control and failing adult hearts. *J. Clin. Invest.* 88:323–30

9. Braun, T., Bober, E., Winter, B., Rosenthal, N., Arnold, H. H. 1990. Myf-6, a new member of the human gene family of myogenic determination factors: evidence for a gene cluster on chromosome 12. *EMBO J.* 9:821–31

10. Buskin, J. N., Hauschka, S. D. 1989. Identification of a myocyte nuclear factor that binds to the muscle-specific enhancer of the mouse muscle creatine kinase gene. *Mol. Cell. Biol.* 9:2627–40

11. Carr, C. S., Sharp, P. A. 1990. A helix-loop-helix protein related to the immunoglobulin E box-binding proteins. *Mol. Cell. Biol.* 10:4384–88

12. Chien, K. R., Knowlton, K. U., Zhu, H., Chien, S. 1991. Regulation of cardiac gene expression during myocardial growth and hypertrophy: Molecular studies of an adaptive physiologic response. *FASEB J.* 5:3037–46

13. Cserjesi, P., Olson, E. N. 1991. Myogenin induces the myocyte-specific enhancer binding factor MEF-2 independently of other muscle-specific gene products. *Mol. Cell. Biol.* 11:4854–62

14. Edmondson, D. G., Olson, E. N. 1989. A gene with homology to the myc similarity region of MyoD1 is expressed during myogenesis and is sufficient to activate the muscle differentiation program. *Genes Dev.* 3:628–40

15. Evans, S. M., O'Brien, T. X. 1992. Id-1 mRNA expression during mouse development. Submitted

16. Evans, S. M., Walsh, B., Newton, C., Thorburn, J., van Bilsen, M., et al. 1992. The potential role of helix-loop-helix proteins in cardiac gene expression. Submitted

17. Field, L. J. 1988. Atrial natriuretic factor-SV40 T antigen transgenes produce tumors and cardiac arrhythmias in mice. *Science* 239:1029–33

18. Geisterfer-Lowrance, A. A., Kass, S., Tanigawa, G., Vosberg, H. P., McKenna, W., et al. 1990. A molecular basis for familial hypertrophic cardiomyopathy: a beta cardiac myosin heavy chain gene missense mutation. *Cell* 62:999–1006

19. Gorza, L., Schiaffino, S., Vitadello, M. 1988. Heart conduction system: a neural crest derivative. *Brain Res.* 457:360–66

20. Gossett, L. A., Kelvin, D. J., Sternberg, E. A., Olson, E. N. 1989. A new myocyte-specific enhancer-binding factor that recognizes a conserved element associated with multiple muscle-specific genes. *Mol. Cell. Biol.* 9:5022–33

21. Deleted in proof

22. Harris, A., Chen, Y. F., Rauscher, F., Chien, K. R. 1992. The Wilm's tumor gene product activates the expression of the ANF gene in cultured ventricular cardiac muscle cells. Submitted

22. Harris, A. N., Chen, Y. F., Chien, K. R. 1992. Multiple *cis* regulatory elements mediate inducibility of the ANF gene by RAS and α-adrenergic agonists. Submitted

23. Haubruck, H., McCormick, F. 1991. Ras p21: effects and regulation. *Biochim. Biophys. Acta.* 1072(2–3):215–29

24. Deleted in proof

25. Henderson, S. A., Spencer, M., Sen, A., Kumar, C., Siddiqui, M. A., Chien, K. R. 1989. Structure, organization, and expression of the rat cardiac myosin light chain-2 gene: Identification of a 250-base pair fragment which confers cardiac-specific expression. *J. Biol. Chem.* 264:18142–48

26. Horlick, R. A., Benfield, P. A. 1989. The upstream muscle-specific enhancer of the rat muscle creatinine kinase gene is composed of multiple elements. *Mol. Cell. Biol.* 9:2396–413

27. Horlick, R. A., Hobson, G. M., Patterson, J. H., Mitchell, M. T., Benfield, P. A. 1990. Brain and muscle creatine kinase genes contain common AT-rich recognition protein-binding regulatory elements. *Mol. Cell. Biol.* 10:4826–36

28. Iannello, R. C., Mar, J. H., Ordahl, C. P. 1991. Characterization of a promoter element required for transcription in myocardial cells. *J. Biol. Chem.* 266: 3309–16

29. Iwaki, K., Sukhatme, V. P., Shubeita, H. E., Chien, K. R. 1990. α and β adrenergic stimulation induce distinct patterns of immediate early gene expression in neonatal rat myocardial cells: fos/jun expression is associated with sarcomere assembly; Egr-1 induction is primarily an α1 mediated response. *J. Biol. Chem.* 265:13809–17

30. Izumo, S., Lompre, A. M., Matsuoka, R., Koren, G., Schwartz, K. 1987. Myosin heavy chain messenger RNA and protein isoform transitions during cardiac hypertrophy: Interaction between hemodynamic and thyroid hormone-induced signals. *J. Clin. Invest.* 79:970–77

31. Izumo, S., Nadal-Ginard, B., Mahdavi, V. 1988. Proto-oncogene

induction and reprogramming of cardiac gene expression produced by pressure overload. *Proc. Natl. Acad. Sci. USA* 85:339–43

32. Johnson, J. E., Wold, B. J., Hauschka, S. D. 1989. Muscle creatine kinase sequence elements regulating skeletal and cardiac muscle expression in transgenic mice. *Mol. Cell. Biol.* 9:3393–99

33. Kariya, K., Karns, L. R., Simpson, P. C. 1991. Expression of a constitutively activated mutant of the beta-isozyme of protein kinase C in cardiac myocytes stimulates the promoter of the beta-myosin heavy chain isogene. *J. Biol. Chem.* 266:10023–26

34. Kariya, K.-I., Karns, L. R., Simpson, P. C. 1992. *J. Mol. Cell. Cardiol.* 24:S101 (Abstr.)

35. Knowlton, K. U., Baracchini, E., Ross, R. S., Harris, A. N., Henderson, S. A., et al. 1991. Co-regulation of the atrial natriuretic factor and cardiac myosin light chain-2 genes during α-adrenergic stimulation of neonatal rat ventricular cells. *J. Biol. Chem.* 266:7759–68

36. Knowlton, K. U., Michel, M., Shubeita, H., Itani, M., Yanagi, K., et al. 1992. The α1A-receptor subtype mediates inositol phosphate accumulation and the transcriptional activation of an embryonically expressed gene (ANF) in cultured neonatal ventricular myocytes. *J. Biol. Chem.* In press

37. Deleted in proof

38. Komuro, I., Kaida, T., Shibazaki, Y., Kurabayashi, M., Katoh, Y., et al. 1990. Stretching cardiac myocytes stimulates proto-oncogene expression. *J. Biol. Chem.* 265:3595–98

39. Komuro, I., Kurabayashi, M., Takaku, F., Yazaki, Y. 1988. Expression of cellular oncogenes in the myocardium during the developmental stage and pressure-overloaded hypertrophy of the rat heart. *Circ. Res.* 62:1075–79

40. Kovacic-Milivojevic, B., Gardner, D. G. 1992. Divergent regulation of the human atrial natriuretic peptide gene by c-jun and c-fos. *Mol. Cell. Biol.* 12:292–301

41. La Morte, V., Thorburn, J., Knowlton, K., Chien, K. R., Feramisco, J. 1992. Inhibition of GQ blocks α adrenergic induction of ANF gene expression during cardiac muscle cell hypertrophy. Submitted

42. Lee, H., Henderson, S., Reynolds, R., Dunnmon, P., Yuan, D., Chien, K. R. 1988. α-1 adrenergic stimulation of cardiac gene transcription in neonatal rat myocardial cells: Effects on myosin

light chain-2 gene expression. *J. Biol. Chem.* 263:7352–58

43. Lee, K., Rockman, H., Ross, J., Chien, K. R. 1992. Mechanical activation of a MLC- luciferase fusion gene in transgenic mice during in vivo pressure overload hypertrophy. *Proc. Natl. Acad. Sci. USA.* In preparation

44. Lee, K. J., Ross, R. S., Rockman, H. A., Harris, A., O'Brien, T. X., et al. 1992. Myosin light chain 2-luciferase transgenic mice reveal distinct regulatory programs for cardiac and skeletal muscle specific expression of a single contractile protein gene. *J. Biol. Chem.* 276:15875–86

45. Litvin, J., Montgomery, M., Gonzalez-Sanchez, A., Bader, D. 1992. Commitment and differentiation of cardiac myo- cytes. *Trends Cardiovasc. Med.* 2:27–32

46. Lomasney, J. W., Cotecchia, S., Lefkowitz, R. J., Caron, M. G. 1991. Molecular biology of alpha-adrenergic receptors: Implications for receptor classification and for structure-function relationships. *Biochim. Biophys. Acta* 1095:127–39

47. Lompre, A. M., Mercadier, J. J., Schwartz, K. 1991. Changes in gene expression during cardiac growth. *Int. Rev. Cytol.* 124:137–86

48. Long, C. S., Henrich, C. J., Simpson, P. C. 1991. A growth factor for cardiac myocytes is produced by cardiac nonmyocytes. *Cell Reg.* 2:1081–95

49. Lyons, G. E., Schiaffino, S., Sassoon, D., Barton, P., Buckingham, M. 1990. Developmental regulation of myosin gene expression in mouse cardiac muscle. *J. Cell. Biol.* 111:2427–36

50. Mar, J. H., Antin, P. B., Cooper, T. A., Ordahl, C. P. 1988. Analysis of the upstream regions governing expression of the chicken cardiac troponin T gene in embryonic cardiac and skeletal muscle cells. *J. Cell. Biol.* 107:573–85

51. Mar, J. H., Ordahl, C. P. 1988. A conserved CATTCCT motif is required for skeletal muscle-specific activity of the cardiac troponin T gene promoter. *Proc. Natl. Acad. Sci. USA* 85:6404–8

52. Deleted in proof

53. Miller-Hance, W., Evans, S. M., Robbins, J., Chien, K. R. 1992. An in vitro model of ventricular specification of the MLC-2 gene during the differentiation of embryonic stem cells into embryoid bodies. Submitted

54. Miner, J. H., Miller, J. B., Wold, B. J. 1992. Skeletal muscle phenotypes

initiated by ectopic MyoD in transgenic mouse heart. *Development* 114:853–60

55. Miner, J. H., B. Wold. 1990. Herculin, a fourth member of the MyoD family of myogenic regulatory genes. *Proc. Natl. Acad. Sci. USA* 87:1089–93

56. Minty, A., Kedes, L. 1986. Upstream regions of the human cardiac actin gene that modulate its transcription in muscle cells: Presence of an evolutionary conserved repeated motif. *Mol. Cell Biol.* 6:2125–46

57. Murre, C., McCaw, P. S., Baltimore, D. 1989. A new DNA binding and dimerization motif in immunoglobulin enhancer binding, *daughterless, MyoD,* and *myc* proteins. *Cell* 56:777–83

58. Murre, C., McCaw, P. S., Vaessin, H., Caudy, M., Jan, L. Y., et al. 1989. Interactions between heterologous helix-loop-helix proteins generate complexes that bind specifically to a common DNA sequence. *Cell* 58:537–44

59. Nagai, R., Pritzl, N., Low, R. B., Stirewalt, W. S., Zak, R., et al. 1987. Myosin isozyme synthesis and mRNA levels in pressure-overloaded rabbit hearts. *Circ. Res.* 60:692–99

60. Navankasattusas, S., Zhu, H., Garcia, A., Evans, S. M., Chien, K. R. 1992. A ubiquitous factor (HF-1a) and a muscle factor (HF-1b/MEF-2) forms an E-box independent pathway for cardiac muscle specific expression. *Mol. Cell Biol.* 12(4):1469–79

61. Nelson, C., Shen, L.-I., Meister, A., Fodor, E., Rutter, W. J. 1990. Pan: a transcriptional regulator that binds chymotrypsin, insulin, and AP-4 enhancer motifs. *Genes Dev.* 4:1035–43

62. Nguyen, V., Brown, A., Garcia, A., Zhu, H., Chien, K. R. 1992. HF-1b and the induction of the MLC-2 gene during cardiac muscle cell hypertrophy. Submitted

63. O'Brien, T. X., Lee, K., Chien, K. R. 1992. A morphogenetic field of MLC-2 gene expression in the primordial heart tube of normal and MLC-luciferase transgenic mice. Submitted

64. Olson, E. N. 1992. Regulatory mechanisms for skeletal muscle differentiation and their relevance to cardiac morphogenesis. *Trends Cardiovasc. Med.* 2: In press

65. Olson, E. N. 1990. MyoD family: a paradigm for development? *Genes Dev.* 4:1454–61

66. Olson, E. N., Cjerjesi, P., Lilly, B., Bryson, L., et al. 1992. M-Hox: A mesodermally restricted homeodomain protein that binds an essential site in the muscle creatine kinase enhancer. *Development*. In press

67. Otto, M. O., Bober, E., Lyons, G., Arnold, H., Buckingham, M. 1991. Early expression of the myogenic regulatory gene, myf-5, in precursor cells of skeletal muscle in the mouse embryo. *Development* 111:1097–107

68. Parker, T. G., Chow, K. L., Schwartz, R. J., Schneider, M. D. 1992. Positive and negative control of the skeletal alpha-actin promoter in cardiac muscle. A proximal serum response element is sufficient for induction by basic fibroblast growth factor (FGF) but not for inhibition by acidic FGF. *J. Biol. Chem.* 267:3343–50

69. Parker, T. G., Packer, S. E., Schneider, M. D. 1990. Peptide growth factors can provoke "fetal" contractile protein gene expression in rat cardiac myocytes. *J. Clin. Invest.* 85:507–14

70. Parmacek, M. S., Leiden, J. M. 1989. Structure and expression of the murine slow/cardiac troponin C gene. *J. Biol. Chem.* 264:13217–25

71. Parmacek, M. S., Vora, A. J., Tingliang, S., Barr, E., Jung, F., Leiden, J. M. 1992. Identification and characterization of a cardiac specific transcriptional regulatory element in the slow/cardiac troponin C gene. *Mol. Cell. Biol.* 12:1967–76

72. Pelton, R. W., Dickinson, M. E., Moses, H. L., Hogan, B. L. 1990. In situ hybridization analysis of TGF beta 3 RNA expression during mouse development: comparative studies with TGF beta 1 and beta 2. *Development* 110:609–20

73. Peters, K. G., Werner, S., Chen, G., Williams, L. T. 1992. Two FGF receptor genes are differentially expressed in epithelial and mesenchymal tissues during limb formation and organogenesis in the mouse. *Development* 114: 233–43

74. Pollock, R., Treisman, R. 1991. Human SRF-related proteins: DNA-binding properties and potential regulatory targets. *Genes Dev.* 5:2327–41

75. Rhodes, S. J., Konieczny, S. F. 1989. Identification of MRF4: a new member of the muscle regulatory factor gene family. *Genes Dev.* 3:2050–61

76. Robbins, J., Gulick, J., Sanchez, A., Howles, P., Doetschman, T. 1990. Mouse embryonic stem cells express the cardiac myosin heavy chain genes during development in vitro. *J. Biol. Chem.* 265:11905–9

77. Rockman, H. A., Ross, R. S., Harris, A. N., Knowlton, K. U., Steinhelper,

M. E., et al. 1991. Segregation of atrial specific and inducible expression of an ANF transgene in an in vivo murine model of cardiac hypertrophy. *Proc. Natl. Acad. Sci. USA* 88:8277–81

79. Rosenzweig, A., Halazonetis, T. D., Seidman, C. E. 1991. Proximal regulatory domains of rat atrial natriuretic factor gene. *Circulation* 84:1256–65

79. Rosenzweig, A., Seidman, C. E. 1991. Atrial natriuretic factor and related peptide hormones. *Annu. Rev. Biochem.* 60:229–55

80. Sartorelli, V., Kedes, L. 1992. Myocardial activation of the human cardiac α-actin promoter by helix-loop-helix proteins. *Proc. Natl. Acad. Sci. USA* 89:4047–51

81. Sassoon, D., G. Lyons, W. E., Wright, V., Lin, A.. Lassar, et al. 1989. Expression of two myogenic regulatory factors myogenin and MyoDI during mouse embryogenesis. *Nature* 341: 303–7

82. Schiaffino, S., Samuel, J. L., Sassoon, D., Lompre, A. M., Garner, I., et al. 1989. Nonsynchronous accumulation of alpha-skeletal actin and beta-myosin heavy chain mRNAs during early stages of pressure-overload—induced cardiac hypertrophy demonstrated by in situ hybridization. *Circ. Res.* 64(5):937–48

83. Deleted in proof

84. Seidman, C. E., Wong, D. W., Jarcho, J. A., Bloch, K. D., Seidman, J. G. 1988. *Cis*-acting sequences that modulate atrial natriuretic factor gene expression. *Proc. Natl. Acad. Sci. USA* 85(11):4104–8

85. Shubeita, H. E., Martinson, E., Chien, K. R., Brown, J. H. 1992. Expression of a constitutively active protein kinase C gene activates the transcription of the ANF and MLC-2 genes in cultured myocardial cells. *Proc. Natl. Acad. Sci. USA* 89:1305–9

86. Shubeita, H. E., McDonough, P. M., Harris, A., Knowlton, K. U., Glembotski, C., et al. 1990. Endothelin induction of inositol phospholipid hydrolosis, sarcomere assembly, and cardiac gene expression in ventricular myocytes: A paracrine mechanism for myocardial cell hypertrophy. *J. Biol. Chem.* 265: 20555–62

87. Shubeita, H. E., Thorburn, J., Chien, K. R. 1992. Microinjection of antibodies and expression vectors into living myocardial cells. Development of

a novel approach to identify candidate genes that regulate cardiac growth and hypertrophy. *Circulation.* 85:2236–46

88. Tanigawa, G., Jarcho, J. A., Kass, S., Solomon, S. D., Vosberg, H. P. 1990. A molecular basis for familial hypertrophic cardiomyopathy: an alpha/beta cardiac myosin heavy chain hybrid gene. *Cell* 62:991–98

89. Thompson, W. R., Nadal-Ginard, B., Mahdavi, V. 1991. A myoD1 independent muscle- specific enhancer controls the expression of the beta-myosin heavy chain gene in skeletal and cardiac muscle cells. *J. Biol. Chem.* 266: 22678–88

90. Thorburn, A., Thorburn, J., Chen, S. Y., Powers, S., Shubeita, H. E., et al. 1992. HRas dependent pathways can activate morphological and genetic markers of cardiac muscle cell hypertrophy. *J. Biol. Chem.* In press

91. Vitadello, M., Matteoli, M., Gorza, L. 1990. Neurofilament proteins are co-expressed with desmin in heart conduction system myocytes. *J. Cell Sci.* 97:11–21

92. Weintraub, H., Davis, R., Tapscott, S., Thayer, M., Krause, M., et al. 1991. The myoD gene family: nodal point during specification of the muscle cell lineage. *Science* 251:761–66

93. Wright, W. E., Sassoon, D. A., Lin, V. K. 1989. Myogenin, a factor regulating myogenesis, has a domain homologous to MyoD. *Cell* 56:607–17

94. Wu, J. P., Kovacic-Milivojevic, B., Lapointe, M. C., Nakamura, K., Gardner, D. G. 1991. *Cis*-active determinants for cardiac-specific expression in the human atrial natriuretic peptide gene. *Mol. Endocrinol.* 5(9):1311–22

95. Zhu, H., Brown, A., Nguyen, V., Pourhosseini, A., Garcia, A., Chien, K. R. 1992. A novel SP-1 like zinc finger gene (HF-1b) mediates an E box independent pathway for cardiac muscle gene expression. Submitted

96. Zhu, H., Garcia, A., Ross, R. S., Evans, S. M., Chien, K. R. 1991. A conserved 28 bp element (HF-1) within the rat cardiac myosin light chain-2 gene confers cardiac specific and α-adrenergic inducible expression in neonatal rat myocardial cells. *Mol. Cell Biol.* 11: 2273–81

97. Markham, B. 1993. *J. Biol. Chem.* In press

Annu. Rev. Physiol. 1993. 55:97–114

TRANSGENIC MICE IN CARDIOVASCULAR RESEARCH

Loren J. Field

Krannert Institute of Cardiology, Indiana University, School of Medicine, Indianapolis, Indiana 46202–4800

KEY WORDS: gene transfer of recombinant DNA, retroviral transfection, genomic clones natriuretic factor, cardiovascular regulation

INTRODUCTION

Our understanding of cardiovascular regulation has advanced primarily through the pharmacological, surgical, and/or physiological manipulation of whole animal models. Information gained from these direct intervention approaches has been augmented by the existence of numerous heritable forms of cardiovascular disease, both in humans and in other animals. The complex relationship that exists between expression of variant genes and manifestation of a phenotypic trait is readily apparent in genetic diseases that affect cardiovascular function, particularly in instances where the disease is multi-genic in nature.

Recently, techniques have emerged that permit direct manipulation of the genome, and thereby produce "transgenic" animals that heritably express genes that have been modified in vitro. The transgenic approach enables investigators to make unequivocal correlations between aberrant gene expression and a physiologic trait. The goal of this review is to provide a primer on the use of transgenic mice in the study of cardiovascular regulation.

Development of Transgenic Technology

The ability to produce transgenic animals evolved from technical advances in the embryo manipulation and recombinant DNA fields. The first successful transgenic model was reported in 1981 by Ruddle and co-workers (33). In the 1980s it became apparent that transgenic experiments could be applied to

97

a wide variety of biomedical research. Transgenic models of oncology, immunology, endocrinology, physiology, and developmental biology were reported. Transgenic models of the cardiovascular system have recently been reviewed (29, 57, 59).

Three methods are currently used to produce transgenic animals. The most popular approach relies on direct microinjection of recombinant DNA molecules, or transgenes, into the pronucleus of one-celled embryos (41). The embryos are then surgically implanted into surrogate mothers. Approximately 20% of the microinjected embryos will integrate the transgene into their genomes. In most instances, the integrated transgene will be passed on to subsequent generations, thereby establishing a lineage of transgenic mice. Although embryo microinjection is relatively easy to set up and master, the requisite equipment can be somewhat expensive (upwards of $50,000). However, most investigators quickly realize that these expenses pale when compared to those incurred for animal purchase and per diem charges. When using the embryo microinjection approach, it is difficult to precisely control the transgene copy number. In addition, the site of transgene integration is random. Both of these variables may negatively effect transgene expression.

Two other methodologies have been used to produce transgenic animals. One approach relies on gene transfer of recombinant DNA into pluripotent embryonic stem cells (ES cells, see 68). Chimeric animals are then generated by injection of the transfected ES cells into host blastocysts. If the ES cells contribute to the germ line, transgenic lineages derived entirely from the ES cells can be established. Although this methodology is difficult to master, it forms the basis for gene targeting experiments. Additionally, the method is quite useful if transgene expression causes developmental anomalies; large numbers of chimeric animals are readily produced once a transgenic ES cell line is generated.

Transgenic animals can also be produced by retroviral transfection (46). In this approach, embryos are transfected with a recombinant retrovirus carrying the gene of interest. The transfected embryos are then implanted into surrogate mothers. Retroviral integration is not associated with rearrangement of host sequences, as is frequently observed in embryo microinjections. In addition, the multiplicity of infection is easily adjusted to give each embryo upwards of ten unique integrations events. The viral genome provides a useful molecular tag that facilitates rapid cloning of host sequences flanking the integration site. These features make retroviral transgenesis the method of choice for random mutagenesis studies. The main disadvantage of retroviral transgenesis is the physical constraints on transgene size since it must be packaged as part of the retroviral genome.

Hogan et al (41) have compiled an excellent handbook that deals with the practical aspects of producing transgenic animals. Additionally, protocols for identifying founder animals and for establishing transgenic lineages are included. The book also has numerous helpful suggestions for microinjection facility design and animal husbandry practices, as well as a listing of vendors for requisite materials and supplies.

Practical Considerations for Designing Transgenic Models

Many factors may influence the final outcome of a given transgenic experiment. Failure to consider these factors could result in a model that fails to express the transgene, or alternatively a model in which the phenotype cannot be measured. Several issues that should be considered when designing a transgenic model are discussed below.

FUSION GENE DESIGN   Manifestation of a phenotype in transgenic animals is ultimately dependent upon fusion gene expression. It is clear that several aspects of transgene design may often negatively influence expression.

cDNA vs genomic clones Investigators frequently must choose between the use of cDNA vs genomic sequences when designing transgenes. Several groups have reported that cDNAs tend to express poorly in transgenic animals and, as a rule, they should be avoided if possible (9, 40). However, in most instances, cDNAs are isolated prior to the corresponding genomic clones. Additionally, many genes are large, and manipulation of fragments greater than 10 to 15 kb in length can be difficult, particularly in instances where unique restriction endonuclease sites must be engineered into the construct. Cassettes carrying heterologous introns and polyadenylation sites that efficiently target expression of cDNA inserts have recently been reported (64).

Vector sequences Vector sequences are required for the growth and selection of cloned genes in bacteria. When designing a transgene, many investigators will engineer restriction sites that permit separation of vector sequences from the transgene insert prior to microinjection. It has been suggested that vector sequences may negatively interfere with transgene expression (10), presumably by providing a target for DNA methylation. Although it is sometimes difficult to incorporate suitable restriction sites that permit insert isolation, when one considers the time and money invested in generating transgenic mice, any effort that might enhance transgene expression should be seriously entertained.

Homologous vs heterologous sequences Many transgenic mice expressing genes from other species have been generated. However, it is possible that transgene expression in a heterologous system may give an unexpected result. This is best illustrated by the mouse renin gene. Inbred mice fall into two categories with respect to the structure of the renin locus. Some mice carry a single renin structural gene, designated $Ren-1^c$, while other mice carry two renin structural genes, designated $Ren-1^d$ and $Ren-2^d$. These genes have markedly different patterns of tissue-specific expression (27). There is no overt pathophysiology associated with the expression of the endogenous $Ren-2^d$ gene in mice. Moreover, transgenic mice that carry a $Ren-2^d$ transgene in a $Ren-1^c$ genetic background are also phenotypically normal (61, 91). However, transgenic rats that carry the same $Ren-2^d$ transgene develop hypertension in the absence of elevated plasma renin activity (60). It has been suggested that the phenotype in these animals may be due to differences in the patterns of expression between the murine $Ren-2^d$ gene and the rat renin gene. Thus transgene expression can elicit markedly different phenotypes in homologous vs heterologous environments.

BACKGROUND CONSIDERATIONS   Many laboratories produce transgenic animals in outbred or random bred backgrounds. This practice stems largely from the observation that outbred mice tend to produce more and heartier embryos as compared to inbred animals. However, phenotypic variation resulting from allelic segregation in a random bred population can detract from a given transgenic model. For example, it is clear that while blood pressure values are consistent within a given inbred line of mice, significant variation is observed between different lines. Schlager has reported that systolic pressures range from 83 mm Hg for BALB/cJ mice to 151 mm Hg for aged C3H mice (73). Similar variation in other physiologic parameters, including water balance, heart rate, blood volume, and electrolyte balance have been reported (7). Given these observations, allelic segregation in an outbred population will increase the variability of the baseline physiological profile and consequently may obscure any phenotype arising from transgene expression.

Allelic segregation in mixed genetic backgrounds may also have a direct influence on transgene expression. For example, Storb and co-workers have identified a locus called SSM-1 (for strain-specific modifier) that influences transgene expression (25). There is a direct correlation between inhibition of transgene expression, transgene methylation, and segregation of the C57Bl/6J SSM-1 allele. In contrast, high levels of transgene expression were observed in the presence of the DBA/2J SSM-1 allele. The use of inbred DBA/2J mice would eliminate variable transgene expression caused by segregation of SSM-1 alleles in this model.

SPECIES CONSIDERATIONS   Although this review is limited to transgenic mice, it is becoming abundantly clear that transgenic experiments can be performed in a number of species. To date, transgenic models in mice, rats, rabbits, pigs, cows, and goats have been reported. The fact that mice have been predominately used for transgenic experiments is in part historic, as the transgenic technology was first developed in this species. Additionally, fiscal considerations favor the use of mice. Other advantages include the well-defined murine linkage map, the availability of numerous well characterized inbred lines and genetic mutants, and the ability to perform rapid linkage analyses (53).

Despite these advantages, one can easily make a case for the use of other species in transgenic experiments. For example, physiological manipulations are more readily performed in larger animals. In addition, numerous surgical and pharmacological cardiovascular models have already been developed in the rat, dog, and pig. There are also well characterized genetic models of cardiovascular disease in the rat, hamster, and rabbit. The ability to directly interface these model systems with transgenic technology is quite appealing. Thus depending on the system under study, one may well benefit by choosing a species other than the mouse.

ALTERATION OF CARDIOVASCULAR FUNCTION WITH TRANSGENIC MICE

Regulation of the cardiovascular system is dependent upon the coordinated interaction of numerous hormonal and neuronal systems. It is relatively easy to envision transgenic models in which these regulatory cascades are manipulated. For example, one can produce a model that aberrantly expresses an important regulatory gene product or, alternatively, produce a model in which a mutant regulatory gene product is expressed. The advantage of the transgenic approach lies in the fact that experimental and control animals differ only by the presence or absence of the transgene. Consequently any phenotypic differences observed between the two groups are attributable, either directly or indirectly, to transgene expression. Given that the transgene is inherited as a Mendelian trait, large numbers of experimental animals are easily produced. Moreover, if the transgenic model is made in an inbred background, phenotypic variation resulting from allelic segregation is eliminated.

Survey of Current Models

Transgenic models that exhibit altered cardiovascular function are described in Table 1. As can be seen, transgene expression can impinge on a variety of different regulatory pathways. For example, several laboratories have generated models that aberrantly express proteins involved in blood pressure regulation. Transgene expression in these animals results in chronically altered blood pressure and a variety of other phenotypes. In other models, neuroendocrine function, apolipoprotein metabolism, erythropoiesis, or blood clotting activities have been altered.

Table 1 Alteration of cardiovascular function in transgenic mice

Gene	Comments	References
Genes affecting blood pressure and electrolyte regulation		
AVP	Expression targeted with the metallothionein promoter results in vasop-ressinemia and nephrogenic diabetes insipidus	35, 36
ANF	Expression targeted with the transthyretin promoter results 10–20 fold increase in plasma ANF levels and induces marked hypotension in the absence of chronic natriuresis	16, 30, 49, 83, 94
Renin	Expression of the mouse renin gene in transgenic rats produces severe hypertension in the absence of elevated plasma renin activity	60
Renin/ANG	Targeted expression of the rat renin and angiotensin genes with the metallothionein promoter induces mild hypertension	63
Expression of other hormones		
GH	Targeted expression with the metallothionein promoter results in vascular remodeling	21
GH and GHRF	Targeted expression of growth hormone and growth hormone releasing factor with the metallothionein induces progressive glomeruloscler-osis secondary to renal mesangial cell growth	22, 23, 24, 67, 87
Insulin	Expression of the human insulin gene results in hyperinsulinemia	55
Alteration of LDL and apolipoprotein metabolism		
LDL rec.	Targeted expression of the human LDL receptor with the metallothio-nein promoter causes enhanced elimination of exogenous LDL and resistance to experimentally-induced atherosclerosis	40, 65, 100
Apo CIII	Expression of the human Apo CIII gene results in elevated Apo CIII levels and severe hypertryglyceridemia	42
Apo E	Transgenic mice with the human apolipoprotein E gene display normal levels of plasma human Apo E despite the absence of high levels of liver expression	80
Apo A1	A human apolipoprotein A-1 transgene protects mice that are genetical-ly susceptible to atherosclerosis when maintained on a high fat diet. Additionally, several groups have independently shown that these animals display diminished selective uptake of HDL cholesteryl esters	13, 69, 70
Alteration of erythropoiesis and globin gene expression		
α and β^S	Several groups have targeted either wild-type human globin genes or the human α and β-sickle globin genes. Collectively, these studies have shown functional α/β hemoglobin dimers are formed. Additionally, expression of the β^S globin allele results in sickled pheno-type when the RBCs are deoxygenated	6, 71, 72, 89, 93
EPO	Targeted expression of the human erythropoietin gene produces polycythemia in transgenic mice	74
Alteration of plasminogen activator metabolism		
uPA	Targeted expression of the urokinase-type plasminogen activator under the albumin promoter induces spontaneous intestinal and intra-abdominal bleeding	39
PAI-1	Targeted expression of the human plasminogen activator inhibitor gene results in the development of venous, but not arterial, occlusions	26

Transgenic Mice With Chronically Elevated Plasma ANF

Atrial natriuretic factor (ANF) is a cardiac hormone with potent vasoactive and natriuretic activities. Although the effects of acute ANF administration are well documented, the role of the hormone in chronic cardiovascular regulation has remained controversial. To address this issue, our laboratory has generated a transgenic mouse model that exhibits chronically elevated plasma ANF levels (83). These animals, designated TTR-ANF, carry a transgene comprised of the mouse transthyretin (TTR) promoter and the mouse ANF structural gene. We postulated that transgene expression would target ANF synthesis to hepatocytes and that the hepatic ANF would in turn be constitutively secreted into the circulation. Radio-immune assays demonstrated that plasma ANF levels in the TTR-ANF mice were elevated ca tenfold as compared to their nontransgenic litter mates. Elevated plasma ANF levels were detected as early as three weeks of age and persisted throughout the entire lifespan of the mice (83).

The TTR-ANF transgenic mice provide an interesting model system with which to assess the consequences of chronically elevated plasma ANF. A physiological profile of these animals is shown in Table 2. Mean arterial pressure was approximately 25 mm Hg lower in the transgenic mice as compared to their nontransgenic litter mates. Hypotension was observed in both conscious (83) and anesthetized (30) animals. Although the TTR-ANF mice persistently exhibited a slight tendency towards natriuresis and tachycardia, water balance, plasma and urinary electrolytes, and heart rates were not significantly altered in our initial studies (Table 2A). The levels of several cardiovascular hormones were studied to determine if any compensatory humoral pathways were activated in the hypotensive TTR-ANF mice (94). Interestingly, aldosterone levels were elevated; other hormones, including AVP, catecholamines and ACTH, as well as plasma renin activity, were not significantly different from the nontransgenic controls (Table 2B). The increased plasma aldosterone levels were surprising because it is well documented that acute ANF administration inhibits aldosterone production (1).

Studies were initiated to measure the renal response to intravascular fluid volume expansion (30). After a control period, extracellular volume was expanded by approximately 25%. During the control period, average blood pressure was about 20 mm Hg lower in TTR-ANF mice, but baseline urine volumes and sodium excretions were not different from nontransgenic controls. After blood volume expansion, both diuresis and natriuresis were markedly elevated in the TTR-ANF mice as compared to controls, even though blood pressure remained relatively depressed (30). There were no differences in glomerular filtration rates or hematocrit between groups, either before or after volume expansion. These data suggest that the ANF-induced decrease

Table 2 Physiological characterization of TTR-ANF mice

Variable	Nontransgenic	TTR-ANF
A. Baseline physiological profile		
Mean arterial pressure (mm Hg)	103.9 ± 2.0	75.5 ± 0.9
Heart rate (beats/min)	704.4 ± 15.6	719.4 ± 14.6
Plasma [Na$^+$] (meq/l)	142.2 ± 1.5	142.2 ± 2.0
Plasma [K$^+$] (meq/l)	4.7 ± 0.2	5.1 ± 0.2
Water intake (ml/mouse/day)	6.50 ± 0.25	6.60 ± 0.44
Urine volume (ml/mouse/day)	2.69 ± 0.13	3.03 ± 0.16
Urine Na$^+$ (meq/mouse/day)	0.48 ± 0.03	0.48 ± 0.04
B. Plasma hormone profile		
ANF (pg/ml)	577 ± 83	5,185 ± 514
AVP (ng/ml)	3.16 ± 0.55	3.72 ± 0.71
ACTH (ng/ml)	0.183 ± 0.004	0.182 ± 0.017
Aldosterone (ng/ml)	0.74 ± 0.07	1.37 ± 0.21
Norepinephrine (pg/ml)	1206 ± 384	1280 ± 265
Epinephrine (pg/ml)	2106 ± 549	1307 ± 220
Plasma renin activity (ng AI/ml/hr)	11.5 ± 2.3	13 ± 4.4
C. Profile during hypoxia-induced pulmonary hypertension		
Normoxic RV/LV + S (mg/mg)	0.27 ± 0.01	0.30 ± 0.01
Normoxic RV systolic pressure (mm Hg)	16.8 ± 0.5	15.7 ± 0.5
Hypoxic RV/LV + S (mg/mg)	0.45 ± 0.02	0.39 ± 0.01
Hypoxic RV systolic pressure (mm Hg)	29.2 ± 1.9	25.4 ± 1.6
D. Baroreflex profile		
BRS; no blockade (msec/mm Hg)	11.9 ± 0.8	4.8 ± 0.8
BRS; atenolol blockade (msec/mm Hg)	4.8 ± 0.9	4.9 ± 1.0

Data from references 16, 30, 49, 83, 94, and L. Field et al, unpublished.

in arterial pressure (and consequently reduced renal perfusion pressure) directly counteracts the natriuretic effects of the peptide, thus allowing maintenance of salt balance. However, when volume is expanded acutely, the relatively elevated ANF levels in the transgenic group exaggerate the renal response (30).

The effects of chronically elevated plasma ANF levels on experimentally induced pulmonary hypertension were studied in the TTR-ANF mice (49). Animals were maintained in either a normoxic or hypoxic (0.5 atm) environment for a period of three weeks. In the normoxic group, the TTR-ANF mice had similar right ventricle/left ventricle + septum (RV/LV+S) ratios as compared to the nontransgenic sibs (Table 2C). Right ventricular systolic pressures were also similar between the two groups. Following hypoxia, the extent of right ventricular hypertrophy, as well as the degree of pulmonary hypertension, were markedly reduced in the transgenic animals (Table 2C).

Previous studies by Oparil and co-workers detected a similar protective effect following acute ANF administration (47).

Additional studies were initiated to determine if the baroreflex was altered in hypotensive TTR-ANF mice (16). Baroreflex slope (BRS; change in interbeat interval vs change in systolic arterial pressure) in response to phenylephrine infusion was assessed in conscious animals with chronic arterial and venous canulas. The BRS in the transgenic mice was half that observed in the nontransgenic animals (Table 2D). Atenolol-induced sympathetic blockade had no effect on BRS in the TTR-ANF mice. In contrast, atenolol administration resulted in a marked attenuation of the BRS in nontransgenic mice; indeed BRS was reduced to a value similar to that observed in the transgenic animals (Table 2D). These results suggest that sustained elevation of plasma ANF levels dampens sympathetic modulation of the carotid baroreflex.

In summary, chronic elevation of plasma ANF levels in the TTR-ANF transgenic mice produces a marked hypotensive phenotype without the expected alterations in natriuresis and diuresis. Thus it would appear that the transgenic mice are able to counteract the natriuretic effects of ANF, but not the hemodynamic effects. Further analysis of this model may provide insights into the role of ANF in chronic cardiovascular regulation.

GENERATING CELL LINES WITH TRANSGENIC MICE

Transgenic mice have been widely used in targeted oncogenesis studies. These experiments typically utilize transgenes comprised of a strong cell-specific promoter fused to an oncogene. Animals that carry such transgenes frequently develop tumors in the targeted cell type. This experimental paradigm has been used successfully to document the tumorigenic potential of many oncogenes (reviewed in 17, 38). In addition, tumors derived from transgenic animals have proven to be an invaluable resource for cell culture experiments.

Survey of Current Models

Although the spectrum of cardiovascular cell-types that have been subjected to targeted oncogenesis is limited (Table 3), interesting pathophysiological abnormalities have frequently been observed in these models. This is best exemplified by the myocardial fibrosis seen in mice expressing the v-fps oncogene in cardiac fibroblasts (15, 99) and by the occurrence of polycystic kidney disease in mice expressing c-myc in the kidney (92). Tumors derived from transgenic mice have on occasion yielded cell lines. In some instances, the cell lines have retained highly differentiated characteristics typical of the progenitor cell type. For example, Gross and co-workers have derived cell lines from mice expressing a renin-SV40 T antigen fusion gene (77). These cells exhibit properties similar to renal juxtaglomerular cells and secrete processed renin in response to secretagogues.

Transgenic Mice with Myocardial Tumors

Several groups have described transgenic models that develop myocardial tumors (Table 3). In our laboratory, cardiac tumorigenesis was induced by a transgene comprised of the human ANF promoter linked to a 2.7 kb restriction fragment of the SV40 early region. This transgene, designated ANF-TAG, targets expression of the SV40 large T antigen oncogene (T-Ag) to the atria. Five transgenic lineages carrying the ANF-TAG transgene were generated (28). Virtually every ANF-TAG mouse developed unilateral right atrial hyperplasia; the right atrium typically grew to a mass greater than that of the ventricles. Right atrial tumorigenesis in the ANF-TAG mice was accompanied by severe cardiac arrhythmias. The severity and frequency of cardiac arrhythmias increased proportionally with tumor mass (28, 85).

Immunohistology studies indicate that the bulk of atrial tumor cells express sarcomeric myosin (86). This result was supported by electron microscopy

Table 3 Abnormal cardiovascular function due to targeted oncogene expression

Gene	Comments	References
Cardiac models		
fps	Targeted expression of the *fps* oncogene with the β-globin promoter induces progressive cardiac fibrosis and hypertrophy	15, 99
v-myc	Targeted expression of *myc* with the RSV-LTR results in mild developmental hyperplasia in cardiomyocytes	43, 44
PVLT	Expression of the polyoma virus large T-antigen under the metalalothionein promoter results in cardiomyopathy secondary to cardiomyocyte hypertrophy; cultured cells reported	14
SV40 T-Ag	Targeted expression of the *SV40* large T-antigen oncogene with either the ANF or the protamine promoter induces atrial tumorigenesis and cardiac arrhythmias; cultured cells reported	5, 20, 28, 32, 50, 85, 86
SV40 T-Ag	Targeted expression of T-Ag with the α-cardiac MHC promoter induces both atrial and ventricular tumors; cultured cells reported	48, 84
Renal models		
c-myc	Expression of a β-globin-*c-myc* transgene results in polycystic kidney disease secondary to renal tubule epithelial hyperplasia	92
SV40 T-Ag	Targeted expression of *SV40* T-Ag with the renin promoter induces vascular smooth muscle proliferation; cultured cells reported	45, 76, 77, 81
SV40 T-Ag	Mice harboring the *SV40* early region develop renal sclerosis; glomerular epithelial, mesangial, and endothelial cell lines reported; cells reactive to ANG II	54
Other models		
PVLT	Expression of the polyoma virus early region causes hemangiomas in mice; cultured cells reported	3, 58, 96, 98

(EM) studies; cardiomyocytes with well differentiated myofibrils and immunoreactive ANF secretory granules were observed throughout the tumors. ^{3}H-Thymidine incorporation indicated a extremely high rate of DNA synthesis in the tumor cardiomyocytes, which suggests that these cells proliferate rapidly (86). Collectively, these results indicate that T-Ag can induce proliferation of differentiated atrial cardiomyocytes in transgenic animals.

Initial cell culture experiments with primary ANF-TAG tumor cardiomyocytes failed to establish a cell line. This result prompted us to test the capacity of ANF-TAG atrial tissue to proliferate in syngeneic hosts (84, 86), an attribute that is a hallmark of transformed cells. ANF-TAG atrial tissue was minced and injected subcutaneously into syngeneic hosts. Only 20% of the injected mice developed palpable tumors, and only after long latent periods (9–24 months). In most instances, no enhanced growth was observed with subsequent passage. However, one transplant tumor, designated AT-1, did exhibit markedly enhanced growth characteristics upon subsequent passage.

The initial AT-1 tumor appeared after a 20 month latent period. In subsequent passages, AT-1 tumors appeared within a period of 2–3 months. There was also an increase in the efficiency of transplantation; greater than 90% of mice receiving injections of AT-1 cardiomyocytes developed tumors. This heritable change in latency suggests that AT-1 cardiomyocytes have undergone an adaptive genetic alteration that potentiates ectopic growth. Unlike primary ANF-TAG cardiomyocytes, AT-1 cardiomyocytes actively divide when placed into culture (86). Once confluent, the cells exhibit spontaneous contractile activity, with the entire dish beating synchronously. Intracellular recordings revealed action potentials that are very similar to those generated by normal cultured atrial cells (86). Importantly, AT-1 cardiomyocytes can be passaged a limited number of times.

We have analyzed AT-1 tumors and cultured AT-1 cardiomyocytes for the expression of a series of atrial-, cardiac-, and muscle-specific markers (Table 4). These studies have shown that AT-1 cardiomyocytes retain a differentiated cardiac phenotype at the molecular level (86, 50). Additionally, EM analyses indicate that cultured AT-1 cardiomyocytes retain a highly organized ultrastructure typical of normal adult atrial tissue (20, 86). Well organized myofibrils with prominent Z densities, ANF-containing secretory granules, and well organized T-tubules are all readily apparent.

The above results indicate that T-Ag can induce atrial cardiomyocyte proliferation. To determine the proliferative potential of ventricular cardiomyocytes, we have generated additional transgenic mice that express T-Ag under the control of the rat α cardiac myosin heavy chain promoter (MHC-TAG mice, see 48). Adult MHC-TAG mice exhibit gross bilateral atrial hyperplasia, with the right atrium invariably exhibiting a greater degree of growth than the left. In addition, extensive ventricular pathology is also apparent; hyperplastic cardiomyocytes are readily observed throughout the ventricular septum dis-

Table 4 Summary of gene expression in transgenic cardiomyocytes

Gene product	AT-1 tumors	Cultured AT-1 cells	Control atrial myocytes
α-Cardiac myosin heavy chain	+	+	+
β-Cardiac myosin heavy chain	−	−	−
α-Cardiac actin	+	+	+
α-Skeletal actin	−	−	−
β-Actin	+	+	−
Connexon 43	+	+	+
Atrial natriuretic factor	+	+	+
Desmin	+	+	+
Vimentin	−	−	−
Peptidyl α-amidating monooxygenase	+	ND	+
Sarcoplasmic reticulum calcium-ATPase	+	ND	+
Calsequestrin	+	ND	+
Phospholamban	−	−	−
Creatine kinase-MM isoform	+	ND	+
Creatine kinase-MB isoform	+	ND	−
Creatine kinase-BB isoform	−	ND	−
p53	+	+	+
Retinoblastoma gene product	−	−	−
Cardiac troponin$_C$	ND	+	+

Data from references 28, 50, 85, 86, and L. Field et al, unpublished.

tributed from the midline to the apex. Immunohistological analysis indicates that the proliferating cells continue to express sarcomeric myosin. Electron microscopic examination reveals that adult cardiomyocytes in various stages of the cell cycle retain ultrastructural characteristics typical of differentiated heart cells (48).

In summary, these studies demonstrate that the targeted expression of T-Ag can induce cardiomyocyte proliferation in transgenic mice. Both atrial and ventricular cardiomyocytes respond to T-Ag. These cells may prove to be a useful model system for the study of cardiomyocyte cell cycle regulation and myofibril assembly in vitro.

OTHER APPLICATIONS OF TRANSGENIC TECHNOLOGY

Promoter Studies

Transgenic animals have been extensively used to study promoter function. Frequently the putative promoter is fused to an easily scored enzymatic reporter gene as, for example, the chloramphenicol acetyltransferase (CAT), β-galactosidase (β-GAL), or luciferase genes. Expression assays for these recorder enzymes are easily performed and produce quantitative data. Alternatively, more traditional transgene-specific probes (i.e. Northern blot, primer extension, RNAse protection, or PCR amplification) can be employed if there are concerns regarding differences in mRNA stability between a given reporter and a given test gene transcript. This approach is also warranted if intragenic regulatory sequences are present.

To date, many promoters have been analyzed in transgenic mice. Indeed, a literature survey identified 63 citations for the analysis of 18 independent cardiovascular promoters. Space limitations preclude a comprehensive listing of these studies. However, it is interesting to note that the globin, renin, and apolipoprotein loci have been extensively studied in transgenic animals. The reader is referred to the following review articles: globin promoters, see 18, 34, 52, 66, 82, 88, 90; renin promoters, see 62, 75; apolipoprotein promoters, see 78, 95.

Random Mutagenesis as an Experimental Paradigm

Each transgene integration event disrupts a portion of the host genome and consequently has the potential to generate a loss of function mutation. This has prompted many investigators to breed their transgenic mice to homozygosity in an effort to identify potentially interesting mutations. To date several insertional mutants affecting cardiovascular function and/or development have been identified. For example, Jaenisch and co-workers identified a retroviral insertional mutation that develops nephrotic syndrome. Affected animals exhibit progressive glomerular sclerosis and chronic renal failure (97). In other studies, Potter and co-workers identified an insertional mutation that exhibited a legless phenotype (56, 79). Interestingly, these animals also exhibit situs inversus, a developmental defect associated with transposition of the great vessels and congenital heart defects in both humans and mice (51). The use of insertional mutagenesis as an experimental paradigm has recently been reviewed (19).

SUMMARY AND FUTURE DIRECTIONS

The studies described in this review demonstrate that transgenic animals can readily be employed to study cardiovascular regulation. It is certain that the number and scope of cardiovascular transgenic models will rapidly increase. Our ability to perform sophisticated physiological analyses in mice will also improve.

Currently several cardiovascular transgenic models are conspicuously absent. For example, targeted expression of growth factors and oncogenes to vascular smooth muscle and vascular endothelial cells would provide an exciting area of research. Cardiovascular innervation can also be easily manipulated in transgenic animals. Cell lineages of interest to the cardiovascular system can be ablated through the targeted expression of an intracellular diphtheria toxin (4). Alternatively, conditional ablation using the Herpes thymidine kinase gene and the nucleotide analogue gancyclovir is also a viable approach (2, 8).

Finally, transgenic approaches are limited by the fact that transgene expression is superimposed upon the host genome. Consequently, the transgene must encode a dominant activity in order to elicit a physiological effect. The advent of gene targeting via homologous recombination will enable investigators to study recessive alterations (that is, loss of function models, reviewed in 11, 12, 31). Gene targeting should also enable us to study the effects of discrete structural alterations. This can be accomplished by the expression of a structurally modified transgene in a null background. Alternatively, as homologous recombination methodologies are refined, it may be possible to directly target subtle alterations. Several groups are actively perusing gene targeting experiments with relevant cardiovascular proteins. These latter experiments will undoubtedly generate new and exciting models.

Literature Cited

1. Atarashi, K., Mulrow, P. J., Franco-Saenz, R., Snajdar, R., Rapp, J. 1984. Inhibition of aldosterone production by an atrial extract. *Science* 224:992–94

2. Baird, S. M., Hyman, R., Evans, R. M. 1989. Thymidine kinase obliteration: creation of transgenic mice with controlled immune deficiency. *Proc. Natl. Acad. Sci. USA* 86:2698–702

3. Bautch, V. L. 1989. Effects of polyoma virus oncogenes in transgenic mice. *Mol. Biol. Med.* 6:309–17

4. Behringer, R. R., Mathews, L. S., Palmiter, R. D., Brinster, R. L. 1988. Dwarf mice produced by genetic ablation of growth hormone-expressing cells. *Genes Dev.* 2:453–61

5. Behringer, R. R, Peschon, J. J., Messing, A., Gartside, C. L., Hauschka, S. D., et al. 1988. Heart and bone tumors in transgenic mice. *Proc. Natl. Acad. Sci. USA* 85:2648–52

6. Behringer, R. R., Ryan, T. M., Reilly, M. P., Asakura, T., Palmiter, R. D., et al. 1989. Synthesis of functional human hemoglobin in transgenic mice. *Science* 245:971–33

7. Bernstein, S. 1975. Physiological characteristics. In *Biology of the Laboratory Mouse*, ed. E. L. Green, pp. 337–50. Toronto:General Publ.

8. Borrelli, E., Heyman, R. A., Arias, C., Sawchenko, P. E., Evans, R. M. 1989. Transgenic mice with inducible dwarfism. *Nature* 339:538–41

9. Brinster, R. L., Allen, J. M., Behringer, R. R., Gelinas, R. E., Palmiter, R. D. 1988. Introns increase transcriptional efficency in transgenic mice. *Proc. Natl. Acad. Sci. USA* 85:836–40

10. Brinster, R. L., Chen, H. Y., Trumbauer, M. E., Yagle, M. K., Palmiter, R. D. 1985. Factors affecting the efficiency of introducing foreign DNA into mice by microinjecting eggs. *Proc. Natl. Acad. Sci. USA* 82:4438–42

11. Camerini-Otero, R. D., Kucherlapati, R. 1990. Right on target. *New Biol.* 2:337–41

12. Cappechi, M. R. 1989. Altering the genome by homologous recombination. *Science* 1989:1288–92

13. Chajek-Shaul, T., Hayek, T., Walsh, A., Breslow, J. L. 1991. Expression of the human apolipoprotein A-I gene in transgenic mice alters high density lipoprotein (HDL) particle size distribution and diminishes selective uptake of HDL cholesteryl esters. *Proc. Natl. Acad. Sci. USA* 88:6731–35

14. Chalifour, L. E., Gomes, M. L., Wang, N.-S., Mes Masson, A. M. 1990. Polyoma large T-antigen expression in

the heart of transgenic mice causes cardiomyopathy. *Oncogene* 5:1719–26

15. Chow, L. H., Yee, S. P., Pawson, T., McManus, B. M. 1991. Progressive cardiac fibrosis and myocyte injury in v-fps transgenic mice. A model for primary disorders of connective tissue in the heart? *Lab. Invest.* 64:457–62

16. Cochrane, K. L., Field, L. J. 1990. Baroreflex function in hypotensive transgenic mice overexpressing ANF. *Neurosci. Abstr.* 16:220

17. Compere, S. J., Baldacci, P., Jaenisch, R. 1988. Oncogenes in transgenic mice. *Biochim. Biophys. Acta* 948:129–49

18. Constantoulakis, P., Costantini, F., Josephson, B., Fry, D., Mangahas L., et al. 1990. A transgenic mouse model for studying the induction of fetal hemoglobin in the adult. *Trans. Assoc. Am. Physicians* 103:80–89

19. Costantini, F., Radice, G., Lee, J. L., Chada, K., Perry, W., et al. 1989. Insertional mutagenesis in transgenic mice. *Prog. Nucleic Acids Res. Mol. Biol.* 36:159–69

20. Delcarpio, J. B., Lanson, N. A. Jr., Field, L. J., Claycomb, W. C. 1991. Morphological characterization of cardiomyocytes isolated from a transplantable cardiac tumor derived from transgenic mouse atria (AT-1 cells). *Circ. Res.* 69:159–60

21. Dilley, R. J., Schwartz, S. M. 1989. Vascular remodeling in the growth hormone transgenic mouse. *Circ. Res.* 65:1233–40

22. Doi, T., Striker, L. J., Gibson, C. C., Agodoa, L. Y., Brinster, R. L., et al. 1990. Glomerular lesions in mice transgenic for growth hormone and insulin-like growth factor-I. I. Relationship between increased glomerular size and mesangial sclerosis. *Am. J. Pathol.* 137:541–52

23. Doi, T., Striker, L. J., Kimata, K., Peten, E. P., Yamada, Y., et al. 1991. Glomerulosclerosis in mice transgenic for growth hormone. Increased mesangial extracellular matrix is correlated with kidney mRNA levels. *J. Exp. Med.* 173: 1287–90

24. Doi, T., Striker, L. J., Quaife, C., et al. 1988. Progressive glomerulosclerosis develops in transgenic mice chronically expressing growth hormone and growth hormone releasing factor but not in those expressing insulin-like growth factor-1. *Am. J. Pathol.* 131: 398–403

25. Engler, P., Haasch, D., Pinkert, C. A., Doglio, L., Glymour, M., et al. 1991. A strain-specific modifier on mouse chromosome 4 controls the methylation of independent transgene loci. *Cell* 65: 939–47

26. Erickson, L. A., Fici, G. J., Lund, J. E., Boyle, T. P., Polites, H. G., et al. 1990. Development of venous occlusions in mice transgenic for the plasminogen activator inhibitor-1 gene. *Nature* 346:74–76

27. Fabian, J. R., Field, L. J., McGowan, R. M., Mullins, J. J., Sigmund, C. D., Gross, K. W. 1989. Allele-specific expression of the murine *Ren-1* genes. *J. Biol. Chem.* 264:17589–94

28. Field, L. J. 1988. Atrial natriuretic factor SV40 T antigen transgenes produce tumors and cardiac arrhythmias in mice. *Science* 239:1029–33

29. Field, L. J. 1991. Transgenic models of cardiovascular disease. *Trends Cardiovasc. Med.* 1:141–46

30. Field, L. J., Veress, A. T., Steinhelper, M. E., Cochrane, K., Sonnenberg, H. 1991. Kidney function in ANF transgenic mice: effect of blood volume expansion. *Am. J. Physiol.* 260 (29): R1–5

31. Frohman, M. A., Martin, G. R. 1989. Cut, paste and save: new approaches to altering specific genes in mice. *Cell* 56:145–47

32. Gardner, D. G., Camargo, M. J., Behringer, R. R., Brinster, R. L., Baxter, J. D., et al. 1992. Atrial natriuretic peptide synthesis in atrial tumors of transgenic mice. *Am. J. Physiol.* 262:E524–31

33. Gordon, J. W., Ruddle, F. H. 1981. Integration and stable germ line transmission of genes injected into the mouse pronucleus. *Science* 214:1244–46

34. Grosveld, F., Greaves, D., Philipsen, S., Talbot, D., Pruzina, S., et al. 1990. The dominant control region of the human beta-globin domain. *Ann. NY Acad. Sci.* 612:152–59

35. Habener, J. F., Cwikel, B. J., Hermann, H., Hammer, R. E., Palmiter, R. D., et al. 1989. Metallothionein-vasopressin fusion gene expression in transgenic mice. Nephrogenic diabetes insipidus and brain transcripts localized to magnocellular neurons. *J. Biol. Chem.* 264: 18844–52

36. Habener, J. F., Cwikel, B., Hermann, H., Hammer, R. E., Palmiter, R. D., et al. 1988. Expression of a metallothionein-vasopressin fusion gene in transgenic mice produces hypervasopressine- mia and manifestations of nephrogenic diabetes insipidus. *Trans. Assoc. Am. Physicians* 101:155–62

37. Habener, J. F., Cwikel, B. J., Her-

mann, H., Hammer, R. E., Palmiter, R. D., et al. 1989. Metallothionein-vasopressin fusion gene expression in transgenic mice. Nephrogenic diabetes insipidus and brain transcripts localized to magnocellular neurons. *J. Biol. Chem.* 264 (31):18844–52

38. Hanahan, D. 1989. Transgenic mice as probes into complex systems. *Science* 246:1265–75

39. Heckel, J. L., Sandgren, E. P., Degen, J. L., Palmiter, R. D., Brinster, R. L. 1990. Neonatal bleeding in transgenic mice expressing urokinase-type plasminogen activator. *Cell* 62:447–56

40. Hofmann, S. L., Russell, D. W., Brown, M. S., Goldstein, J. L., Hammer, R. E. 1988. Overexpression of low density lipoprotein (LDL) receptor eliminates LDL from plasma in transgenic mice. *Science* 239:1277–81

41. Hogan, B., Costantini, F., Lacy, L. 1986. *Manipulating the Mouse Embryo--A Laboratory Manual.* Cold Spring Harbor, N Y:Cold Spring Harbor Lab. 332 pp.

42. Ito, Y., Azrolan, N., O'Connell, A., Walsh, A., Breslow, J. 1990. Hypertriglyceridemia as a result of human Apo CIII gene expression in transgenic mice. *Science* 249:790–93

43. Jackson, T., Allard, M. F., Sreenan, C. M., Doss, L. K., Bishop, S. P., et al. 1990. The c-myc proto-oncogene regulates cardiac development in transgenic mice. *Mol. Cell. Biol.* 10:3709–16

44. Jackson, T., Allard, M. F., Sreenan, C. M., Doss, L. K., Bishop, S. P., et al. 1991. Transgenic animals as a tool for studying the effect of the c-myc proto-oncogene on cardiac development. *Mol. Cell. Biochem.* 104:15–19

45. Jacob, H. J., Sigmund, C. D., Shockley, T. R., Gross, K. W., Dzau, V. J. 1991. Renin promoter SV40 T-antigen transgenic mouse. A model of primary renal vascular hyperplasia. *Hypertension* 17: 1167–72

46. Jaenisch, R., Jahner, D., Nobis, P., Simon, I., Lohler, J., et al. 1981. Chromosomal position and activation of retroviral genomes inserted into the germline of mice. *Cell* 24:519–29

47. Jin, H., Yang, R.-H., Chen, Y.-F., Jackson, R. M., Oparil, S. 1990. Atrial natriuretic peptide attenuates the development of pulmonary hypertension in rats adapted to chronic hypoxia. *J. Clin. Invest.* 85:115–20

48. Katz, E., Steinhelper, M. E., Daud, A., Delcarpio, J. B., Claycomb, W.

C., et al. 1992. Ventricular cardiomyocyte proliferation in transgenic mice expressing α-cardiac myosin heavy chain-SV40 T antigen fusion genes. *Am. J. Physiol.* 262(31):H1867–76

49. Klinger, J. R., Petit, R., Curtain, L., Warburton, R., Field, L. J., Hill, N. 1991. Attenuation of hypoxia-induced pulmonary hypertension in transgenic mice with overexpression of ANF. *Am. Rev. Resp. Dis.* 143:A187

50. Lanson, N. A. Jr., Glembotski, C. C., Steinhauer, M. E., Field, L. J., Claycomb, W. C. 1992. Gene expression and ANF processing and secretion in cultured AT-1 cells. *Circulation.* 85:1835–41

51. Layton, W. M. Jr. 1985. The biology of asymmetry and the development of the cardiac loop. In *Cardiac Morphogenesis*, ed. A. Ferrens, pp. 134–40. New York:Elsevier

52. Ley, T. J. 1991. The pharmacology of hemoglobin switching: of mice and men. *Blood* 77:1146–152

53. Lyon, M. F., Searle, A. G. 1989. *Genetic Variation and Strains of the Laboratory Mouse.* Oxford: Oxford Univ. Press 2nd ed. 876 pp.

54. MacKay, K., Striker, L. J., Elliot, S., Pinkert, C. A., Brinster, R. L., et al. 1988. Glomerular epithelial, mesangial, and endothelial cell lines from transgenic mice. *Kidney Int.* 33:677–84

55. Marban, S. L., DeLoia, J. A., Gearhart, J. D. 1989. Hyperinsulinemia in transgenic mice carrying multiple copies of the human insulin gene. *Dev. Genet.* 10:356–64

56. McNeish, J. D., Thayer, J., Walling, K., Sulik, K. K., Potter, S. S., et al. 1990. Phenotypic characterization of the transgenic mouse insertional mutation, legless. *J. Exp. Zool.* 253:151–62

57. Mockrin, S. C., Dzau, V. J., Gross, K. W., Horan, M. J. 1991. Transgenic animals: new approaches to hypertension research. *Hypertension* 17:394–99

58. Montesano, R., Pepper, M. S., Mohle-Steinlein, U., Risau, W., Wagner, E. F., et al. 1990. Increased proteolytic activity is responsible for the aberrant morphogenetic behavior of endothelial cells expressing the middle T oncogene. *Cell* 62:435–45

59. Mullins, J. J., Ganten, D. 1990. Transgenic animals: new approaches to hypertension research. *J. Hypertension (Suppl.)* 8:S35–37

60. Mullins, J. J., Peters, J., Ganten, D. 1990. Fulminant hypertension in trans-

genic rats harbouring the mouse *Ren-2* gene. *Nature* 344:541–44

61. Mullins, J. J., Sigmund, C. D., Kane-Haas, C., Gross, K. W. 1989. Expression of the DBA/2J ren-2 gene in the adrenal gland of transgenic mice. *EMBO J.* 8:4065–72

62. Mullins, J. J., Sigmund, C. D., Kane-Haas, C., Wu, C. Z., Pacholec, F., et al. 1988. Studies on the regulation of renin genes using transgenic mice. *Clin. Exp. Hypertension Prt. A* 10:1157–67

63. Ohkubo, H., Kawakami, H., Kakehi, Y., Takumi, T., Arai, H., et al. 1990. Generation of transgenic mice with elevated blood pressure by introduction of the rat renin and angiotensinogen genes. *Proc. Natl. Acad. Sci. USA* 87:5153–57

64. Palmiter, R. D., Sandgren, E. P., Avarbock, M. R., Allen, D. D., Brinster, R. L. 1991. Heterologous introns can enhance expression of transgenes in mice. *Proc. Natl. Acad. Sci. USA* 88:478–82

65. Pathak, R. K., Yokode, M., Hammer, R. E., Hofmann, S. L., Brown, M. S., et al. 1990. Tissue specific sorting of the human LDL receptor in polarized epithelia of transgenic mice. *J. Cell Biol.* 111:347–59

66. Perez-Stable, C., Magram, J., Niederreither, K., Costantini, F. 1989. Analysis of human gamma and beta globin gene regulation using transgenic mice. *Prog. Clin. Biol. Res.* 316A:203–15

67. Pesce, C. M., Striker, L. J., Peten, E., Elliot, S. J., Striker, G. E. 1991. Glomerulosclerosis at both early and late stages is associated with increased cell turnover in mice transgenic for growth hormone. *Lab. Invest.* 65:601–5

68. Robertson, E., Bradley, A., Kuehn, M., Evans, M. 1986. Germ-line transmission of genes introduced into cultured pluripotent cells by retroviral vector. *Nature* 323:445–48

69. Rubin, E. M., Ishida, B. Y., Clift, S. M., Krauss, R. M. 1991. Expression of human apolipoprotein A-I in transgenic mice results in reduced plasma levels of murine apolipoprotein A-I and the appearance of two new high density lipoprotein size subclasses. *Proc. Natl. Acad. Sci. USA* 88:434–38

70. Rubin, E. M., Krauss, R. M., Spangler, E. A., Verstuyft, J. G., Clift, S. M. 1991. Inhibition of early atherogenesis in transgenic mice by human apolipoprotein AI. *Nature* 353:265–67

71. Rubin, E. M., Witkowska, H. E.,

Spangler, E., Curtin, P., Lubin, B. H., et al. 1991. Hypoxia induced in vivo sickling of transgenic mouse red cells. *J. Clin. Invest.* 87:639–47

72. Ryan, T. M., Townes, T. M., Reilly, M. P., Asakura, T., Palmiter, R. D., et al. 1990. Human sickle hemoglobin in transgenic mice. *Science* 247:566–68

73. Schlager, G. 1966. Systolic blood pressure in eight inbred strains of mice. *Nature* 201:519–20

74. Semenza, G. L., Traystman, M. D., Gearhart, J. D., Antonarakis, S. E. 1989. Polycythemia in transgenic mice expressing the human erythropoietin gene. *Proc. Natl. Acad. Sci. USA* 86:2301–5

75. Sigmund, C. D., Gross, K. W. 1991. Structure, expression, and regulation of the murine renin genes. *Hypertension* 18(4):446–57

76. Sigmund, C. D., Jones, C. A., Jacob, H. J., Ingelfinger, J., Kim, U., et al. 1991. Pathophysiology of vascular smooth muscle in renin promoter-T antigen transgenic mice. *Am. J. Physiol.* 260:F249–57

77. Sigmund, C. D., Okuyama, K., Ingelfinger, J., Jones, C. A., Mullins, J. J., et al. 1990. Isolation and characterization of renin expressing cell lines containing a renin promoter viral oncogene construct. *J. Biol. Chem.* 265:19916–922

78. Simonet, W. S., Bucay, N., Lauer, S. J., Pitas, R. E., Weisgraber, K. H., et al. 1990. Downstream regulatory elements stimulate expression of the human apolipoprotein E gene in the liver and suppress expression in the kidney of transgenic mice. *Trans. Assoc. Am. Physicians* 103:119–28

79. Singh, G., Supp, D. M., Schreiner, C., McNeish, J., Merker, H. J., et al. 1991. Legless insertional mutation: morphological, molecular, and genetic characterization. *Genes Dev.* 5:2245–55

80. Smith, J. D., Plump, A. S., Hayek, T., Walsh, A., Breslow, J. L. 1990. Accumulation of human apolipoprotein E in the plasma of transgenic mice. *J. Biol. Chem.* 265:14709–12

81. Sola, C., Tronik, D., Dreyfus, M., Babinet, C., Rougeon, F. 1989. Renin-promoter SV40 large T antigen transgenes induce tumors irrespective of normal cellular expression of renin genes. *Oncogene Res.* 5:149–53

82. Stamatoyannopoulos, G. 1991. Human hemoglobin switching. *Science* 252:383

83. Steinhelper, M. E., Cochrane, K. L., Field, L. J. 1990. Hypotension in transgenic mice expressing atrial natri-

uretic factor fusion genes. *Hypertension* 16(3): 301–7

84. Steinhelper, M. E., Field, L. J. 1990. SV40 large T-Antigen induces cardiocyte proliferation in transgenic mice. In *The Development and Regenerative Potential of Cardiac Muscle*, ed. J. Oberpriller, J. Oberpriller, A. Mauro, pp. 365–84. New York:Harwood Academic

85. Steinhelper, M. E., Field, L. J. 1990. Cardiac tumors and dysrhythmias in transgenic mice. *Toxicol. Pathol.* 18: 464–69

86. Steinhelper, M. E., Lanson, N., Dresdner, K., Claycomb, W., Wit, A., et al. 1990. Proliferation in vivo and in culture of differentiated adult atrial cardiomyocytes from transgenic mice. *Am. J. Physiol.* 259 (28):H1826–34

87. Striker, L. J., Doi, T., Conti, F., Striker, G. E. 1991. Role of mesangial cells in glomerulosclerosis. *J. Diabetic Complications* 5:60–61

88. Tanaka, M., Nolan, J. A., Bhargava, A. K., Rood, K., Collins, F. S., et al. 1990. Expression of human globin genes in transgenic mice carrying the beta-globin gene cluster with a mutation causing G gamma beta and hereditary persistence of fetal hemoglobin. *Ann. NY Acad. Sci.* 612:167–78

89. Townes, T. M., Behringer, R. R. 1990. Human globin locus activation region (LAR): role in temporal control. *Trends Genet.* 6:219–23

90. Townes, T. M., Ryan, T. M., Behringer, R. R., Palmiter, R. D., Brinster, R. L. 1989. DNase I super-hypersensitive sites direct high level erythroid expression of human alpha-, beta- and beta s- globin genes in transgenic mice. *Prog. Clin. Biol. Res.* 316A:47–61

91. Tronik, D., Dreyfus, M., Babinet, C., Rougeon, F. 1897. Regulated expression of the *ren-2* gene in transgenic mice derived from parental strains carrying only the *ren-1* gene. *EMBO J.* 6:983–87

92. Trudel, M., D'Agati, V., Costantini, F. 1991. C-myc as an inducer of polycystic kidney disease in transgenic mice. *Kidney Int.* 39:665–71

93. Trudel, M., Saadane, N., Garel, M. C., Bardakdjian-Michau, J., Blouquit, Y., et al. 1991. Towards a transgenic mouse model of sickle cell disease: hemoglobin SAD. *EMBO J.* 10:3157–165

94. Veress, A. T., Field, L. J., Steinhelper, M. E., Sonnenberg, H. 1992. Effect of potassium infusion on renal function in ANF transgenic mice. *Clin. Invest. Med.* In press

95. Walsh, A., Ito, Y., Breslow, J. L. 1991. Apolipoprotein A-I gene expression in transgenic mice. *Biotechnology* 16: 227–35

96. Wang, R., Bautch, V. L. 1991. The polyomavirus early region gene in transgenic mice causes vascular and bone tumors. *J. Virol.* 65:5174–83

97. Weiher, H., Noda, T., Gray, D. A., Sharpe, A., Jaenisch, R. 1990. Transgenic mouse model of kidney disease: insertional inactivation of ubiquitously expressed gene leads to nephrotic syndrome. *Cell* 62:425–34

98. Williams, R. L., Courtneidge, S. A., Wagner, E. F. 1988. Embryonic lethalities and endothelial tumors in chimeric mice expressing polyoma virus middle T oncogene. *Cell* 52:121–31

99. Yee, S. P., Mock, D., Maltby, V., Silver, M., Rossant, J., et al. 1989. Cardiac and neurological abnormalities in v-fps transgenic mice. *Proc. Natl. Acad. Sci. USA* 86:5873–77

100. Yokode, M., Hammer, R. E., Ishibashi, S., Brown, M. S., Goldstein, J. L. 1990. Diet-induced hypercholesterolemia in mice: prevention by overexpression of LDL receptors. *Science* 250:1273–75

Annu. Rev. Physiol. 1993. 55:115–30

ALDOSTERONE ACTION

John W. Funder

Baker Medical Research Institute, Victoria, Australia

KEY WORDS: mineralocorticoid, receptor, 11-hydroxysteroid, dehydrogenase, 18-methyloxidase

INTRODUCTION

Aldosterone was discovered by Simpson and her co-workers in 1953, although the salt-retaining (mineralocorticoid) steroid, deoxycorticosterone (DOC), had been previously characterized and extensively studied. Since that time, aldosterone action has been studied in a number of ways. In 1956, Ussing and his colleagues (1a) developed the toad bladder as a model to study transepithelial flux, and in 1961 Crabbe (8a) used this preparation to show that aldosterone promoted transepithelial Na^+ transport. In 1956 Kagawa (27) first published details of the bioassay that bears his name, where the mineralocorticoid activity of a test substance is gauged by its ability to alter urinary Na^+/K^+ ratios in the adrenalectomized rat. Denton and his colleagues (6a) used salivary Na^+/K^+ ratios in the sheep to similar ends.

Over the past two decades the emphasis in studies on aldosterone action has evolved from bioassay— often used as an index in studies on the control of aldosterone secretion, or to test candidate mineralocorticoid agonists and antagonists— to biochemistry, to the elucidation of the molecular mechanisms by which aldosterone promotes unidirectional transepithelial Na^+ flux. The first studies on aldosterone binding to specific Type I (mineralocorticoid) receptors were published by Edelman's laboratory in 1972 (18, 46), and hippocampal high affinity corticosterone-preferring binding sites were detailed by McEwen and his colleagues shortly thereafter (12). It was not until almost a decade later that renal aldosterone-binding mineralocorticoid receptors and hippocampal high affinity glucocorticoid receptors were both shown to be identical Type I receptors (6, 29).

In 1987 the human renal mineralocorticoid receptor was cloned by Evans' group (5) and shown to be highly homologous with the human glucocorticoid

115

0066–4278/93/0315–0115$02.00

receptor, sharing 94% amino acid identity in the DNA-binding region and 57% in the ligand-binding domain. The rat mineralocorticoid receptor (43) was subsequently cloned from a hippocampal library by Watson and his co-workers, using the human renal sequence as a probe, which underlined the commonality of the renal Type I mineralocorticoid receptor and the hippocampal corticosterone-preferring (rather than dexamethasone) high affinity glucocorticoid receptor.

The cloning and expression of the mineralocorticoid receptor also threw into sharp relief its lack of specificity for aldosterone, in that it showed equivalent affinity for the physiologic glucocorticoids cortisol and corticosterone, which circulate at much higher total (and free) concentrations than aldosterone. This had been previously noted in cytosol preparations (30), and the difference between the in vivo aldosterone selectivity of mineralocorticoid targets and their in vitro lack of binding specificity was similarly detailed (50, 51). There is no doubt, however, that the cloning of the mineralocorticoid receptor provided considerable further impetus to studies designed to explore this conundrum of non-selectivity, first noted some fifteen years before (19).

The evolution of our knowledge of mineralocorticoid receptors over the past two decades and the mechanisms conferring aldosterone-selectivity on Type I sites in physiologic mineralocorticoid target tissues are discussed in some detail in this chapter. Beyond the receptor, aldosterone action currently awaits definition at a number of levels. Twenty years ago in a review (15) similar in scope to this, three contending theories of action were canvassed; activation of a permease enzyme, increased activity of key tricarboxylic acid enzymes, and increases in Na^+/K^+ ATPase activity. Twenty years later the actions of aldosterone on epithelial tissues are still unresolved in terms of post-receptor mechanism(s); specifically, whereas a number of genes have been characterized as clearly responsive to glucocorticoids, vitamin D, or the sex steroids in transcriptional terms, to date no uniquely aldosterone-responsive or Type I receptor-regulated genes have been reported. In a subsequent section of this review, the possibility that there are no uniquely aldosterone-regulated genes will be addressed and the physiological implications of such a possibility will be discussed.

So far we have focused on the epithelial actions of aldosterone, in line with Crabbe's definition of a mineralocorticoid as a hormone promoting unidirectional transepithelial Na^+ transport (8a). We need to distinguish between aldosterone action and Type I receptor-mediated effects. First, Type I receptors in the hippocampus and septum do not appear to be protected in vivo against occupancy by circulating glucocorticoids; in these organs (and in tissues such as heart and liver) such sites thus appear to be high affinity glucocorticoid receptors, and not substantially occupied by aldosterone under physiologic conditions. Although the reports of antagonistic actions of Type I and Type

II receptor activation in studies on hippocampal slices (26) may have implications for the question of a unique mineralocorticoid response element (MRE) distinct from the classical glucocorticoid response element (GRE), such actions are likely to reflect hippocampal Type I receptor occupancy by cortisol or corticosterone, and not by aldosterone itself. Secondly, and importantly, there are a variety of reports of aldosterone-specific actions on non-epithelial tissues; if these are substantiated, they will extend or even overturn the narrow, classical definition restricting the site of aldosterone action to epithelial tissues.

Of the variety of studies dealing with aldosterone action on non-epithelial tissue, three are discussed here in some detail. First, there is impressive evidence for aldosterone-selective intracranial Type I receptors, from studies by McEwen and his colleagues on salt appetite (36). Aldosterone infused intracerebroventricularly at low concentrations has effects on salt seeking and ingestion that are neither mimicked nor blocked by equal or substantially higher doses of corticosterone, but are very largely blocked by specific Type I receptor antagonists. Other effects of intracerebroventricular infusion of aldosterone, for example, blood pressure elevation in the uninephrectomized rat (24), are clearly via Type I receptors, which are not aldosterone-selective, since the hypertensive effect is antagonized by similar doses of corticosterone infused simultaneously. Although the mechanism conferring aldosterone selectivity on the Type I receptors subserving salt appetite remains to be established, it may well be similar or identical to that operating in epithelial tissues. Whatever the mechanism, there appears in this instance to be excellent evidence for specific non-epithelial actions of aldosterone, consistent with the prime epithelial effects as part of a larger, coherent physiology of Na^+ homeostasis.

Secondly, there are a series of recent reports of an increase in cardiac fibrosis in experimental hypertension in animals or in patients where levels of aldosterone are inappropriately high for the Na^+ status of the organism (7, 56). On the basis of the documented presence of Type I receptors in cardiac muscle (44), and of the prevention of experimental cardiac fibrosis by the concurrent administration of subtherapeutic (in terms of blood pressure) doses of spirolactone (7), it has been proposed that such cardiac fibrosis represents a direct effect of aldosterone on collagen synthesis by cardiac myocytes and/or fibroblasts. The role of the inappropriately high Na^+ (for the ambient steroid state) is still unexplored.

There are a number of difficulties, however, in such a direct action hypothesis. First, cardiac Type I receptors appear unprotected, in the same way as are hippocampal Type I receptors, and unlike Type I receptors in kidney, colon, and parotid gland; therefore, they might be expected to function as high affinity glucocorticoid receptors (23). Secondly, in rat cardiac myocytes and fibroblasts cultured separately or together, we have been unable to show any effect of aldosterone on ^{3}H-proline incorporation into collagen (M. Fullerton & J. Funder, in preparation). Third, again in studies on cultured rat cardiac cells, Nichols and co-workers demonstrated an identical domain of induced and repressed proteins after mineralocorticoid or glucocorticoid exposure, as determined by two-dimensional gel electrophoresis (41). On the other hand, in none of these studies was aldosterone exposure equal to that (4–8 weeks) found in in vivo studies on cardiac fibrosis; similarly the effect of inappropriately high whole body Na$^+$ status on Type I receptor specificity, for example, is awaiting exploration.

Finally, there have been several studies on aldosterone binding to and actions on circulating mononuclear leukocytes. Armanini and his colleagues originally demonstrated low levels ($\sim$ 300 sites/cell) of classical Type I receptors in this accessible cell type (3), which defined the syndrome of pseudohypo-aldosteronism (PHA) (8) as one reflecting either low levels or absent Type I receptors in both epithelial and non-epithelial tissues (2). In further studies, addition of aldosterone was shown to block the ion flux that otherwise occurs during the process of cell preparation by Ficoll-Hypaque centrifugation; the effect was seen at nanomolar concentrations of aldosterone, but was neither blocked nor mimicked by cortisol (58). More recently, following the demonstration of very rapid effects of nanomolar levels of aldosterone on cell volume, Wehling and his colleagues demonstrated the existence of high-affinity membrane receptors for aldosterone, by the use of ^{125}I-aldosterone as tracer, and claimed that the affinity and specificity of these sites correlate much better with the observed effects on cell size and ion flux than the classical intracellular Type I receptors in the same cells (57). This system has been described at some length, inasmuch as it may well extend our concepts of aldosterone action, not only in terms of target tissue (non-epithelial vs epithelial), but also in terms of classical intracellular vs membrane-bound receptors. In parallel, the recent demonstration of a high affinity G protein-linked membrane receptor for corticosterone in *Ticarda*, and its demonstrated role in the amphibian (42), indicate similar possibilities for aldosterone being of physiological importance.

PHYSIOLOGY OF ALDOSTERONE BIOSYNTHESIS

Any consideration of aldosterone action needs to be prefaced by a brief description of the regulation of its biosynthesis, to set action in a physiologic context. The four predominant stimuli to aldosterone synthesis are angiotensin II, K$^+$, ACTH, and Na$^+$. Although angiotensin is a potent stimulus of glucocorticoid secretion from adrenal fasciculata cells in vitro, and ACTH stimulates aldosterone secretion from glomerulosa cells, in most species angiotensin and K^+ appear to be the prime stimulators in terms of aldosterone biosynthesis. Na^+ has its major effects via the renin-angiotensin system, and ACTH is responsible for the observed circadian variation in synthesis and plasma levels.

The unique feature of aldosterone, from which its name derives, is the existence of an aldehyde rather than a methyl group at C_{18}. Although the conversion of methyl to aldehyde occurs uniquely in the zona glomerulosa, the specificity of the enzymes concerned has, until recently, been the subject of considerable debate summarized in a timely review (38). Currently, it has been established that in man, two distinct genes (CYP 11B1, CYP 11B2), located in tandem on chromosome 8q22, code for 11β hydroxylase (P4501B1) and 18 methyloxidase (P4501B2).

These two enzymes have 95% amino acid identity; 11βOHase is expressed in both zona fasciculata and zona glomerulosa, under ACTH control, whereas 18 methyloxidase expression is confined to the zona glomerulosa, and can be induced in cultured cells by angiotensin. Chimeric genes, formed by an unequal crossover between the 5′ end of 11βOHase and the 3′ end of 18 methyloxidase, have been described in a number of kindred with the syndrome of glucocorticoid remediable aldosteronism and recently documented by Lifton et al (34).

These two facets of aldosterone biosynthesis are mentioned for a particular reason. The operation of the 18 methyloxidase, which confers the unique C_{18} aldehyde group on aldosterone, appears to be one of the two major enzymatic determinants of mineralocorticoid specificity that allows aldosterone to escape metabolism in target tissues and thus occupy Type I receptors in the face of much higher glucocorticoid levels. This will be more fully covered below.

Secondly, if we are to erect models for a physiology of aldosterone action, it is important to consider that the predominant factors affecting its synthesis and secretion are stimuli. Even though we are less used to thinking about tonic inhibition than about baseline and stimulus systems, stimulatory control of aldosterone secretion requires careful consideration. For carnivores, and particularly those on a Western diet, aldosterone and/or epithelial Type I receptors might thus be viewed as evolutionary baggage; the treatment of receptor deficiency (pseudohypoaldosteronism) is very much simpler (salt) and effective than that of apparent mineralocorticoid excess, where cortisol inappropriately occupies and activates renal mineralocorticoid receptor mechanisms, and patients commonly die at a young age. The physiological context of aldosterone action is thus one of Na^+ retention, presumably reflecting evolutionary pressures; what may be entirely appropriate in terms of fine-tuning distal tubular (and perhaps colonic) Na^+ flux in states of Na^+ deficit, may be less appropriate in terms of its dynamic range in the face of a relatively constant high Na^+ intake. The zona glomerulosa of the hamster, which does not appear to make aldosterone (60), may provide a useful point of departure for speculation on this issue.

MINERALOCORTICOID (TYPE I) RECEPTORS

The earliest studies in which aldosterone was shown to bind to two sites with relatively high affinity were performed using rat kidney cytosol (47), in buffers that in retrospect were very suboptimal in terms of receptor stability. More definitive studies on kidney slices from adrenalectomized rats and on in vivo binding in adrenalectomized rats (19) clearly showed that aldosterone bound to two classes of sites in the kidney. Those with higher affinity (Type I sites) were shown to be functionally equivalent to mineralocorticoid receptors, by studies in which binding and action were simultaneously blocked by spirolactone (35); those with lower affinity (Type II sites) were shown to represent classical, dexamethasone-binding glucocorticoid receptors (20). In the early kidney slice/in vivo studies (19), corticosterone was calculated to have 2–4% the affinity of aldosterone for Type I sites, and in addition to be >tenfold more highly bound in plasma; together, these findings were adduced as evidence for the ability of aldosterone to occupy mineralocorticoid receptors despite the much higher total circulating levels of glucocorticoids.

Simultaneously with these studies by Edelman and his colleagues (19, 34), McEwen and his co-workers described two varieties of glucocorticoid receptors in the rat hippocampus and septum (12). One of these bound injected ^{3}H-dexamethasone with high affinity; the other appeared to have a higher affinity for injected ^{3}H-dexamethasone and were dubbed corticosterone-preferring binding sites. Further experiments from McEwen's (40) and de Kloet's (9–11) laboratories showed that these sites were high affinity glucocorticoid receptors that responded to corticosterone but not dexamethasone. These receptors were physiologically glucocorticoid, in that aldosterone (unlike corticosterone) did not restore the deficits induced by adrenalectomy, but did block the restorative action of corticosterone when given simultaneously.

The finding that renal mineralocorticoid receptors and hippocampal corticosterone-preferring sites were identical Type I receptors, with equivalent affinity in cytosol preparations for aldosterone and physiological glucocorticoids, raised more questions than it answered. One question resolved was the apparent mineralocorticoid specificity of binding, previously demonstrated in rat kidney cytosols, and now shown to reflect binding of corticosterone by contaminating transcortin (29). The questions raised, however, had wider implications. First, even though cytosol preparations of Type I receptors from both tissues bound steroids identically in the absence of transcortin, were receptors identical by criteria other than ligand binding? Second, given the much higher circulating levels of glucocorticoids, how was the in vivo aldosterone-selectivity of Type I receptors in physiologic mineralocorticoid target tissues achieved? This selectivity was clearly at the level of binding, as well as action. Although in vitro corticosterone and aldosterone bound equally well to Type I sites in all tissues, in vivo this was true for the hippocampus, but not kidney or colon, where corticosterone binding was shown to be very much lower than that of aldosterone (50, 51).

The cloning of the human and subsequently rat Type I receptors answered the first of these questions. The Type I receptor appears identical in terms of sequence in all tissues studied. Although differences have been noted between kidney and hippocampus in terms of regulation of receptor levels, particularly in response to adrenalectomy and steroid administration (46), such differences are not unexpected. The specificity studies on recombinant human mineralocorticoid receptors, however, echoed those previously done in rat tissue extracts. Recombinant mineralocorticoid receptors bound ^{3}H-aldosterone with appropriately high affinity (5); this binding, in turn, was equally well displaced by aldosterone, corticosterone, or cortisol, which underlines the non-selectivity of receptor, and further points to the question of how the physiologic glucocorticoids are excluded in vivo.

11β-HYDROXYSTEROID DEHYDROGENASE

The mechanism whereby the physiologic glucocorticoids are excluded from Type I sites in classical aldosterone target tissues appears to involve two enzymes, one in the adrenal zona glomerulosa and the other in the target tissue. The target tissue enzyme is 11β OH steroid dehydrogenase (11-HSD), which catalyzes the oxidoreduction of appropriately C11 substituted steroids: in the kidney, for example, cortisol is converted to its 11-keto, receptor-inactive analogue, cortisone, and corticosterone is converted to 11-dehydrocorticosterone, which is similarly receptor inactive. Aldosterone is a very poor substrate for 11-HSD, so that it is not converted to 11-ketoaldosterone which, like cortisone and 11-dehydrocorticosterone, has very low affinity I (or Type II) receptors. What confers this status on aldosterone is the action of the adrenal glomerulosa enzyme responsible for the unique, highly reactive aldehyde group at C18, which cyclizes with the hydroxyl at C11 to form a very stable 11, 18 hemiketal.

The initial insights into the enzymatic mechanisms conferring aldosterone selectivity on renal Type I receptors came from studies on patients with the syndrome of Apparent Mineralocorticoid Excess (AME), a rare and relatively rapidly lethal condition first described by New and her colleagues in 1977 (54). Children with this syndrome show marked salt retention and have very high blood pressures, reflecting their inability to convert cortisol to cortisone in the kidney, and the consequent spill-over of cortisol into normally "forbidden" receptors. Although circulating cortisone levels are normally much lower than those of cortisol, in some tissues (e.g. kidney) the direction of the reaction catalyzed by 11-HSD is predominantly conversion of cortisol to cortisone, so that normal urinary levels of cortisone-derived metabolites are similar to those that are cortisol-derived. In patients with classical AME this ratio of urinary metabolites ranges from 10:1 to 50:1, despite normal circulating cortisol levels and commonly suppressed or low normal aldosterone levels.

The fact that the salt retention and hypertension seen in AME were causally related to low levels of 11-HSD activity was shown by the elegant studies of Edwards and his colleagues (52), who administered licorice to normal human volunteers and demonstrated blockade of the enyzme by its active principles, glycyrrizic acid and its aglycone, glycyrrhetinic acid. Licorice ingestion has long been known to mimic mineralocorticoid excess and to cause hypertension and hypokakalemia. By showing a modest change in urinary ratios of cortisol to cortisone metabolites, and a doubling of the half-time of clearance of infused radioactive cortisol in subjects eating licorice, the Edinburgh group was able to establish a chain of causation between 11-HSD blockade, salt retention, and hypertension.

The drug carbenoxolone sodium was widely used in the 1970s for the treatment of peptic ulcer; despite its therapeutic efficacy, it was subsequently displaced by equally effective anti-ulcer agents without the side-effects of salt and water retention, and blood pressure elevation. Such side effects, in retrospect, may not seem so surprising, given that carbenoxolone is the water-soluble hemisuccinate of glycyrrhetinic acid. That 11-HSD was the physiologic mechanism excluding glucocorticoids from renal Type I receptors was demonstrated in this laboratory by studies in which rats were pretreated with carbenoxolone to block the enzyme, and then the in vivo selectivity of Type I receptors in various tissues determined by their uptake of injected ^{3}H-aldosterone or ^{3}H-corticosterone, in the presence of excess RU28362, to exclude tracer from classical Type II glucocorticoid receptors (23). Under such circumstances there is no difference in hippocampal binding of either steroid, with or without carbenoxolone. In contrast, the aldosterone selectivity of uptake and retention in the kidney and parotid is abolished by carbenoxolone pretreatment and in colon is very substantially reduced. 11-HSD activity, measured in vitro by the conversion of ^{3}H-cortisol to ^{3}H-cortisone, was high in kidney and parotid, modest in colon, and absent in hippocampus. The dose of carbenoxolone used in the binding studies was clearly sufficient to inhibit 11-HSD activity; tissues harvested after in vivo injection of carbenoxolone showed profoundly depressed enzyme activity over two hr incubation at 37°C, which suggests that carbenoxolone may act as a suicide substrate for the enzyme.

These findings, and parallel studies on the in vitro binding of ^{3}H-cortico-sterone in glycyrrhetinic acid treated rats (14), established 11-HSD activity as a crucial determinant of Type I receptor selectivity for aldosterone in physiologic mineralocorticoid target tissue. At the same time, the enzyme was purified from rat liver membranes by Monder and his associates (32), used to raise antibodies, and eventually cloned (1). In immunohistochemical studies, the purified and cloned enzyme appears at high concentration in tissues (testis, liver, lung, renal proximal convoluted tubule) not currently considered to be mineralocorticoid targets; in particular, it appears not to colocalize with Type I receptors detected immunohistochemically in distal tubular structures (48), and when transfected into a toad bladder cell line, 11-HSD acts uniquely as a reductase rather than as a dehydrogenase (13). This species of 11-HSD activity has been dubbed 11-HSD 1 (17), and splice variants with and without signal peptide have been described in rat kidney (31); neither variant, however, appears to fulfill the localization criteria required for intracellular protection of Type I receptors in aldosterone target tissues. Such protection is thus presumed to reflect the activity of a second putative member of this large dehydrogenase family (29), dubbed 11-HSD 2. Currently, although 11-HSD 2 is yet to be purified or cloned, its activity has been distinguished on immunocytochemical grounds from 11-HSD 1 by the NAD-dependent dehydrogenation of 11-keto androstenedione in renal distal tubule sections in vitro (37).

The current position, in brief, is that 11-HSD activity appears to confer aldosterone selectivity on otherwise promiscuous Type I receptors in at least some mineralocorticoid target tissue, and that the species of 11-HSD purified and cloned at the time of writing probably represents an enzyme that modulates glucocorticoid access to classical Type II glucocorticoid receptors in tissues other than the mineralocorticoid target tissues. There are a number of areas, clinical and basic, where questions remain to be answered:

—at the clinical level, the classical syndrome of AME appears to reflect an impaired ability to convert cortisol to cortisone, with the rise in ratio of urinary metabolites a consequence of this impairment. More recently, a variant of this syndrome has been described (AME Type II), in which both reduction and dehydrogenation appear impaired (55). Given that both reduction and dehydrogenation reflect the action of a single enzyme species, the mechanism whereby dehydrogenation alone is impaired in AME Type I remains to be explored;

—in AME the failure to convert cortisol to cortisone is only one of a series of abnormalities of steroid metabolism. For example, the normal ratios of 5α- to 5β-reduced dihydro metabolites are similarly perturbed by the blockade of 5βreduction (53). The coincidence of multiple enzyme blockade in the syndrome suggests that the lesion is not at the level of the gene coding for 11-HSD, but may reflect either inhibition of gene expression via coordinate regulatory mechanisms, or direct blockade of the active sites of the various enzymes;

—the latter appears to be favored by observations of the effects on steroid metabolism of glycyrrhetinic acid and carbenoxolone (33). Both carbenoxolone and glycyrrhetinic acid block a range of enzyme activities that parallel those impaired in AME (e.g. 11-HSD, 5βreductase, 3α,20β reductase). In addition, whereas after licorice (glycyrrhetinic acid) ingestion, the urinary metabolite profile resembles that in AME Type I, after carbenoxolone administration, two independent studies have shown normal urinary ratios of cortisol to cortisone metabolites, as in AME Type II;

—the possibility thus exists that AME Type I represents increased circulating levels of or sensitivity to an endogenous glycyrrhetinic acid equivalent and that AME Type II reflects the activity of increased endogenous carbenoxolone. Candidate molecules to date for such activity are the amidated bile acids, (45), which have been shown to inhibit 11-HSD activity with IC_{50} values as low as $10^{-7}M$ (45); the role of these or other effectors in AME and the mechanism of unidirectional (AME Type I) or bidirectional (AME Type II) blockade remain to be explored;

—at a more basic, physiological level, there remain questions about the universality of the 11-HSD mechanism in terms of Type I receptor protection, and in terms of target tissues and potential competing steroids. For example, the colon has extremely modest levels of 11-HSD activity measured by conversion of cortisol to cortisone, and levels of 11-HSD 1 gene expression are below detection by solution hybridization, yet it boasts the highest levels of Type I receptors of any epithelial tissue. It is thus possible that this tissue has only highly localized 11-HSD 2 activity, perhaps co-expressed in cells containing Type I receptors, and lacks 11-HSD 1 activity. Alternatively, the very low levels found may reflect activity in mesenteric vascular tissue (22) and the absence of activity in the colon itself. Evidence consistent with the former possibility comes from studies on isolated rat rectal mucosa by Hierholzer and his colleagues, who showed patterns of dexamethasone metabolism quite distinct from that seen with 11-HSD-1 (16).

—in terms of potential competing steroids, deoxycorticosterone has affinity for Type I receptors equal to aldosterone, and progesterone is 15–20% as effective as aldosterone. Although both are clearly more highly bound in plasma than is aldosterone, total deoxycorticosterone levels are similar to those of aldosterone in conditions of normal sodium intake and, unlike aldosterone, they are not suppressed by elevated sodium intake. Progesterone levels in the luteal phase, and more particularly as pregnancy progresses, can be considerably higher than those of aldosterone. Neither has an oxygen function at

C11 to serve as substrate for 11-HSD: as agonist (deoxycorticosterone) or antagonist (progesterone) both may be adventitious occupants of Type I receptors, unless excluded by mechanisms other than 11-HSD.

—the existence of such mechanisms is suggested by the patterns of metabolism by the isolated perfused rat kidney of corticosterone compared with aldosterone (25). Whereas aldosterone is predominantly 5α-reduced, corticosterone is in addition not only 11-dehydrogenated, as expected, but also 20β-reduced, which suggests the presence and selective activity of 3α,20β steroid reductase in the rat kidney. Deoxycorticosterone may also be a substrate for this enzyme in distal tubular elements, as suggested by immunocytochemical studies of Mercer & Krozowski (37), who showed carbenoxolone-inhibitable reduction of tetranitrazolium blue by such cells in kidney slices incubated with NAD and 11βOH androstenedione, but not corticosterone. Given the importance of reduced NADH in producing the color reaction, these authors reasoned that the failure of corticosterone to produce an equivalent reaction may reflect consumption of reducing equivalents by 20β reduction, an interpretation strengthened by the ability of equimolar deoxycorticosterone to block the color reaction seen with 11βOH androstenedione. Direct studies exploring the localization of 3α,20β reductase and its role in the exclusion of deoxycorticosterone and progesterone from renal Type I receptors are currently in progress in this laboratory.

PHYSIOLOGICAL CONTEXT, FUTURE STUDIES

Although details of the post-receptor events in aldosterone are outside the admittedly narrow focus of this review and have recently been extensively reviewed elsewhere (49), there is one aspect of this area worthy of further comment in the present discussion of physiological context. In studies on cultured cortical collecting tubules in vitro (39) and in adrenalectomized rats and patients with pseudohypoaldosteronism (congenital absence of Type I receptors) in vivo (21), glucocorticoids, including the highly Type II selective steroid RU28362, were shown to be as effective as aldosterone in terms of transepithelial sodium flux. In vivo, 11-HSD was blocked by carbenoxolone, and in vitro tenfold higher glucocorticoid concentrations were used. Whereas the interpretation of the clinical studies on AME was that unmetabolized cortisol was occupying and activating renal Type I receptors to cause the observed sodium retention, the interpretation of the studies from Naray-Fejes-Toth and her colleagues (39), and from this laboratory (21), is far more radical— that the gold-standard effect of mineralocorticoids can be indistinguishably produced by Type II glucocorticoid receptor activation providing, of course, that the steroid can access the receptor.

The implications of this finding for the way we view the physiological role of aldosterone are profound. There is clear evidence that the physiologic glucocorticoids can activate mineralocorticoid responses via Type I or Type II receptors, that the affinity of cortisol/corticosterone for Type I receptors is an order of magnitude higher than for Type II (30), and that in transfection studies activated Type I receptors increase reporter gene transcription to levels only 5–10% of those with Type II receptor activation (4). Given this evidence, there would appear to be two systems whereby glucocorticoids activate the genomic mechanisms responsible for sodium retention; a higher sensitivity, possibly lower amplitude Type I response, and a lower sensitivity, perhaps higher amplitude Type II response. Both these mechanisms are abrogated by 11-HSD in the distal tubules; as noted previously evidence is perhaps less for such protection in other classic mineralocorticoid target tissues, and in some (e.g. sweat gland) it may be completely absent.

For many years it has been assumed that aldosterone is the crucial determinant of Na^+ status, despite the fact that the adrenalectomized rat lives longer than its intact litter mate provided it has normal saline to drink, and that patients with PHA lacking Type I receptors are similarly very well controlled by salt supplementation in infancy. A pointer, perhaps, to the relative importance of aldosterone vs unprotected receptors is the very different natural history of PHA to that of AME, in that the latter is commonly lethal in youth despite vigorous therapeutic interventions. What remains a conundrum is the Type I receptor and its evolutionary role: given its occurrence and documented functions in non-epithelial tissues, for example, and its maintained equal affinity for cortisol and corticosterone as for aldosterone, it may be presumptuous to view its evolution as driven by salt-retention, or indeed its cognate ligand as aldosterone.

In some sense it is clearly impertinent to speculate why a specific aldosterone receptor has not evolved, particularly given the power and flexibility of the steroid/thyroid/retinoic acid/orphan receptor family: the answer to such speculation is that we have not. On the other hand, the speculation might be reformatted as pondering the possible evolutionary gain in pressing a high affinity glucocorticoid receptor into service, in some (but perhaps not all) epithelial tissues, as a species to which aldosterone has privileged access reflecting its resistance to target tissue metabolism. If this is the case, then the Type I receptor rather than aldosterone may become the pivotal point in sodium homeostasis, and there are a number of ways in which such an hypothesis can be addressed. Such studies might include

—an examination of Type I receptor affinity in the guinea pig for cortisol. Such receptors have been reported to have an unremarkable (nanomolar) affinity for aldosterone, as in other species (28); plasma aldosterone levels are similarly like those in other species (59), in contrast with levels of free cortisol, which are up to two orders of magnitude higher. Type II receptor affinity is commensurately much lower than in other species; the affinity of guinea pig Type I receptors for cortisol may thus provide evidence for which steroid is the cognate ligand, and by extension for the physiological role of glucocorticoids in unprotected Type I receptors;

—an examination of whether or not hamsters have Type I receptors, and if so their relative affinity for cortisol and aldosterone. As noted previously, there is no evidence, despite an intensive and sophisticated search (60), for aldosterone biosynthesis by hamster adrenals after 8 weeks of salt deprivation. The presence or absence of Type I receptors and, if present, their relative affinities for cortisol and aldosterone, plus the exploration of a role for variation in 11-OHSD activity in sodium homeostasis, may provide data on which more credible models of sodium homeostasis can be based;

—and finally, a reexamination of the relative importance of the roles of cortisol and aldosterone in modulation of sodium loss via the sweat gland. It has been estimated that working hard in the tropics occasions a sweat loss of a gallon per hour, equivalent to approx 700 meq of sodium if no reabsorption takes place. In adrenalectomized subjects, Type I receptors in sweat glands will clearly be activated by lower doses of aldosterone than cortisol given the higher transcortin binding of glucocorticoid, whether or not such sites are protected by 11-HSD. A much more coherent physiology can be made for such sites being unprotected, normally occupied and largely activated by baseline cortisol, and very promptly saturated by the rapid rise in cortisol following heavy exertion. If this is the case, then in some epithelia (sweat glands, perhaps some areas of gut) sodium conservation may be the physiologic province of glucocorticoids via Type I receptors, and only in sites like kidney distal tubules and ruminant parotid tubules is aldosterone the physiologic mineralocorticoid.

Whether or not this is the case is to a large extent susceptible to experimental resolution. The studies sketched above and others may provide a clearer vantage point from which to view aldosterone action, in the context of its being but one potential ligand for a highly conserved receptor in a variety of epithelial and non-epithelial tissues. For many years it has been much simpler to give a coherent account of aldosterone physiology than that of the glucocorticoids. With the benefit of our current knowledge of receptors and prereceptor specificity conferring mechanisms, it now appears that such confidence may have been misplaced and that perhaps aldosterone action may only be properly seen as one part of a much less well-defined series of actions of corticosteroids via Type I receptors.

Literature Cited

1. Agarwal, A. K., Monder, C., Eckstein, B., White, P.C. 1989. Cloning and expression of rat cDNA encoding corticosteroid 11 β-dehydrogenase. *J. Biol. Chem.* 264:18939–43

1a. Anderson, B., Ussing, H. H. 1957. Solvent drag on non-electrolytes during osmotic flow through isolated toad skin and its response to antidiuretic hormone. *Acta Physiol. Scand.* 39(2–3): 228–39

2. Armanini, D., Kuhnle, U., Strasser, T., Dorr, H., Weber, P. C., et al. 1985. Aldosterone-receptor deficiency in pseudohypoaldosteronism. *N. Engl. J. Med.* 313:1178–81

3. Armanini, D., Strasser, T., Weber, P. C. 1985. Characterization of aldosterone binding sites in circulatory human mononuclear leukocytes. *Am. J. Physiol.* 248:E388–90

4. Arriza, J., Simerly, R. B., Swanson, L. W., Evans, R. M. 1988. Neuronal mineralocorticoid receptor as a mediator of glucocorticoid response. *Neuron* 1:887–900

5. Arriza, J. L., Weinberger, C., Glaser, T., Handelin, B. L., Housman, D. E., et al. 1987. Cloning of human mineralocorticoid receptor complementary DNA; structural and functional kinship with the glucocorticoid receptor. *Science* 237:268–75

6. Beaumont, K., Fanestil, D. D. 1983. Characterization of rat brain aldosterone receptors reveals high affinity for corticosterone. *Endocrinology* 113:2043–51

6a. Blair-West, J. R., Coghlan, J. P., Denton, D. A., Goding, J. R., Wright, R. D. 1963. The effect of aldosterone, cortisol, and corticosterone on sodium and potassium content of sheep's parotid saliva. *J. Clin. Invest.* 42:484–96

7. Brilla, C. G., Weber, K. T. 1991. Prevention of myocardial fibrosis in hypertension: role of fibroblast corticoid receptors and spirolactone. *FASEB J.* 5:A1256 (Abstr.)

8. Cheek, D. B., Perry, J. W. 1958. A salt-washing syndrome in infancy. *Arch. Dis. Child.* 33:252–56

8a. Crabbe, J. 1961. Stimulation of active Na transport across isolated toad bladder after injection of aldosterone to the animal. *Endocrinology* 69:673–82

9. de Kloet, E. R., Kovacs, G. L., Szabo, G., Telegdy, D., Bohus, B., et al. 1982. Decreased serotonin turnover in the dorsal hippocampus of rat brain shortly after adrenalectomy: selective normalization after corticosterone substitution. *Brain Res.* 239:659–63

10. de Kloet, E. R., Sybesma, H., Reul, J. H. M. 1986. Selective control by corticosterone of serotonin-1 receptor capacity raphe-hippocampal system. *Neuroendocrinology* 42:513–21

11. de Kloet, E. R., Versteeg, D. H. G., Kovacs, G. L. 1983. Aldosterone blocks the response to corticosterone in the raphe-hippocampal serotonin system. *Brain. Res.* 264:323–27

12. de Kloet, E. R., Wallach, G., McEwen, B. S. 1975. Differences in corticosterone and dexamethasone binding to rat brain and pituitary. *Endocrinology* 96:598–609

13. Duperrex, H., Gaeggeler, H.-P., Kenouch, S., Farman, N., Rossier, B. C. 1992. Expression of rat liver 11 β-hydroxysteroid-dehydrogenase (11 β-OHSD) in TBM cells, an aldosterone responsive cell line. *24th Ann. Meeting USGEB/USSBE (Abstr.)*

14. Edwards, C. R. W., Stewart, P. M., Burt, D., Brett, L., McIntyre, M. A., et al. 1988. Localization of 11 β-hydroxysteroid dehydrogenase–tissue specific protector of the mineralocorticoid receptor. *Lancet* 2:986–89

15. Feldman, D., Funder, J. W., Edelman, I. S. 1972. Subcellular mechanisms in the action of adrenal steroids. *Am. J. Med.* 53:545

16. Fromm, M., Epple, H. J., Schulzke, J. D., Hierholzer, K. 1991. Dose-response of aldosterone and ten other corticosteroids on electrogenic Na$^+$ transport in rat rectal colon in vitro. *Proc. Int. Symp. Aldosterone* 215:334 (Abstr.)

17. Funder, J. W. 1990. 11 β-hydroxysteroid dehydrogenase and the meaning of life. *Mol. Cell. Endocrinol.* 68:C3–5

18. Funder, J. W., Feldman, D., Edelman, I. S. 1972. Specific aldosterone binding in rat kidney and parotid. *J. Steroid Biochem.* 3:209–18

19. Funder, J. W., Feldman, D., Edelman, I. S. 1973. The roles of plasma binding and receptor specificity in the mineralocorticoid action of aldosterone. *Endocrinology* 92:994–1004

20. Funder, J. W., Feldman, D., Edelman, I. S. 1973. Glucocorticoid receptors in the rat kidney: the binding of tritiated dexamethasone. *Endocrinology* 92:1005–13

21. Funder, J. W., Pearce, P., Myles, K., Roy, L.P. 1990. Apparent mineralocorticoid excess, pseudohypoaldosteronism and urinary electrolyte excretion: towards a redefinition of "mineralocorticoid" action. *FASEB J.* 4:3234–38

22. Funder, J. W., Pearce, P. T., Smith, R., Campbell, J. 1989. Vascular Type I aldosterone binding sites are physiological mineralocorticoid receptors. *Endocrinology* 125:2224–26

23. Funder, J. W., Pearce, P. T., Smith, R., Smith, A. I. 1988. Mineralocorticoid action: target-tissue specificity is enzyme, not receptor, mediated. *Science* 242:583–85

24. Gomez-Sanchez, E. P., Venkataraman, M. T., Thwaites, D., Fort, C. 1990. Intracerebroventricular infusion of corticosterone antagonizes ICV-aldosterone hypertension. *Am. J. Physiol.* 258: E649–53

25. Hierholzer, K., Schoneshofer, M., Siebe, H., Tsiakiras, D., Weskamp, P. 1984. Corticosteroid metabolism in isolated rat kidney in vitro. *Pflügers Arch.* 400:363–71

26. Joels, M., de Kloet, E. R. 1990. Mineralocorticoid receptor-mediated changes in membrane properties of rat CA1 pyramidal neurons in vitro. *Proc. Natl. Acad. Sci. USA* 87:4495–98

27. Kagawa, C. M., Cella, J. A., Van Arman, C. G. 1957. Action of new steroids in blocking effects of aldosterone and deoxycorticosterone on salt. *Science* 126:1015–16

28. Kraft, N., Hodgson, A. J., Funder, J. W. 1979. Glucocorticoid receptor and effector mechanisms: a comparison of the corticosensitive mouse with the corticoresistant guinea-pig. *Endocrinology* 104:344–49

29. Krozowski, Z. S. 1992. 11β-Hydroxysteroid dehydrogenase and the short-chain alcohol dehydrogenase (SCAD) superfamily. *Mol. Endocrinol.* 84:C25–31

30. Krozowski, Z. S., Funder, J. W. 1983. Renal mineralocorticoid receptors and hippocampal corticosterone binding species have identical intrinsic steroid specificity. *Proc. Natl. Acad. Sci. USA* 80:6056–60

31. Krozowski, Z. S., Stuchbery, S., White, P., Monder, C., Funder, J. W. 1990. Characterization of 11β-hydroxysteroid dehydrogenase expression: identification of multiple unique forms of messenger ribonucleic acid in the rat kidney. *Endocrinology* 127:3009–13

32. Lakshmi, V., Monder, C. 1989. Purification and characterization of the corticosteroid 11β-dehydrogenase component of the rat liver 11β-hydroxysteroid dehydrogenase complex. *Endocrinology* 23:2390–98

33. Latif, S. A., Conca, J. J., Morris, D. J. 1990. The effect licorice derivative, glycyrrhetinic acid, on hepatic 3α- and 3β-hydroxysteroid dehydrogenase and 5α- and 5β-reductase pathways of metabolism of aldosterone in male rats. *Steroids* 55:52–58

34. Lifton, R. P., Dluhy, R. G., Powers, M., Rich, G. R., Cook, S., et al. 1992. A chimaeric 11β-hydrolase-aldosterone synthase gene causes glucocorticoid-remediable aldosteronism and human hypertension. *Nature* 355:262–65

35. Marver, D., Stewart, J., Funder, J. W., Feldman, D., Edelman, I. S. 1975. Renal aldosterone receptors: studies with [³H]aldosterone and the antimineralocorticoid [³H]spirolactone (SC-26304). *Proc. Natl. Acad. Sci. USA* 71:1431–35

36. McEwen, B. S., Lambdin, L. T., Rainbow, T. C., Denicola, A. F. 1986. Aldosterone effects on salt appetite in adrenalectomized rats. *Neuroendocrinology* 43:38–43

37. Mercer, W. R., Krozowski, Z. S. 1992. Localization of an 11β-hydroxysteroid dehydrogenase activity to the distal nephron of the rat kidney. Evidence for the existence of two species of dehydrogenase in the rat kidney. *Endocrinology* 130:540–43

38. Muller, J. 1991. Aldosterone biosynthesis in bovine, rat, and human adrenal: commonalities and challenges. *Mol. Cell. Endocrinol.* 78(3):C119–24

39. Naray-Fejes-Toth, A., Fejes-Toth, G. 1990. Glucocorticoid receptors mediate mineralocorticoid-like effects in cultured collecting duct cells. *Am. J. Physiol.* 259:F672–78

40. Nestler, E. J., Rainbow, T. C., McEwen, B. S., Greengard, P. 1981. Corticosterone increases the level of protein 1, a neuron-specific protein in rat hippocampus. *Science* 212:1162–64

41. Nichols, N. R., Khalid, B. A. K., Fuller, P. J., Rayson, B. M., Funder, J. W. 1984. A common 43K protein induced by glucocorticoids in a variety of cells and tissues. *Mol. Cell. Endocrinol.* 37:197–204

42. Orchinik, M., Murray, T. F., Moore, F. L. 1991. Corticosteroid receptor in neuronal membranes. *Science* 252:1848–51

43. Patel, P. D., Sherman, T. G., Gold-

man, D. J., Watson, S. J. 1989. Molecular cloning of a mineralocorticoid (Type I) receptor complementary DNA for rat hippocampus. *Mol. Endocrinol.* 3: 1877–85

44. Pearce, P., Funder, J. W. 1987. High affinity aldosterone binding sites (Type I receptors) in rat heart. *Clin. Exp. Pharmacol. Physiol.* 14:859–66

45. Perschel, F. H., Buhler, H., Hierholzer, K. 1991. Bile acids and their amidates inhibit 11-hydroxysteroid dehydrogenase obtained from rat kidney. *Pflügers Arch.* 418:538–43

46. Reul, J. M. H. M., Pearce, P. T., Funder, J. W., Krozowski, Z. S. 1989. Type I and Type II corticosteroid receptor gene expression in the rat: effect of adrenalectomy and dexamethasone administration. *Mol. Endocrinol.* 3: 1674–80

47. Rousseau, G., Baxter, J. D., Funder, J. W., Edelman, I. S. Tomkins, G. M. 1972. Glucocorticoid and mineralocorticoid receptors for aldosterone. *J. Steroid Biochem.* 3:219–27

48. Rundle, S. E., Funder, J. W., Lakshmi, V., Monder, C. 1989. The intrarenal localization of mineralocorticoid receptors and 11β-dehydrogenase: immunocytochemical studies. *Endocrinology* 125:1700–4

49. Schafer, J. A., Hawk, C. T. 1992. Regulation of Na^+ channels in the cortical collecting duct by AVP and mineralocorticoids. *Kidney Int.* 41: 255–68

50. Sheppard, K., Funder, J. W. 1987. Mineralocorticoid specificity of renal Type I receptors: in vivo binding studies. *Am. J. Physiol.* 252:E224–29

51. Sheppard, K., Funder, J. W. 1987. Type I receptors in parotid, colon and pituitary are aldosterone-selective in vivo. *Am. J. Physiol.* 253:E467–71

52. Stewart, P. M., Valentino, R., Wallace, A. M., Burt, D., Shackleton, C. H. L., et al. 1987. Mineralocorticoid

activity of liquorice: 11β-hydroxysteroid dehydrogenase deficiency comes of age. *Lancet* ii:821–24

53. Ulick, S., Levine, L. S., Gunczler, P., Zanconato, G., Ramirez, L. C., et al. 1979. A syndrome of apparent mineralocorticoid excess associated with defects in the peripheral metabolism of cortisol. *J. Clin. Endocrinol. Metab.* 49:757–64

54. Ulick, S., Ramirez, L. C., New, M. 1977. An abnormality in reductive metabolism in a hypertensive syndrome. *J. Clin. Endocrinol. Metab.* 44:799–802

55. Ulick, S., Teddle, R., Mantero, F. 1990. Pathogenesis of the type 2 variant of the syndrome of apparent mineralocorticoid excess. *J. Clin. Endocrinol. Metab.* 70:200–6

56. Weber, K. T., Brilla, C. G. 1991. Pathological hypertrophy and cardiac interstitium: fibrosis and renin-angiotensin-aldosterone system. *Circulation* 83:1849–65

57. Wehling, M., Christ, M., Theisen, K. 1991. High affinity aldosterone binding to plasma membrane rich fractions from mononuclear leukocytes: is there a membrane receptor for mineralocorticoids? *Biochem. Biophys. Res. Commun.* 181:1306–12

58. Wehling, M., Armanini, D., Strasser, T., Weber, P. C. 1987. Effect of aldosterone on sodium and potassium concentrations in human mononuclear leukocytes. *Am. J. Physiol.* 252:E505–8

59. Whipp, G. T., Wintour, E. M., Coghlan, J. P., Scoggins, B. A. 1976. Regulation of aldosterone in the guinea-pig; effect oestrous cycle, pregnancy and sodium status. *Aust. J. Exp. Biol Med.* 54: 71

60. Wiseman, J. S., Nichols, J. S., Wright, C. L., Chen, T.-M., Johnston, J. O. 1992. Metabolism of 11-deoxycorticosterone hamster adrenal mitochondria. *J. Steroid Biochem. Mol. Biol.* In press

Annu. Rev. Physiol. 1993. 55:131–53

THE INSULIN-LIKE GROWTH FACTORS

W. S. Cohick and D. R. Clemmons

Department of Medicine, University of North Carolina, Chapel Hill, North Carolina 27599

KEY WORDS: binding proteins, somatomedin, receptors, growth, differentiation

INTRODUCTION

The insulin-like growth factors (IGF-I and IGF-II) are single-chain polypeptides with structural homology to proinsulin. They regulate proliferation and differentiation of a multitude of cell types and are capable of exerting insulin-like metabolic effects. Unlike insulin, they are produced by most tissues of the body and are abundant in the circulation. Thus the IGFs have the potential to act via endocrine as well as autocrine and/or paracrine mechanisms.

The IGFs exert their effects at the cellular level by interacting with the Type-I IGF receptor (IGF-I receptor). They also bind to the Type II/mannose-6-phosphate receptor (IGF-II receptor) and insulin receptors, as well as high affinity binding proteins (IGFBPs). Like the IGFs, the IGFBPs are produced by multiple cell types and have been shown to modulate IGF bioactivity. The recent availability of cDNA probes and antibodies for the IGFs, IGF receptors, and IGFBPs has led to a substantial increase in published studies of IGF physiology. This review attempts to integrate recent information regarding coordinate regulation and function of the IGFs, their receptors, and IGFBPs.

BIOLOGICAL ACTIONS OF IGFS IN VITRO

Effects on Growth and Differentiation

The actions of the IGFs in stimulating growth and differentiation of a wide variety of cell types has been recently reviewed (70). Despite an extensive list of cell types that are responsive to the IGFs, the intracellular mechanisms

131

0066–4278/93/0315–0131$02.00

mediating these events are not defined. IGF-I acts as a progression factor in the cell cycle and synergizes with competence factors such as PDGF and FGF. Recent evidence indicates that ras proteins may be required for the mitogenic signal generated by IGF-I late in G1, whereas they are not essential for the action of PDGF or EGF during the Go/G1 transition. In contrast, inhibition of the G protein alpha subunit inhibits the action of PDGF and EGF, but does not affect the IGF-I stimulation of DNA synthesis (72).

IGF-I has been shown to stimulate terminal myogenic differentiation of L6 myoblasts by inducing expression of the myogenin gene. The increase in myogenin mRNA levels in response to IGF-I is blunted by inhibitors of myogenic differentiation, and an oligodeoxyribonucleotide complementary to the amino terminal sequence of myogenin blocks the stimulation of differentiation by the IGFs. The inhibition by the antisense oligomer is specific for differentiation, as none of the other anabolic effects of IGF-I on L6 myoblasts is affected (43, 44).

Autocrine/Paracrine Actions

While the liver is the major source of circulating IGFs, local production is thought to be important in the regulation of growth and differentiation. Induction of differentiation of skeletal muscle cells in vitro by serum withdrawal is associated with increases in IGF-II mRNA levels and IGF-II cell-surface receptors (108, 129). Differentiation of muscle cells is inhibited by an oligonucleotide complementary to the first five codons of IGF-II and addition of IGF-II overcomes the inhibition, thus providing direct evidence that autocrine secretion of IGF-II stimulates myoblast differentiation (45).

Muscle cells secrete several forms of IGFBPs in culture that may modulate the effect of the IGFs on differentiation. The secretion of IGFBP-5 is induced 30-fold within 16 hr of the onset of differentiation in C2 skeletal muscle cells (128), while increased expression of IGF-II during differentiation is associated with decreased expression of IGFBP-2 and IGFBP-5 in mouse myoblasts (41). A shift in the pattern of IGFBP production has also been reported during differentiation of L6 muscle cells (86).

Connective tissue cells have been shown to synthesize IGF-I, IGF-II, and IGFBPs in vitro, and growth hormone (GH), as well as other trophic hormones, regulates their synthesis at the tissue level. IGF-I and -II mRNAs are expressed in human dermal fibroblasts and in connective tissue stromal cells in multiple tissues (70). IGF-I mRNA is expressed in chondrocytes of the epiphyseal growth plate of 28-day old rats. IGF-I mRNA levels are decreased in chondrocytes of hypophysectomized rats and partially restored by GH treatment (96), which supports a role for locally produced IGF-I in mediating the effect of GH on longitudinal bone growth. In addition to GH,

PTH stimulates rapid increases in IGF-I mRNA and peptide levels in osteoblasts, which may be mediated via increases in cAMP production (81). IGF-II synthesis by osteoblasts was constitutive in one study and not regulatable by PTH or other trophic agents (82); however, PTH stimulation of IGF-I and -II release from neonatal mouse calvaria has been reported (69). PTH also stimulates synthesis of IGFBP-4 via a cAMP-dependent mechanism in human osteoblasts (65). Since IGFBP-4 has been shown to inhibit the mitogenic effects of the IGFs in human osteoblasts, the acute effects of PTH on bone resorption could be mediated by the increased production of IGFBP-4 (89). Release of IGF-II from mouse calvaria is stimulated by $1,25\text{-}(OH)_2D_3$ to a similar extent as PTH, but release of IGF-I is inhibited (69). Estrogen also modulates IGF-I, IGFBP-2, and IGFBP-4 levels in osteoblasts, and estrogen stimulation of osteoblast proliferation is blocked by an antibody against IGF-I (21, 42).

Genes for IGF-I and -II are expressed in human and rat ovary, however, cellular sites of synthesis vary between the two species. The granulosa cell is the primary site of IGF-I mRNA expression in the rat (57), whereas IGF-II transcripts are present in theca-interstitial cells, but not granulosa (58). Human luteinized granulosa cells express IGF-II mRNA, but not IGF-I mRNA, while IGF-I peptide is localized in the theca-interstitium (56). Estrogen treatment of immature, hypophysectomized rats increases ovarian levels of IGF-I mRNA while decreasing hepatic levels of IGF-I mRNA and ovarian IGF-II mRNA (57, 58). In the rat ovary, the mRNAs for IGFBP-2, -3, and -4 are localized to interstitial cells, corpora lutea, and atretic granulosa cells, respectively, while IGFBP-5 mRNA is expressed in atretic granulosa cells, corpora lutea, and the surface epithelium (40, 95). IGFBP-1 mRNA is not detectable in the rat ovary; however, it is present in the human ovary (63). Several forms of IGFBPs are secreted by granulosa cells in culture and have been shown to inhibit FSH stimulation of ovarian function (11, 130). Regulation of local production of IGF-I in the uterus may also be important. Estrogen induces IGF-I mRNA levels in the ovariectomized rat uterus, while decreasing IGF-I mRNA abundance in the liver, and IGF-I potentiates the effect of estrogen on DNA synthesis in rat uterus in organ culture (93).

A number of human tumor cell lines have been shown to synthesize IGFs and IGFBPs and to have IGF-I or IGF-II receptors (75). Some of these cell lines grow in the absence of exogenous growth factors, and proliferation in serum-free media can be inhibited by antibodies that bind IGF-I, IGF-II, or the IGF-I receptor. Thus the IGFs may serve as autocrine regulators of tumor growth. Recently, IGF-II has been overexpressed in a breast tumor epithelial cell line (MCF-7), which does not constitutively express IGF-I or -II. IGF-II-expressing clones showed marked morphological changes in anchor-age-dependent culture and grew in soft agar, while wild-type MCF-7 cells did not show these properties. An antibody against the IGF-I receptor inhibited the growth of IGF-II- expressing clones in serum-free medium (35).

In summary, multiple cell types have been shown to synthesize the IGFs. Furthermore, antibodies against either IGF-I or -II or the IGF-I receptor have been shown to block bioactivity in several systems, thus indicating that autocrine/paracrine growth regulation is a likely possibility. Most of these cell types also secrete IGFBPs, although their specific functions in most systems remain to be determined.

BIOLOGICAL ACTIONS OF IGFS IN VIVO

Effects of IGF Infusion on Growth

Infusion of IGF-I in GH-deficient, mature rats stimulates body weight gain, tibial epiphyseal width, and longitudinal bone growth. However, direct comparison with GH treatment indicates that GH is more potent (70). In one study, infusion of IGF-I or -II to neonatal hypophysectomized rats had no effect on body weight gain, despite normalization of serum IGF-I levels, while GH was stimulatory (52). Although GH treatment causes proportionate organ enlargement, IGF-I treatment consistently results in greater increases in kidney, spleen, and thymus weights (52, 70). These differences may be related to the distinct changes in serum IGFBP profiles that are induced by the two treatments. While IGF-I induces IGFBP-3, GH is required for production of the acid-labile subunit of the large molecular weight ternary complex. This complex is present in GH-treated, but not IGF-I-treated animals (136). This alteration in the carrier complex for IGF-I and -II may alter tissue delivery. It is also possible that these differences reflect direct effects of GH on tissue growth that are independent of its induction of IGF-I.

Transgenic Animal Models

Transgenic mice overexpressing the IGF-I gene have increased body weight gain compared to controls, but the increases are less than those of littermates expressing the GH gene (80). However, in these studies the levels of IGF-I in serum and certain organs were lower in the animals expressing the IGF-I gene compared to the GH-expressing animals. Recently, a transgenic line of mice expressing IGF-I has been crossed to a line of dwarf transgenic mice lacking GH-expressing cells (10). The mice that express IGF-I in the absence of GH grow larger than their GH-deficient transgenic littermates and exhibit weight gain and linear growth similar to that of their nontransgenic siblings. However, analysis of organ growth suggests that GH and IGF-I have some effects that are distinct. GH appears to be necessary to attain normal liver size, while IGF-I can stimulate brain growth (10).

Renal Function

IGF-I peptide and mRNA are colocalized in the collecting duct epithelium, and IGF-I levels are regulated by GH. Levels of IGF-I peptide, but not IGF-I mRNA, rise in the kidney following unilateral nephrectomy in adult rats, which suggests that changes in translation or in clearance may be occurring (55). Expression of IGF-I and IGF receptor genes following unilateral nephrectomy has recently been shown to be age-dependent, with increases in mRNA levels of IGF-I, IGF-I receptor, and IGF-II receptor observed in remnant kidneys of immature, but not adult rats (91). While kidney cells have been shown to produce IGFBPs (28), their role in regulating the action of IGF-I in the kidney is largely unknown. However, IGF-I and IGFBP-1 are colocalized in the same cell types in multiple nephron segments (62).

Direct infusion of IGF-I increases kidney weight relative to somatic growth in several animal model systems (46, 66, 77) and increases glomerular filtration rate and renal plasma flow in humans (53). This suggests that IGF-I may be a physiologic regulator of renal function. Whether IGF-I has a role as a therapeutic agent in patients with renal insufficiency has not been determined.

MODULATION OF IGF ACTION BY IGFBPS

The IGFBP Family

While attempting to purify IGF-I and -II from serum, investigators found that the IGFs were bound to higher molecular weight carrier proteins. Western ligand blotting, a technique that utilizes the binding properties of the IGFBPs for IGF-I or -II, has been used to obtain molecular weight estimates of several forms of IGFBPs and to determine which forms are present in multiple biological fluids (87, 107). Recently, cDNA cloning has been used to determine the sequences of the genes encoding each of the IGFBPs.

The complete primary structures of six forms of IGFBP have now been determined. They have been designated IGFBP-1 through 6. The mature proteins each consist of 200 to 300 amino acids, with signal sequences of 20 to 40 amino acids. The IGFBPs have 18 cysteine residues in their amino- and carboxyterminal ends whose alignment is conserved, suggesting disulfide bonding may be important in forming the specific high-affinity IGF binding site. An exception is IGFBP-6, which lacks 2 and 4 of the homologous cysteines in the rat and human, respectively. In addition to the 18 cysteines, two additional cysteines are present in rat and human IGFBP-4. IGFBP-1 and

-2 contain an RGD sequence in their carboxyterminal end, which is found in many extracellular matrix proteins and often serves as a recognition sequence for cell surface integrin receptors. Four of the IGFBPs (3 though 6) are glycosylated to varying degrees, which may be important for adherence to cell surfaces.

The first IGFBP to be completely characterized was human IGFBP-1. This protein was purified from human amniotic fluid and decidua. The cDNA sequences of human and rat IGFBP-1 are 58% homologous (87). IGFBP-1 binds IGF-I and -II with approximately equal affinity. At pH 7.0 its affinity constant for IGF-I is fivefold greater than that of the IGF-I receptor. IGFBP-1 mRNA expression is high in human decidua, endometrium, and fetal liver. In the adult rat, IGFBP-1 mRNA expression is highest in the kidney, liver, and decidua (94).

The complete structures of human, rat, and bovine IGFBP-2 have been determined from cDNA sequence analysis (16, 87). The proteins from all three species are approximately 85% homologous. The liver is the predominant site of IGFBP-2 expression in the fetus, although kidney, stomach, lung, and brain also express moderate message levels. Expression is very high in rat brain and higher in fetal than adult tissues (101, 102). The affinity of IGFBP-2 for IGF-II is threefold higher than for IGF-I, but its affinity for both is greater than that of IGFBP-1 at pH 7.4.

IGFBP-3 is the IGF-binding subunit of the 150 kd GH-dependent binding complex that is present in serum (8). IGFBP-3 was originally purified from human plasma, and its primary structure was determined from clones obtained from human liver cDNA libraries. Porcine, rat, and bovine IGFBP-3 have subsequently been cloned. In adult rats, abundant levels of IGFBP-3 are present in the kidney, liver, stomach, placenta, uterus, and ovary (2). IGFBP-3 has a very high affinity for both IGF-I and -II and is the most abundant form of IGFBP in serum. These properties account for the fact that it binds greater than 95% of the IGF-I and -II in the circulation.

IGFBP-4 has been purified from human and rat serum and from media conditioned by a human osteosarcoma cell line (61, 89, 115). Its primary structure has been determined from cDNA sequence analysis (61, 65, 114). The human and rat proteins are 92% homologous. While IGFBP-4 contains a single N-linked glycosylation site, it is generally present in a non-glycosylated form. Higher M_r forms of 28 to 30 kd have been detected in serum and conditioned medium of neuroblastoma cells (22, 61). A single mRNA transcript of 2.6 kb is present in multiple tissues of adult rats, with liver exhibiting the highest expression (95, 114). IGFBP-4 transcripts of 2.0 to 2.3 kb have been detected in human tissues and fetal fibroblasts (19, 61, 65). IGFBP-4 has a high affinity for IGF-I and -II that is nearly equal to that of IGFBP-3 at pH 7.4.

IGFBP-5 has been purified from human and rat sources (3, 7, 113), and its primary structure has been obtained from clones isolated from rat ovary, human placenta, and human osteosarcoma cDNA libraries (60, 113). The rat and human proteins are 97% conserved, and M_rs of the mature proteins are 28,428 and 28,553, respectively (113). While IGFBP-5 contains no potential N-linked glycosylation sites, the protein migrates as a doublet at 31 to 32 kd on SDS gels under nonreducing conditions. IGFBP-5 has the highest affinity for IGF-I and -II of all the IGFBPs, which is 50-fold greater than that of the IGF-I receptor at pH 7.4.

A single 6.0 kb IGFBP-5 mRNA transcript has been detected in all tissues examined of adult rats. Several tissues have higher levels of mRNA compared to the liver, with the highest expression observed in the kidney (113). A single 6.0 kb transcript is also present in human fetal fibroblasts (19). In addition to the 6.0 kb transcript, a 1.7 to 1.8 kb transcript has been detected in rat ovarian tissue and human osteosarcoma cells (40, 60).

IGFBP-6 has been purified from several human sources, including serum, cerebrospinal fluid, and conditioned media of fibroblasts and osteosarcoma cells (3, 47, 79, 106, 137). The complete primary structure of rat and human IGFBP-6 has been determined from cDNA sequence analysis of clones obtained from rat ovary, human placenta, and human osteosarcoma cells (61, 112). The estimated M_rs of the mature proteins are 22, 847 and 21,461 for the human and rat, respectively. The protein has a 10- to 100-fold higher affinity for IGF-II than for IGF-I (47, 79, 106), which is similar to the affinity of IGFBP-3 for IGF-I. A single transcript of 1.3 kb is abundant in all tissues that have been examined (112).

The human IGFBP-1, 2, 3, 4, and 5 genes are located on chromosomes 7, 2, 7, 17, and 5, respectively (113). The human IGFBP-1, human IGFBP-3, and rat IGFBP-2 genes span 5.2, 8.9, and at least 8 kb, respectively, and have similar structural organization (17, 33, 34). The IGFBP-1 and IGFBP-2 genes contain four exons, while the IGFBP-3 gene contains a fifth exon. The promoter regions of IGFBP-1 and IGFBP-3 each contain a TATA box and a consensus promoter element located upstream from a single mRNA cap site within a CpG island. Liver factor B1 (LFB1) appears to regulate basal IGFBP-1 promoter activity in HepG2 cells by binding the CCAAT promoter element (126). This element is absent from the IGFBP-3 promoter, which contains sequences that could bind Sp1 and AP2. In contrast to IGFBP-1 and -3, the IGFBP-2 gene lacks a TATA box near the transcription start site. Its promoter region contains recognition sequences for several transcription factors including Sp1, ETF, AP-1, AP-2, and LFB1.

Regulation of IGF Bioavailability

The majority of IGF-I and -II in the circulation is associated with a 150 kd complex that is composed of glycosylated IGFBP-3, an 85 kd acid-labile subunit and IGF-I or -II (8). The acid-labile subunit and IGFBP-3 do not interact in the absence of IGFs. The smaller M_r complex of 40 kd contains IGFBP-1, -2, -4, and -6 and contains most of the unsaturated IGF binding sites in serum (61, 137). IGFBP-5 has not been identified in this complex; however, it has been purified from human serum and very small amounts are detectable in human and bovine serum by immunoblot analysis. Serum levels of IGFBP-3, -2, and -1 in the adult human are approximately 5 ug/ml, 150 ng/ml, and 50 ng/ml, respectively. The half-lives of the IGFs are dependent on their association with IGFBPS. The 10 min half-life of ^{125}I-IGF-I is extended to 30 min when bound to the 40,000 M_r complex and greater than 10 to 15 hr when bound to the 150,000 M_r complex. Radiolabeled des(1-3)IGF-I, which has reduced affinity for IGFBPs, is cleared more rapidly (4, 54).

IGFBPs may also be important in mediating transport of the IGFs from the vascular space. IGFBP-1, -2, -3, and -4 have been shown to cross intact vascular endothelium, either alone or when crosslinked to IGF-I (6, 12a). However, it is not known whether the IGFs can also leave the vasculature in an unbound form. Insulin stimulates transport of IGFBP-1, but not IGFBP-2, across intact capillaries (5), which could be a mechanism by which insulin acutely lowers IGFBP-1 concentrations.

Modulation of IGF Action at the Cellular Level

IGFBPs both inhibit and potentiate the metabolic and mitogenic effects of the IGFs at the cellular level. Addition of purified IGFBP-1, -2, -3, or -4 inhibits binding of IGFs to cell surfaces and thus attenuates IGF bioactivity by sequestering the peptide and preventing receptor interaction (12, 18, 22, 32, 48, 89, 109). At equimolar concentrations, IGFBP-3 is more effective than either IGFBP-2 or IGFBP-1 in blocking cell surface binding (84).

Preincubation of fibroblasts with IGFBP-3 results in potentiation of IGF-I activity, while co-incubation of IGFBP-3 and IGF-I is inhibitory (8, 32). The potentiating effect is associated with increased binding of IGF-I to membrane-associated IGFBP-3 (32). IGFBP-3 released from cell surfaces of fetal fibroblasts has a greater affinity for IGF-I than that remaining on the cell surface (85). Therefore, the potentiating effect of cell-surface associated IGFBP-3 may be the result of a decrease in its binding affinity, which would permit a more favorable equilibrium with the IGF-I receptor. The mechanism by which IGFBP-3 adheres to cell surfaces is unknown, but does not appear to require glycosylation (31).

IGFBP-1 and -2 also potentiate the mitogenic activity of IGF-I; however, IGFBP-1 is more potent than IGFBP-2 and also induces a greater increase in IGF-I binding to the cell surface (16, 24). Two forms of IGFBP-1 have been isolated from amniotic fluid, but only one form potentiates IGF-I activity, and this form associates with cell membranes (87). The mechanism by which cell-surface associated IGFBPs potentiate IGF activity is unknown. Studies with IGF analogues with altered affinity for IGFBPs and the IGF-I receptor indicate that binding of IGF-I to both IGFBP-1 and the IGF-I receptor is required for potentiation (23).

IGFBP-5 has been shown to potentiate the proliferative actions of IGF-II in osteoblasts (7), while a mixture of IGFBP-5 and -6 enhances IGF-I stimulation of mitogenesis in human osteosarcoma cells (3). Preincubation with the IGFBPs was not necessary to elicit the potentiating effect on IGF activity, and their ability to associate with cell membranes was not determined.

IGFBP-1 is phosphorylated in vitro by human hepatoma (HepG2) and endometrial cells in culture (49, 59). Human amniotic fluid and fetal serum contain both nonphosphorylated and phosphorylated IGFBP-1, whereas HepG2 and decidual cells secrete predominantly phosphorylated isoforms. The phosphorylated IGFBP-1 secreted by HepG2 cells has a sixfold higher affinity for IGF-I than it does after dephosphorylation. IGFBP-3 is also phosphorylated, however, its affinity for IGF-I has not been determined. Dephosphorylated IGFBP-1 purified from amniotic fluid potentiates the effect of IGF-I on DNA synthesis, while the phosphorylated form appears to be inhibitory.

REGULATION OF IGF AND IGFBP SYNTHESIS

Hormonal Regulation

The regulation of circulating concentrations and tissue synthesis of IGF-I by GH is well documented (8, 36). Circulating levels of IGFBP-3 are also regulated by GH; however, this effect is likely mediated by IGF-I since infusion of IGF-I to hypophysectomized rats induces IGFBP-3 (26, 136). While serum levels of IGF-I and IGFBP-3 decrease in a coordinate fashion in hypophysectomized rats, mRNA levels are not coordinately regulated in all tissues. In liver, mRNA levels of IGF-I and IGFBP-3 are decreased to 10 and 50% of controls, respectively, and partially restored with GH treatment. Levels of IGF-I mRNA in the kidney follow a similar pattern; however, kidney IGFBP-3 mRNA levels increase twofold in hypophysectomized rats and are not reduced by GH (2). Synthesis of IGFBP-3 by multiple cell types including chondrocytes, fibroblasts, endometrial and breast carcinoma cells is also stimulated by IGF-I or -II (20, 23, 111). TGF-beta also stimulates IGFBP-3 secretion by human skin fibroblasts (78).

In contrast to IGFBP-3, blood levels of IGFBP-2 are inversely related to GH status. IGFBP-2 levels increase twofold in patients with hypopituitarism (25), and decrease fourfold in lactating dairy cows treated with GH (29). However, GH does not affect IGFBP-2 levels in calorically restricted adults, which suggests that a normal caloric intake is required for GH to suppress IGFBP-2 (25). Infusion of IGF-I in healthy adults increases circulating

IGFBP-2, while patients with non-islet cell tumor hypoglycemia, in which IGF-II is overexpressed, also have elevated IGFBP-2 levels (137). Thus, GH and IGF-I appear to regulate IGFBP-2 in a dis-coordinate manner.

IGFBP-4 secretion is decreased following exposure to IGF-I or -II in fetal fibroblasts and breast carcinoma cells, while insulin at concentrations sufficient to stimulate the IGF-I receptor increases secretion of IGFBP-4 (19, 20). However, this effect appears to be cell-type specific since IGF-I stimulates IGFBP-4 secretion in L6 muscle cells (86). The decrease in IGFBP-4 secretion by fetal fibroblasts that occurs with IGF-I treatment is not accompanied by a decrease in mRNA abundance (19).

There are presently no reports on regulation of IGFBP-5 in vivo. The findings that hepatic abundance of IGFBP-5 mRNA is low and that serum contains very little detectable protein suggest that circulating IGFBP-5 has a minor regulatory role. In contrast, IGFBP-5 that is synthesized by connective tissue cells and localized in extracellular matrix may be important. IGF-I increases IGFBP-5 abundance in fibroblast conditioned media six- to eightfold while causing no change in mRNA levels. In addition, insulin, at doses that should act through the IGF-I receptor, fails to increase IGFBP-5 levels, which indicates that IGF-I is not acting via its receptor to stimulate IGFBP-5 secretion (19). This effect is mediated by a unique mechanism whereby fibroblasts secrete a protease that specifically degrades IGFBP-5. When IGF-I or -II binds to IGFBP-5, degradation is inhibited.

IGFs and IGFBPs have been suggested to play a role in the growth inhibitory effects seen with glucocorticoid excess. Dexamethasone reduces body weight gain and hepatic and tibial IGF-I mRNA abundance in the adult rat without affecting serum IGF-I concentrations, while at the same time increasing IGFBP-1 serum and hepatic mRNA levels (73). Hepatic IGFBP-1 mRNA levels are also increased during dexamethasone-induced growth retardation in fetal rats, however, mRNA levels of IGF-I and -II are not decreased (104). Dexamethasone increases IGFBP-1 mRNA levels by increasing gene transcription (103, 131). Treatment of 4-day old rats with dexamethasone decreases both hepatic IGF-II and IGFBP-2 mRNA levels (102), while treatment of 4-week old rats increases serum and hepatic mRNA levels of IGFBP-3 (74). Secretion of IGFBP-3 and IGFBP-5 by fetal fibroblasts in vitro is decreased by dexamethasone (19).

Nutritional Regulation

Adequate nutrition is essential for IGF-I to promote growth. During undernutrition, attenuation of growth is accompanied by decreases in serum IGF-I that cannot be normalized by GH treatment (27). The decline in IGF-I concentrations during fasting is due to a decrease in binding of GH to its hepatic receptor. These changes are accompanied by decreases in hepatic

IGF-I and GH receptor mRNA abundance (15, 120). A reduction in the rate of IGF-I gene transcription does not account for the decrease in IGF-I mRNA, which suggests that regulation is primarily at the posttranscriptional level (120). Reductions in IGF-I and GH receptor mRNA levels are also observed in nonhepatic tissues, although the two mRNAs are not coordinately regulated in all tissues (15, 71). IGF-I receptor mRNA appears to be up-regulated in several tissues (71). IGF-I treatment has been shown to partially restore the growth rate of malnourished rats (110), thus suggesting that some degree of tissue sensitivity to IGF-I is maintained.

In contrast to the decrease in hepatic GH binding observed during fasting, dietary protein restriction appears to cause GH resistance by a postreceptor mechanism (27). Reductions of IGF-I mRNA levels in liver and skeletal muscle are observed during protein restriction in growing rats (121, 132). However, infusion of IGF-I into protein-restricted rats fails to normalize tail length, weight, or tibial epiphyseal width despite normalization of serum IGF-I levels and enhancement of spleen and kidney growth (127). This suggests that dietary protein restriction causes organ-specific resistance to IGF-I.

Serum levels of IGF-I, IGFBP-3, and IGFBP-2 are relatively constant over the day. In contrast, IGFBP-1 levels show a marked diurnal variation that is inversely related to insulin status and blood glucose levels and is independent of GH secretory status. The regulation of IGFBP-1 in serum has been extensively studied, and a role in glucose counter-regulation has been proposed (67). Administration of an IGF-I/IGFBP-1 complex to rats blocks the hypoglycemic response to exogenous IGF-I, while injection of IGFBP-1 alone increases plasma glucose levels (68). These data suggest that the IGFs may play a role in glucose homeostasis. The effects of insulin on IGFBP-1 appear to be both direct, as well as secondary, to changes in glucose concentrations (116, 124).

Alterations in IGFBP-1 levels due to metabolic status are reflected at the level of hepatic synthesis, although insulin has also been shown to stimulate transport from the vasculature. Hepatic IGFBP-1 production is increased by glucagon, substrate deprivation, and factors that increase cAMP, whereas insulin is inhibitory (67). Insulin decreases IGFBP-1 mRNA levels in rat hepatoma cells by directly decreasing gene transcription (131). Therefore, the regulation of hepatic IGFBP-1 synthesis may be an important determinant of serum IGFBP-1 levels.

Extreme variations in nutrient intake such as fasting also regulate IGFBPs. Plasma levels of IGFBP-3 are decreased by fasting or protein deprivation in growing rats (26), while hepatic mRNA levels of IGFBP-2 and IGFBP-1 are increased by fasting or protein deprivation (94, 101, 102, 121). Maternal fasting increases IGFBP-1 mRNA levels in fetal liver, while having no effect on IGFBP-2 mRNA levels (119). Levels of IGFBP-1 are increased in serum of neonatal piglets after 48 hr of fasting when analyzed by ligand blot and radio-immunoassay (RIA). In contrast, IGFBP-2 levels are increased by RIA, but decreased by ligand blot analysis, which indicates that an IGFBP-2-specific protease may regulate IGFBP-2 levels in neonatal serum (88).

Developmental Regulation

The IGFs are believed to be important in fetal development, and direct evidence of a role for IGF-II in fetal growth has been demonstrated (38). IGF-I and -II mRNA transcripts are present in virtually all fetal tissues, although their abundance and ontogeny of expression varies among organs. In the fetal rat, IGF-II gene expression is abundant in most tissues, but decreases dramatically at birth in all tissues except the brain. The decrease in IGF-II mRNA levels corresponds to the decrease in circulating levels of IGF-II postnatally. However, this decrease may be unique to the rat, as studies in other species, including humans, have shown that significant serum levels of IGF-II are maintained postnatally. IGF-I transcripts in fetal liver, kidney, and heart are lower in abundance compared with IGF-II and rise progressively with increasing postnatal age, as does serum IGF-I, while expression in fetal lung, muscle, and stomach is higher than it is postnatally (1). In mid-gestation, IGF-I and -II transcripts are found predominately in mesenchymal cells; however, early in organogenesis these transcripts are not always coexpressed, and in the case of IGF-II, not restricted to cells of mesenchymal origin (14).

Levels of IGFBP-1 and -2 are also developmentally regulated, with transcripts for each expressed in a variety of fetal tissues. Expression of both mRNAs is higher in the liver than in other fetal tissues, with abundant levels of IGFBP-2 also present in fetal kidney, brain, and stomach (101). IGFBP-2 transcripts are predominately localized to cells of ectodermal and endodermal origin and expressed in discrete locations in the nervous system during early organogenesis. They are not colocalized with IGF-II mRNA (135). Message and serum levels of IGFBP-1 and -2 fall postnatally in the rat. IGFBP-3 is not present in serum of fetal rats; however, IGFBP-3 mRNA is present in the kidney and liver of 1-day old rats and increases in both organs by week 1. Levels remain constant thereafter, while the levels of hepatic IGF-I mRNA continue to increase up to 8 weeks (2). In contrast to the rat, IGFBP-3 levels are abundant in fetal serum of other species, such as the sheep, cow, and pig, although circulating concentrations are significantly higher in postnatal life.

IGFs and IGFBPs are altered in maternal serum during pregnancy. In the rat, serum IGF-I and hepatic IGF-I mRNA levels are decreased during pregnancy, while serum IGF-II levels are unchanged (37, 39). In the human, serum IGF-I and IGFBP-3 levels determined by RIA increase during pregnancy (8). In contrast, IGFBP-3 is virtually undetectable by ligand blot analysis in pregnant serum of both humans and rodents (37, 39, 50). This decrease has been attributed to the presence of a protease that would produce fragments that are unable to bind the IGFs, but would react immunologically (37, 51). However, this discrepancy has also been attributed to an alteration in the ability of IGFBP-3 to bind iodinated IGF (122, 123). The exact physiological role that this protease plays in IGF function during pregnancy is not clear. The abundance of liver IGFBP-3 mRNA is not altered during preganancy in the rat, while IGFBP-1 and -4 mRNA levels are increased (39).

THE IGF-I RECEPTOR

The IGF-I receptor mediates most of the biological actions of IGF-I and IGF-II and is present in a wide variety of tissues and cell lines. The affinity (kd) of the IGF-I receptor for IGF-I is approximately 1 nM, 2- to 10-fold lower for IGF-II, and 100- to 500-fold lower for insulin. The IGF-I receptor is an $alpha_2beta_2$ transmembrane glycoprotein that is structurally similar to the insulin receptor and contains tyrosine protein kinase domains in the cytoplasmic portion of the beta subunit. The gene is located on human chromosome 15 and mouse chromosome 7 (125). Promoters of the human and rat IGF-I receptor genes lack TATA and CAAT boxes upstream of a unique transcription start site and contain potential binding sites for several transcription factors (76, 133).

IGF-I Receptor Function

Expression studies of cloned IGF-I and insulin receptor cDNAs indicate that both receptors are capable of mediating short-term metabolic effects, as well as long-term mitogenic effects. The physiological roles of both insulin and IGF-I are therefore likely to be determined by the distribution and abundance of their receptors on the cell surface. However, studies with chimeric receptors containing the extracellular ligand-binding domain of the insulin receptor and the intracellular domain of the IGF-I receptor indicate that while the IGF-I and insulin receptors mediate short-term responses such as glucose transport similarly, receptors containing an IGF-I intracellular domain are more effective in stimulating DNA synthesis than the insulin receptor (64). Thus, insulin and IGF-I receptors have similar, yet distinct, signaling potentials that are defined by the cytoplasmic domain.

The intrinsic tyrosine kinase activity of the IGF-I receptor may mediate the biological actions of IGF-I by phosphorylating endogenous cellular substrates. Several substrates for IGF-I receptor kinases have been identified. The phosphoprotein pp185 is an endogenous substrate of both the IGF-I and insulin receptor kinases. This protein has recently been purified and sequenced and is now designated Insulin Receptor Substrate-1 (IRS-1) (109a, 124a). IRS-1 has been proposed as a multi-site "docking" protein, which upon phosphorylation associates with cellular proteins such as phosphatidylinositol 3' kinase, most likely through src-homology 2 (SH2) domains (20a). The phosphoprotein pp175 is also an endogenous substrate for the IGF-I and insulin receptors in FRTL5 thyroid cells and in L6 myoblasts in which it is associated with the cytoskeleton (9, 30). In undifferentiated L6 cells, stimulation by IGF-I increases IGF-I receptor phosphorylation and pp175 induction, whereas IGF-I-induced phosphorylation of pp175 is almost undetectable after cells differentiate into myotubes. Sequence analysis of pp175 will determine whether this protein is identical to IRS-1, which appears likely. The ability of IGF-I to stimulate mitogenesis, but not glucose transport, is inhibited in cells expressing a kinase-defective insulin receptor. IGF-I mediated phosphorylation of pp170 and pp220 is inhibited in these cells (83). Therefore, while the specific functions of phosphorylated endogenous substrates are unknown, evidence that they may be important mediators of biological activity is accumulating.

IGF-I Insulin Receptor Hybrids

Some tissues and cell types have been shown to express hybrid receptors composed of one insulin receptor alpha and beta subunit and one IGF-I receptor alpha and beta subunit. These receptors may account for the appearance of two beta subunits with different M_r that are frequently observed following IGF-I stimulation. The presence of hybrid receptors was suggested by findings that monoclonal antibodies specific for the insulin receptor immunoprecipitated IGF-I binding activity (117). Evidence that this cross-reactivity is produced by hybrid receptors came from studies in which an antibody specific for the human insulin receptor immunopreciptiated IGF-I binding activity only after expression of the human insulin receptor in rodent cell lines and, conversely, an antibody specific for the human IGF-I receptor acquired the ability to immunoprecipitate insulin-binding activity following expression of human IGF-I receptors in a mouse cell line (118). The hybrid receptor has higher affinity for IGF-I than insulin, and IGF-I is more effective than insulin in inducing a conformational change in the receptor and in activating autophosphorylation (90, 118). Therefore, the hybrid receptor appears to function more as an IGF receptor than as an insulin receptor. The extent to which hybrid receptors constitute the total receptor population has not been defined for most systems. However, in placenta, 70% of the receptors are estimated to be hybrids (117). This suggests that in some tissues these receptors may play an important role in coordinating IGF action.

Developmental Regulation

Levels of IGF-I receptor mRNA decrease in multiple tissues throughout postnatal development in the rat in comparison to fetal levels. In contrast,

IGF-I mRNA levels increase in liver, heart, and kidney postnatally (134). During early organogenesis, mRNA for the IGF-I receptor is widely distributed in fetal tissues and is most prominent in the developing nervous system and muscle. IGF-II mRNA is also widespread and more abundant than IGF-I message, which is relatively localized, suggesting that the actions of IGF-II may be mediated via the IGF-I receptor in the fetus (14). Recently, two cellular patterns of IGF-I receptor gene expression have been described during development of the rat brain (13). Cells of neuroepithelial lineage have a basal level of receptor gene expression that could represent a target for IGFs in CSF and mediate a basic metabolic or trophic function. Superimposed on this constitutive pattern are sets of neurons that show high levels of IGF-I receptor mRNA in conjunction with IGF-I mRNA expression during the period of postnatal differentiation. This suggests that these may represent specific areas of paracrine IGF-I action in the brain parenchyma (13).

THE IGF-II RECEPTOR

Physiological Significance

The IGF-II receptor is identical to the cation-independent mannose-6-phosphate (M6P) receptor, which functions as a lysosomal enzyme targeting protein. This receptor consists of a single polypeptide chain with a large extracellular domain containing separate binding sites for IGF-II and M6P, a very short cytoplasmic region that lacks intrinsic protein kinase activity, and a single transmembrane domain. The majority of the metabolic and mitogenic effects of IGF-II are mediated through the IGF-I or insulin receptors. The limited studies that indicate a role for the IGF-II receptor in mediating the biologic responses of IGF-II are difficult to interpret and have been recently reviewed (98). Therefore, the function of the IGF-II receptor with respect to IGF-II growth promoting activity remains to be elucidated.

Signal Transduction

Recently, the IGF-II receptor has been shown to be coupled to Gi_2, a GTP-binding protein (G protein). In phospholipid vesicles, IGF-II directly couples purified rat IGF-II receptor with porcine Gi_2 (97). In reconstituted vesicles containing clonal human IGF-II receptor and purified G proteins, the stimulatory effect of IGF-II on Gi_2 activation is inhibited by M6P, while Gi_2 is not activated by M6P alone (92). A 14 amino acid segment of the cytoplasmic domain of the IGF-II receptor is able to activate Gi_2, and its activation is blocked by an antibody against this segment (99, 100). Further evidence that IGF-II may signal intracellular events by activating G proteins via the IGF-II receptor comes from the finding that low concentrations of

IGF-II stimulate production of inositol triphosphate in kidney proximal tubular membranes (105). However, this effect is potentiated by M6P, which indicates that the G protein involved may not be analagous to Gi_2. The relationship of this G protein signaling mechanism to the IGF-related growth response has not been defined.

SUMMARY

The recent availablity of reagents to study the IGFs, their receptors, and binding proteins has led to an explosive growth in the study of IGF physiology. However, most studies to date have been descriptive, and studies delineating mechanisms of action are limited. It is apparent that most organ systems synthesize several components of the IGF system necessary for IGF to function in an autocrine or paracrine fashion and that regulation of this system occurs at the local level. However, the relative importance of locally produced IGF vs circulating IGF remains unclear. The mechanisms by which the IGFBPs modulate IGF activity are crucial to understanding this system, and identification of specific roles for each of these proteins will be required. Of critical importance is the identity of the intracellular signal transduction system by which the IGF receptor mediates the effects of the IGFs, and the delineation of mechanisms by which the IGFBPs interact with the receptor at the cellular level. It is also of interest to determine what role, if any, the IGF-II receptor plays in mediating the growth-promoting effects of the IGFs.

The ubiquitous distribution of the IGFs, IGFBPs, and IGF receptors indicates that they may play a role in the regulation of coordinate growth amoung several tissues and cell types. Understanding the mechanisms by which these components interact to coordinate growth responses between different cell types should greatly enhance our understanding of normal growth and development.

Literature Cited

1. Adamo, M., Lowe, W. L. Jr., LeRoith, D., Roberts, C. T., Jr. 1989. Insulin-like growth factor I messenger ribonucleic acids with alternative 5'-untranslated regions are differentially expressed during development of the rat. *Endocrinology* 124:2737–44

2. Albiston, A. L., Herington, A. C. 1992. Tissue distribution and regulation of insulin-like growth factor (IGF)-binding protein-3 messenger ribonucleic acid (mRNA) in the rat: comparison with IGF-I mRNA expression. *Endocrinology* 130:497–502

3. Andress, D. L., Birnbaum, R. S. 1991. A novel human insulin-like growth factor binding protein secreted by osteoblast-like cells. *Biochem. Biophys. Res. Commun.* 176:213–18

4. Ballard, F. J., Knowles, S. E., Walton, P. E., Edson, K., Owens, P. C., et al. 1991. Plasma clearance and tissue distribution of labelled insulin-like growth factor-I (IGF-I), IGF-II and des(1–3) IGF-I in rats. *J. Endocrinol.* 128:197–204

5. Bar, R. S., Boes, M., Clemmons, D. R., Busby, W. H., Sandra, A., et al.

1990. Insulin differentially alters trans-capillary movement of intravascular IGFBP-1, IGFBP-2 and endothelial cell IGF-binding proteins in the rat heart. *Endocrinology* 127:497–99

6. Bar, R. S., Boes, M., Dake, B. L., Sandra, A., Bayne, M., et al. 1990. Tissue localization of perfused endothelial cell IGF binding protein is markedly altered by association with IGF-I. *Endocrinology* 127:3243–45

7. Bautista, C. M., Baylink, D. J., Mohan, S. 1991. Isolation of a novel insulin-like growth factor (IGF) binding protein from human bone: a potential candidate for fixing IGF-II in human bone. *Biochem. Biophys. Res. Commun.* 176: 756–63

8. Baxter, R. C., Martin, J. L. 1989. Binding proteins for the insulin-like growth factors: structure, regulation and function. *Prog. Growth Factor Res.* 1:49–68

9. Beguinot, F., Kahn, C. R., Moses, A. C., White, M. F., Smith, R. J. 1989. Differentiation-dependent phosphorylation of a 175,000 molecular weight protein in response to insulin and insulin-like growth factor-I in L6 skeletal muscle cells. *Endocrinology* 125:1599–605

10. Behringer, R. R., Lewin, T. M., Quaife, C. J., Palmiter, R. D., Brinster, R. L., et al. 1990. Expression of insulin-like growth factor I stimulates normal somatic growth in growth hormone-deficient transgenic mice. *Endocrinology* 127:1033–40

11. Bicsak, T. A., Shimonaka, M., Malkowski, M., Ling, N. 1990. Insulin-like growth factor-binding protein (IGF-BP) inhibition of granulosa cell function: effect on cyclic adenosine 3′,5′-monophosphate, deoxyribonucleic acid synthesis, and comparison with the effect of an IGF-I antibody. *Endocrinology* 126:2184–89

12. Blat, C., Delbe, J., Villaudy, J., Chatelain, G., Golde, A., et al. 1989. Inhibitory diffusible factor 45 bifunctional activity. As a cell growth inhibitor and as an insulin-like growth factor I-binding protein. *J. Biol. Chem.* 264:12449–54

12a. Boes, M., Booth, B. A., Sandra, A., Dake, B. L., Bergold, A., Bar, R. S. 1992. Insulin-like growth factor binding protein (IGFBP)4 accounts for the connective tissue distribution of endothelial cell IGFBPs perfused through the isolated heart. *Endocrinology* 131:327–30

13. Bondy, C., Werner, H., Roberts, C. T. Jr., LeRoith, D. 1992. Cellular

pattern of type-I insulin-like growth factor receptor gene expression during maturation of the rat brain: comparison with insulin-like growth factors I and II. *Neuroscience* 46:909–23

14. Bondy, C. A., Werner, H., Roberts, C. T. Jr., LeRoith, D. 1990. Cellular pattern of insulin-like growth factor-I (IGF-I) and type I IGF receptor gene expression in early organogenesis: comparison with IGF-II gene expression. *Mol. Endocrinol.* 4:1386–98

15. Bornfeldt, K. E., Arnqvist, H. J., Enberg, B., Mathews, L. S., Norstedt, G. 1989. Regulation of insulin-like growth factor-I and growth hormone receptor gene expression by diabetes and nutritional state in rat tissues. *J. Endocrinol.* 122: 651–56

16. Bourner, M. J., Busby, W. H., Siegel, N. R., Krivi, G. G., McCusker, R. H., et al. 1992. Cloning and sequence determination of bovine insulin-like growth factor binding protein-2 (IGFBP-2): comparison of its structural and functional properties with IGFBP-1. *J. Cell. Biochem.* 48:215–26

17. Brown, A. L., Rechler, M. M. 1990. Cloning of the rat insulin-like growth factor-binding protein-2 gene and identification of a functional promoter lacking a TATA box. *Mol. Endocrinol.* 4:2039–51

18. Burch, W. M., Correa, J., Shively, J. E., Powell, D. R. 1990. The 25-kilodalton insulin-like growth factor (IGF)-binding protein inhibits both basal and IGF-I-mediated growth of chick embryo pelvic cartilage in vitro. *J. Clin. Endocrinol. Metab.* 70:173–80

19. Camacho-Hubner, C., Busby, W. H. Jr., McCusker, R. H., Wright, G., Clemmons, D. R. 1992. Identification of the forms of insulin-like growth factor binding proteins produced by human fibroblasts and the mechanisms that regulate their secretion. *J. Biol. Chem.* 267:11949–56

20. Camacho-Hubner, C., McCusker, R. H., Clemmons, D. R. 1991. Secretion and biological actions of insulin-like growth factor binding proteins in two human tumor-derived cell lines in vitro. *J. Cell. Physiol.* 148:281–89

20a. Cantley, L. C., Auger, K. R., Carpenter, C., Duckworth, B., Graziani, A., et al. 1991. Oncogenes and signal transduction. *Cell* 64:281–302

21. Chen, T. L., Liu, F., Bates, R. L., Hintz, R. L. 1991. Further characterization of insulin-like-growth factor binding proteins in rat osteoblast-like cell cultures: modulation by 17 beta-

estradiol and human growth hormone. *Endocrinology* 128:2489–96

22. Cheung, P. T., Smith, E. P., Shimasaki, S., Ling, N., Chernausek, S. D. 1991. Characterization of an insulin-like growth factor binding protein (IGFBP-4) produced by the B104 rat neuronal cell line: chemical and biological properties and differential synthesis by sublines. *Endocrinology* 129:1006–15

23. Clemmons, D. R., Cascieri, M. A., Camacho-Hubner, C., McCusker, R. H., Bayne, M. L. 1990. Discrete alterations of the insulin-like growth factor I molecule which alter its affinity for insulin-like growth factor-binding proteins result in changes in bioactivity. *J. Biol. Chem.* 265:12210–16

24. Clemmons, D. R., Gardner, L. I. 1990. A factor contained in plasma is required for IGF binding protein-1 to potentiate the effect of IGF-I on smooth muscle cell DNA synthesis. *J. Cell. Physiol.* 145:129–35

25. Clemmons, D. R., Snyder, D. K., Busby, W. H. Jr. 1991. Variables controlling the secretion of insulin-like growth factor binding protein-2 in normal human subjects. *J. Clin. Endocrinol. Metab.* 73:727–33

26. Clemmons, D. R., Thissen, J. P., Maes, M., Ketelslegers, J. M., Underwood, L. E. 1989. Insulin-like growth factor-I (IGF-I) infusion into hypophysectomized or protein-deprived rats induces specific IGF-binding proteins in serum. *Endocrinology* 125:2967–72

27. Clemmons, D. R., Underwood, L. E. 1991. Nutritional regulation of IGF-I and IGF binding proteins. *Annu. Rev. Nutr.* 11:393–412

28. Cohick, W. S., Clemmons, D. R. 1991. Regulation of insulin-like growth factor binding protein synthesis and secretion in a bovine epithelial cell line. *Endocrinology* 129:1347–54

29. Cohick, W. S., McGuire, M. A., Clemmons, D. R., Bauman, D. E. 1992. Regulation of insulin-like growth factor-binding proteins in serum and lymph of lactating cows by somatotropin. *Endocrinol.* 130:1508–14

30. Condorelli, G., Formisano, P., Villone, G., Smith, R. J., Beguinot, F. 1989. Insulin and insulin-like growth factor I (IGF I) stimulate phosphorylation of a M_r 175,000 cytoskeleton-associated protein in intact FRTL5 cells. *J. Biol. Chem.* 264:12633–38

31. Conover, C. A. 1991. Glycosylation of insulin-like growth factor binding protein-3 (IGFBP-3) is not required for potentiation of IGF-I action: evidence for processing of cell-bound IGFBP-3. *Endocrinology* 129:3259–68

32. Conover, C. A., Ronk, M., Lombana, F., Powell, D. R. 1990. Structural and biological characterization of bovine insulin-like growth factor binding protein-3. *Endocrinology* 127:2795–803

33. Cubbage, M. L., Suwanichkul, A., Powell, D. R. 1989. Structure of the human chromosomal gene for the 25 kilodalton insulin-like growth factor binding protein. *Mol. Endocrinol.* 3:846–51

34. Cubbage, M. L., Suwanichkul, A., Powell, D. R. 1990. Insulin-like growth factor binding protein-3. Organization of the human chromosomal gene and demonstration of promoter activity. *J. Biol. Chem.* 265:12642–49

35. Cullen, K. J., Lippman, M. E., Chow, D., Hill, S., Rosen, N., et al. 1992. Insulin-like growth factor-II overexpression in MCF-7 cells induces phenotypic changes associated with malignant progression. *Mol. Endocrinol.* 6: 91–100

36. Daughaday, W. H., Rotwein, P. 1989. Insulin-like growth factors I and II. Peptide, messenger ribonucleic acid and gene structures, serum, and tissue concentrations. *Endocrinol. Rev.* 10: 68–91

37. Davenport, M. L., Clemmons, D. R., Miles, M. V., Camacho-Hubner, C., D'Ercole, A. J., et al. 1990. Regulation of serum insulin-like growth factor-I (IGF-I) and IGF binding proteins during rat pregnancy. *Endocrinology* 127: 1278–86

38. DeChiara, T. M., Efstratiadis, A., Robertson, E. J. 1990. A growth-deficiency phenotype in heterozygous mice carrying an insulin-like growth factor II gene disrupted by targeting. *Nature* 345:78–80

39. Donovan, S. M., Giudice, L. C., Murphy, L. J., Hintz, R. L., Rosenfeld, R. G. 1991. Maternal insulin-like growth factor-binding protein messenger ribonucleic acid during rat pregnancy. *Endocrinology* 129:3359–66

40. Erickson, G. F., Nakatani, A., Ling, N., Shimasaki, S. 1992. Localization of insulin-like growth factor-binding protein-5 messenger ribonucleic acid in rat ovaries during the estrous cycle. *Endocrinology* 130:1867–78

41. Ernst, C. W., McCusker, R. H., White, M. E. 1992. Gene expression and secretion of insulin-like growth factor-binding proteins during myoblast dif-

ferentiation. *Endocrinology* 130: 607–15

42. Ernst, M., Heath, J. K., Rodan, G. A. 1989. Estradiol effects on proliferation, messenger ribonucleic acid for collagen and insulin-like growth factor-I, and parathyroid hormone-stimulated adenylate cyclase activity in osteoblastic cells from calvariae and long bones. *Endocrinology* 125:825–33

43. Florini, J. R., Ewton, D. Z. 1990. Highly specific inhibition of IGF-I-stimulated differentiation by an antisense oligodeoxyribonucleotide to myogenin mRNA. No effects on other actions of IGF-I. *J. Biol. Chem.* 265: 13435–37

44. Florini, J. R., Ewton, D. Z., Roof, S. L. 1991. Insulin-like growth factor-I stimulates terminal myogenic differentiation by induction of myogenin gene expression. *Mol. Endocrinol.* 5:718–24

45. Florini, J. R., Magri, K. A., Ewton, D. Z., James, P. L., Grindstaff, K., et al. 1991. "Spontaneous" differentiation of skeletal myoblasts is dependent upon autocrine secretion of insulin-like growth factor-II. *J. Biol. Chem.* 266: 15917–23

46. Flyvbjerg, A., Bornfeldt, K. E., Orskov, H., Arnqvist, H. J. 1991. Effect of insulin-like growth factor I infusion on renal hypertrophy in experimental diabetes mellitus in rats. *Diabetologia* 34: 715–20

47. Forbes, B., Ballard, F. J., Wallace, J. C. 1990. An insulin-like growth factor-binding protein purified from medium conditioned by a human lung fibroblast cell line (He[39]L) has a novel N-terminal sequence. *J. Endocrinol.* 126:497–506

48. Frauman, A. G., Tsuzaki, S., Moses, A. C. 1989. The binding characteristics and biological effects in FRTL5 cells of placental protein-12, an insulin-like growth factor-binding protein purified from human amniotic fluid. *Endocrinology* 124:2289–96

49. Frost, J. P., Linda, T. 1991. Insulin-like growth factor-binding protein-1 is phosphorylated by cultured human endometrial stromal cells and multiple protein kinases in vitro. *J. Biol. Chem.* 266: 18082–88

50. Gargosky, S. E., Owens, P. C., Walton, P. E., Owens, J. A., Robinson, J. S., et al. 1991. Most of the circulating insulin-like growth factors-I and -II are present in the 150 kDa complex during human pregnancy. *J. Endocrinol.* 131: 491–97

51. Giudice, L. C., Farrell, E. M., Pham, H., Lamson, G., Rosenfeld, R. G. 1990. Insulin-like growth factor binding proteins in maternal serum throughout gestation and in the puerperium: effects of a pregnancy-associated serum protease activity. *J. Clin. Endocrinol. Metab.* 71:806–16

52. Glasscock, G. F., Hein, A. N., Miller, J. A., Hintz, R. L., Rosenfeld, R. G. 1992. Effects of continuous infusion of insulin-like growth factor I and II, alone and in combination with thyroxine or growth hormone, on the neonatal hypophysectomized rat. *Endocrinology* 130:203–10

53. Guler, H. P., Eckardt, K. U., Zapf, J., Bauer, C., Froesch, E. R. 1989. Insulin-like growth factor I increases glomerular filtration rate and renal plasma flow in man. *Acta Endocrinol. Copenhagen* 121:101–6

54. Guler, H. P., Zapf, J., Schmid, C., Froesch, E. R. 1989. Insulin-like growth factors I and II in healthy man. Estimations of half-lives and production rates. *Acta. Endocrinol. Copenhagen* 121:753–58

55. Hammerman, M. R. 1989. The growth hormone-insulin-like growth factor axis in kidney. *Am. J.Physiol.* 257:F503–14

56. Hernandez, E. R., Hurwitz, A., Vera, A., Pellicer, A., Adashi, E. Y., et al. 1992. Expression of the genes encoding the insulin-like growth factors and their receptors in the human ovary. *J. Clin. Endocrinol. Metab.* 74:419–25

57. Hernandez, E. R., Roberts, C. T. Jr., LeRoith, D., Adashi, E. Y. 1989. Rat ovarian insulin-like growth factor I (IGF-I) gene expression is granulosa cell-selective: 5'-untranslated mRNA variant representation and hormonal regulation. *Endocrinology* 125:572–74

58. Hernandez, E. R., Roberts, C. T. Jr., Hurwitz, A., LeRoith, D., Adashi, E. Y. 1990. Rat ovarian insulin-like growth factor II gene expression is theca-interstitial cell-exclusive: hormonal regulation and receptor distribution. *Endocrinology* 127:3249–51

59. Jones, J. I., D'Ercole, A. J., Camacho-Hubner, C., Clemmons, D. R. 1991. Phosphorylation of insulin-like growth factor (IGF)-binding protein 1 in cell culture and in vivo: effects on affinity for IGF-I. *Proc. Natl. Acad. Sci. USA* 88:7481–85

60. Kiefer, M. C., Ioh, R. S., Bauer, D. M., Zapf, J. 1991. Molecular cloning of a new human insulin-like growth factor binding protein. *Biochem. Biophys. Res. Commun.* 176:219–25

61. Kiefer, M. C., Masiarz, F. R., Bauer, D. M., Zapf, J. 1991. Identification and molecular cloning of two new 30-kDa insulin-like growth factor binding proteins isolated from adult human serum. *J. Biol. Chem.* 266:9043–49

62. Kobayashi, S., Clemmons, D. R., Venkatachalam, M. A. 1991. Colocalization of insulin-like growth factor-binding protein with insulin-like growth factor I. *Am. J.Physiol.* 261:F22–28

63. Koistinen, R., Suikkari, A. M., Titinen, A., Kontula, K., Seppala, M. 1990. Human granulosa cells contain insulin-like growth factor binding protein (IGFBP) mRNA. *Clin. Endocrinol.* 32:635–40

64. Lammers, R., Gray, A., Schlessinger, J., Ullrich, A. 1989. Differential signalling potential of insulin- and IGF-1-receptor cytoplasmic domains. *EMBO J.* 8:1369–75

65. Latour, D., Mohan, S., Linkhart, T. A., Baylink, D. J., Strong, D. D. 1990. Inhibitory insulin-like growth factor-binding protein: cloning, complete sequence, and physiological regulation. *Mol. Endocrinol.* 4:1806–14

66. Lemmey, A. B., Martin, A. A., Read, L. C., Tomas, F. M., Owens, P. C., et al. 1991. IGF-I and the truncated analogue des-(1–3)IGF-I enhance growth in rats after gut resection. *Am. J. Physiol.* 260:E213–19

67. Lewitt, M. S., Baxter, R. C. 1991. Insulin-like growth factor-binding protein-1: a role in glucose counterregulation? *Mol. Cell. Endocrinol.* 79:C147–52

68. Lewitt, M. S., Denyer, G. S., Cooney, G. J., Baxter, R. C. 1991. Insulin-like growth factor-binding protein-1 modulates blood glucose levels. *Endocrinology* 129:2254–256

69. Linkhart, T. A., Keffer, M. J. 1991. Differential regulation of insulin-like growth factor-I (IGF-I) and IGF-II release from cultured neonatal mouse calvaria by parathyroid hormone, transforming growth factor-beta, and 1,25-dihydroxyvitamin D3. *Endocrinology* 128:1511–18

70. Lowe, W. L. Jr. 1991. Biological actions of the insulin-like growth factors. In *Insulin-Like Growth Factors: Molecular and Cellular Aspects,* ed. D. LeRoith, pp. 49–85. Boca Raton: CRC Press

71. Lowe, W. L. Jr., Adamo, M., Werner, H., Roberts, C. T., Jr., LeRoith, D. 1989. Regulation by fasting of rat insulin-like growth factor I and its receptor. Effects on gene expression and binding. *J. Clin. Invest.* 84:619–26

72. Lu, K., Campisi, J. 1992. Ras proteins are essential and selective for the action of insulin-like growth factor 1 late in the G1 phase of the cell cycle in BALB/c murine fibroblasts. *Proc. Natl. Acad. Sci. USA* 89:3889–93

73. Luo, J., Reid, R. E., Murphy, L. J. 1990. Dexamethasone increases hepatic insulin-like growth factor binding protein-1 (IGFBP-1) mRNA and serum IGFBP-1 concentrations in the rat. *Endocrinology* 127:1456–62

74. Luo, J. M., Murphy, L. J. 1990. Regulation of insulin-like growth factor binding protein-3 expression by dexamethasone. *Mol. Cell. Endocrinol.* 74:213–19

75. Macaulay, V. M. 1992. Insulin-like growth factors and cancer. *Br. J. Cancer* 65:311–20

76. Mamula, P. W., Goldfine, I. D. 1992. Cloning and characterization of the human insulin-like growth factor-I receptor gene 5'-flanking region. *DNA Cell. Biol.* 11:43–50

77. Martin, A. A., Tomas, F. M., Owens, P. C., Knowles, S. E., Ballard, F. J., et al. 1991. IGF-I and its variant, des-(1–3)IGF-I, enhance growth in rats with reduced renal mass. *Am. J. Physiol.* 261:F626–33

78. Martin, J. L., Baxter, R. C. 1991. Transforming growth factor-beta stimulates production of insulin-like growth factor-binding protein-3 by human skin fibroblasts. *Endocrinology* 128:1425–33

79. Martin, J. L., Willetts, K. E., Baxter, R. C. 1990. Purification and properties of a novel insulin-like growth factor-II binding protein from transformed human fibroblasts. *J. Biol. Chem.* 265:4124–30

80. Mathews, L. S., Hammer, R. E., Behringer, R. R., D'Ercole, A. J., Bell, G. I., et al. 1988. Growth enhancement of transgenic mice expressing human insulin-like growth factor I. *Endocrinology* 123:2827–33

81. McCarthy, T. L., Centrella, M., Canalis, E. 1990. Cyclic AMP induces insulin-like growth factor I synthesis in osteoblast-enriched cultures. *J. Biol. Chem.* 265:15353–56

82. McCarthy, T. L., Centrella, M., Canalis, E. 1992. Constitutive synthesis of insulin-like growth factor-II by primary osteoblast-enriched cultures from fetal rat calvariae. *Endocrinology* 130:1303–8

83. McClain, D. A., Maegawa, H., Thies,

R. S., Olefsky, J. M. 1990. Dissection of the growth versus metabolic effects of insulin and insulin-like growth factor-I in transfected cells expressing kinase-defective human insulin receptors. *J. Biol. Chem.* 265:1678–82

84. McCusker, R. H., Busby, W. H., Dehoff, M. H., Camacho-Hubner, C., Clemmons, D. R. 1991. Insulin-like growth factor (IGF) binding to cell monolayers is directly modulated by the addition of IGF-binding proteins. *Endocrinology* 129:939–49

85. McCusker, R. H., Camacho-Hubner, C., Bayne, M. L., Cascieri, M. A., Clemmons, D. R. 1990. Insulin-like growth factor (IGF) binding to human fibroblast and glioblastoma cells: the modulating effect of cell released IGF binding proteins (IGFBPs). *J. Cell. Physiol.* 144:244–53

86. McCusker, R. H., Camacho-Hubner, C., Clemmons, D. R. 1989. Identification of the types of insulin-like growth factor- binding proteins that are secreted by muscle cells in vitro. *J. Biol. Chem.* 264:7795–800

87. McCusker, R. H., Clemmons, D. R. 1992. The insulin-like growth factor binding proteins: structure and biological function. In *The Insulin-Like Growth Factors: Structure and Biological Function*, ed. P. N. Schofield, pp. 110–50. Oxford: Oxford Univ. Press

88. McCusker, R. H., Cohick, W. S., Busby, W. H., Clemmons, D. R. 1991. Evaluation of the developmental and nutritional changes in porcine insulin-like growth factor-binding protein-1 and -2 serum levels by immunoassay. *Endocrinology* 129:2631–38

89. Mohan, S., Bautista, C. M., Wergedal, J., Baylink, D. J. 1989. Isolation of an inhibitory insulin-like growth factor (IGF) binding protein from bone cell-conditioned medium: a potential local regulator of IGF action. *Proc. Natl. Acad. Sci. USA* 86:8338–42

90. Moxham, C. P., Duronio, V., Jacobs, S. 1989. Insulin-like growth factor I receptor beta-subunit heterogeneity. Evidence for hybrid tetramers composed of insulin- like growth factor I and insulin receptor heterodimers. *J. Biol. Chem.* 264:13238–44

91. Mulroney, S. E., Haramati, A., Werner, H., Bondy, C., Roberts, C. T. Jr., et al. 1992. Altered expression of insulin-like growth factor-I (IGF-I) and IGF receptor genes after unilateral nephrectomy in immature rats. *Endocrinology* 130:249–56

92. Murayama, Y., Okamoto, T., Ogata, E., Asano, T., Iiri, T., et al. 1990. Distinctive regulation of the functional linkage between the human cation-independent mannose 6-phosphate receptor and GTP-binding proteins by insulin-like growth factor II and mannose 6-phosphate. *J. Biol. Chem.* 265:17456–62

93. Murphy, L. J., Ghahary, A. 1990. Uterine insulin-like growth factor-1: regulation of expression and its role in estrogen-induced uterine proliferation. *Endocrinol. Rev.* 11:443–53

94. Murphy, L. M., Seneviratne, C., Ballejo, G., Croze, F., Kennedy, T. G. 1990. Identification and characterization of a rat decidual insulin-like growth factor binding protein complementary DNA. *Mol. Endocrinol.* 4:329–36

95. Nakatani, A., Shimasaki, S., Erickson, G. F., Ling, N. 1991. Tissue-specific expression of four insulin-like growth factor- binding proteins (1, 2, 3, and 4) in the rat ovary. *Endocrinology* 129:1521–29

96. Nilsson, A., Carlsson, B., Isgaard, J., Isaksson, O. G., Rymo, L. 1990. Regulation by GH of insulin-like growth factor-I mRNA expression in rat epiphyseal growth plate as studied with in-situ hybridization. *J. Endocrinol.* 125:67–74

97. Nishimoto, I., Murayama, Y., Katada, T., Ui, M., Ogata, E. 1989. Possible direct linkage of insulin-like growth factor-II receptor with guanine nucleotide-binding proteins. *J. Biol. Chem.* 264:14029–38

98. Nissley, P., Kiess, W., Sklar, M. 1991. The insulin-like growth factor-II/mannose 6-phosphate receptor. See Ref. 70, pp. 111–50

99. Okamoto, T., Katada, T., Murayama, Y., Ui, M., Ogata, E., et al. 1990. A simple structure encodes G protein-activating function of the IGF-II/mannose 6-phosphate receptor. *Cell* 62:709–17

100. Okamoto, T., Nishimoto, I. 1991. Analysis of stimulation-G protein subunit coupling by using active insulin-like growth factor II receptor peptide. *Proc. Natl. Acad. Sci. USA* 88:8020–23

101. Ooi, G. T., Orlowski, C. C., Brown, A. L., Becker, R. E., Unterman, T. G., et al. 1990. Different tissue distribution and hormonal regulation of messenger RNAs encoding rat insulin-like growth factor-binding proteins-1 and -2. *Mol. Endocrinol.* 4:321–28

102. Orlowski, C. C., Brown, A. L., Ooi,

G. T., Yang, Y. W., Tseng, L. Y., et al. 1990. Tissue, developmental, and metabolic regulation of messenger ribonucleic acid encoding a rat insulin-like growth factor- binding protein. *Endocrinology* 126:644–52

103. Orlowski, C. C., Ooi, G. T., Brown, D. R., Yang, Y. W., Tseng, L. Y., et al. 1991. Insulin rapidly inhibits insulin-like growth factor-binding protein-1 gene expression in H4-II-E rat hepatoma cells. *Mol. Endocrinol.* 5:1180–87

104. Price, W. A., Stiles, A. D., Moats-Staats, B. M. 1992. Gene expression of insulin-like growth factors (IGFs), the type I IGF receptor, and IGF-binding proteins in dexamethasone-induced fetal growth retardation. *Endocrinology* 130:1424–32

105. Rogers, S. A., Hammerman, M. R. 1989. Mannose 6-phosphate potentiates insulin-like growth factor II-stimulated inositol trisphosphate production in proximal tubular basolateral membranes. *J. Biol. Chem.* 264:4273–76

106. Roghani, M., Lassarre, C., Zapf, J., Povoa, G., Binoux, M. 1991. Two insulin-like growth factor (IGF)-binding proteins are responsible for the selective affinity for IGF-II of cerebrospinal fluid binding proteins. *J. Clin. Endocrinol. Metab.* 73:658–66

107. Rosenfeld, R. G., Lamson, G., Pham, H., Oh, Y., Conover, C., et al. 1990. Insulinlike growth factor-binding proteins. *Recent. Prog. Horm. Res.* 46:99–159

108. Rosenthal, S. M., Brunetti, A., Brown, E. J., Mamula, P. W., Goldfine, I. D. 1991. Regulation of insulin-like growth factor (IGF) I receptor expression during muscle cell differentiation. Potential autocrine role of IGF-II. *J. Clin. Invest.* 87:1212–19

109. Ross, M., Francis, G. L., Szabo, L., Wallace, J. C., Ballard, F. J. 1989. Insulin-like growth factor (IGF)-binding proteins inhibit the biological activities of IGF-1 and IGF-2 but not des-(1–3)-IGF-1. *Biochem. J.* 258:267–72

109a. Rothenberg, P. L., Lane, W. S., Karasik, A., Backer, J., White, M., et al. 1991. Purification and partial sequence analysis of pp185, the major cellular substrate of the insulin receptor tyrosine kinase. *J. Biol. Chem.* 266:8302–11

110. Schalch, D. S., Yang, H., Ney, D. M., DiMarchi, R. D. 1989. Infusion of human insulin-like growth factor I (IGF-I) into malnourished rats reduces hepatic IGF-I mRNA abundance. *Biochem. Biophys. Res. Commun.* 160:795–800

111. Schmid, C., Zapf, J., Froesch, E. R. 1989. Production of carrier proteins for insulin-like growth factors (IGFs) by rat osteoblastic cells. Regulation by IGF I and cortisol. *FEBS Lett.* 244:328–32

112. Shimasaki, S., Gao, L., Shimonaka, M., Ling, N. 1991. Isolation and molecular cloning of insulin-like growth factor- binding protein-6. *Mol. Endocrinol.* 5:938–48

113. Shimasaki, S., Shimonaka, M., Zhang, H. P., Ling, N. 1991. Identification of five different insulin-like growth factor binding proteins (IGFBPs) from adult rat serum and molecular cloning of a novel IGFBP-5 in rat and human. *J. Biol. Chem.* 266:10646–53

114. Shimasaki, S., Uchiyama, F., Shimonaka, M., Ling, N. 1990. Molecular cloning of the cDNAs encoding a novel insulin-like growth factor-binding protein from rat and human. *Mol. Endocrinol.* 4:1451–58

115. Shimonaka, M., Schroeder, R., Shimasaki, S., Ling, N. 1989. Identification of a novel binding protein for insulin-like growth factors in adult rat serum. *Biochem. Biophys. Res. Commun.* 165:189–95

116. Snyder, D. K., Clemmons, D. R. 1990. Insulin-dependent regulation of insulin-like growth factor-binding protein-1. *J. Clin. Endocrinol. Metab.* 71:1632–36

117. Soos, M. A., Siddle, K. 1989. Immunological relationships between receptors for insulin and insulin-like growth factor I. Evidence for structural heterogeneity of insulin-like growth factor I receptors involving hybrids with insulin receptors. *Biochem. J.* 263:553–63

118. Soos, M. A., Whittaker, J., Lammers, R., Ullrich, A., Siddle, K. 1990. Receptors for insulin and insulin-like growth factor-I can form hybrids. *Biochem. J.* 270:383–90

119. Straus, D. S., Ooi, G. T., Orlowski, C. C., Rechler, M. M. 1991. Expression of the genes for insulin-like growth factor-I (IGF-I), IGF-II, and IGF-binding proteins-1 and -2 in fetal rat under conditions of intrauterine growth retardation caused by maternal fasting. *Endocrinology* 128:518–25

120. Straus, D. S., Takemoto, C. D. 1990. Effect of fasting on insulin-like growth factor-I (IGF-I) and growth hormone receptor mRNA levels and IGF-I gene

transcription in rat liver. *Mol. Endocrinol.* 4:91–100

121. Straus, D. S., Takemoto, C. D. 1990. Effect of dietary protein deprivation on insulin-like growth factor (IGF)-I and -II, IGF binding protein-2, and serum albumin gene expression in rat. *Endocrinology* 127:1849–60

122. Suikkari, A. M., Baxter, R. C. 1991. Insulin-like growth factor (IGF) binding protein-3 in pregnancy serum binds native IGF-I but not iodo-IGF-I. *J. Clin. Endocrinol. Metab.* 73:1377–79

123. Suikkari, A. M., Baxter, R. C. 1992. Insulin-like growth factor-binding protein-3 is functionally normal in pregnancy serum. *J. Clin. Endocrinol. Metab.* 74:177–83

124. Suikkari, A. M., Koivisto, V. A., Koistinen, R., Seppala, M., Yki-Jarvinen, H. 1989. Dose-response characteristics for suppression of low molecular weight plasma insulin-like growth factor-binding protein by insulin. *J. Clin. Endocrinol. Metab.* 68: 135–40

124a. Sun, X. J., Rothenberg, P., Kahn, C. R., Backer, J. M., Araki, E., et al. 1991. Structure of the insulin receptor substrate IRS-1 defines a unique signal transduction protein. *Nature* 352:73–77

125. Sundaresan, S., Francke, U. 1989. Insulin-like growth factor I receptor gene is concordant with c-Fos protooncogene and mouse chromosome 7 in somatic cell hybrids. *Somat. Cell Mol. Genet.* 15:373–76

126. Suwanichkul, A., Cubbage, M. L., Powell, D. R. 1990. The promoter of the human gene for insulin-like growth factor binding protein-1. Basal promoter activity in HEP G2 cells depends upon liver factor B1. *J. Biol. Chem.* 265: 21185–93

127. Thissen, J. P., Underwood, L. E., Maiter, D., Maes, M., Clemmons, D. R., et al. 1991. Failure of insulin-like growth factor-I (IGF-I) infusion to promote growth in protein-restricted rats despite normalization of serum IGF-I concentrations. *Endocrinology* 128: 885–90

128. Tollefsen, S. E., Lajara, R., McCusker, R. H., Clemmons, D. R., Rotwein, P. 1989. Insulin-like growth factors (IGF) in muscle development. Expression of IGF-I, the IGF-I receptor, and an IGF binding protein during myoblast differentiation. *J. Biol. Chem.* 264: 13810–17

129. Tollefsen, S. E., Sadow, J. L., Rotwein, P. 1989. Coordinate expression of insulin-like growth factor II and its receptor during muscle differentiation. *Proc. Natl. Acad. Sci. USA* 86:1543–47

130. Ui, M., Shimonaka, M., Shimasaki, S., Ling, N. 1989. An insulin-like growth factor-binding protein in ovarian follicular fluid blocks follicle-stimulating hormone-stimulated steroid production by ovarian granulosa cells. *Endocrinology* 125:912–16

131. Unterman, T. G., Oehler, D. T., Murphy, L. J., Lacson, R. G. 1991. Multihormonal regulation of insulin-like growth factor-binding protein-1 in rat H4IIE hepatoma cells: the dominant role of insulin. *Endocrinology* 128: 2693–701

132. VandeHaar, M. J., Moats-Staats, B. M., Davenport, M. L., Walker, J. L., Ketelslegers, J. M., et al. 1991. Reduced serum concentrations of insulin-like growth factor-I (IGF-I) in protein-restricted growing rats are accompanied by reduced IGF-I mRNA levels in liver and skeletal muscle. *J. Endocrinol.* 130:305–12

133. Werner, H., Stannard, B., Bach, M. A., LeRoith, D., Roberts, C. T. Jr. 1990. Cloning and characterization of the proximal promoter region of the rat insulin-like growth factor I (IGF-I) receptor gene. *Biochem. Biophys. Res. Commun.* 169:1021–27

134. Werner, H., Woloschak, M., Adamo, M., Shen-Orr, Z., Roberts, C. T. Jr., et al. 1989. Developmental regulation of the rat insulin-like growth factor I receptor gene. *Proc. Natl. Acad. Sci. USA* 86:7451–55

135. Wood, T. L., Brown, A. L., Rechler, M. M., Pintar, J. E. 1990. The expression pattern of an insulin-like growth factor (IGF)- binding protein gene is distinct from IGF-II in the midgestational rat embryo. *Mol. Endocrinol.* 4: 1257–63

136. Zapf, J., Hauri, C., Waldvogel, M., Futo, E., Hasler, H., et al. 1989. Recombinant human insulin-like growth factor I induces its own specific carrier protein in hypophysectomized and diabetic rats. *Proc. Natl. Acad. Sci. USA* 86:3813–17

137. Zapf, J., Kiefer, M., Merryweather, J., Musiarz, F., Bauer, D., et al. 1990. Isolation from adult human serum of four insulin-like growth factor (IGF) binding proteins and molecular cloning of one of them that is increased by IGF I administration and in extrapancreatic tumor hypoglycemia. *J. Biol. Chem.* 265:14892–98

Annu. Rev. Physiol. 1993. 55:155–79

MECHANICAL FACTORS IN LUNG LIQUID DISTRIBUTION

Stephen J. Lai-Fook

Center for Biomedical Engineering, University of Kentucky,
Lexington, Kentucky 40506

KEY WORDS: interstitial compartments, interstitial pressure, alveolar liquid, microvascular
fluid exchange

INTRODUCTION

The general principles of microvascular fluid exchange that apply to the lung are similar to those of all body organs. Fluid filtration across the pulmonary capillary membrane is governed by osmotic and fluid pressures of interstitial liquid and capillary blood according to the Starling equation. The degree of interstitial hydration results from a balance between the net filtration and the rate of clearance by lymphatics. Homeostasis in interstitial volume is maintained by compensations in osmotic and fluid pressure gradients and by changes in lymphatic absorption. These principles apply to the lung treated as a single homogeneous unit (38). However, the lung has unique properties with regard to fluid exchange because of its tissue-air interfaces and its ability to change volume with breathing. These properties result in a heterogeneous interstitium in which interstitial pressure is not uniformly distributed throughout the lung. Because the lung is air-filled, its density is much less than that of a liquid, and the gravitational force results in vertical variations in lung expansion, blood flow and fluid filtration. These variations may affect regional lung water.

The distribution of extravascular lung water is uniform throughout the normal lung because the lymphatic clearance matches the normal filtration. However, during abnormally high filtration, lymphatic clearance becomes inadequate and excess microvascular filtrate results in interstitial swelling, alveolar flooding, and eventually impaired gas exchange. This review focuses on the mechanical factors, such as interstitial pressure, resistance, and compliance, that determine the movement of liquid within the lung interstitium

155

0066–4278/93/0315–0155$02.00

and how these factors interact to determine the distribution of extravascular lung during edema formation. General reviews of lung fluid balance have appeared elsewhere (101, 106).

INTERSTITIAL COMPARTMENTS

Excess liquid can accumulate in three interstitial compartments in the lung (103, 110): the interstitium around capillaries in the alveolar wall (alveolar vessels), the loose connective (perivascular) interstitium around large blood vessels that includes arterioles and venules (extra-alveolar vessels), and the alveolar air spaces. The perivascular interstitium is contiguous with the interstitium surrounding capillaries in the alveolar walls. Liquid may pass directly between the periarterial and perivenous interstitial spaces via anastomoses (69).

On a macroscopic scale encompassing several alveoli, the amount of water in the interstitial space is uniformly distributed in the normal lung. The wet-to-dry weight ratio of the normal lung is constant among species, ~ 4.7 (101). The interstitium surrounding alveolar wall capillaries varies from relatively thick parts to vanishingly thin parts (110). The interstitial cuff thickness surrounding extra-alveolar vessels as measured in the dog is $\sim 1\%$ of vessel diameter, but it can increase more than 100-fold during edema formation (78, 79). The expandable interstitium during pulmonary edema formation consists of the thick parts in alveolar walls, the interstitial cuffs around extra-alveolar vessels greater than ~ 100 μm in diameter, and the bronchi (18, 19). The liquid that lines the alveolar surface is extremely thin. In lungs fixed by vascular perfusion, the alveolar liquid lining layer appears to be continuous; its thickness is ~ 0.1 μm on the flat part of the alveolar wall and is somewhat greater in corners (110). No reliable information on the amount of free alveolar liquid exists. Electron microscopic studies of frozen guinea pig lungs indicate that the liquid lining peripheral airways near alveolar ducts is ~ 6 μm thick at both functional residual capacity (FRC) and total lung capacity (TLC) (118), similar to the thickness of the liquid lining the larger airways (120).

INTERCOMPARTMENTAL RELATIONSHIPS

Sequence of Edema Formation

The following sequence of pulmonary edema formation reported by Staub and co-workers some 25 years ago (103) has formed the conceptual framework of numerous studies from which a mechanical theory of liquid distribution in edematous lungs has emerged. Fluid that leaks across capillaries flows into the alveolar corners where it is absorbed by lymphatic vessels located near alveolar junctions (65). The lymphatics course through the interstitium around extra-alveolar vessels and carry the fluid out of the lung at the lung hilum. During pulmonary edema formation, the capacity of the lymphatics is overwhelmed and excess microvascular filtrate first appears as liquid cuffs around extra-alveolar blood vessels and bronchi. Perivascular filling occurs from alveolar junctions parallel to lymph flow (121). This is followed by alveolar wall interstitial thickening and alveolar edema. Although edema has been observed by electron microscopy in the alveolar wall interstitium during the initial stages of cuff formation (20), its relation to perivascular cuff volume has not been determined. Alveolar edema first appears after the lung has gained 30–50% of its initial weight in extravascular water (50). Alveolar edema occurs by a process of quantal filling of alveoli (all or none). In addition to absorption by lymphatics and the circulation, edema fluid is cleared by bulk flow into the pleural space (10).

Mechanisms of Alveolar Flooding

It is uncertain why alveolar flooding occurs in view of the fact that the alveolar epithelium is in general a barrier that is tight enough (pore size of $\sim$ 1 nm radius) to restrict the passage of plasma proteins (96, 105a, 106). Alveolar edema fluid has a protein concentration near to that of plasma; this indicates that interstitial liquid leaks into the alveolar air spaces across a system of large pores (102). One possibility is that parts of the airway epithelium have large pores, and liquid leaks through these pores only after interstitial pressure increases with hydration. Terminal bronchioles have been proposed as the leakage site (102). However, recent anatomical studies using fluorescent probes locate leaks at the alveolar wall level (14). Another possibility is that the increase in interstitial pressure due to interstitial edema expands the normally tight alveolar epithelium (106). Studies of the clearance of albumin solutions deposited in lobular segments show that the albumin concentration of the alveolar liquid increases as the liquid is cleared from the air spaces (75). Clearance takes place against an increasing osmotic pressure gradient, which suggests an active ionic pump as the primary mechanism for the removal of excess alveolar liquid. Accordingly, the large epithelial pores that allow the passage of protein molecules during alveolar flooding are not essential for the clearance of albumin solution from lobular segments. A transient increase in epithelial pore size from $\sim$ 1 to 4 nm radius, a value sufficiently large to allow protein molecules to pass, has been described in the newborn lung (23). This effect may be related to the degree of interstitial hydration, similar to the conditions that exist in the adult lung during alveolar flooding.

Growth of Perivascular Liquid Cuffs

In liquid-filled dog lungs, perivascular interstitial cuff volume as a fraction of vascular volume increases with the inflation pressure (15, 32). Based on the compliance of the surrounding lung parenchyma (64, 99), interstitial compliance is inversely proportional to the inflation pressure. If interstitial pressure initially were to equal pleural pressure, cuff size as a fraction of vessel size would be constant at all inflation pressures. However, perivascular interstitial pressure of large vessels falls below pleural pressure with lung inflation (36), so that changes in interstitial pressure with edema formation should be greater at higher inflation pressures, and cuff size should increase with lung inflation.

The growth of perivascular liquid cuffs has been studied extensively in liquid-filled dog, sheep, and rabbit lungs by Conhaim and co-workers (15–19, 67). Interstitium surrounding peripheral vessels (<0.5 mm diameter) does not expand homogeneously. A large fraction of these vessels do not form cuffs, and vessels smaller than 0.1 mm diameter are devoid of cuffs. The latter behavior probably reflects the fact that perivascular pressure is close to alveolar air pressure, a result of the lack of alveolar wall attachments to the vessel wall. These studies indicate that interstitial cuffs grow to a maximum size at rates that are species-dependent. Cuffs around smaller vessels grow earlier followed by cuffs around large vessels. The time constants of cuff growth are 3, 9, and 60 min for the dog, sheep, and rabbit lungs, respectively. The maximum cuff area as a fraction of vessel area is independent of vessel size and reaches values of 3.5, 2.5, and 1.2 for the dog, sheep, and rabbit lung, respectively. At 90% TLC, the maximum interstitial cuff volume is 5–9% of the air space volume in dog (19) and sheep lungs (18). The albumin concentration of cuff liquid is 37% of alveolar liquid concentration and independent of the inflation pressure (16). Thus the airway epithelium restricts the passage of plasma proteins, but the epithelial permeability does not change with lung inflation (17). Tracer experiments suggest a multiple pore system (1–400 nm) for the alveolar epithelium (16).

In liquid-filled lungs perivascular cuffs attain their maximum size when interstitial pressure reaches the alveolar or inflation pressure. This was substantiated in liquid-inflated dog and rabbit lungs in which the interstitial pressure around a surface vein measured at the lung hilum equilibrated to values near the alveolar pressure (15, 67). By contrast, in the air-filled lung, interstitial pressure equilibrates to a value below the alveolar air pressure (7, 53, 68). This value depends on alveolar surface tension (Figure 1). Thus cuff

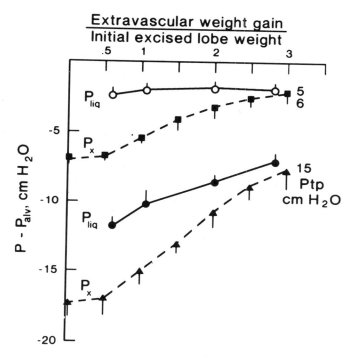

Figure 1 Comparison between perivascular (perivenous) pressure (P_x) measured at the lung hilum and alveolar liquid pressure (P_{liq}) measured in isolated dog lung lobes is shown plotted vs W/Wo, ratio of lung weight to initial lung weight. Transpulmonary pressures were held constant at 5–6 cm H_2O and 15 cm H_2O. P_x and P_{liq} were measured by the micropuncture method. Reproduced from Lai-Fook & Beck (55) with permission.

size in the air-filled lung depends on the response in interstitial pressure to the edema formation. The protein concentration measured in the hilar perivascular and perivenous interstitium shows marked differences, indicating a heterogeneous interstitium (92).

Cuff Growth in the Newborn Lung

The growth of perivascular cuffs has been studied in the rabbit as it changes from the fetal liquid-filled state to the air-filled state after birth (8, 9). Lung liquid is reduced just before birth, which serves to reduce both the amount of alveolar liquid and the perivascular cuff volume so that the reduced alveolar liquid can be absorbed into the interstitium after birth (8). Perivascular cuffs attain a maximum size at 30 min after birth and decrease to the prenatal size by 6 hr (1, 9). This relatively slow clearance of lung liquid contrasts to the more rapid clearance found in other studies (73). Alveolar liquid is partially cleared by transepithelial reabsorption via active sodium (Na^+) ionic pumps into the circulation. The role of active transport mechanisms in the production and clearance of alveolar liquid has been reviewed by Strang (104). The increase in perivascular cuffs after birth is attributed to the effect of lung inflation, analogous to the behavior of adult lungs (9). How this is accomplished in fetal and newborn lungs in which extra-alveolar vascular volume becomes compressed with lung inflation is uncertain (74, 109). Based on a maximum perivascular cuff volume of 5–9% of the airspace volume (18, 19), the perivascular interstitium accommodates only a small fraction of the alveolar liquid after birth. From observations in adult lungs, cuff growth in the neonatal lung may be strongly species-dependent. For example, in the liquid-inflated adult rabbit lung, the time constant of cuff growth is ~ 60 min (67), much greater than that of the adult sheep and dog lungs (18, 19). By contrast, alveolar liquid absorption in the adult rabbit lung is faster than in the adult sheep and dog lungs (5, 31, 75).

INTERSTITIAL PRESSURE

Theoretical Basis

Interstitial pressure has been a topic of controversy because there has been a lack of a theoretical basis for reconciling measurements made in subcutaneous tissue that showed a negative interstitial pressure relative to the boundary or surface (atmospheric) pressure (37). In the lung, the concept of a negative interstitial pressure has gained wide acceptance because passive forces resulting from both lung static recoil and alveolar surface tension act in a direction to lower interstitial pressure below the ambient pressure (alveolar air pressure). The transmission of forces within the interstitium is described within the context of a conservative system, in which the interstitium is considered a porous material (94). The laws governing force equilibrium apply. Interstitial fluid pressure results from a balance among the forces acting in the interstitial liquid, in the interstitial solid, and on the interstitial boundaries. The pressure developed in the liquid is balanced by the isotropic normal stress (solid tissue pressure) in the solid tissue. A negative interstitial fluid pressure can be generated either by reducing the boundary pressure or by decreasing the volume of the interstitium surrounded by a compliant boundary. A negative interstitial fluid pressure in equilibrium with boundary forces requires the interstitial tissue elements to be in tension. By contrast, a negative interstitial pressure relative to the boundary pressure requires the tissue elements to be in compression (77). Compressive tissue force has been postulated to result from lymphatic suction (38).

Choice of the Reference Pressure

The reference pressure for interstitial fluid pressure is chosen in relation to the particular force acting on the boundary of each compartment. The interstitium around capillaries is acted upon by the alveolar air pressure via a thin film of surfactant lining alveolar surfaces. Surface tension of the air-liquid interface reduces the alveolar air pressure acting on curved alveolar walls. Hence the reference pressure for both the alveolar wall interstitial pressure and alveolar liquid pressure is the alveolar air pressure.

By contrast, the pressure exerted on structures much larger than an alveolus is the surface-averaged pressure, which equals the difference between the alveolar air pressure and the pressure exerted by the connecting alveolar membranes (76). At the pleural surface, the surface-averaged pressure is the pleural pressure. Within the lung, the applied pressure acting on regions that are surrounded by uniformly expanded parenchyma is the pleural pressure. The pressure exerted by the lung parenchyma on structures, such as blood vessels, may differ from the pleural pressure to the extent that the lung parenchyma is distorted locally. Accordingly, the reference pressure for the interstitial pressure around extra-alveolar vessels is chosen as the pleural pressure.

Measurement of Interstitial Fluid Pressure

Since the original experiments of Guyton and co-workers (77), who estimated interstitial fluid pressure from perforated capsules implanted in dog lungs, considerable advances have been made with the use of open-ended needles, wick catheters, and the micropipette-servonulling method. Large catheters (1 mm diameter) inserted in the interstitial spaces around large blood vessels in isolated lungs result in a reliable measure of interstitial pressure because the perivascular interstitium has a relatively large compliance and the volume expansion caused by insertion of the catheter has only a small effect on interstitial pressure. The micropipette method is necessary for measuring perivascular interstitial pressure around subpleural vessels (20–60 μm diameter). Micropipettes can be inserted only in the interstitium just beneath the pleural surface. Thus the surface pressure acting on the interstitium in regions within the lung parenchyma may be different from the surface pressure acting on the subpleural interstitium. A limitation of the micropuncture method is the uncertainty of the location of the micropipette tip within the lung parenchyma.

Alveolar Wall Interstitial Fluid Pressure

The interstitial pressure around capillaries in the alveolar wall has not been directly measured because the size of the micropipette (2–5 μm tip diameter) is much larger than the thickness (~ 0.1 μm) of alveolar wall interstitium (110). Wiederhielm (112) has measured subcutaneous interstitial pressure with 0.1 μm tip diameter micropipettes.

On theoretical grounds the pressure within the alveolar wall should be equal to the alveolar gas pressure (P_{alv}) minus the effects of any alveolar wall tension and alveolar surface tension (13, 38, 101). Using the Laplace equation as it is applied to a spherical membrane, the interstitial pressure P_i equals P_{alv} − $(2T/R)$, where T is the combined tension of the alveolar wall and the alveolar liquid film, and R is the local radius of curvature. Since both alveolar wall and surface tensions are small at FRC, about 1–3 dynes/cm (97), and the mean alveolar radius curvature in the human is ~70 μm, interstitial pressure within the alveolar wall should be slightly (<1 cm H_2O) below alveolar air pressure. That alveolar air pressure is transmitted unattenuated to the pericapillary interstitium is supported by the virtual stoppage of blood flow when alveolar air pressure exceeds capillary pressure (Zone 1) (111).

Alveolar Liquid Pressure

The micropipette method has been used to measure the liquid pressure in the alveolar liquid spaces in edematous, isolated adult dog (3, 4, 55, 91) and rabbit (26, 60) lungs, in nonedematous adult rabbit lungs (30), in perfused newborn rabbit (25) and adult dog lungs (7), and in immature (89) and neonatal rabbit lungs (26, 89). Alveolar liquid pressure in nonedematous air-filled rabbit lungs is slightly above the pleural pressure at all lung volumes, but relative to the alveolar air pressure is −2 cm H_2O at FRC ($\sim50\%$ TLC) and is reduced to −20 cm H_2O at TLC (30). These results are attributed to the effect of alveolar surface tension, which decreases with lung deflation (97). Surface tension calculated from the interfacial pressure (the difference between alveolar air and liquid pressures) and a radius of curvature of 30 μm, shows a reduction in surface tension with lung deflation from 30 dynes/cm at TLC to ~3 dynes/cm at FRC (30), consistent with in situ estimates (97). Alveolar edema has a minor effect on the alveolar liquid pressure (Figure 2) (26, 55, 60). More negative values (−10 cm H_2O relative to alveolar air pressure) for alveolar liquid pressure (termed pulmonary interstitial pressure) have been measured in vivo by micropuncture (82–84). However, these results have not been confirmed; independent studies indicate that alveolar liquid pressure in vivo is similar to that measured in the isolated lung (29).

In adult lungs with increases in lung static recoil associated with an elevated alveolar surface tension, alveolar liquid pressure is reduced compared to control lungs at the same lung volume (4). A similar result is obtained when alveolar liquid pressure, measured in immature air-filled fetal rabbit lung with an increased lung recoil due to a deficiency of surfactant, is compared to

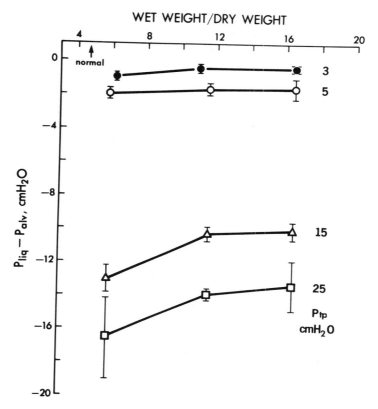

Figure 2   Alveolar liquid pressure (P_{liq}) relative to alveolar air pressure (P_{alv}) measured in isolated edematous rabbit lungs is plotted vs ratio of lung wet weight to lung dry weight. Isopleths of transpulmonary pressure (P_{tp}) of 3, 5, 15, and 25 cm H_2O are shown. P_{liq} was measured by the micropuncture method. Reproduced from Lai-Fook & Kaplowitz (60) with permission.

mature air-filled lungs with normal static recoil (89). The lower interstitial pressure predisposes immature lungs to edema formation, a characteristic of respiratory distress syndrome of the newborn.

Several investigators (82–84, 116) have interpreted the pressure measured by micropuncture of the lung parenchyma as interstitial pressure in the belief that the micropipette tip was embedded in interstitium. To address this issue, alveolar liquid pressure was measured in kerosene-filled rabbit lungs (30). Alveolar liquid pressure was slightly (1–2 cm H_2O) below the pressure exerted by the kerosene and the difference between the kerosene and alveolar liquid pressures was reduced with lung deflation. This indicated a small kerosene-surfactant interfacial tension, which has been verified in vitro using a captive bubble technique (30). The micropipette tip must have been in the surfactant layer rather than in the kerosene or interstitial tissue because (a) the micropuncture technique cannot measure pressure in low electrically conducting liquids such as kerosene, and (b) the pressure measured was unlikely to be interstitial pressure because in air-filled nonedematous lungs, interstitial pressure is near the pleural pressure, not the alveolar pressure (7, 25, 33, 34, 90).

The question remains how a micropipette can measure a pressure in an alveolar liquid layer that is considerably smaller than the micropipette tip. A similar question pertains to the interstitial tissue in which free liquid is vanishingly small. This question does not apply under edematous conditions. The answer lies in the fact that the micropuncture method depends on the establishment of electrical conductivity between the alveolar or interstitial liquid and the liquid within the micropipette, which can occur by surface contact. Surface contact would be facilitated by the location of the micropipette tip in alveolar corners, where liquid pools are maximal, and by tissue distortion that causes pooling of liquid around the micropipette tip.

Mechanical Stability of the Alveolar Liquid Layer

The contribution of passive forces to the control of alveolar liquid in the adult lung is still largely unknown. Reliable estimates of the protein concentration of normal alveolar liquid are not available. Alveolar liquid samples withdrawn by micropuncture showed no decrease in surface tension with surface film compression (93), contrary to the behavior observed in situ (97). Contamination of the alveolar liquid during micropuncture was the likely reason. Transepithelial reabsorption of alveolar liquid by active transport mechanisms has been postulated (75, 104) and the supporting evidence has been reviewed (21).

In perfused newborn rabbit lungs, alveolar liquid pressure is identical to perivascular interstitial pressure surrounding small venules (20–40 μm) (25). The virtual equilibrium in pressure between the alveolar liquid space and the adjoining perivascular interstitium supports the following negative feedback mechanism for the control of alveolar liquid (93, 115). A transient increase in interstitial pressure from equilibrium causes a flow from the interstitium into an alveolar corner and increases the radius of curvature of the air-liquid interface. By the law of Laplace there will be an increased alveolar liquid pressure that will reduce the interstitial-to-alveolar liquid pressure gradient until the flow is eliminated. This control of alveolar liquid continues until the alveolar air-liquid interface becomes spherical, at which point an increase in alveolar liquid reduces the radius of curvature and decreases the alveolar liquid pressure, an unstable condition that would result in rapid filling of the alveolus with liquid. This explains why in lungs with alveolar edema, the flooding of alveoli appears to be "all or none" (103).

Perivascular and Peribronchial Surface and Interstitial Pressures

Lung inflation increases the capacity of large blood vessels and reduces the (surface) pressure exerted at the boundary of the parenchyma and the blood vessel (47, 70). Structural analyses show the following behavior for the perivascular (surface) pressure (52, 98). (a) At constant vascular pressure, perivascular pressure is near pleural pressure at FRC and decreases with lung inflation. (b) At constant transpulmonary pressure, perivascular pressure is reduced with a decrease in vascular pressure. (c) Periarterial pressure is more negative than perivenous pressure.

While perivascular pressure falls below pleural pressure with lung inflation, peribronchial pressure remains near to or increases above pleural pressure with lung inflation (49, 58, 95). This is partly due to the fact that intrabronchial pressure follows the alveolar pressure, which increases relative to pleural pressure with lung inflation, while the vascular pressure varies independently. In addition, there is a complex distribution of pressure around bronchi and blood vessels that results from the interaction among the bronchus, artery, and lung parenchyma (59). A structural analysis of this interaction indicates a significant shape change and non-uniform peritubular pressure distribution that are reduced with edema formation (56).

Following the prediction of the perivascular surface pressure behavior, several investigators (36, 43, 51, 64) measured the fluid pressure in the interstitium between the bronchus and artery at the hilum of isolated dog lungs by inserting wick-catheters and open-ended needles. Perivascular interstitial fluid pressure is -2 to -5 cm H_2O relative to pleural pressure at FRC and becomes more negative with lung inflation and with decreases in vascular pressure. The similar behavior of perivascular interstitial and surface pressures indicates that the interstitial fluid pressure reflects the mechanical stress exerted by the lung parenchyma on the blood vessel.

The micropipette method has been used to measure the interstitial pressure in the hilar perivenous interstitium (7, 53, 67), in the perivenular (25) and periarteriolar adventitial spaces (7, 33-34), and in the alveolar junctions (7). Interstitial pressure in the hilar spaces is 1–3 cm H_2O below the pleural pressure at conditions near FRC and falls with lung inflation (53), similar to the interstitial pressure response measured using liquid-filled catheters in the peribronchoarterial space. Interstitial pressure in the periarteriolar space, perivenular space, and in the alveolar junctions is near (within 1 cm H_2O) pleural pressure at FRC and remains near pleural pressure with lung inflation (7, 25, 33-34), similar to values of alveolar liquid pressure.

INTERSTITIAL FLUID RESISTANCE

Conceptual Framework

The interstitium is not a simple fluid but a complex mixture of tissue components and water. Described as a porous material (94), the driving pressure for unidirectional flow through the interstitium is proportional to fluid velocity. The fluid resistance (reciprocal of fluid conductance) is defined as the ratio of the driving pressure gradient to flow and is described by the ratio (v/K) of fluid viscosity (v) to an interstitial permeability constant (K). Reliable estimates of interstitial resistance in both the normal and edematous lung have been difficult to establish. The enormous interstitial expansion during edema formation makes it difficult to separate any change in permeability from the effects of changes in cross-sectional area. Interstitial resistance estimated from cuff growth experiments includes that of the airway epithelium and is appropriate to the edematous lung.

Perivascular Interstitial Resistance

Conhaim and co-workers measured the rate of cuff formation around blood vessels in dog (19), sheep (18), and rabbit (67) lungs inflated with liquid to 90% TLC. From electrical analogue models used to describe the cuff growth data, values of v/K were 40, 300, and 1100 cm H_2O. min.cm^{-2} for the dog, sheep and rabbit, respectively. Interstitial resistance may depend on the inflation pressure which was 14, 19, and 5 cm H_2O for the dog, sheep, and rabbit lungs, respectively.

We recently developed a method to measure directly the pressure-flow characteristics through the perivascular interstitium of a 1–3 mm diameter vessel of an isolated rabbit lung (54, 57, 62, 105). Values of v/K were ~70 cm H_2O. min.cm^{-2}, in line with estimates from cuff growth data of the dog. Perivascular interstitial resistance is a function of protein concentration (62), electric charge of the solute molecules (57), and hyaluronan concentration (62). Interstitial fluid resistance decreased with albumin concentration under hydrated conditions, but increased with albumin concentration under conditions near normal (105).

Interstitial resistance in the above studies is partly due to the presence of hyaluronan since hyaluronidase increases interstitial conductivity. This observation is supported by studies of the isolated rabbit lung, in which hyaluronidase decreases the time constant of both cuff growth (67) and the response in hilar interstitial pressure to edema (68). The increased conductivity of the interstitium due to hyaluronidase (62) is also hydration-dependent (105). In sheep, washout of interstitial hyaluronan observed in pulmonary lymph occurs with interstitial hydration caused by left atrial pressure elevation (66). In rabbits, hyaluronidase reduces extravascular lung water (6). Thus in vivo hyaluronan appears to be essential for maintaining normal lung fluid balance.

Interstitial Resistance of the Alveolar Wall and the Alveolar Liquid Space

The fluid resistance of the alveolar wall interstitium has not been measured directly. Theoretical calculations indicate that for a typical flow through an alveolar wall, the pressure drop is much less than 1 cm H_2O (38, 101). Recently the interstitial resistance to flow from the microvasculature into the alveolar liquid space was estimated from an electrical analogue that was used to fit measurements of perivascular interstitial pressure vs edema formation (68). Interstitial resistance for flow into the alveolar liquid space was fivefold smaller than that for flow into the perivascular interstitium.

INTERSTITIAL COMPLIANCE: Effect of Edema on Interstitial Pressure

Perivascular Interstitial Compliance

The effect of hydration on interstitial pressure is important for evaluating the buffering effect of interstitial pressure on the filtration rate. A measure of this effect is the interstitial compliance, defined as the change in interstitial volume divided by the change in interstitial pressure. Direct estimates of the compliance of the perivascular interstitial and alveolar liquid compartments have been made from measurements of perivascular interstitial (7, 64) and alveolar liquid pressures (26, 55, 60) as a function of extravascular water accumulation. However, the heterogeneity of the lung interstitium poses major difficulties in the interpretation of these estimates. Only indirect estimates of alveolar wall interstitial compliance are available. Compliance of the alveolar liquid space is an order of magnitude larger than that of the perivascular interstitium. Perivascular interstitial compliance is lower during dehydration than during hydration (33).

At FRC, the interstitial fluid pressure measured in the peribronchovascular interstitium at the hilum increases by ~3 cm H_2O for an increase in extravascular lung water of ~0.3 times the initial lung weight (64). The perivascular interstitial compliance was ~0.1 g H_2O $^{-1}$ per g wet lung weight, threefold smaller than the value estimated from studies using the micropipette method (7). These values of interstitial compliance may be an overestimate because (a) liquid collects in the alveolar liquid space before reaching the hilar interstitium, the site of pressure measurement, and (b) there is a tendency for liquid to drain to dependent sites by gravity.

The compliance of the perivascular interstitium can also be estimated from the maximum cuff size measured in isolated liquid-inflated lungs (18, 19, 67). Compliance based on changes in cuff area is defined as maximum cuff-to-vessel area ratio divided by inflation pressure. Perivascular interstitial compliance was in the range of $0.13–0.25$ cm^2.cm^2.cm H$_2$O^{-1} for dog, sheep, and rabbit lungs. With the assumption that vascular weight equals one-third lung weight, these values are equivalent to $0.04–0.08$ g.g^{-1}.cm H$_2$O^{-1}. It is assumed that perivascular pressure is equal to pleural pressure prior to cuff growth. Since perivascular interstitial pressure of large vessels is normally below pleural pressure, these values of compliance may be an overestimate.

With lung inflation from a transpulmonary pressure of 5 to 25 cm H$_2$O, perivascular interstitial compliance decreases threefold (64). This behavior supports the notion that the perivascular interstitial compliance is the sum of the parenchymal compliance and the compliance of the blood vessel (64, 99). Neglecting the smaller vessel wall compliance, interstitial compliance based on parenchymal expansion is $(\Delta D/D)/DP_i = 1/(2G)$, where G is the shear modulus of the lung parenchyma and D is cuff diameter. Using a shear modulus of 0.7 times the transpulmonary pressure measured by indentation tests (39), interstitial compliance based on a change in cuff area is 0.38 cm^2.cm^2.cm H$_2$O^{-1} at a transpulmonary pressure of 5 cm H$_2$O and is reduced to 0.077 cm^2.cm^2.cm H$_2$O at a transpulmonary pressure of 25 cm H$_2$O (67). These values are equivalent to 0.13 and 0.026 g.g^{-1}.cm H$_2$O^{-1}, with the assumption that vascular weight equals one third the lung weight. Based on these compliance values, the effect on fluid filtration from a transient increase in interstitial volume would be negligible. That interstitial cuff expansion occurs primarily by outward expansion of the surrounding parenchyma is consistent with results that show little change in vascular diameter (80) or in vascular resistance (90) with edema formation. Compliance based on the parenchymal expansion ignores the intrinsic compliance of the interstitial tissue, which is much smaller than that of the lung parenchyma (28) and which depends on interstitial macromolecular composition (100).

Alveolar Wall Interstitial Compliance

No direct estimate of the alveolar wall interstitial compliance is available. The indirect isogravimetric method has been used to estimate the alveolar wall interstitial compliance (35, 71, 106, 108). In this method an isolated lung is perfused to a constant weight and the change in weight is measured in response to a step change in vascular pressure. The change in interstitial pressure is assumed, and filtration is estimated from the change in lung weight. Studies of filtration using optical measurements of protein concentration have questioned the accuracy of the isogravimetric method (41).

Early estimates of interstitial compliance using the isogravimetric technique were in the range $0.001–0.01$ g.g^{-1}.cm H$_2$O^{-1} (35, 71, 85, 108), one to two orders of magnitude lower than the direct estimates for the perivascular interstitium. By contrast, a recent study showed that interstitial compliance increased from 0.03 to 0.09 $g \cdot g^{-1} \cdot cm$ H_2O^{-1} as the lung weight increased above 40% (88). The latter values for the compliance of the alveolar wall interstitium are close to values of perivascular interstitial compliance estimated from the cuff growth experiments.

The mechanical basis of alveolar wall interstitial compliance has not been resolved. The relatively high estimates of interstitial compliance support the view that the alveolar walls do not resist expansion (101). It has been suggested that fibroblast pillars spanning epithelial basal laminae resist the outward expansion by interstitial pressure and thereby regulate alveolar wall interstitial compliance (110).

Compliance of the Alveolar Liquid Space

Micropuncture measurements of alveolar liquid pressure as a function of lung water in isolated adult dog (55) and rabbit lungs (60) as well as in newborn rabbit lungs (26) indicate a compliance of ~ 1 $g \cdot g^{-1} \cdot cm$ H_2O^{-1} at a transpulmonary pressure of 5 cm H_2O. This compliance value is reduced by a factor of 3–7 at 25 cm H_2O transpulmonary pressure. A similar behavior is observed for the perivascular interstitial compliance (64). These values are 10- to 20-fold larger than estimates of the perivascular interstitial compliance based on the maximum cuff size (18, 19, 67). Perivascular interstitial pressure measured as a function of edema formation near the hilum of isolated dog lungs indicates an initial rapid increase in interstitial pressure followed by a slower increase (64). This behavior is interpreted as the filling of the perivascular interstitium followed by the flooding of the alveolar air-spaces. The estimate of the compliance of the alveolar liquid space is ~ 0.60 $g \cdot g^{-1} \cdot cm$ H_2O^{-1}, sixfold greater than the perivascular interstitial compliance. An electrical analogue model chosen to fit the hilar interstitial pressure in response to edema formation indicated a compliance of the alveolar liquid space of 1.2 $g \cdot g^{-1} \cdot cm$ H_2O^{-1}, 15-fold larger than the value of 0.08 $g \cdot g^{-1} \cdot cm$ H_2O^{-1} for perivascular interstitial compliance based on cuff growth (68). Micropuncture studies in intact rabbits have suggested that interstitial pressure increased from -10 cm H_2O to 6 cm H_2O relative to alveolar pressure with only slight edema (82). This result is unsupported by any other study.

Alveolar surface tension is reduced with surface film compression (97). This behavior is the mechanical basis for the compliance of the alveolar liquid space. At a constant lung volume, an increase in alveolar liquid volume reduces the surface area of the air-liquid interface thereby causing a compression of the surface film. The effect is to reduce alveolar surface tension and the interfacial pressure so that alveolar liquid pressure is increased relative to the alveolar air pressure (Figure 1). The slope of the surface area (A) vs surface tension (τ) curve decreases with surface area, and this behavior reflects the compliance of the alveolar liquid space at different lung volumes. Thus compliance of the alveolar liquid space is greatest at low lung volumes where the A-τ curve is steepest and decreases near TLC where the slope of the curve is reduced.

TIME CONSTANT FOR PERIVASCULAR INTERSTITIAL FILLING

The rate at which the perivascular interstitium fills during edema formation determines, in part, the time course of alveolar flooding. In terms of a single interstitial compartment that consists of a resistive element in series with a compliant element, the time constant for filling the compartment is the product of resistance and compliance. The time constants for perivascular interstitial filling in liquid-filled dog, sheep, and rabbit lungs (18, 19, 67) are 3, 9, 60 min, respectively. The longer time constant of the rabbit results from the larger interstitial resistance because perivascular interstitial compliance in the three species is comparable.

GRADIENTS IN INTERSTITIAL PRESSURE

Longitudinal Gradients in Interstitial Pressure

Micropuncture studies indicate a longitudinal gradient in interstitial pressure between the alveolar liquid space and the perivenous interstitium at the lung hilum (53, 55). Figure 1 shows a comparison between alveolar liquid pressure (P_{liq}) and perivenous pressure (P_x) at the lung hilum measured at two levels of transpulmonary pressure, 5–6 cm H_2O and 15 cm H_2O. P_{liq} and P_x relative to alveolar air pressure (P_{alv}) are plotted vs water accumulation. Alveolar liquid pressure is initially 5 cm H_2O above the perivenous interstitial pressure at the lung hilum at both levels of transpulmonary pressure. However, this pressure gradient is reduced to zero with water accumulation. Even at equilibrium, when both pressures are equal, the interstitial pressure is below alveolar air pressure, -1 and -7 cm H_2O relative to alveolar air pressure at transpulmonary pressure of 5–6 and 15 cm H_2O, respectively. This is attributed to the effect of alveolar surface tension that is still present in very edematous lungs. Similar studies have reported a longitudinal gradient in interstitial pressure that persisted with edema formation (7). A longitudinal gradient in perivascular interstitial pressure is also formed with the growth of perivascular cuffs during edema formation.

Absence of an Hydrostatic Gradient in Interstitial Pressure

Micropuncture studies show a vertical gradient of interstitial pressure that is not hydrostatic (1 cm H_2O/cm height). In isolated lungs at constant transpulmonary pressure, alveolar liquid pressure (3, 116) and interstitial pressure at alveolar junctions (7) are constant at different heights. With severe edema there is a small vertical gradient in interstitial pressure (0.3 cm H_2O/cm) due to the increased extravascular water and interstitial pressure at the more edematous dependent lung regions (7).

A vertical gradient in perivascular interstitial pressure is also absent in the perivenous interstitium near the lung hilum (61). This was demonstrated in saline-filled sheep lungs, in which perivenous pressure was measured at two locations 2 cm apart in height by micropuncture. While the vertical gradient in alveolar liquid pressure was hydrostatic, interstitial pressure was uniform with height.

Why hydrostatic equilibrium is never attained in interstitium has to do with the fact that interstitial fluid pressure is a reflection of the pressure exerted by the compliant interstitial boundary coupled with the large interstitial fluid resistance. Viscous forces predominate in such a system. Perivascular interstitial pressure is determined by parenchymal forces around large vessels, and alveolar liquid pressure is determined by alveolar surface tension. These forces are uniform with height in uniformly expanded lungs, and the force of gravity is balanced by viscous forces caused by the downward flow of interstitial liquid. This principle also applies to the pleural liquid space (63).

Effect of the Vertical Gradient in Transpulmonary Pressure

In most body positions, there is a vertical gradient in transpulmonary pressure, the upper regions of the lung are more expanded than the lower regions (81). An exception is the prone position where lung expansion is uniform with respect to height (63). Because perivascular, perivenular, and alveolar liquid pressures vary with transpulmonary pressure, a vertical gradient in transpulmonary pressure results in a vertical gradient in interstitial pressure. In upright humans the vertical gradient in pleural or transpulmonary pressure at FRC is ~ 0.3 cm H_2O/cm height (81). At the lung hilum, perivascular pressure relative to alveolar air pressure decreases by 1.5 cm H_2O per cm H_2O increase in transpulmonary pressure (36). Thus in vivo perivascular pressure relative to alveolar air pressure would vary by $1.5 \times 0.3 = 0.45$ cm H_2O per cm height. Except for lung volumes near TLC, perivenular or alveolar liquid pressure relative to pleural pressure remains constant with lung inflation (26, 55, 60). Thus the vertical gradient in perivenous or alveolar liquid pressure is equal to the vertical gradient in pleural pressure; that is, 0.3 cm H_2O/cm height. If alveolar interstitial pressure were equal to or constant relative to alveolar air pressure, alveolar wall interstitial pressure would be invariant with lung inflation caused by spontaneous ventilation, and its vertical gradient would be equal to zero.

In the intact chest of supine dogs, the pressure measured in occluded liquid-filled lobular region and implanted perforated capsules showed a vertical gradient of 0.6 cm H_2O/cm height (87). With inversion to the prone position, the vertical gradient is reduced. Thus the pressure measured by these techniques is a reflection of the vertical gradient in transpulmonary pressure, which is greater in the supine than in the prone position (44, 48, 114).

Vertical Gradients in Extravascular Lung Water

In the normal lung, the extravascular water content is uniform with respect to height because the lymphatics absorb the entire microvascular filtrate (2, 27). The resistance to flow downwards through the normal interstitium is much greater than the resistance to flow towards the lymphatic stomata. With edema formation, the interstitial resistance decreases, and the downward flow may become greater than the outflow through the lymphatics. As a result, there may be net accumulation of liquid at the lung base (3).

The distribution of extravascular water in edematous lungs often appears to be uniform with height in spite of the force of gravity tending to drain liquid toward the lung base and the hydrostatic gradient in vascular pressure (40, 107, 113). This is the result of other forces that act to offset the effect of gravity. Longitudinal gradients in interstitial pressure may drive excess liquid toward the perivascular interstitium of large central vessels and airways. This process is aided by breathing, which during inspiration decreases the perivascular interstitial pressure of extra-alveolar vessels. At the alveolar level, alveolar surface forces acting on alveolar liquid dominate gravitational forces, and as a result liquid is retained in alveoli. Complete filling of alveoli associated with an alveolar duct causes the movement of excess liquid to the adjoining peripheral airways via the alveolar duct. Increased airway liquid exacerbates the bronchoconstriction caused by perivascular cuffs (119). As edema liquid moves from the peripheral airways to the larger central airways, gravitational forces dominate the effects of surface tension, and at this level liquid drains downwards. Thus the drainage of edema to the lung base occurs only after sufficient interstitial, alveolar, and airway edema have formed.

Differences in regional lung expansion among different body positions may affect the distribution of edema between the perivascular interstitium and alveolar liquid space. This may result in profound differences in gas exchange. For example, gas exchange in lungs made edematous by oleic acid is better in the prone than in the supine position, in spite of the uniform distribution of extravascular lung water in both body positions (113). This behavior results from the relative distribution of edema in the perivascular interstitium and alveolar liquid space at different lung volumes. In the supine position, the superior lung regions are more expanded than the dependent lung regions, while in the prone position lung volume is more uniform (44, 48, 114). Thus in the supine position, the dependent lung regions, which are least expanded, have a smaller perivascular interstitial capacity (15, 32) so that alveolar flooding and airway closure result in poor ventilation of these regions. By contrast, in the prone position, dependent lung regions are more expanded and more water is retained in the perivascular interstitium (72).

EFFECT OF LUNG INFLATION ON LUNG FLUID BALANCE

Whether lung inflation increases extravascular lung water is an issue that is important to critical care medicine where mechanical ventilation with positive-end expiratory pressure is frequently used. Previous studies showed that continuous positive pressure ventilation results in no change in lung fluid balance (46, 117), while recent studies indicate an increase in extravascular lung water after mechanical ventilation to a high end-inspiratory pressure (86), with increased tidal volume, or with positive end-expiratory pressure (12). Clearly the effect on lung fluid balance depends on the degree of lung inflation imposed in these studies. Although lung inflation increases fluid filtration, extravascular lung water would not increase if the lymphatics could accommodate the increased filtration. During alveolar flooding, lung inflation results in absorption of alveolar liquid by the perivascular interstitium and in this manner improves gas exchange (72). There are several reasons why lung inflation can be expected to increase the transudation rate across microvessels.

First the vascular-to-interstitial pressure gradient increases with lung inflation because both perivascular interstitial (36) and alveolar liquid pressures (25) are reduced relative to vascular pressure. The latter effect will be compounded in surfactant-deficient adult lungs with an increased shear modulus of the lung parenchyma caused by the increased surface tension (4). This mechanism would not apply to fetal lungs, where lung inflation compresses extra-alveolar vessels (74, 109). However, in immature fetal lungs, like adult lungs, surfactant deficiency would reduce alveolar liquid pressure relative to alveolar air pressure, while capillary pressure might remain constant so that the capillary-to-alveolar liquid pressure difference might increase. In immature lungs, an increased lung static recoil reduces the alveolar liquid pressure compared to control lungs (89). The effect of left atrial pressure on the microvascular-to-interstitial pressure gradient has been examined recently in newborn (25) and adult rabbit lungs (24) by micropuncture studies. First, arteriolar pressure relative to alveolar air pressure remains constant while periarteriolar interstitial pressure remains near pleural pressure with lung inflation. Thus the transmural pressure of arterioles always increases with lung inflation. However, the transmural pressure of venules increases with lung inflation only if the left atrial pressure remains above the airway pressure (Zone 3). Second, lung inflation increases the volume of peripheral extra-alveolar vessels and their surface area for fluid filtration (47). Third, lung inflation may increase the permeability of the microvascular barrier, as found recently in lungs made edematous by oleic acid (42). Whether this effect occurs in the normal lung is not known.

CONCLUDING REMARKS

In view of the longitudinal gradient in perivascular interstitial pressure (Figure 1), the sequence of alveolar flooding in relation to perivascular filling occurs in two phases. The first phase is associated with the filling of the perivascular interstitium of large central vessels where interstitial pressure is below pleural pressure (36). During this phase, interstitial pressure of peripheral vessels and of alveolar liquid is near pleural pressure (25). The second phase starts when perivascular interstitial pressure of the central vessels rises to equal that of the peripheral vessels, at which point edema collects in the interstitial and alveolar liquid compartments simultaneously. The rates of edema formation in the two compartments will depend on their compliances and fluid resistances (68).

A mechanical theory of interstitial fluid movement during edema formation requires the knowledge of properties such as the spatial distribution of interstitial fluid pressure, interstitial compliance, and interstitial resistance, and the effects of lung inflation on these properties. Interstitial pressure and compliance are well characterized in certain parts of the interstitium. There is a paucity of even rudimentary information concerning interstitial resistance. Even less is known of the effects of lung development on interstitial resistance. Indirect data from cuff growth experiments suggest that the time course and distribution of edema among the interstitial compartments may vary widely among species. Bronchovascular constriction lowers interstitial pressure and results in increased perivascular cuffs. Such effects may be associated with asthma (119) and hypoxia (11, 45), and here the role of the bronchial circulation may be crucial (22).

ACKNOWLEDGMENTS

This research was supported by National Institutes of Health grants HL40362 and HL36597 from the National Heart Lung and Blood Institute.

Literature Cited

1. Aherne, W., Dawkins, M. J. R. 1964. The removal of fluid from the pulmonary airways after birth in the rabbit and the effect on this of prematurity and prenatal hypoxia. *Biol. Neonate* 7:214–29

2. Baile, E. M., Pare, P. D., Dahlby, R., Hogg, J. C. 1979. Regional distribution of extravascular water and hematocrit in the lung. *J. Appl. Physiol.* 46:937–42

3. Beck, K. C., Lai-Fook, S. J. 1983. Effect of height on alveolar liquid pressure in isolated edematous dog lung. *J. Appl. Physiol.* 54:619–22

4. Beck, K. C., Lai-Fook, S. J. 1983. Alveolar liquid pressure in excised edematous dog lung with increased static recoil. *J. Appl. Physiol.* 55:1277–83

5. Berthiaume, Y., Broaddus, V. C., Gropper, M. A., Tanita, T., Matthay, M. A. 1988. Alveolar liquid and protein clearance from normal dog lungs. *J. Appl. Physiol.* 65:583–93

6. Bhattacharya, J., Cruz, T., Bhattacharya, S., Bray, B. 1989. Hyaluronan affects extravascular water in lungs of unanesthetized rabbits. *J. Appl. Physiol.* 66: 2595–99

7. Bhattacharya, J., Gropper, M. A., Staub, N. C. 1984. Interstitial fluid pressure gradient measured by micropuncture in excised dog lung. *J. Appl. Physiol.* 56:271–77

8. Bland, R. D., Hansen, T. N., Haberkern, C. M., Bressack, M. A., Hazinski, T. A., et al. 1982. Lung fluid balance in lambs before and after birth. *J. Appl. Physiol.* 53:992–1004

9. Bland, R. D., McMillan, D. D., Bressack, M. A., Dong, L. 1980. Clearance of liquid from lungs of newborn rabbits. *J. Appl. Physiol.* 49:171–77

10. Broaddus, V. C., Wiener-Kronish, J. P., Staub, N. C. 1990. Clearance of lung edema into the pleural space of volume-loaded anesthetized sheep. *J. Appl. Physiol.* 68:2623–30

11. Brower, R. G., Gottlieb, J., Wise, R. A., Permutt, S., Sylvester, J. T. 1987. Locus of hypoxic vasoconstriction in isolated ferret lungs. *J. Appl. Physiol.* 63:58–65

12. Bshouty, Z., Ali, J., Younes, M. 1988. Effect of tidal volume and PEEP on rate of edema formation in in situ perfused canine lobes. *J. Appl. Physiol.* 64:1900–7

13. Clements, J. A. 1961. Pulmonary edema and permeability of alveolar membranes. *Arch. Environ. Health* 2:280–83

14. Conhaim, R. L. 1989. Airway level at which edema liquid enters the air space of isolated dog lung. *J. Appl. Physiol.* 67:2234–42

15. Conhaim, R. L. 1986. Growth rate of perivascular cuffs in liquid-inflated dog lung lobes. *J. Appl. Physiol.* 61:647–53

16. Conhaim, R. L., Eaton, A., Staub, N.C., Heath, T. D. 1988. Equivalent pore estimate for the alveolar-airway barrier in isolated dog lung. *J. Appl. Physiol.* 64:1134–42

17. Conhaim, R.L., Gropper, M. A., Staub, N. C. 1983. Effect of lung inflation on alveolar-airway barrier protein permeability in dog lung. *J. Appl. Physiol.* 55:1249–56

18. Conhaim, R. L., Lai-Fook, S. J., Eaton, A. 1989. Sequence of perivascular liquid accumulation in liquid-inflated sheep lung lobes. *J. Appl. Physiol.* 66:2659–66

19. Conhaim, R. L., Lai-Fook, S. J., Staub, N. C. 1986. Sequence of perivascular liquid accumulation in liquid-inflated dog lung lobes. *J. Appl. Physiol.* 60: 513–20

20. Cottrell, T. S., Levine, 0. R., Senior, R. M., Wiener, J., Spiro, D., Fishman, A. P. 1967. Electron microscopic alterations at the alveolar level in pulmonary edema. *Circ. Res.* 21:783–97

21. Crandall, E. D., Kim, K.J. 1991. Alveolar epithelial barrier properties. In *The Lung: Scientific Foundations,* ed. R. G. Crystal, J. B. West, P. J. Barnes, N. S. Cherniack, E. R. Weibel, Chapt. 3.1.12, pp. 273–87. New York: Raven

22. Deffebach, M. E., Charan, N. B., Lakshminarayan, S., Butler, J. 1987. The bronchial circulation. Small, but a vital attribute of the lung. *Am. Rev. Resp. Dis.* 135:463–81

23. Egan, E. A., Olver, R. E., Strang, L. B. 1975. Changes in non-electrolyte permeability of alveoli and the absorption of lung liquid at the start of breathing in the lamb. *J. Physiol.* 244: 161–79

24. Fike, C. D., Kaplowitz, M. R. 1990. Effect of airway and vascular outflow pressures on the microcirculation in adult rabbit lungs. *FASEB J.* 4:A1075 (Abstr.)

25. Fike, C. D., Lai-Fook, S. J. 1990.

Effect of airway pressure and left atrial pressure on microvascular pressure in newborn rabbit lung. *J. Appl. Physiol.* 69:1063–72

26. Fike, C. D., Lai-Fook, S. J., Bland, R. D. 1988. Alveolar liquid pressure in newborn and adult rabbit lungs. *J. Appl. Physiol.* 64:1629–35

27. Flick, M. R., Perel, A., Kageler, W., Staub, N. C. 1979. Regional extravascular lung water in normal sheep. *J. Appl. Physiol.* 46:932–38

28. Ford, T. R., Sacks, J. R., Grotberg, J. B., Glucksberg, M. R. 1991. Perialveolar interstitial resistance and compliance in isolated rat lung. *J. Appl. Physiol.* 70:2750–56

29. Ganesan, S., Lai-Fook, S. J. 1992. Alveolar liquid and pleural pressures measured in the intact rabbit chest by micropuncture. *FASEB J.* 6:A1534 (Abstr.)

30. Ganesan, S., Lai-Fook, S. J., Schurch, S. 1989. Alveolar liquid pressures in nonedematous and kerosene-washed rabbit lung by micropuncture. *Respir. Physiol.* 78:281–96

31. Gates, L., Matthay, M. A. 1988. Effects of amiloride and phloridzin on alveolar and lung liquid clearance in rabbits. *FASEB J.* 2:A707 (Abstr.)

32. Gee, M. H., Williams, D. O. 1979. Effect of lung inflation on perivascular cuff fluid volume in isolated dog lung lobes. *Microvasc. Res.* 17:192–201

33. Glucksberg, M. R., Bhattacharya, J. 1989. Effect of dehydration on interstitial pressure in the isolated dog lung. *J. Appl. Physiol.* 67:839–45

34. Glucksberg, M. R., Bhattacharya, J. 1991. Effect of alveolar and pleural pressures on interstitial pressures in isolated dog lung. *J. Appl. Physiol.* 70:914–18

35. Goldberg, H. S. 1980. Pulmonary interstitial compliance and microvascular filtration coefficient. *Am. J. Physiol.* 239:H189–98

36. Goshy, M., Lai-Fook, S. J., Hyatt, R. E. 1979. Perivascular pressure measurements by wick-catheter technique in isolated dog lobes. *J. Appl. Physiol.* 46:1003–10

37. Guyton, A. C., Scheel, K., Murphree, D. 1966. Interstitial fluid pressure. III. Its effect on resistance to tissue fluid motility. *Cir. Res.* 19:412–19

38. Guyton, A. C., Taylor, A. E., Drake, R. E., Parker, J. C. 1976. Dynamics of subatmospheric pressures in the pulmonary interstitial fluid. In *Lung Liquids*, ed. R. Porter, M. O'Connors, pp. 77–96. Amsterdam: Elsevier

39. Hajji, M. A., Wilson, T. A., Lai-Fook, S. J. 1979. Improved measurements of shear modulus and pleural membrane tension of the lung. *J. Appl. Physiol.* 47:175–81

40. Hales, C. A., Kanarek, D. J., Ahluwalia, B., Latty, A., Erdmann, J., et al. 1981. Regional edema formation in isolated perfused dog lungs. *Circ. Res.* 48:121–27

41. Hancock, B. J., Landolfo, K. P., Hoppensack, M., Oppenheimer, L. 1990. Slow phase of transvascular fluid flux reviewed. *J. Appl. Physiol.* 69:456–64

42. Hernandez, L. A., Coker, P. J., May, S., Thompson, A. L., Parker, J. C. 1990. Mechanical ventilation increases microvascular permeability in oleic acid-injured lungs. *J. Appl. Physiol.* 69:2057–61

43. Hida, W., Inoue, H., Hildebrandt, J. 1982. Lobe weight gain and vascular, alveolar, and peribronchial interstitial fluid pressure. *J. Appl. Physiol.* 52:173–83

44. Hoffman, E. A., Ritman, E. L. 1985. Effect of body orientation on regional lung expansion in dog and sloth. *J. Appl. Physiol.* 59:481–91

45. Homik, L. A., Bshouty, Z., Light, R. B., Younes, M. 1988. Effect of alveolar hypoxia on pulmonary fluid filtration in in situ dog lung. *J. Appl. Physiol.* 65:46–52

46. Hopewell, P. C., Murray, J. F. 1976. Effects of continuous positive pressure ventilation in experimental pulmonary edema. *J. Appl. Physiol.* 40:568–74

47. Howell, J. B. L., Permutt, S., Proctor, D. F., Riley, R. L. 1961. Effect of inflation of the lung on different parts of the vascular bed. *J. Appl. Physiol.* 16:71–76

48. Hubmayr, R. D., Walters, B. J., Chevalier, P. A., Rodarte, J. R., Olson, L. E. 1983. Topographic distribution of regional lung volume in anesthetized dogs. *J. Appl. Physiol.* 54:1048–56

49. Hyatt, R. E., Flath, R. E. 1966. Influence of lung parenchyma on pressure-diameter behavior of dog bronchi. *J. Appl. Physiol.* 21:1448–52

50. Iliff, L. D. 1971. Extra-alveolar vessels and edema development in excised dog lungs. *Circ. Res.* 28:524–32

51. Inoue, H., Inoue, C., Hildebrandt, J. 1980. Vascular and airway pressures, and interstitial edema, affect peribronchial fluid pressure. *J. Appl. Physiol.* 48:177–85

52. Lai-Fook, S. J. 1979. A continuum mechanics analysis of pulmonary vas-

cular interdependence in isolated dog lobes. *J. Appl. Physiol.* 46:419–29

53. Lai-Fook, S. J. 1982. Perivascular interstitial fluid pressure measured by micropipettes in isolated dog lung. *J. Appl. Physiol.* 52:9–15

54. Lai-Fook, S. J. 1988. Pressure-flow behavior of pulmonary interstitium. *J. Appl. Physiol.* 64:2372–80

55. Lai-Fook, S. J., Beck, K. C. 1982. Alveolar liquid pressure measured by micropipettes in isolated dog lung. *J. Appl. Physiol.* 53:737–43

56. Lai-Fook, S. J., Beck, K. C., Sutcliffe, A. M., Donaldson, J. T. 1984. Effect of edema and height on bronchial diameter and shape in excised dog lung. *Respir. Physiol.* 55:223–37

57. Lai-Fook, S. J., Brown, L. V. 1991. Effect of electric charge on hydraulic conductivity of pulmonary interstitium. *J. Appl. Physiol.* 70:1928–32

58. Lai-Fook, S. J., Hyatt, R. E., Rodarte, J. R. 1978. Effect of parenchymal shear modulus and lung volume on bronchial pressure-diameter behavior. *J. Appl. Physiol.* 44:859–68

59. Lai-Fook, S. J., Kallok, M. J. 1982. Bronchial-arterial interdependence in isolated dog lung. *J. Appl. Physiol.* 52:1000–7

60. Lai-Fook, S. J., Kaplowitz, M. R. 1984. Alveolar liquid pressure measured using micropipettes in isolated rabbit lungs. *Respir. Physiol.* 57:61–72

61. Lai-Fook, S. J., Kaplowitz, M. R. 1984. Perivascular interstitial pressure versus height in isolated saline filled sheep lung. *Microvasc. Res.* 27:250 (Abstr.)

62. Lai-Fook, S. J., Rochester, N. L., Brown, L. V. 1989. Effects of albumin, dextran, and hyaluronidase on pulmonary interstitial conductivity. *J. Appl. Physiol.* 67:606–13

63. Lai-Fook, S. J., Rodarte, J. R. 1991. Pleural pressure distribution and its relationship to lung volume and interstitial pressure. *J. Appl. Physiol.* 70: 967–78

64. Lai-Fook, S. J., Toporoff, B. 1980. Pressure-volume behavior of perivascular interstitium measured in isolated dog lung. *J. Appl. Physiol.* 48:939–46

65. Lauweryns, J. M. 1970. The juxta-alveolar lymphatics in the human adult lung. *Am. Rev. Respir. Dis.* 102:877–85

66. Lebel, H., Smith, L., Risberg, B., Gerdin, R., Laurent, T. C. 1988. Effect of increased hydrostatic pressure on lymphatic elimination of hyaluronan from sheep lung. *J. Appl. Physiol.* 64:1327–32

67. Li, J., Lai-Fook, S. J., Conhaim, R. L. 1992. Effect of hyaluronidase on the interstitial cuff and pressure response in liquid-inflated rabbit lung. *J. Appl. Physiol.* 72:1261–69

68. Li, J., Lai-Fook, S. J. 1992. Effect of hyaluronidase on interstitial pressure response to edema formation in air-inflated rabbit lung. *Respir. Physiol.* 89: 133–46

69. Luchtel, D. L., Embree, L., Guest, R., Albert, R. K. 1991. Extra-alveolar veins are contiguous with, and leak fluid into, periarterial cuffs in rabbit lungs. *J. Appl. Physiol.* 71:1606–13

70. Macklin, C. C. 1946. Evidence of increase in the capacity of the pulmonary arteries and veins of dogs, cats and rabbits during inflation of the freshly excised lung. *Rev. Can. Biol.* 5:199–232

71. Magno, M., Atkinson, B., Katz, A., Fishman, A. P. 1980. Estimation of pulmonary interstitial fluid space compliance in isolated perfused rabbit lung. *J. Appl. Physiol.* 48:677–83

72. Malo, J., Ali, J., Wood, L. D. H. 1984. How does positive end-expiratory pressure reduce intrapulmonary shunt in canine pulmonary edema? *J. Appl. Physiol.* 57:1002–10

73. Maloney, J. E., Condo, C., Takahashi, Y., Dickson, V., Grant, D., Schoel, W. M. 1989. Lung aeration and lung water dynamics in artificially ventilated newborn lambs. *J. Appl. Physiol.* 66:1–7

74. Mansell, A. L., McAteer, A. L. 1990. Interdependence of extraalveolar arteries and parenchyma in newborn piglet lungs. *Physiologist* 33:Al02 (Abstr.)

75. Matthay, M. A., Berthiaume, Y., Staub, N. C. 1985. Long-term clearance of liquid and protein from the lungs of unanesthetized sheep. *J. Appl. Physiol.* 59:928–34

76. Mead, J., Takishima, T., Leith, D. 1970. Stress distribution in lungs: a model of pulmonary elasticity. *J. Appl. Physiol.* 28:596–608

77. Meyer, B. J., Meyer, A., Guyton, A. C. 1968. Interstitial fluid pressure. V. Negative pressure in the lung. *Circ. Res.* 22:263–71

78. Michel, R. P., Hakim, T. S., Smith, T. T., Poulsen, R. S. 1983. Quantitative morphology of permeability lung edema in dogs induced by alpha-naphthylthiourea. *Lab. Invest.* 49:412–19

79. Michel, R. P., Smith, T. T., Poulsen, R. S. 1984. Distribution of fluid in bronchovascular bundles with permeability lung edema induced by alpha-

naphthylthiourea in dog lungs. *Lab. Invest.* 51:97–103

80. Michel, R. P., Zocchi, L., Rossi, A., Cardinal, G. A., Ploy-Song-Sang, Y., et al. 1987. Does interstitial lung edema compress airways and arteries? A morphometric study. *J. Appl. Physiol.* 62: 108–15

81. Milic-Emili, J., Henderson, J. A. M., Dolovich, M. B., Trop, D., Kaneko, K. 1966. Regional distribution of inspired gas in the lung. *J. Appl. Physiol.* 21:749–59

82. Miserocchi, G., Negrini, D., Del Fabbro, M. 1991. Pulmonary interstitial pressure measured with micropipettes in in-situ lungs during saline loading. *FASEB J.* 5:A771 (Abstr.)

83. Miserocchi, G., Negrini, D., Gonano, C. 1990. Direct measurements of interstitial pulmonary pressure in in situ lung with intact pleural space. *J. Appl. Physiol.* 69:2168–74

84. Miserocchi, G., Negrini, D., Gonano, C. 1991. Parenchymal stress affects interstitial and pleural pressures in in situ lung. *J. Appl. Physiol.* 71:1967–72

85. Mitzner, W., Robotham, J. L. 1979. Distribution of interstitial compliance and filtration coefficient in canine lung. *Lymphology* 12:140–48

86. Parker, J. C., Hernandez, L. A., Longenecker, G. L., Peevy, K., Johnson, W. 1990. Lung edema caused by high peak inspiratory pressures in dogs. Role of increased microvascular filtration and permeability. *Am. Rev. Respir. Dis.* 142:321–28

87. Parker, J. C., Taylor, A. E. 1982. Comparison of capsular and intraalveolar fluid pressures in the lung. *J. Appl. Physiol.* 52:1444–52

88. Parker, J. C., Townsley, M. I., Cartledge, J. T. 1989. Lung edema increases transvascular filtration rate but not filtration coefficient. *J. Appl. Physiol.* 66:1553–60

89. Raj, J. U. 1987. Alveolar liquid pressure measured by micropuncture in isolated lungs of mature and immature fetal rabbits. *J. Clin. Invest.* 79:1579–88

90. Raj, J. U., Bland, R. D., Lai-Fook, S. J. 1986. Microvascular pressure measured by micropipettes in isolated rabbit lung. *J. Appl. Physiol.* 60:539–45

91. Raj, J. U., Conhaim, R. L., Bhattacharya, J. 1987. Micropuncture measurements of alveolar liquid pressure in excised dog lung lobes. *J. Appl. Physiol.* 62: 781–84

92. Raj, J. U., Anderson, J. 1992. Regional differences in interstitial fluid albumin concentration in edematous lamb lungs. *J. Appl. Physiol.* 72:699–705

93. Reinfenrath, R. 1975. The significance of alveolar geometry and surface tension in the respiratory mechanics of the lung. *Respir. Physiol.* 24:115–37

94. Richardson, J. G. 1961. Flow through porous media. In *Handbook of Fluid Dynamics,* ed. V. L. Streeter, pp. 1–16. New York: McGraw-Hill

95. Sasaki, H., Hoppin, F. G. Jr., Takishima, T. 1978. Peribronchial pressure in excised dog lung. *J. Appl. Physiol.* 45: 858–69

96. Schneeberger, E. E., Karnovsky, M. J. 1971. The influence of intravascular fluid volume on the permeability of newborn and adult mouse lungs to ultrastructural protein tracers. *J. Cell Biol.* 49:319–34

97. Schurch, S., Goerke, J., Clements, J. A. 1976. Direct determination of surface tension in the lung. *Proc. Natl. Acad. Sci. USA* 73:4698–702

98. Smith, J. C., Mitzner, W. 1980. Analysis of pulmonary vascular interdependence in excised dog lobes. *J. Appl. Physiol.* 48:450–67

99. Smith, J. C., Mitzner, W. 1983. Elastic characteristics of the lung perivascular interstitial space. *J. Appl. Physiol.* 54: 1717–25

100. Snashall, P. D., Keyes, S. J., Morgan, B. M., Chung, K. F. 1982. Pulmonary interstitial compliance: a function of osmotic constituents of the interstitium. *J. Appl. Physiol.* 53:324–29

101. Staub, N.C. 1974. Pulmonary edema. *Physiol. Rev.* 54:678–811

102. Staub, N. C., Gee, M. H., Vreim, C. E. 1976. Mechanism of alveolar flooding in acute pulmonary edema. In *Lung Liquids,* ed. R. Porter, M. O'Connor, pp. 255–72. Amsterdam: Elsevier

103. Staub, N.C., Nagano, H., Pearce, M. L. 1967. Pulmonary edema in dogs, especially the sequence of fluid accumulation in lungs. *J. Appl. Physiol.* 22:227–40

104. Strang, L. B. 1991. Fetal lung liquid: secretion and reabsorption. *Physiol. Rev.* 71:991–1016

105. Tajaddini, A., Brown, L. V., Lai-Fook, S. J. 1992. Effect of interstitial pressure on the interstitial conductivity response to the flow of albumin and hyaluronidase. *FASEB J* 6:A1534 (Abstr.)

105a. Taylor, A. E., Garr, K. A. 1970. Estimation of equivalent pore radii of pulmonary capillary and alveolar membranes. *Am. J. Physiol.* 218:1133–40

106. Taylor, A. E., Parker, J. C. 1985. Pulmonary interstitial spaces and lymphatics. In *Handbook of Physiology. The Respiratory system. Circulation and Nonrespiratory Functions*, Sect. 3, pp. 167–230. Bethesda: Am. Physiol. Soc.

107. Tsang, J. Y., Baile, E. M., Hogg, J. C. 1986. Relationship between regional pulmonary edema and blood flow. *J. Appl. Physiol.* 60:449–57

108. Unruh, H. W., Goldberg, H. S., Oppenheimer, L. 1984. Pulmonary interstitial compartments and tissue resistance to fluid flux. *J. Appl. Physiol.* 57:1512–19

109. Walker, A. M., Ritchie, B. C., Adamson, T. M., Maloney, J. E. 1988. Effect of changing lung liquid volume on the pulmonary circulation of fetal lambs. *J. Appl. Physiol.* 64:61–67

110. Weibel, E. R., Bachofen, H. 1979. Structural design of the alveolar septum and fluid exchange. In *Pulmonary Edema*, ed. A. P. Fishman, E. M. Renkin, Chapt. 1, p. 1. Bethesda: Am. Physiol. Soc.

111. West, J. B., Dollery, C. T., Naimark, A. 1964. Distribution of blood flow in isolated lung; relation to vascular and alveolar pressures. *J. Appl. Physiol.* 19:713–24

112. Wiederhielm, C. A. 1969. The interstitial space and lymphatic pressures in the bat wing. In *The Pulmonary Circulation and the Interstitial Space*, ed. A. P. Fishman, H. H. Hecht, p. 29. Chicago: Univ. Chicago Press

113. Wiener, C. W., Kirk, W., Albert, R. K. 1990. The prone position reverses the gravitational distribution of perfusion in dog lungs with oleic acid-induced edema. *J. Appl. Physiol.* 68: 1386–92

114. Wiener-Kronish, J. P., Gropper, M. A., Lai-Fook, S. J. 1985. Pleural liquid pressure in dogs measured using a rib capsule. *J. Appl. Physiol.* 59:597–602

115. Wilson, T. A. 1981. Effect of alveolar wall shape on alveolar water stability. *J. Appl. Physiol.* 50:222–24

116. Wiig, H., Opdahl, H., Nicolaysen, A., Nicolaysen, G. 1985. Interstitial fluid pressure in isolated perfused rabbit lung. *Acta Physiol. Scand.* 125:601–7

117. Woolverton, W. C., Brigham, K. L., Staub, N. C. 1978. Effect of positive pressure breathing on lung lymph flow and water content in sheep. *Circ. Res.* 42:550–57

118. Yager, D., Bastacky J., Kamm, R. D., Drazen, J. M. 1991. Thickness of the epithelial liquid layer of guinea-pig small airways at FRC and TLC. *FASEB J.* 5:A1134 (Abstr.)

119. Yager, D., Butler, J. P., Bastacky, J., Israel, E., Smith, G., Drazen, J. M. 1989. Amplification of airway constriction due to liquid-filling of airway interstices. *J. Appl. Physiol.* 66:2873–84

120. Yoneda, K. 1976. Mucous blanket of rat bronchus: ultrastructural study. *Am. Rev. Resp. Dis.* 14:837–42

121. Zumsteg, T. A., Havell, A. M., Gee, M. H. 1982. Relationships among lung extravascular fluid compartments with alveolar flooding. *J. Appl. Physiol.* 53:267–71

Annu. Rev. Physiol. 1993. 55:181–207

GENE TRANSFECTION OF LUNG CELLS IN VITRO AND IN VIVO

Thomas A. Hazinski

Department of Pediatrics, Vanderbilt University School of Medicine, Nashville, Tennessee 37232-2586

KEY WORDS: gene therapy, gene expression, liposome, lung

INTRODUCTION

This review focuses on the use of gene transfection as a tool with which to examine pulmonary function at the molecular, cellular, and whole organ level. The term transfection is defined as the introduction of one or more copies of a gene or cDNA into eukaryotic cells in order to permit either transient or permanent transcription and, usually, translation of a gene product, whose presence can be detected directly or inferred from functional assays. Although the term has also been applied to the introduction of DNA into embryonal cells to produce transgenic animals, this topic is not discussed in our review. Rather we describe various transfection techniques as well as experiments in which transfection-based methods have yielded new insights into pulmonary biology. We also discuss recent reports of successful in vivo lung cell transfection.

In general, there are three reasons to consider gene transfection as an experimental approach. First, DNA can be transfected into a eukaryotic cell in order to produce a normal or mutated protein; the protein can then be characterized in terms of its structure and function in a physiologically relevant context. Two experiments utilizing the cystic fibrosis (CF) transmembrane conductance regulator (CFTR) gene illustrate this approach. In the first experiment, the CFTR cDNA was transfected into cells that lacked cAMP-regulated chloride conductance (1, 2); this ion transport capability is known to be absent or reduced in cells obtained from patients with CF. Both

181

0066–4278/93/0315–0181$02.00

investigators demonstrated that CFTR protein and cAMP-stimulated chloride efflux were now present in transfected cells. These studies showed that the CFTR gene product alone could function as an ion channel and did not encode a channel regulatory protein or channel subunit as was originally proposed.

In the second experiment, investigators examined the functional importance of several domains in the CFTR protein by transfecting a series of mutated CFTR cDNAs that would predictably alter specific sites in the CFTR protein (3). These studies showed that transfected DNA constructs containing mutations in the R domain of the CFTR protein (which contains four serine residues that can be phosphorylated by cAMP) resulted in the loss of CFTR-directed ion transport, while mutations in other regions did not. This study clearly demonstrated the functional importance of the R domain of the CF protein in ion channel function.

In both of these examples, the transfection of precisely-defined DNA constructs into appropriate target cells permitted the study of the molecular physiology of the CFTR protein without the use of nonspecific reagents or drugs that could confound interpretation of results.

The second and most frequent use of gene transfection is to study the regulation of gene expression. In this approach, the gene of interest is not transfected, and its gene product is not analyzed. Rather, regions of genomic DNA that flank or interrupt the transcribed portions of the gene of interest (i.e. portions of exons and introns) are studied with respect to their ability to confer cell specificity and transcriptional regulation. To perform such studies, putative regulatory regions are isolated from genomic DNA libraries using standard techniques. These regions are sequenced, mapped with regard to restriction sites, and cloned into vectors that permit amplification and/or mutation of selected regions. Using these techniques, a series of precisely characterized DNA sequences from nontranscribed regions of genomic DNA are linked to so-called reporter genes to yield a fusion gene construct or expression cassette. The expression cassette is then transfected into cultured cells that have been chosen because they are thought to contain the same transcriptional factors that control the expression of the gene of interest in vivo. The amount, activity, or sites of reporter gene expression are then assayed under a series of experimental perturbations; changes in reporter gene expression are assumed to reflect changes in transcription rate of the gene of interest, which is driven by the promoter portion of the fusion gene construct. A reporter gene is used instead of the endogenous gene because most transfection methods deliver multiple copies of fusion genes per transfected cell, while most cultured cells contain only two copies; thus the use of a reporter gene results in a high signal-to-noise transcription signal. Reporter gene expression is also easily detectable at either the RNA or protein level, while the gene product of the gene of interest may be difficult or impossible to measure, or may be in such low abundance to preclude regulation studies. Thus the transfection method enables questions to be asked regarding the position, sequence, and relevance of DNA regions that regulate the expression of their respective genes. Using these methods, genomic DNA sequences (so called *cis*-acting sequences) have been identified that confer hormonal, cytokine, and cyclic-nucleotide regulation and cell-specificity for many eukaryotic genes (4, 5) and have been recently applied to genes expressed in the lung. For example, the 5′-flanking region of the surfactant protein-C (SP-C) gene has been found to contain a region within 400 base pairs of the transcription start site that confines gene expression to alveolar type II cells and its progenitors (J. Whitset, personal communication). Similarly, several regions of the 5′ flank of the surfactant protein-A (SP-A) gene, which permit induction of gene expression by glucocorticoids and cyclic-AMP, have been identified (7). In addition, as shown in Figure 1, fusion gene transfection studies have also been used to demonstrate that lung cell specificity of SP-A gene expression may require DNA sequences from intronic segments (8). To date, only a handful of lung cell-specific promoter regions have been analyzed in detail. In addition to the surfactant proteins A and C (9), the CFTR (10, 11), CC-10 (uteroglobin) (12–15), and secretory leucocyte protease inhibitor (SLPI) (16) promoter elements have been examined using in vitro transfection methods.

The third way in which cell transfection has been used is to confer a new phenotypic property or to augment an existing metabolic capability and to assess the physiological consequences of fusion gene expression. For example, Rich et al (17) transfected cultured respiratory epithelial cells from CF patients with a normal CFTR gene and corrected the ion transport defect. In another example, Warner et al (18) tested the hypothesis that augmentation of manganese superoxide dismutase (MnSOD) enzyme activity would protect cultured cells from oxidant injury. They transfected recombinant Chinese hamster ovary (CHO) cell lines with the MnSOD gene driven by a viral promoter. The cells transfected with the MnSOD gene had higher levels of MnSOD enzyme activity and tolerated oxidant stress much better than sham-transfected cells. In this example, the transfection of the MnSOD gene permitted the direct assessment of the importance of this enzyme free of the confounding effects of more nonspecific experimental designs that involve the use of pharmacologic manipulation of enzyme levels.

Lung cell transfection has also been used to preserve or restore phenotypic characteristics to cultured lung cells. Primary cultures of alveolar type II cells (19) and airway epithelial cells (20) have been transfected in order to establish long-term cell lines which, it is hoped, will retain many of the phenotypic properties typical of cells in vivo.

Another application of cell transfection has been to clone other genes whose

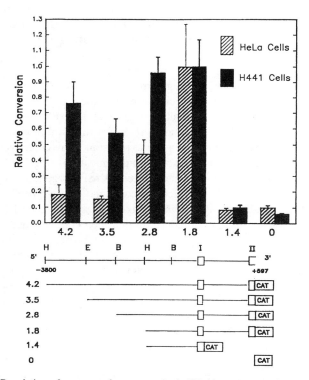

Figure 1 Regulation of mouse surfactant protein A (SP-A) gene expression examined by the transient transfection method. In this example, a family of five fusion genes was constructed, each containing a portion of the proposed SP-A promoter region and the reporter gene chloramphenicol acetlytransferase (CAT). Below the bar graph is a schematic representation of the five transfected gene constructs; the top figure represents the mouse wild-type putative promoter, which is thought to include the first intron and the first two exons (*small rectangles*). The fusion genes were cloned in plasmids and transfected by calcium phosphate precipitation into HeLa cells and H441 cells. In this example, the region deleted in construct 1.4 (i.e. portions of exon 1 and 2 and all of the first intron) reduced CAT expression to the level measured in the promoterless plasmid (construct 0), which indicates that sequences in or adjacent to the first intron of the SP-A gene determine constructive expression in both cell types (figure provided by T. Korfhagen) (8).

products may be physiologically active in lung cells. For example, the gene encoding the cell surface receptor for platelet activating factor (PAF) was cloned from oocytes transfected with the PAF gene derived from guinea pig lung. Those oocytes, which developed typical PAF-induced electrophysiologic responses, were assumed to contain a functional PAF receptor and were analyzed further for the presence of the receptor gene (21).

GENERAL REQUIREMENTS FOR GENE TRANSFER TO LUNG CELLS

The general requirements for gene transfection experiments are construction of a fusion gene or expression cassette; choice of gene delivery method; and choice of an appropriate cell line as a transfection target.

Construction of a Fusion Gene or Expression Cassette

A fusion gene or expression cassette contains three essential elements: (*a*) a promoter region containing nucleotide sequences that permit the binding and/or interaction with constitutively-expressed eukaryotic transcription factors and enzymes; this region, which is positioned 5′ or upstream from the gene, may also contain putative regulatory sequences; (*b*) a well-characterized gene or cDNA whose RNA transcript or translated protein can be unambiguously detected; and (*c*) DNA sequences at the 3′ end of the gene or cDNA that influence the splicing, polyadenylation, post-translational processing, and stability of the primary RNA transcript. These three elements are then inserted into a variety of DNA configurations (or vectors) for amplification and recovery in suitable amounts in order to perform transfection experiments. Each of these elements is described below.

PROMOTER REGION   The choice of a promoter region depends on the objective of the transfection experiment. If the objective of the experiment is to produce translated protein in cultured cells to study structure/function relationships or to influence cell phenotype, commercially available promoter sequences derived from viruses can be used. Such sequences have been found by trial and error to be effective in many eukaryotic cell lines. Promoter and enhancer sequences from the long terminal repeat sequences of the SV-40 (22), cytomegalovirus (CMV) (23), mouse mammary tumor virus (MMTV) (24), rous sarcoma virus (RSV) (25), and herpes simplex thymidine kinase promoter (26) are often used in fusion gene construction. The promoter element derived from MMTV is especially useful because it contains several glucocorticoid response elements that enhance transcription in glucocorticoid-treated cells that contain glucocorticoid receptors (26a). Constitutive viral promoters within the genome of retroviruses, adenovirus, adeno-associated virus, and other DNA viruses can also be used to drive fusion gene expression. In addition, enhancer sequences can be added to the promoter region to enhance gene expression (27).

If the goal of the transfection experiment is to study gene regulation, precisely defined potential regulatory regions must be carefully designed and verified prior to being cloned into vectors containing reporter genes.

PURIFIED GENE, CDNA OR REPORTER GENE   The fusion gene construct also contains a gene or cDNA that codes for either the gene of interest or a reporter gene; that is, a gene whose RNA transcript or translated protein can be easily and unambiguously identified in the transfected cells. If a gene or cDNA is used, it must be carefully purified and verified with regard to size and structure. This point cannot be overemphasized. The widespread practice of "cloning by phone" and gene sharing has resulted in the appearance or disappearance of genomic sequences caused by inevitable cloning modifications that are usually innocuous but sometimes significant. Subcloning may have inadvertently removed the gene's functional activity or rendered the gene unable to be expressed appropriately. A gene construct may contain extraneous sequences that yield positive results, but are misleading. For example, some plasmid vectors that contain promoterless reporter genes may be transcribed nonspecifically in cultured cells, presumably because of read-through of the plasmid vector (28). On the other hand, extraneous genomic sequences induced by cloning can be extremely helpful. For example, recent transfection studies employing the CFTR gene have taken advantage of viral sequences induced by cloning in order to distinguish transfected CFTR RNA from endogenous CFTR RNA, since the former produces predicted changes in RNA size (29) and resultant PCR product (30).

If a reporter gene is used to study gene expression, the gene must be unambiguously detectable at the RNA, protein, or enzyme activity level in transfected cells. Prokaryotic genes are often used because they are not constitutively expressed in eukaryotic cells. For example, since the bacteria-derived chloramphenicol acetyltransferase (CAT) (31–34) and β-galactosidase (Lac-Z) genes (35–41) are not present in eukaryotic cells, assays of these genes have been used in many transfection experiments. Many commercially available plasmid transfection vectors already contain these genes (42, 43). For both genes, assays of functional enzyme activity, RNA quantitation by blots, and in situ hybridization, and immunohistochemical detection methods are available. The β-galactosidase gene product metabolizes the substrate X-gal into an insoluble blue metabolite that can be detected at the electron or light microscopic level. Two photo-detectable reporter genes, firefly luciferase (44, 45) and jellyfish aequorin (46), are also available. The human growth hormone (hGH) gene has been used as a reporter gene because specific radioimmunoassay and immunohistochemical methods can distinguish it from nonhuman growth hormones in cells and in serum-containing media (47–48). Moreover, because it is a secreted gene product, it can be measured in culture media or even in lung secretions in vivo. The gene for beta-globin (49–51), SV 40 T antigen (52, 14), and diphtheria toxin (53) have been used to detect eukaryotic promoter-driven fusion gene expression. Some of the advantages and disadvantages of selected reporter genes are given in Table 1 and have

Table 1 Advantages and disadvantages of frequently used reporter genes

Reporter gene	Detection method	Advantages	Disadvantages
Chloramphenicol acetyl-transferase (CAT)	Activity assay using thin layer chromotography or scintillation counter Immunoblot Immunohistochemistry RNA blots PCR In situ hybridization	CAT enzyme is thermostable Some assays quantitative Low background	Some cells contain CAT-like or de-acetylation activity CAT activity is reduced in frozen tissue
Luciferase	Enzyme activity by luminometry	Very high sensitivity Multiple isoforms available that permit multiple transfections Quantitative Low background	Enzyme unstable in some lung cell lines
Beta-galactosidase (*Lac Z* gene)	Activity assay by spectro-photometry Cytostaining of X-gal metabolite Cell fluorescence	Quantitative X-gal metabolite insoluble	Enzyme cross-reactivity with endogenous glucosidases and galactosidases in some tissues
Human growth hormone	RIA/ELISA of hGH protein Immunoblot Immunohistochemistry	Culture media or lung lavage can be assayed	Assays do not detect functional enzyme
Beta-globin	Enzyme activity by spectro-photometry RNA blots Primer extension In situ hybridization PCR	Stable mRNA in many cell lines Low background expression in non(myeloid) cells	Enzyme activity unstable in some cells

been reviewed recently (54, 55). It must be recognized that reporter gene expression at the protein level is sufficient for some applications, but not for others. For example, if the goal of transfection is to produce protein in specific cells, the detection of protein amount or activity is adequate. However, if protein-based assays are used to study the mechanisms of transcriptional regulation, protein activity must be considered an indirect estimate of transcription rate since the pool size of translated protein is influenced by many factors other than transcription (4, 56). In these cases, transcriptional regulation must be confirmed by direct measurement of transcription rate by nuclear run-on assay or less directly by primer extension analysis.

RNA PROCESSING AND ENHANCER ELEMENTS   Fusion gene constructs also contain sequences that determine splicing, polyadenylation processing, and stability of the primary RNA transcript from the gene or cDNA. These DNA sequences can be provided by the 3' end of the gene or cDNA or can be provided by additional portions of viral sequences contained within the vector itself. DNA sequences from SV-40 are often used for this purpose. Sequences added from this region may also influence RNA transcript stability and thus transfection efficiency (57).

In addition to these three DNA elements, other nucleotide elements are necessary in the vector to produce sufficient quantities of fusion genes to perform transfection studies. Fusion genes can be constructed, inserted, grown in large amounts, and recovered from many vectors: plasmids, phages, cosmids, viruses, or bacteria. A detailed description of each of these DNA formats is beyond the scope of this article but is available in excellent molecular biology manuals (58–60). These DNA formats also may carry additional genes that allow selection and amplification of successfully transfected cells in vitro. For example, the *neo* gene codes for a enzyme that destroys aminoglycoside antibiotic. As a result, eukaryotic cells transfected with vectors containing both the *neo* gene and the fusion gene will grow in the presence of toxic concentrations of this drug while untransfected cells will not (61).

Choice of Cell Line

A cell line must be chosen as a target for either transient or stable transfection. Ideally, the cell line should constitutively contain the proper amounts of all of the relevant transcriptional and translational control factors that are present in vivo, but this is obviously difficult to ascertain. Immortalized cell lines, which are available commercially and have simple well-characterized nutrient requirements, are the easiest to study, but may not express the gene of interest. By contrast, cells derived from lung tissue may be difficult to maintain in culture, have meticulous growth requirements, and probably have substantial genetic diversity (62). Therefore, the choice of a transfection target inevitably involves many trade-offs and the investigator must search for optimized conditions and "look where the light is best". For example, the airway cell line H441 constitutively expresses SP-A, but HeLa and airway cell-derived H558 cells do not (8). Eukaryotic cells in culture often have unstable genomes or can differentiate, de-differentiate, or become polyploid. Some cells require special growth factors, matrix or serum components to support growth. Cultured cells also develop other idiosyncracies that must be considered when interpreting and generalizing from the results. The number of cell lines available for transfection studies is rapidly increasing; at least 100 lung-derived cell lines are available commercially and individual laboratories are producing their own.

DNA Transfer Methods

Although linear DNA containing little or no promoter region can be added to the media of cultured cells or injected in vivo (63), large amounts must be used, and transfection efficiency is usually low and erratic. Therefore most investigators resort to one of several methods to introduce expression cassettes into cells. These methods can be grouped into three general categories: (*a*) methods that transiently disrupt the plasma membrane to permit the entry of free or precipitated DNA; (*b*) methods to attach DNA to ligands, lipids, or viral particles to create conjugates that can traverse cell membranes via endocytosis or receptor-mediated pathways; and (*c*) virus-based methods whereby the expression cassette is carried within the genome of a replication defective virus.

METHODS THAT DISRUPT CELL MEMBRANES   In cultured cells, co-precipitation of DNA (usually plasmid DNA) with calcium phosphate (64) or DEAE-dextran (60) are commonly used methods because of their simplicity and low reagent cost. Moreover, as with any method used widely, trouble-shooting and strategies to optimize transfection conditions for a variety of target cells are widely available. This method has been used frequently to transfect lung-derived cells in culture. Electroporation is a transfection technique that utilizes high voltage pulsations to transiently permeabilize cell membranes, thereby permitting DNA to enter. Generally a low DNA copy number is transfected, which is desirable in some applications (65). Microinjection involves direct injection of DNA into individual cells such as frog oocytes or mouse embryonal cells (66). This method is obviously impractical for cultured cells, or for in vivo applications. Generally with these methods, large amounts of DNA enter each cell and are transiently expressed. In all of these methods, gene transcription occurs episomally, but stable integration, when it occurs, often results in the insertion of large tandem-repeating DNA units (66).

LIPOSOME AND LIGAND CONJUGATE-MEDIATED CELL TRANSFECTION   Lung cells have been transfected in vitro and in vivo with expression cassettes complexed with cationic, neutral, or acidic liposomes. This new technique has been termed lipofection (67) (Figure 2). Cationic liposomes can complex spontaneously with linear or plasmid DNA (or RNA) (68) in aqueous solution. These DNA:lipid aggregates can then fuse to plasmid membranes, enter via nonreceptor-mediated endocytosis, and rapidly reach the nucleus after addition to culture media. Neutral and acidic lipids can also usher DNA into some cultured cells with an effectiveness that equals or exceeds other chemical methods (69–72). Lung cells can be transfected with good efficiency with any of these lipid carriers (73–76). Critical parameters include lipid composition, the lipid and DNA concentration ratio, the degree of DNA:lipid aggregation, the degree of DNA supercoiling and sensitivity to culture conditions including serum concentration. Because liposomes have detergent-like properties, high concentrations may be toxic to cell lines (70). Recently investigators have added additional substances to the lipid:DNA complexes to improve lipofection efficiency and cell targeting. For example, investigators have added macromolecules (77), protein ligands for cell-surface receptors (78, 79) and other proteins (80) to lipid:DNA complexes and have demonstrated enhanced efficiency of transfection. The addition of surfactant proteins, some of which are taken up by airway cells (81), to liposomes might also enhance lung cell transfection, but this possibility has not yet been evaluated. Such approaches

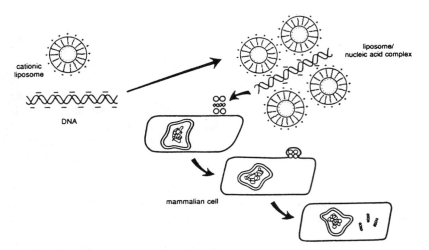

Figure 2   Schematic representation of cationic liposome-mediated transfection method (from Felgner & Ringold, 129). Negatively charged DNA complexes with positively charged DNA (or RNA) and is taken up by cells via non-receptor-mediated endocytosis. See text for details.

may be important for in vivo applications where cell targeting will be essential. Liposome technology is rapidly improving and liposome-based in vivo lung cell transfection has emerged as a realistic alternative to virus-based transfection methods (see below).

Another approach to gene transfection in vitro has been the use of well-characterized receptor-mediated endocytosis pathways as entry portals for DNA. Wu et al targeted hepatic cells in vivo by linking a galactose-containing glycoprotein to plasmid DNA that was taken up via a cell surface galactose receptor (82). Curiel et al transfected the transformed respiratory epithelial cell line HBE-1 with a plasmid fusion gene linked to transferrin via a polylysine linker (83) (see Figure 3). The transferrin portion of the DNA polylysine:transferrin conjugate is thought to bind to the transferrin receptor with subsequent internalization and the formation of vesicles that fuse with lysosomes. Although lysosomal fusion results in DNA degradation and subsequent loss of transfection efficiency, strategies to avoid or delay lysosomal DNA degradation with chloroquine (84) or monensin (85) have also been described.

Curiel et al, in another novel approach, conjugated plasmid DNA to a

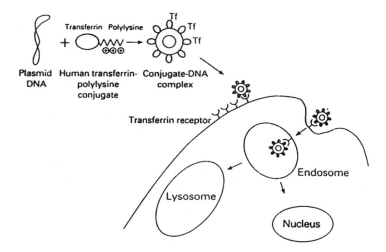

Figure 3 Strategy for gene transfer via the transferrin internalization pathway utilizing transferrin-polylysine conjugates. Interaction of plasmid DNA with human transferrin-polylysine conjugates results in the formation of conjugate-DNA complexes in which the DNA is condensed into compact transferrin-coated particles. The transferrin moiety of the complex binds to the cellular receptors for transferrin, which allows the internalization of the complex by the receptor-mediated endocytosis pathway. After internalization, the transferred DNA is localized within the endosomes, whereupon it is either targeted for lysosomal degradation, or alternatively, achieves escape from the endosome to reach the nucleus, where foreign gene expression is effected.

polylysine linker and then attached replication-defective adenovirus particles (86). These DNA/polylysine/adenovirus conjugates were used to transfect respiratory epithelial cells with high efficiency. Because the adenovirus possesses a mechanism to avoid lysosomal degradation, the addition of adenovirus to the transfection vector may overcome the limitations of other receptor-mediated transfection methods. Such conjugates may also be less likely to enter cells that do not have surface receptors for the viral glycoproteins. If this is true, such an approach should be useful for in vivo gene therapy where specific epithelial cells are the desired targets.

VIRUS-BASED TRANSFECTION METHODS   By far the most efficient gene transfection methods for many cell lines utilize viruses as vectors to carry DNA into eukaryotic cells. Retroviruses, containing two strands of RNA that are reverse transcribed after the retrovirus enters the cell, can be rendered replication-defective, can accommodate heterologous genes in their genomes, and have strong promoter elements to drive transcription of single gene copies in the host cell (87). The development of new retrovirus packaging cells has also advanced this method (88). Retrovirus-based transfection methods have played a pivotal role in the study of gene regulation and in human gene therapy (89, 90). Retroviruses have been used to produce immortal cell lines from primary lung cell cultures (91), to permanently confer new phenotypic properties to cultured cells, to restore genetic information extinguished during prolonged culture (19, 20), or to transfect human tracheal cells prior to their re-seeding onto tracheal explants (92). Retrovirus-based transfection methods result in the random integration of a single gene copy into the genome of dividing cells with subsequent stable expression for prolonged periods (93). The integration site and copy number influence the magnitude and duration of transfected gene expression. In vivo transfection efficiency can approach 100% with retrovirus-based methods if the cells are actively dividing. However, several factors limit their utility as a transfection tool in pulmonary biology. Retroviruses may be difficult to grow to high titer, especially when foreign DNA is added to their genome. Moreover, their small genome size precludes the insertion of large genes and regulatory elements. Moreover, nondividing cells, such as lung explants and some primary cultures of alveolar type II, endothelial and smooth muscle cells, cannot be transfected using retroviruses. However, some arrested cell lines can be transfected in vitro during brief periods in the cell cycle, which suggests that even arrested cells may be transfectable by retroviruses (94). In addition, retroviruses may re-acquire replication-competence (95).

DNA viruses, such as adenovirus (96, 97) and adeno-associated virus (AAV), have also been used to transfect lung cells in culture. Steele et al (19) used an adenovirus vector to immortalize rat alveolar type II cells, and immortalized airway epithelial cells have also been produced (98). The replication-deficient adenovirus has several properties that render it useful as a gene transfer agent. It is easy to grow in high titer and has a relatively strong constitutive promoter. Its deleted genome accommodates large genes or cDNAs (up to 7.5 kb). Moreover, unlike retroviruses, the adenovirus can transfect nondividing cells, and its genome is transcribed episomally unless large doses are transfected (99). In addition, some adenovirus strains are tropic to pulmonary epithelium, which may offer substantial advantages for in vivo transfection.

The adeno-associated virus (AAV) is a member of the parvovirus family and has been used successfully to transfect reporter genes and selectable marker genes into cultured cells (100, 101). The AAV genome has the remarkable property of stably integrating at low copy number into a specific site on chromosome 19 of actively dividing human cells (102). In some cell lines, the AAV promoter is constitutively active. However, it can only accommodate small (< 3 kb) DNA fragments and is difficult to grow to high titer when its genome includes a fusion gene. Other DNA viruses such as the herpes virus (103), and vaccinia virus (104) have also been used as transfection vectors.

INTRACELLULAR FATE OF TRANSFECTED DNA

After DNA is transferred across the plasma membrane, it can be found in cell organelles and the nucleus within minutes (105), which suggests that nuclear membrane traversal is not a rate-limiting step in transfection. The mechanisms by which DNA enters the nucleus, integrates or remains episomal, and interacts with the transcription apparatus are uncertain. It is likely that much of the transfected DNA is destroyed in the cytoplasm by uptake into vesicles, endosomes, or phagosomes and then into lysosomes, since in some studies, agents that block lysosomal degradation can enhance transfection efficiency. The intracellular fate of transfected DNA probably depends on many factors including the DNA configuration, the target cell type, and experimental conditions.

Rationale for the Development of in Vivo Lung Transfection Methods

After several decades of empirical efforts, there is now a wide choice of transfection methods, fusion genes, vectors, target cell lines, cell culture methods, and unpublished tricks of the trade that have been optimized to yield acceptable results in vitro. In in vitro transfection methods, the cytotoxicity of transfection methods can be accommodated as long as a high signal-to-noise ratio and minimum variability are achieved. Moreover, some inefficient in vitro transfection methods are rendered useful by the use of sensitive reporter gene assays that detect gene expression at levels that may be insufficient for in vivo detection or correction of a physiological abnormality. Although many important lessons have been learned and should be considered when designing in vivo gene transfer methods, the ultimate value of any transfection method will only be known by studies in relevant animal models.

If gene transfection is exploited to treat lung diseases, methods that render in vivo gene transfection safe, efficient, regulatable, and targetable should be developed. Several transfection methods have been used successfully to transfer DNA into lung cells in vivo. Although transfection efficiency has been low and difficult to quantitate, there are compelling reasons to develop somatic cell gene delivery methods. First, correction of many devastating lung diseases may require only a low transfection efficiency. For example, in vitro (104) and in vivo (106) evidence suggests that relatively small amounts of transfected CFTR are needed to maintain or restore normal cellular physiology in cystic fibrosis lung cells. In addition, a few lung cell-specific promoters have been characterized that might be useful in confining gene expression to specific cell types. Moreover, the study of integrated gene regulation will require the analysis of in vivo transfection studies since results obtained from cultured cells may not be applicable to the more complex in vivo environment (4). Transient transfection of lung cells in situ may also be a realistic and less expensive alternative to the development of transgenic animal models to test the functional consequences of expression or overexpression of genes in the lung. Finally, despite advances in non-gene based therapies, patients with potentially lethal lung disorders, such as cancer, cystic fibrosis, emphysema, and acute inhalational injuries, may be willing to risk gene therapy to gain substantial benefit. Such informed risk-taking has been observed in AIDS treatment trials and in the development of organ transplantation methods (107). In addition, it is possible that lung transfection in vivo, even if transient, could be clinically beneficial or that frequent dosing schedules could overcome both low efficiency and transient expression.

Because of its large accessible epithelial and endothelial surface area, the lung appears at first glance to be a highly suitable target for in vivo gene therapy. In addition, well-defined regulators of gene expression, such as corticosteroids or cAMP inducers, are already used to treat patients with pulmonary disorders and are routinely given by the inhaled route. Inhalation therapy technology is well established and improving (108–110). In addition, physical forces active on the lung surface favor homogenous particle deposition following intra-tracheal administration (111).

However, both the normal and injured lung create special challenges for gene transfer therapy. First, while many cell-specific promoters have been characterized in other organs, only a few lung-cell-specific promoters have been described and, except for our recent studies, have not yet been evaluated for their ability to target genes to the specific lung cells in vivo. In addition, many useful in vitro gene transfer methods are not applicable to in vivo gene therapy because of the physical and biological realities of the intact lung. For example, lung epithelial cell turnover is very slow (112–114), and therefore retroviral gene transfer methods, which have proven so effective for ex vivo gene therapy in humans (90), may be inefficient in vivo unless the targeted lung cell population is proliferating. Second, if progenitor cells are appropriate targets for gene transfection, there is uncertainty regarding the precise progenitor cells in the mammalian lung. Third, it is possible that the highly efficient immune surveillance system in the mammalian lung may reduce the efficiency of any gene transfer method especially if they contain protein (115). Moreover, the role of the immune system in many lung disorders is incompletely understood and it is possible that the immune response to protein-containing vectors may further impair lung function (116). Fifth, since the human lung has a complex epithelium while rodent epithelium is simple and contains few mucous glands (117), even promising results obtained in rodent lung transfection models may not be applicable to humans. Therefore, nonrodent animal models should be targeted for lung transfection studies.

Gene transfer to the intact lung has been accomplished recently using a viral vector. The replication-deficient adenovirus and its promoter have been used to transfect the α_1 antitrypsin (118) and CFTR (30) genes to rat lung epithelial cells in vivo. In the latter experiment, CFTR RNA transcripts were detectable for up to six weeks after a single intratracheal transfection in a broad spectrum of airway epithelial cells (119). This vector, which tranfects nondividing cells and is transcribed episomally, holds great promise for in vivo gene therapy to the lung. Potential limitations are that either pre-existing immunity or immunity that develops during therapy may reduce transfection efficiency.

The use of liposomes as gene transfer agents may offer some significant advantages for in vivo lung transfection. First, liposomes have already been used to deliver drugs to humans with both normal and injured lungs (120–122). In these studies as well as in animal studies, there appears to be a wide margin of safety and low toxicity when even high doses are delivered to lung (123–125). By themselves, empty liposomes are neither immunogenic nor pro-inflammatory (124, 125). Second, unlike viruses, liposomes permit the induction of nonreplicating DNA that cannot be rendered replication-competent. Third, liposome composition and charge can be altered to improve transfection efficiency (125, 126). Protein conjugates added to lipid:DNA complexes can also enhance lung cell targeting. For example, if a monoclonal antibody to a lung endothelial cell antigen is added to liposomes, 15–20-fold more lipid can accumulate in the lung after intravenous injection (127). The addition of ligands for specific cell surface receptors presumably increases the duration of contact between the liposome and cell membrane in vivo, thereby facilitating cell fusion and endocytosis of the lipid:DNA complex (128). Another advantage is that liposome complexed DNA can transfect both resting and dividing cells (67, 129). Moreover, large DNA constructs can be accommodated within liposomes so that large expression cassettes can be transfected. In addition, liposome-mediated gene transcription probably occurs episomally, thereby avoiding or reducing the hazards of random chromosome integration (129).

Liposomes as gene transfer agents have disadvantages as well, particularly when injected into the intravascular space. First, despite the large endothelial surface area of the lung, most but not all investigators have found that intravenous injection of lipid:DNA complexes does not produce high level of gene expression in the lung (128, 130). The addition of targeting proteins to the intravenously injected lipid:DNA complexes improves lung endothelial cell targeting, but extra-pulmonary expression appears inevitable and may well have unanticipated consequences. Second, although liposome-mediated gene transfer has been shown to be long-lived in porcine vascular grafts (131), the efficiency and duration of lung epithelial gene expression with intratracheal lipofection have been low in a small number of reported attempts. Other ligands that might improve airway cell targeting include proteins that bind to specific airway epithelial cells via specific receptors (132). For example, the glucocorticoid receptor protein has been added to liposomes to enhance in vivo transfection efficiency (133). However, it is possible that protein-containing liposomes may be either immunogenic or rapidly engulfed by macrophages, thereby reducing long-term transfection efficiency.

Recently, lung cells have been successfully transfected in vivo by several groups. Brigham et al (134) complexed plasmid DNA with cationic liposomes and found reporter gene expression in mouse lung after either intravenous or intratracheal injection. Hazinski et al (135) intratracheally injected liposome-complexed plasmid DNA into rats and found that reporter gene expression was confined to lung. In both of these studies, viral promoters were used to drive reporter gene expression and in the latter study, reporter gene expression was inducible by glucocorticoid treatment when the fusion gene included the MMTV promoter. Recently, Yoshimura et al (136) lipofected the CFTR gene into mice and detected CFTR gene expression at the RNA level for up to four weeks.

The lipofection experiments described above have used viral promoters to drive transfected gene expression. Eukaryotic promoters have also been used to drive reporter gene expression in vivo. Hazinski et al (137, 138) used the SP-C promoter (which confines SP-C gene expression to lung epithelial cells and is induced by corticosteroids and O_2 in vivo) (139) in liposome:fusion genes constructs and injected these intratracheally into rats. Reporter gene expression was confined to alveolar type II cells and increased at least tenfold in rats that breathed oxygen. Surprisingly, dexamethasone treatment over a wide dose range did not increase reporter gene expression. This finding suggests that integrated regulation of eukaryotic genes in vivo may not be predictable by in vitro studies.

In summary, although viral-based methods hold great promise for the delivery of therapeutic genes to lung cells in vivo, liposome-based methods have enjoyed similar success in vivo and deserve further study. Important gaps exist in our knowledge of those factors that determine transfection efficiency by any method in the normal lung, and even larger gaps exist in our understanding of the injured lung's response to transfection. A summary of some of the relevant features of potential in vivo transfection vectors is shown in Table 2.

Potential Determinants of Lung Transfection Efficiency in Vivo

DNA TOPOLOGY   The topological state of DNA (i.e. supercoiled, relaxed, nicked, or linear) plays an important role in determining transfection efficiency in cultured cells. Plasmid DNA can exist as a closed circular duplex species whose nucleotide strands are intertwined (supercoiled). The degree of supercoiling is defined in terms of a linking number that specifies the number of times the two strands are intertwined. Supercoiled DNAs may be over 100-fold more effective than linear DNAs in transcription assays. These differences cannot be explained by differences in nuclear uptake or degradation (140). The efficiency enhancing of supercoiling is most demonstrable in plasmids that contain upstream enhancer sequences in the fusion gene constructs (23). Moreover, when supercoiled and nonsupercoiled plasmids are cotransfected, transfection efficiency falls, which suggests that nonsupercoiled DNA competes for binding of one or more transcription factors, but is not efficiently transcribed (129). These observations indicate that DNA topology may be a critical determinant for transfection efficiency in vivo. The effect of DNA topology on in vivo lung gene transfer has not been studied. Because liposomes complex with all topological forms of DNA equally well, a liposome-based transfection system would be ideal to examine this issue in vivo. If a high degree of supercoiling is necessary for efficient episomal transcription, then one way to optimize in vivo gene therapy using liposomes would be to ensure that transfected DNA was highly supercoiled.

CELL-SPECIFIC PROMOTER ELEMENTS   We and others have transfected lung cells in vivo with fusion genes that contain constitutive, viral, and eukaryotic

Table 2 Potential in vivo gene transfer vectors for lung transfection

Feature	Retrovirus	Adenovirus	AAV	Liposomes	DNA-protein conjugates
Tropism for airway cells	Unknown	Perhaps	Unknown	Potential	Potential
Naturally disease-causing?	Probably	Yes	Yes	No	No
Titer necessary to produce expression	$\approx 10^6$	$>10^{10}$	$\approx 10^8$	NA	NA
Dividing cells needed?	Yes	No	?	No	No
Persistence	$+++$	?	$+$	?	?
Integration	Yes	Dose-dependent	$+$	?	?
Site-specific	No	—	Yes	—	—
In vivo lung transfection demonstrated	No	Yes	No	Yes	No
Efficiency	30–40% (ex vivo tracheal grafts)	$\approx 60\%$?	ND	$\approx 3\%$ Type II $\approx 40\%$ airway cells	Unknown
Immune response					
Preexisting?	Unknown	Yes	Yes	No	No
Likely after administration	Unknown	Perhaps	Perhaps	No	Perhaps
Oncogenic potential?	Low	Unknown	Unknown	Very low	Unknown
Environmental risk	Low	Unknown	Unknown	Very low	Very low
Necessity for repetitive dosing	Unknown	Probably yes	Unknown	Probably yes	Probably yes

Adapted from Collins & Wilson. 1991. *Conference on Gene Therapy for Cystic Fibrosis.* Williamsburg, VA.

promoter regions. However, the most essential requirement for in vivo transfection is to confer a controllable level of cell-specific expression. This requirement may be met by incorporating lung cell-specific promoter elements in fusion gene construction. Unfortunately, only a few lung epithelial cell-specific promoters have been characterized and only one has been used for in vivo transfection experiments (133, 134). Recently, we lipofected a fusion gene that contained a 3.3 kb fragment of the rabbit uteroglobin 5' flanking region; this region contains a lung cell-specific regulatory sequence that confers gene expression to broncho-alveolar cells in rabbit and mouse lung (14, 15). The lung-specific sequence within the promoter has not yet been characterized, but fusion genes containing this promoter were successfully transfected into the intact lung and expressed with an efficiency that exceeded that of viral-promoter driven expression (T. Hazinski et al, unpublished data).

Other factors related to fusion gene construction may influence in vivo transfection efficiency. For example, some strong viral promoters, such as the long terminal repeat sequence of the cytomegalovirus (CMV) promoter, may confer in vivo gene expression to specific cells. In our recent study, this promoter, when fused to the *E. coli Lac-Z* gene, confined X-gal staining to rat airway epithelial cells (135). It is likely that some plasmid vectors will be more efficient than others under in vivo conditions. For example, some plasmids contain noncoding sequences that have been found to increase or decrease in vitro transfection efficiency in eukaryotic cells (23). The mechanisms responsible for this effect are uncertain, but probably include enhancement of RNA stability, prevention of read-through, or enhanced translation.

COMPARATIVE MORPHOLOGY OF MAMMALIAN LUNGS   There are at least 12 cell types lining the airways of mammals, and not all cell types are found in all mammals (112–114). Moreover, their frequency distribution and sites vary widely across species. For example, mucous-secreting surface epithelial cells are common throughout the tracheobronchial epithelium of cats, ferrets, sheep, and human, but are rarely found beyond the trachea in rodents. Basal cells, flat triangular-shaped cells not normally exposed to the epithelial surface, may be progenitor cells for human airway epithelium that also vary in number with location and with the species (rat trachea has about 20 basal cells per square millimeter, while primates have more than 100) (117). Mucous glands, which consist of compound tubular glands and acinar glands, are found only in cartilaginous airways and extend to the bronchioles in human, sheep, and ferret, but are absent in rodents. These gland cells, isolated from the trachea of CF patients, demonstrate typical ion transport abnormalities (142) and abnormal CFTR (143), which indicate that CFTR function is abnormal in these specialized cells. Although it is uncertain what role the secretions from these glands play in the pathogenesis of CF or in normal mucous production in the lung, these data indicate that animals with more complex lung epithelial structures should be examined in in vivo lung transfection studies.

Although there are constraints to the degree to which lung cells in vivo can be optimized to permit efficient transfection, it is logical to believe that strategies can be developed that enhance lung cell turnover or might have a beneficial effect on gene transfection efficiency. For example, treatment with chloroquine, which inhibits lysosomal function and thus slows DNA and RNA degradation, might enhance transfection efficiency in vivo as it does in vitro (83). On the other hand, chloroquine intercalates into DNA, which may interfere with efficient transcription of transfected genes (84). Moreover, many in vitro transfection methods rely on transient permeabilization of cell membranes; these methods may be considered a form of sublethal cell injury. Therefore, it is possible that acute lung injury itself may enhance lung cell transfection in vivo. These results would also be relevant to the clinical situation where individuals with already injured lungs would be candidates for gene transfer.

Another way to induce transfection efficiency in vivo would be to stimulate lung cell proliferation without resorting to lung injury. For example, in ferrets (144, 145) and rats (146), partial pneumonectomy stimulates the remainder of the lung to proliferate. This proliferation occurs at both the airway and acinar levels. Similarly, epithelial cell proliferation can be induced in vivo with large doses of intravenous epidermal growth factor (147, 148).

It will also be important to determine whether chronically infected airway epithelium, such as that seen in patients with lung disease, can be transfected in vivo. A rat model of pseudomonas bronchial pneumonia may be useful in answering this question (149, 150).

In summary, both virus-based and lipid-based transfection methods have shown promise in vivo. Lipofection uses nonreplicating vectors, and large DNA constructs can be transcribed episomally in nondividing cells. Thus, an effective and safe in vivo liposome-based DNA transfer method should be developed pari pasu with viral vector development. Lipofection avoids many of the pitfalls of virus-based methods and could play a major role in the development of somatic gene therapy for acute and chronic lung disorders. Liposome-based methods might also permit rapid and inexpensive analysis of putative therapeutic gene constructs in vivo prior to the application of more hazardous virus-based methods. In addition, lipofection may serve as a useful tool to better understand regulatory DNA sequences that are responsible for the integrated regulation of cell-specific gene expression in the intact lung that cannot be modeled by in vitro or transgenic models. If it were possible, by any transfection method, to render an animal "transiently transgenic," such a technique would permit inexpensive testing of a wide variety of hypotheses concerning the role of specific gene products in lung disorders. Even if liposome-based methods prove inefficient for long-term correction of a physiologic abnormality, transient transfection studies should yield valuable insight into fusion gene design and techniques that take into account the unique features of the intact lung. These insights will be important in somatic gene therapy development and in understanding gene regulation in vivo (151).

ACKNOWLEDGMENTS

This work is supported by HL 14214 and by grants from the Cystic Fibrosis Foundation and American Lung Association.

Literature Cited

1. Kartner, N., Hanrahan, J. W., Jensen, T. J., Naismith, A. L., Sun, S. Z., et al. 1991 Expression of the cystic fibrosis gene in nonepithelial invertebrate cells produce a regulated anion conductance. *Cell* 64:681–92

2. Anderson, M. P., Rich, D. P., Gregory, R. J., Smith, A. E., Welsh, M. J. 1991. Generation of cAMP activated chloride currents by expression of CFTR. *Science* 251:679–82

3. Cheng, S. H., Rich, D. P., Marshall, J., Gregory, R. J., Welsh, M. J., Smith, A. E. 1991. Phosphorylation of the R domain by cAMP-dependent protein kinase regulates the CFTR chloride channel. *Cell* 66:1027–36

4. Granner, D., O'Brien, R., Imai, E., Forest, C., Mitchell, J., Lucas, P. 1991. Complex hormone response unit regulating transcription of the phosphoenolpyruvate carboxykinase gene: from metabolic pathways to molecular biology. *Recent Prog. Horm. Res.* 47:319–48

5. Grayson, D. R., Costa, R. H., Darnell, J. E. 1989. Regulation of hepatocyte-specific gene expression. *Ann. NY Acad. Sci.* 557:243–56

6. Deleted in proof

7. Alcorn, J. L., Gerard, R. D., Smith, M. E., Mendelson, C. R. 1992. Analysis of genomic regions involved in cyclic AMP and cell-specific regulation of rabbit surfactant protein A (SP-A) gene expression. *Am. Rev. Respir. Dis.* 145:A224 (Abstr.)

8. Korfhagen, T., Bruno, M., Glasser, S., Ciraolo, P., Lattier, D. 1992. Transcriptional activity of murine SP-A gene sequences in transfected cells.

Am. Rev. Respir. Dis. 145:A225 (Abstr.)

9. Glasser, S. W., Korfhagen, T. R., Bruno, M. D., Dey, C., Whitsett, J. A. 1990. Structure and expression of the pulmonary surfactant protein SP-C gene in the mouse. *J. Biol. Chem.* 265:21986–91

10. Yoshimura, K., Nakamura, H., Trapnell, B. C. 1991. The cystic fibrosis gene has a "housekeeping"-type promoter and is expressed at low levels in cells of epithelial origin. *J. Biol. Chem.* 266:9140–44

11. Chou, J. L., Rozmahel, R., Tsui, L. C. 1991. Characterization of the promoter region of the cystic fibrosis transmembrane conductance regulator gene. *J. Biol. Chem.* 266:24471–76

12. Hagen, G., Wolf, M., Katyal, S. L., Singh, G., Beato, M., Suske, G. 1990. Tissue-specific expression, hormonal regulation and 5'-flanking gene region of the rat Clara cell 10 kDa protein: comparison to rabbit uteroglobin. *Nucleic Acids Res.* 18:2939–45

13. Singh, G., Katyal, S. L., Brown, W. E., Phillips, S., Kennedy, A. L., et al. 1988. Amino acid and nucleotide sequences of human Clara cell 10 kDa protein. *Biochim. Biophys. Acta* 950: 329–37

14. DeMayo, F. J., Finegold, M. J., Hansen, T. N., Stanley, L. A., Smith, B., Bullock, D. W. 1991. Expression of SV40 T antigen under control of rabbit uteroglobin promoter in transgenic mice. *Am. J. Physiol.* 261:L70–76

15. DeMayo, F. J., Damak, S., Hansen, T. N., Bullock, D. W. 1991. Expression and regulation of the rabbit

uteroglobin gene in transgenic mice. *Mol. Endocrinol.* 5:311–18

16. Abe, T., Kobayashi, N., Yoshimura, K., Trapnell, B. C., Kim, H., et al. 1991. Expression of the secretory leukoprotease inhibitor gene in epithelial cells. *J. Clin. Invest.* 87:2207–15

17. Rich, D. P., Anderson, M. P., Gregory, R. J., Cheng, S. H., Paul, S., et al. 1990. Expression of cystic fibrosis transmembrane conductance regulator corrects defective chloride channel regulation in cystic fibrosis airway epithelial cells. *Nature* 347:358–63

18. Warner, B. B., Heile, M., Papes, R., Wispe, J. R. 1992. Overexpression of MnSOD protects recombinant cell lines against oxidative injury. *Pediatr. Res.* 31:326A (Abstr.)

19. Steele, M. P., Levine, R. A., Joyce-Brady, M., Brody, J. S. 1992. A rat alveolar type II cell line developed by adenovirus 12SE1A gene transfer. *Am. J. Respir. Cell Mol. Biol.* 6:50–56

20. Yankaskas, J. R., Boucher, R. C. 1990. Transformation of airway epithelial cells with persistence of cystic fibrosis or normal ion transport phenotypes. *Methods Enzymol.* 192:565–71

21. Honda, Z., Nakamura, M., Miki, I., Minami, M., Watanabe, T., et al. 1991. Cloning by functional expression of platelet-activating factor receptor from guinea-pig lung. *Nature* 349:342–46

22. McKnight, S., Tjian, R. 1986. Transcriptional selectivity of viral genes in mammalian cells. *Cell* 46:795–805

23. Boshart, M., Weber, F., Jahn, G., Dorschhasler, K., Fleckenstein, B., Schaffner, W. 1985. A very strong enhancer is located upstream of an immediate early gene of human cytomegalorvirus. *Cell* 41:521–30

24. Yamamoto, K. R. 1985. Steroid receptor regulated transcription of specific genes and gene networks. *Annu. Rev. Genet.* 19:209–52

25. Gorman, C. M., Merlino, G. T., Willingham, M. C., Pastan, I., Howard, B. H. 1982. The rous sarcoma virus long terminal repeat is a strong promoter when introduced into a variety of eukaryotic cells by DNA-mediated transfection. *Proc. Natl. Acad. Sci. USA* 79:6777–81

26. Shimotohno, K., Temin, H. M. 1981. Formation of infectious progeny virus after insertion of herpes simplex thymidine kinase gene into DNA of an avian retrovirus. *Cell* 26:67–77

26a. Beato, M. 1989. Gene regulation by steroid hormones. *Cell* 56:335–44

27. Jobling, S. A., Gehrke, L. 1987. Enhanced translation of chimeric messenger RNAs containing a plant viral untranslated leader sequence. *Nature* 325:622–25

28. Fridovich-Keil, J., Gudas, J. M., Bryan, I. B., Pardee, A. B. 1991. Improved expression vectors for eukaryotic promoter/enhancer studies. *BioTechniques* 11:572–79

29. Drumm, M. L., Pope, H. A., Cliff, W. H., Rommens, J. M., Marvin, S. A., et al. 1990. Correction of the cystic fibrosis defect *in vitro* by retrovirus-mediated gene transfer. *Cell* 62:1227–33

30. Rosenfeld, M. A., Yoshimura, K., Trapnell, B. C., Yoneyama, K., Rosenthal, E. R., et al. 1992. In vivo transfer of the human cystic fibrosis transmembrane conductance regulator gene to the airway epithelium. *Cell* 68:143–55

31. Gorman, C. M., Moffat, L. F., Howard, B. H. 1982. Recombinant genomes which express chloramphenicol acetyltransferase in mammalian cells. *Mol. Cell. Biol.* 2:1044–51

32. Nordeen, S. K., Green, P. P., Fowlkes, D. M. 1987. A rapid, sensitive, and inexpensive assay for chloramphenicol acetyltransferase. *DNA* 6:173–78

33. Nielsen, D. A., Chang, T. C., Shapiro, D. J. 1989. A highly sensitive, mixed-phase assay for chloramphenicol acetyltransferase activity in transfected cells. *Anal. Biochem.* 179:19–23

34. Luckow, B., Schutz, G. 1987. CAT constructions with multiple unique restriction sites for the functional analysis of eukaryotic promoters and regulatory elements. *Nucleic Acids Res.* 15:5490

35. Robbins, J., Subramaniam, A., Gulick, J. 1989. A multipurpose vector for the study of transcriptional control. *Gene* 85:541–44

36. Zhang, Y., Naleway, J. J., Larison, K. D., Huang, Z., Haugland, R. P. 1991. Detecting *lacZ* gene expression in living cells with new lipophilic, fluorogenic β-galactosidase substrates. *FASEB J.* 5:3108–13

37. MacGregor, G. R., Nolan, G. P., Fiering, S., Roederer, M., Herzenberg, L. A. 1991. Use of *E. coli lacZ* (β-galactosidase) as a reporter gene. In *Methods in Molecular Biology*, ed. E. J. Murray, 7:217–35. Clifton, NJ: Humana

38. MacGregor, G. R., Mogg, A. E., Burke, J. F., Caskey, C. T. 1987. Histochemical staining of clonal mammalian cell lines expressing *E. coli*

b-galactosidase indicates heterogenous expression of the bacterial gene. *Somat. Cell Mol. Genet.* 132:253–65

39. Dannenberg, A. M., Suga, M. 1981. Histochemical stains for macrophages in cell smears and tissue sections: β-galactosidase, acid phosphatase, non-specific esterase, succine dehydrogenase, and cytochrome oxidase. In *Methods for Studying Mononuclear Phagocytes,* ed. D. O. Adams, P. J. Edelson, H. S. Koren, pp. 375–77. New York: Academic

40. Pearson, B., Wolf, P. L., Vazquez, J. 1963. A comparative study of a series of new indolyl compounds to localize β-galactosidase in tissues. *Lab. Invest.* 12:1249–59

41. Walsh, C., Cepko, C. L. 1988. Clonally related cortical cells show several migration patterns. *Science* 241:1342–45

42. Prost, E., Moore, D. D. 1986. CAT vectors for analysis of eukaryotic promoters and enhancers. *Gene* 45:107–11

43. An, G., Hidaka, K., Siminovitch, L. 1982. Expression of bacterial β-galactosidase in animal cells. *Mol. Cell. Biol.* 2:1628–32

44. DeWet, J. R., Wood, K. V., DeLuca, M., Helinski, D. R., Subramani, S. 1987. Firefly luciferase gene: structure and expression in mammalian cells. *Mol. Cell Biol.* 7:725–37

45. Williams, T. M., Burlein, J. E., Ogden, S., Kricka, L. J., Kant, J. A. 1989. Advantages of firefly luciferase as a reporter gene: application to the interleukin-2 gene promoter. *Anal. Biochem.* 176:28–32

46. Tanahashi, H., Takashi, I., Inouye, S., Tsuji, F. I., Sakaki, Y. 1990. Photoprotein aequorin use as a reporter enzyme in studying gene expression in mammalian cells. *Gene* 96:249–55

47. Behringer, R. R., Mathews, L. S., Palmiter, R. D., Brinster, R. L. 1988. Dwarf mice produced by genetic ablation of growth hormone-expressing cells. *Gene Dev.* 2:453–61

48. Selden, R. F., Burke, H. K., Rowe, M. E., Goodman, H. M., Moore, D. D. 1986. Human growth hormone as a reporter gene in regulation studies employing transient gene expression. *Mol. Cell Biol.* 6:3173–79

49. Ross, H. J., Sato, N., Ueyama, Y., Koeffler, H. P. 1991. Cytokine messenger RNA stability is enhanced in tumor cells. *Blood* 77:1787–95

50. Fridovich-Keil, J. L., Gudas, J. M., Bryan, I. B., Pardee, A. B. 1991. Improved expression vectors for eukaryotic promoter/enhancer studies. *BioTechniques* 11:572–79

51. Simpson, E., Lauber, M., Demeter, M., Stirling, D., Rodgers, R., et al. 1991. Regulation of expression of the genes encoding steroidogenic enzymes. *J. Steroid Biochem. Mol. Biol.* 40:45–52

52. Sigmund, C. F., Jones, C. A., Fabian, J. R., Mullins, J. J., Gross, K. W. 1990. Tissue and cell specific expression of a renin promoter reporter gene construct in transgenic mice. *Biochem. Biophys. Res. Commun.* 170:344–50

53. Korfhagen, T. R., Glasser, S. W., Wert, S. E., Bruno, M. D., Daugherty, C. C., et al. 1990. *Cis*-acting sequences from a human surfactant protein gene confer pulmonary-specific gene expression in transgenic mice. *Proc. Natl. Acad. Sci. USA* 87:6122–26

54. Gallie, D. R., Feder, J. N., Schimke, R. T., Walbot, V. 1991. Post-transcriptional regulation in higher eukaryotes: the role of the reporter gene in controlling expression. *Mol. Gen. Genet.* 228:258–64

55. Alam, J., Cook, J. L. 1990. Reporter genes: application to the study of mammalian gene transcription. *Anal. Biochem.* 188:245–54

56. Weaver, T. E., Whitsett, J. A. 1991. Function and regulation of expression of pulmonary surfactant-associated proteins. *Biochem. J.* 273:249–64

57. Shaw, G., Kamen, R. 1986. A conserved AU sequence from the 3′ untranslated region of GM-CSF mRNA mediates selective mRNA degradation. *Cell* 46:659–67

58. Sambrook, J., Fritsch, E. F., Maniatis, T. 1989. Expression of cloned genes in cultured mammalian cells. In *Molecular Cloning: A Laboratory Manual,* p. 16.5. New York: Cold Spring Harbor Lab. Press

59. Ausubel, F. M., Brent, R., Kingston, R. E., Moore, D. D., Seidman, J. G., Smith, J. A., Struhl, K., eds. 1989. *Current Protocols in Molecular Biology,* Vol. 1. New York: Wiley & Sons

60. Murray, E. J., ed. 1991. *Gene Transfer and Expression Protocols.* Clinton, NJ: Humana

61. Davies, J., Smith, D. I. 1978. Plasmid-determined resistance to antimicrobial agents. *Annu. Rev. Microbiol.* 32:469–518

62. Siminski, J. T., Kavanagh, T. J., Chi, E., Raghu, G. 1992. Long-term maintenance of mature pulmonary parenchyma cultured in serum-free

conditions. *Am. J. Physiol.* 262:L105–10

63. Wolff, J. A., Malone, R. W., Williams, P., Chong, W., Acsadi, G., et al. 1990. Direct gene transfer into mouse muscle in vivo. *Science* 247:1465–68

64. Graham, F. L., van der Eb, A. J. 1973. A new technique for the assay of infectivity of human adenovirus 5. *Virology* 52:456–67

65. Toneguzzo, F., Keating, A., Glynn, S., McDonald, K. 1988. Electric field-mediated gene transfer: characterization of DNA transfer and patterns of integration in lymphoid cells. *Nucleic Acids Res.* 16:5515–32

66. Folger, K. R., Wong, E. A., Wahl, G., Capecchi, M. R. 1982. Patterns of integration of DNA microinjected into cultured mammalian cells: evidence for homologous recombination between injected plasmid DNA molecules. *Mol. Cell Biol.* 2:1372–87

67. Felgner, P. L., Gadek, T. R., Holm, M., Roman, R., Chan, H. W., et al. 1987. Lipofection: A highly efficient lipid-mediated DNA-transfection procedure. *Proc. Natl. Acad. Sci. USA* 84:7413–17

68. Malone, R. W., Felgner, P. L., Verma, I. M. 1989. Cationic liposome-mediated RNA transfection. *Proc. Natl. Acad. Sci. USA* 86:6077–81

69. Conner, J., Huang, L. 1987. Acid-induced fusion of liposomes. In *Cell Fusion,* ed. A. E. Sowers, pp. 285–99. New York: Plenum

70. Leventis, R., Silvius, J. R. 1990. Interactions of mammalian cells with lipid dispersions containing novel metabolizable cationic amphiphiles. *Biochem. Biophys. Acta* 1023:124–32

71. Rose, J. K., Buonocore, L., Whitt, M. A. 1991. A new cationic liposome reagent mediating nearly quantitative transfection of animal cells. *BioTechniques* 10:520–25

72. Wang, C. Y., Huang, L. 1987. pH-sensitive immunoliposomes mediate target-cell-specific delivery and controlled expression of a foreign gene in mouse. *Proc. Natl. Acad. Sci. USA* 84:7851–55

73. Lu, L., Zeitlin, P. L., Guggino, W. B., Craig, R. W. 1989. Gene transfer by lipofection in rabbit and human secretory epithelial cells. *Pflügers Arch.* 415:198–203

74. Debs, R., Pian, M., Gaensler, K., Clements, J., Friend, D., et al. 1992. Prolonged transgene expression in rodent lung cells. *Am. J. Respir. Cell Mol. Biol.* In press

75. Brigham, K. L., Meyrick, B., Christman, B., Berry, L. C., King, G. 1989. Expression of a prokaryotic gene in cultured lung endothelial cells after lipofection with a plasmid vector. *Am. J. Respir. Cell. Mol. Biol.* 1:95–100

76. Gao, X. A., Huang, L. 1991. A novel cationic liposome reagent for efficient transfection of mammalian cells. *Biochem. Biophys. Res. Commun.* 179:280–85

77. Tikchonenko, T. I., Glushakova, S. E., Kislina, O. S., Grodnitskaya, N. A., Manykin, A. A., Naroditsky, B. S. 1988. Transfer of condensed viral DNA into eukaryotic cells using proteoliposomes. *Gene* 63:321–30

78. Holmberg, E., Maruyama, K., Litzinger, D. C., Wright, S., Davis, M., et al. 1989. Highly efficient immunoliposomes prepared with a method which is compatible with various lipid compositions. *Biochem. Biophys. Res. Commun.* 165:1272–78

79. Wang, C. Y., Huang, L. 1987. pH-sensitive immunoliposome mediate target-cell-specific delivery and controlled expression of a foreign gene in mouse. *Proc. Natl. Acad. Sci. USA* 84:7851–55

80. Kaneda, Y., Iwai, K., Uchida, T. 1989. Increased expression of DNA cointroduced with nuclear protein in adult rat liver. *Science* 244:375–78

81. Wright, J. R., Wager, R. E., Hawgood, S., Dobbs, L., Clements, J. A. 1987. Surfactant apoprotein M_r 26,000-36,000 enhances uptake of liposomes by type II cells. *J. Biol. Chem.* 262:2888–94

82. Wu, G. Y., Wu, C. H. 1988. Receptor-mediated gene delivery and expression in vivo. *J. Biol. Chem.* 263:14621–24

83. Curiel, D. T., Agaral, S., Ramer, M. U., Wagner, E., Cotten, M., et al. 1992. Gene transfer to respiratory epithelial cells via the receptor-mediated endocytosis pathway. *Am. J. Respir. Cell. Mol. Biol.* 6:347–52

84. Pruitt, S. C., Reeder, R. H. 1984. Effect of intercalating agents on RNA polymerase I promoter selection in *Xenopus laevis. Mol. Cell. Biol.* 4:3851–57

85. Amitay, R., Bar-Nun, S., Haimovich, J., Rabinovich, E., Shachar, I. 1991. Post-translational regulation of IgM expression in B lymphocytes. *J. Biol. Chem.* 266:12568–73

86. Curiel, D. T., Wagner, E., Cotten, M., Birnstiel, M. L., Agarwal, S., et al. 1992. High-efficiency gene transfer mediated by adenovirus coupled to DNA-polylysine complexes. *Hum. Gene Ther.* 3:147–54

87. McLachin, J. R., Cornetta, K., Eglitis, M. A., Anderson, W. F. 1990. Retroviral-mediated gene-transfer. *Prog. Nucleic Acids Res. Mol. Biol.* 38:92–135

88. Miller, A. D. 1990. Retrovirus packaging cells. *Hum. Gene Ther.* 1:5–14

89. Rosenberg, S. A., Aebersold, P., Cornetta, K., Kasid, A., Morgan, R. A., et al. 1990. Gene transfer into humans— immunotherapy of patients with advanced melanoma, using tumor-infiltrating lymphocytes modified by retroviral gene transduction. *N. Engl. J. Med.* 323:570–78

90. Culver, K. W., Berger, M., Miller, A. D., Anderson, W. F., Blaese, R. M. 1992. Lymphocyte gene therapy for adenosine deaminase deficiency. *Pediatr. Res.* 31:149A (Abstr.)

91. Johnson, L. G., Olsen, J. C., Wong, M., Yankaskas, J., Boucher, R. C. 1991. Optimization of retroviral-mediated gene transfer in transformed and primary human airway epithelial cells. *Am. Res. Respir. Dis.* 143:139A (Abstr.)

92. Engelhardt, J. F., Allen, E. D., Wilson, J. M. 1991. Reconstitution of tracheal grafts with a genetically modified epithelium. *Proc. Natl. Acad. Sci. USA* 88:11192–96

93. Grandgenett, D. P., Mumm, S. R. 1990. Unraveling retrovirus integration. *Cell* 60:3–4

94. Friedmann, T., Xu, L., Wolff, J., Yee, J. K., Miyanohara, A. 1989. Retrovirus vector-mediated gene transfer into hepatocytes. *Mol. Biol. Med.* 6:117–25

95. D'Onofrio, C., Bonmassar, E. 1990. An immunopharmacological approach for prevention of retrovirus-associated disease in human pathology. *Pharmacol. Res.* 22:645–59

96. Smith, C. L., Hager, G. L., Pike, J. W., Marx, S. J. 1991. Overexpression of the human vitamin D3 receptor in mammalian cells using recombinant adenovirus vectors. *Mol. Endocrinol.* 5:867–78

97. Berkner, K. L. 1988. Development of adenovirus vectors for the expression of heterologous genes. *BioTechiques* 6:616–29

98. Zeitlin, P. L., Lu, L., Rhim, J., Cutting, G., Stetten, G., et al. 1991. A cystic fibrosis bronchial epithelial cell line: immortalization by adeno-12-SV40 infection. *Am. J. Respir. Cell. Mol. Biol.* 4:313–19

99. Straus, S. E. 1984. Adenovirus infections in humans. In *The Adenoviruses*, ed. H. S. Ginsberg, pp. 451–96. New York: Plenum

100. Tratschin, J. D., Miller, I. L., Smith, M. G., Carter, B. J. 1985. Adeno-associated virus vector for high-frequency integration, expression, and rescue of genes in mammalian cells. *Mol. Cell. Biol.* 5:3251–60

101. Dixit, M., Webb, M. S., Smart, W. C., Ohi, S. 1991. Construction and expression of a recombinant adeno-associated virus that harbors a human β-globin-encoding cDNA. *Gene* 104:253–57

102. Samulski, R. J., Zhu, X., Xiao, X., Brook, J. D., Houseman, D. E., et al. 1991. Targeted integration of adeno-associated virus (AAV) into human chromosome 19. *EMBO J.* 10:3941–50

103. Geller, A. I., Keyomarsi, K., Bryan, J., Pardee, A. B. 1990. An efficient deletion mutant packaging system for defective herpes simplex virus vectors: potential applications to human gene therapy and neuronal physiology. *Proc. Natl. Acad. Sci. USA* 87:8950–54

104. Rich, D. P., Anderson, M. P., Gregory, R. J., Cheng, S. H., Paul, S., et al. 1990. Expression of cystic fibrosis transmembrane conductance regulator corrects defective chloride channel regulation in cystic fibrosis airway epithelial cells. *Nature* 347:358–63

105. Cudd, A., Nicolau, C. 1985. Intracellular fate of liposome-encapsulated DNA in mouse liver. Analysis using electron microscope autoradiography and subcellular fractionation. *Biochim. Biophys. Acta* 845:477–91

106. Chu, C. S., Trapnell, B. C., Murtagh, J. J., Moss, J., Dalemans, W., et al. 1991. Variable detection of exon 9 coding sequences in cystic fibrosis and in normal bronchial epithelium. *EMBO J.* 10:1355–63

107. FDA Center for Biologies Evaluation and Research. 1991. Points to consider in human somatic cell therapy and gene therapy. *Hum. Gene Ther.* 2:251–56

108. Brain, J. D., Valberg, P. A. 1979. Deposition of aerosol in the respiratory tract. *Am. Rev. Respir. Dis.* 120:1325–73

109. Summers, Q. A. 1991. Inhaled drugs and the lung. *Clin. Exp. Allergy* 21:259–68

110. Ilowite, J. S., Niederman, M. S., Fein, A. M. 1991. Delivery of topical antibiotics: pharmacokinetics and clinical problems. *Semin. Respir. Infect.* 6:158–67

111. Gehr, P., Schurch, S. 1992. Surface

forces displace particles deposited in airways toward the epithelium. *News Physiol. Sci.* 7:1–5

112. St. George, J., Edmonson, S., Wong, V., Cranz, D., Weir, A., et al. 1986. Control of differentiation of mucous cells from nonhuman primate respiratory airways. *J. Cell. Biol.* 103:200

113. St. George, J., Wu, R., Neu, K., Plopper, C. G. 1987. Growth and differentiation of fetal rhesus airway epithelium in vivo. *Am. Rev. Respir. Dis.* 135:A364 (Abstr.)

114. Evans, M. J., Shami, S. G. 1989. Lung cell kinetics. In *Lung Cell Biology*, ed. C. Lenfant, D. Massaro, pp. 1–36. New York: Dekker

115. Smina, T., van der Brugge-Gamelkoorn, F. J., Jeurissen, S. H. 1989. Structure and function of bronchus-associated lymphoid tissue. *Crit. Rev. Immunol.* 9:119–50

116. Moss, R. B., Hsu, Y. P., Lewiston, N. J. 1986. Association of systemic immune complexes, complement activation, and antibodies to *P. aeruginosa* lipopolysaccharide and exotoxin A with motality in CF. *Am. Rev. Respir. Dis.* 133:648–52

117. Brewer, N. R. 1989. Comparative morphophysiology of the mammalian lung part II. The epithelium. *Synapse* 22:8–17

118. Rosenfeld, M. A., Siegfried, W., Yoshimura, K., Yoneyama, K., Fukayama, M., et al. 1991. Adenovirus-mediated transfer of a recombinant α1-antitrypsin gene to the lung epithelium in vivo. *Science* 252:431–34

120. Sculier, J. P., Body, J. J. 1991. Intravenous administration of amphotericin B entrapped in liposomes: induction of high serum levels of TNF alpha. *Ann. Oncol.* 2:141–44

121. Thomas, D. A., Myers, M. A., Wichert, B., Schreier, H., Gonzalez-Rothi, R. J. 1991. Acute effects of liposome aerosol inhalation on pulmonary function in healthy human volunteers. *Chest* 99:1268–70

122. Katz, N. M., Pierce, P. F., Anaeck, R. A., et al. 1990. Liposomal amphotericin B for treatment of pulmonary aspergillosis in a heart transplant patient. *J. Heart Transplant* 9:14–17

123. Pettenazzo, A., Jobe, A., Ikegami, M., Abra, R., Hogue, E., Mihalko, P. 1989. Clearance of phosphatidylcholine and cholesterol from liposomes, liposomes loaded with metaproterenol, and rabbit surfactant from adult rabbit lungs. *Am. Rev. Respir. Dis.* 139:752–58

124. Meisner, D., Pringle, J., Mezei, M. 1989. Liposomal pulmonary drug delivery. *J. Microencapsul.* 6:379–87

125. Gregoriadis, G. 1989. The physiology of the liposome. *News Physiol. Sci.* 4:146–51

126. Hug, P., Sleight, R. G. 1991. Liposomes for the transformation of eukaryotic cells. *Biochim. Biophys. Acta* 1097:1–17

127. Hughes, B. J., Kennel, S., Lee, R., Huang, L. 1989. Monoclonal antibody targeting of liposomes to mouse lung in vivo. *Cancer Res.* 49:6214–20

128. Maruyama, K., Holmberg, E., Kennel, S. J., Klibanov, A., Torchilin, V. P., Huang, L. 1990. Characterization of in vivo immunoliposome targeting to pulmonary endothelium. *J. Pharmacol. Sci.* 79:978–84

129. Felgner, P. L., Ringold, G. M. 1989. Cationic liposome-mediated transfection. *Nature* 337:387–88

130. Maruyama, K., Kennel, S. J., Huang, L. 1990. Lipid composition is important for highly efficient target binding and retention of immunoliposomes. *Proc. Natl. Acad. Sci. USA* 87:5744–48

131. Nabel, E. G., Plautz, G., Nabel, G. J. 1990. Site-specific gene expression in vivo by direct gene transfer into the arterial wall. *Science* 249:1285–88

132. Jankowski, M., Hornsleth, A., Olsen, P. G. 1990. IgG-subclass-specific antibody reactivity to respiratory syncytial virus polypeptides investigated by Western blot. *Res. Virol.* 141:343–53

133. Debs, R. J., Freedman, L.P., Edmunds, S., Gaensler, K. L., Duzgunes, N., Yamamoto, K. R. 1990. Regulation of gene expression in vivo by liposome-mediated delivery of a purified transcription factor. *J. Biol. Chem.* 265:10189–92

134. Brigham, K. L., Meyrick, B., Christman, B., Magnuson, M., King, G., et al. 1989. In vivo transfection of murine lungs with a functioning prokaryotic gene using a liposome vehicle. *Am. J. Med. Sci.* 298:278–81

135. Hazinski, T. A., Ladd, P. A., DeMatteo, C. A. 1991. Localization and induced expression of fusion genes in the rat lung. *Am. J. Respir. Cell. Mol. Biol.* 4:206–9

136. Yoshimura, K., Rosenfeld, M. A., Nakamura, H., Scherer, E. M., Pavirani, A., et al. 1992. Expression of the human cystic fibrosis transmembrane conductance regulator gene in the mouse lung after in vivo intra-tracheal plasmid-mediated gene transfer.

Am. Rev. Respir. Dis. 145:689A (Abstr.)

137. Hazinski, T. A. 1992. Prospects for gene therapy in acute lung injury. *Am. J. Med. Sci.* 304(4):131–35

138. Hazinski, T. A. 1992. Liposome-mediated transfer of fusion genes to the intact lung. *Semin. Perinatol.* 16(3): 200–4

139. Glasser, S. W., Korfhagen, T. R., Wert, S. E., Bruno, M. D., McWilliams, K. M., et al. 1991. Genetic element from human surfactant protein SP-C gene confers bronchiolar-alveolar cell specificity in transgenic mice. *Am. J. Physiol.* 261:L349–56

140. Weintraub, H., Cheng, P. F., Conrad, K. 1986. Expression of transfected DNA depends on DNA topology. *Cell* 46:115–22

141. Deleted in proof

142. Yamaya, M., Finkbeiner, W. E., Widdicombe, J. H. 1991. Altered ion transport by tracheal glands in cystic fibrosis. *Am. J. Physiol.* 261: L491–94

143. Trezise, A. E. O., Buchwald, M. 1991. In vivo cell-specific expression of the cystic fibrosis transmembrane conductance regulator. *Nature* 353:434–37

144. McBride, J. T. 1985. Postpneumonectomy airway growth in the ferret. *J. Appl. Physiol.* 58:1010–14

144. Gellert, M. 1981. DNA topoisomerases. *Annu. Rev. Biochem.* 50: 879–910

145. Kirchner, K. K., McBride, J. T. 1990. Changes in airway length after unilateral pneumonectomy in weanling ferrets. *J. Appl. Physiol.* 68:187–92

146. Berger, L. C., Burri, P. H. 1985. Timing of the quantitative recovery in the regenerating rat lung. *Am. Rev. Respir. Dis.* 132:777–83

147. Stahlman, M. T., Gray, M. E., Chytil, F., Sundell, H. 1988. Effect of retinol on fetal lamb tracheal epithelium, with and without epidermal growth factor. *Lab. Invest.* 59:25–35

148. Sundell, H. W., Gray, M. E., Serenius, F. S., Escobedo, M. B., Stahlman, M. T. 1980. Effects of epidermal growth factor on lung maturation in fetal lambs. *Am. J. Pathol.* 100:707–25

149. Cash, H. A., Woods, D. E., McCullough, B., Johanson, W. G., Bass, J. A. 1979. A rat model of chronic respiratory infection with *Pseudomonas aeruginosa*. *Am. Rev. Respir. Dis.* 119:453–59

150. Graham, L. M., Vasil, A., Vasil, M. L., Voelkel, N. F., Stenmark, K. R. 1990. Decreased pulmonary vasoreactivity in an animal model of chronic *Pseudomonas* pneumonia. *Am. Rev. Respir. Dis.* 142:221–29

151. Friedmann, T. 1989. Progress toward human gene therapy. *Science* 244:1275–80

Annu. Rev. Physiol. 1993. 55:209–26

INTERRELATIONSHIP OF PLEURAL AND PULMONARY INTERSTITIAL LIQUID

Jeanine P. Wiener-Kronish

Departments of Anesthesia and Medicine, and Cardiovascular Research Institute, University of California, San Francisco, San Francisco, California 94143

V. Courtney Broaddus

Department of Medicine, San Francisco General Hospital, and Cardiovascular Research Institute, University of California, San Francisco, San Francisco, California 94110

KEY WORDS: pulmonary edema, alveolar epithelium, systemic circulation, permeability, pressure gradient

INTRODUCTION

The close proximity of the pleural space and the pulmonary interstitial space makes it reasonable to ask whether liquid can flow from one space to the other. Such liquid flow could have great consequences for regulation of lung interstitial liquid volume. Because the two spaces have different lymphatic drainage pathways, a flexibility in liquid flow could endow functional advantages in clearing excess liquid. In this review, we discuss the accumulating evidence about the existence and the significance of liquid flow between the pulmonary interstitium and pleural space.

THE INTERRELATIONSHIP OF PLEURAL AND PULMONARY INTERSTITIAL LIQUID DURING NORMAL CONDITIONS

In the normal lung, as in all organs, there is a net outward flow of liquid and protein from the vasculature into the extravascular interstitial space. This normal interstitial filtrate is removed by the lung lymphatics. Most investiga-

209

tors believe that normal pleural liquid has little or no relationship to the lung interstitial liquid, but rather originates from the high-pressure systemic capillaries of the pleura (46, 52).

The evidence that normal pleural liquid originates from the systemic circulation, not the pulmonary circulation, is based in large part on the protein concentration of pleural liquid. In sheep, a species with a similar pleural anatomy to that of humans, normal pleural liquid contains 1–1.5 g/dl total protein while normal lung interstitial liquid contains 4.5 g/dl total protein (19, 56). The protein concentration of the pleural liquid is comparable to that of filtrate from systemic microvessels. The low protein concentration results from a high degree of sieving across the microvascular membrane driven by the gradient between microvascular and perimicrovascular pressures. Presuming there are no changes in the permeability of the systemic microvascular membrane, the protein concentration would vary with the microvascular pressure and the pleural pressure, which is a major determinant of the subpleural, perimicrovascular, pressure. In two studies, pleural liquid protein concentration has been examined in animals with different systemic pressures. Spontaneously hypertensive rats were found to have a significantly lower pleural liquid protein concentration than were control (Wistar-Kyoto) normotensive rats (29). Sheep, during development from the fetal to the adult stage, demonstrated a progressive increase in systemic blood pressure and a decrease in pulmonary artery pressure. Pleural liquid protein concentrations were found to decrease with development, as expected if the source was the systemic circulation, and the lung interstitial liquid (lymph) protein concentrations were found to increase, as expected if the source was the pulmonary circulation (Figure 1) (12). Changes in pleural pressure can also alter the pressure gradient across the systemic pleural microvessels. In the latter study, some of the decrease in pleural liquid protein concentration in the developing sheep possibly was due to a lower pleural pressure with increasing size. Avery & Cook found that pleural pressure decreased from 0 to −2 to −3.3 mm Hg with development from fetal to newborn to adult goats, which they attributed to an increasing stiffness of the chest wall (5). In an examination of five different species of different size, Miserrochi and co-workers found that both pleural pressure and pleural liquid protein concentration decreased with increasing body mass (38). In these studies, changes in the transvascular pressure gradient across the systemic microvessels of the pleura led to expected changes in protein concentration of the pleural liquid.

Of the two pleural membranes, it is likely that the parietal is the major source of normal pleural liquid. For one reason, the parietal pleura is supplied by systemic vessels in all species examined, whereas the visceral pleura is not. Larger mammalian species (cow, pig, sheep, horse, and human) have a thick visceral pleura supplied by the bronchial circulation, whereas smaller

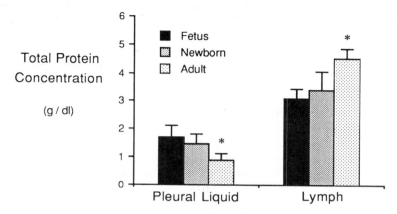

Figure 1 Developmental changes in total protein concentrations of pleural liquid and lung lymph in sheep. At each age, pleural liquid differs significantly from lymph. During development, the protein concentration of pleural liquid significantly decreases, whereas that of lymph increases. * = significantly different from fetal and newborn values (reproduced with permission from 12).

species (rat, rabbit, cat, dog) have a thin visceral pleura consisting of little more than a mesothelial cell layer overlying the lung parenchyma and supplied by the pulmonary circulation (34). For another reason, even in those larger species in which both pleurae are supplied by systemic microvessels, parietal pleural microvessels are closer to the pleural space (10–12 μm) than are visceral pleural microvessels (20–50 μm) (52). Finally, the microvascular pressure in the parietal pleura is likely to be higher than that of the visceral pleura because the bronchial vessels supplying the visceral pleura drain into low-pressure pulmonary, not systemic, veins (3). Pleural liquid formation has been measured noninvasively in both the sheep, an animal with a systemic circulation to both the parietal and visceral pleura, and the rabbit, an animal with a systemic circulation to the parietal pleura only, and expressed as the rate per pleural surface area. The fact that the rates are quite similar (2.5 ml $\cdot$ m^{-2} $\cdot$h^{-1}, rabbit; 2.0 ml$\cdot$m$^{-2}\cdot$ h^{-1}, sheep) suggests that the parietal pleura is the major source of the liquid. And yet, other evidence suggests that, at least during invasive procedures that might induce inflammation, the visceral pleura and its bronchial circulation also contribute liquid. In experiments in which sheep lungs were isolated in a water-tight bag to allow collection of pleural liquid, ligation of the bronchoesophageal artery led to a 54% decrease in pleural liquid collected (57). We conclude that it is the systemic circulation of the parietal, and sometimes visceral, pleural membranes that is the source of normal pleural liquid.

Once formed, pleural liquid flows along intrapleural pressure gradients toward interlobular fissures, the hilum, or the dependent regions of the pleural space. Such flows have been demonstrated by the movement of small radiolabeled boluses of liquid instilled into the pleural space (39), deduced from the finding of a vertical pressure gradient significantly less than a static 1 cm/cm height gradient (30), or measured with a minimally invasive, dependent pleural catheter (10). The pleural liquid ultimately drains into stomata connecting the pleural space to parietal pleural lymphatics. It was recognized by early investigators that lymphatics on the visceral pleural side did not open into the pleural space: carbon or dyes instilled into the pleural space stained the parietal pleura, not the visceral (17). Normal rates of exit of pleural liquid equal the slow rates of pleural liquid entry that have been measured in sheep as 0.01 $ml\cdot kg^{-1}\cdot h^{-1}$ (56), in rabbits as 0.017 $ml\cdot kg^{-1}\cdot h^{-1}$(10), and in dogs as 0.020 and 0.019 $ml\cdot kg^{-1}\cdot h^{-1}$ (37, 42). These slow rates, equivalent to approximately 0.6–1.2 ml/h in a 60 kg human, are comparable to known rates of interstitial liquid production.

Normal pulmonary interstitial liquid, on the other hand, is filtered across pulmonary microvessels, either at the alveolar or the extra-alveolar capillaries. The constant pulmonary filtrate flows to alveolar junctions where the liquid enters the initial pulmonary lymphatics. From this point, the pulmonary lymphatics carry lung lymph to the hilum and to mediastinal lymphatics. No pulmonary lymphatics open upon or drain into the pleural space. Therefore, we believe that there is little, if any, interrelationship of pleural and pulmonary interstitial liquids when lung liquid content is normal. The distinction becomes more blurred when the lungs become edematous.

THE INTERRELATIONSHIP OF PLEURAL AND PULMONARY LIQUID DURING PULMONARY EDEMA

Conditions Allowing Movement of Liquid to Pleural Space

When the filtration of liquid across the pulmonary vessels increases, some of the excess liquid is drained by the lung lymphatics, while other liquid collects in peribronchial interstitial spaces (51). The edema in these extra-lymphatic interstitial spaces constitutes a sequestered pool, in continuity not with pulmonary lymphatics, but with other interstitial spaces of the lung (20). The route of clearance of this interstitial edema has been unclear; some studies have shown that the lymphatic clearance alone does not account for the observed rate of edema clearance (31). Possible routes of interstitial edema clearance include the pulmonary circulation (8), airways (54), mediastinum (21), or pleural space. Flow from the lung interstitium into the pleural space would be a function of two factors: (a) the liquid pressure gradient across the visceral pleura, and (b) the permeability of the pleural membrane.

The subpleural pressure is more positive than that of the pleural space, and this pressure gradient increases with the development of edema. Using micropuncture in isolated dog lungs with different amounts of edema, Bhattacharya and co-workers measured a gradient of 1.3 cm H_2O from the subpleural alveolar junctions to the pleural space in non-edematous lungs that increased to 3.0–4.4 cm H_2O during moderate to severe edema (7). The subpleural junctional pressure rose steeply after the lung water reached 5.0 g/g dry lung and reached a plateau at a lung water of 6.0 g/g dry lung. Liquid flow across the visceral pleura in these experiments was not measured.

The pleural membranes themselves are leaky to liquid and protein. Such conclusions arise from the study of the pleural membrane itself and that of the closely related peritoneal membrane (40). Whether studied after excision (25, 44) or in situ (43), the pleural membranes appear to offer little resistance to the movement of liquid and protein. When studying the intact lung, however, Kinasewitz and co-workers measured a higher resistance to protein and liquid flow out across the visceral pleura, a resistance expected of endothelium. The investigators concluded that the major barrier to liquid and protein flow out of the lung was the endothelial membrane of the subpleural microvessels, not the visceral pleural membrane (26, 27). Thus once liquid has flowed across an endothelial membrane, there is little to prevent its movement across the visceral pleural membrane.

Given a gradient of pressure across the visceral pleura into the pleural space and a leaky membrane as a barrier, it is not surprising that liquid could move from the lung into the pleural space. What is the evidence for such a route of liquid movement and of what importance could this route be to the clearance of lung edema?

Flow of Liquid from Lung Interstitium to Pleural Space

HYDROSTATIC EDEMA   The study of the source of pleural effusion in the face of elevated pulmonary and/or systemic pressures has been complicated by the difficulty of isolating the different pressure changes and the multiple effects of these pressure changes. Systemic pressure elevation could lead to pleural effusion by increasing filtration across the systemic circulation of parietal membranes as well as by decreasing lymphatic flow through increases in the downstream venous pressure. Pulmonary pressure elevation could lead to pleural effusion by increasing filtration across the pulmonary circulation and across the systemic circulation of the thick visceral pleura, which drains into pulmonary veins. The timing of these changes may matter; for example, a short-lived increase in pulmonary venous pressure may not lead to the extent of interstitial edema needed to see liquid flow into the pleural space, and a chronic increase in systemic venous pressure may lead to adaptation in lymphatic contractility and increased pleural liquid clearance.

In a careful attempt to separate the effects of pulmonary from systemic pressure elevation, Mellins and co-workers inflated balloons in either the left atrium or at the right atrium prior to volume-loading anesthetized dogs (35). After 2 hr of pressure elevation to 25 mm Hg, the investigators recovered more pleural liquid from the animals with systemic pressure elevation (68 ml) than from those with pulmonary pressure elevation (26 ml). Elevation of both pressures had an additive effect on the pleural effusion volume recovered (88 ml). Based on later studies, we have suggested that 2 hr is insufficient to observe the contribution from the lung (14). This study, however, does demonstrate the contribution to pleural effusion of both the systemic pleural circulation and the chest wall, which is the sole location of the systemic pleural circulation in the dog.

In clinical studies, there was also confusion about whether pleural liquid accumulated more from pulmonary or from systemic pressure elevation (47, 55). Older clinical studies were limited to clinical and roentgenographic examination and necropsy findings. In modern clinical studies, however, all hemodynamic pressures can be measured. In an important clinical study, Wiener-Kronish and co-workers compared the elevation of different pressures with the presence of pleural effusion using ultrasound, a sensitive technique for detecting pleural liquid. They found a close association between the elevation of pulmonary artery wedge pressure and the presence of pleural effusion (61). In order to determine whether systemic venous pressure could independently affect pleural effusion formation, a companion study was performed in which only patients with elevated pulmonary artery and right atrial pressures were examined (60). In this group, no pleural effusion could be detected. Although these studies necessarily were of patients with chronic changes in pressures, they lent strong support to the connection between elevated pulmonary artery wedge pressure and the presence of excess pleural liquid.

In experimental studies, we and others have confirmed that lung edema enters the pleural space and have estimated the relative importance of the pleural route of edema clearance. The initial experimental evidence that pleural liquid was coming from the lung was the observation that the protein concentration ratio (pleural/plasma) of pleural liquid increased after volume-loading (Table 1) (14). If the liquid arose from systemic vessels, a higher hydrostatic pressure and liquid flow would be expected to create a filtrate with a lower protein concentration ratio. The higher ratio strongly suggested that the liquid arose from a different source, the pulmonary circulation. Indeed, the pleural liquid protein concentration ratio was similar to that of lung lymph. In order to isolate the lung and avoid confounding effects of the chest wall with its liquid formation and absorption, we exposed the lungs of some sheep and enveloped them in impermeable bags (14). To compare pleural liquid to lung interstitial liquid, we collected lung lymph. After volume-loading to elevate the pulmonary capillary wedge pressure by 10–30 cm H_2O, liquid began to flow from the lung across the visceral pleura. This flow reached a steady state by 2 hr. Terminally, the pleural liquid contained the same protein concentration as that of the lung lymph and of peribronchovascular cuff interstitial liquid sampled from the frozen lungs. The frozen lungs showed extensive edema in the subpleural space continuous with the intrapulmonary septae (Figure 2). When the amount of edema exiting by the pleural route was compared to the amounts of edema (excess liquid) exiting the lung by lymph and remaining in the lung, the pleural liquid accounted for 23% (at 20 cm H_2O PCWP elevation) and 29% (at 30 cm H_2O) of the total edema formed. There are several points to be made. First, it took 2 hr of volume-loading before this route of edema clearance reached a steady state; we think this time was necessary for the liquid to accumulate beneath the visceral pleura. Second, by measuring and accounting for absorption rates from the pleural space in the face of elevated systemic pressures, we were able to show that the lung leakage accounted for most of the pleural effusion volume found in the closed-chest sheep. Finally, although we subtracted conservative estimates of the visceral pleural membrane contribution, we could not completely exclude a contribution from it and its bronchial circulation to the liquid collected. Since that time, however, we have shown similar leakage from edematous in situ lungs of rabbits, a species without a separate pleural circulation (V. C. Broaddus, unpublished observations).

Other studies have shown leakage of lung edema across the visceral pleura in different settings. Pleural liquid has leaked from isolated edematous lungs (16, 28). In anesthetized sheep, left atrial pressure elevation for 6–24 hr led to the development of pleural effusion. In the five sheep with extravascular lung water above 4.5 g/g dry lung, all had pleural effusions (50–240 ml) with a high pleural protein concentration ratio (0.46) (4). In a study of anesthetized dogs with hydrostatic edema induced by left-atrial balloon inflation and volume-loading, pleural effusion was found to account for approximately 21% of the total edema formed, although in this study of closed-chested animals, the effects of the chest wall on both pleural liquid formation and absorption were not taken into account (derived from Table 2, Reference 9).

From these clinical and experimental studies, we conclude that hydrostatic pulmonary edema clears the lung via the pleural space, as well as by the lymphatics and other routes. Once in the pleural space, this liquid will exit through the parietal pleural lymphatics. The pleural space therefore constitutes an additional safety factor against the development of alveolar edema.

INCREASED PERMEABILITY EDEMA   Unlike hydrostatic edema, increased permeability edema can be more easily induced selectively in the lung. The

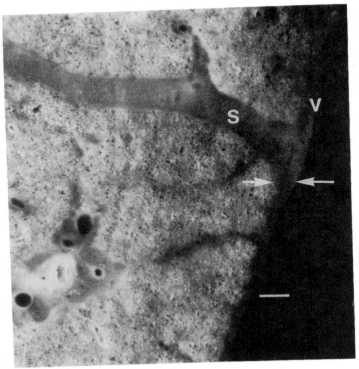

Figure 2   Frozen lung and visceral pleura from the closed side of the chest of a volume-loaded sheep. There is a band of edema (between arrows) present in the visceral pleura (*V*) continuous with edema in intrapulmonary septae (*S*). Horizontal bar, 1 mm (reproduced with permission from 14).

Table 1   Pleural liquid in sheep with both sides of the chest closed with and without volume-loading[a]

Wedge pressure elevation (cm H_2O)	Number of sheep	Protein concentration		Volume on both sides (ml)
		g/dl	pleural liquid/plasma	
0	21	1.0 ± 0.5	0.15 ± 0.07	3.7 ± 2.9
20	4	1.0 ± 0.1	0.27 ± 0.03^b	30.8 ± 8.8
30	3	1.1 ± 0.2	0.44 ± 0.10^c	120.0 ± 58.8

[a] Values represent mean ± one standard deviation. [b] Significantly different from values at 0 cm H_2O pressure elevation. [c] Significantly different from values at 0 and 20 cm H_2O pressure elevation (from 14).

presence of pleural effusion can therefore be attributed to lung leakage with less concern about other possible sources of liquid such as the pleural membranes.

EXPERIMENTAL STUDIES   The association of increased permeability pulmonary edema and pleural effusion has been most consistently observed after alpha-naphthyl thiourea (ANTU) administration to many species. The reason for this association was perhaps first examined by Richter in a study of rats exposed to ANTU (48). He observed that lung edema reached a maximum approximately 1 hr after intraperitoneal ANTU administration, while high protein pleural effusion did not appear until the third hour. Richter concluded that the effusion probably arose from the lungs and only after the lungs were well-filled. In later studies of the histology of ANTU-induced injury, investigators concluded that ANTU caused selective injury to pulmonary capillaries (18). They did not, however, examine the visceral pleura. In another study, the investigators hypothesized that hypoxemia did not occur in their rats exposed to ANTU because lung interstitial edema was cleared into the pleural space (53), and thus alveolar edema was avoided. By light and electron microscopy, the edema was located in the peribronchovascular cuffs and in the visceral subpleural tissues (mistakenly referred to as parietal). In a study in which dogs were given ANTU 24 hr previously, pleural effusion was noted only in those animals with an extravascular lung water greater than 5.0 g/g dry lung (45), and the protein concentration of the pleural liquid was the same as that of right duct lymph, approximately 73% of plasma.

Pleural effusions have also been described following other types of lung-specific injuries, such as those due to hyperoxia (15, 49, 50) or intravenous ethchlorvynol (36). In a study designed to show the origin of pleural effusion in hyperoxic rats, Bernaudin and co-workers used intravenous anti-horseradish peroxidase (HRP) IgG as a morphologic tracer (6). On light and electron microscopy, they described edema of the subpleural tissues and formation of focal submesothelial blebs caused by the distention of the visceral mesothelial layer. As early as 5–10 min after intravenous injection, the anti-HRP antibodies were found in the subpleural tissues, in the distended submesothelial spaces, and in intercellular spaces between mesothelial cells. No tracer was found beneath the parietal pleura. They concluded that hyperoxic pleural effusion formed from lung edema flowing across the visceral pleura into the pleural space.

In order to measure all pleural liquid formed and to determine the role of the pleural route of edema clearance to that of other routes of edema clearance, we isolated the lungs of anesthetized sheep and measured pleural liquid at different times after intravenous oleic acid (58). Within 1 hr of oleic acid administration, copious pulmonary edema froth could be obtained from the endotracheal tubes of the sheep. Pleural effusion, however, did not appear until 3 hr after lung edema formation (Table 2). By morphologic assessment, subpleural edema was greatest at 5 and 8 hr, intrapulmonary septae were distended, and there was no evidence of pleural injury (Figures 3, 4). The protein concentration of the pleural liquid was approximately 75% of that of plasma. This was the same as that reported for lymph collected in another study of oleic acid injury in sheep (24). Finally, by comparing the quantity of pleural liquid to that of lung edema and of lymph flow in oleic-acid injury (24), we estimated that 21% of the lung edema flowed into the pleural space. The pleural space therefore was an important pathway for edema clearance and of similar importance in increased permeability as in hydrostatic edema.

CLINICAL STUDIES   Pleural effusion develops in humans with increased permeability pulmonary edema. Recent findings contrast with previous reports that pleural effusion is rare in patients with acute lung injury (22, 23). In a radiographic study of patients with both hydrostatic and increased-permeability edema, we determined the presence of pleural effusion without knowledge of the type of edema (1). For each patient, a sample of pulmonary edema liquid and plasma had been obtained at the time of intubation in order to classify patients as having either hydrostatic edema (edema to plasma protein concentration ratio < 0.60) or increased permeability edema (ratio > 0.70). All clinical and hemodynamic data were found to be consistent with the classification based on the edema protein ratio. There was no difference in the incidence of pleural effusion in the two groups of patients; in the 15 patients with hydrostatic edema, 40% had pleural effusion, and in the 25 patients with increased permeability edema, 36% had pleural effusion. In

Table 2 Closed-chest sheep: pleural fluid collected compared with pulmonary pressures and extravascular lung water following intravenous oleic acid

Time	Pulmonary arterial pressure (cm H_2O)	Pulmonary arterial wedge pressure (cm H_2O)	EVLW (g water/g dry lung)	Pleural fluid volume (ml/thorax)
Control (n = 12)	23 ± 5	13 ± 3	3.6 ± 0.25[a]	1.8 ± 1.5[a]
Oleic acid				
1 hr (n = 12)	37 ± 14	16 ± 7	6.0 ± 0.7 (n = 2)	2.1 ± 0.8 (n = 2)
3 hr (n = 10)	26 ± 12	11 ± 5	6.5 ± 0.7 (n = 4)	13.6 ± 8.7 (n = 4)
5 hr (n = 6)	47 ± 22	14 ± 1	8.0 ± 0.4 (n = 3)	48.5 ± 16.9 (n = 3)
8 hr (n = 3)	38 ± 8	14 ± 3	6.6 ± 0.6 (n = 3)	45.5 ± 16.9 (n = 3)

All data are expressed as the mean ± one standard deviation. [a] Significantly different by analysis of variance from other experimental periods (from 58).

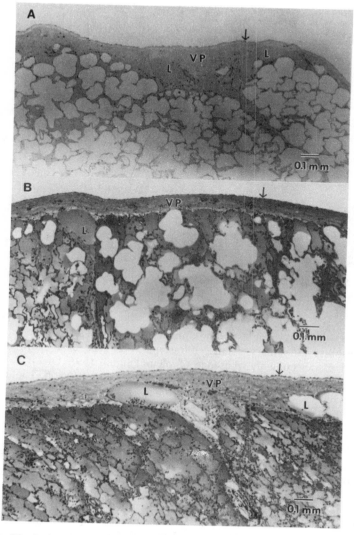

Figure 3   Histologic view of the sheep's lung and visceral pleura (*A*) 1 hr after oleic acid infusion, (*B*) 3 hr after oleic acid infusion, and (*C*) 8 hr after oleic acid infusion. Alveolar edema and infiltration of leukocytes were the first signs of acute lung injury. The visceral pleura (*VP*) gradually became washed out and swollen by tracking of the edema liquid along the interlobular septae. Lymphatics (*L*) in the visceral pleura also become distended. Mesothelial cells (*arrows*) on the visceral pleural surface remained intact at all experimental time points that were studied (reproduced with permission from 58).

Figure 4   Macroscopic view of the lung's surface from a sheep given oleic acid for 1 hr. The interlobular septae (*S*) are partially distended with edema liquid (reproduced with permission from 58).

another study of patients with clinical acute lung injury and increased permeability pulmonary edema, ultrasound was used as a more sensitive method of detecting the presence of pleural liquid (59). Of eight patients examined with ultrasound, all had high-protein pleural effusion. These results suggest that severe pulmonary edema from any cause is associated with pleural effusion.

Flow of Liquid from Alveolar Space to Pleural Space

Depending on the integrity of the alveolar epithelial barrier, alveolar liquid may represent a pool separate from the interstitial and pleural liquid (62). In our study of sheep with increased permeability edema due to oleic acid, the protein concentration of alveolar edema liquid was significantly different from that of pleural liquid (Table 3) (58). In these experiments, the protein concentration in alveolar edema liquid probably increased because of ongoing liquid clearance across the alveolar epithelium (32). Comparable increases in alveolar edema protein concentration have been found for patients with edema caused by either hydrostatic edema or increased permeability edema, and can be attributed to a recovery of normal barrier and active transport functions of the alveolar epithelium (33). In situations in which the alveolar epithelial barrier recovers, alveolar liquid becomes a separate liquid pool, and its protein

Table 3 Comparison of total protein concentration ratio in pleural liquid and alveolar edema liquid in closed-chest sheep

Time	Protein concentration (pleural liquid/plasma)	Protein concentration (alveolar liquid/plasma)
Control[a] (n = 23)	0.2 ± 0.1[b]	—
Oleic acid		
1 hr (n = 2)	0.2 ± 0.2	1.0
3 hr (n = 4)	0.6 ± 0.1[c]	1.1 ± 0.1
5 hr (n = 3)	0.6 ± 0.1[c]	1.0 ± 0.3
8 hr (n = 3)	0.7 ± 0.1[c]	1.3 ± 0.1

[a] Data are expressed as mean ± one standard deviation. [b] Based on 23 normal sheep. [c] Significantly higher than baseline by analysis of variance (from 58).

concentration diverges from that of lung interstitial liquid. In those circumstances, pleural liquid more accurately represents lung interstitial liquid and lymph than does alveolar liquid.

In experiments in which the alveolar epithelium is severely injured and fails to recover barrier functions, pleural effusions can form that are representative of alveolar liquid. We have found that instillation of live *Pseudomonas aeruginosa* (10^9 bacteria) into the airspaces of the lung consistently causes epithelial injury (J. Wiener-Kronish, unpublished observations). Using an experimental protocol that allows the quantification of the flux of instilled alveolar protein tracers, we found instillation of live *P. aeruginosa* increased the efflux of an alveolar tracer into the blood and also the influx of a vascular tracer into the airspaces of the lung. Associated with this, protein-rich pleural effusions formed that clearly originated from the airspaces of the lung because they contained the protein tracer and bacteria introduced into the airspaces. When either *E. coli* endotoxin, a lower inoculum of bacteria, or mutated bacteria missing virulence products were instilled into the airspaces of the lung, the alveolar epithelium was not damaged and pleural effusion was not found (J. Wiener-Kronish, unpublished observations). Therefore, alveolar epithelial injury by *P. aeruginosa* allows alveolar liquid to enter the interstitium and to leave the lung in part via the pleural space.

THE INTERRELATIONSHIP OF PLEURAL AND PULMONARY LIQUID DURING PLEURAL EFFUSION

Early investigators reasoned that pleural liquid was normally absorbed across the visceral pleura into the low-pressure pulmonary capillaries. Such arguments failed to take into account several facts: pleural liquid is absorbed by bulk flow (with no change in protein concentration), not by diffusion (which would cause a progressive increase in protein concentration), and the pressure of the low-pressure pulmonary capillaries still exceeds the pleural pressure. Clearly, in the normal situation, pleural liquid is absorbed into lymphatics, not into the lung.

Under some circumstances, there is evidence that pleural liquid can flow across the visceral pleura into the lung. When the lung was isolated in an impermeable bag, Starling forces could be adjusted to the point that pleural liquid was absorbed across the visceral pleura into the lung (26). When very large instillates (20 ml/kg) were introduced into the pleural space of rabbits, the water content of the adjacent lung increased by 33% (41). Thus the question arises whether, in the face of pleural effusion, pleural liquid flows into the lung.

Even when excess pleural liquid accumulates, evidence fails to support a reversed flow of liquid from the pleural space into the lung. It is true that when pleural liquid accumulates, pleural pressures increase (2). As long as the lung is inflated, however, the pleural pressure should be lower than the subpleural pressure of the lung. When moderate-sized pleural effusions (10 ml/kg) were instilled into one pleural space of sheep, it was evident that almost all pleural liquid absorption could be accounted for by lymphatic flow, not by diffusion as would be expected with liquid flow into the lung (13). First, there was no difference in extravascular lung water between the lung on the side of the instillate and the lung on the opposite side at 2–24 hr after instillation. Second, during absorption of the effusions, pleural liquid protein and albumin concentrations remained constant and erythrocytes were readily cleared. Following hyperoxic-induced lung injury and pleural effusion formation in rats, a tracer instilled into the pleural effusion heavily stained the parietal pleura, but did not enter the visceral pleura (6). Even when pleural liquid volume is increased, the pleural liquid does not appear to enter the lung. Presumably, if pleural liquid is increased to an extreme point where supra-atmospheric pleural pressures develop exceeding the pressures in the adjacent lung, a reversed flow can be induced (41).

SUMMARY

When the lung interstitium fills with liquid, lung interstitial liquid may flow across the visceral pleura into the pleural space. This route of interstitial liquid flow does not apparently depend on the type of edema because it is used equally in both hydrostatic and increased permeability edema. The route of flow depends mostly on the quantity and location of extravascular lung water. In experimental studies of hydrostatic and increased permeability edema, pleural effusion develops when extravascular lung water has reached a certain level for a certain amount of time. The necessary level of edema appears to be greater than 5.0 g/g dry lung, whether in hydrostatic edema [5.2–6.2 g/g dry lung (14); 5.0–6.5 g/g dry lung (4)] or in increased permeability edema due either to ANTU [5.1–9.3 g/g dry lung (45)], oleic-acid [6.5–8.0 g/g dry lung (58)], or alveolar *P. aeruginosa* [5.4–6.7 g/g dry lung (J. Wiener-Kronish, unpublished observations)]. The amount of lung edema necessary for pleural effusion formation is similar to the amount of edema Bhattacharya and co-workers found to be associated with the steep rise in subpleural pressure (7). The time before appearance of pleural effusion appears to be approximately 2 hr after the development of lung edema, whether the effusion results from hydrostatic edema (14) or increased permeability edema due to ANTU (48) or oleic acid (58). This delay may be necessary for the interstitial liquid to accumulate and the interstitial pressure to increase in the subpleural tissues to the point that liquid flows across the visceral pleura at a rate greater than the rate at which the parietal lymphatics can clear it.

Consequences of a pleural route of edema clearance are several. Pleural effusion that develops in the course of lung edema represents lung interstitial edema and can be sampled in lieu of sampling lung lymph. Indeed, pleural liquid may be a better sample of lung interstitial liquid than is alveolar edema liquid. The flow of lung interstitial liquid to the pleural space can protect against the development of alveolar edema by transferring excess liquid from the lung interstitium to the pleural space, where the effects on lung function are relatively minor. Obliteration of the pleural space may either lower the threshold for development of alveolar edema in the adjacent lungs, or slow the clearance of established edema; with chronic edema, other routes of clearance would likely adapt to compensate for the loss of the pleural clearance route.

ACKNOWLEDGMENTS

Both authors were supported in part by the National Heart Lung Blood Institute Pulmonary Vascular Specialized Center of Pulmonary Vascular Research Grant (HL-19155). In addition, Dr. Wiener-Kronish was supported by a California American Lung Association Established Investigator Award; Dr. Broaddus was supported by a National Heart Lung Blood Institute Clinical Investigator Award (HL-01893).

Literature Cited

1. Aberle, D. R., Wiener-Kronish, J. P., Webb, W. R., Matthay, M. A. 1988. The diagnosis of hydrostatic versus increased permeability edema based on chest radiographic criteria in critically ill patients. *Radiology* 168:73–79
2. Agostoni, E., D'Angelo, E. 1969. Thickness and pressure of the pleural liquid at various heights and with various hydrothoraces. *Resp. Physiol.* 6:330–42
3. Albertine, K. H., Wiener-Kronish, J. P., Roos, P. J., Staub, N. C. 1982. Structure, blood supply, and lymphatic vessels of the sheep's visceral pleura. *Am. J. Anat.* 165:277–94

4. Allen, S., Drake, J., Gabel, R. 1989. Left atrial hypertension causes pleural effusion formation in unanesthetized sheep. *Am. J. Physiol.* 257(26):H690–92

5. Avery, M. E., Cook, C. D. 1961. Volume-pressure relationships of lungs and thorax in fetal, newborn, and adult goats. *J. Appl. Physiol* 16:1034–38

6. Bernaudin, J. F., Theven, D., Pinchon, M. C., Brun-Pascaud, M., Bellon, B., Pocidalo, J. J. 1986. Protein transfer in hyperoxic induced pleural effusion in the rat. *Exp. Lung Res.* 10:23–38

7. Bhattacharya, J., Gropper, M. A., Staub, N. C. 1984. Interstitial fluid pressure gradient measured by micropuncture in excised dog lung. *J. Appl. Physiol.* 56:271–77

8. Bland, R., Hansen, T., Haberkern, C., Bressack, M., Hazinski, T., et al. 1982. Lung fluid balance in lambs before and after birth. *J. Appl. Physiol* 53:992–1004

9. Blomqvist, H., Berg, B., Frostell, C., Wickerts, C.-J., Hedenstierna, G. 1990. Net fluid leakage (LN) in experimental pulmonary oedema in the dog. *Acta Anaesthesiol. Scand.* 34:377–83

10. Broaddus, V. C., Araya, M. 1992. Liquid and protein dynamics using a new, minimally invasive pleural catheter in rabbits. *J. Appl. Physiol.* 72:851–57

11. Deleted in proof

12. Broaddus, V. C., Araya, M., Carlton, D. P., Bland, R. D. 1991. Developmental changes of pleural liquid protein concentration in sheep. *Am. Rev. Resp. Dis.* 143:38–41

13. Broaddus, V. C., Wiener-Kronish, J. P., Berthiaume, Y., Staub, N. C. 1988. Removal of pleural liquid and protein by lymphatics in awake sheep. *J. Appl. Physiol.* 64:384–90

14. Broaddus, V. C., Wiener-Kronish, J. P., Staub, N. C. 1990. Clearance of lung edema into the pleural space of volume-loaded, anesthetized sheep. *J. Appl. Physiol.* 68:2623–30

15. Charbonneau, P., Brun, M., Azoulay, E., Blayo, J. F., Bernaudin, M. C., Pocidalo, J. J. 1982. Respiratory and non-respiratory causes of death in the rat exposed to normobaric oxygen. *Bull. Eur. Physiopathol. Respir.* 18:633–42

16. Conhaim, R. L. 1986. Growth rate of perivascular cuffs in liquid-inflated dog lung lobes. *J. Appl. Physiol.* 61:647–53

17. Courtice, F. C., Simmonds, W. J. 1954. Physiological significance of lymph drainage of the serous cavities and lungs. *Physiol. Rev.* 34:419–48

18. Cunningham, A. L., Hurley, J. V. 1972. Alpha-naphthyl-thiourea-induced pulmonary oedema in the rat: a topographical and electron-microscope study. *J. Pathol.* 106:25–35

19. Erdmann, A. J., Vaughan, T. R., Brigham, K. L., Woolverton, W. C., Staub, N. C. 1975. Effect of increased vascular pressure on lung fluid balance in unanesthetized sheep. *Circ. Res.* 37:271–84

20. Gee, M. H., Havill, A. M. 1980. The relationship between pulmonary perivascular cuff fluid and lung lymph in dogs with edema. *Microvasc. Res.* 19:209–16

21. Jerome, E. H., Broaddus, V. C., Arakawa, M., Osorio, O., Neuburger, M., Staub, N. C. 1989. Evidence for mediastinal clearance of interstitial pulmonary edema. *FASEB J.* 3:A374 (Abstr.)

22. Joffre, N. 1974. The adult respiratory distress syndrome. *Am. J. Roentgen.* 122:719–34

23. Johnson, T. H., Altman, A. R., McCaffree, R. D. 1982. Radiologic considerations in ARDS treated with PEEP. *Clin. Chest Med.* 3:89–100

24. Julien, M., Hoeffel, J. M., Flick, M. R. 1986. Oleic acid injury in sheep. *J. Appl. Physiol.* 60:433–40

25. Kim, K. J., Critz, A. M., Crandall, E. D. 1979. Transport of water and solutes across sheep visceral pleura. *Am. Rev. Resp. Dis.* 120:883–92

26. Kinasewitz, G. T., Fishman, A. P. 1981. Influence of alterations in Starling forces on visceral pleural fluid movement. *J. Appl. Physiol.* 51:671–77

27. Kinasewitz, G. T., Groome, L. J., Marshall, R. P., Diana, J. N. 1983. Permeability of the canine visceral pleura. *J. Appl. Physiol.* 55:121–30

28. Lai-Fook, S. J. 1982. Perivascular interstitial fluid pressure measured by micropipettes in isolated dog lung. *J. Appl. Physiol.* 52:9–15

29. Lai-Fook, S. J., Kaplowitz, M. R. 1988. Pleural protein concentration and liquid volume in spontaneously hypertensive rats. *Microv. Res.* 35:101–8

30. Lai-Fook, S. J., Rodarte, J. R. 1991. Pleural pressure distribution and its relationship to lung volume and interstitial pressure. *J. Appl. Physiol.* 70:967–78

31. Mackersie, R. C., Christensen, J., Lewis, F. R. 1987. The role of pulmonary lymphatics in the clearance of

hydrostatic pulmonary edema. *J. Surg. Res.* 43:495–504

32. Matthay, M. A., Landolt, C. C., Staub, N. C. 1982. Differential liquid and protein clearance from the alveoli of anesthetized sheep. *J. Appl. Physiol.* 53:96–104

33. Matthay, M. A., Wiener-Kronish, J. P. 1990. Intact epithelial barrier function is critical for the resolution of alveolar edema in man. *Am. Rev. Respir. Dis.* 142:1250–57

34. McLaughlin, R. F., Tyler, W. S., Canada, R. O. 1961. A study of the subgross pulmonary anatomy in various mammals. *Am. J. Anat.* 108:149–65

35. Mellins, R. B., Levine, O. R., Fishman, A. P. 1970. Effect of systemic and pulmonary venous hypertension on pleural and pericardial fluid accumulation. *J. Appl. Physiol.* 29:564–69

36. Miller, K. S., Harley, R. A., Sahn, S. A. 1989. Pleural effusions associated with ethchlorvynol lung injury result from visceral pleural leak. *Am. Rev. Respir. Dis.* 140:764–70

37. Miniati, M., Parker, J. C., Pistolesi, M., Cartledge, J. T., Martin, D. J., et al. 1988. Reabsorption kinetics of albumin from the pleural space of dogs. *Am. J. Physiol.* 255:H375–85

38. Miserocchi, G., Negrini, D., Mortola, J. P. 1984. Comparative features of Starling-lymphatic interaction at the pleural level in mammals. *J. Appl. Physiol.* 56:1151–56

39. Miserocchi, G., Pistolesi, M., Miniati, M., Bellina, C. R., Negrini, D., Giuntini, C. 1984. Pleural liquid pressure gradients and intrapleural distribution of injected bolus. *J. Appl. Physiol.* 56:526–32

40. Nagel, W., Kuschinsky, W. 1970. Study of the permeability of the isolated dog mesentery. *Eur. J. Clin. Invest.* 1:149–54

41. Negrini, D., Bhattacharya, J. 1988. Liquid flow from pleura to lung parenchyma during pleural effusion in rabbits. *FASEB J.* 2:A1702

42. Negrini, D., Pistolesi, M., Miniati, M., Bellina, R., Giuntini, C., Miserocchi, G. 1985. Regional protein absorption rates from the pleural cavity in dogs. *J. Appl. Physiol.* 58:2062–67

43. Negrini, D., Townsley, M., Taylor, A. 1989. Hydraulic conductivity of the parietal pleura in dogs. *FASEB J.* 3:2713 (Abstr.)

44. Payne, D. K., Kinasewitz, G. T., Gonzalez, E. 1988. Comparative permeability of canine visceral and pa-

rietal pleura. *J. Appl. Physiol.* 65:2558–64

45. Pine, M. B., Beach, P. M., Cottrell, T. S., Scola, M., Turino, G. M. 1976. The relationship between right duct lymph flow and extravascular lung water in dogs given α-naphthylthiourea. *J. Clin. Invest.* 58:482–92

46. Pistolesi, M., Miniati, M., Giuntini, C. 1989. Pleural liquid and solute exchange: state of the art. *Am. Rev. Resp. Dis.* 140:825–47

47. Race, G. A., Scheifley, C. H., Edwards, J. E. 1957. Hydrothorax in congestive heart failure. *Am. J. Med.* 22:83–89

48. Richter, C. P. 1952. The physiology and cytology of pulmonary edema and pleural effusion produced in rats by alpha-naphthyl thiourea (ANTU). *J. Thorac. Surg.* 23:66–91

49. Robinson, F. R., Thomas, A. A., Rendon, L. 1968. Analysis of pleural effusion from rats exposed to high concentrations of oxygen. *Clin. Chem.* 14:1066–73

50. Royston, B. D., Webster, N. R., Nunn, J. F. 1990. Time course of changes in lung permeability and edema in the rat exposed to 100% oxygen. *J. Appl. Physiol.* 69:1532–37

51. Staub, N. C., Nagano, H., Pearce, M. L. 1967. Pulmonary edema in dogs, especially the sequence of fluid accumulation in lungs. *J. Appl. Physiol.* 22:227–40

52. Staub, N. C., Wiener-Kronish, J. P., Albertine, K. H. 1985. Transport through the pleura: physiology of normal liquid and solute exchange in the pleural space. In *The Pleura in Health and Disease*, ed. J. Chreacutetien, J. Bignon, A. Hirsch, pp. 169–93. New York: Dekker

53. Vivet, P., Brun-Pascaud, M., Mansour, H., Pocidalo, J. J. 1983. Non-hypoxaemic pulmonary oedema induced by α-naphthyl thiourea in the rat. *Br. J. Exp. Pathol.* 64:361–66

54. Vreim, C. E., Snashall, P. D., Demling, R. H., Staub, N. C. 1976. Lung lymph and free interstitial fluid protein composition in sheep with edema. *Am. J. Physiol.* 230:1650–53

55. White, P. D., August, S., Michie, C. R. 1947. Hydrothorax in congestive heart failure. *Am. J. Med. Sci.* 214:243–47

56. Wiener-Kronish, J. P., Albertine, K. H., Licko, V., Staub, N. C. 1984. Protein egress and entry rates in pleural fluid and plasma in sheep. *J. Appl. Physiol.* 56:459–63

57. Wiener-Kronish, J. P., Albertine, K. H., Osorio, O., Neuberger, M., Staub, N. C. 1988. The contribution of the bronchial and pulmonary circulation to liquid formation across the visceral pleura in anesthetized sheep. *Fed. Proc.* 2:A952

58. Wiener-Kronish, J. P., Broaddus, V. C., Albertine, K. H., Gropper, M. A., Matthay, M. A., Staub, N. C. 1988. Relationship of pleural effusions to increased permeability pulmonary edema in anesthetized sheep. *J. Clin. Invest.* 82:1422–29

59. Wiener-Kronish, J. P., Goldstein, R., Matthay, M. A. 1988. Pleural effusions are frequently associated with the adult respiratory distress syndrome. *Am. Rev. Respir. Dis.* 137:227 (Abstr.)

60. Wiener-Kronish, J. P., Goldstein, R., Matthay, R. A., Bionidi, J. W., Broaddus, V. C., et al. 1987. Lack of association of pleural effusion with chronic pulmonary arterial and right atrial hypertension. *Chest* 92:967–70

61. Wiener-Kronish, J. P., Matthay, M. A., Callen, P. W., Filly, R. A., Gamsu, G., Staub, N. C. 1985. Relationship of pleural effusions to pulmonary hemodynamics in patients with heart failure. *Am. Rev. Respir. Dis.* 132:1253–56

62. Zumsteg, T. A., Havill, A. M., Gee, M. H. 1982. Relationships among lung extravascular fluid compartments with alveolar flooding. *J. Appl. Physiol.* 53:267–71

Annu. Rev. Physiol. 1993. 55:227–48

NEUTROPHIL-ENDOTHELIAL CELL INTERACTIONS IN THE LUNG

Marlys H. Gee and Kurt H. Albertine

Departments of Physiology and Medicine, Division of Pulmonary Medicine and Critical Care, Jefferson Medical College, Thomas Jefferson University, 1020 Locust Street, Philadelphia, Pennsylvania 19107

KEY WORDS: lung injury, adherence proteins, cytokines, neutrophil margination

INTRODUCTION

It has proven surprisingly difficult to determine the relationship between neutrophils and pulmonary endothelial cells under normal conditions in the intact lung, let alone under conditions that result in endothelial injury. Some of the issues that bear directly on this problem include the size of the marginated pool of neutrophils in the lung, the distribution of neutrophils in the lung, the conditions governing neutrophil margination in the lung, the effect of margination on neutrophil and endothelial cell function, and the effect of activation on marginated and sequestered neutrophils and pulmonary endothelial cells. All of these issues are addressed in this chapter with particular emphasis on in situ studies of neutrophil-endothelial cell interaction and on issues that, in our opinion, have not been adequately studied as yet.

DEFINITIONS

Neutrophils within a circulatory bed can exist in several pools. Cells can be part of the circulating pool of neutrophils. Morphologically, we define the circulating pool in lung tissue sections as neutrophils that are free from contact with a vascular wall. In histological sections of lung tissue, this definition is applied to neutrophils that are greater than 10 μm from endothelial cells lining pre- and postcapillary vessels. This distance is greater than the diameter of neutrophils in situ (6 to 8 μm) (3, 55). Therefore, circulating cells contribute

227

to the total number of neutrophils within a particular vascular bed, but not to the marginated pool of neutrophils.

The marginated pool of neutrophils is comprised of cells that are transiently removed from the circulating pool. The disposition of these noncirculating, hence retained, cells has been demonstrated by intravital microscopy, first using systemic microvascular beds such as the mesentery (19, 26) and cheek pouch (9), and later using superficial pulmonary microvessels along the visceral pleura (35). When viewed by intravital microscopy, neutrophils (and other granulocytes) in this pool are seen rolling along the vessel wall, making transient physical contact with endothelial cells. Because of their physical contact with endothelial cells, such neutrophils are truly marginated. This morphological relationship provides a more exact definition of margination, in our opinion, than the physiological use of the term "margination," which identifies the portion of the total blood leukocyte pool not circulating, regardless of location or cause.

The marginated pool of neutrophils should function as a readily mobilizable store of cells for repletion of the circulating pool. The implication is that marginated and circulating neutrophils are in dynamic equilibrium (12). Unfortunately, we know more about the release of neutrophils developing in hematopoietic tissue than we know about the dynamic relationship between marginated neutrophils in the lung and the circulating pool.

Disappearance of neutrophils from the circulating pool can also be the result of sequestration, or increased retention, within a vascular bed. Sequestration is not synonymous with margination; sequestration is an abrupt, and sometimes sustained, change in the dynamic equilibrium between the marginated and circulating pools of neutrophils. Sequestration implies an active process representing a change in circulating neutrophils and endothelial cells. The change need not involve activation of neutrophils sufficient to produce measurable endothelial injury, however. An event as seemingly innocuous as placement of a flow-directed catheter in a pulmonary artery through an introducer in an external jugular vein can produce transient sequestration of neutrophils in awake sheep.

Emigration is the movement of neutrophils from the vascular compartment into an extravascular space which, in the lung, means either the interstitial compartment or the airspace. Emigration shares common features with sequestration. First, emigration is an active process in which some event (disruption of or injury to vascular endothelium) or chemical (chemotaxin) changes neutrophil and/or endothelial cell function to arrest neutrophil flux in microvessels and induce directed movement. Second, emigration of neutrophils is not sufficient evidence to infer that tissue injury is neutrophil-mediated (62).

Activation of neutrophils, in the context of tissue injury, is defined as an induced change in neutrophil function that results in release of reduced oxygen metabolites and proteolytic enzymes from primary and/or secondary granules. This is a very specific and restrictive definition of activation. Others have used the term much more broadly to argue that any change in neutrophil phenotype is activation. We reject this argument for the following reasons. First, margination of neutrophils may involve a change in neutrophil phenotype although margination is part of normal neutrophil function. Second, sequestration and emigration are processes that undoubtedly involve a change in neutrophil phenotype, yet these phenomena need not be associated with any pathophysiologic change in the function of endothelial cells, platelets, other phagocytic cells or epithelial cells (62). In other words, margination, sequestration, and emigration are necessary for neutrophil function as a phagocyte, but they are not sufficient for killing. Third, secretion of oxygen metabolites and proteolytic enzymes is necessary for bacterial killing. Therefore, it is reasonable to set these secretory activities apart from other events that are necessary, but not sufficient, for neutrophil bactericidal function.

NEUTROPHIL-ENDOTHELIAL CELL INTERACTIONS IN NORMAL LUNGS

The Size of the Marginated Neutrophil Pool in the Lung

The number of neutrophils in the normal lung is about three times the circulating pool of neutrophils (55). Although there are no estimates of the number of circulating neutrophils in the lung relative to the number of marginated cells, the majority of lung neutrophils are undoubtedly marginated because most of the vascular surface area is comprised of capillaries. Pulmonary neutrophils represent a true vascular pool since over 95% of the cells are in the vascular compartment with less than 4% in the pulmonary interstitium and alveolar airspace (55). Three different studies have shown that about 65% of the marginated neutrophils are in parenchymal vessels, primarily alveolar capillaries (Figure 1). A significant fraction of the marginated pool, however, is in pulmonary arteries (about 25%), with only 10% of the neutrophils in pulmonary veins.

In systemic microvessels, neutrophil margination occurs primarily in postcapillary venules (9, 19, 26). Margination in precapillary arterioles and capillaries is infrequently observed. This is in stark contrast to the primary site of margination of neutrophils in pulmonary microvessels (3, 35, 55). Thus postcapillary venules in systemic organs behave as alveolar capillaries in the lung with respect to the primary site of neutrophil margination.

Why capillaries in the lung are the major site of neutrophil margination

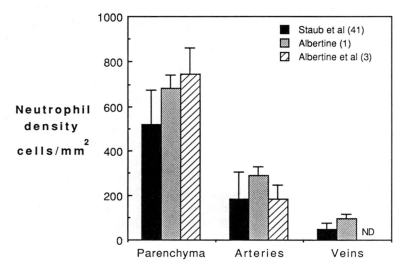

Figure 1   Distribution of marginated neutrophils in the pulmonary circulation of sheep. Data (X ± SD) were extracted from the references listed in the legend. ND means the measurement was not done.

and sequestration remains to be determined. Among the explanations is the unique anatomy of pulmonary capillaries. For example, the alveolar capillary bed is massive. Under normal circumstances, capillary blood volume is approximately equal to the stroke volume (60 to 75 ml). This large volume is accomodated by an enormous number of capillary segments, 277×10^9, (61) that span an average distance of about 800 μm (54) from the arterial beginning to the venous end of the pulmonary capillary bed. Since each capillary segment is only about 8 μm in length (61), neutrophils leaving a pulmonary arteriole would flow through roughly 100 capillary segments before reaching a pulmonary venule. The surface area, about 70 m^2, of the lung's capillary bed is also massive (61). The combination of blood volume, vessel length, and vessel total surface area for alveolar capillaries likely contributes to the enormous marginated pool of neutrophils by facilitating neutrophil-endothelial cell interaction.

Effect of Margination on Neutrophils

Margination in the lung clearly affects neutrophils since the size of the cells is dependent on vascular location. Albertine and co-workers (3) showed that the cross-sectional area of neutrophils is least for cells circulating in small pulmonary arteries and largest for cells moving in alveolar capillaries (Figure 2). A 40% increase in the cross-sectional area of neutrophils during passage through the pulmonary circulation is an extraordinary new finding since changes in size of this magnitude are normally attributed to neutrophil activation.

Sheep neutrophils also increase volume by 25 to 35% from circulating cells in pulmonary arteries to neutrophils in alveolar capillaries (3). To put this volume increase in perspective, increases in neutrophil volume of 50 to 60% have been measured for activated, phagocytozing cells in vitro (49, 50). Worthen et al (64) measured a volume increase of 90% for rabbit neutrophils recruited and activated in the alveolar airspace. Therefore, the volume increase observed as quiescent, circulating neutrophils enter alveolar capillaries is one third to one half of the volume increase measured with neutrophil activation.

Similar studies of neutrophil size and volume in systemic vascular beds have not been reported to our knowledge. It is a matter of some consequence since the distribution of neutrophils in systemic circulations is predominantly in postcapillary vessels. The systemic distribution has been explained by differences in shear forces in different parts of the circulation. However, Perry & Granger (45) found the distribution to be independent of shear rate. These authors suggest that the density distribution of ligands for adherence proteins may be less for arteriolar compared to venular endothelial cells. Although this is an intriguing possibility, the question of why endothelial cell properties change pre- and postcapillary remains unanswered.

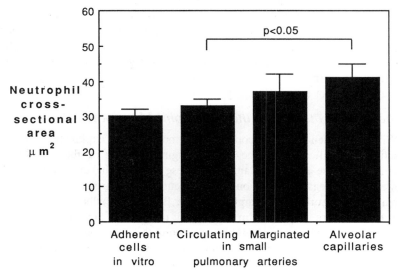

Figure 2 The cross-sectional area of sheep neutrophils in vitro and in situ in the pulmonary circulation. Data (X ± SD) are from Albertine et al (3).

Marginated neutrophils in the pulmonary circulation are morphologically and functionally normal; that is, the cells have not been activated using our definition of activation. The comparisons illustrated in Figure 3 show that neutrophils have lost the smooth round contour, apparent for circulating cells, by passage into alveolar capillaries. There is no evidence, however, of degranulation or vacuole formation characteristic of neutrophil activation in vitro and in situ (3). Furthermore, when marginated neutrophils are washed from the pulmonary circulation, the ability of marginated cells to release superoxide anion is the same as that measured in neutrophils isolated from the circulating pool in peripheral blood (36) (Figure 4). These results are in keeping with other known functions of neutrophils. For example, neutrophils must change shape during emigration from the vascular to the interstitial compartments, but this movement need not be associated with initiation of the respiratory burst or secretion of phagocytic enzymes.

Effect of Neutrophil Margination on Pulmonary Endothelial Cells

There is no direct evidence on the effect of neutrophil margination on pulmonary endothelial cell function. The morphology of endothelial cells in contact with neutrophils is the same as that of endothelial cells alone (Figure 5). However, morphologic changes generally associated with injury are gross changes most often seen with irreversible injury. Most physiologic studies of acute lung injury produce much more subtle changes in endothelial cell function and structure. Studies that have compared pulmonary hemodynamics and lung lymph flow in sheep before and after treatments to deplete circulating neutrophils showed no change in these variables as the result of neutrophil depletion (18, 25, 55). The possibility that marginated neutrophils may contribute to normal endothelial cell metabolic functions or to cell surface properties has not been adequately investigated.

Adherence Proteins and the Neutrophil Marginated Pool

With no evidence to the contrary, the most logical explanation for the functional significance of the large marginated pool in the pulmonary circulation is the ready availability of these cells to the circulating pool. However, this begs the question of why neutrophils marginate in the lung. Ismail and co-workers (30) argue that the β_2 integrin adherence proteins, CD11/CD18, are important in neutrophil margination in the pulmonary circulation. In their experiments, human neutrophils were incubated with an antibody directed against CD11b prior to assessing sequestration of the cells in isolated, perfused rat lungs. They found that sequestration of the antibody-treated neutrophils was inhibited. This study may not be definitive, however, since the neutrophil isolation procedure and the exposure of neutrophils to the

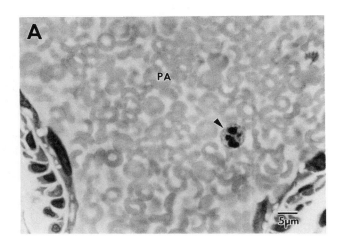

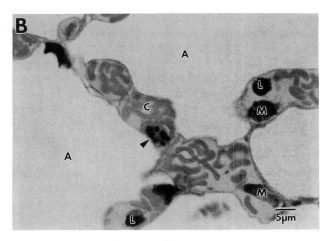

Figure 3 Histological appearance of neutrophils (*arrowhead*) in a pulmonary arteriole (*panel A*) and in an alveolar capillary (*panel B*) from a normal sheep. The neutrophil in the pulmonary arteriole (PA) is located in the center of the lumen, more than 10 μm from the endothelium. We designate it a "circulating" neutrophil. Circulating neutrophils have a round, smooth profile in tissue section. By comparison, neutrophils in alveolar capillaries (C) appear more elongated and their surfaces are uneven. The alveolar capillary neutrophil is truly marginated because it is apposed to the capillary endothelium. Also visible in the lumen of the capillary segments are lymphocytes (L), which appear round, and intravascular macrophages (M).

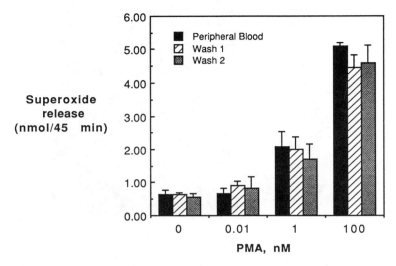

Figure 4 Superoxide anion release (X ± SEM) from adherent neutrophils isolated from peripheral blood and from successive washes of the pulmonary circulation of lungs removed from normal sheep [reprinted from McKenna et al (36) with permission *Am. J. Physiol.*].

in vitro perfusion apparatus could have stimulated expression of adherence proteins that may not occur in vivo. On the other hand, Yoder et al (66) argue that CD11/CD18 adherence proteins are not normally involved in neutrophil retention. These investigators measured the transit time of neutrophils through lung surface microvessels in intact dogs. Fluorescein-labeled neutrophils isolated from normal donor dogs and neutrophils from a dog with leukocyte adhesion-deficiency disease, an inherited deficiency of the CD11/CD18 adherence proteins, demonstrated equivalent transit times. Although the results quoted above suggest that CD11/CD18 integrins are not required for neutrophil margination in the lung, the issue is by no means settled. Other adherence molecules on the surface of neutrophils, such as L-selectin (LAM-1), may be involved (24 and references therein). Furthermore, adhesion molecules on endothelial cells may be expressed normally at low levels (ICAM-1) or may be expressed constitutively (ICAM-2) (24 and references therein). Others, such as P-selectin (CD62, GMP-140), can be rapidly mobilized to the endothelial surface. Much more must be done to determine the expression of these molecules on endothelium in different parts of the pulmonary circulation under normal conditions. Furthermore, studies that have utilized antibodies to adherence proteins have not documented the effect of this treatment on the number and distribution of marginated neutrophils in the normal pulmonary circulation. Until these issues are addressed for the

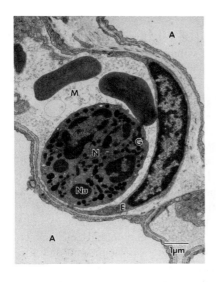

Figure 5 Sheep neutrophil (N) in an alveolar microvessel (M) of a control animal infused with autologous plasma. Control, unactivated neutrophils are round and smooth in contour, the cytoplasm is filled with granules (G) and nuclear lobes (Nu). The portion of the endothelial cell (E) juxtaposed to the neutrophil does not appear different from other parts of the endothelial cell. (A, alveolus).

currently characterized neutrophil and endothelial cell adherence proteins and their ligands, the mechanism of neutrophil margination in the normal lung will remain an open question.

NEUTROPHILS AND ENDOTHELIAL CELL INJURY

Requirements for Neutrophil-Mediated Endothelial Cell Injury

To produce endothelial injury, secretory responses of neutrophils must be activated. Most studies have shown that reduced metabolites of oxygen released from activated neutrophils are sufficient to produce injury to endothelial cells in culture (32). Secretion of proteolytic enzymes from primary and secondary granules in neutrophils may also contribute to endothelial cell injury, but does not appear to be necessary to demonstrate injury (51). Shasby and co-workers (51) showed that activated neutrophils must contact cultured endothelial cells to produce injury. This study demonstrated the need for points of contact between activated neutrophils and endothelial cells. The hypothesis is that these points of contact create a microenvironment between the two cell types that allows access of labile neutrophil activation products, such as free radicals, to the endothelial cell surface. As we have seen (Figures 3 and 5), points of contact between neutrophils and endothelial cells occur normally, particularly in alveolar capillaries. The missing element is activation of neutrophils.

There are clear cytochemical and morphological changes that occur with neutrophil activation. Cytochemical staining for myeloperoxidase and alkaline phosphatase has been used to demonstrate secretion of proteolytic enzymes from primary and secondary granules, respectively, in activated neutrophils (3). Neutrophils also increase in size and volume with activation, and they develop cytoplasmic vacuoles, the significance of which is not clear (3). These cytochemical and morphological features of activated neutrophils have been quantitated for neutrophils in situ in the pulmonary circulation (3).

Figure 6 shows activated neutrophils within alveolar capillaries in a sheep lung. Neutrophils in alveolar microvessels during infusion of zymosan-activated plasma demonstrated characteristics of activation including cytoplasmic vacuole formation and polarization of cell shape and in the distribution of organelles. Cells in zymosan-activated plasma-treated sheep were both vacuolated and more elongated than their counterparts in control plasma-treated sheep. Also evident was polarization of organelle distribution in neutrophils in zymosan-activated plasma-treated sheep. Cytoplasmic vacuoles were congregated away from regions of neutrophil-endothelial cell contact, whereas nuclear lobes were positioned toward regions of neutrophil-endothelial cell contact. Neutrophils in plasma-treated sheep lacked cytoplasmic vacuoles, and the nuclear lobes were randomly distributed in the cytoplasm. The alignment of the secretory apparatus of activated neutrophils away from regions of neutrophil-endothelial cell contact observed in our work has not been appreciated previously. We recently reported similar polarization of cell organelles in neutrophils activated in vitro at high density where neutrophil-neutrophil interactions are prominent (46). The polarization of cell contents was accompanied by a general down-regulation of the biochemical changes associated with neutrophil activation. Because similar structural features have

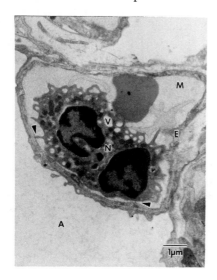

Figure 6   Activated sheep neutrophil (N) in situ in a pulmonary capillary at 30 min of intravenous infusion of autologous zymosan-activated plasma. Activated neutrophils in the lumen of alveolar microvessels (M) have polarized morphology. Along the zone of neutrophil-endothelial cell (E) contact (*arrow-heads*), the neutrophil's surface is smooth, and points of cell-cell contact are visible. The neutrophil's luminal surface, in contrast, is ruffled and contains numerous clear cytoplasmic vacuoles (V), (A, alveolus).

now been identified in vivo, we suggest that cell-cell interactions may be a mechanism for directing neutrophil secretory products away from endothelial cells, at least in the initial stimulation of secretion during activation. Although quantitative studies have not compared neutrophil cytochemistry and morphology in situ with different activating stimuli, qualitative results show that these features are largely independent of the activating agent used (1, 3, 37). An important exception to this statement is the effect different activating agents have on mobilization of primary and secondary granules. As far as is known, the description that follows is independent of the activating agent used.

The cross-sectional area of adherent neutrophils activated in vitro increased by about 33% (3) (Figure 7). Activated neutrophils in situ in the pulmonary circulation increased in the cross-section area 24 to 35%. Interestingly, the cross-sectional area of activated neutrophils was dependent on vascular location to exactly the same extent as documented for quiescent neutrophils. The cross-sectional area of neutrophils in alveolar capillaries was larger than "circulating" neutrophils in pulmonary arteries regardless of whether the neutrophils were activated or quiescent. This is additional indirect evidence supporting the hypothesis that site-specific changes in neutrophil size may be

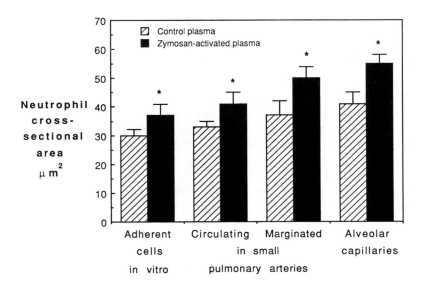

Figure 7   The cross-sectional area of sheep neutrophils measured in vitro and in situ. Neutrophils were either quiescent after exposure to control plasma or activated by exposure to zymosan-activated plasma in vitro and in vivo. The data (X ± S.D) from quiescent cells are the same as those shown in Figure 2 [results excerpted from Albertine et al (2)].

related to blood flow characteristics and the anatomy of lung capillaries rather than expression of adherence glycoproteins, which we assume is different in quiescent vs activated neutrophils. The morphological and cytochemical data show the presence of activated neutrophils in the pulmonary circulation during a time when endothelial injury is measurable as an increase in net transvascular fluid and protein flux.

There is abundant in vivo evidence that supports conclusions reached by placing activated neutrophils in contact with an endothelial cell monolayer in vitro. Administration of free radical scavengers in a prevention protocol has been shown to reduce pulmonary endothelial injury produced by complement anaphylatoxins (44), air embolization (39), or endotoxin (6). These data provide presumptive evidence showing that reduced oxygen metabolites may injure pulmonary endothelial cells measurably in an intact animal; they do not provide evidence that activated neutrophils were the sole source, or even an important source, of the oxygen radicals.

It is tempting to conclude that neutrophils are the source of the oxygen free radicals since most of the stimuli listed above are associated with sequestration of circulating neutrophils in the pulmonary circulation. As Staub and co-workers (55) first noted, sequestration is not evidence that neutrophils produce endothelial injury. Measurement of the circulating leukocyte count and differential is a convenient means, in an intact animal, of documenting neutrophil sequestration, perhaps reflecting a change in neutrophil adherence and/or neutrophil activation. Therefore, circulating leukocyte count and differential can be one indication that cell function has changed. As noted above, however, the number of marginated neutrophils in the lung is greater than the circulating pool so there is little reason to suggest that additional neutrophils must be retained in the lung to produce injury. Furthermore, not all insults that presumably produce neutrophil-dependent injury in the lung are associated with sequestration of neutrophils in the pulmonary circulation. Air embolization is a good example of this point (1, 18).

Neutrophil Depletion Studies

Several studies in which the number of circulating neutrophils has been reduced in vivo by chemical treatment or by treatment with an antineutrophil antibody have shown that neutrophil depletion reduces the increase in net transvascular fluid and protein flux produced by many different insults associated with pulmonary endothelial cell injury (5, 18, 25, 55, 56). None of these studies, however, has documented the degree to which treatment reduced the much larger pool of marginated neutrophils within the lung. One study did address this problem and reported that treatment that decreased circulating neutrophils by 98% decreased pulmonary vascular neutrophils only 77% (1). Interestingly, the same distribution of neutrophils within the pulmonary circulation (parenchymal vessels → pulmonary arteries → pulmonary veins) was observed before and after leukocyte depletion (Figure 8). These data raise the same issue as neutrophil sequestration from a different perspective: how many neutrophils are required to produce endothelial injury? Even though the number of neutrophils in parenchymal vessels was reduced by about two thirds by leukocyte depletion, 100 to 200 neutrophils/mm^2 tissue (15,000 to 30,000 neutrophils/mm^3 blood volume) in lung microvessels remains a significant cell density that may have contributed to the residual endothelial injury measured in the Albertine study (1). It is difficult to address the issue of depletion of marginated neutrophils; however, it must be considered in interpreting data that are available.

Adherence Proteins and Neutrophil-Mediated Endothelial Injury

If we assume (as most evidence suggests) that activated neutrophils in the pulmonary circulation can produce endothelial injury, the question of how activated neutrophils and endothelial cells interact must be addressed. Worthen et al (65) showed that activated neutrophils are stiffer than quiescent cells, which presumably makes activated neutrophils less prone to deformation as they circulate through capillary beds. We have shown that emigration of neutrophils in skin and into the airspace of the lung is inhibited by intravascular

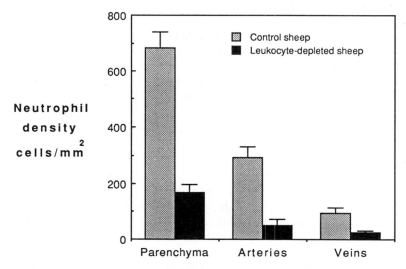

Figure 8 The distribution of neutrophils in the pulmonary circulation of control sheep and sheep after treatment with nitrogen mustard to deplete circulating leukocytes. The control data (X ± SD) are the same as one of the sets illustrated in Figure 1 [results excerpted from Albertine (1)].

activation of the cells (2). These results are also consistent with the hypothesis that activated neutrophils are stiffer and less easily deformed than quiescent cells. The decreased deformability, together with the increase in cross-sectional area that occurs with activation, may be sufficient to retard movement of activated neutrophils through alveolar capillaries and provide ample opportunity for release of oxygen metabolites and proteolytic enzymes in close proximity to the endothelial cell surface. Yoder's (66) study showed that the transit time of complement-activated neutrophils through lung surface microvessels was increased when normal dog neutrophils were measured, but not when neutrophils from the CD11/CD18-deficient dog were measured. This result suggests that adherence proteins are necessary for retention of activated neutrophils in pulmonary capillaries. To our knowledge, however, a study on the increase in size and stiffness of adhesion-deficient neutrophils with activation has not been done.

Another way to approach this problem is to passively immunize animals using antibodies directed against specific adhesion proteins. This approach has been limited to studies in small animals because of availability of appropriate antibodies. Methods used to assess acute lung injury in these experiments include histologic evidence of edema formation and isolated perfused lung studies measuring the filtration coefficient. Vedder and co-workers (58) used a hemorrhage and fluid resuscitation protocol in rabbits, treating some of the animals with a monoclonal antibody to CD18. They found that antibody treatment improved survival and limited injury in the liver and gut. The pulmonary circulation, however, did not benefit from antibody treatment. In contrast, studies from Malik's laboratory showed that acute lung injury and pulmonary edema were inhibited by treatment with an antibody to CD18, or an antibody to ICAM-1, the endothelial cell ligand for CD18 (27, 28). In these studies, rabbits were subjected to 24 hr of unilateral pulmonary artery occlusion followed by 2 hr of reperfusion before the filtration coefficient and weight gain were measured in lungs perfused with albumin-supplemented buffer. These investigators also radiolabeled the ICAM-1 antibody and showed increased uptake of the antibody in lungs subjected to occlusion/reperfusion compared to the contralateral lung (27). Using immunocytochemical methods, they found antibody that appeared to be associated with alveolar wall structures in the lung subjected to occlusion and reperfusion, but not in the control, contralateral lung. In another study, the weight gain in isolated guinea pig lungs produced by adding neutrophils and opsonized zymosan to the perfusate was also prevented by treatment with a CD18 antibody (33).

These studies illustrate several important points. The results are contradictory, with some protocols showing that inhibiting adherence protein binding reduced lung injury, while other experiments failed to show a beneficial effect. One problem is that the experiments and the endpoints used to assess acute lung injury are not comparable. Experiments are needed in protocols that permit continuous estimates of pulmonary endothelial permeability in intact animals over time. These types of experiments are becoming feasible with the increasing availability of reagents and antibodies for testing. Furthermore, ongoing in vitro studies may well provide nonimmunologic approaches to modify the expression of or the interaction between adherence proteins and ligands.

The apparent contradiction also illustrates the complexity of what seemed to be a simple question of the effect of adherence proteins on neutrophil-mediated acute lung injury. One thing that has become apparent from the elegant in vitro studies that have appeared in the literature is that this is a complex problem involving the interaction of adherence proteins representing different supergene families, their ligands, cytokines, and different cell types, including platelets and endothelial cells in addition to neutrophils. Given the biological and biochemical complexity, the question of the regulation of neutrophil-endothelial cell interactions will be answered in measured and cumulative steps.

Another way to study the role of adherence glycoproteins in the pulmonary circulation is to measure emigration of neutrophils into the alveolar airspace. Doerschuk and co-workers (16) implanted sponges treated with *Streptococcus pneumonia,* endotoxin, phorbol myristate acetate (PMA), or hydrochloric acid into the abdominal cavity of rabbits or instilled these agents intratracheally. Rabbits were pretreated with intravenous saline or an antibody to CD18. They found that antibody treatment inhibited neutrophil emigration into the abdominal wall regardless of the stimulus used. In contrast, antibody treatment had no effect on neutrophil emigration into the alveolar airspace in response to *Streptococcus pneumonia* or hydrochloric acid, partially inhibited emigration in response to endotoxin, and abolished PMA-induced emigration. Clearly, integrins do not have the same effect on neutrophil-endothelial cell interaction in pulmonary and systemic vascular beds because the effect of antibody treatment was absolute in the abdomen while it was stimulus-specific in the pulmonary circulation.

There is no ready explanation for why the integrins have different effects in the lung vs other organs. There is no reason to believe that the ability of neutrophils to express adherence glycoproteins depends on whether the neutrophil is located temporarily in the pulmonary or systemic circulation. One possible explanation is that pulmonary, but not systemic, vascular endothelium is specialized to express adherence glycoproteins in a stimulus-specific manner. Although this could be the case, we think it is unlikely. Recently, data have emerged that suggest that the presence of macrophages, both alveolar and intravascular, may explain what appeared to be CD18-independent neutrophil adherence and emigration in the lung (24 and references therein). The hypothesis is that macrophages are the source of an as yet unidentified adherence protein. This intriguing possibility highlights the complexities associated with the issue of adherence proteins and acute lung injury, as discussed above.

We have presented data showing that neutrophil size is dependent on vascular location in the pulmonary circulation. The low blood pressure, huge vascular surface area, long capillary segments, and different shear forces may combine to make the lung's effect on neutrophils unique. If similar changes in neutrophil size with location were not apparent in systemic vascular beds, then adherence proteins might play a much more important role in retarding neutrophil transit through systemic vascular beds. Based on this supposition, antibodies to adherence proteins should have little or no effect on the number and distribution of activated or quiescent neutrophils in the pulmonary circulation. Clearly, measurements of neutrophil density and size in pulmonary and systemic arteries, capillaries, and veins are needed under a variety of treatment conditions.

Our suggestion that integrins and selectins have little role in neutrophil margination in the lung normally does not imply that adherence proteins have no role in neutrophil-mediated lung injury. Horgan et al (28) argued, based on studies by Nathan (41, 43), that adherence proteins may have an amplifying effect on neutrophil secretory responses to an activating stimulus. The hypothesis is that neutrophil attachment via adherence proteins may augment the respiratory burst and release of other neutrophil-derived mediators of tissue injury. This is an intriguing hypothesis that will require considerable ingenuity and patience to test. If both of the hypotheses concerning the role of adherence proteins in the pulmonary circulation are correct, then treatment with antibodies to adherence proteins will not alter neutrophil margination, but may reduce tissue injury caused by neutrophil activation.

Cytokines, Neutrophils and Endothelial Injury

Cytokines have also been implicated as peptides affecting neutrophil-endothelial cell interactions. In vitro studies have shown that incubation of neutrophils with tumor necrosis factor (TNFα) or interleukin-1 (IL-1β) stimulates neutrophil adherence to endothelium by mechanisms dependent on expression of integrins and selectins (10, 20, 22). In vivo studies of endotoxin-induced circulatory shock have shown that inhibition of the end-organ effects of TNFα or IL-1β reduced lethality associated with endotoxin shock (7, 57, 59). Sloane et al (52) showed that prolonged infusion of endotoxin in awake sheep resulted in synthesis and release of TNFα, but the circulating concentration of TNFα did not correlate with the severity of acute lung injury or outcome in the sheep.

Human recombinant TNFα has been infused into awake or anesthetized sheep in several laboratories (29, 31, 34, 47). The results show that TNFα increased lung microvascular permeability. Interestingly, Horvath et al (29) showed that neutrophil depletion did not prevent TNFα-induced acute lung injury, which suggests that the injury may not be dependent on neutrophil-endothelial cell interaction. It is necessary to temper this conclusion with the fact that neutrophil depletion is not complete, particularly in the pulmonary circulation (1).

The study of cytokines, like adherence proteins, is a rapidly developing science. Many of the in vitro studies support the hypothesis that one action of cytokines is hormone-like, i.e. to regulate leukocyte-leukocyte and leukocyte-endothelial cell interactions. These data represent the beginning of what may prove to be a unique opportunity to use innovative techniques to study neutrophil-endothelial cell interactions in normal and injured lungs. Like the selectins and integrins, cytokines are proteins, which means that immunocytochemical techniques can be adapted for in situ measurements. The cells responsible for cytokine synthesis can be identified using these techniques. In addition, the relationship between cytokine synthesis and expression of adherence proteins on neutrophils and endothelial cells can be addressed by studying the cells in situ under a variety of circumstances.

OTHER LEUKOCYTES IN THE PULMONARY CIRCULATION

We have focused exclusively on neutrophil-endothelial cell interactions since neutrophils are the only leukocyte directly implicated as a mediator of endothelial cell injury. Clearly, more research is needed on the possible involvement of other leukocytes, either as mediators of endothelial injury, or as cells capable of modifying neutrophil-endothelial cell interactions.

Macrophages, their circulating counterpart the blood monocyte, and eosinophils can be activated to release eicosanoids, cytokines, oxygen metabolites, and proteolytic enzymes (8, 42). These cells are biochemically capable of producing endothelial cell injury and, as such, deserve greater scrutiny. Mileski et al (38) suggested that macrophages promote CD18-independent neutrophil adhesion and emigration. This observation could be of particular importance in the lung because of the presence of intravascular as well as alveolar macrophages.

Intravascular macrophages have been identified in alveolar microvessels in many species including humans (14, 53, 63). They resemble hepatic Kupffer cells of liver sinusoids. One of the unique structural features of pulmonary intravascular macrophages is the presence of junctional complexes at sites of cell-to-cell contact with pulmonary endothelial cells. The junctional complexes are reminiscent of desmosomes between contiguous cells. The role of adherence molecules in promoting firm and prolonged attachment of pulmonary intravascular macrophages to pulmonary endothelial cells in vivo is not known.

Functionally, pulmonary intravascular macrophages clearly play a role in the clearance of blood-borne microbial agents, particulates, and formed elements of blood such as erythrocytes and neutrophils (53, 63). During phagocytosis in vivo, intravascular macrophages secrete eicosanoids, which affect both vascular and airway smooth muscle (4, 40). These studies have established the fact that secretory processes can be activated in vivo that have physiologically significant effects. It is highly likely, therefore, that intravascular macrophages can also be stimulated to release cytokines or stimulate adherence of neutrophils. These cells are certainly well placed to directly produce endothelial cell injury through the release of oxygen metabolites or proteolytic enzymes, or to produce injury indirectly by activating neutrophils marginated in alveolar microvessels. Since it is difficult to harvest intravascular macrophages and be confident that their function is normal, immunocytochemistry of cytokines and adherence proteins may prove to be particularly valuable in identifying a role for these cells under conditions associated with acute lung injury.

There are no in vivo studies that have focused on blood monocytes as cells producing endothelial injury in the lung. The fact that there are few circulating monocytes relative to the numbers of neutrophils and lymphocytes make such a study particularly difficult. Given the lack of hard data, it seems reasonable to assume that blood monocytes may function much like intravascular macrophages; capable of directly producing endothelial injury and indirectly of activating neutrophils to produce injury.

Eosinophils have been studied much more extensively as cells contributing to airway inflammation (13, 17, 21). These cells have an abundance of inflammatory mediators that can be released extracellularly. Of these mediators, major basic protein is particularly cytotoxic to both endothelial and epithelial cells. Eosinophils also have been shown to accumulate in the alveolar airspaces in disease conditions such as the acute respiratory distress syndrome (23), which indicates that further study of the potential role of eosinophils in acute endothelial injury is needed.

There is another reason to be concerned about leukocytes in addition to neutrophils. Rapidly emerging data show that different leukocytes utilize different adherence mechanisms to marginate and emigrate. In vitro studies have shown that monocytes, eosinophils, lymphocytes, and basophils express the very late antigen (VLA-4), while neutrophils lack this antigen (10, 11, 15, 48, 60). The ligand for VLA-4 is vascular cell adhesion molecule (VCAM-1). Another example of selective cell recruitment via specific adherence molecules is the CD11/CD18-independent emigration of lymphocytes. This selectivity appears to be related to expression of L-selectin

(LECAM-1) on the surface of lymphocytes, and its ligand, E-selectin (ELAM-1), on endothelial cells. Although interactions among leukocytes with different adherence mechanisms have not been well defined, these types of interactions may provide an explanation for why neutrophil and monocyte emigration is not completely inhibited in patients whose leukocytes lack CD11/CD18 integrins. As demonstrated by the complexity of adherence proteins and ligands, it is also possible that neutrophils and monocytes may use other, as yet unidentified, adherence molecules and ligands.

SUMMARY

The large marginated pool of neutrophils normally present in the pulmonary circulation provides a unique opportunity to study the relationship between neutrophils and endothelial cells in situ. Unlike other organs in which neutrophil density in the vascular space is low, adequate numbers of cells are readily available in the lung to assess such important characteristics as distribution, density, size, volume, and immunocytochemical and cytochemical characteristics. To take advantage of such a large marginated pool, morphologic techniques should be more universally applied in studies of neutrophil-mediated tissue injury.

From the data presented, it seems clear that factors governing neutrophil-endothelial cell interactions may differ in the lung compared to systemic vascular beds. We have suggested that this difference may be related to the unique characteristics of the lung with regard to anatomy and blood flow rather than site-specific differences in endothelial cells. With the discovery of specialized proteins involved in cell adhesion and the increasing availability of appropriate antibodies to adhesion proteins, unprecedented opportunities exist to address these questions. It is an exciting time to study neutrophil-endothelial cell interactions in the lung.

Literature Cited

1. Albertine, K. H. 1988. Lung injury and neutrophil density during air embolization in sheep after leukocyte depletion with nitrogen mustard. *Am. Rev. Respir. Dis.* 138:1444–53
2. Albertine, K. H., Koh, Y. Y., Peters, S. P., Gee, M. H., McKenna, P. J. 1991. Activated sheep neutrophils demonstrate decreased transvascular migration in response to chemoattractants in alveolar airspaces and skin. *Am. Rev. Respir. Dis.* 143:A542
3. Albertine, K. H., Rosolia, D. L., Peters, S. P., Gee, M. H. 1992. Neu-

trophil activation in vivo in the lung during ZAP infusion is characterized by changes in physical and cytochemical properties of neutrophils. *J. Appl. Physiol.* In press
4. Albertine, K. H., Staub, N. C. 1986. Vascular tracers alter hemodynamics and airway pressure in anesthetized sheep. *Microvasc. Res.* 32:279–88
5. Barie, P. S., Tahamont, M. V., Malik, A. B. 1982. Prevention of increased pulmonary vascular permeability after pancreatitis by granulocyte depletion

in sheep. *Am. Rev. Respir. Dis.* 126: 904–8

6. Bernard, G. R., Lucht, W. D., Niedermeyer, M. E., Snapper, J. R., Ogletree, M. L., Brigham, K. L. 1984. Effect of N-acetylcysteine on pulmonary response to endotoxin in the awake sheep and upon in vitro granulocyte function. *J. Clin. Invest.* 73:1772–84

7. Beutler, B. A., Milsark, I. W., Cerami, A. 1985. Passive immunization against cachectin/tumor necrosis factor protects mice from lethal effect of endotoxin. *Science* 229:860–71

8. Bevilacqua, M. P., Pober, J. S., Majeau, G. R., Cotran, R. S., Gimbrone, M. A. Jr. 1984. Interleukin 1 (IL-1) induces biosynthesis and cell surface expression of procoagulant activity in human vascular endothelial cells. *J. Exp. Med.* 160:618–23

9. Bjork, J., Smedegard, G. 1984. The microvasculature of the hamster cheek pouch as a model for studying acute immune-complex-induced inflammatory reactions. *Int. Arch. Allergy Appl. Immunol.* 74:178–85

10. Bochner, B. S., Luscinskas, F. W., Gimbrone, M. A. Jr., Newman, W., Sterbinsky, S. A., et al. 1991. Adhesion of human basophils, eosinophils, and neutrophils to interleukin 1-activated human vascular endothelial cells: Contributions of endothelial cell adhesion molecules. *J. Exp. Med.* 173:1553–56

11. Carlos, T. M., Schwartz, B. R., Kovach, N. L., Yee, E., Rosa, M., et al. 1990. Vascular cell adhesion molecule-1 mediates lymphocyte adherence to cytokine-activated cultured human endothelial cells. *Blood* 76:965–70

12. Cartwright, G. E., Athens, I. W., Wintrobe, M. M. 1964. The kinetics of granulopoiesis in normal man. *Blood* 24:780–803

13. Collins, D. S., Dupuis, R., Gleich, G. J., Bartemes, K. R., Koh, Y., et al. 1992. Increased vascular permeability is associated with eosinophilic inflammation after segmental antigen challenge in allergic individuals. *Am. Rev. Respir. Dis.* In press

14. Dehring, D. J., Wismar, B. L. 1989. Intravascular macrophages in pulmonary capillaries of humans. *Am. Rev. Respir. Dis.* 139:1027–29

15. Dobrina, A., Menegazzi, R., Carlos, T. M., Nardon, E., Cramer, R., et al. 1991. Mechanisms of eosinophil adherence to cultured vascular endothelial cells. *J. Clin. Invest.* 88:22–26

16. Doerschuk, C. M., Winn, R. K., Coxson, H. O., Harlan, J. M. 1990. CD18-dependent and -independent mechanisms of neutrophil emigration in the pulmonary and systemic microcirculation of rabbits. *J. Immunol.* 144: 2327–33

17. Dupuis, R., Collins, D. S., Koh, Y. Y., Pollice, M., Albertine, K. H., et al. 1992. Effect of antigen dose on the recruitment of inflammatory cells to the lung by segmental antigen challenge. *J. Allergy Clin. Immunol.* 89:850–58

18. Flick, M. R., Perel, A., Staub, N. C. 1981. Leukocytes are required for increased lung microvascular permeability after microembolization in sheep. *Circ. Res.* 48:344–51

19. Frashier, W. G. Jr., Wayland, H. 1972. A repeating modular organization of the microcirculation of cat mesentery. *Microvasc. Res.* 4:62–76

20. Gamble, J. R., Skinner, M. P., Berndt, M. C., Vadas, M. A. 1990. Prevention of activated neutrophil adhesion to endothelium by soluble adhesion protein GMP140. *Science* 249:414–17

21. Gleich, G. J. 1990. The eosinophil and bronchial asthma: current understanding. *J. Allergy Clin. Immunol.* 85:422–36

22. Hakkert, B. C., Kuijpers, T. W., Leeuwenberg, J. F. M., Van Mourik, J. A., Roos, D. 1991. Neutrophil and monocyte adherence to and migration across monolayers of cytokine-activated endothelial cells: The contribution of CD18, ELAM-1, and VLA-4. *Blood* 78:2721–26

23. Halgren, R., Samuelson, T., Venge, P., Modig, J. 1987. Eosinophil activation in the lung is related to lung damage in adult respiratory distress syndrome. *Am. Rev. Respir. Dis.* 135: 639–42

24. Harlan, J. M., Winn, R. K., Vedder, N. B., Doerschuk, C. M., Rice, C. L. 1992. In vivo models of leukocyte adherence to endothelium. In *Adhesion: Its Role in Inflammatory Disease*, ed. J. M. Harlan, D. Y. Liu, 6:117–50. New York: Freeman

25. Heflin, A. C., Brigham, K. L. 1981. Prevention by granulocyte depletion of increased vascular permeability of sheep following endotoxemia. *J. Clin. Invest.* 68:1253–60

26. Hernandez, L. A., Grisham, M. B., Twohig, B., Arfors, K. E., Harlan, J. M., Granger, D. N. 1987. Role of neutrophils in ischemia-reperfusion induced microvascular injury. *Am. J. Physiol.* 253:H699–703

27. Horgan, M. J., Ge, M., Gu, J., Rothlein, R., Malik, A. B. 1991. Role of ICAM-1 in neutrophil-mediated lung vascular injury after occlusion and reperfusion. *Am. J. Physiol.* 261: H1578–84

28. Horgan, M. J., Wright, S. D., Malik, A. B. 1990. Antibody against leukocyte integrin (CD18) prevents reperfusion-induced lung vascular injury. *Am. J. Physiol.* 259:L315–19

29. Horvath, C. J., Ferro, T. J., Jesmok, G., Malik, A. B. 1988. Recombinant tumor necrosis factor increases pulmonary vascular permeability independent of neutrophils. *Proc. Natl. Acad. Sci. USA* 85:9219–23

30. Ismail, G., Morganroth, M. L., Todd, R. F. III, Boxer, L. A. 1987. Prevention of pulmonary injury in isolated perfused rat lungs by activated human neutrophils preincubated with anti-Mo1 monoclonal antibody. *Blood* 69:1167–74

31. Johnson, J., Meyrick, B., Jesmok, G., Brigham, K. L. 1989. Human recombinant tumor necrosis factor alpha infusion mimics endotoxemia in awake sheep. *J. Appl. Physiol.* 66:1448–54

32. Kaslovsky, R. A., Gibbs, L., Malik, A. B. 1991. Neutrophils from chronic granulomatous disease fail to increase endothelial permeability. *Am. J. Physiol.* 261:H1226–30

33. Kaslovsky, R. A., Horgan, M. J., Lum, H., McCandless, B. K., Gilboa, N., et al. 1990. Pulmonary edema induced by phagocytosing neutrophils: Protective effect of monoclonal antibody against phagocyte CD18 integrin. *Circ. Res.* 67:795–802

34. Kreil, E. A., Greene, E., Fitzgibbon, C., Robinson, D. R., Zapol, W. M. 1989. Effects of recombinant human tumor necrosis factor alpha, lymphotoxin, and *Escherichia coli* lipopolysaccharide on hemodynamics, lung microvascular permeability, and eicosanoid synthesis in anesthetized sheep. *Circ. Res.* 65:502–14

35. Lien, D. C., Wagner, W. W. Jr., Capen, R. L., Haslett, C., Hanson, W. L., et al. 1987. Physiological neutrophil sequestration in the lung: visual evidence for localization in capillaries. *J. Appl. Physiol.* 62:1236–43

36. McKenna, P. J., Rosolia, D. L., Ishihara, Y., Albertine, K. H., Staub, N. C., Gee, M. H. 1992. Down regulation of blood and bone marrow neutrophils prevents expression of acute lung injury in sheep. *Am. J. Physiol.* In press

37. Meyrick, B., Brigham, K. L. 1983. Acute effects of *Escherichia coli* endotoxin on the pulmonary microcirculation of anesthetized sheep. Structure:function relationships. *Lab. Invest.* 48:458–70

38. Mileski, W. Harlan, J., Rice, C., Winn, R. 1990. Streptococcus pneumoniae-stimulated macrophages induce neutrophils to emigrate by a CD18-independent mechanism of adherence. *Circ. Shock* 31:259–67

39. Milligan, S. A., Hoeffel, J. M., Goldstein, I. M., Flick, M. R. 1988. Effect of catalase on endotoxin-induced acute lung injury in unanaesthetized sheep. *Am. Rev. Respir. Dis.* 137:420–28

40. Miyamoto, K., Schultz, E. Heath, T., Mitchell, M. D., Albertine, K. H., Staub, N. C. 1988. Pulmonary intravascular macrophages and hemodynamic effects of liposomes in sheep. *J. Appl. Physiol.* 54:1143–52

41. Nathan, C. F. 1987. Neutrophil activation on biological surfaces: massive secretion of hydrogen peroxide in response to products of macrophages and lymphocytes. *J. Clin. Invest.* 80:1550–60

42. Nathan, C. F., Murray, H. W., Cohn, Z. A. 1980. The macrophage as an effector cell. *N. Engl. J. Med.* 303:622–26

43. Nathan, C., Srimal, S., Farber, C., Sanchez, E., Kabbash, L., et al. 1989. Cytokine-induced respiratory burst of human neutrophils: Dependence on extracellular matrix proteins and CD11/CD18 integrins. *J. Cell Biol.* 109:1341–49

44. Perkowski, S. Z., Havill, A. M., Flynn, J. T., Gee, M. H. 1983. Role of intrapulmonary release of eicosanoids and superoxide anion as mediators of pulmonary dysfunction and endothelial injury in sheep with intermittent complement activation. *Circ. Res.* 53:574–83

45. Perry, M. A., Granger, D. N. 1991. Role of CD11/CD18 in shear rate-dependent leukocyte-endothelial cell interactions in cat mesenteric venules. *J. Clin. Invest.* 87:1798–804

46. Peters, S. P., Cerasoli, F. Jr., Albertine, K. H., Gee, M. H., Ishihara, Y. 1990. "Autoregulation" of human neutrophil activation in vitro. Regulation of phorbol myristate acetate-induced neutrophil activation by cell density. *J. Leuko. Biol.* 47:457–74

47. Redl, H., Schlag, G., Lamche, H., Vogl, C., Paul, E., et al. 1990. TNF-

and LPS-induced changes of lung vascular permeability: Studies in unanesthetised sheep. *Circ. Shock* 31:183–92

48. Rice, G. E., Munro, J. M., Bevilacqua, M. P. 1990. Inducible cell adhesion molecule 110 (INCAM-110) is an endothelial receptor for lymphocytes. A CD11/CD18-independent adhesion mechanism. *J. Exp. Med.* 171:1369–74

49. Rothe, G., Kellermann, W., Valet, G. 1990. Flow cytometric parameters of neutrophil function as early indicators of sepsis- or trauma-related pulmonary or cardiovascular organ failure. *J. Lab. Clin. Med.* 115:52–61

50. Rothe, G., Valet, G. 1988. Phagocytosis, intracellular pH, and cell volume in the multifunctional analysis of granulocytes by flow cytometry. *Cytometry* 9:316–24

51. Shasby, D. M., Shasby, S. S., Peach, M. J. 1983. Granulocytes and phorbol myristate acetate increase permeability to albumin of cultured endothelial monolayers and isolated perfused lungs: Role of oxygen radicals and granulocyte adherence. *Am. Rev. Respir. Dis.* 127:72–76

52. Sloane, P. J., Elsasser, T. H., Spath, J. A. Jr., Albertine, K. H., Gee, M. H. 1992. Plasma tumor necrosis factor alpha during long term endotoxemia in awake sheep. *J. Appl. Physiol.* In press

53. Staub, N. C. 1989. *The Pulmonary Intravascular Macrophage.* Mount Kisko, NY: Futura

54. Staub, N. C., Schultz, E. L. 1968. Pulmonary capillary length in dog, cat and rabbit. *Respir. Physiol.* 5:371–78

55. Staub, N. C., Schultz, E. L., Albertine, K. H. 1982. Leucocytes and pulmonary microvascular injury. *Ann. NY Acad. Sci.* 384:332–42

56. Tahamont, M. V., Malik, A. B. 1983. Granulocytes mediate the increase in pulmonary vascular permeability after thrombin embolism. *J. Appl. Physiol.* 54:1489–95

57. Tracey, K. J., Fong, Y., Hesse, D. G., Manogue, K. R., Lee, A. T., et al. 1987. Anti-cachetin/TNF monoclonal antibodies prevent septic shock during lethal bacteremia. *Nature* 330:662–64

58. Vedder, N. B., Winn, R. K., Rice, C. L., Chi, E. Y., Arfors, K. E., Harlan, J. M. 1988. A monoclonal antibody to the adherence-promoting leukocyte glycoprotein, CD18, reduces organ injury and improves survival from hemorrhagic shock and resuscitation in rabbits. *J. Clin. Invest.* 81:939–44

59. Wakabayashi, G., Gelfand, J. A., Burke, J. F., Thompson, R. C., Dinarello, C. A. 1991. A specific receptor antagonist for interleukin 1 prevents *Escherichia coli*-induced shock in rabbits. *FASEB J.* 5:338–43

60. Walsh, G. M., Mermod, J. J., Hartnell, A., Kay, A. B., Wardlaw, A. J. 1991. Human eosinophil, but not neutrophil, adherence to IL-1-stimulated human umbilical vascular endothelial cells is a4b1 (very late antigen-4) dependent. *J. Immunol.* 146:3419–23

61. Weibel, E. R. 1963. *Morphometry of the Human Lung.* New York: Academic

62. Wiener-Kronish, J. P., Albertine, K. H., Matthay, M. A. 1991. Differential responses of the endothelial and epithelial barriers of the lung in sheep to *Escherichia coli* endotoxin. *J. Clin. Invest.* 88:864–75

63. Winkler, G. C. 1988. Pulmonary intravascular macrophages in domestic animal species: review of structural and functional properties. *Am. J. Anat.* 181:217–34

64. Worthen, G. S., Henson, P. M., Rosengren, S. R., Downey, G. P., Hyde, D. M. 1992. Neutrophil migration into the airspaces is associated with an increase in cellular volume. *Am. Rev. Respir. Dis.* 145:A697

65. Worthen, G. S., Schwab, B. III, Elson, E. L., Downey, G. P. 1989. Mechanics of stimulated neutrophils: Cell stiffening induces retention in capillaries. *Science* 245:183–86

66. Yoder, M. C., Checkley, L. L., Giger, U., Hanson, W. L., Kirk, K. R., et al. 1990. Pulmonary microcirculatory kinetics of neutrophils deficient in leukocyte adhesion-promoting glycoproteins. *J. Appl. Physiol.* 69:207–13

Annu. Rev. Physiol. 1993. 55:249–65

ENDOTHELIN PEPTIDES AND THE KIDNEY

M. S. Simonson and M. J. Dunn[*]

Departments of Medicine and Physiology and [*]Biophysics, Case Western Reserve University, Division of Nephrology, University Hospitals of Cleveland, Cleveland, Ohio 44106

KEY WORDS: regulatory peptides, endothelium-derived mediators, renal hemodynamics, glomerular filtration rate, growth factors

INTRODUCTION

Endothelin Peptides and Renal Function: An Overview

Renal homeostasis reflects a delicate balance of diverse signaling systems controlling renal blood flow, glomerular filtration rate, and tubular reabsorption and secretion. Regulatory peptides such as angiotensin II, arginine vasopressin, and atrial natriuretic factor help maintain homeostasis by controlling virtually every aspect of renal function (9, 18). It is perhaps surprising that one of the most potent renal peptides, endothelin (ET), was only recently discovered (131). Although our understanding remains fragmentary, the basic outline of how ET peptides regulate renal physiology is now becoming clear. ET is secreted by the endothelium and at several other sites in the kidney, where it acts in a paracrine or autocrine signaling mode on target cells. By virtue of its vasoactive properties, ET probably regulates, in part, the long-term control of renal blood flow (RBF), glomerular filtration rate (GFR), and sodium and water excretion. ET has direct effects on tubular transport of sodium and water at different nephron sites, especially in the collecting duct. ET is also a potent mitogen for glomerular mesangial cells. Finally, it has been postulated that ET contributes to renal pathophysiology in such disorders as acute renal failure, cyclosporine-mediated renal toxicity, and perhaps even glomerular inflammation.

The purpose of this review is to describe what is known about the actions of ET in the kidney and indicate what is less certain or unknown. We begin

249

0066–4278/93/0315–0249$02.00

with a brief overview of aspects of the cellular and molecular biology of ET peptides that are pertinent to renal physiology. After a brief outline of the sites of ET secretion and localization of ET receptors in the kidney, we discuss in greater detail the mechanisms by which ET affects renal hemodynamics, glomerular function, and sodium and water transport. We conclude with some brief comments about possible roles for ET in the development of renal pathophysiology. In a review of this length, it is impossible to fully reference the vast literature on ET and the kidney; thus, the reader is referred to several other reviews that focus on specific aspects of ET and give a more detailed discussion of the experimental models and interpretation of results (51, 106).

An important backdrop for the experiments described here is the extensive knowledge of ET structure, function, and pathways of secretion. ET also has a surprisingly diverse array of actions in other organ systems. This diversity results from cell-type-specific regulation of the response to ET, distribution of ET receptors, and localization of ET secretion. These topics have been the subject of some recent reviews (1, 61, 93, 132), while other reviews have focused on aspects of the signal transduction pathways evoked by activated ET receptors (70, 108, 113).

OVERVIEW OF ET PEPTIDES

Structure and Molecular Biology of ET Peptides

The term endothelin refers to a family of homologous, 21-amino acid peptides found in three distinct isoforms: ET-1, ET-2, and ET-3 (13, 38, 41, 130, 131). Two intrachain disulfide bonds constrain the molecule in a hairpin loop configuration with the COOH terminus extended. The hydrophobic COOH terminus of ET is essential for bioactivity, but the loop configuration also contributes to activity (44). Although the biological significance of ET isoforms is not entirely clear, it is certain that there are significant cell- and tissue-specific differences in ET isoform secretion and in the biological response to the different isopeptides. Thus it seems likely that these distinct ET isopeptides have evolved to serve diverse signaling roles in different tissues. It is also important to note that ET peptides are nearly identical to sarafotoxins, small peptides isolated from venom of the burrowing asp *Atractaspis engaddensis* (46). In mammals, sarafotoxin peptides cause intense vasoconstriction, often followed by cardiac arrest, by interacting with cognate ET receptors. The high degree of sequence homology and conserved bioactivity between ET and sarafotoxins suggests that they constitute a supergene family with common evolutionary origins (47, 56, 81).

Genomic blotting reveals that each ET isopeptide is encoded by a distinct gene (12, 13, 38, 39, 94). In humans, both genetic mapping and in situ hybridization demonstrate separate chromosomal loci for each preproET gene: preproET-1 to chromosome 6 (4, 12), preproET-2 to chromosome 1 (4, 13), and preproET-3 to chromosome 20 (4, 11). Considerable allelic variation has been shown for the preproET-1 locus, but the biological consequences of this variation are unknown (36). With the exception of an Alu repetitive element, nucleotide sequences in the preproET-1 gene show little homology with other gene families (39). The structural arrangement of the human preproET-1 (12, 39) and preproET-3 (11) genes is similar and consists of five exons and four introns. Nucleotide sequences encoding the mature ET peptide reside within the second exon, while the third exon encodes a 15-amino acid ET-like peptide, with little or no biological activity. Diverse 5' *cis*-acting sequences have been identified that control endothelial cell type-specific and inducible transcription of the preproET-1 gene (57, 59). ET-1 has been postulated to autoregulate transcription of the preproET-1 gene via its ability to increase the activity of AP-1 transcription factors, which stimulate preproET-1 transcription via an AP-1 *cis*-element within the promoter (58, 114).

ET Secretion and Mode of Signaling

Although ET secretion was originally thought to be localized exclusively in the vascular endothelium, it is now clear that preproET genes are widely expressed in both vascular and avascular tissues (1, 93, 112, 132). ET secretion is thought to occur in most cells exclusively via a constitutive pathway. Thus up-regulation of ET secretion occurs by de novo gene expression and appears to take place 3–6 hr after stimulation by ligands such as transforming growth factor β (55, 85, 92), thrombin (68, 78, 100, 131), tumor necrosis factor (19, 85), and fluid-mechanical shear stress (75, 134). In contrast, the presence of secretory granules containing ET in cells of the posterior pituitary (133) suggests that in some cells secretion occurs by a regulated pathway. Similar to other regulatory peptides or neurotransmitters, ET isopeptides arise from post-translational processing of large (approximately 200 amino acid), isopeptide-specific prohormones (11, 12, 38, 41, 96, 131). The first step in post-translational processing is recognition by dibasic pair-specific endopeptidases (i.e. Lys-Arg or Arg-Arg) that cleave the preproET polypeptide at two residues to generate a 38- or 39-amino acid proET and NH_2 and COOH terminal peptides. The next step in ET processing involves a putative endothelin-converting enzyme activity that recognizes a unique cleavage site between Trp^{21}-Val^{22} of proET (131). This enzyme has been difficult to characterize, but it appears to be a metal-dependent neutral endopeptidase (73, 98); however, several different enzymes might contribute to the observed activity (71, 99, 121). Further understanding of the pathway of ET secretion will undoubtedly follow the successful isolation and cloning of the endothelin-converting enzyme gene. The specificity of endothelin-converting enzyme makes it an attractive candidate for the development of pharmacological antagonists of ET secretion.

Normal human plasma contains low concentrations of ET (approximately 0.5–5 pM), which are well below the K_d for ET receptors (0.1–2.0 nM) (see 108 for review). ET injected intravenously into normal mammals is rapidly cleared from the plasma with a $t_{1/2}$ of less than 1 min (2, 24, 90, 127). Thus the ability of target cells to respond to ET probably depends not on circulating levels of ET, but on local synthesis and secretion. In the kidney, as in other organs, the anatomic location of cells capable of secreting ET is probably the major determinant of the local concentration of ET. However, the concept of ET as a local peptide might have to be reassessed in light of recent evidence suggesting that in some pathophysiological states, circulating levels of ET are elevated and might have biological significance (60, 61, 112, 132).

SITES OF ET ACTION IN THE KIDNEY

Localization of ET Secretion

Analysis of ET secretion in the kidney is hampered by the extensive compartmentalization and heterogeneity of renal tissue. Northern RNA blot analysis of total RNA from adult rat kidney reveals abundant expression of a preproET-1 mRNA transcript (66, 84, 96). PreproET-1 transcripts have also been identified in the cortex and medulla of adult pig kidney by the polymerase chain reaction (83). PreproET gene expression in the kidney has been localized by in situ hybridization using radiolabeled oligodeoxynucleotide probes complementary to preproET-1 mRNA (66, 83). PreproET mRNA was expressed primarily in the medulla, corresponding to vasa recta bundles, and at discrete vascular sites in both the cortex and medulla. However, the absence of preproET expression at other sites in the kidney probably reflects the inability of in situ hybridization to detect preproET mRNA at diffuse sites (i.e. the glomerular endothelium) since ET expression as been documented throughout the kidney by other techniques. For example, immunocytochemical studies demonstrate ET-1 peptide at numerous sites in the rat kidney including vascular endothelium of arcuate arteries, veins, glomerular capillaries and arterioles, peritubular capillaries, and vasa recta of distal nephron segments (129). Vascular expression of ET was not uniform and was instead highly compartmentalized. Glomerular ET was localized in the glomerular endothelial cells and weak staining was observed in the mesangium. Immunoreactive ET peptides have also been localized by weak focal staining in the cytoplasm of collecting ducts and in the proximal tubule brush border (129). Further experiments are necessary to determine whether ET is actually secreted at all of these renal cellular sites, or whether the presence of immunoreactive ET reflects diffusion of ET secreted by neighboring cells.

Experiments in different renal cell culture models suggest that ET is secreted by numerous cells in the kidney and that gene expression is not limited to vascular endothelium. Cultured glomerular endothelial cells express preproET-1 mRNA and secrete mature ET-1 peptide into the culture medium (68). Secretion of ET-1 by glomerular endothelial cells is markedly stimulated by bradykinin, thrombin, ATP, and platelet-activating factor (68). Glomerular mesangial cells also express a 2.3 kb preproET-1 mRNA transcript and secrete mature ET-1 peptide (7, 95, 136). Primary epithelial cell cultures derived from microdissected nephron segments demonstrate that renal tubule cells secrete abundant amounts of ET-1 and lesser amounts of ET-3 (49). ET secretion is much greater in cultures derived from medullary segments with inner medullary collecting ducts > medullary thick ascending limb > cortical collecting ducts > proximal tubule. ET-1 secretion has also been documented from five renal cell lines of putative medullary origin (54, 85, 104), thus confirming the notion that the medulla is an active site of ET secretion. Collectively, these experiments demonstrate that numerous cells in the kidney secrete ET, but that localization of ET secretion is tightly regulated.

Identification of ET Receptors

Molecular cloning reveals that ET receptors belong to the G protein-coupled receptor family and that at least two subtypes exist, the ET_A and ET_B isoforms (3, 62, 97). Northern RNA blot analysis shows that the kidney expresses abundant mRNA transcripts for both the ET_A (3) and ET_B (97) receptors. The ET_A receptor is expressed by renal vascular smooth muscle cells including glomerular arterioles (36a). ET_B receptor mRNA is localized to endothelial cells of glomeruli, vasa recta bundles, and thin segments of Henle's loop (36a). Receptor autoradiography with [^{125}I]-labeled ET peptides has been used to map ET receptors to glomeruli, loops of Henle, and collecting ducts (43, 50, 66, 80, 125). ET binding sites are similarly localized in the kidneys of different mammals including humans, monkeys, rabbits, dogs, and rats, which suggests that the renal actions of ET have been conserved in evolution (43). A high density of ET-1 binding sites is also present in vasa recta bundles in the inner stripe of the outer medulla. Several studies have demonstrated a moderate density of ET receptors in the proximal tubule (50, 125). [^{125}I]ET-1 binding is highly specific and is not displaced by heterologous ligands such as angiotensin II, atrial natriuretic peptide, arginine vasopressin, and numerous Ca^{2+} channel blockers. It is important to note that in many systems binding of ET-1 to its receptor is nearly irreversible, but the functional significance of this remains unclear (108, 132). To date little is known about the regulation of ET receptor expression and function in any tissue, including the kidney.

The proximal location in the kidney of ET receptors and cells that secrete ET is consistent with the hypothesis that ET signals principally in a paracrine or autocrine mode. The glomerulus provides a good example: glomerular endothelial cells are thought to secrete ET-1, which diffuses into the mesangium and binds to a high-affinity receptor on adjacent mesangial cells to signal in a paracrine mode. Glomerular endothelial cells also express ET receptors, which suggests that ET might function in an autocrine mode. Mesangial cells secrete modest levels of ET-1, so one can infer that under some circumstances ET might also function as an autocrine peptide for mesangial cells. As discussed below, the mode of ET signaling (i.e. paracrine/autocrine vs endocrine) is an important consideration when postulating physiological roles for ET in the kidney.

ET AND RENAL HEMODYNAMICS

Regulation of Renal Vascular Tone: Experiments in Vivo and in Vitro

ET is one of the most potent vasoconstrictors of the renal vasculature yet tested, and by virtue of its ability to regulate renal hemodynamics, ET controls numerous aspects of renal function. Systemic infusions of ET-1 increase renal vascular resistance and markedly decrease RBF (6, 17, 20, 31, 32, 35, 45, 74). Analogous to the systemic effect of ET on mean arterial pressure, renal vasoconstriction is often preceded by transient renal vasodilatation. The decline in RBF is dose-dependent and occurs rapidly. The maximal decline in RBF usually occurs 20–30 min after infusion of ET-1 and slowly returns to basal after approximately 1–2 hr. Indomethacin or aspirin, which block prostaglandin synthesis, amplify the increase in renal vascular resistance, which implies that vasodilatory prostaglandins function as negative feedback signals to attenuate ET-induced renal vasoconstriction (20, 21, 76). Systemic infusions of ET increase circulating atrial natriuretic peptide (32, 74), but it remains uncertain whether under physiological conditions atrial natriuretic peptide antagonizes renal vasoconstriction induced by ET (51, 93). It is also important to note that ET induces a decline in both cortical and medullary blood flow, although the cortical vasculature is more sensitive to ET (124). ET-induced vasoconstriction results from contraction of the glomerular arterioles and the arcuate and interlobular arteries (6, 26, 35, 53, 65).

Although the data with systemic infusions of ET generally support the hypothesis that ET is a potent vasoconstrictor in the kidney, this interpretation is complicated by several factors. First, systemic infusions are usually at high concentrations that reflect pharmacological rather than physiological concentrations of ET peptide; moreover, systemic infusions probably mimic an endocrine signaling mode as opposed to the mostly paracrine/autocrine signaling mode of ET in vivo. Second, it is difficult to separate systemic from intrarenal effects of ET because kidney function is regulated by numerous baroreceptor reflexes. Thus in order to directly observe the intrarenal actions of ET, investigators have employed the isolated perfused kidney, and these experiments prove that ET is indeed a potent renal vasoconstrictor. For example, ET-1 (>0.01 nM) causes a dose-dependent increase in renal vascular resistance when added to isolated perfused rat and rabbit kidneys (15, 27, 82, 88). ET-1 is approximately 30 times more potent than angiotensin II and 50 times more potent than norepinepherine (15). Due to discrepant results with cyclooxygenase inhibitors (27, 88), the effects of prostaglandins on ET-induced vasoconstriction remain uncertain and warrant further study.

Molecular Mechanisms of ET-Induced Vasoconstriction

Information regarding the molecular mechanisms of ET-induced renal vasoconstriction is incomplete (see 113 for review). Presumably ET is released by the endothelium and diffuses to vascular smooth muscle where binding to cognate, high-affinity G protein-coupled receptors occurs. Activated ET receptors then elevate intracellular free $[Ca^{2+}]$, which is generally thought to mediate the contractile response to ET (70, 108) (Figure 1). Protein kinase C has been implicated in the tonic contraction of vascular smooth muscle by ET (23, 48, 117), but the underlying mechanisms of this response are unclear. ET does not bind to or directly activate voltage-gated Ca^{2+} channels, and dihydropyridine and phenylakylamine Ca^{2+} channel blockers have a minimal effect on ET-induced renal vasoconstriction (17, 67). ET increases Ca^{2+} by evoking the phosphoinositide cascade, thereby releasing Ca^{2+} from the inositol $(1,4,5)P_3$-sensitive stores and promoting Ca^{2+} influx through receptor-operated Ca^{2+} channels (70, 108). Although pharmacomechanical coupling has not been studied in renal vascular smooth muscle, it appears to be a universal pathway for ET-induced contraction in other cell types including glomerular mesangial cells (107, 111, 115). It is important to note, however, that in isolated vascular smooth muscle cells, ET can increase the probability of a voltage-gated Ca^{2+} channel opening by an indirect modulatory pathway (33, 40, 105). ET would, therefore, enhance contraction in response to an initial depolarizing stimulus (Figure 1). Indirect modulation of voltage-gated Ca^{2+} channel activity might explain why dihydropyridine channel blockers attenuate ET-induced contraction of afferent glomerular arterioles (26, 65). The simplest interpretation of the experiments described above is that ET contracts renal vascular smooth muscle by pharmacomechanical coupling, but modulation of voltage-gated Ca^{2+} channels probably enhances contraction by classical excitation-contraction coupling. The diversity of ET-sensitive Ca^{2+}

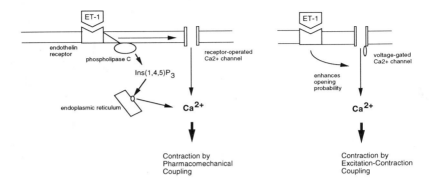

Figure 1   Schematic illustration of the postulated pathways for ET-induced vasoconstriction. In one model (*left*), ET directly induces contraction by pharmacomechanical coupling. Intracellular free $[Ca^{2+}]$ is increased by the release of Ca^{2+} from intracellular stores and by the influx of extracellular Ca^{2+} through receptor-operated Ca^{2+} channels. In another model (*right*), ET indirectly enhances contraction in response to a depolarizing stimulus by increasing the probability of opening of classical voltage-gated Ca^{2+} channels. These mechanisms are not mutually exclusive and might act in concert to contract vascular smooth muscle in the renal vasculature. See text for details.

channels suggests that specific ET antagonists will be required to block ET-induced renal vasoconstriction.

ET AND GLOMERULAR FUNCTION

Control of GFR

Bolus infusion of ET-1 in rats and dogs produces a dose-dependent, sustained decrease in GFR (6, 17, 20, 32, 35, 45, 67, 74). Experiments with the isolated perfused kidney also demonstrate that ET reduces GFR (15, 27, 82, 88). Although the precise mechanism(s) remain unclear, a decline in the net filtration pressure across the glomerular capillary (P_{UF}) and in the ultrafiltration coefficient (K_f) contributes to the fall in GFR. The decline in P_{UF} appears to result from contraction of the afferent and efferent arterioles (26). However, mildly pressor doses of ET-1 cause a proportionately greater increase in efferent than afferent arteriolar contraction and increase P_{UF} (45). This would appear to favor filtration, but a decline in K_f and a modest fall in glomerular capillary flow rate (Q_A) cause GFR to remain relatively constant at these low doses of ET. Micropuncture studies of individual glomeruli demonstrate that ET-1 directly reduces K_f (6, 45, 53). Little is known regarding the mechanism whereby ET-1 reduces K_f, but the observation that ET-1 contracts cultured mesangial cells makes it tempting to speculate that mesangial contraction reduces filtering surface area and reduces K_f (6, 107, 109). Contraction of mesangial cells by ET appears to occur via pharmacomechanical coupling (109, 111, 115).

Regulation of Mesangial Cell Biology

There is good evidence that glomerular mesangial cells are one of the important renal targets for ET. In addition to the potent contractile actions discussed above, ET is also a growth factor for mesangial cells in culture (6, 25, 42, 64, 115). ET stimulates prostaglandin synthesis in mesangial cells, which might act to attenuate ET-induced contraction (109). Mesangial cells express both an ET_A-like receptor and an ET_B-like receptor (5, 8, 69), but the receptor subtype responsible for the contractile and mitogenic actions of ET on mesangial cells is not well characterized (109, 115). The presence of two ET receptor subtypes in mesangial cells is also supported by chemical cross-linking of ET to its receptor followed by fractionation on SDS-PAGE gels (69, 118). The observation that ET is mitogenic illustrates an important point about ET, namely that these peptides can also induce long-term changes in cell phenotype that require differential regulation of gene expression (108). The mitogenic actions of ET also confirm the emerging concept that ligands activating G protein-coupled receptors can act as growth factors (34, 102). ET-1 induces several genes in quiescent mesangial cells including *fos* and *jun* family genes (114), collagenase (114), platelet-derived growth factor A and B chains (42), and prostaglandin endoperoxide synthase (116). In contrast to our extensive knowledge of the signal transduction pathways mediating the short-term actions of ET, little is known about the pathways of nuclear signaling. In mesangial cells both mitogen-activated protein kinase (126) and AP-1 transcription factors (114) have been postulated to mediate the growth factor actions of ET.

EFFECTS OF ET ON SODIUM AND WATER BALANCE

Diverse Actions of ET Regulate Sodium Balance

Current experiments to address the role of ET in renal sodium handling have generated a confusing, often contradictory, picture. Several lines of evidence point to an antinatriuretic effect of ET. First, systemic infusions of ET tend to decrease sodium excretion because of the reduction in filtered load (32, 35, 74). Infusion of ET-1 also increases circulating aldosterone (32, 74), which might reflect local stimulation of adrenal glomerulosa cells by ET (22), or instead be the result of increased levels of plasma renin (32, 74). The increase in circulating plasma renin levels is probably secondary to activation of intrarenal baroreceptor- and macula densa-mediated pathways of renin secretion. Both the decrease in filtered load and the increase in circulating aldosterone occur when ET is tested in essentially an endocrine signaling mode (i.e. systemic infusions).

In contrast, other lines of evidence support a natriuretic role for ET. For example, several studies document a natriuretic effect of ET despite a fall in RBF and GFR (30, 45, 87). In addition, studies in the isolated perfused kidney have consistently shown an increase in sodium excretion despite a dramatic decline in GFR (27, 82, 88). Several mechanisms have been proposed for the natriuretic effect of ET including a direct effect on juxtaglomerular cells to inhibit renin release (72, 77, 91, 119, 120, 122), stimulation of cardiac myocytes to increase atrial natriuretic peptide secretion (29, 37, 101), and reduction in the electrochemical gradient favoring sodium reabsorption through inhibition of Na^+-K^+-ATPase activity in the medullary collecting duct (135).

Perhaps the simplest explanation to consolidate these apparently contradictory findings is that ET acting in an intrarenal, paracrine, or autocrine mode would be natriuretic, whereas ET acting in an endocrine mode would be anti-natriuretic. As the current evidence favors an intrarenal role for ET in the kidney, it seems likely that the physiological role for ET in renal sodium handling would be natriuresis. It will be of great interest to determine the mechanism of the natriuretic effect of ET and to investigate other possibilities such as modulation of sympathetic output to the tubules and the effects of prostaglandin synthesis.

ET and Renal Water Handling

Several studies have documented that ET increases urine flow rate despite a decrease in RBF and GFR (6, 32), which suggests that ET inhibits water reabsorption. Consistent with this hypothesis, ET-1 specifically inhibits arginine vasopressin-mediated cAMP accumulation in the cortical collecting duct and in the outer and inner medullary collecting duct (123). Direct evidence for inhibition of arginine vasopressin-stimulated water permeability comes from studies in microperfused inner medullary collecting duct segments where ET reversibly inhibits the increase in osmotic water permeability by arginine vasopressin (86). The ability of ET to attenuate water reabsorption in the collecting duct could explain in part the ability of ET to increase urinary volume despite the fall in RBF and GFR.

POSSIBLE ROLES FOR ET IN RENAL PATHOPHYSIOLOGY

Given the potent effects of ET on renal homeostasis, several studies have investigated the possible involvement of ET peptides in renal disease (51,

110). Cyclosporine increases ET secretion (16, 52, 79, 89), and ET secretion has been postulated to mediate the intense renal vasoconstriction and glomerular dysfunction associated with cyclosporine-induced renal toxicity. Because hypoxia is a potent stimulus for ET secretion, several laboratories have postulated a role for ET in hemodynamically-mediated renal failure (28, 53, 63, 103, 128). In fact, in one model of post-ischemic renal failure, neutralizing antibodies against ET ameliorated the decline in RBF and GFR (53). In addition, several lines of evidence point to a role for ET in glomerular inflammation (10, 14, 110). It should be stressed, however, that these findings are preliminary at this stage and much work will be necessary to document a role for ET in renal disease.

CONCLUDING REMARKS

It is now clear that ET peptides have striking effects on renal physiology, but many important questions remain unanswered. For instance, it will be critical to define the relevant physiological stimuli for ET secretion in the kidney. Does hemodynamic shear stress, for example, mediate ET secretion in the kidney or do soluble mediators also contribute? Many questions remain regarding the effects of ET on sodium handling. In addition, it will be essential to map the pathways of nuclear signaling by ET receptors that mediate long term changes in cell phenotype. The development of pharmacological tools to block ET secretion and ET receptors will undoubtedly provide answers to many of these questions and allow us to develop an integrated view of the control of renal homeostasis by ET.

ACKNOWLEDGMENTS

This work was supported by National Institutes of Health grant HL22563.

Literature Cited

1. Anggard, E., Botting, R., Vane, J. R. 1990. Endothelins. *Blood Vessels* 27: 269–81
2. Anggard, E., Galton, S., Rae, G., Thomas, R., McLoughlin, L., et al. 1989. The fate of radioiodinated endothelin-1 and endothelin-3 in the rat. *J. Cardiovasc. Pharmacol* 13(S5):S46–49
3. Arai, H., Hori, S., Aramori, I., Ohkubo, H., Nakanishi, S. 1990. Cloning and expression of a cDNA encoding an endothelin receptor. *Nature* 348: 730–32
4. Arinami, T., Ishikawa, M., Inoue, A., Yanagisawa, M., Masaki, T., et al. 1991. Chromosomal assignments of the human endothelin family genes: the endothelin-1 gene (EDN1) to 6p23-p24, the endothelin-2 gene (EDN2) to 1p34, and the endothelin-3 gene (EDN3) to 20q13.2-q13.3. *Am. J. Hum. Genet.* 48:990–96
5. Badr, K. F., Munger, K. A., Sugiura, M., Snajdar, R. M., Schwartzberg, M., Inagami, T. 1989. High and low affinity binding sites for endothelin on cultured rat glomerular mesangial cells. *Biochem. Biophys. Res. Commun.* 161: 776–81

6. Badr, K. F., Murray, J. J., Breyer, M. D., Takahashi, K., Inagami, T., Harris, R. C. 1989. Mesangial cell, glomerular, and renal vascular responses to endothelin in the kidney. *J. Clin. Invest.* 83:336–42

7. Bakris, G. L., Fairbanks, R., Traish, M., Akerstrom, V., Kern, S. 1991. Arginine vasopressin stimulates human mesangial cell production of endothelin. *J. Clin. Invest.* 87:1158–64

8. Baldi, E., Dunn, M. J. 1991. Endothelin binding and receptor downregulation in rat glomerular mesangial cells. *J. Pharmacol. Exp. Ther.* 256: 581–86

9. Ballermann, B. J., Zeidel, M. L., Gunning, M. E., Brenner, B. M. 1991. Vasoactive peptides and the kidney. In *The Kidney*, ed. B. M. Brenner, F. J. Rector, pp. 510–83. St. Louis: Saunders

10. Benigni, A., Perico, N., Gaspari, F., Zoja, C., Bellizzi, L., et al. 1991. Increased renal endothelin production in rats with reduced renal mass. *Am. J. Physiol.* 260:F331–39

11. Bloch, K. D., Eddy, R. L., Shows, T. B., Quertermous, T. 1989. cDNA cloning and chromosomal assignment of the gene encoding endothelin 3. *J. Biol. Chem.* 264:18156–61

12. Bloch, K. D., Friedrich, S. P., Lee, M.-E., Eddy, R. L., Shows, T. B., Quertermous, T. 1989. Structural organization and chromosomal assignment of the gene encoding endothelin. *J. Biol. Chem.* 264:10851–57

13. Bloch, K. D., Hong, C. C., Eddy, R. L., Shows, T. B., Quertermous, T. 1991. cDNA cloning and chromosomal assignment of the endothelin 2 gene: vasoactive intestinal contractor peptide is rat endothelin 2. *Genomics* 10:236–42

14. Brooks, D. P., Contino, L. C., Storer, B., Ohlstein, E. H. 1991. Increased endothelin excretion in rats with renal failure induced by partial nephrectomy. *Br. J. Pharmacol.* 104:987–89

15. Cairns, H. S., Rogerson, M. E., Fairbanks, L. D., Neild, G. H., Westwick, J. 1989. Endothelin induces an increase in renal vascular resistence and a fall in glomerular filtration rate in the rabbit isolated perfused kidney. *Br. J. Pharmacol.* 98:155–60

16. Cairns, H. S., Rogerson, M., Fairbanks, L. D., Westwick, J., Neild, G. H. 1988. Endothelin and cylosporin nephrotoxicity. *Lancet* 24:1496–97

17. Cao, L., Banks, R. O. 1990. Cardiovascular and renal actions of endothelin: effects of calcium-channel blockers. *Am. J. Physiol.* 258:F254–58

18. Carmines, P. K., Fleming, J. T. 1990. Control of the renal microvasculature by vasoactive peptides. *FASEB J.* 4: 3300–9

19. Casey, M. L., Word, R. A., MacDonald, P. C. 1991. Endothelin-1 gene expression and regulation of endothelin mRNA and protein biosynthesis in avascular human amnion. *J. Biol. Chem.* 266: 5762–68

20. Chou, S.-Y., Dahhan, A., Porush, J. G. 1990. Renal actions of endothelin: interaction with prostacyclin. *Am. J. Physiol.* 259:F645–52

21. Chou, S.-Y., Dahhan, A., Porush, J. G. 1990. Renal actions of endothelin: interaction with prostacyclin. *Am. J. Physiol.* 259:F645–52

22. Cozza, E. N., Gomez-Sanchez, C. E., Foecking, M. F., Chiou, S. 1989. Endothelin binding to cultured calf adrenal zona glomerulosa cells and stimulation of aldosterone secretion. *J. Clin. Invest.* 84:1032–35

23. Danthuluri, N. R., Brock, T. A. 1990. Endothelin receptor-coupling mechanisms in vascular smooth muscle: A role for protein kinase C. *J. Pharmacol. Exp. Ther.* 254:393–99

24. deNucci, G., Thomas, R., D'Orleans-Juste, P., Antunes, E., Walder, C., et al. 1988. Pressor effects of circulating endothelin are limited by its removal in the pulmonary circulation and by the release of prostacyclin and endothelium-derived relaxing factor. *Proc. Natl. Acad. Sci. USA* 85:9797–800

25. Dunlop, M. E., Larkins, R. G. 1990. Insulin-dependent contractility of glomerular mesangial cells in response to angiotensin II, platelet-activating factor and endothelin is attenuated by prostaglandin E2. *Biochem. J.* 272: 561–68

26. Edwards, R. M., Trizna, W. T., Ohlstein, E. H. 1990. Renal microvascular effects of endothelin. *Am. J. Physiol.* 259: F217–21

27. Ferrario, R. G., Foulkes, R., Salvati, P., Patrono, C. 1989. Hemodynamic and tubular effects of endothelin and thromboxane in the isolated perfused rat kidney. *Eur. J. Pharmacol.* 171: 127–34

28. Firth, J. D., Raine, A. E., Ratcliffe, P. J., Ledingham, J. G. 1988. Endothelin: An important factor in acute renal failure. *Lancet* 19:1179–81

29. Fukada, Y., Hirata, Y., Yoshimi, H. 1988. Endothelin is a potent secretagogue for atrial natriuretic peptide in

cultured rat atrial myocytes. *Biochem. Biophys. Res. Commun.* 155:167–71

30. Garcia, R., Lachance, D., Thibault, G. 1990. Positive inotropic action, natriuresis and atrial natriuretic factor release induced by endothelin in the conscious rat. *J. Hypertens.* 8: 725–31

31. Goetz, K. L., Wang, B. C., Leadley, R. J., Zhu, J. L., Madwed, J., Bie, P. 1989. Endothelin and sarafotoxin produce dissimilar effects on renal blood flow, but both block the antidiuretic effects of vasopressin. *Proc. Soc. Exp. Biol. Med.* 191:425–27

32. Goetz, K. L., Wang, B. C., Madwed, J. B., Zhu, J. L., Leadley, R. J. 1988. Cardiovascular, renal, and endocrine responses to intravenous endothelin in conscious dogs. *Am. J. Physiol.* 255: R1064–68

33. Goto, K., Kasuya, Y., Matsuki, N., Takuwa, Y., Kurihara, H., et al. 1989. Endothelin activates the dihydropyridine-sensitive, voltage-dependent Ca^{2+} channel in vascular smooth muscle. *Proc. Natl. Acad. Sci. USA* 86:3915–18

34. Gupta, S. K., Gallego, C., Johnson, G. L. 1992. Mitogenic pathways regulated by G protein oncogenes. *Mol. Biol. Cell* 3:123–28

35. Hirata, Y., Matsuoka, H., Kimura, K., Fukui, K., Hayakawa, H., et al. 1989. Renal vasoconstriction by the endothelial cell-derived peptide endothelin in spontaneously hypertensive rats. *Circ. Res.* 65:1370–79

36. Hoehe, M. R., Ehrenreich, H., Caenazzo, L., Berrettini, W. H. 1991. Taq1 identifies a four allele DNA polymorphism of the human endothelin-1 gene (EDN1). *Nucleic Acids Res.* 19: 3161–63

36a. Hori, S., Komatsu, Y., Shigemoto, R., Mizuno, N., Nakanishi, S. 1992. Distinct tissue distribution and cellular localization of two messenger ribonucleic acids encoding different subtypes of rat endothelial receptors. *Endocrinology* 130:1885–95

37. Hu, J. R., Berninger, U. G., Lang, R. E. 1988. Endothelin stimulates atrial natriuretic peptide (ANP) release from rat atria. *Eur. J. Pharmacol.* 158:177–80

38. Inoue, A., Yanagisawa, M., Kimura, S., Kasuya, Y., Miyauchi, T., et al. 1989. The human endothelin family: Three structurally and pharmacologically distinct isopeptides predicted by three separate genes. *Proc. Natl. Acad. Sci. USA* 86:2863–67

39. Inoue, A., Yanagisawa, M., Takuwa, Y., Mitsui, Y., Kobayashi, M., Masaki, T. 1989. The human preproendothelin-1 gene. *J. Biol. Chem.* 264:14954–59

40. Inoue, Y., Oike, M., Kitamura, K., Kuriyama, H. 1990. Endothelin augments unitary calcium channel currents on the smooth muscle cell membrane of guinea-pig portal vein. *J. Physiol.* 423:171–91

41. Itoh, Y., Yanagisawa, M., Ohkubo, S., Kimura, C., Kosaka, T., et al. 1988. Cloning and sequence analysis of cDNA encoding the precursor of a human endothelium-derived vasoconstrictor peptide, endothelin: identity of human and porcine endothelin. *FEBS Lett.* 231:440–44

42. Jaffer, F. E., Knauss, T. C., Poptic, E., Abboud, H. E. 1990. Endothelin stimulates PDGF secretion in cultured human mesangial cells. *Kidney Int.* 38:1193–98

43. Jones, C. R., Hiley, C. R., Pelton, J. T., Miller, R. C. 1989. Autoradiographic localization on endothelin binding sites in kidney. *Eur. J. Pharmacol.* 163:379–82

44. Kimura, S., Kasuya, Y., Sawamura, T., Shinmi, O., Sugita, Y., et al. 1988. Structure-activity relationships of endothein: importance of the C-terminal moiety. *Biochem. Biophys. Res. Commun.* 156:1182–86

45. King, A. J., Brenner, B. M., Anderson, S. 1989. Endothelin: a potent renal and systemic vasoconstrictor peptide. *Am. J. Physiol.* 256:F1051–58

46. Kloog, Y., Ambar, I., Sokolovsky, M., Wollberg, Z. 1988. Sarafotoxin, a novel vasoconstrictor peptide: phosphoinositide hydrolysis in rat heart and brain. *Science* 242:268–70

47. Kloog, Y., Sokolovsky, M. 1989. Similarities in mode and sites of action of sarafotoxins and endothelins. *Trends Pharmacol. Sci.* 10:212–14

48. Kodama, M., Kanaide, H., Abe, S., Hirano, K., Kai, H., Nakamura, M. 1989. Endothelin-induced Ca-independent contraction of the porcine coronary artery. *Biochem. Biophys. Res. Commun.* 160:1302–8

49. Kohan, D. E. 1991. Endothelin synthesis by rabbit renal tubule cells. *Am. J. Physiol.* 261:F221–26

50. Kohzuki, M., Johnston, C. I., Chai, S. Y., Casley, D., Mendelsohn, F. A. O. 1989. Localization of endothelin receptors in rat kidney. *Eur. J. Pharmacol.* 160:193–94

51. Kon, V., Badr, K. F. 1991. Biological actions and pathophysiologic signifi-

cance of endothelin in the kidney. *Kidney Int.* 40:1–12

52. Kon, V., Sugiura, M., Inagami, T., Harvie, B. R., Ichikawa, I., Hoover, R. L. 1990. Role of endothelin in cyclosporine-induced glomerular dysfunction. *Kidney Int.* 37:1487–91

53. Kon, V., Yoshioka, T., Fogo, A., Ichikawa, I. 1989. Glomerular actions of endothelin in vivo. *J. Clin. Invest.* 83:1762–67

54. Kosaka, T., Suzuki, N., Matsumoto, H., Itoh, Y., Yasuhara, T., 1989. Synthesis of the vasoconstrictor peptide endothelin in kidney cells. *FEBS Lett.* 249:42–46

55. Kurihara, H., Yoshizuma, M., Sugiyama, T., Takaku, F., Yanagisawa, M., et al. 1989. Transforming growth factor-b stimulates the expression of endothelin mRNA by vascular endothelial cells. *Biochem. Biophys. Res. Commun.* 159: 1435–40

56. Landan, G., Bdolah, A., Wollberg, Z., Kochva, E., Graur, D. 1991. Evolution of the sarafotoxin/endothelin superfamily of proteins. *Toxicon* 29:237–44

57. Lee, M.-E., Bloch, K. D., Clifford, J. A., Quertermous, T. 1990. Functional analysis of the endothelin-1 gene promoter. *J. Biol. Chem.* 265:10446–50

58. Lee, M.-E., Dhadly, M. S., Temizer, D. H., Clifford, J. A., Yoshizumi, M., Quertermous, T. 1991. Regulation of endothelin-1 gene expression by fos and jun. *J. Biol. Chem.* 266:19034–39

59. Lee, M.-E., Temizer, D. H., Clifford, J. A., Quertermous, T. 1991. Cloning of the GATA-binding protein that regulates endothelin-1 gene expression in endothelial cells. *J. Biol. Chem.* 266: 16188–92

60. Lerman, A., Hildebrand, F. L., Aarhus, L. L., Burnett, J. C. 1991. Endothelin has biological actions at pathophysiological concentrations. *Circulation* 83: 1808–14

61. Lerman, A., Hildebrand, F. L., Margulies, K. B., O'Murchu, B., Perrella, M. A., Heublien, D. M., Schwab, T. R., Burnett, J. C. 1990. Endothelin: A new cardiovascular regulatory peptide. *Mayo Clin. Proc.* 65:1441–55

62. Lin, H.-Y., Kaji, E. H., Winkel, G. K., Ives, H. E., Lodish, H. F. 1991. Cloning and functional expression of a vascular smooth muscle endothelin-1 receptor. *Proc. Natl. Acad. Sci. USA* 88:3185–89

63. Lopez-Farre, A., Gomez-Garre, D., Bernabeu, F., Lopez-Novoa, J. M. 1991. A role for endothelin in the maintenance of post-ischemic renal failure in the rat. *J. Physiol.* 444:513–22

64. Lopez-Farre, A., Gomez-Garre, D., Bernabeu, F., Montanes, I., Millas, I., Lopez-Novoa, J. M. 1991. Renal effects and mesangial cell contraction induced by endothelin are mediated by PAF. *Kidney Int.* 39:624–30

65. Loutzenhiser, R., Epstein, M., Hayashi, K., Horton, C. 1990. Direct visualization of effects of endothelin on the renal microvasculature. *Am. J. Physiol.* 258:F61–68

66. MacCumber, M. W., Ross, C. A., Glaser, B. M., Synder, S. H. 1989. Endothelin: Visualization of mRNAs by in situ hybridization provides evidence for local action. *Proc. Natl. Acad. Sci. USA* 86:7285–89

67. Madeddu, P., Yang, X., Anania, V., Troffa, C., Pazzola, A., et al. 1990. Efficacy of nifedipine to prevent systemic and renal vasoconstrictor effects of endothelin. *Am. J. Physiol.* 259: F304–11

68. Marsden, P. A., Dorfman, D. M., Collins, T., Brenner, B. M., Orkin, S., Ballermann, B. J. 1991. Regulated expression of endothelin 1 in glomerular capillary endothelial cells. *Am. J. Physiol.* 261:F117–25

69. Martin, E. R., Brenner, B. M., Ballermann, B. J. 1990. Heterogeneity of cell surface endothelin receptors. *J. Biol. Chem.* 265:14044–49

70. Masaki, T., Yanagisawa, M., Takuwa, Y., Kasuya, Y., Kimura, S., Goto, K. 1990. Cellular mechanism of vasoconstriction induced by endothelin. *Adv. Sec. Messenger Phosphoprotein Res.* 24:425–28

71. Matsumura, Y., Ikegawa, R., Tsukahara, Y., Takaoka, M., Morimoto, S. 1990. Conversion of big endothelin-1 to endothelin-1 by two types of metalloproteinases derived from porcine aortic endothelial cells. *FEBS Lett.* 272:166–70

72. Matsumura, Y., Nakase, K., Ikegawa, R., Hayashi, K., Ohyama, T., Morimoto, S. 1989. The endothelium-derived vasoconstrictor peptide endothelin inhibits renin release in vitro. *Life Sci.* 44:149–57

73. McMahon, E. G., Palomo, M. A., Moore, W. M., McDonald, J. F., Stern, M. K. 1991. Phosphoramidon blocks the pressor activity of porcine big endothelin-1-(1–39) in vivo and conversion of big endothelin-1-(1–39) to endothelin-1-(1–21) in vitro. *Proc. Natl. Acad. Sci. USA USA* 88:703–7

74. Miller, W. L., Redfield, M. M., Bur-

nett, J. C. 1989. Integrated cardiac, renal, and endocrine actions of endothelin. *J. Clin. Invest.* 83:317–20

75. Milner, P., Bodin, P., Loesch, A., Burnstock, G. 1990. Rapid release of endothelin and ATP from isolated aortic endothelial cells exposed to increase flow. *Biochem. Biophys. Res. Commun.* 170:649–56

76. Miura, K., Yukimura, T., Yamashita, Y., Shimmen, T., Okumura, M., et al. 1991. Renal and femoral vascular responses to endothelin-1 in dogs: role of prostaglandins. *J. Pharmacol. Exp. Ther.* 256:11–17

77. Moe, O., Tejedor, A., Campbell, W. B., Alpern, R. J., Henrich, W. L. 1991. Effects of endothelin on in vitro renin secretion. *Am. J. Physiol.* 260: E521–25

78. Moon, D. G., Horgan, M. J., Andersen, T. T., Krystek, S. R., et al. 1989. Endothelin-like pulmonary vasoconstrictor peptide release by a-thrombin. *Proc. Natl. Acad. Sci. USA* 86: 9529–33

79. Nambi, P., Pullen, M., Contino, L. C., Brooks, D. P. 1990. Upregulation of renal endothelin receptors in rats with cyclosporine A-induced nephrotoxicity. *Eur. J. Pharmacol.* 187:113–16

80. Nayler, W. G. 1990. Endothelin: isoforms, binding sites, and possible implications in pathology. *Trends Pharmacol. Sci.* 11:96–99

81. Niall, H. D. 1982. The evolution of peptide hormones. *Annu. Rev. Physiol.* 44:615–24

82. Nitta, K., Naruse, M., Sanaka, T., Tsuchiya, K., Naruse, K., et al. 1990. Natriuretic and diuretic effects of endothelin in isolated perfused rat kidney. *Endocrinol. Jpn.* 36:887–90

83. Nunez, D. J., Brown, M. J., Davenport, A. P., Neylon, C. B., Schofield, J. P., Wyse, R. K. 1990. Endothelin-1 mRNA is widely expressed in porcine and human tissues. *J. Clin. Invest.* 85: 1537–41

84. Nunez, D. J., Taylor, E. A., Oh, V. M., Schofield, J. P., Brown, M. J. 1991. Endothelin-1 mRNA expression in the rat kidney. *Biochem. J.* 275:817–19

85. Ohta, K., Hirata, Y., Imai, T., Kanno, K., Emori, T., Shichiri, M., Marumo, F. 1990. Cytokine-induced release of endothelin-1 from porcine renal epithelial cell line. *Biochem. Biophys. Res. Commun.* 169:578–84

86. Oishi, R., Nonoguchi, H., Tomita, K., Marumo, F. 1991. Endothelin-1 inhibits AVP-stimulated osmotic water permeability in rat inner medullary collecting duct. *Am. J. Physiol.* 261:F951–56

87. Perico, N., Cornejo, R. P., Benigni, A., Malanchini, B., Ladny, J. R., Remuzzi, G. 1991. Endothelin induces diuresis and natriuresis in the rat by acting on proximal tubular cells through a mechanism mediated by lipoxygenase products. *J. Am. Soc. Nephrol.* 2:57–69

88. Perico, N., Dadan, J., Gabanelli, M., Remuzzi, G. 1990. Cyclooxygenase products and atrial natriuretic peptide modulate renal response to endothelin. *J. Pharmacol. Exp. Ther.* 252:1213–20

89. Perico, N., Dadan, J., Remuzzi, G. 1990. Endothelin mediates the renal vasoconstriction induced by cyclosporine in the rat. *J. Am. Soc. Nephrol.* 1:76–83

90. Pernow, J., Hemsen, A., Lundberg, J. M. 1989. Tissue specific distribution, clearance, and vascular effects of endothelin in the pig. *Biochem. Biophys. Res. Commun.* 161:647–53

91. Rakugi, H., Nakamaru, M., Saito, H., Higaki, J., Ogihara, T. 1988. Endothelin inhibits renin release from isolated rat glomeruli. *Biochem. Biophys. Res. Commun.* 155:1244–47

92. Resink, T. J., Hahn, A. W., Scott-Burden, T., Powell, J., Weber, E., Buhler, F. R. 1990. Inducible endothelin mRNA expression and peptide secretion in cultured human vascular smooth muscle cells. *Biochem. Biophys. Res. Commun.* 168:1303–10

93. Rubanyi, G. M., Parker Botelho, L. H. 1991. Endothelins. *FASEB J.* 5: 2713–20

94. Saida, K., Mitsui, Y., Ishida, N. 1989. A novel peptide, vasoactive intestinal constrictor, of a new (endothelin) peptide family. *J. Biol. Chem.* 264:14613–16

95. Sakamoto, H., Sasaki, S., Hirata, Y., Imai, T., Ando, K., Ida, T., et al. 1990. Production of endothelin-1 by rat cultured mesangial cells. *Biochem. Biophys. Res. Commun.* 169:462–68

96. Sakurai, T., Yanagisawa, M., Inoue, A., Ryan, U. S., Kimura, S., et al. 1991. cDNA cloning, sequence analysis and tissue distribution of rat preproendothelin-1 mRNA. *Biochem. Biophys. Res. Commun.* 175:44–47

97. Sakurai, T., Yanagisawa, M., Takuwa, Y., Miyazaki, H., Kimura, S., et al. 1990. Cloning of a cDNA encoding a non-isopeptide-selective subtype of the endothelin receptor. *Nature* 348:732–35

98. Sawamura, T., Kasuya, Y., Matsushita, Y., Suzuki, N., Shinmi, O., et al.,

1991. Phosphoramidon inhibits the intracellular conversion of big endothelin-1 to endothelin-1 in cultured endothelial cells. *Biochem. Biophys. Res. Commun.* 174:779–84

99. Sawamura, T., Kimura, S., Shinmi, O., Sugita, Y., Kobayashi, M., et al. 1990. Characterization of endothelin converting enzyme activities in soluble fraction of bovine cultured endothelial cells. *Biochem. Biophys. Res. Commun.* 169: 1138–44

100. Schini, V. B., Hendrickson, H., Heublein, D. M., Burnett, J. C., Vanhoutte, P. M. 1989. Thrombin enhances the release of endothelin from cultured porcine aortic endothelial cells. *Eur. J. Pharmacol.* 165:2–3

101. Sei, C. A., Glembotski, C. C. 1990. Calcium-dependence of phenylepherine-stimulated, endothelin-stimulated, and potassium chloride-stimulated atrial natriuretic factor secretion from longterm primary neonatal rat atrial cardiocytes. *J. Biol. Chem.* 265:7166–72

102. Seuwen, K., Pouyssegur, J. 1990. Serotonin as a growth factor. *Biochem. Pharmacol.* 39:985–90

103. Shibouta, Y., Suzuki, N., Shino, A., Matsumoto, H., Terashita, Z.-I., et al. 1990. Pathophysiological role of endothelin in acute renal failure. *Life Sci.* 46:1611–18

104. Shichiri, M., Hirata, Y., Emori, T., Ohta, K., Nakajima, T., et al. 1989. Secretion of endothelin and related peptides from renal epithelial cell lines. *FEBS Lett.* 253:203–6

105. Silberberg, S. D., Poder, T. C., Lacerda, A. E. 1989. Endothelin increases single-channel calcium currents in coronary arterial smooth muscle cells. *FEBS Lett.* 247:68–72

106. Simonson, M. S. 1993. Endothelins: Multifunctional renal peptides. *Physiol. Rev.* In press

107. Simonson, M. S., Dunn, M. J. 1990. Endothelin: Pathways of transmembrane signaling. *Hypertension* 15(S1):I5–12

108. Simonson, M. S., Dunn, M. J. 1990. Cellular signaling by peptides of the endothelin gene family. *FASEB J.* 4: 2989–3000

109. Simonson, M. S., Dunn, M. J. 1990. Endothelin-1 stimulates contraction of rat glomerular mesangial cells and potentiates β-adrenergic-mediated cyclic adenosine monophosphate accumulation. *J. Clin. Invest.* 85:790–97

110. Simonson, M. S., Dunn, M. J. 1991. Endothelin peptides: A possible role in glomerular inflammation. *Lab. Invest.* 64:1–4

111. Simonson, M. S., Dunn, M. J. 1991. Ca^{2+} signaling by distinct endothelin peptides in glomerular mesangial cells. *Exp. Cell Res.* 192:148–56

112. Simonson, M. S., Dunn, M. J. 1991. Endothelins: A family of regulatory peptides. *Hypertension* 17:856–63

113. Simonson, M. S., Dunn, M. J. 1992. The molecular mechanisms of cardiovascular and renal regulation by endothelin peptides. *J. Lab. Clin. Med.* 119:622–39

114. Simonson, M. S., Jones, J. M., Dunn, M. J. 1992. Differential regulation of fos and jun gene expression and AP-1 cis-element activity by endothelin isopeptides: Possible implications for mitogenic signaling by endothelin. *J. Biol. Chem.* 267:8643–49

115. Simonson, M. S., Wann, S., Mene, P., Dubyak, G., Kester, M., et al. 1989. Endothelin stimulates phospholipase C, Na^+/H^+ exchange, c-fos expression, and mitogenesis in rat mesangial cells. *J. Clin. Invest.* 83:708–12

116. Simonson, M. S., Wolfe, J. A., Konieczkowski, M., Sedor, J. R., Dunn, M. J. 1991. Regulation of prostaglandin endoperoxide synthase gene expression in cultured rat mesangial cells: Induction by serum via a protein kinase-C-dependent mechanism. *Mol. Endocrinol.* 5:441–51

117. Sugiura, M., Inagami, T., Harem, G. M., Johns, J. A. 1989. Endothelin action: inhibition by protein kinase C inhibitor and involvement of phosphoinositols. *Biochem. Biophys. Res. Commun.* 158: 170–76

118. Sugiura, M., Snadjar, R. M., Schwartzberg, M., Badr, K. F., Inagami, T. 1989. Identification of two types of specific endothelin receptors in rat mesangial cell. *Biochem. Biophys. Res. Commun.* 162:1396–401

119. Takagi, M., Matsuoka, H., Atarashi, K., Yagi, S. 1988. Endothelin: a new inhibitor of renin release. *Biochem. Biophys. Res. Commun.* 157:1164–68

120. Takagi, Y., Tsudada, H., Matsuoka, H., Yagi, S. 1989. Inhibitory effect of endothelin on renin release in vitro. *Am. J. Physiol.* 257:E833–38

121. Takaoka, M., Hukumori, Y., Shiragami, K., Ikegawa, R., Matsumura, Y., Morimoto, S. 1990. Proteolytic processing of porcine big endothelin-1 catalyzed by cathepsin D. *Biochem. Biophys. Res. Commun.* 173: 1218–23

122. Tejedor, A., Moe, O., Alpern, R. J., Campbell, W. B., Henrich, W. L.

ENDOTHELIN 265

1989. Endothelin inhibits in vitro renin release. *Clin. Res.* 37:585A
123. Tomita, K., Nonoguchi, H., Marumo, F. 1990. Effects of endothelin on peptide-dependent cyclic adenosine monophosphate accumulation along the nephron segments of the rat. *J. Clin. Invest.* 85:2014–18
124. Tsuchiya, K., Naruse, M., Sanaka, T., Naruse, K., Nitta, K., et al. 1989. Effects of endothelin on renal regional blood flow in dogs. *Eur. J. Pharmacol.* 166:541–43
125. Waeber, C., Hoyer, D., Palacios, J.-M. 1990. Similar distribution of [125I] sarafotoxin-6b and [^{125}I] endothelin 1,2,3 binding sites in the human kidney. *Eur. J. Pharmacol.* 176:233–36
126. Wang, Y., Simonson, M. S., Pouyssegur, J., Dunn, M. J. 1992. Endothelin rapidly stimulates mitogen-activated protein kinase activity in rat mesangial cells. *Biochem. J.* In press
127. Westcott, J. Y., Henson, J., McMurtry, I. F., OBrien, R. F. 1990. Uptake and metabolism of endothelin in the isolated perfused rat lung. *Exp. Lung Res.* 16: 521–32
128. Wilkes, B. M., Pearl, A. R., Mento, P. F., Maita, M. E., Macica, C. M., Girardi, E. P. 1991. Glomerular endothelin receptors during initiation and maintenance of ischemic acute renal failure in rats. *Am. J. Physiol.* 260: F110–18
129. Wilkes, B. M., Susin, M., Mento, P. F., Macica, C. M., Girardi, E. P., et al. 1991. Localization of endothelin-like immunoreactivity in rat kidneys. *Am. J. Physiol.* 260:F913–20
130. Yanagisawa, M., Akihiro, I., Ishikawa,

T., Kasuya, Y., Kimura, S., et al. 1988. Primary stucture, synthesis, and biological activity of rat endothelin, an endothelium-derived vasconstictor. *Proc. Natl. Acad. Sci. USA* 85:6964–67
131. Yanagisawa, M., Kurihara, H., Kimura, S., Tombe, Y., Kobayashi, M., et al. 1988. A novel potent vasoconstrictor peptide produced by vascular endothelial cells. *Nature* 332: 411–15
132. Yanagisawa, M., Masaki, T. 1989. Endothelin, a novel endothelium-derived peptide. *Biochem. Pharmacol.* 38: 1877–83
133. Yoshizawa, T., Shinmi, O., Giaid, A., Yanagisawa, M., Gibson, S. J., et al. 1990. Endothelin: A novel peptide in the posterior pituitary system. *Science* 247:462–64
134. Yoshizuma, M., Kurihara, H., Sugiyama, T., Takaku, F., Yanagisawa, M., et al. 1989. Hemodynamic shear stress stimulates endothelin production by cultured endothelial cells. *Biochem. Biophys. Res. Commun.* 161:859–64
135. Zeidel, M. L., Brady, H. R., Kone, B. C., Gullans, S. R., Brenner, B. M. 1989. Endothelin, a peptide inhibitor of Na$^+$-K$^+$-ATPase in intact renal tubular cells. *Am. J. Physiol.* 257: C1101–7
136. Zoja, C., Orisio, S., Perico, N., Benigni, A., Morigi, M., et al. 1991. Constitutive expression of endothelin gene in cultured human mesangial cells and its modulation by transforming growth factor b, thrombin, and a thromboxane A2 analogue. *Lab. Invest.* 64:16–25

Annu. Rev. Physiol. 1993. 55:267–88

FUNCTION AND REGULATION OF COLLECTING DUCT INTERCALATED CELLS

Victor L. Schuster

Departments of Medicine and Physiology/Biophysics, Albert Einstein College of Medicine, Bronx, New York 10461

KEY WORDS: acidification, anion exchange, mineralocorticoids, hydrogen ATPases

INTRODUCTION

Renal intercalated cells (IC) are interspersed among the segment-specific majority (principal) cells of the distal convoluted tubule, connecting tubule, and collecting duct (71, 144). Ultrastructurally, ICs are distinguished by their dark cytoplasm, high mitochondrial density, cytoplasmic tubulovesicular structures, and apical microprojections (87). There are two major collecting duct IC subtypes, and they mediate H^+ and HCO_3 secretion, and Cl and K^+ reabsorption (116–119, 123).

This review focuses on immunocytochemistry and perfused tubule data from ICs of rabbit and rat cortical collecting duct (CCD) and outer medullary collecting duct (OMCD), with emphasis on six areas: (*a*) functional and immunocytochemical characteristics of IC subtypes; (*b*) axial distribution along the collecting duct; (*c*) regulation by β-adrenergic agonists; (*d*) regulation by systemic acid-base perturbations; (*e*) regulation by aldosterone; and (*f*) plasticity of IC transporter polarity and expression.

SUBTYPES: Functional and Immunocytochemical Characteristics

The nomenclature of IC subtypes is, unfortunately, somewhat confusing. The two major subtypes of the turtle bladder mitochondria-rich cells, equivalent to mammalian ICs, were first named α and β by Stetson and Steinmetz (132, 133). Subsequently, rat ICs were called types A and B (87), whereas rabbit

267

0066–4278/93/0315–0267$02.00

ICs followed the original turtle bladder designation as α and β (123). For simplicity, in this review I use the α/β nomenclature.

The α cell, abundant in the OMCD, but also present in the CCD, absorbs HCO_3 via H^+ secretion. The β cell, found only in the CCD, secretes HCO_3 and absorbs Cl via apical Cl-HCO_3 exchange (116, 117). One or both cell types may absorb K^+ via an H^+K^+ATPase (see below). Both IC types have a high density of mitochondria (26, 71) and an apical membrane of high electrical resistance (31, 63–65, 97, 98, 103). In the rat, the two IC subtypes are readily distinguished by transmission electron microscopy (TEM) (71, 144), but in the rabbit it can be impossible to differentiate between the two except by immunocytochemistry or scanning electron microscopy (SEM) (26, 106). Figure 1 presents a comparison of the expression and polarity of primary transporters in α and β ICs.

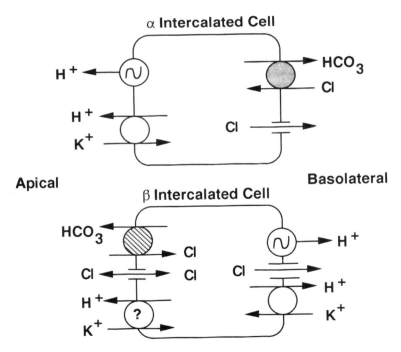

Figure 1   Acid-base transporters of the two major types of rat and rabbit collecting duct intercalated cells. Not all components have been shown to be present in both rat and rabbit. The polarity of some transporters is still uncertain. α cells of the cortical collecting duct may not be identical to those of the medullary collecting duct. A small subset of cells may combine features of both α and β types. See text for details.

Polarity and Function of H^+ ATPases

Expression of vacuolar H^+ATPase is one of the most characteristic features of ICs. One isoform of the vacuolar H^+ATPase 56-kd subunit is IC-specific (102). In the rat, a subset of ICs of both the CCD and OMCD exhibits definite apical immunocytochemical staining for vacuolar H^+ATPase (α ICs) (1, 6, 10, 11, 62, 147), whereas another subset of ICs exhibits distinct basolateral staining (β ICs) (1, 6, 10, 11). Other staining patterns for vacuolar H^+ATPase in the rat CCD are also seen (6) (see below). In the rabbit, as in the rat, α ICs of the CCD and OMCD have distinct apical H^+ATPase labeling (122). In contrast, at the light microscope level, the staining pattern of β IC H^+ATPase in the rabbit is diffuse across the cell, i.e. no cells exhibit the well-polarized basal staining seen in rat β ICs (122). Nonetheless, some labeling of vacuolar H^+ATPase over the rabbit β IC basolateral membrane has been reported by ultrastructural immunocytochemistry (149).

Functional studies using the H^+ATPase inhibitor N-ethylmaleimide (NEM) are consistent with the immunocytochemistry. Na^+-independent H^+ extrusion by single rabbit α ICs is inhibited by apical, but not basolateral, NEM (46, 74), and Na^+-independent H^+ extrusion by single rabbit β ICs is inhibited by basolateral NEM (92, 160). Basolateral NEM also depolarizes rabbit β ICs, a result consistent with inhibition of electrogenic H^+ extrusion (31).

Unfortunately, NEM inhibits not only the vacuolar H^+ATPase but also the E1-E2 class of ATPases, which includes the H^+K^+ATPase (7). Thus, the exact interpretation of the NEM studies is not clear. There is a preliminary report that the newer inhibitor bafilomycin, at a concentration highly specific for vacuolar H^+ATPase (7), decreases H^+ secretion by rabbit OMCD cells in primary culture (these cells are probably α ICs) (68). However, there are no data on the effect of basolateral bafilomycin on H^+ extrusion by single β ICs or on HCO_3 secretion by the perfused CCD. Therefore, although the NEM data are suggestive, it remains to be proven that the vacuolar H^+ATPase present immunocytochemically at the basolateral membrane of β ICs (1, 6, 10, 11, 62, 147, 149) provides the major driving force for CCD HCO_3 secretion.

Indeed, recent data suggest a major role for a basolateral H^+K^+ATPase in mediating HCO_3 secretion by the perfused rat CCD. H^+K^+ATPase is extensively reviewed elsewhere in this volume by C. Wingo & B. Cain. Although H^+K^+ATPase is enzymatically present in the dissected rat CCD and OMCD (16, 19, 96), Wingo et al found that immunocytochemical labeling for H^+K^+ATPase was present in only a subset of rat CCD ICs (155). In a functional correlate, Gifford et al have now reported that the H^+K^+ATPase inhibitor SCH28080, at a concentration that does not affect NEM-sensitive H^+ATPase (16), markedly inhibits HCO_3 secretion by perfused rat CCDs when added to the basolateral membrane (37). Taken with the immunocytochemical results, it seems likely that most HCO_3 secretion by rat CCD β cells is driven by a basolateral H^+K^+ATPase, at least under conditions of acute chloride-depletion metabolic alkalosis.

As in the rat, H^+K^+ATPase is enzymatically present in dissected rabbit CCDs (35, 36), and by immunocytochemistry is probably present in both IC subtypes (155). Unlike the rat, however, recent preliminary functional studies on isolated rabbit CCDs suggest that the H^+K^+ATPase in CCD α and β ICs is apical (77, 127, 157). The immunocytochemical labeling of rabbit CCD principal cells for H^+K^+ATPase is negative (155).

In contrast to the evolving functional role, uncertain distribution, and species differences surrounding the H^+K^+ATPase in the CCD, in the OMCD the majority of functional, enzymatic, and immunocytochemical evidence in rat and rabbit supports a role for an apical H^+K^+ATPase in mediating H^+ secretion and K^+ reabsorption (37, 156, 158) [see (46) for an exception].

Ion Exchangers

A basolateral Cl-HCO_3 exchanger in α cells facilitates HCO_3 exit (134). Recently, the exchanger has been studied by following the dependence of intracellular pH (pH_i) on basolateral Cl (8, 45, 46, 75, 125, 161). The reported $K_{1/2}$ for extracellular Cl varies, depending upon the conditions and preparation, from 10 mM (8) to 30 mM (161) to 113 mM (45). Cl-HCO_3 exchange in α ICs is inhibited by disulfonic stilbenes (8, 45, 66, 75, 91, 125, 134, 161); indeed, stilbene binding to OMCD cells occurs with the same affinity as to erythrocytes (54). Functional studies on perfused rabbit OMCDs argue strongly against apical Cl-HCO_3 exchange in α cells (42).

Several laboratories have used antibodies raised to the erythrocyte Cl-HCO_3 exchanger (anion exchanger-1, AE1) to probe for a similar protein in the rat and rabbit collecting duct. Immunoreactivity is present at the basolateral membrane of CCD and OMCD α ICs, but is not found in principal cells or β ICs (1, 2, 20, 21, 25, 50, 62, 85a, 121, 147, 148). In the rat and mouse kidney, the primary AE1 transcript undergoes alternative splicing with deletion of exons 1–3 (9, 73).

Schwartz et al first reported that rabbit β ICs functionally have an apical Cl-HCO_3 exchanger (124). This non-AE1 anion exchanger has several interesting features. It engages in substantial Cl self-exchange (123, 138, 139). In the perfused rabbit CCD the $K_{1/2}$ for lumen [Cl] required to drive HCO_3 secretion is ~ 11 mM (115), roughly comparable to the $K_{1/2}$ of 19 mM determined for the apical Cl-HCO_3 exchanger in single β cells (31). Unlike the AE1 exchanger of α ICs, luminal stilbenes do not inhibit the β IC apical exchanger (22, 114, 126, 138). An especially intriguing finding is that the β IC apical Cl-HCO_3 exchanger does not mediate pH_i recovery at alkaline pH_i (154). Univalent anion exchange by AE1 is known not to activate at alkaline

pH_i, whereas $Cl-HCO_3$ exchange by AE2 and AE3 does activate (80). In this regard, both CCD and OMCD principal cells have a basolateral $Cl-HCO_3$ exchanger (75, 152, 153), and at least the CCD principal cell exchanger does activate at alkaline pH_i (154). Taken with the persistent inability of investigators to find AE1 immunocytochemically in β ICs (1, 2, 20, 21, 25, 50, 62, 85a, 121, 147, 148), the lack of activation at alkaline pH_i raises the possibility that the β cell apical exchanger is not part of the AE1-2-3 family.

The evidence for a similar apical β cell $Cl-HCO_3$ exchanger in the rat is inferential. The isolated, perfused rat CCD dissected from $NaHCO_3$-loaded or alkalotic animals does secrete HCO_3 (3, 38, 145), and this HCO_3 secretion requires luminal Cl (38, 145). However, apical β cell $Cl-HCO_3$ exchange in the rat has not been studied at the single-membrane level using measurements of pH_i as in the rabbit.

Both α and β ICs, as well as principal cells, appear to have a basolateral Na^+/H^+ exchanger (8, 15, 74, 153, 159). This almost certainly serves to regulate pH_i. Na^+/H^+ exchange does not drive HCO_3 secretion by β ICs, since CCD HCO_3 secretion is Na^+-independent (114, 129), is uninhibited by basolateral amiloride (114), and proceeds in the presence of ouabain (90, 129).

Chloride Channels

Chloride channels have been described in both α and β ICs. Microelectrode and patch-clamp experiments by Koeppen et al have shown that the α ICs of perfused rabbit OMCDs or of OMCDs in primary culture have a basolateral Cl channel (63, 64, 69, 104). Patch-clamp studies on a rabbit collecting duct cell line that exhibits several α properties indicate the presence of a basolateral Cl channel with a single-channel conductance of 35–75 pS (17).

Several flux studies of perfused rabbit CCDs suggest that β ICs also have a basolateral Cl conductance (89, 123, 140). This interpretation has now been confirmed by direct microelectrode study (31, 98, 104). In addition, at the apical membrane of rabbit β ICs there is evidence for a stilbene-inhibitable Cl conductance (31). Patch-clamp analysis of single channels from β ICs in primary culture has revealed an apical 300 pS Cl channel that probably functions in volume regulation (83, 128). Additional 4 and 8 pS apical Cl channels reported in rabbit CCD cells in primary culture may also derive from β ICs (137).

Enzymes, Metabolism, and Solute Transporters

Both α and β ICs have carbonic anhydrase activity as assessed by the histochemical Hansson's technique (12, 18, 106). Recent immunocytochemical studies using antibodies specific to carbonic anhydrase isoenzymes have shown that α and β ICs have cytoplasmic staining for type II, but not type IV, carbonic anhydrase (13, 55, 60, 62). The lack of strong apical membrane labeling is consistent with studies indicating the absence of functional luminal carbonic anhydrase activity in perfused rabbit CCD and OMCD (outer stripe) (130, 131).

Histochemical, immunocytochemical, and functional studies indicate that principal cells have abundant $Na^+K^+ATPase$ at the basolateral membrane. In contrast, studies using these methods indicate that both α and β ICs express significantly lower levels of the Na^+ pump (28, 49, 50, 56, 106, 113, 136).

The metabolic source for primary active H^+ secretion by ICs is probably glycolysis. Indeed, the collecting duct is highly glycolytic (4, 40, 146), and ATP-dependent H^+ extrusion by OMCD segments is normal when oxidative phosphorylation is inhibited, but glycolysis is left intact (162). The necessary transporters and enzymes are present: the basolateral membranes of rat CCD ICs label strongly for the GLUT1 glucose transporter (141, 143), and immunocytochemical staining for the glycolytic enzymes hexokinase I and glyceraldehehyde-3-phosphate dehydrogenase (GAPDH) is most prominent in rat α ICs (25, 79).

AXIAL DISTRIBUTION OF IC SUBTYPES

The distribution of α vs β ICs varies along the length of the cortical and outer medullary collecting duct (axial heterogeneity). Rat and rabbit CCDs have both α and β IC subtypes. In the rat, estimates of the percentage of total ICs that are of the α type vary by investigator and technique, e.g. 38 (6), 40 (11), 46 (1), and 60% (50, 150). In the rabbit CCD, the fraction of α ICs also varies: 5 (124), 9–19 (125), 20 (98), 29 (121, 122), and 32–53% (23). The somewhat larger variability in the rabbit may be due to the fact that the data are derived from both immunocytochemical and functional markers, whereas all of the data in the rat are morphological or immunocytochemical. Another possible reason for the variation is the position of the CCD within the cortex at which the counting is performed. At least in the rabbit, there is axial heterogeneity of ICs within the CCD itself. LeFurgey & Tisher noted that the fraction of microplicated ICs (α ICs) appeared to increase along the CCD as it reached the cortico-medullary junction (81). Four subsequent quantitative studies in the rabbit CCD, in which α and β ICs were defined by various functional, morphological, or histochemical markers, have also found that the percentage of α ICs increases from the mid-cortical region to the cortico-medullary junction, whereas the fraction of β ICs decreases (23, 26, 125, 159).

In both rat and rabbit, the OMCD has only α ICs (10, 26, 121, 122). In the rabbit inner stripe, the ICs have numerous small apical microvilli (26, 81), basolateral AE1, and a well-polarized apical $H^+ATPase$. In the rabbit outer stripe, the ICs have apical microplicae (26, 81), basolateral AE1, and diffuse or apical H^+ATPase staining (122).

Most discussions of ICs consider α ICs of the CCD to be functionally equivalent to those in the OMCD. However, some evidence suggests that this may not be the case. First, the H^+K^+ATPase inhibitor, SCH28080, lowers H^+ secretion from the lumen in the rat OMCD, but not in the CCD (37). Moreover, H^+K^+ATPase appears not to be present immunocytochemically in both CCD and OMCD α ICs in the rat (155). These results suggest that the rat OMCD α IC expresses the H^+K^+ATPase, whereas the rat CCD α IC does not. Second, a recent report suggests that the AE1 anion exchanger is distributed in intracellular vesicles and multivesicular bodies in rabbit CCD α ICs, but not in OMCD α ICs (85a). Finally, another preliminary report suggests that metabolic alkalosis down-regulates AE1 in rat CCD α ICs, but produces no change in AE1 in OMCD α ICs (2). If these axial differences in α IC function are born out by further study, the issue arises as to whether they may be due to the some factor in the tubule environment in the cortex vs medulla, e.g. osmolarity or pH.

Some evidence suggests that division of rabbit ICs into only two types (α and β), especially in the rabbit, may be an oversimplification. Using SEM, Lefurgey & Tisher and Evans et al reported not two, but four distinct surface patterns on ICs from the rabbit outer CCD to the OMCD inner stipe (26, 81). Although it seems reasonable that the rabbit CCD ICs that bind peanut lectin are β ICs (reviewed in 119), clearly some ICs have basolateral AE1 or apical H^+ATPase and also bind peanut lectin apically (hybrid cells) (122). ICs that express apical H^+ATPase but no basolateral AE1 have been described in the rat CCD (1).

REGULATION BY β-ADRENERGIC AGONISTS

The rat CCD is innervated by sympathetic nerves (5), and thus might be expected to respond to adrenergic agonists. Studies on single dissected rat and rabbit tubules by Morel et al showed that the β-adrenergic agonist isoproterenol increased cAMP formation in the CCD, but not in the OMCD (95). Subsequent studies in which rabbit CCD principal cells were sorted away from ICs have demonstrated that isoproterenol increases cAMP exclusively in ICs (predominantly β ICs) (28). In sorted ICs derived from the rabbit OMCD (α only), isoproterenol also produces a substantial increase in cAMP (14, 70). Thus isoproterenol probably increases cAMP in both α and β ICs.

Extensive functional studies support this interpretation. Isoproterenol and/or cAMP in the rabbit CCD stimulate net Cl reabsorption (51), net HCO_3 secretion (114), unidirectional HCO_3 secretion (115), and Cl-Cl self-exchange (138). All of these results are consistent with stimulation of β ICs. In the rabbit, cAMP and forskolin increase electrogenic H^+ secretion and HCO_3 reabsorption by the perfused OMCD, which suggests that transport by α ICs is increased as well (48). Also, cAMP stimulates flow of equivalent positive current by the rabbit CCD (i.e. the lumen becomes more positive) (115), a result consistent with stimulation by cAMP of electrogenic H^+ secretion by cortical α ICs.

A recent micropuncture study found that the rate of net HCO_3 reabsorption by the rat distal tubule was decreased by denervation (151). Although this is consistent with an effect of renal nerves in the rat to stimulate H^+ secretion or inhibit HCO_3 secretion, it is also consistent with a stimulatory effect of nerves/isoproterenol on both IC types. One need only postulate a larger response per α IC and/or a higher α/β ratio in the rat vs rabbit cortex (see above).

The cellular mechanisms by which cAMP stimulates β IC transport have been examined by determining pH_i in single ICs. Emmons & Stokes reported that 8-bromo-cAMP caused a transient increase in pH_i of rabbit β ICs that persisted even when the apical $Cl-HCO_3$ exchanger was blocked, a result consistent with a primary effect on H^+ secretion (24). In contrast, Hayashi et al reported that pH_i fell and that the turnover rate of the apical $Cl-HCO_3$ exchanger was enhanced by 8-bromo-cAMP (43). The reasons for these opposite results are not apparent.

Koeppen et al have examined cAMP effects on primary cultured rabbit OMCD cells, which exhibit functional properties of α ICs (69). As expected for AE1, the $Cl-HCO_3$ exchange was stilbene-sensitive. Addition of isoproterenol or cAMP increased the rate of $Cl-HCO_3$ exchange, and this increase was blocked by pre-treatment with a Cl channel blocker, which suggests that cAMP stimulated $Cl-HCO_3$ exchange primarily by increasing a basolateral Cl channel (88). Further studies using whole-cell patch-clamp analysis confirmed that cAMP, isoproterenol, and protein kinase A increase α IC Cl currents (104). Similar results have been reported by Dietl et al in the transformed rabbit collecting duct cell line RCCT-28A, which shares a number of properties with α ICs (17).

REGULATION BY SYSTEMIC ACID-BASE PERTURBATIONS

α Intercalated Cells of OMCD

Since the OMCD has the highest rate of H^+ secretion (HCO_3 reabsorption) (3, 78, 84, 91), and the apical staining for the vacuolar $H^+ATPase$ is the most intense in OMCD α ICs (10, 122), it is reasonable to ask whether the

H^+ pump and/or the basolateral AE1 Cl-HCO_3 exchanger of the OMCD α ICs are regulated by metabolic or respiratory acidosis.

Evidence for induction of H^+ATPase in the rat OMCD by chronic acidosis is mixed. Two groups reported an increase in enzymatic activity of NEM-sensitive H^+ATPase in the rat OMCD (33, 57), whereas another laboratory found no change (108). Oral acid loading is not associated with a change in the protein level, as assessed by immunoblotting, or the steady-state mRNA level of the vacuolar H^+ATPase 31-kd subunit (6).

On the other hand, there is evidence for an acidosis-induced redistribution of the H^+ATPase within the OMCD α IC. Madsen & Tisher found that giving rats an oral acid load for 15 days produced an increase in the surface density of the apical plasma membrane and a concomitant depletion of apical tubulovesicular structures in rat OMCD α ICs. They suggested that these changes might be indicative of an increase in H^+ secretion (86). In a recent immunocytochemical study at the light-microscope level, Bastani et al presented evidence that acid loading may induce a shift in the distribution of vacuolar H^+ATPase in the rat OMCD from cytoplasmic vesicles to the plasma membrane (6).

The AE1 exchanger of the OMCD may also be increased by chronic acidosis: the steady-state level of AE1 mRNA is increased about twofold in rat medulla after 5 days of respiratory acidosis (142), and oral acid loading has been reported to increase the intensity of basolateral AE1 staining in rat OMCD α ICs (2).

If these changes in the distribution of H^+ATPase or the intensity of AE1 are physiologically relevant, one might expect acidosis to induce an accompanying change in H^+ secretion by the perfused OMCD. Since the OMCD has no β ICs, inferences about regulation of α ICs can be made by studying HCO_3 transport by this segment. The data from such perfusion experiments have recently been summarized (119). Surprisingly, none of the studies of chronic acidosis using oral acid loading or chronic high pCO_2 exposure has resulted in a significant alteration in the rate of net HCO_3 reabsorption (H^+ secretion) by rat or rabbit OMCD (3, 52, 78, 84, 91). A recent analysis at the single-cell level using measurements of pH_i also failed to see an effect of systemic acidosis on H^+ extrusion by OMCD α ICs (53). Needless to say, these negative functional data call into question the significance of the morphological, immunocytochemical, molecular biological, and enzymatic results. To reconcile the results one could postulate that the activities of the apical H^+ pump or basolateral anion exchanger are enhanced, but that back-leak of reabsorbed HCO_3 or secreted H^+ is also enhanced. This is not very satisfying because it suggests that any apparently adaptive mechanisms are futile. It is also possible that the OMCD adapts in vivo, but that this adaptation is quickly lost when a tubule is dissected out and perfused in vitro.

This also seems unlikely: if anything, HCO_3 secretion in the CCD, not HCO_3 reabsorption, has been reported to decline in vitro (3). In summary, the discrepancy between the functional and non-functional data remains a serious unsolved problem.

Intercalated Cells of the CCD

In marked contrast to the OMCD, essentially every functional study using micropuncture or the perfused tubule to examine the effect of acidosis or alkalosis on transport by the rat or rabbit CCD has found evidence for regulation in this segment (3, 32, 37, 38, 41, 52, 78, 82, 84, 90, 111, 124, 139).

Indeed, the case for regulation of the CCD β IC is quite strong. Immunocytochemical data show that systemic acidosis results in fewer rat CCD ICs that exhibit the "pure" β (well-polarized basal) staining pattern for vacuolar H^+ATPase, and more ICs with a diffuse staining pattern (6). Systemic alkalosis results in an increase in basolateral membrane complexity and basolateral membrane vacuolar H^+ATPase staining in rat CCD β ICs (59, 147), whereas acidosis causes the opposite changes (59).

The functional data are even stronger. The unidirectional rate of HCO_3 secretion (bath-to-lumen) in perfused CCDs can be estimated by determining the HCO_3 flux after removing perfusate HCO_3. In two studies, systemic in vivo acid-base perturbations altered unidirectional HCO_3 secretion (β IC function) by the isolated CCD (32, 41). In vivo acid loading decreases the rate of H^+ extrusion across the basolateral membrane of individual CCD β ICs (160), and in vivo acidosis and alkalosis change the rate of CCD Cl-Cl exchange, a marker of activity of the β IC apical Cl-HCO_3 exchanger (123, 139). In addition to these in vivo effects, in vitro acidosis applied to the perfused CCD results in a clear-cut decrease in function of the β IC apical Cl-HCO_3 exchanger (111, 160) and a decrease in the rate of basolateral H^+ extrusion (160) within individual β ICs. The time required to induce β cell adaptation is surprisingly small. Experiments by Gifford et al in the rat have shown that 30 min of peritoneal dialysis with a 154 mM HCO_3 solution causes the subsequently-perfused in vitro CCD to secrete HCO_3 at high rates for up to 3 hr despite normalization of peritubular fluids to 25 mM HCO_3 (38).

As with the OMCD α IC, the evidence for regulation of the CCD α IC is somewhat mixed. Although changes in CCD NEM-sensitive H^+ATPase activity with acid-base manipulations have been reported (108), these are very difficult to interpret given the mixture of α and β ICs in a dissected CCD. On the other hand, immunocytochemical methods have shown that, with acidosis, there is an increase in labeling for apical vacuolar H^+ATPase and for basolateral AE1 in rat CCD α ICs (59). Conversely, with alkalosis there is a decrease in basolateral AE1 intensity in rat CCD α ICs (2) and a decrease in apical membrane area and labeling for vacuolar H^+ATPase (147). Chronic respiratory acidosis has been reported to increase the steady-state mRNA for AE1 in rat renal cortex; this suggests regulation of α ICs since AE1 expression in the CCD is restricted to these cells (142).

There are also perfused tubule data from the rabbit CCD. H^+ secretion by CCD α ICs has been assessed in two ways. First, the steady-state lumen pH, factored for the transepithelial voltage, has been used to estimate the degree to which lumenal H^+ is accumulated above electrochemical equilibrium. Metabolic acidosis produced by starvation resulted in a lumen $[H^+]$ in the CCD that was further off equilibrium than that of control CCDs (52), a result consistent with regulation of α ICs. Other studies have estimated the rate of H^+ secretion from the unidirectional lumen-to-bath HCO_3 fluxes while bathing in HCO_3-free bath. Neither of these two studies found regulation of these fluxes by in vivo acid loading (32, 41). Thus, as is the case with OMCD α ICs, there is some inconsistency between the flux studies and the other data with regard to regulation of the CCD α IC, albeit to a lesser degree than in the OMCD.

There is some preliminary evidence that metabolic or respiratory acidosis increases the steady-state levels of mRNA for the H^+K^+ATPase in rat kidney (39, 105). However, as with the vacuolar H^+ATPase, these results are difficult to interpret given that H^+K^+ATPase in the rat may be distributed in CCD β ICs and OMCD α ICs (37, 155).

REGULATION BY ALDOSTERONE

α Intercalated Cells of OMCD

There is substantial evidence that H^+ secretion by OMCD α ICs is stimulated by aldosterone. Administered at physiological doses to adrenalectomized rats or rabbits, aldosterone increases the enzymatic activity of NEM-sensitive H^+ATPase in the OMCD (34, 58). Stone and co-workers found that the rate of H^+secretion ($J_H{}^+$) by perfused OMCD (inner stripe) segments dissected from control or adrenalectomized rabbits was decreased following adrenalectomy and was restored to control levels by in vivo or in vitro aldosterone replacement (135). Subsequent studies on the outer stripe are consistent with this result (91).

At the single-cell level, Hays et al and Kuwahara et al have reported that adrenalectomy decreases, and DOCA administration increases, both $J_H{}^+$ across the apical membrane and $Cl-HCO_3$ exchange across the basolateral membrane in OMCD α ICs (44, 47, 76). The DOCA-induced change in $J_H{}^+$

by OMCD α ICs is inhibited by lumen NEM, but not by the H^+K^+ATPase inhibitor SCH28080 (76), which suggests an effect on the vacuolar H^+ATPase. This result is consistent with three other findings: (a) mineralocorticoids increase the lumen-positive voltage in OMCD (135); (b) staining for the vacuolar H^+ATPase undergoes a shift toward the plasma membrane in OMCD (inner stripe) with DOCA treatment (5a); and (c) aldosterone produces no change in enzymatic H^+K^+ATPase activity in dissected OMCD tubules (36).

In complementary studies by two separate groups, immunocytochemical examination at the light microscope level indicates the presence of mineralocorticoid receptors (MR) in all cells of the rabbit OMCD (27, 85). Distribution of MR in the rat OMCD has not been described (72, 107). Taken together, the data strongly suggest a stimulatory effect of aldosterone via the mineralocorticoid receptor on the apical electrogenic (vacuolar) H^+ATPase. There is perhaps an additional effect on the basolateral AE1 anion exchanger.

Intercalated Cells of the CCD

Because of the mixture of α and β ICs in the CCD, interpretation of the effects of aldosterone on this segment is more difficult. Enzymatic studies indicate that aldosterone increases the activities of NEM-sensitive H^+ATPase in the rat and rabbit CCD (34, 58) and of H^+K^+ATPase in the rabbit CCD (36). It is not clear, however, which cell type is responsible, because the enzyme activities are determined on the whole tubule. DOCA-induced changes in lumen pH are difficult to interpret because of concommitant changes in Na^+ and K^+ transport, and thus the transepithelial voltage (52, 67).

Although there is evidence that DOCA increases the transport rate of the basolateral Na^+/H^+ exchanger in rabbit CCD β ICs (159), most of the functional studies argue against a major aldosterone effect on the CCD β IC. In perfused tubule studies, Garcia-Austt et al showed that DOCA had no effect on unidirectional HCO_3 secretion when concomitant alkalosis was prevented (32). Perfusion studies on rabbit CCD have shown no effect of DOCA Cl-Cl self-exchange, a β IC marker (V. Schuster, unpublished). Adrenalectomy produces no change in the basolateral membrane voltage of randomly impaled rabbit CCD ICs (97). As such random impalements are probably numerically dominated by β cells, one can tentatively conclude that aldosterone has no net effect on conductive pathways in the β IC. Finally, immunocytochemical studies on MR in the rat and rabbit have indicated that many, if not all, CCD ICs are negative (27, 72, 85, 107). It is not clear at present whether both α and β ICs are devoid of the receptor. However, from the number of ICs in the rabbit CCD that are unreactive, it appears that at least the β cells have no MR (27, 85). Considering all of the data, one can conclude that aldosterone probably does not significantly regulate the β IC.

PLASTICITY OF TRANSPORTER POLARITY AND EXPRESSION

In 1985, Schwartz et al put forth the provocative hypothesis that intercalated cells might reverse their functional polarity under certain conditions, e.g. that metabolic acidosis could functionally convert β ICs into α ICs (124). This led to the idea that ICs possess "plasticity" of expression of the various acid-base transporters. In subsequent years, substantial experimental effort has gone into testing the polarity reversal hypothesis. It now appears that ICs can, indeed, display plasticity, but that the degree to which this is the case is strongly influenced by the experimental system.

Plasticity in Cell Culture

Using cell type-specific monoclonal antibodies as empirical cell surface markers, Fejes-Toth and Naray-Fejes-Toth immunodissected and sorted rabbit CCD cells into β ICs or principal cells. When placed separately into primary culture, it was found that principal cells remained unchanged, as judged by Na^+ absorption, K^+ secretion, and surface markers. In contrast, a culture that was seeded as 98% β ICs became, with subsequent cell divisions, a mixture of α ICs, β ICs, and principal cells (29, 30). DNA replication was highest in those cultures seeded with sorted β ICs, which suggests that these cells were dividing rapidly and giving rise to the other cell types. Indeed, surface markers allowed the identification of asymmetric cell division in a mouse CCD cell line, i.e. the segregation of IC and principal cell surface markers from a single cell into two daughter cells during mitosis (29, 30). These important studies suggest that when CCD ICs are placed into culture, β ICs may function as stem cells for the formation of α ICs and principal cells (29, 30).

There are, however, two problems with extrapolating these results to the adult CCD in situ. First, cell division is extremely rare in the adult CCD (26, 53a, 124), but is very rapid in tissue culture. Second, ICs in culture are obviously not in their normal in vivo milieu. One model system that provides the appropriate in vivo milieu, but still allows for rapid cell division, is the neonatal kidney.

Plasticity in the Neonatal Collecting Duct

Extensive studies by Satlin and co-workers and by others have shown that there is post-natal centrifugal growth and cell division in the rat and rabbit collecting duct, especially in the CCD (26, 93, 101, 109, 110). Although the newborn rabbit CCD is devoid of ICs, during the first few weeks after birth, cells gradually appear that have the immunocytochemical, morphological, and functional characteristics of β ICs (26, 109, 110, 112). Similar findings using morphological criteria have been reported in the rat CCD: at 2 weeks some α ICs are seen, whereas β ICs are increasingly seen from 3 weeks on (101).

What is the source of these new ICs ? Minuth et al reported that neonatal collecting duct cells stained positively with either wheat germ agglutinin (principal cells) or peanut agglutinin [β ICs (121)]. In contrast, cells in the ampullary bud, a possible site of stem cells for the collecting duct, co-labeled with both lectins (93, 94). These principal/intercalated cells, reminiscent of the cell culture results discussed above (29, 30), raise the possibility that CCD ICs and principal cells develop from a common precursor.

Given the plasticity inducible during rapid cell division in culture, is seems likely that plasticity could be induced in the proliferating cells of the newborn CCD. Indeed, Narbaitz et al induced metabolic acidosis or alkalosis in pregnant rabbits and examined the effect on the IC subtypes of their newborn offspring. Neither maneuver changed the number of ICs relative to principal cells in the collecting duct. However, maternal alkalosis increased the percentage of β ICs in both the OMCD and CCD and decreased the percentage of α ICs in the OMCD (99, 100). Acidosis, in contrast, slightly decreased the percentage of OMCD β ICs, but had no effect on the α ICs (99). These experiments do not necessarily imply that there is α-to-β or β-to-α interconversion. Rather, in a setting in which stem or precursor cells may be rapidly dividing, systemic acid-base perturbations appear to be capable of changing the direction of differentiation of these cells. This could be called a form of plasticity.

Plasticity in the Perfused CCD From the Adult

What, then, of the original plasticity hypothesis as it applies to the adult CCD perfused in vitro? To prove this hypothesis, it must be shown that an individual IC, followed temporally in vitro, responds to an in vitro acid-base signal by decreasing its β transporters and simultaneously expressing new α transporters (or vice versa). Since the same cell must be followed during the adaptation, sequential immunocytochemical or molecular biological approaches seem unsuited. Rather, one would like to record a given IC as it functionally reverses its transporters in response to an in vitro stimulus. Studies by Satlin et al (111) have attempted just this. Although an in vitro acidosis applied to the perfused rabbit CCD clearly causes a reduction, via endocytosis, in the β IC apical $Cl-HCO_3$ exchanger and apical peanut lectin binding sites, it has not been unequivocally demonstrated that a new $Cl-HCO_3$ exchanger appears at the basolateral membrane of these cells.

On the other hand, several reports raise the possibility that a given CCD IC may have the capacity to express properties that one would normally categorize as both α and β. Weiner & Hamm presented data consistent with the presence of basolateral Cl-HCO$_3$ exchange in rabbit CCD β ICs (154). Emmons & Kurtz, using the perfused rabbit CCD, reported that most CCD ICs possess both apical and basolateral Cl-OH exchangers (22). Also, Merot et al also have presented evidence that is consistent with the expression of new basolateral Cl-HCO$_3$ exchangers in rabbit β ICs following an intracellular acid load (92). The precise molecular nature of these basolateral anion exchangers in β ICs remains unknown, nor has it been examined whether the polarized expression of NEM-sensitive or SCH28080-sensitive H$^+$ extrusion processes can be reversed within a single cell followed temporally.

Increasingly, various investigators are reporting small numbers of ICs within the adult CCD that express markers of both α and β cells (1, 28, 29, 122). There is clearly much work ahead before IC plasticity is completely understood.

ACKNOWLEDGMENTS

The author is an Established Investigator of the American Heart Association and is supported by a Hirschl-Weill-Caulier Trust award and by National Institutes of Health grant DK38095.

Literature Cited

1. Alper, S. L., Natale, J., Gluck, S., Lodish, H. F., Brown, D. 1989. Subtypes of intercalated cells in rat kidney collecting duct defined by antibodies against erythroid band 3 and renal vacuolar H$^+$-ATPase. *Proc. Natl. Acad. Sci. USA* 86: 5429–33

2. Alper, S. L., Sabolic, I., Tyszkowski, R., Brown, D. 1991. Metabolic acidosis and alkalosis modulate anion exchanger (AE1) expression in kidney collecting ducts. *J. Am. Soc. Nephrol.* 2:693 (Abstr.)

3. Atkins, J. L., Burg, M. B. 1985. Bicarbonate transport by isolated perfused rat collecting ducts. *Am. J. Physiol.* (249)18:F485–89

4. Bagnascao, S., Good, D., Balaban, R., Burg, M. 1985. Lactate production in isolated segments of the rat nephron. *Am. J. Physiol.* (248)17:F522–26

5. Barajas, L., Powers, K., Wang, P. 1985. Innervation of the late distal nephron: an autoradiographic and ultrastructural study. *J. Ultrastruct. Res.* 92:146–57

5a. Bastani, B., Kalkbrenner, M., Gluck, S. 1991. Chronic DOCA administration increases polarization of H$^+$ATPase in medullary intercalated cells. *J. Am. Soc. Nephrol.* 2:694 (Abstr.)

6. Bastani, B., Purcell, H., Hemken, P., Trigg, D., Gluck, S. 1991. Expression and distribution of renal vacuolar proton-translocating adenosine triphosphatase in response to chronic acid and alkali loads in the rat. *J. Clin. Invest.* 88(1):126–36

7. Bowman, E. J., Siebers, A., Altendorf, K. 1988. Bafilomycins: A class of inhibitors of membrane ATPases from microorganisms, animal cells, and plant cells. *Proc. Natl. Acad. Sci. USA* 85: 7972–76

8. Breyer, M. D., Jacobson, H. R. 1989. Regulation of rabbit medullary collecting duct cell pH by basolateral Na$^+$/H$^+$ and Cl$^-$/base exchange. *J. Clin. Invest.* 84:996–1004

9. Brosius, F. C. III, Alper, S. L., Garcia, A. M., Lodish, H. F. 1989. The major kidney band 3 gene transcript predicts an amino-truncated band 3 polypeptide. *J. Biol. Chem.* 264:7784–87

10. Brown, D., Hirsch, S., Gluck, S. 1988. Localization of a proton-pumping ATPase in rat kidney. *J. Clin. Invest.* 82:2114–26

11. Brown, D., Hirsch, S., Gluck, S.

1988. An H^+ATPase is present in opposite plasma membrane domains in subpopulations of kidney epithelial cells. *Nature* 331:622–24

12. Brown, D., Kumpulainen, T. 1985. Immunocytochemical localization of carbonic anhydrase on ultrathin frozen sections with protein A-gold. *Histochemistry* 83:153–58

13. Brown, D., Zhu, X. L., Sly, W. S., 1990. Localization of membrane-associated carbonic anhydrase type IV in kidney epithelial cells. *Proc. Natl. Acad. Sci. USA* 87:7457–561

14. Burnatowska-Hledin, M. A., Spielman, W. S. 1988. Immunodissection of mitochondria-rich cells from rabbit outer medullary collecting tubule. *Am. J. Physiol.* (254)23:F907–11

15. Chaillet, J. R., Lopes, A. G., Boron, W. F. 1985. Basolateral Na-H exchange in the rabbit cortical collecting tubule. *J. Gen. Physiol.* 86:795–812

16. Cheval, L., Barlet-Bas, C., Khadouri, C., Feraille, E., Marsy, S., et al. 1991. K^+ATPase-mediated Rb^+ transport in rat collecting tubule: modulation during K^+ deprivation. *Am. J. Physiol.* (260) 29:F800–5

17. Dietl, P., Stanton, B. A. 1992. Conductive properties of a rabbit cortical collecting duct cell line: regulation by isoproterenol. *Am. J. Physiol.* 262:F578–82

18. Dobyan, D. C., Bulger, R. E. 1982. Renal carbonic anhydrase. *Am. J. Physiol.* (243)12:F311–24

19. Doucet, A., Marsy, S. 1987. Characterization of K-ATPase activity in distal nephron: stimulation by potassium depletion. *Am. J. Physiol.* (253)22:F418–23

20. Drenckhahn, D., Merte, C. 1987. Restriction of the human band 3-like anion exchanger to specialized subdomains of the basolateral plasma membrane of intercalated cells. *Eur. J. Cell. Biol.* 45:107–15

21. Drenckhahn, D., Schluter, K., Allen, D. P., Bennett, V. 1985. Co-localization of band 3 with ankyrin and spectrin at the basal membrane of intercalated cells in the rat kidney. *Science* 230:1287–89

22. Emmons, C. L., Kurtz, I. 1991. The majority of outer CCD intercalated cells have both apical and basolateral Na^+independent Cl^-base exchangers. *J. Am. Soc. Nephrol.* 2:699 (Abstr.)

23. Emmons, C. L., Matsuzaki, K., Stokes, J. B., Schuster, V. L. 1991. Axial heterogeneity of rabbit cortical collecting duct. *Am. J. Physiol.* 260:F498–505

24. Emmons, C. L., Stokes, J. B. 1990. Mechanism of cAMP-induced HCO_3 secretion by rabbit cortical collecting ducts. *Kidney Int.* 37:536 (Abstr.)

25. Ercolani, L., Brown, D., Stuart-Tilley, A., Alper, S. L. 1992. Colocalization of GAPDH and band 3 (AE1) proteins in the rat erythrocytes and kidney intercalated cell membranes. *Am. Physiol.* 262:F892–96

26. Evan, A. P., Satlin, L. M., Gattone, V. H., Conners, B., Schwartz, G. J. 1991. Postnatal maturation of rabbit renal collecting duct. II. Morphological observations. *Am. J. Physiol.* 261:F91–107

27. Farman, N., Oblin, M. E., Lombes, M., Delahaye, F., Westphal, H. M., et al. 1991. Immunolocalization of gluco- and mineralocorticoid receptors in rabbit kidney. *Am. J. Physiol.* 260: C226–33

28. Fejes-Toth, G., Naray-Fejes-Toth, A. 1989. Isolated principal and intercalated cells: hormone responsiveness and Na^+K^+ATPase activity. *Am. J. Physiol.* (256)25:F742–50

29. Fejes-Toth, G., Naray-Fejes-Toth, A. 1992. Differentiation of renal β-intercalated cells to α-intercalated and principal cells in culture. *Proc. Natl. Acad. Sci. USA* 89:5487–91

30. Fejes-Toth, G., Naray-Fejes-Toth, A. 1991. Cell differentiation and stem cell renewal via asymmetric cell division in the renal collecting duct. *J. Cell Biol.* 115:148a (Abstr.)

31. Furuya, H., Breyer, M. D., Jacobson, H. R. 1991. Functional characterization of α- and β-intercalated cell types in rabbit cortical collecting duct. *Am. J. Physiol.* 261:F377–85

32. Garcia-Austt, J., Good, D. W., Burg, M. B., Knepper, M. A. 1985. Deoxycorticosterone-stimulated bicarbonate secretion in rabbit cortical collecting ducts: effects of luminal chloride removal and in vivo acid loading. *Am. J. Physiol.* (249)18:F205–12

33. Garg, L. C., Narang, N. 1985. Stimulation of an N-ethylmaleimide-sensitive ATPase in the collecting duct segment of the rat nephron by metabolic acidosis. *Can. J. Physiol. Pharmacol.* 63:1291–96

34. Garg, L. C., Narang, N. 1988. Effects of aldosterone on NEM-sensitive ATPase in rabbit nephron segments. *Kidney Int.* 34:13–17

35. Garg, L. C., Narang, N. 1988. Ouabain-insensitive K-adenosine triphosphatase in distal nephron segments of the rabbit. *J. Clin. Invest.* 81:1204–8

36. Garg, L. C., Narang, N. 1990. Effects of aldosterone on ouabain-insensitive K-ATPase activity in rabbit nephron segments. *J. Am. Soc. Nephrol.* 1:684 (Abstr.)

37. Gifford, J. D., Rome, L., Galla, J. H. 1992. H^+K^+ATPase activity in rat collecting duct segments. *Am. J. Physiol.* 262:F692–95

38. Gifford, J. D., Sharkins, K., Work, J., Luke, R. G., Galla, J. H. 1990. Total CO_2 transport in rat cortical collecting duct in chloride-depletion alkalosis. *Am. J. Physiol.* (258) 27:F848–53

39. Gifford, J. D., Ware, M. W., Crowson, S., Shull, G. E. 1991. Expression of a putative rat distal colonic H^+K^+ATPase mRNA in rat kidney: effect of respiratory acidosis. *J. Am. Soc. Nephrol.* 2:700 (Abstr.)

40. Grupp, C., Pavenstadt-Grupp, I., Grunewald, R. W., Bevan, C., Stokes, J. B., et al. 1989. A Na-K-Cl cotransporter in isolated rat papillary collecting duct cells. *Kidney Int.* 36:201–9

41. Hamm, L. L., Hering-Smith, K. S., Vehaskari, V. M. 1989. Control of bicarbonate transport in collecting tubules from normal and remnant kidneys. *Am. J. Physiol.* (256)25:F680–87

42. Hayashi, M., Schuster, V. L., Stokes, J. B. 1988. Absence of transepithelial anion exchange by rabbit OMCD: evidence against reversal of cell polarity. *Am. J. Physiol.* (255)24:F220–28

43. Hayashi, M., Yamaji, Y., Iyori, M., Kitajima, W., Saruta, T. 1991. Effect of isoproterenol on intracellular pH of the intercalated cells in the rabbit cortical collecting ducts. *J. Clin. Invest.* 87:1153–57

44. Hays, S. R. 1991. Mineralocorticoid deficiency inhibits apical membrane H pump and basolateral Cl/HCO3 exchange activities in parallel in the inner stripe of the outer medullary collecting duct. *J. Am. Soc. Nephrol.* 2:702 (Abstr.)

45. Hays, S. R., Alpern, R. J. 1990. Basolateral membrane Na^+-independent Cl^-/HCO3 exchange in the inner stripe of the rabbit outer medullary collecting tubule. *J. Gen. Physiol.* 95:347–67

46. Hays, S. R., Alpern, R. J. 1990. Apical and basolateral membrane H^+ extrusion mechanisms in inner stripe of rabbit outer medullary collecting duct. *Am. J. Physiol.* 259:F628–35

47. Hays, S. R., Alpern, R. J. 1990. Mineralocorticoids stimulate apical membrane H^+ pump and basolateral membrane Cl/HCO3 exchange activities in parallel in the inner stripe of the outer medullary collecting duct. *J. Am. Soc. Nephrol.* 1:650 (Abstr.)

48. Hays, S. R., Kokko, J. P., Jacobson, H. R. 1986. Hormonal regulation of proton secretion in rabbit medullary collecting duct. *J. Clin. Invest.* 78:1279–86

49. Holthofer, H., Schulte, B. A., Pasternack, G., Siegel, G. J., Spicer, S. S. 1987. Immunocytochemical characterization of carbonic anhydrase-rich cells in the rat kidney collecting duct. *Lab. Invest.* 57:150–56

50. Holthofer, H., Schulte, B. A., Pasternack, G., Siegel, G. J., Spicer, S. S. 1987. Three distinct cell populations in rat kidney collecting duct. *Am. J. Physiol.* (253)22:C323–28

51. Iino, Y., Troy, J. L., Brenner, B. M. 1981. Effects of catecholamines on electrolyte transport in cortical collecting tubule. *J. Membr. Biol.* 61:67–73

52. Ishibashi, K., Sasaki, S., Yoshiyama, N., Shiigai, T., Takeuchi, J. 1987. Generation of pH gradient across the rabbit collecting duct segments perfused in vitro. *Kidney Int.* 31:930–36

53. Iyori, M., Hayashi, M., Yamaji, Y., Saruta, T. 1991. Metabolic alkalosis decreases H^+ pump activity in the inner stripe of outer medullary collecting ducts (OMCDₛs). *J. Am. Soc. Nephrol.* 2:702 (Abstr.)

53a. Jakobbson, B., Bohman, S.-O., Sundelin, B., Aperia, A. 1988. Mitotic response to high protein intake in different renal cell types in weanling rats. *Kidney Int.* 33:662–66

54. Janoshazi, A., Ojcius, D. M., Kone, B., Seifter, J. L., Solomon, A. K. 1988. Relation between the anion exchange protein in kidney medullary collecting duct cells and red cell band 3. *J. Membr. Biol.* 103:181–89

55. Karhukorpi, E. K. 1991. Carbonic anhydrase II in rat acid secreting cells: comparison of osteoclasts with gastric parietal cells and kidney intercalated cells. *Acta Histochem.* 90:11–20

56. Kashgarian, M., Biemesderfer, D., Caplan, M., Forbush, B. III. 1985. Monoclonal antibody to Na,K-ATPase: Immunocytochemical localization along nephron segments. *Kidney Int.* 28:899–913

57. Khadouri, C., Marsy, S., Barlet-Bas, C., Cheval, L., Doucet, A. 1992. Effect of metabolic acidosis and alka-

losis on NEM-sensitive ATPase in rat nephron segments. *Am. J. Physiol.* (262) 31: F583–90

58. Khadouri, C., Marsy, S., Barlet-Bas, C., Doucet, A. 1989. Short-term effect of aldosterone on NEM-sensitive ATPase in rat collecting tubule. *Am. J. Physiol.* (257)26:F177–81

59. Kim, J., Shami, H., Tisher, C. C., Madsen, K. M. 1991. Immunocytochemical response of intercalated cells in rat collecting duct to metabolic acidosis and hypokalemia. *J. Am. Soc. Nephrol.* 2:703 (Abstr.)

60. Kim, J., Tisher, C. C., Linser, P. J., Madsen, K. M. 1990. Ultrastructural localization of carbonic anhydrase II in subpopulations of intercalated cells of the rat kidney. *J. Am. Soc. Nephrol.* 1:245–56

61. Deleted in proof

62. Kim, J., Welch, W. J., Cannon, J. K., Tisher, C. C., Madsen, K. M. 1992. Immunocytochemical response of type A and type B intercalated cells to increased sodium chloride delivery. *Am. J. Physiol.* 262:F288–302

63. Koeppen, B. M. 1985. Conductive properties of the rabbit outer medullary collecting duct: inner stripe. *Am. J. Physiol.* 248 17:F500–6

64. Koeppen, B. M. 1986. Conductive properties of the rabbit outer medullary collecting duct: outer stripe. *Am. J. Physiol.* (250)19:F70–76

65. Koeppen, B. M. 1987. Electrophysiological identification of principal and intercalated cells in the rabbit outer medullary collecting duct. *Pflugers Arch.* 409:138–41

66. Koeppen, B. M. 1989. Electrophysiology of collecting duct H^+ secretion: effect of inhibitors. *Am. J. Physiol.* (256)25:F79–84

67. Koeppen, B. M., Helman, S. I. 1982. Acidification of luminal fluid by the rabbit cortical collecting tubule perfused in vitro. *Am. J. Physiol.* (242) 11:F521–31

68. Koeppen, B. M., Manger, T. M., Pappas, C. A. 1991. Effect of bafilomycin A1 on primary cultures of rabbit outer medullary collecting duct cells (OMCDi). *J. Am. Soc. Nephrol.* 2:704 (Abstr.)

69. Koeppen, B. M., Pappas, C. A., Manger, T. M., Oyler, O. 1991. Cellular mechanisms of Cl transport in outer medullary collecting duct. *Kidney Int. 40, Suppl.* 33:S131–35

70. Koseki, C., Yamaguchi, Y., Furusawa, M., Endou, H. 1988. Isolation by monoclonal antibody of intercalated cells of rabbit kidney. *Kidney Int.* 33: 543–54

71. Kriz, W., Kaissling, B. 1992. Structural organization of the mammalian kidney. In *The Kidney: Physiology and Pathophysiology,* ed. D. W. Seldin, G. Giebisch, pp. 707–77. New York: Raven 2nd ed.

72. Krozowski, Z. S., Rundle, S. E., Wallace, C., Castell, M. J., Shen, J.-H., et al. 1989. Immunolocalization of renal mineralocorticoid receptors with an antiserum against a peptide deduced from the complementary deoxyribonucleic acid sequence. *Endocrinology* 125:192–98

73. Kudrycki, K. E., Shull, G . E., 1989. Primary structure of the rat kidney band 3 anion exchange protein deduced from a cDNA. *J. Biol. Chem.* 264: 8185–92

74. Kuwahara, M., Sasaki, S., Marumo, F., 1990. Cell pH regulation in rabbit outer medullary collecting duct cells: Mechanisms of HCO_3-independent processes. *Am. J. Physiol.* 259:F902–9

75. Kuwahara, M., Sasaki, S., Marumo, F., 1991. Cl^-HCO_3 exchange and Na-HCO_3 symport in rabbit outer medullary collecting duct cells. *Am. J. Physiol.* 260:F635–42

76. Kuwahara, M., Sasaki, S., Marumo, F. 1992. Mineralcorticoids and acidosis regulate H^+/HCO_3 transport of intercalated cells. *J. Clin. Invest.* 89:1388–94

77. Laski, M. E. 1991. Luminal K removal inhibits pH_i recovery in type A intercalated cells of the rabbit cortical collecting tubule. *J. Am. Soc. Nephrol.* 2:704 (Abstr.)

78. Laski, M. E., Kurtzman, N. A. 1990. Collecting tubule adaptation to respiratory acidosis induced in vivo. *Am. J. Physiol.* (258)27:F15–20

79. Lawrence, G. M., Trayer, I. P. 1984. Histochemical and immunohistochemical localization of hexokinase isoenzymes in rat kidney. *Histochem. J.* 16:697–708

80. Lee, B. S., Gunn, R. B., Kopito, R. R. 1991. Functional differences among nonerythroid anion exchangers expressed in a transfected human cell line. *J. Biol. Chem.* 266:11448–54

81. LeFurgey, A., Tisher, C. C. 1979. Morphology of rabbit collecting duct. *Am. J. Anat.* 155:111–23

82. Levine, D. Z., Iacovitti, M., Nash, L., Vandorpe, D. 1988. Secretion of bicarbonate by rat distal tubules in vivo. Modulation by overnight fasting. *J. Clin. Invest.* 81:1873–78

83. Light, D. B., Schwiebert, E. M., Fejes-Toth, G., Naray-Fejes-Toth, A., Karlson, K. H., et al. 1990. Chloride channels in the apical membrane of cortical collecting duct cells. *Am. J. Physiol.* (258)27:F273–80

84. Lombard, W. E., Kokko, J. P., Jacobson, H. R. 1983. Bicarbonate transport in cortical and outer medullary collecting tubules. *Am. J. Physiol.* (244)13:F289–96

85. Lombes, M., Farman, N., Oblin, M. E., Baulieu, E. E., Bonvalet, J. P., et al. 1990. Immunohistochemical localization of renal mineralocorticoid receptor by using an anti-idiotypic antibody that is an internal image of aldosterone. *Proc. Natl. Acad. Sci. USA* 87:1086–88

85a. Madsen, K. M., Kim, J., Tisher, C. C. 1992. Intracellular band 3 immunostaining in type A intercalated cells of rabbit kidney. *Am. J. Physiol.* 262: F1015–22

86. Madsen, K. M., Tisher, C. C. 1984. Response of intercalated cells of rat outer medullary collecting duct to chronic metabolic acidosis. *Lab. Invest.* 51:268–76

87. Madsen, K. M., Tisher, C. C. 1986. Structural-functional relationships along the distal nephron. *Am. J. Physiol.* (250)19:F1–15

88. Manger, T. M., Koeppen, B. M. 1991. β adrenergic regulation of Cl/HCO3 antiporter activity in primary cultures of rabbit outer medullary collecting duct cells. *J. Am. Soc. Nephrol.* 2:706 (Abstr.)

89. Matsuzaki, K., Schuster, V. L., Stokes, J. B. 1989. Reduction in sensitivity to Cl channel blockers by HCO3/CO2 in rabbit cortical collecting duct. *Am. J. Physiol.* (257)26:C102–09

90. McKinney, T. D., Burg, M. B. 1978. Bicarbonate secretion by rabbit cortical collecting tubules in vitro. *J. Clin. Invest.* 61:1421–27

91. McKinney, T. D., Davidson, K. K. 1987. Bicarbonate transport in collecting tubules from outer stripe of outer medulla in rabbit kidneys. *Am. J. Physiol.* (253)22:F816–22

92. Merot, J., Geibel, J., Giebisch, G. 1991. Plasticity of β intercalated cells in the rabbit cortical collecting duct. *J. Am. Soc. Nephrol.* 2:706 (Abstr.)

93. Minuth, W. W., Gilbert, P., Rudolph, U., Spielman, W. S. 1989. Successive histochemical differentiation steps during postnatal development of the collecting duct in rabbit kidney. *Histochemistry* 93:19–25

94. Minuth, W. W., Rudolph, U. 1990. Successive lectin-binding changes within the collecting duct during postnatal development of the rabbit kidney. *Pediatr. Nephrol.* 4:505–9

95. Morel, F., Doucet, A. 1986. Hormonal control of kidney function at the cell level. *Physiol. Rev.* 66:377–468

96. Mujais, S. K., Chen, Y., Al-Sheika, M. W., Batlle, D. C. 1991. Profile of H:K ATPase along the collecting duct: effect of K depletion. *J. Am. Soc. Nephrol.* 2:746 (Abstr.)

97. Muto, S., Giebisch, G., Sansom, S. 1987. Effects of adrenalectomy on CCD; evidence for differential response of two cell types. *Am. J. Physiol.* (253) 22:F742–52

98. Muto, S., Yasoshima, K., Yoshitomi, K., Imai, M., Asano, Y. 1990. Electrophysiological identification of α- and β-intercalated cells and their distribution along the rabbit distal nephron segments. *J. Clin. Invest.* 86:1829–39

99. Narbaitz, R. A., Kapal, V. K., Levine, D. Z. 1991. Induction of population changes of intercalated cells in medullary collecting ducts of newborn rat pups from acid and alkali loaded mothers. *J. Am. Soc. Nephrol.* 2:(Abstr.)

100. Narbaitz, R. A., Tran, N. T., Levine, D. Z. 1990. Induction of early appearance of B intercalated cells in neonatal rat cortical collecting tubule by bicarbonate loading. *J. Am. Soc. Nephrol.* 1:726 (Abstr.)

101. Narbaitz, R. A., Vandorpe, D., Levine, D. Z. 1991. Differentiation of renal intercalated cells in fetal and postnatal rats. *Anat. Embryol.* 183:353–61

102. Nelson, R. D., Guo, X.-L., Masood, K., Brown, D., Kalkbrenner, M., Gluck, S. 1991. Selectively amplified expression of an isoform of the vacuolar H+ATPase 56 kilodalton subunit in renal intercalated cells. *Proc. Natl. Acad. Sci. USA* 89:3541–45

103. O'Neil, R. G., Hayhurst, R. A. 1985. Functional differentiation of cell types of cortical collecting duct. *Am. J. Physiol.* (248)17:F449–53

104. Pappas, C. A., Koeppen, B. M. 1991. β adregergic regulation of Cl currents in primary cultures of rabbit outer medullary collecting duct cells. *J. Am. Soc. Nephrol.* 2:747

105. Reuben, M. A., Naco, G., Starr, F. L., Sachs, G., Kraut, J. A. 1991. Evidence for a H-K-ATPase-like mRNA in rat kidney. *J. Cell Biol.* 115:201a (Abstr.)

106. Ridderstrale, Y., Kashgarian, M., Koeppen, B. M., Giebisch, G., Stetson,

D. L., et al. 1988. Morphological heterogeneity of the rabbit collecting duct. *Kidney Int.* 34:655–70

107. Rundle, S. E., Smith, A. I., Stockman, D., Funder, J. W. 1989. Immunocytochemical demonstration of mineralocorticoid receptors in rat and human kidney. *J. Steroid Biochem.* 33:1235–42

108. Sabatini, S., Laski, M. E., Kurtzman, N. A. 1990. NEM-sensitive ATPase activity in rat nephron: Effect of metabolic acidosis and alkalosis. *Am. J. Physiol.* (258)27:F297–304

109. Satlin, L. M., Matsumoto, T., Schwartz, G. J. 1992. Postnatal maturation of rabbit renal collecting duct III. Peanut lectin-binding intercalated cells. *Am. J. Physiol.* (262)31:F199–208

110. Satlin, L. M., Schwartz, G. J. 1987. Postnatal maturation of rabbit renal collecting duct: intercalated cell function. *Am. J. Physiol.* (253)22:F622–35

111. Satlin, L. M., Schwartz, G. J. 1989. Cellular remodeling of HCO_3-secreting cells in rabbit renal collecting duct in response to an acidic environment. *J. Cell Biol.* 109:1279–88

112. Satlin, L. M., Schwartz, G. J. 1991. Maturation of H^+/HCO_3 transport pathways in β intercalated cells of the rabbit cortical collecting duct. *J. Am. Soc. Nephrol.* 2:711 (Abstr.)

113. Sauer, M., Dorge, A., Thurau, K., Beck, F. X. 1989. Effect of ouabain on electrolyte concentrations in principal and intercalated cells of the isolated perfused cortical collecting duct. *Pflügers Arch.* 413:651–55

114. Schuster, V. L. 1985. Cyclic AMP-stimulated bicarbonate secretion in rabbit cortical collecting tubules. *J. Clin. Invest.* 75:2056–64

115. Schuster, V. L. 1986. Cyclic AMP-stimulated anion transport in rabbit cortical collecting duct: kinetics, stoichiometry, and conductive pathways. *J. Clin. Invest.* 78:1621–30

116. Schuster, V. L. 1990. Organization of collecting duct intercalated cells. *Kidney Int.* 38:668–72

117. Schuster, V. L. 1990. Bicarbonate reabsorption and secretion by the cortical and outer medullary collecting tubule. *Semin. Nephrol.* 10:139–47

118. Schuster, V. L. 1991. Control mechanisms for bicarbonate secretion. *Am. J. Kidney Dis.* 13:348–52

119. Schuster, V. L. 1991. Cortical collecting duct bicarbonate secretion. *Kidney Int. 40, Suppl.* 33:S47–50

120. Deleted in proof

121. Schuster, V. L., Bonsib, S. M., Jennings, M. L. 1986. Two types of collecting duct mitochondria-rich (intercalated cells): lectin and band 3 cytochemistry. *Am. J. Physiol.* (251)20:C347–55

122. Schuster, V. L., Fejes-Toth, G., Naray-Fejes-Toth, A., Gluck, S. 1991. Colocalization of H^+-ATPase and band 3 anion exchanger in rabbit collecting duct intercalated cells. *Am. J. Physiol.* 260:F506–17

123. Schuster, V. L., Stokes, J. B. 1987. Chloride transport by the cortical and outer medullary collecting duct. *Am. J. Physiol.* (253)22:F203–12

124. Schwartz, G. J., Barasch, J., Al-Awqati, Q. 1985. Plasticity of functional epithelial polarity. *Nature* 318:368–71

125. Schwartz, G. J., Satlin, L. M., Bergman, J. E. 1988. Fluorescent characterization of collecting duct cells: a second H^+-secreting type. *Am. J. Physiol.* (255) 24:F1003–14

126. Shimizu, T., Yoshitomi, K., Nakamura, M., Imai, M. 1988. Site and mechanism of action of trichloromethiazide in rabbit distal nephron segments perfused in vitro. *J. Clin. Invest.* 82:721–30

127. Silver, R. B., Frindt, G., Palmer, L. G. 1991. Functional identification of an H-K ATPase in mammalian cortical collecting duct. *J. Am. Soc. Nephrol.* 2:751 (Abstr.)

128. Stanton, B. A., Dietl, P., Schwiebert, E. M. 1990. Cell volume regulation in the cortical collecting duct: Stretch-activated Cl channels. *J. Am. Soc. Nephrol.* 1:692 (Abstr.)

129. Star, R. A., Burg, M. B., Knepper, M. A. 1985. Bicarbonate secretion and chloride absorption by rabbit cortical collecting ducts. Role of chloride/bicarbonate exchange. *J. Clin. Invest.* 76:1123–30

130. Star, R. A., Burg, M. B., Knepper, M. A. 1987. Luminal disequilibrium pH and ammonia transport in outer medullary collecting duct. *Am. J. Physiol.* (252)21:F1148–57

131. Star, R. A., Kurtz, I., Mejia, R., Burg, M. B., Knepper, M. A. 1987. Disequilibrium pH and ammonia transport in isolated perfused cortical collecting ducts. *Am. J. Physiol.* (253)22:F1232–42

132. Stetson, D. L., Beauwens, R., Palmisano, J., Mitchell, P. P., Steinmetz, P. R. 1985. A double-membrane model for urinary bicarbonate secretion. *Am. J. Physiol.* (249)18:F546–52

133. Stetson, D. L., Steinmetz, P. R. 1985. alpha and beta types of carbonic anhydrase-rich cells in turtle bladder. *Am. J. Physiol.* (249)18:F553–65

134. Stone, D. K., Kokko, J. P., Jacobson, H. R. 1983. Anion dependence of rabbit medullary collecting duct acidification. *J. Clin. Invest.* 71:1505–8

135. Stone, D. K., Seldin, D. W., Kokko, J. P., Jacobson, H. R. 1983. Mineralocorticoid modulation of rabbit medullary collecting duct acidification. A sodium-independent effect. *J. Clin. Invest.* 72:77–83

136. Strange, K. 1989. Ouabain-induced cell swelling in the rabbit cortical collecting tubule: NaCl transport by principal cells. *J. Membr. Biol.* 107:249–61

137. Superdock, K. R., Snyders, D. J., Breyer, M. D. 1991. Highly selective low conductance chloride channels in apical membrane of the rabbit cortical collecting duct. *J. Am. Soc. Nephrol.* 2:752 (Abstr.)

138. Tago, K., Schuster, V. L., Stokes, J. B. 1986. Regulation of Cl self-exchange by cAMP in cortical collecting tubule. *Am. J. Physiol.* (251)20:F40–48

139. Tago, K., Schuster, V. L., Stokes, J. B. 1986. Stimulation of chloride transport by HCO3-CO2 in rabbit cortical collecting tubule. *Am. J. Physiol.* (251) 20:F49–56

140. Tago, K., Warden, D. H., Schuster, V. L., Stokes, J. B. 1986. Effects of inhibitors of Cl conductance on Cl self-exchange in rabbit cortical collecting tubule. *Am. J. Physiol.* (251) 20: F1009–17

141. Takata, K., Kasahara, T., Kasahara, M., Ezaki, O., Hirano, H. 1991. Localization of Na$^+$-dependent active type and erythrocyte/HepG2-type glucose transporters in rat kidney: Immunofluorescence and immunogold study. *J. Histochem. Cytochem.* 39:287–98

142. Teixeira da Silva, J. C. Jr., Perrone, R. D., Johns, C. A., Madias, N. E. 1991. Rat kidney band 3 mRNA modulation in chronic respiratory acidosis. *Am. J. Physiol.* 260:F204–9

143. Thorens, B., Lodish, H. F., Brown, D. 1990. Differential localization of two glucose transporter isoforms in rat kidney. *Am. J. Physiol.* (259)28:C286–94

144. Tisher, C. C., Madsen, K. M. 1991. Anatomy of the kidney. In *The Kidney*, ed. B. M. Brenner, F. C. Rector, pp. 3–75. Philadelphia: Saunders 4th ed.

145. Tomita, K., Pisano, J. J., Burg, M. B., Knepper, M. A. 1986. Effects of vasopressin and bradykinin on anion transport by the rat cortical collecting duct. Evidence for an electroneutral sodium chloride transport pathway. *J. Clin. Invest.* 77:136–41

146. Uchida, S., Endou, H. 1988. Substrate specificity to maintain cellular ATP along the mouse nephron. *Am. J. Physiol.* (255)24:F977–83

147. Verlander, J. W., Madsen, K. M., Galla, J. H., Luke, R. G., Tisher, C. C. 1992. Response of intercalated cells to chloride depletion metabolic alkalosis. *Am. J. Physiol.* 262:F309–19

148. Verlander, J. W., Madsen, K. M., Low, P. S., Allen, D. P., Tisher, C. C. 1988. Immunocytochemical localization of band 3 protein in the rat collecting duct. *Am. J. Physiol.* (255) 24:F115–25

149. Verlander, J. W., Madsen, K. M., Stone, D. K., Tisher, C. C. 1991. Ultrastructural localization of H$^+$ATPase in rabbit cortical collecting duct. *J. Am. Soc. Nephrol.* 2:714 (Abstr.)

150. Verlander, J. W., Madsen, K. M., Tisher, C. C. 1987. Effect of acute respiratory acidosis on two populations of intercalated cells in rat cortical collecting duct. *Am. J. Physiol.* (253)22:F1142–56

151. Wang, T., Chan, Y. L. 1989. Neural control of distal tubular bicarbonate and fluid transport. *Am. J. Physiol.* (257)26:F72–76

152. Wang, X., Kurtz, I. 1990. H$^+$/base transport in principal cells characterized by confocal fluorescence imaging. *Am. J. Physiol.* 259:C365–73

153. Weiner, I. D., Hamm, L. L. 1990. Regulation of intracellular pH in the rabbit cortical collecting tubule. *J. Clin. Invest.* 85:274–81

154. Weiner, I. D., Hamm, L. L. 1991. Regulation of Cl$^-$/HCO3 exchange in the rabbit cortical collecting tubule. *J. Clin. Invest.* 87:1553–58

155. Wingo, C. S., Madsen, K. M., Smolka, A., Tisher, C. C. 1990. H-K-ATPase immunoreactivity in cortical and outer medullary collecting duct. *Kidney Int.* 38:985–90

156. Wingo, C. S., Straub, S. 1990. Rb efflux by rabbit inner stripe outer medullary collecting duct (OMCD$_i$): effect of gastric H-K-ATPase inhibitor SCH28080. *Kidney Int.* 37:575. (Abstr.)

157. Wingo, C. S., Straub, S. 1991. Ouabain-insensitive Cl reabsorption by the cortical collecting duct is mediated by

$H^+K^+ATPase$. *J. Am. Soc. Nephrol.* 2:755 (Abstr.)

158. Wingo, C. S., Straub, S. G. 1989. Active proton secretion and potassium absorption in the rabbit outer medullary collecting duct. Functional evidence for proton-potassium-activated adenosine triphosphatase. *J. Clin. Invest.* 84:361–65

159. Yamaji, Y., Hayashi, M., Iyori, M., Kitijima, Y., Saruta, T. 1992. Chronic DOC treatment enhances Na^+/H^+ exchanger activity of β intercalated cells in rabbit CCD. *Am. J. Physiol.* 262: F712–17

160. Yamaji, Y., Hayashi, M., Iyori, M., Saruta, T. 1991. Peritubular metabolic acidosis decreases H^+-pump activity of β intercalated cell. *J. Am. Soc. Nephrol.* 2:717 (Abstr.)

161. Zeidel, M. L., Silva, P., Seifter, J. L. 1986. Intracellular pH regulation in rabbit renal medullary collecting duct cells. Role of chloride-bicarbonate exchange. *J. Clin. Invest.* 77: 1682–88

162. Zeidel, M. L., Silva, P., Seifter, J. L. 1986. Intracellular pH regulation and proton transport by rabbit renal medullary collecting duct cells. Role of plasma membrane proton adenosine triphosphatase. *J. Clin. Invest.* 77:113–20

Annu. Rev. Physiol. 1993. 55:289–304

REGULATION OF THE RENAL BRUSH BORDER MEMBRANE Na^+-H^+ EXCHANGER

E. J. Weinman

Department of Medicine, VA Medical Center, Sepulveda, California 91343

S. Shenolikar

Department of Pharmacology, Duke University, Durham, North Carolina 27710

KEY WORDS: renal physiology, cAMP-dependent protein kinase, calcium-phospholipid-dependent protein kinase, calcium-calmodulin-dependent multifunctional protein kinase, renal electrolyte transport

INTRODUCTION

Murer and co-workers described the presence of an electroneutral Na^+-H^+ exchanger in brush border membrane (BBM) preparations from the kidney and small intestine (52). This was the first description of such a transport mechanism in mammalian tissue. Subsequently, Na^+-H^+ exchange transport was found to be present in many, if not all, cells of the body. Initially, it was not known if the Na^+-H^+ exchanger present in different organs represented a single transporter or a family of transport proteins, but numerous lines of functional evidence suggested that the renal and small intestinal BBM Na^+-H^+ exchanger differed from that found in non-epithelial tissue. For example, Haggerty et al reported the presence of Na^+-H^+ exchange transport in both the apical and basolateral membranes of LLC-PK1 cells: cells that possess properties of renal proximal tubule cells (23). One key observation in this cultured cell line was the greater sensitivity of the basolateral as compared to the brush border membrane exchanger to inhibition by amiloride. Studies by others using these cells indicated differences in the mode of regulation of the basolateral vs the apical membrane Na^+-H^+ exchanger (7). While these functional distinctions might reflect differences in the lipid environment between the two cell borders and/or the presence or absence of specific cofactors, the general conclusion was that LLC-PK1 cells contain more than one type of Na^+-H^+ exchanger.

In 1989 Sardet and co-workers cloned a cDNA from human fibroblasts that encodes a Na^+-H^+ exchange transport protein (65a). This transport protein has a wide tissue distribution and is highly conserved between species. Recent cloning experiments have isolated cDNAs from the kidney of rat and rabbit, and from LLC-PK1 cells that are homologous to the cloned human Na^+-H^+ exchanger (29, 54, 60). In situ hybridization studies using a cDNA to the cloned Na^+-H^+ exchanger in the rat kidney indicate a different distribution along the nephron than that of the BBM exchanger as determined from functional studies (39). Antibodies to fusion proteins of the cloned exchanger do not localize to the BBM of renal proximal tubule cells (6). Antipeptide antibodies to specific domains of the cloned exchanger also do not correlate with functional expression of the BBM exchanger (74). Thus it has been concluded that the exchanger elucidated by Sardet et al is the widely distributed "housekeeping" form of the Na^+-H^+ exchanger. Another designation for this Na^+-H^+ exchanger is NHE-1.

Study of the structure of the renal BBM Na^+-H^+ exchanger is an area of intensive investigative interest. Some information regarding reactive sites of the BBM Na^+-H^+ exchanger has been gained using chemical modifying agents, but to date this information is incomplete (16, 33). Donowitz and co-workers have reported results of preliminary studies suggesting that there is a family of Na^+-H^+ exchangers, of which some bear homology to NHE-1 in the transmembrane domains, but differ in the cytosolic domains (M. Donowitz, personal communication). These latter Na^+-H^+ exchangers have a more restricted tissue distribution and may represent the BBM form of the exchanger. Elucidation of the structure of the BBM form of the exchanger will greatly facilitate the study of the structure-function relations of the BBM Na^+-H^+ exchanger.

Both the NHE-1 and other forms of the Na^+-H^+ exchanger are electroneutral transporters, are inhibited by amiloride and amiloride analogues and, at least in most tissues, possess internal modifier sites that are sensitive to the free hydrogen ion concentration in the cell (3, 37, 45). The housekeeping Na^+-H^+ exchanger functions in defense of cell pH and cell volume (18). In many tissues, this form of the Na^+-H^+ exchanger is stimulated by mitogenic stimuli (35, 40). While the BBM form of the exchanger may subserve similar functions in renal and small intestinal cells, this transporter is more likely to be involved in transepithelial transport of electrolytes. The functional importance of the apical membrane Na^+-H^+ exchanger in the renal proximal tubule is evidenced by estimates that this transporter mediates the reabsorption of approximately one third of the filtered load of sodium and the bulk of the secretion of hydrogen ions (8, 31, 57).

REGULATION OF THE RENAL BBM Na^+-H^+ EXCHANGER

A large body of experimental data is now available to define changes in Na^+-H^+ exchange activity in renal BBM in response to a variety of experimental maneuvers. To a first approximation, two types of regulatory responses have been observed (20). First, there may be recycling or the net addition or removal of transporters from the BBM. Kinetic studies have demonstrated that there is a change in the V_{max} of the BBM Na^+-H^+ exchanger in response to administration of thyroxine, glucocorticoids, and long-term acidosis (9, 14, 38). It should be noted, however, that measurement of V_{max} is not synonymous with the number of transporters. Measurement of the actual number of transporters must await the development of specific chemical ligands or antibodies to the BBM form of the exchanger. Second, the activity of the BBM Na^+-H^+ exchanger may be altered by changes in the affinity for sodium or hydrogen ions, or in the response of transporter to hydrogen ions on its internal modifier site. A number of agents and maneuvers appear to affect Na^+-H^+ exchange activity by such mechanisms (19, 21, 49). Generally, changes in V_{max} occur under circumstances associated with chronic adaptation of the Na^+-H^+ exchanger, while changes in ion affinity are associated with more rapid regulation of the rates of transport.

A particular focus of study from our laboratory has been the regulation of the renal BBM Na^+-H^+ exchanger by processes involving reversible protein phosphorylation (78). Specific emphasis has been placed on the study of three protein kinases present in the renal proximal convoluted tubule; cAMP-dependent protein kinase (PKA), calcium-phospholipid-dependent protein kinase (PKC), and calcium- calmodulin-dependent multifunctional protein kinase II (CaM-KII). In conjunction with studies on the mechanisms of signal transduction in the renal proximal tubule, a framework for understanding the regulation of the renal BBM Na^+-H^+ exchanger has begun to emerge.

This review summarizes the current understanding of the mechanisms of regulation of renal BBM exchanger by processes involving activation of PKA, PKC, and CaM-KII. Although other protein kinases may also regulate components of BBM Na^+-H^+ exchange activity, currently little direct information is available on this form of regulation. In addition, protein phosphatases and/or protein phosphatase inhibitors may be sites of regulatory control, but these interactions remain to be defined. Accordingly, these latter topics are not discussed.

SHORT-TERM REGULATION OF THE BBM Na$^+$-H$^+$ EXCHANGER BY PHOSPHORYLATION/ DEPHOSPHORYLATION REACTIONS

Cyclic Adenosine Monophosphate-Dependent Protein Kinase

In 1971, Agus et al using recollection micropuncture techniques reported that the administration of parathyroid hormone (PTH) to dogs resulted in a decrease in the reabsorption of phosphate in the proximal tubule and an increase in phosphate excretion in the urine (1). Although not a focus of these experiments, a decrease in sodium and water reabsorption in the proximal tubule was observed. Infusion of a permeable analogue of cAMP also resulted in a decrease in the reabsorption of phosphate, sodium, and water in the proximal tubule. Studies in the rat and rabbit established that cAMP inhibited sodium transport in the proximal tubule (34, 73). An insight into the mechanism by which cAMP inhibited sodium transport in this nephron segment was provided by Dennis (11), who reported that the inhibitory effect of PTH on sodium transport in the isolated perfused proximal convoluted tubule of the rabbit required the presence of bicarbonate in the luminal perfusion solution. Dennis raised the possibility that cAMP inhibited the renal apical membrane Na$^+$-H$^+$ exchanger, but offered no direct evidence to support this idea. However, it was shown that cAMP inhibited the reabsorption of bicarbonate in the renal proximal tubule when methods were developed to measure the concentration of bicarbonate in tubular fluid samples (46, 58).

It is interesting from an historic perspective to note that while cAMP-mediated inhibition of the renal brush border Na$^+$-H$^+$ exchanger was suggested by the above experiments, other possibilities were also considered. For example, studies in both the rat and rabbit proximal tubule suggested that PTH and/or cAMP increased the passive backleak of bicarbonate in the proximal tubule via a paracellular pathway (34, 43, 44). Experiments in the rat suggested that PTH inhibited carbonic anhydrase activity (5). At the present time, however, neither of these mechanisms is believed to play an important physiologic role in mediating the effect of PTH on the reclamation of filtered bicarbonate in the renal proximal tubule.

Dolson et al incubated an enriched suspension of rabbit proximal tubules in solutions containing PTH or cAMP (12). Both PTH and cAMP inhibited oxygen consumption; the onset of action for PTH being 7 to 10 min, that of cAMP being approximately 5 min. Dolson et al provided evidence that PTH-mediated inhibition of oxygen consumption was the result of decreased sodium entry into the cells of the proximal tubule and not the result of PTH or cAMP-associated inhibition of Na$^+$-K$^+$ ATPase. In the intact cell, however, it is not possible to control rigorously the intracellular concentration of electrolytes such that an effect of PTH or cAMP on the cell concentration of sodium, buffering capacity, or pH could not be excluded. Kahn et al designed experiments to determine if PTH and cAMP inhibited the renal BBM Na^+-H^+ exchanger directly (36). A suspension of rabbit proximal tubules was incubated with PTH or cAMP. Isolated renal BBM vesicles were prepared from this suspension for study of proton gradient-stimulated, amiloride inhibitable sodium uptake; an operative definition of Na^+-H^+ exchange transport. This approach had the advantage of permitting study of the transporter in control and experimental membrane vesicles under the same initial conditions. It was demonstrated that incubation of the tubules in PTH or a permeable analogue of cAMP resulted in a 25 to 35% decrease in Na^+-H^+ exchange activity, as assayed in BBM, but no change in the sodium-dependent transport of glucose. These results have been confirmed in the rat (22, 51) and provide initial evidence that PTH and cAMP directly inhibit the activity of the renal BBM Na^+-H^+ exchanger. A concurrent publication by Pollock et al using a proximal cell line derived from the opossum kidney also suggests that PTH and cAMP inhibit the Na^+-H^+ exchanger in the apical membrane (55).

The above experiments established that PTH stimulated the production of cAMP in the renal proximal convoluted tubule and that cAMP inhibited the activity of the BBM Na^+-H^+ exchanger. The major, if not the sole, binding protein of biologic importance for cAMP is the regulatory component of cAMP-dependent protein kinase (PKA). cAMP binds to the regulatory subunit, which results in the dissociation of the regulatory subunit from the catalytic subunit and increased protein kinase activity. While PKA is known to be present in the cytosol of cells, studies in the BBM of dog and rabbit suggest that PKA is also an intrinsic BBM membrane protein (24, 67). The experiments of Shenolikar et al, for example, provide biochemical and immunologic evidence that the rabbit BBM contains a tightly associated regulatory component (RII) of PKA (67).

Direct proof of the involvement of PKA with subsequent phosphorylation of BBM proteins in regulating Na^+-H^+ exchange activity was provided by Weinman et al (82). BBM prepared by precipitation with divalent cations assume a predominantly right-side-out orientation. Most likely critical regulatory sites of BBM transporters occur on the cytosolic side of the membranes, the inner side of the closed membrane vesicles. Closed BBM vesicles have limited permeability to proteins such as PKA and to ATP. Incubation of rabbit renal BBM in isotonic phosphorylation solutions containing ATP, magnesium, and cAMP, or purified catalytic subunit of PKA, resulted in no change in Na^+-H^+ exchanger activity. Incubation of rabbit renal BBM vesicles in a hypotonic solution rendered the vesicles permeable to the reactants and resulted in a decrease in Na^+-H^+ exchange activity. This decrease in transporter activity was dependent on ATP and was inhibited by the specific inhibitor of PKA. Sodium-dependent glucose transport was not affected. These studies established that cAMP acting via PKA inhibited the BBM Na^+-H^+ exchanger by a process involving the phosphorylation of one or more BBM proteins.

SDS-PAGE analysis of rabbit renal BBM phosphorylated by PKA indicated rapid and reversible phosphorylation of 10 to 15 BBM proteins (82). The number of substrate proteins for PKA in rabbit BBM rendered it impossible to identify unique polypeptides that were responsible for PKA-mediated regulation of the Na^+-H^+ exchanger. More detailed study of the substrate proteins for PKA in BBM required development of methods to solubilize BBM proteins and to reconstitute Na^+-H^+ exchanger activity. Weinman & Shenolikar solubilized rabbit renal BBM in the detergent, octyl glucoside, and demonstrated electroneutral, proton gradient-stimulated uptake of sodium after reconstitution of the proteins into soybean phospholipid vesicles (81). Heating of the solubilized BBM proteins destroyed transport activity. Na^+-H^+ exchange activity in the reconstituted proteoliposomes was inhibited in a dose-dependent manner by amiloride and amiloride analogues with a rank order of specificity similar to that established in native BBM membrane vesicles.

By contrast to native BBM vesicles, solubilized BBM proteins demonstrate little or no endogenous protein kinase or protein phosphatase activity (77). This fortuitous finding provided the opportunity to study the specific effect of individual protein kinases under experimental conditions that obviate the problem of the time-dependent dephosphorylation of substrate proteins. Incubation of solubilized BBM proteins in a solution containing ATP, magnesium, and purified catalytic subunit of PKA inhibited Na^+-H^+ exchange activity as assayed after reconstitution (77). The effect of PKA was dependent on the presence of ATP and was inhibited by a specific inhibitor of this protein kinase. These results supported the conclusions deduced from experiments using native BBM. However, the possibility that phosphorylation of proteins(s) altered the efficiency of reconstitution of the Na^+-H^+ exchanger could not be excluded with certainty.

In subsequent experiments, three lines of evidence were advanced to indicate that the activity of the Na^+-H^+ exchanger could be dissociated from its regulation by PKA. Freeze-thawing of solubilized BBM proteins resulted in a somewhat higher basal rate of Na^+-H^+ exchange transport, but near total loss of regulation by PKA (77). Subjecting solubilized BBM proteins to limited trypsin digestion resulted in similar findings (75). Finally, studies involving fractionation of solubilized BBM proteins by anion exchange chromatography indicated that the more anionic proteins, those eluting between 0.2 and 0.4 M NaCl, demonstrated Na^+-H^+ exchange activity, but were not regulated by PKA (83). Coreconstitution experiments using trypsinized solubilized BBM proteins and the 0.2–0.4 M NaCl fraction of solubilized BBM proteins with other BBM protein fractions obtained by size exclusion and/or anion exchange chromatography suggested that the inhibitory effect of PKA on Na$^+$-H$^+$ exchange activity required a 42-kd polypeptide. This 42-kd polypeptide does not appear to mediate Na$^+$-H$^+$ exchange activity itself, but rather is a necessary cofactor for the expression of the effects of PKA on the exchanger. The 42-kd regulatory protein that is a substrate for PKA is inactivated by heat, freeze/thawing, and trypsin. Studies are currently in progress to purify this 42-kd polypeptide and to determine its structure and function (84).

Calcium-Phospholipid-Dependent Protein Kinase

There is a convincing body of experimental data that indicates that the housekeeping form of the Na$^+$-H$^+$ exchanger (NHE-1) is stimulated by activation of PKC in a variety of tissues (53, 56, 62, 71). Less information is available on the effect of PKC on the activity of the renal BBM Na$^+$-H$^+$ exchanger. Moreover, studies on the effect of PKC on the BBM Na$^+$-H$^+$ exchanger have not been consistent. Hammerman and co-workers reported that PKC resulted in alkalinization of dog proximal tubules studied in suspension (48). This alkalinization was dependent on sodium in the medium and was inhibited by amiloride. It is likely, although not proven, that these results are best explained by activation of the renal BBM Na$^+$-H$^+$ exchanger rather than activation of a basolateral NHE-1 form of the exchanger. Functional evidence for Na$^+$-H$^+$ exchange activity has not been observed in isolated basolateral membrane preparations (BLM) of the kidney (70). In preliminary immunologic studies, antipeptide antibodies to NHE-1 have not localized to the BLM of renal proximal tubules of the rabbit (74). Preliminary immunohistochemical studies in the rabbit, using an antibody to a fusion protein of NHE-1, suggest that this transporter is localized to BLM of segments of juxtamedullary proximal convoluted tubules and in more distal nephron segments (6). A recent study by Krapf & Solioz, using reverse transcription and the polymerase chain reaction, indicates that the mRNA for NHE-1 is expressed in S1 and S2 segments of juxtamedullary nephrons in the kidney of the rat (39). The mRNA is expressed only weakly in midcortical proximal tubule nephrons, but is not expressed in superficial proximal tubules. Comparable studies in the kidney of the dog, however, have not yet been reported. Accordingly, the experiments of Hammerman et al can not be interpreted with certainty.

Two direct lines of evidence provide support for the conclusion that PKC activation stimulates the activity of the BBM Na$^+$-H$^+$ exchanger in the kidney of the rabbit. Rabbit BBM were incubated in a phosphorylation solution containing ATP, calcium, magnesium, and either an active phorbol ester or partially purified PKC (80). The phosphorylation solution was rendered hypotonic to permit entry of the reactants into the vesicle space and exposure to the cytosolic face of these right-side-out vesicles. Activation of endogenous BBM PKC by phorbol esters, or provision of exogenous PKC, resulted in an increase in the amiloride-sensitive component of proton gradient-stimulated uptake of sodium. The stimulatory effect of PKC had an absolute requirement for ATP. Sodium-dependent glucose transport was not affected by activation of PKC. In later experiments, octyl glucoside-extracted BBM proteins of the rabbit kidney were phosphorylated using ATP, calcium, magnesium, and PKC (76). Na^+-H^+ exchange activity was stimulated when assayed after reconstitution of the solubilized proteins into artificial lipid vesicles. The stimulatory effect of PKC had an absolute requirement for ATP and calcium. These experiments demonstrate that protein phosphorylation mediated by PKC stimulates the activity of the BBM Na^+-H^+ exchanger.

The conclusion that PKC activation stimulates the BBM Na^+-H^+ exchanger is supported by preliminary studies in the rat. Kidney slices from the cortex of the rat were incubated in a solution containing an active phorbol ester (22, 51). Na^+-H^+ exchange activity was assayed in BBM derived from the slices and was found to be increased significantly. In addition, Alpern and co-workers observed that an active phorbol ester stimulated Na^+-H^+ exchange activity using a primary culture of rabbit renal proximal tubule cells (30). For reasons already discussed, it appears most likely that the BBM exchanger was stimulated. It is worth noting, however, that in the experiments of Alpern et al, the active phorbol ester increased the steady state expression of the mRNA of NHE-1. Baum & Hays reported that activators of PKC inhibited sodium, water, and bicarbonate reabsorption in microperfused superficial rabbit proximal convoluted tubules (4). In a later study using a similar protocol, Wang & Chan observed that phorbol esters stimulated sodium, water, and bicarbonate reabsorption initially. After approximately 15 to 30 min of perfusion with phorbol esters, there was a decrease in these measured parameters (72). The reduction in transport corresponded in time to that observed by Baum & Hays. Thus it appears that activation of PKC does stimulate Na^+-H^+ activity in intact rabbit renal proximal tubules. In addition, phorbol esters rapidly down-regulate the activity of PKC in this nephron segment with a resultant decrease in the activity of the exchanger.

Murer and co-workers observed a decrease in Na^+-H^+ exchange activity in cultured opossum kidney proximal tubule cells exposed to activators of PKC (59). It is difficult to reconcile these observations with those discussed above. One possible explanation is that the cultured opossum kidney cells behave differently than the proximal convoluted tubule cells of rabbit, rat, or dog. As will be discussed below, the integrated response to PKC in intact cells vs membrane preparations may include regulation of other pathways that affect the activity of the BBM Na$^+$-H$^+$ exchanger. The interactions between the regulatory pathways may be different in cultured opossum proximal tubule cells. Additional experiments will be required to resolve these questions.

The mechanism by which PKC alters the activity of the BBM exchanger is not known with certainty. Studies using isolated rabbit BBM and solubilized proteins from these membranes indicate that PKC-mediated regulation of the Na$^+$-H$^+$ exchanger is the result of phosphorylation of one or more BBM proteins (80, 76). Studies from our laboratory indicate that PKC phosphorylates a significant number of BBM proteins that are different from those phosphorylated by PKA (80). By one dimensional SDS-PAGE, however, both protein kinases appear to phosphorylate some of the same BBM proteins. The NHE-1 form of the Na$^+$-H$^+$ exchanger contains several consensus sequences for phosphorylation by PKC (65a). A 110-kd polypeptide representing NHE-1 was shown to be phosphorylated in the intact cell (65). In addition, the phosphorylation state of this polypeptide is increased when the cells are treated with growth factors. The structure of the BBM Na$^+$-H$^+$ exchanger has not been elucidated, and it is not possible to predict if the BBM Na$^+$-H$^+$ exchanger is a direct substrate for PKC, or if other regulatory phosphoprotein factors are required.

Calcium-Calmodulin-Dependent Multifunctional Protein Kinase II

An increase in the cytosolic concentration of calcium in renal proximal tubules has been reported to have a variable effect on sodium transport in the proximal convoluted tubule (15, 66, 86). The reason for this variability is not known, but probably relates to differences in experimental design and in the use of different drugs and agents to increase the calcium concentration inside the cell. Despite some conflicting results, the general consensus is that an increase in the cytosolic concentration of calcium is associated with a decrease in the reabsorption of sodium in the renal proximal tubule. The mechanism by which calcium inhibits the rate of sodium transport, however, was not elucidated by such studies. An important target for calcium-mediated cell signaling is the ubiquitous calcium-binding protein, calmodulin, with the subsequent activation of numerous calcium-calmodulin-regulated proteins including several protein kinases (47). Studies from our laboratory have focused on the potential role of calcium-calmodulin-dependent multifunctional protein kinase II (CaM-KII). This protein kinase has broad substrate specificity and a wide distribution in tissues as compared to other known calmodulin-activated protein kinases (17, 27, 69). A cDNA to the alpha-subunit of rat brain CaM-KII hybridized to a single mRNA of appropriate size in the renal cortex and medulla of the rabbit kidney, and in total RNA extracted from a suspension of rabbit renal proximal convoluted tubules (25). In addition, cytosolic extracts of rabbit renal proximal convoluted tubule cells demonstrated CaM-KII activity using a selective bioassay. Taken together, these experiments indicate that rabbit renal proximal tubules contain CaM-KII. No attempt was made in these experiments to determine if this protein kinase was present in BBM. A later study by Donowitz et al identified CaM-KII in the BBM of cells of the rabbit small intestine (10).

The possible interaction between CaM-KII and the BBM Na^+-H^+ exchanger was examined using detergent-solubilized rabbit renal BBM proteins incubated in a solution containing ATP, calcium, magnesium, calmodulin, and purified CaM-KII (76). As assayed after reconstitution, CaM-KII inhibited the Na^+-H^+ exchanger in a calcium-, calmodulin-, and ATP-dependent manner. Indirect preliminary studies in LLC-PK1 cells confirm the inhibitory effect of CaM-KII on BBM Na^+-H^+ exchange activity (7). Similar results have been reported in BBM of rabbit small intestine (63).

Although the mechanism by which CaM-KII inhibits the renal BBM Na^+-H^+ exchanger has not been established at the present time, it would appear that it involves different phosphoproteins than those mediating the inhibitory effects of PKA. The phosphorylation patterns for PKA and CaM-KII in rabbit renal BBM are quite different (77, 76). In addition, as discussed earlier, a chromatographic fraction of octyl glucoside-extracted rabbit renal BBM proteins, which retains transport activity but is not regulated by PKA, has been identified. Na^+-H^+ exchange activity in this fraction, however, is inhibited by CaM-KII, which further suggests that different substrates are involved in the regulation of the rabbit renal BBM Na^+-H^+ exchanger by PKA and CaM-KII (83, 79).

IMPLICATIONS OF IN VITRO STUDIES FOR UNDERSTANDING THE REGULATION OF THE BBM Na^+-H^+ EXCHANGER IN INTACT RENAL PROXIMAL TUBULE CELLS

Studies involving the use of isolated BBM and solubilized BBM proteins have permitted examination of the effect of activation of specific protein kinases on transport activity. In intact cells, however, the physiologic regulation of the Na^+-H^+ exchanger by hormones and other agonists is likely to be more complex. A full discussion of all the potential interactions between signal transduction pathways and regulation of associated transporters would be highly speculative, but a few illustrations may serve to highlight these complexities.

Teitelbaum et al have reported a mutual inhibitory interaction between PKA and PKC (68). While these experiments were not performed in the renal proximal tubule, it is likely that similar interactions could be present in the cells of this nephron segment. Hanley and co-workers have reported that phorbol esters result in a decrease in the steady-state concentration of the mRNA for the alpha-subunit of CaM-KII in the rabbit proximal tubule (26). Thus an activating mechanism (PKC) results in down-regulation of an inactivating mechanism (CaM-KII); a process that could amplify the effects of PKC on the activity of the BBM Na$^+$-H$^+$ exchanger. The interaction between cell signaling mechanisms has become of considerable physiologic interest based on recent evidence that some agonists are capable of activating more than one signal transduction pathway. For example, PTH, in addition to activating adenylate cyclase and the production of cAMP, also activates PKC (32). Murer and co-workers reported that in opossum kidney cells studied in culture, lower concentrations of PTH are required to activate PKC than are required to stimulate production of cAMP (50). In rat proximal tubules, Liu & Cogan and others have reported that angiotensin II stimulates Na$^+$-H$^+$ exchange activity by mechanisms that include a decrease in the cell concentration of cAMP and stimulation of PKC activity (41, 42, 85).

In the intact cell, Na$^+$-H$^+$ exchange transport activity is affected by the prevailing transmembrane ion gradient for sodium and by the hydrogen ion concentration of the cell. The major determinant of the transcellular concentration of sodium is the Na$^+$-K$^+$ ATPase pump. In initial studies of suspended rabbit proximal convoluted tubules, PTH was not demonstrated to affect Na$^+$-K$^+$ ATPase activity (12). Mandel and co-workers reviewed existing literature and noted that the inhibitory effect of PTH on sodium transport in the renal proximal tubule cells often exceeded that achieved by cAMP alone. Studies by these investigators demonstrated that PTH, but not cAMP, inhibited the activity of the Na$^+$-K$^+$ ATPase pump in suspended rabbit proximal convoluted tubules (61). Dopamine stimulates the production of cAMP in the renal proximal tubule and inhibits the activity of the BBM Na$^+$-H$^+$ exchanger in this nephron segment (13). In addition, dopamine inhibits Na$^+$-K$^+$ ATPase activity (2). Simultaneous inhibition of the Na$^+$-H$^+$ exchanger and the Na$^+$-K$^+$ ATPase pump would provide a synergistic mechanism by which to limit sodium reabsorption. Arruda and co-workers reported that PKA, PKC, and possibly CaM-KII regulate the activity of the sodium-dependent transport of bicarbonate across the basolateral membrane of the proximal tubule (64). The independent regulation of this bicarbonate exit mechanism would be predicted to alter the hydrogen ion concentration in the cell and secondarily affect the activity of the BBM Na$^+$-H$^+$ exchanger.

Finally, Hensley and co-workers proposed another mechanism of regulation of the BBM Na$^+$-H$^+$ exchanger by PTH and cAMP (28). Na$^+$-H$^+$ exchange activity was measured by a functional assay in density gradient fractions of the rat kidney. In control basal conditions, the bulk of transport activity was localized to the BBM. Following administration of PTH, however, Na$^+$-H$^+$

exchange activity was translocated from the BBM to intracellular compartments. These experiments suggest that a mode of regulation of the BBM Na^+-H^+ exchanger involves a recycling mechanism with the insertion and removal of BBM transporters and/or regulatory proteins. The development of antibodies or specific ligands for the BBM Na^+-H^+ exchanger will be essential to delineate the relative contribution of covalent modification vs transporter recycling in the overall control of the renal BBM Na^+-H^+ exchanger.

FUTURE DIRECTIONS

Critical to a detailed understanding of the regulation of the renal BBM Na^+-H^+ exchanger will be the elucidation of the structure of this exchanger. From the structure, it should be possible to develop monospecific antibodies to the BBM Na^+-H^+ exchanger and perform site-directed mutagenesis experiments. The availability of a cDNA and antibodies to the BBM cation exchanger will greatly facilitate the study of its regulation. While the present review has focused on the effect of three protein kinases, it remains possible that other serine/threonine and, perhaps, tyrosine protein kinases may regulate the activity the BBM Na^+-H^+ exchanger. Regulation of the activity of protein phosphatases that mediate dephosphorylation of substrate proteins and protein phosphatase inhibitors in renal tissue have not been studied in detail (12a, 67a). The possible participation of other regulatory cofactor proteins may also be an area of fruitful investigation.

Finally, the interaction between cell signaling pathways in the renal proximal tubule requires better definition. Also important is a clearer understanding of the relation between the various transporters in the renal proximal tubule that influence the activity of each other. It is likely that the use of molecular and cellular biologic techniques in conjunction with presently available methodologies will provide answers to existing questions and open new areas of investigative inquiry.

Literature Cited

1. Agus, Z. S., Puschett, J. B., Senesky, D., Goldberg, M. 1971. Mode of action of parathyroid hormone and cyclic adenosine 3'- 5' monophosphate on renal-tubular phosphate reabsorption in the dog. *J. Clin. Invest.* 50:617–26
2. Aperia, A., Bertorello, A., Seri, I. 1987. Dopamine causes inhibition of Na^+-K^+-ATPase activity in rat proximal convoluted tubule segments. *Am. J. Physiol.* 252(21): F39–F45

3. Aronson, P. S. 1985. Kinetic properties of the plasma membrane Na^+-H^+ exchanger. *Annu. Rev. Physiol.* 47:545–60
4. Baum, M., Hays, S. 1988. Phorbol myristate and dioctanoylglycerol inhibit transport in rabbit proximal convoluted tubule. *Am. J. Physiol.* 254(23):F9–14
5. Beck, N., Kim, K. S., Wola, M., Davis, B. B. 1975. Inhibition of carbonic anhydrase by parathyroid hor-

mone and cyclic AMP in rat renal cortex in vivo. *J. Clin. Invest.* 55:149–56

6. Biemesderfer, D., Reilly R. F., Exnaer, M., Hilderbrandt, F., Igarashi, P., Aronson, P. S. 1991. Immunochemical characterization of an epithelial Na$^+$-H$^+$ exchanger. *J. Am. Soc. Nephrol.* 2:696 (Abstr.)

7. Burns, K. D., Homma, T., Harris, R. C. 1990. Calmodulin antagonism inhibits basolateral and activates apical Na$^+$-H$^+$ exchange in LLC-PK/Cl4. *J. Am. Soc. Nephrol.* 1:714 (Abstr.)

8. Chantrelle, B., Cogan, M. G., Rector, F. C. Jr. 1982. Direct evidence for coupled sodium-hydrogen exchange in the rat superficial proximal convoluted tubule. *Pflügers Arch.* 395:186–89

9. Cohn, D. E., Klahr, S., Hammerman, M. R. 1983. Metabolic acidosis and parathyroidectomy increase Na$^+$-H$^+$ exchange in brush border membrane vesicles. *Am. J. Physiol.* 245:F217–22

10. Cohen, M. E., Reinlib, L., Watson, A. J. M., Gorelick, F., Rys-Sikora, K., et al. 1990. Rabbit ileal villus cell brush border Na$^+$-H$^+$ exchange is regulated by Ca^{2+}/calmodulin-dependent protein kinase II, a brush border membrane protein. *Proc. Natl. Acad. Sci. USA* 87:8990–94

11. Dennis, V. 1976. Influence of bicarbonate on parathyroid hormone induced changes in fluid reabsorption by the proximal tubule. *Kidney Int.* 10:373–80

12. Dolson, G. M., Hise, M. K., Weinman, E. J. 1985. Relationship among parathyroid hormone, cAMP, and calcium on proximal tubule sodium transport. *Am. J. Physiol.* 249(18):F409–16

12a. Elbrecht, A., DiRenzo, J., Smith, R., Shenolikar, S. 1990. Molecular cloning of the cDNA for protein phosphatase inhibitor-1 and its expression in rat and rabbit tissue. *J. Biol. Chem.* 265:13415–18

13. Felder, C. C., Campbell, T., Albrecht, F., Jose, P. 1990. Dopamine inhibits Na$^+$-H$^+$ exchanger activity in renal BBM by stimulation of adenylate cyclase. *Am. J. Physiol.* 259(28):F297–303

14. Freiberg, J. M., Kinsella, J., Sacktor, B. 1982. Glucocorticoids increase the Na$^+$-H$^+$ exchange and decrease the Na$^+$ gradient dependent phosphate uptake systems in renal brush border membranes. *Proc. Natl. Acad. Sci. USA* 79:4932–36

15. Friedman, P. A., Figueiredo, J. F., Windhager, E. E. 1981. Sodium-calcium interactions in the renal proximal

convoluted tubule of the rabbit. *Am. J. Physiol.* 240(9):F558–68

16. Friedrich, T., Sablotni, J., Burckhardt, G. 1986. Identification of the renal Na$^+$-H$^+$ exchanger with N,N′-dicyclohexylcarbondiimide (DCCD) and amiloride analogues. *J. Membr. Biol.* 94: 253–66

17. Fukunaga, K., Seto, H., Takatsu, K., Tominaga, A., Miyamoto, E. 1986. Monoclonal antibody against a multifunctional calmodulin-dependent protein kinase from rat brain and the tissue distribution of the enzyme. *Biomed. Res.* 7:405–13

18. Grinstein, S., Clark, C. A., Rothstein, A. 1983. Activation of Na$^+$-H$^+$ exchange in lymphocytes by osmotically induced volume changes and by cytoplasmic acidification. *J. Gen. Physiol.* 82:619–38

19. Grinstein, S., Furuya, W. 1984. Amiloride-sensitive Na$^+$/H$^+$ exchange in human neutrophils: Mechanism of activation by chemotactic factors. *Biochem. Biophys. Res. Commun.* 122:755–62

20. Grinstein, S., Rothstein, A. 1986. Mechanisms of regulation of the Na$^+$-H$^+$ exchanger. *J. Membr. Biol.* 90:1–12

21. Grinstein, S., Rothstein, A., Cohen, S. 1985. Mechanism of osmotic activation of the Na$^+$/H$^+$ exchange in rat thymic lymphocytes. *J. Gen. Physiol.* 85:765–87

22. Guntupalli, J., Phelps, R., Morell, G., Weinman, E. J. 1991. Role of protein kinase C (PKC) and cAMP in the regulation of Na-P$_i$ and Na$^+$-H$^+$ exchange in rat proximal tubular brush border membranes (BBM). *J. Am. Soc. Nephrol.* 1:576

23. Haggerty, J. G., Agarwal, N., Reilly, R. F., Adelberg, E. A., Slayman, C. W. 1988. Pharmacologically different antiporters on the apical and basolateral surfaces of cultured kidney cells (LLC-PK1). *Proc. Natl. Acad. Sci. USA* 85:6797–801

24. Hammerman, M. R. 1986. Phosphorylation of type II cAMP-dependent protein kinase in renal brush border membranes. *Am. J. Physiol.* 250 (19):F659–66

25. Hanley, R. M., Pollack, J., Steplock, D., Weinman, E. J. 1990. Identification of calcium-calmodulin multifunctional protein kinase II in rabbit kidney proximal convoluted tubule. *Kidney Int.* 38:63–66

26. Hanley, R. M., Weinman, E. J. 1991. The effect of phorbol esters on the expression of mRNA for the alpha

subunit of calcium/calmodulin dependent protein kinase II in rabbit proximal tubule. *Adv. Sec. Messengers Phosphoprotein Res.* 13:111–16

27. Hashimoto, Y., Soderling, T. R. 1987. Calcium calmodulin-dependent protein kinase II and calcium phospholipid-dependent protein kinase activities in rat tissues assayed with a synthetic peptide. *Arch. Biochem. Biophys.* 252:418–25

28. Hensley, C. B., Bradley, M. E., Mircheff, A. K. 1989. Parathyroid hormone-induced translocation of antiporters in rat proximal tubules. *Am. J. Physiol.* 257(26):C637–45

29. Hildebrant, F., Reilly, R. F., Sardet, C., Pouysségur, J., Slayman, C., et al. 1990. Cloning of a cDNA encoding a rabbit renal Na^+-H^+ exchanger. *Kidney Int.* 37:539 (Abstr.)

30. Horie, S., Moe, O., Miller, R. T., Alpern, R. J. 1992. Long-term activation of protein kinase C causes chronic Na/H antiporter stimulation in cultured proximal tubule cells. *J. Clin. Invest.* 89: 365–72

31. Howlin, K. J., Alpern, R. J., Rector, F. C. Jr. 1985. Amiloride inhibition of proximal tubular acidification. *Am. J. Physiol.* 248(17):F773–78

32. Hruska, K. A., Moskowitz, D., Esbrit, P., Civitelli, R., Westbrook, S., Huskey, M. 1987. Stimulation of inositol triphosphate and diacylglycerol production in renal tubular cells by parathyroid hormone. *J. Clin. Invest.* 79:230–39

33. Igarashi, P., Aronson, P. S. 1987. Covalent modification of the renal Na^+-H^+ exchanger by N,N'-dicyclohexylcarbodiimide. *J. Biol.Chem.* 262:860–68

34. Jacobson, H. R. 1979. Altered permeability in the proximal tubule response to cyclic AMP. *Am. J. Physiol.* 253:F71–79

35. Johnson, J. D., Epel, D., Paul, M. 1976. Intracellular pH and activation of sea urchin eggs after fertilization. *Nature* 262:661–64

36. Kahn, A. M., Dolson, G. M., Hise, M. K., Bennett, S. C., Weinman, E. J. 1985. Parathyroid hormone and dibutyryl cyclic AMP inhibit Na^+/H^+ countertransport in brush border membrane vesicles isolated from a suspension of rabbit proximal tubules. *Am. J. Physiol.* 248(17):F212–81

37. Kinsella, J. L., Aronson, P. S. 1980. Properties of the Na^+-H^+ exchanger in renal microvillus membrane vesicles. *Am. J. Physiol.* 238:F461–69

38. Kinsella, J. L., Sactor, B. 1985. Thyroid hormones increased Na^+-H^+ exchange activity in renal brush border membranes. *Proc. Natl. Acad. Sci. USA* 82:3606–10

39. Krapf, R., Solioz, M. 1991. Na^+/H^+ antiporter mRNA expression in single nephron segments of rat kidney cortex. *J. Clin. Invest.* 88:783–88

40. L'Allemain, G., Franchi, A., Cragoe, E. Jr., Pouysségur, J. 1984. Blockade of the Na^+-H^+ antiport abolishes growth factor-induced DNA synthesis in fibroblasts. *J. Biol. Chem.* 259: 4313–19

41. Liu, F., Cogan, M. G. 1988. Angiotensin II stimulation of hydrogen ion secretion in the early proximal tubule. *J. Clin. Invest.* 82:601–7

42. Liu, F., Cogan, M. G. 1989. Angiotensin II stimulates early proximal bicarbonate reabsorption in the rat by decreasing cyclic adenosine monophosphate. *J. Clin. Invest.* 84:83–91

43. Lorentz, W. B. Jr. 1974. The effect of cyclic AMP and dibutyryl cyclic AMP on the permeability characteristics of the renal tubule. *J. Clin. Invest.* 55:1250–57

44. Lorentz, W. B. Jr. 1976. Effect of parathyroid hormone on renal tubular permeability. *Am. J. Physiol.* 231: 1401–7

45. Mahnensmith, R. L., Aronson, P. S. 1985. The plasma membrane sodium-hydrogen exchanger and its role in physiological and pathophysiological processes. *Circ. Res.* 57:773–88

46. McKinney, T. D., Meyers, P. 1980. Bicarbonate transport by proximal tubules: Effect of parathyroid hormone and dibutyryl cyclic AMP. *Am. J. Physiol.* 238:F166–79

47. Means, A. R., Tash, J. S., Chafouleas, J. G. 1982. Physiological implications of the presence, distribution, and regulation of calmodulin in eucaryotic cells. *Physiol. Rev.* 62:1–39

48. Mellas, J., Hammerman, M. . 1986. Phorbol ester-induced alkalinization of canine renal proximal tubular cells. *Am. J. Physiol.* 250(19):F451–59

49. Moolenaar, W. H., Tsien, R. Y., van der Saag, P. T., de Laat, S. W. 1983. Na^+/H^+ exchange and cytoplasmic pH in the action of growth factors in human fibroblasts. *Nature* 304:645–48

50. Moran, A. M., Montrose, M. H., Murer, H. 1988. Regulation of Na^+-H^+ exchange in cultured opossum kidney cells by parathyroid hormone, atrial natriuretic peptide and cyclic nucleo-

tides. *Biochim. Biophys. Acta* 969:49–56

51. Morell, G., Guntupalli, J., Phelps, R., Weinman, E. J. 1990. Regulation of the Na-P$_i$ transporter in rat proximal tubular brush border membranes (BBM) by protein kinase C and PTH. *Clin. Res.* 38:315A (Abstr.)

52. Murer, H., Hopfer, U., Kinne, R. 1976. Sodium/proton antiport in brush border membrane vesicles isolated from rat small intestine and kidney. *Biochem. J.* 154:597–604

53. Nishizuka, Y. 1984. The role of protein kinase C in cell surface signal transduction and tumor promotion. *Nature* 308:693–97

54. Pearce, D., Krapf, R., Rector, F. C., Reudelhuber, T. L. 1990. Cloning of a partial length rat kidney cDNA homologous to the human Na$^+$/H$^+$ antiporter. *Kidney Int.* 37:233 (Abstr.)

55. Pollock, A. S., Warnock, D. G., Strewler, G. J. 1986. Parathyroid hormone inhibition of Na$^+$-H$^+$ antiporter activity in cultured renal cell line. *Am. J. Physiol.* 250(19):F217–25

56. Pouysségur, J., Franchi, A., L'Allemain, G., Paris, S. 1985. Cytoplasmic pH, a key determinant of growth factor-induced DNA synthesis in quiescent fibroblasts. *FEBS Lett.* 190:115–19

57. Preisig, P. A., Rector, F. C. Jr. 1988. Role of Na$^+$-H$^+$ antiport in rat proximal tubule NaCl absorption. *Am. J. Physiol.* 255(24):F461–65

58. Puschett, J. B., Zurbach, P., Sylk, D. 1976. Acute effects of parathyroid hormone on proximal bicarbonate transport in the dog. *Kidney Int.* 9:501–10

59. Quamme, G., Pfeilschiffer, J., Murer H. 1989. Parathyroid hormone inhibition of Na$^+$/phosphate cotransport in OK cells: requirement of protein kinase C-dependent pathway. *Biochim. Biophys. Acta* 1013(2):159–65

60. Reilly, R. F., Hildebrant, F., Sardet, C., Pouysségur, J., Adelberg, E., et al. 1990. Cloning of a cDNA encoding a Na$^+$/H$^+$ exchanger in LLC-PK1 cells. *Kidney Int.* 37:233 (Abstr.)

61. Ribeiro, C. P., Mandel, L. J. 1992. Parathyroid hormone inhibits proximal tubule Na$^+$-K$^+$-ATPase activity. *Am. J. Physiol.* 262(31):F209–16

62. Rosengurt, E. 1986. Early signals in the mitogenic response. *Science* 234:161–66

63. Rood, R. P., Emmer, E., Wesolek, J., McCullen, J., Husain, Z., et al. 1988. Regulation of the rabbit ileal brush-border Na$^+$-H$^+$ exchanger by ATP-requiring Ca^{2+}/calmodulin-mediated process. *J. Clin. Invest.* 82:1091–97

64. Ruiz, O., Arruda, J. A. L. 1990. Modulation of renal Na$^+$-HCO$_3$$^-$ cotransporter by protein kinases A and C. *Kidney Int.* 37:1:544 (Abstr.)

65. Sardet, C., Counillion, L., Franchi, A., Pouysségur, J. 1990. Growth factors induce phosphorylation of the Na$^+$-H$^+$ antiporter, a glycoprotein of 110 kD. *Science* 247:723–26

65a. Sardet, C., Franchi, A., Pouysségur, J. 1989. Molecular cloning, primary structure and expression of human growth factor-activatable Na$^+$-H$^+$ antiporter. *Cell* 56:271–80

66. Senekjian, H. O., Knight, T. F., Ince, A., Weinman, E. J. 1978. Effect of ionophore RO 2–2985 on the efflux of calcium from the rat nephron. *Am. J. Physiol.* 235(4):F381–84

67. Shenolikar, S., Fischer, K., Chang, L., Weinman, E. J. 1988. Type II cAMP-dependent protein kinase is associated with the rabbit kidney brush border membranes. *Adv. Sec. Messengers Phosphoprotein Res.* 12:95–104

67a. Shenolikar, S., Maim, A. 1991. Protein phosphatases: recent progress. *Adv. Sec. Messenger Phosphoprotein Res.* 23:1–121

68. Teitelbaum, I. 1990. Cyclic adenosine monophosphate and diacylglycerol. Mutually inhibitory second messengers in cultured rat inner medullary collecting duct cells. *J. Clin. Invest.* 86:46–51

69. Tobimatsu, T., Fujisawa, H. 1989. Tissue-specific expression of four types of rat calmodulin-dependent protein kinase II mRNAs. *J. Biol. Chem.* 264:17907–12

70. Tsai, C. J., Ives, H. E., Alpern, R. J., Yee, V. J., Warnock, D. G., Rector, F. C. 1984. Increased V$_{max}$ for Na/H antiporter activity in proximal tubule brush border vesicles from rabbits with metabolic acidosis. *Am. J. Physiol.* 247(16):F339–43

71. Villereal, M. L., Mix-Muldoon, L. L., Vincentini, L. M., Jamieson G. A. Jr., Owen N. 1986. Mechanisms of growth factor stimulation of Na$^+$-H$^+$ exchange in cultured fibroblasts. In *Current Topics in Membranes and Transport,* ed. P. S. Aronson, W. Boron, 26:175–92. New York: Academic

72. Wang, T., Chan, Y. L. 1990. Time-and dose-dependent effects of protein kinase C on proximal bicarbonate transport. *J Membr. Biol.* 117:131–39

73. Weinman, E. J., Bennett, S. C., Brady, R. C., Harper, J. F., Hise, M. K.,

Kahn, A. M. 1984. Effect of cAMP and calmodulin inhibitors on water absorption in rat proximal tubule. *Proc. Soc. Exp. Biol. Med.* 176:322–26

74. Weinman, E. J., Corry, D., Steplock, D., Shenolikar, S. 1992. Western immunoblot analysis of rabbit renal BBM and BLM using polyclonal antibodies to the cloned "housekeeping" Na^+-H^+ exchanger. *J. Am. Soc. Nephrol.* (Abstr.) In press

75. Weinman, E. J., Dubinsky, W. P., Dinh, Q., Steplock, D., Shenolikar, S. 1989. The effect of limited trypsin digestion on the renal Na^+-H^+ exchanger and it regulation by cAMP dependent protein kinase. *J. Membr. Biol.* 109:233–41

76. Weinman, E. J., Dubinsky, W. P., Fischer, K., Steplock, D., Dinh, Q., et al. 1988. Regulation of reconstituted renal Na^+-H^+ exchanger by calcium dependent protein kinases. *J. Membr. Biol.* 103:237–44

77. Weinman, E. J., Dubinsky, W. P., Shenolikar, S. 1988. Reconstitution of cAMP-dependent protein kinase regulated renal Na^+-H^+ exchanger. *J. Membr. Biol.* 101:11–18

78. Weinman, E. J., Dubinsky, W., Shenolikar, S. 1989. Regulation of the renal Na^+-H^+ exchanger by protein phosphorylation. *Kidney Int.* 36:519–25

79. Weinman, E. J., Hanley, R. M., Morell, G., Shenolikar, S. 1990. Calcium-calmodulin dependent multifunctional protein kinase II (CaM-KII) inhibition of the rabbit renal brush border membrane (BBM) Na^+-

H^+ exchanger. *Clin. Res.* 38:469A (Abstr.)

80. Weinman, E. J., Shenolikar, S. 1986. Protein kinase C activates the renal apical membrane Na^+-H^+ exchanger. *J. Membr. Biol.* 93:133–39

81. Weinman, E. J., Shenolikar, S., Cragoe, E. J. Jr., Dubinsky, W. P. 1988. Solubilization and reconstitution of renal brush border Na^+-H^+ exchanger. *J. Membr. Biol.* 101:1–9

82. Weinman, E. J., Shenolikar, S., Kahn, A. M. 1987. cAMP-associated inhibition of Na^+-H^+ exchanger in rabbit kidney brush-border membranes. *Am. J. Physiol.* 252(21):F19–25

83. Weinman, E. J., Steplock, D., Bui, G., Yuan, N., Shenolikar, S. 1990. Regulation of the renal Na^+-H^+ exchanger by cAMP dependent protein kinase. *Am. J. Physiol.* 258(27):F1254–58

84. Weinman, E. J., Steplock, D., Shenolikar, S. 1991. Studies of the regulatory protein mediating cAMP dependent protein kinase (PKA) inhibition of the renal BBM Na^+-H^+ exchanger. *J. Am. Soc. Nephrol.* (Abstr.) In press

85. Wirthensohn, G., Guder, W. G. 1985. Stimulation of phospholipid turnover by angiotensin II and phenylephrine in proximal convoluted tubules microdissected from mouse nephron. *Pflügers Arch.* 404:94–96

86. Yang, J. M., Lee, C. O., Windhager, E. E. 1988. Regulation of cytosolic free calcium in isolated perfused proximal tubules of *Necturus*. *Am. J. Physiol.* 255(24):F787–99

Annu. Rev. Physiol. 1993. 55:305–21

ROLE OF GROWTH FACTORS IN REGULATION OF RENAL GROWTH

Marc R. Hammerman, Michael O'Shea, and Steven B. Miller

George M. O'Brien Kidney and Urological Diseases Center, Renal Division, Departments of Internal Medicine, Cell Biology, and Physiology, Washington University School of Medicine, St. Louis, Missouri 63110

KEY WORDS: epidermal growth factor, fibroblast growth factor, hepatocyte growth factor, insulin-like growth factor, nerve growth factor, platelet-derived growth factor, transforming growth factor-α, transforming growth factor-β

INTRODUCTION

The kidney is a "target" organ for a number of polypeptide growth factors. Certain of these peptides interact with sensitive renal cells as classical endocrine hormones. Others are produced within the kidney and exert actions on the cell of origin or on adjacent cells in an autocrine or paracrine fashion. A number of studies support roles for one or more of these agents as causative of the increase in renal size and changes in renal function that occur in conditions such as hypersomatotropism, compensatory hypertrophy, and diabetes mellitus. Growth factors are thought to mediate adaptations in renal function that occur in chronic reduction of functional renal mass and to promote regeneration following acute renal injury. While the adaptations induced by growth factors are probably initially salutary, the effects of continuing renal growth factor expression may be maladaptive. In addition to their roles in kidneys of the adult, polypeptide growth factors regulate renal growth and development during embryogenesis. Any understanding of the biology of growth factors in kidney, requires a detailed knowledge of renal anatomy, renal physiology, renal embryology, and the biochemistry, cellular, and molecular biology of polypeptide growth factors. The purpose of this review is to summarize what is known about growth factor participation in processes of kidney growth, regulation of renal function, repair following

305

renal injury, and nephrogenesis within the context of the cellular and molecular biology of these growth promoting agents.

Growth Factor Families of Importance in Renal Tissue

The polypeptide growth factors/growth factor families, the physiology of which within kidney is best characterized, are the insulin-like growth factors (IGFs) (13, 48), epidermal growth factor/transforming growth factor-α (EGF/TGF-α) (19, 32, 70), transforming growth factor-β (TGF-β) (10, 92, 106), platelet-derived growth factor (PDGF) (62, 98, 106), fibroblast growth factor (FGF) (8, 18, 40, 90, 106), nerve growth factor (NGF) (9, 68, 114), and hepatocyte growth factor (HGF) (79, 80).

IGFS I AND II   IGF I is a single chain insulin-like polypeptide that is 70 amino acids in length. It circulates in tight non-covalent association with specific carrier proteins. The functions of the carrier proteins are incompletely defined. In vitro, one or another carrier protein has been shown to function as both agonist and antagonist for the biological activity of IGF I. IGF I is the major growth hormone (GH)-dependent growth factor. It is produced in several tissues in a GH-dependent manner. The collecting duct is a major source of IGF I production within the adult kidney (13). Both GH (94) and EGF (95) enhance IGF I production at this site. IGF I is also produced by glomerular mesangial cells in culture (4, 23). IGF-binding proteins are synthesized within the kidney (1, 63). Receptors for IGF I are present in glomeruli (3, 4, 23) and on the basolateral membrane of the renal proximal tubular cell (50). IGF II is slightly smaller than IGF I (67 amino acids). It also circulates in tight non-covalent association with the carrier proteins that bind IGF I. Because levels of IGF II mRNA in all tissues, except neural tissue, and levels of circulating IGF II fall precipitously in rodents following birth, it has been postulated that IGF II functions predominantly as a fetal growth factor. However, no such fall occurs in humans, consistent with a role for IGF II in adult physiology (48). IGF II receptors are present in glomeruli (56) and in both basolateral and brush border membranes of the proximal tubular cell (50).

EGF/TGF-α   EGF and TGF-α are members of the same growth factor family and are thought to act via the same membrane receptor. EGF is a 53 amino acid peptide. Tissue levels are highest in the salivary gland of adult mammals followed by the kidney. In humans, EGF was first purified from urine. The high levels in urine (5×10^{-10} M), compared to blood ($< 10^{-12}$M), suggest that the kidney is the source of urinary EGF. Both EGF and TGF-α precursor proteins contain hydrophobic membrane-spanning regions that anchor them to plasma membranes. The portions that contain mature EGF and TGF-α are located extracellularly (19, 70). Newly synthesized EGF and TGF-α precursors appear to be resistant to cleavage until they reach the plasma membrane. The precursor peptides are biologically active. Therefore, cleavage is not aimed at generating active hormone, but at switching between two active forms, one that is membrane bound and the other that is diffusible. A novel mode of intercellular communication is established by the binding of a membrane-anchored growth factor on one cell to its receptor on an adjacent cell. This form of stimulation has been termed juxtacrine stimulation (70). Whereas the submaxillary gland rapidly processes prepro-EGF to the 53 amino acid form, the precursor accumulates in the kidney. The distal tubule and medullary thick ascending limb of Henle's loop are the predominant sites of EGF production within the adult kidney (32). Glomeruli, proximal tubules, medullary interstitial cells, and the collecting duct all have EGF receptors (16, 122). These receptors are present in the basolateral membranes of the tubular epithelial cells (53, 119). Studies characterizing the localization of immunostainable EGF within the adult kidney show it to be localized to the luminal membrane of distal tubular cells under most conditions (32). The positive immunostaining probably represents prepro-EGF. The peptide must bind to receptors present in the antiluminal membrane of sensitive renal cells to exert biological activity. Recently it was shown that a redistribution of EGF immunoactivity occurs within the distal tubule in a condition under which its synthesis is enhanced, i.e. compensatory renal hypertrophy, such that it is present at both luminal and antiluminal membranes. Such a redistribution of precursor peptide might permit cleavage of mature EGF from basolateral membranes and release of mature peptide into the renal interstitium where it could interact with basolateral membrane receptors (74).

TGF-β   The TGF-β-related family of polypeptides includes a group of closely homologous dimeric proteins and a group of more distantly-related polypeptides. The former include five distinct molecular forms designated TGF-β 1–5. The latter include mullerian-inhibiting substance, the inhibins, and activins. Each member of the TGF-β group is first synthesized as a larger precursor polypeptide. The precursor molecule as well as the mature peptide has biological activity. The mature TGF-β1 polypeptide consists of two identical disulfide-linked monomers each 112 amino acids in length (10, 92). The biological actions of TGF-β in vitro are diverse. They include stimulation or inhibition of proliferation, blocking or initiation of differentiation, stimulation of extracellular matrix formation, and promotion or inhibition of cell migration. Among the most striking effects of TGF-β is its promotion of extracellular matrix formation. These actions suggest that TGF-β functions in the regulation of processes characterized by extensive tissue remodeling (10, 92). TGF-β1 has been localized to the distal tubule of mouse kidney using immunohistochemistry (115). However, the largest quantities of bio-logically active peptide are extractable from glomeruli of rat kidney, and TGF-β1 and β-2 mRNAs are localized in glomeruli consistent with synthesis at this site (66).

PDGF   PDGF is a potent mitogen for cells of connective tissue origin and is thought to play a role in wound healing when released from platelets at the site of injury. The mature growth factor is a dimer, consisting of A and B chains. The genes for A and B chains are located on separate chromosomes. Both A and B chains are synthesized as larger precursors that are processed to mature proteins extractable from tissues as AB heterodimers and smaller amounts of AA and BB homodimers. The oncogene of simian sarcoma virus (v-sis) directs the synthesis of a PDGF BB homologue (62, 98). In the kidney, both glomerular mesangial (108) and renal epithelial cells (62) synthesize PDGF. Production of PDGF mRNA can be induced in human mesangial cells by PDGF itself, EGF, and TGF-α (109). Both cultured Wilms' tumor cells and human fetal kidney cells produce PDGF, consistent with a role for the polypeptide in normal fetal growth and in neoplastic renal cell transformation (37).

FGF   The FGFs are part of a large family of heparin-binding peptides with mitogenic and angiogenic properties. Two separate FGFs, acidic and basic FGF, have been isolated. Acidic FGF is a 140-amino acid single-chain peptide. Basic FGF is composed of 146 amino acids. The two FGFs exhibit greater than 50% homology (18, 81). Both possess two potential binding domains for heparin. While heparin augments the mitogenic activity of acidic FGF, it does not affect that of basic FGF. FGF expression has been detected in a variety of normal and transformed cells in vitro, and both acidic FGF and basic FGF have been isolated from bovine kidney (8, 40).

NGF   The NGF family of growth factors including NGF, brain-derived neurotrophic factor (BDNF), and neurotrophin 3 (NT-3) are important for development and maintenance of neurons (68, 114). A role for one or more of these members of the NGF family in renal tissue is suggested by the presence of receptors for NGF in the glomerulus (20) and mRNA for NT-3 in kidney (68). There is evidence that collecting duct (9) and bladder parenchymal cells (110) can synthesize NGF. NGF immunoreactivity has been localized in mouse to the apical and perinuclear cytoplasm of cells within the collecting tubule of the distal nephron. Intercalated cells lack immunoreactivity (9).

HGF   HGF was first identified in the serum of partially hepatectomized rats and was purified to homogeneity from rat platelets (82). The peptide is a heterodimer consisting of a 68-kd α-subunit and a 34-kd β-subunit. It has a 38% homology with plasminogen, but appears to be related to no other growth factor (80, 81). HGF is produced by cells of mesenchymal origin such as Kupffer cells in the liver and human embryonic lung fibroblasts (113). Receptors for HGF are present in renal plasma membranes. HGF mRNA has been localized within the kidney to endothelial cells that are located between renal tubules (79).

Regulation of Renal Metabolism, Filtration, and Transport by Growth Factors

Several growth factors have been shown to regulate renal metabolic or transport processes in vitro and to control glomerular filtration and renal plasma flow when administered to humans or experimental animals. For example, IGF I stimulates gluconeogenesis in isolated proximal tubular segments (93), enhances phosphate transport in proximal tubule (89), and increases glomerular filtration rate and renal plasma flow when administered systemically to rats (64) or humans (46). IGF II enhances Na^+-H^+ exchange in proximal tubular segments (72). EGF inhibits vasopressin-stimulated hydraulic conductivity (52) and Na^+ reabsorption (119) in isolated-perfused collecting tubule, inhibits gluconeogenesis in proximal tubule in vitro (53), and decreases glomerular filtration rate and renal plasma flow in rats (54). The roles of these growth factors as physiological modulators of metabolic, filtration, and transport processes are not delineated. It is possible that one or more of these agents are important controllers. Alternatively, their effects on these processes may not represent primary regulation, but rather could reflect changes that accompany or mediate the promotion of growth.

Regulation of Renal Growth by Growth Factors

The growth of the kidney that occurs under several conditions is accompanied by enhanced expression of one or more growth factors within the organ. The enhanced synthesis of these agents that occurs in the setting of growth suggests that a causal relationship exists between the two events. The three conditions in which growth factor expression within the kidney has been best studied within the context of renal growth are hypersomatotropism, compensatory renal hypertrophy, and diabetes mellitus.

HYPERSOMATOTROPISM   It has been recognized for over four decades that GH is a renotropin. Hypopituitary humans have small kidneys (29) and acromegalics manifest nephromegaly, which reflects predominantly hypertrophy of glomeruli and proximal tubules (41, 42). Growth hormone increases glomerular filtration rate and renal plasma flow (46, 60, 73). The somatotropic actions of GH as well as its effects on renal function are believed to be mediated by IGF I (64, 73). Levels of circulating IGF I are increased by GH, as are levels of IGF I mRNA and IGF I produced within kidney (75). Whether the renal hypertrophy and hyperfunction that occur in the setting of hypersomatotropism result from the action of circulating IGF I, IGF I of renal origin, or both is not known. A predominant role for IGF I produced within kidney is suggested by the observation that a similar hypertrophy of glomeruli and proximal tubules occurs in compensatory hypertrophy and diabetes mellitus, where renal IGF I production is enhanced, but levels of circulating peptide are not elevated.

COMPENSATORY HYPERTROPHY   The compensatory growth of the contralateral kidney, which follows loss of a kidney in humans and unilateral nephrectomy of experimental animals, is demonstrable within 1–2 days. As in hypersomatotropism, the growth involves primarily the glomerulus and proximal tubule. In adult animals, most of the increase in kidney size following uninephrectomy can be ascribed to hypertrophy of cells. In young animals, hyperplasia is more pronounced (31). Compensatory renal growth in mice (61) and rats (27, 28, 36, 65, 74, 111) is accompanied by increased levels of IGF I and of EGF within the collecting duct (65) and distal tubule (61), respectively. Such findings have prompted speculation that one or both of these growth factors is a renotropic agent under these conditions. There is controversy as to whether the increases in renal IGF I or EGF content occur prior to (36, 61) or following (28, 65, 74, 111) the onset of growth. If the former is true, one or both of these peptides may indeed function as primary renotropic agents. If the latter is the case, it would be difficult to attribute such a role to either agent, at least for the early stages of kidney growth. The increase of renal IGF I is not accompanied by a concomitant change in levels of IGF I mRNA in hypertrophied kidneys of uninephrectomized adult rats (65, 76). However, levels of IGF I mRNA do increase in hypertrophied kidneys of young rats, consistent with age-dependent mechanisms by which expression of the peptide is enhanced (76). Administration of a long-acting somatostatin analogue to uninephrectomized rats prevents both the increase in renal IGF I content and compensatory growth (35). Binding of IGF I and IGF II to kidney membranes and levels of IGF I and IGF II receptor mRNA in whole kidney are increased following unilateral nephrectomy of immature rats, but not adult rats (69, 77). These findings suggest that, at least in young rats, increased binding of IGFs in addition to increased IGF synthesis may stimulate kidney growth. Levels of circulating IGF I do not change in the setting of compensatory hypertrophy (65, 111). A role for GH in compensatory renal growth has been postulated because hypophysectomy inhibits the compensatory response (31). However, compensatory enlargement and increases in renal IGF I content do occur in hypophysectomized rats (111) and in GH-deficient rats (27), consistent with a GH-independent process by which growth is mediated. Levels of HGF mRNA in kidney and HGF activity extractable from kidney are increased within 1 day of unilateral nephrectomy in the rat. The changes in HGF mRNA and HGF activity precede the initial peak of DNA synthesis consistent with a role for this growth factor as an initiator of compensatory renal growth (79).

DIABETES MELLITUS   The onset of diabetes mellitus in humans and in experimental animals is accompanied by a rapid increase in renal mass and enhanced glomerular filtration rate and renal plasma flow. The kidney from diabetic rats is characterized morphologically by early glomerular hypertrophy followed by an increase in proximal tubular cell size (104, 107). Because levels of circulating GH are elevated in humans with diabetes mellitus, it has been implicated as causative of the renal hyperfunction and hypertrophy in this state (51). However, levels of circulating GH as well as IGF I are reduced in diabetic rats (112). Therefore, the changes that occur in this species cannot be attributed to hypersomatotropism. Flyvbjerg and co-workers have demonstrated an increase in renal IGF I within 1 day following induction of diabetes mellitus in rats. Levels returned to baseline within 4 days (36). The increase in IGF I as well as the enhancement in kidney size can be prevented by insulin-treatment of diabetic rats or by administration of a long-acting somatostatin analogue, consistent with a causal relationship between enhanced renal IGF I expression and renal growth (34). Although levels of IGF I peptide are elevated, levels of IGF I mRNA in kidneys are not increased following induction of diabetes mellitus (33). However, levels of IGF I and IGF II receptor mRNA as well as binding of IGF I and IGF II to renal membranes are enhanced (121). Bach & Jerums reported reduced and retarded renal growth and no change in renal IGF I content following induction of diabetes mellitus in prepubertal rats, in contrast to marked growth and increased IGF I in postpubertal animals, consistent with an age-dependent regulation of IGF I expression (7). Observations relating to renal EGF production in diabetes mellitus are contradictory in terms of implicating a role for EGF in diabetic renal growth. EGF excretion in urine falls progressively in diabetic humans (24). Urinary EGF is elevated early following induction of diabetes with streptozotocin in rats. This increase is prevented by insulin-treatment. The elevation in urinary EGF is not accompanied by a concomitant increase in EGF extractable from kidneys (45).

Participation of Growth Factors in Adaptations that Result from Reduction of Functional Renal Mass

CHRONIC RENAL FAILURE   Chronic renal failure is characterized by a series of adaptations in the surviving nephrons of the diseased kidney that allow for maintenance of glomerular filtration and tubular reabsorptive functions (17). Roles for GH-IGF I in mediating some of these adaptations are suggested by a number of observations. Administration of GH to humans or experimental animals with normal renal function increases glomerular filtration rate and renal plasma flow (46, 64). These changes are not mediated directly by GH, but rather by IGF I. A relative resistance of kidney to GH-IGF I is present in the setting of renal disease. The action of GH to enhance glomerular filtration rate in humans with normal renal function cannot be demonstrated in adults or children with chronic renal failure (47, 116, 117). Furthermore, administration of GH or IGF I to rats with reduced functional renal mass does not add to the enhancement of glomerular filtration rate that occurs spontaneously in response to the reduction (73). The renal resistance to GH-IGF I is in contrast to the effectiveness of GH in regulating metabolic events in non-renal tissues of humans (47) or animals (71) with reduced functional renal mass, and to its action as a growth enhancer in children with end-stage kidney failure (116, 117) and in uremic rats (71). The renal resistance to GH-IGF I in the setting of reduced functional renal mass could be explained, at least in part, by dependence on locally-produced IGF I for the adaptations in renal function. The kidney content of IGF I does increase after reduction of renal mass in the rat (28, 36, 65, 111). If IGF I produced in kidney causes the elevation of glomerular filtration rate induced by a reduction in renal mass per se, and if IGF I production in kidney is stimulated by reduction in renal mass such that its effect on glomerular filtration rate is maximal, then neither exogenous GH nor IGF I would be expected to further enhance glomerular filtration rate.

ACUTE RENAL FAILURE   Damaged portions of the nephron undergo regeneration after acute injury. The roles of IGF I and EGF in this process have been examined. Within 3 days following induction of acute ischemic injury in rats, regenerating tubular cells expressing IGF I immunoreactivity can be detected in the damaged S3 region of the proximal tubule. The origin of the cells is uncertain. The cells disappear from the proximal tubule when regeneration is complete, consistent with a role for transiently produced IGF I in the regenerative process (2). The renal synthesis of EGF falls rapidly following induction of acute ischemic injury in the rat. The expression of EGF-precursor mRNA is reduced by 60% at 2 hr post-injury, and the mRNA is undetectable by 24 hr. Urinary EGF excretion falls immediately following induction of ischemia before the decline in EGF-precursor mRNA. EGF excretion returns to only 50% of normal by day 21 (99, 100). Specific binding of ^{125}I-EGF is increased in membrane fractions of renal cortex, inner medulla, and outer medulla within 24 hr after induction of ischemia. Within the cortex, binding capacity is enhanced in the proximal tubule, but not in the glomerulus. The increase in binding may play a role in the regenerative response (99). Enhanced immunoreactivity of EGF is present in the basolateral membrane of rat proximal tubular cells following amikacin-induced acute tubular necrosis, consistent with enhanced binding at this site following drug-induced acute renal failure (118). Administration of EGF to rats has been shown to accelerate recovery from acute ischemic renal injury (58, 83) and from mercuric-chloride-induced acute renal failure (21). The mechanism by which EGF enhances recovery is undetermined.

Maladaptive Effects of Growth Factors in Kidney

INDUCTION OF GLOMERULOSCLEROSIS AND GLOMERULONEPHRITIS   Glomerulosclerosis accompanies hypersomatotropism in rats (25, 75, 88), although not in humans (42). While this condition is observed in rats transgenic for GH, it does not occur in rats transgenic for IGF I, which suggests that the glomerulosclerotic actions of GH are mediated independently of IGF I synthesis (25, 88). Elevated expression of TGF-β1 occurs in glomeruli of rats with experimental glomerulonephritis induced by injection of anti-thymocyte serum (84). Administration to rats of anti-TGF-β1 antiserum at the time of induction of the glomerular disease suppresses the increased production of extracellular matrix and attenuates the histological manifestations of the disease (12). These observations support a causal role for TGF-β1 in the pathogenesis of this model of glomerulonephritis. A role for TGF-β has also been postulated in the pathogenesis of anti-glomerular basement membrane disease in the rabbit (22). PDGF may play a major role in the pathophysiology of glomerulonephritis. In both experimental and human proliferative glomerulonephritis, PDGF and PDGF receptors are up-regulated (30, 44). Expressions of PDGF A-chain and B-chain mRNA, and PDGF receptor β-subunit mRNA and protein are increased in glomeruli of rats with mesangial proliferative nephritis (123). The increase in PDGF B-chain-positive cells is localized to areas of hypercellularity and is associated with an increase in immunostainable PDGF. Complement depletion, which prevents the mesangial cell proliferation, also prevents the enhanced expression of PDGF and its receptor. The identity of the cells within glomeruli that express PDGF B-chain mRNA is uncertain. However, it is suggested that PDGF is produced by a subpopulation of mesangial cells and that the growth factor may act as an autocrine agent in the setting of mesangial proliferative nephritis (59).

Regulation of Metanephric Growth and Development by Polypeptide Growth Factors

An enlarging body of experimental findings documents the participation of several growth factors in the metanephrogenic process. This topic has been recently reviewed (5, 15, 49) and is discussed only briefly here. The metanephric anlage consists initially of two components, the metanephric blastema and the ureteric bud. The metanephric blastema differentiates into all tubular components of the nephron with the exception of the collecting duct. The anlage of collecting duct and the collecting system is the ureteric bud. Growth and differentiation of the metanephric blastema as well as the ureteric bud are dependent on mutual inductive events, the nature of which is unknown (102). A role for one or more polypeptide growth factors has been postulated in one or both inductive processes. No single polypeptide growth factor can induce differentiation of metanephric blastema in vitro, although EGF can be shown to stimulate undifferentiated mesenchymal cells to become stromal cells (120). However, pituitary extract and EGF in concert with a collagen, fibronectin, or laminin matrix can promote tubulogenesis of rat metanephric blastema. Preliminary characterization of the factor in pituitary extract that induces tubulogenesis in combination with EGF is consistent with a protein of M_r 100,000–300,000 (86). It has been established that IGF I (96), IGF II (96), TGF-α (97), and TGF-β (103) are produced in the developing metanephros. IGF I, IGF II, and TGF-α are essential for growth and development of rat metanephric anlage in vitro (96, 97). TGF-β appears to play an inhibitory role in the metanephrogenic process (6). Heparin-binding FGF-like factors produced by metanephric kidney may play a role in nephron vascularization during kidney development (91). A role for NGF in metanephrogenesis is suggested by findings that NGF receptors are transiently synthesized by rat metanephroi in organ culture and disappear from nephrons upon terminal differentiation. Inhibition of NGF receptor expression in developing kidneys by inclusion of antisense oligonucleotides in metanephric cultures inhibits kidney morphogenesis (101).

The Wilms' Tumor Gene Product, Growth Factors, and Kidney Development

Wilms' tumor is a renal malignancy of complex pathology that manifests itself in young children, and constitutes 25% of the tumors found in this population. The embryonic origin of Wilms' tumor is the metanephric blastema (11, 14, 78). Wilms' tumor cells have undergone a deletion of genes located on chromosome 11p13. Recently, mRNA transcripts that are expressed in kidney and map to the Wilms' tumor deletion region have been defined. One cDNA clone (WT1) has characteristics of a tumor-supressor gene and encodes a protein that contains four zinc fingers and a glutamine and proline-rich amino terminus, structural motifs that are associated with binding to DNA and transcriptional-regulatory functions. In fact, the WT1 gene product does repress transcription (67). The WT1 gene is expressed in condensing mesenchyme and in tubular and glomerular epithelia of the developing kidney, consistent with a function in normal kidney differentiation (85, 87). It is possible that the zinc finger protein encoded by the Wilms' tumor locus regulates the pattern of growth factor expression involved in kidney organogenesis. It is well documented that Wilms' tumor tissue expresses high levels of IGF II (55). IGF II mRNA has been localized to the most primitive tumor cells. Adjacent, relatively differentiated epithelial cells show a relative absence of expression (57). Recently, it was shown that the WT1 protein effects transcriptional repression of the IGF II gene (26). Receptors for IGF I are found in Wilms' tumors (38). Antibodies to the IGF I receptor inhibit the growth of Wilms' tumor cells in vitro and of tumors transplanted to athymic mice, consistent with a role for IGF I in oncogenesis (39). In view of the role of metanephric-derived IGF I and IGF II in metanephrogenesis, derangements of their expression could result in neoplastic transformation of the metanephric blastema. Since cultured Wilms' tumor cells also produce PDGF, a role for this growth factor in the pathogenesis of the malignancy is suggested (37).

SUMMARY AND CONCLUSIONS

It is clear that a number of growth factors are synthesized within the adult and the developing kidney. Compelling evidence exists that several of these agents orchestrate the nephrogenic process. A growing body of data supports roles for one or more of these agents in the adult kidney as regulators of renal function, growth, and repair processes. Growth factor expression may be the cause of glomerulosclerosis in one or more pathophysiological states. Our knowledge of the sites of growth factor synthesis and actions in the kidney and of the mechanisms by which growth factor synthesis is regulated and actions are exerted is rudimentary. Expansion of this knowledge base is likely to result in a greater understanding of renal disease mechanisms and thereby generate strategies by which kidney damage can be halted, prevented, or reversed.

ACKNOWLEDGMENTS

We acknowledge the administrative assistance of Ms. Lynn Wesselmann. M. R. Hammerman was supported by National Institutes of Health grants

DK-27600, DK-45181, DK-07126, and DK-20579, by Grant-In-Aid 91006660 from the American Heart Association and by grant 191541 from the Juvenile Diabetes Foundation. M. O. S. was supported in part by National Institutes of Health grant DK-07126. S. B. M. was supported by a Clinician-Scientist Award from the American Heart Association.

Literature Cited

1. Albiston, A. L., Herington, A. C. 1992. Tissue distribution and regulation of insulin-like growth factor (IGF)-binding protein-3 messenger ribonucleic acid (mRNA) in the rat: Comparison with IGF-I mRNA Expression. *Endocrinology* 130:497–502

2. Andersson, G., Jennische, E. 1988. IGF-I immunoreactivity is expressed by regenerating renal tubular cells after ischemic injury in the rat. *Acta Physiol. Scand.* 132:453–57

3. Arnqvist, H. J., Ballermann, B. J., King, G. L. 1988. Receptors for and effects of insulin and IGF-I in rat glomerular mesangial cells. *Am. J. Physiol.* 254: C411–16

4. Aron, D. C., Rosenzweig, J. L., Abboud, H. E. 1989. Synthesis and binding of insulin-like growth factor I by human glomerular mesangial cells. *J. Clin. Endocrinol.* 68:585–91

5. Avner, E. 1990. Polypeptide growth factors and the kidney: A developmental perspective. *Pediatr. Nephrol.* 4:345–53

6. Avner, E. D., Sweeney, W. E. Jr. 1990. Polypeptide growth factors in metanephric growth and segmental nephron differentiation. *Pediatr. Nephrol.* 4: 372–77

7. Bach, L. A., Jerums, G. 1990. Effect of puberty on initial kidney growth and rise in kidney IGF-I in diabetic rats. *Diabetes* 39:557–62

8. Baird, A., Esch, F., Bohlen, P., Ling, N., Gospodarowicz, D. 1985. Isolation and partial characterization of an endothelial cell growth factor from the bovine kidney: Homology with basic fibroblast growth factor. *Reg. Peptides* 12:201–13

9. Barajas, L., Salido, E. C., Laborde, N. P., Fisher, D. A. 1987. Nerve growth factor immunoreactivity in mouse kidney: An immunoelectron microscopic study. *J. Neurosci. Res.* 18: 418–24

10. Barnard, J. A., Lyons, R. M., Moses, H. L. 1990. The cell biology of transforming growth factor β. *Biochim. Biophys. Acta* 1032:79–87

11. Beckwith, J. B. 1983. Wilms' tumor and other renal tumors of childhood: A selective review from the National Wilms' Tumor Study Pathology Center. *Human Pathol.* 14:481–92

12. Border, W. A., Okuda, S., Languino, L. R., Sporn, M. B., Ruoslahti, E. 1990. Suppression of experimental glomerulonephritis by antiserum against transforming growth factor β1. *Nature* 346: 371–74

13. Bortz, J. D., Rotwein, P., DeVol, D., Bechtel, P. J., Hansen, V. A., et al. 1988. Focal expression of insulin-like growth factor I in rat kidney collecting duct. *Am. J. Physiol.* 107:811–19

14. Bove, K. E., McAdams, A. J. 1976. The nephroblastomatosis complex and its relationship to Wilms' tumor: A clinicopathologic treatise. In *Perspectives in Pediatric Pathology.* ed. H. S. Rosenberg, R. P. Bolande, 3:185–223. Chicago: Year Book Med.

15. Brenner, B. M. 1990. Determinants of epithelial differentiation during early nephrogenesis. *J. Am. Soc. Nephrol.* 1:127–39

16. Breyer, M. D., Redha, R., Breyer, J. A. 1990. Segmental distribution of epidermal growth factor binding sites in rabbit nephron. *Am. J. Physiol.* 259: F553–58

17. Bricker, N. S. 1972. On the pathogenesis of the uremic state. An exposition of the "trade-off hypothesis." *N. Engl. J. Med.* 286:1093–99

18. Burgess, W. H., Maciag, T. 1989. The heparin-binding (fibroblast) growth factorfamily of proteins. *Annu. Rev. Biochem.* 58:575–606

19. Carpenter, G., Cohen, S. 1990. Epidermal growth factor. *J. Biol. Chem.* 265:7709–12

20. Chesa, P. G., Rettig, W. J., Thomson, T. M., Old, L. J., Melamed, M. R. 1988. J. Immunohistochemical analysis of nerve growth factor receptor expression in normal and malignant human

tissues. *Histochem. Cytochem.* 36:383–89

21. Coimbra, T. M., Cieslinski, D. A., Humes, H. D. 1990. Epidermal growth factor accelerates renal repair in mercuric chloride nephrotoxicity. *Am. J. Physiol.* 59:F438–43

22. Coimbra, T., Wiggins, R., Noh, J. W., Merritt, S., Phan, S. H. 1991. Tranforming growth factor-β production in anti-glomerular basement membrane disease in the rabbit. *Am. J. Path.* 138:223–34

23. Conti, F. G., Striker, L. J., Elliot, S. J., Andreani, D., Striker, G. E. 1988. Synthesis and release of insulinlike growth factor I by mesangial cells in culture. *Am. J. Physiol.* 255:F1214–19

24. Dagogo-Jack, S., Marshall, S. M., Kendall-Taylor, P., Alberti, K. G. M. M. 1989. Urinary excretion of human epidermal growth factor in the various stages of diabetic nephropathy. *Clin. Endocrinol.* 31:167–73

25. Doi, T., Striker, L. J., Gibson, C. C., Agodoa, L. Y. C., Brinster, R. L., et al. 1990. Glomerular lesions in mice transgenic for growth hormone and insulinlike growth factor-I. *Am. J. Path.* 137:541–52

26. Drummond, I. A., Madden, S. L., Rohwer-Nutter, P., Bell, G. I., Sukhatme, V. K., Rauscher, F. III. 1992. Repression of the insulin-like growth factor II gene by Wilms tumor suppressor WT1. *Science* 257:674–78

27. El Nahas, A. M., Le Carpentier, J. E., Bassett, A. H. 1990. Compensatory renal growth: Role of growth hormone and insulin-like growth factor-I. *Nephrol. Dial. Transpl.* 5:123–29

28. Fagin, J. A., Melmed, S. 1987. Relative increase in insulin-like growth factor I messenger ribonucleic acid levels in compensatory renal hypertrophy. *Endocrinology* 120:718–24

29. Falkheden, T., Wickbom, I. 1965. Renal function and kidney size following hypophysectomy in man. *Acta Endocrin.* 48:348–54

30. Fellstrom, B., Klareskog, L., Heldin, C. H., Larsson, E., Ronnstrand, L., et al. 1989. Platelet-derived growth factor receptors in the kidney—upregulated expression in inflammation. *Kidney Int.* 36:1099–02

31. Fine, L. 1986. The biology of renal hypertrophy. *Kidney Int.* 29:619–34

32. Fisher, D. A., Salido, E. C. Barajase, L. 1989. Epidermal growth factor and the kidney. *Annu. Rev. Physiol.* 51:67–80

33. Flyvbjerg, A., Bornfeldt, K. E., Marshall, S. M., Arnqvist, H. J., Orskov, H. 1990. Kidney IGF-I mRNA in initial renal hypertrophy in experimental diabetes in rats. *Diabetologia* 33:334–38

34. Flyvbjerg, A., Frystyk, J., Thorlacius-Ussing, O., Orskov, H. 1989. Somatostatin analog administration prevents increase in kidney somatomedin C and initial renal growth in diabetic and uninephrectomized rats. *Diabetologia* 32:261–65

35. Flyvbjerg, A., Jorgensen, K. D., Marshall, S. M. Orskov, H. 1991. Inhibitory effect of octreotide on growth hormone-induced IGF-I generation and organ growth in hypophysectomized rats. *Am. J. Physiol.* 260:E568–74

36. Flyvbjerg, A., Thorlacius-Ussing, O., Naeraa, R., Ingerslev, J., Orskov, H. 1988. Kidney tissue somatomedin C and initial renal growth in diabetic and uninephrectomized rats. *Diabetologia* 31:310–14

37. Fraizer, G. E., Bowen-Pope, D. F., Vogel, A. M. 1987. Production of platelet-derived growth factor by cultured Wilms' tumor cells and fetal kidney cells. *J. Cell. Physiol.* 133:169–74

38. Gansler, T., Allen, K. D., Burant, C. F., Inabnett, T., Scott, A., et al. 1988. Detection of type I insulinlike growth factor (IGF) receptors in Wilms' tumors. *Am. J. Pathol.* 130:431–35

39. Gansler, T., Furlanetto, R., Gramling, T. S., Robinson, K. A., Blocker, N., et al. 1989. Antibody to Type I insulinlike growth factor receptor inhibits growth of Wilms' tumor in culture and in athymic mice. *Am. J. Pathol.* 135:961–66

40. Gautshci-Sova, P., Jiang, Z., Frater-Schroder, M., Bohlen, P. 1987. Acidic fibroblast growth factor is present in nonneural tissue: isolation and chemical characterization from bovine kidney. *Biochemistry* 26:5844–47

41. Gershberg, H. 1960. Metabolic and renotropic effects of human growth hormone in disease. *J. Clin. Endocrinol. Metab.* 20:1107–19

42. Gershberg, H., Heinemann, H. O., Stumpf, H. H. 1957. Renal function studies and autopsy report in a patient with gigantism and acromegaly. *J. Clin. Endocrinol. Metab.* 17:377–85

43. Deleted in proof

44. Gesualdo, L., Pinzani, M., Floriano, J. J., Hassan, M. O., Nagy, N. U., et al. 1991. Platelet-derived growth factor expression in mesangial prolif-

erative glomerulonephritis. *Lab. Invest.* 65:160– 67

45. Guh, J.-Y., Lai, Y.-S., Shin, S.-J., Chuang, L.-Y., Tsai, J.-H. 1991. Epidermal growth factor in renal hypertrophy in streptozotocin-diabetic rats. *Nephron* 59:641–47

46. Guler, H.-P., Eckardt, K.-U., Zapf, J., Bauer, C., Froesch, E. R. 1989. Insulin-like growth factor I increases glomerular filtration rate and renal plasma flow in man. *Acta Endocrinol.* 121: 101–6

47. Haffner, D., Zacharewicz, S., Mehls, O., Heinrich, U., Ritz, E. 1989. The acute effect of growth hormone on GFR is obliterated in chronic renal failure. *Clin. Nephrol.* 32:266–69

48. Hammerman, M. R. 1989. The growth hormone-insulin-like growth factor axis in kidney. *Am. J. Physiol.* 257:F503–14

49. Hammerman, M. R. 1992. Growth factors and metanephrogenesis. *Am. J. Physiol.* 262:F523–32

50. Hammerman, M. R., Rogers, S. 1987. Distribution of IGF receptors in the plasma membrane of proximal tubular cells. *Am. J. Physiol.* 253:F841–47

51. Hansen, A. P. Johansen, K. 1970. Diurnal patterns of blood glucose, serum free fatty acids, insulin, glucagon and growth hormone in normals and juvenile diabetics. *Diabetologia* 6:27–33

52. Harris, R. C. 1989. Response of rat inner medullary collecting duct cells to epidermal growth factor. *Am. J. Physiol.* 255:F1191–96

53. Harris, R. C., Daniel, T. O. 1989. Epidermal growth factor binding, stimulation of phosphorylation and inhibition of gluconeogenesis in rat proximal tubule. *J. Cell Physiol.* 139:383–91

54. Harris, R. C., Hoover, R. L., Jacobson, H. R., Badr. K. F. 1988. Evidence for glomerular actions of epidermal growth factor in the rat. *J. Clin. Invest.* 82: 1028–39

55. Haselbacher, G. K., Irminger, J. C., Zapf, J., Ziegler, W. H., Humbel, R. E. 1987. Insulin-like growth factor II in human adrenal pheochromocytomas and Wilms'tumors: Expression at the mRNA and protein level. *Proc. Natl. Acad. Sci. USA* 84:1104–06

56. Haskell, J. F., Pillion, D. J., Meezan, E. 1988. Specific, high affinity receptors for insulin-like growth factor II in the rat kidney glomerulus. *Endocrinology* 123:774–80

57. Hirvonen, H., Sandberg, M., Kalimo, H., Hukkanen, V., Vuorio, E., et al. 1989. The N-myc proto-oncogene and

IGF II growth factor mRNAs are expressed by distinct cells in human fetal kidney and brain. *J. Cell. Biol.* 108:1093–104

58. Humes, H. D., Cieslinski, D. A., Coimbra, T. M., Messana, J. M., Galvao, C. 1989. Epidermal growth factor enhances renal tubule cell regeneration and repair and accelerates the recovery of renal function in postischemic acute renal failure. *J. Clin. Invest.* 84:1757–61

59. Iida, H., Seifert, R., Alpers, C. E., Gronwald, R. G. K., Phillips, P. E., et al. 1991. Platelet-derived growth factor (PDGF) and PDGF receptor are induced in mesangial proliferative nephritis in the rat. *Proc. Natl. Acad. Sci. USA* 88:6560–64

60. Ikkos, D., Ljunggren, H., Luft, R. 1956. Glomerular filtration rate and renal plasma flow in acromegaly. *Acta Endocrinol.* 21:226–36

61. Kanda, S., Saha, P. K., Nomata, K., Taide, M., Nishimura, N., et al. 1991. Transient increase in renal epidermal growth factor content after unilateral nephrectomy in the mouse. *Acta Endocrinol.* 124:188–93

62. Kartha, S., Bradham, D. M., Grotendorst, G. R., Toback, F. G. 1988. Kidney epithelial cells express c-*cis* protooncogene and secrete PDGF-like protein. *Am. J. Physiol.* 255:F800–06

63. Kobayashi, S., Clemmons, D. R., Ventatachalam, M. A. 1991. Colocalization of insulin-like growth factor-binding protein with insulin-like growth factor I. *Am. J. Physiol.* 261: F22–28

64. Kopple, J. D., Hirschberg, R. 1990. Physiological effects of growth hormone and insulin-like growth factor I on the kidney. *Miner. Electrolyte Metab.* 16:82–88

65. Lajara, R., Rotwein, P., Bortz, J. D., Hansen, V. A., Sadow, J. L., et al. 1989. Dual regulation of insulin-like growth factor I expression during renal hypertrophy. *Am. J. Physiol.* 257: F252–61

66. MacKay, K., Kondaiah, P., Danielpour, D., Austin, H. A. III, Brown, P. D. 1990. Expression of transforming growth factor-β1 and β2 in rat glomeruli. *Kidney Int.* 38:1095–100

67. Madden, S. L., Cook, D. M., Morris, J. F., Gashler, A., Sukhatme, V. P., Rauscher, F. J. III 1991. Transcriptional repression mediated by the WT1 Wilms tumor gene product. *Science* 253: 1550–53

68. Maisonpierre, P. C., Belluscio, L., Squinto, S., Ip, N. Y., Furth, M. E., et al. 1990. Neurotrophin-3: A neurotrophic factor related to NGF and BDNF. *Science* 247:1446–51

69. Marshall, S. M., Flyvbjerg, A., Frystyk, J., Korsgaard, L., Orskov, H. 1991. Renal insulin-like growth factor I and growth hormone receptor binding in experimental diabetes and after unilateral nephrectomy in the rat. *Diabetologia* 34:632–39

70. Massagué, J. 1990. Transforming growth factor-α. *J. Biol. Chem.* 265: 21393–96

71. Mehls, O., Ritz, E. Hunziker, B., Eggli, P., Heinrich U., Kapf, J. 1988. Improvement of growth and food utilization by human recombinant growth hormone in uremia. *Kidney Int.* 33:450–52

72. Mellas, J., Gavin, J. R. III, Hammerman, M. R. 1986. Multiplication-stimulating activity-induced alkalinization of canine renal proximal tubular cells. *J. Biol. Chem.* 261:14437–42

73. Miller, S. B., Hansen, V. A., Hammerman, M. R. 1990. Effects of growth hormone and IGF-I on renal function in rats with normal and reduced renal mass. *Am. J. Physiol.* 259:F747–51

74. Miller, S. B., Rogers, S. A., Estes, C. E., Hammerman, M. R. 1992. Increased distal nephron EGF content and altered distribution of peptide in compensatory renal hypertrophy. *Am. J. Physiol.* 262: F1032–38

75. Miller, S. B., Rotwein, P., Bortz, J. D., Bechtel, P. J., Hansen, V. A., et al. 1990. Renal expression of IGF I in hypersomatotropic states. *Am. J. Physiol.* 259:F251–57

76. Mulroney, S. E., Haramati, A., Roberts, C. T. Jr., LeRoith, D. 1991. Renal IGF-1 mRNA levels are enhanced following unilateral nephrectomy in immature rats but not adult rats. *Endocrinology* 128:2660–62

77. Mulroney, S. E., Haramati, A., Werner, H., Bondy, C., Roberts, C. T., et al. 1992. Altered expression of insulin-like growth factor-I (IGF I) and IGF receptor genes after unilateral nephrectomy in immature rats. *Endocrinology* 130:249–56

78. Murphy, G. P., Kawinski, E., Horoszewicz, J. S. 1987. Cell cultures derived from Wilms' tumour animal model. *Cancer Res.* 6:717–20

79. Nagaike, M., Hirao, S., Tajima, H., Noji, S., Taniguchi, S., et al. 1991. Renotropic functions of hepatocyte growth factor in renal regeneration after unilateral nephrectomy. *J Biol. Chem.* 268:22781–84

80. Nakamura, T., Nawa, K., Ichihara, A., Kaise, N., Nishino, T. 1987. Purification and subunit structure of hepatocyte growth factor from rat platelets. *FEBS Lett.* 224:311–16

81. Nakamura, T., Nishizawa, T., Hagiya, M., Seki, T., Shimonishi, M., et al. 1989. Molecular cloning and expression of human hepatocyte growth factor. *Nature* 342:440–43

82. Nakamura, T., Teramoto, H., Ichihara, A. 1986. Purification and characterization of a growth factor from rat platelets for mature parenchymal hepatocytes in primary cultures. *Proc. Natl. Acad. Sci. USA* 83:6489–93

83. Norman, J., Tsau, Y.-K., Bacay, A., Fine, L. G. 1990. Epidermal growth factor accelerates functional recovery from ischaemic acute tubular necrosis in the rat: Role of the epidermal growth factor receptor. *Clin. Sci.* 78:445–50

84. Okuda, S., Languino, L. R., Ruoslahti, E., Border, W. A. 1990. Elevated expression of transforming growth factor-β and proteoglycan production in experimental glomerulonephritis. *J. Clin. Invest.* 86:453–62

85. Pelletier, J., Schalling, M., Buckler, A. J., Rogers, A., Haber, D. A., et al. 1991. Expression of the Wilms' tumor gene WT1 in the murine urogenital system. *Genes Dev.* 5:1345–56

86. Perantoni, A. O., Dove, L. F., Williams, C. L. 1991. Induction of tubules in rat metanephrogenic mesenchyme in the absence of an inductive tissue. *Differentiation* 48:25–32

87. Pritchard-Jones, K., Fleming, S., Davidson, D., Bickmore, W., Porteous, D., et al. 1990. The candidate Wilms' tumour gene is involved in genitourinary development. *Nature* 346:194–97

88. Quaife, C. J., Mathews, L. S., Pinkert, C. A., Hammer, R. E., Brinster, R. L., et al. 1989. Histopathology associated with elevated levels of growth hormone and insulin-like growth factor I in transgenic mice. *Endocrinology* 124: 40–48

89. Quigley, R., Baum, M. 1991. Effects of growth hormone and insulin-like growth factor I on rabbit proximal convoluted tubule transport. *J. Clin. Invest.* 88:368–74

90. Rifkin, D. B., Moscatelli, D. 1989. Recent developments in the cell biology of basic fibroblast growth factor. *J. Cell Biol.* 109:1–6

91. Risau, W., Ekblom, P. 1986. Production of a heparin-binding angiogenesis

factor by the embryonic kidney. *J. Cell Biol.* 103:1101–07

92. Roberts, A. B., Flanders, K. C., Heine, U. I., Jakowlew, S., Kondaiah, P., et al. 1990. Transforming growth factor-β: multifunctional regulator of differentiation and development. *Philos. Trans. R. Soc. London Ser. B* 327:145–54

93. Rogers, S. A., Karl, I. E., Hammerman, M. R. 1989. Growth hormone directly stimulates gluconeogenesis in canine renal proximal tubule. *Am. J. Physiol.* 257:E751–56

94. Rogers, S. A., Miller, S. B., Hammerman, M. R. 1990. Growth hormone stimulates IGF I gene expression in isolated rat renal collecting duct. *Am. J. Physiol.* 259:F474–79

95. Rogers, S. A., Miller, S. B., Hammerman, M. R. 1991. Insulin-like growth factor I gene expression in isolated rat renal collecting duct is stimulated by epidermal growth factor. *J. Clin. Invest.* 87:347–51

96. Rogers, S. A., Ryan, G., Hammerman, M. R. 1991. Insulin-like growth factors I and II are produced in the metanephros and are required for growth and development in vitro. *J. Cell Biol.* 113:1447–53

97. Rogers, S. A., Ryan, G., Hammerman, M. R. 1992. Metanephric transforming growth factor-α is required for renal organogenesis in vitro. *Am. J. Physiol.* 262:F533–39

98. Ross, R., Bowen-Pope, D. F., Raines, E. W. 1990. Platelet-derived growth factor and its role in health and disease. *Philos. Trans. R. Soc. London Ser. B* 327:155–69

99. Safirstein, R., Price, P. M., Saggi, S. J., Harris, R. C. 1990. Changes in gene expression after temporary renal ischemia. *Kidney Int.* 37:1515–21

100. Safirstein, R., Zelent, A. Z., Price, P. M. 1989. Reduced renal prepro-epidermal growth factor mRNA and decreased EGF excretion in ARF. *Kidney Int.* 36:810–15

101. Sariola, H., Saarma, M., Sainio, K., Vaahtokari, A., Thesleff, I., et al. 1991. Dependence of kidney morphogenesis on the expression of nerve growth factor receptor. *Science* 254:571–73

102. Saxen, L. 1987. *Organogenesis of the kidney.* Cambridge: Cambridge Univ. Press. pp. 1–173

103. Schmid, P., Cox, D., Bilbe, G., Maier, R., McMaster, G. K. 1991. Differential expression of TGF β1, β2 and β3 genes during mouse embryogenesis. *Development* 111:117–30

104. Schweiger, J., Fine, L. G. 1990. Renal hypertrophy, growth factors and nephropathy in diabetes mellitus. *Sem. Nephrol.* 10:242–53

105. Scott, J., Cowell, J., Robertson, M. E., Priestly, L. M., Wadey, R., et al. 1985. Insulin-like growth factor-II gene expression in Wilms' tumour and embryonic tissues. *Nature* 317:260–62

106. Segal, R., Fine, L. G. 1989. Polypeptide growth factors and the kidney. *Kidney Int.* 36:S2–10

107. Seyer-Hansen, K. 1983. Renal hypertrophy in experimental diabetes mellitus. *Kidney Int.* 23:643–46

108. Shultz, P. J., DiCorleto, P. E., Silver, B. J., Abboud, H. E. 1988. Mesangial cells express PDGF mRNAs and proliferate in response to PDGF. *Am. J. Physiol.* 255:F674–84

109. Silver, B., Jaffer, F. E., Abboud, H. 1989. Platelet-derived growth factor synthesis in mesangial cells: Induction by multiple peptide mitogens. *Proc. Natl. Acad. Sci. USA* 86:1056–60

110. Steers, W. D., Kolbeck, S., Creedon, D., Tuttle, J. B. 1991. Nerve growth factor in the urinary bladder of the adult regulates neuronal form and function. *J. Clin. Invest.* 88: 1709–15

111. Stiles, A. D., Sosenko, I. R. S., D'Ercole, A. J., Smith, B. T. 1985. Relation of kidney tissue somatomedin-C/insulin-like growth factor I to postnephrectomy renal growth in the rat. *Endocrinology* 117:2397–401

112. Tannenbaum, G. S. 1981. Growth hormone secretory dynamics in streptozotocin diabetes: Evidence of a role for endogenous circulating somatostatin. *Endocrinology* 108:76–82

113. Tashiro, K., Hagiya, M., Nichizawa, T., Seki, T., Shimonishi, M., et al. 1990. Deduced primary structure of rat hepatocyte growth factor and expression of the mRNA in rat tissues. *Proc. Natl. Acad. Sci. USA* 87:3200–04

114. Thoenen, H. 1991. The changing scene of neurotrophic factors. *Trends Neurosci.* 14:165–70

115. Thompson, N. L., Flanders, K. C., Smith, J. M., Ellingsworth, L. R., Roberts, A. B., et al. 1989. Expression of transforming growth factor-β1 in specific cells and tissues of adult and neonatal mice. *J. Cell Biol.* 108:661–69

116. Tonshoff, B., Mehls, O., Heinrich, U., Blum, W. F., Ranke, M. B., et al. 1990. Growth-stimulating effects of recombinant human growth hormone in children with end-stage renal disease. *J. Pediatr.* 116:561–66

117. Tonshoff, B., Mehls, O., Schauer, A., Heinrich, U., Blum, W., Ranke, M. 1989. Improvement of uremic growth failure by recombinant human growth hormone. *Kidney Int.* 36:S201–04

118. Toubeau, G., Nonclercq, D., Zanen, J., Lambricht, P, Tulkens, P. M., et al. 1991. Distribution of epidermal growth factor in the kidneys of rats exposed to amikacin. *Kidney Int.* 40:691–99

119. Vehaskari, V. M., Hering-Smith, K. S., Moskowitz, D. W., Weiner, I. D., Hamm, L. L. 1989. Effect of epidermal growth factor on sodium transport in the cortical collecting tubule. *Am. J. Physiol.* 256:F803–09

120. Weller, A., Sorokin, L., Illgen, E.-M., Ekblom, P. 1991. Development and growth of mouse embryonic kidney in organ culture and modulation of de-velopment by soluble growth factor. *Dev. Biol.* 144:248–61

121. Werner, H., Shen-Orr, Z., Stannard, B., Burguera, B., Roberts, C. T. 1990. Experimental diabetes increases in-sulinlike growth factor I and II receptor concentration and gene expression in kidney. *Diabetes* 39:1490–97

122. Yoshioka, K., Takemura, T., Murakami, K., Akano, N., Matsubara, K., et al. 1990. Identification and localization of epidermal growth factor and its receptor in the human glomer-ulus. *Lab. Invest.* 63:189–96

123. Yoshimura, A., Gordon, K., Alpers, C. E., Floege, J., Pritzl, P., et al. 1991. Demonstration of PDGF β-chain mRNA in glomeruli in mesangial pro-liferative nephritis by in situ hybrid-ization. *Kidney Int.* 40:470–76

Annu. Rev. Physiol. 1993. 55:323–47

THE RENAL H-K-ATPase: Physiological Significance and Role in Potassium Homeostasis

Charles S. Wingo and Brian D. Cain

Department of Medicine, Division of Nephrology, Hypertension, and Transplantation, and Department of Biochemistry and Molecular Biology, University of Florida, and Department of Veterans Affairs Medical Center, Gainesville, Florida 32610

KEY WORDS: active transport, proton pump, potassium, acid-base balance, epithelial transport

INTRODUCTION

Recent work from several laboratories has provided convincing evidence that the kidney possesses a mechanism for primary active potassium (K) absorption that is coupled to proton[1] secretion at the apical membrane of the collecting duct (CD). The mechanism responsible for this process exhibits striking similarity to the mechanism proposed for K and proton (H) transport at the canalicular membrane of the parietal cells in the gastric mucosa (27, 82, 85). The present review considers the hypothesis that this active K absorption by the CD is mediated by H- and K-activated adenosinetriphosphatase (H-K-ATPase) that is similar, but probably not identical, to the H-K-ATPase of the stomach. The existence of a renal H-K-ATPase has only recently gained wide recognition, and the study of the role of this enzyme in H and K transport within the CD is presently an active area of investigation. The purpose of this review is threefold: (*a*) to review the evidence suggesting that the kidney possesses a mechanism of active K absorption; (*b*) to review our current

---

[1]This discussion tacitly accepts the notion that urinary acidification occurs by hydrogen ion or proton secretion. Whether acid secretion actually occurs by proton or hydronium ion (H_3O^+) secretion is beyond the scope of this review.

understanding of this mechanism of active K absorption and proton secretion; and (c) to address the physiologic significance of the renal H-K-ATPase.

K CONSERVATION BY THE KIDNEY

The kidney is the major organ responsible for K elimination and adapts to conserve K when K intake is reduced. The renal H-K-ATPase was initially characterized as a mechanism for active renal K conservation under conditions of K restriction[2] (116). Thus it is appropriate to consider first the physiological, morphological, and biochemical evidence that suggests a role for a renal H-K-ATPase in K conservation. Much of the relevant data is indirect and demands careful review prior to acceptance as evidence for K absorption resulting from the activity of a functional H-K-ATPase in the CD.

Physiological Studies

Renal K conservation is affected by both prior K intake and the extent to which K intake is reduced (95). Moreover, the efficiency of K conservation is influenced by conditions other than K intake. K conservation is promoted if sodium (Na) intake is also reduced, whereas a liberal Na diet impairs K conservation (95). Conversely, K depletion results in significant Na retention, an effect that can be abolished by coincident Na restriction (95, 121). Whereas maximal K conservation in humans is attained by 14–21 days, the renal response in the rat to a low K diet is more rapid and virtually complete within 48 hr (53).

Early metabolic balance and micropuncture studies suggest that the kidney possesses the capacity for active K absorption. Fourman (24) observed that the human kidney possesses the capacity to reduce urinary K concentration below the K concentration of plasma. Moreover, during K deprivation in the rat, fractional urinary K excretion is significantly less than the fractional delivery of K to the late distal tubule[3] (60, 62).

Two alternative interpretations could account for the reduction in fractional

---

[2]The term potassium restriction is defined as a reduction in K intake sufficient to induce renal K conservation (reduced urinary potassium excretion) in the absence of an appreciable reduction in total body K content. The term potassium depletion indicates a reduction in total body K content in excess of nitrogen balance. Thus K restriction deals with a reduction of K intake within the physiologically adaptable range of the organism and compatible with normal growth and health, whereas K depletion implies a pathophysiologic process.

[3]The distal tubule as defined for micropuncture studies (hereafter referred to as the distal convolution) is a heterogeneous structure that includes three anatomically defined segments; the distal convoluted tubule (DCT), the connecting segment (CNT), and initial collecting tubule (ICT). The latter segment represents a functional extension of the cortical collecting duct (CCD). The majority of K secretion in the distal convolution is localized to the CNT and the ICT (95a).

delivery of K between the late distal convolution and the final urine. Either juxtamedullary nephrons conserve K more efficiently than superficial nephrons or the CD possesses the capacity to absorb K. The latter interpretation has now gained wide acceptance. Based upon the results of stationary microperfusion experiments in the distal convolution, Giebisch and co-workers (61) postulated that active K reabsorption from the luminal fluid prevented attainment of electrochemical equilibrium. Subsequent studies further support the role of K absorption by the CD in K conservation (25, 53). Fowler et al (25) and Linas et al (53) examined the urinary recovery of distally microinjected ^{42}K as a function of K intake. Urinary recovery of labeled K markedly decreased after 72 hr adaptation to a low K diet (53). This reduced ^{42}K recovery correlated with K depletion and was independent of mineralocorticoid hormone, which suggests that K reabsorption by the CD contributes to urinary K excretion. Apparently, adaptation to the low K diet increases K absorption along the CD accounting for renal K conservation.

A similar enhancement of K absorption in the medullary CD of K-restricted rats was apparent in microcatherization experiments (2, 35). Under K-replete conditions, net K transport in the medullary CD was negligible. However, after 72 hr adaptation to a low K diet, approximately 85% of K delivered to the medullary CD was reabsorbed prior to the papillary tip (2).

Studies using isolated perfused tubules directly tested the hypothesis that transport in the outer medullary collecting duct from the inner stripe (OMCD$_i$) contributes to K homeostasis. Enhanced K absorptive flux was observed during K restriction, which implicated the OMCD$_i$ as a site of K absorption (115). These studies, conducted under gradient conditions, measured an increase in the apparent permeability of the OMCD$_i$ during K restriction, which indicated that the increase in K absorptive flux could be either transcellular or paracellular. However, subsequent studies showed that K absorption during K restriction is predominantly by a transcellular pathway (116).

Ornt & Tannen examined the mechanism of adaptation to short term K depletion in the isolated perfused kidney (75). Within 72 hr of dietary K deprivation, an intrinsic renal adaptive mechanism for K conservation was activated. K conservation appeared to be largely independent of aldosterone, urinary flow rate, or the luminal pH, ammonium, Na, or anion composition. Further studies indicated that although renal tissue K content was correlated with the rate of K excretion, it did not appear to be the sole mediator of renal K conservation (74).

Although urinary K excretion and K secretion in the distal convolution are generally correlated (60, 62), additional observations provide further evidence that nephron sites distal to the CCD are important for K homeostasis. Certain conditions exhibiting large rates of K secretion in the CNT, ICT, and CCD occur without proportional increases in urinary K excretion. For example, chronic mineralocorticoid stimulation is a potent stimulus for K secretion in the CNT, ICT, and CCD (70, 89, 97, 102, 114). However, this maneuver has only modest effects on net K excretion (62, 97, 114, 118). Similarly, chronic furosemide administration can more than double the rate of K secretion in the distal convolution during a time when urinary K excretion is actually significantly decreased (96). Therefore, additional factors must influence the rate of urinary K excretion in segments distal to the CCD.

Thus there is compelling physiological evidence that K absorption occurs in the medullary CD, and specifically the OMCD$_i$, when K intake is curtailed. Moreover, under certain circumstances enhanced K secretion in the CNT, ICT, and CCD does not result in enhanced K excretion, which suggests a role for the medullary CD in renal K homeostasis.

Morphological Studies

Severe K depletion results in dramatic morphological changes in the kidney and the cells of the CD in particular (52). Early studies noted that severe K depletion was associated with enlarged, pale kidneys and that histologic changes were confined to the mid-medullary zone (17, 86).

Spargo (94) identified the specific anatomic regions of the nephron that underwent morphologic changes in response to K depletion and described a proliferative lesion that was localized to the outer medullary collecting duct (OMCD). The lesion was uniformly present after the sixth day of K depletion and became progressively more severe. Prophetically, he remarked that whereas "the distal tubule is known to be active in ion exchange, the collecting tubules have been generally considered passive. The degree of hyperplasia of this area would make it seem otherwise." Subsequent studies have corroborated these findings (1, 20, 72, 73, 106).

During K depletion, the CD exhibits two morphologically distinct lesions with hyperplastic and hypertrophic changes occurring in the OMCD and a separate lesion occurring in the inner medullary collecting duct (IMCD) (69, 94). The IMCD lesion is characterized by an increased number of lipid droplets, lysosomal-like dense bodies and multivesicular bodies. During severe K depletion, a vacuolar lesion also occurs in the proximal tubule. Hypertrophy of both principal and intercalated cells in the OMCD$_i$ is a consistent finding (36). Moreover, K depletion produces an increase in the relative number of cells in the OMCD$_i$ with a high density of rod-shaped particles without altering the frequency of intercalated cells (99). These changes are associated with a threefold increase in the luminal membrane area of intercalated cells, which suggests that intercalated cells may be involved in K absorption (99).

A recent study examined the effects of chronic potassium depletion in the rat by light and transmission electron microscopy and by morphometric analysis (18). Renal growth was not uniform and hypertrophy of the inner stripe of the outer medulla was most prominent. The histologic changes in the CD included hypertrophy and hyperplasia of both principal cells and intercalated cells. By morphometric analysis there was an increase in luminal and basolateral membrane area of both principal cells and intercalated cells of the $OMCD_i$. However, both apical and basolateral membrane area per unit tubule length approximately doubled in intercalated cells with potassium depletion, whereas the changes in the principal cells were less prominent (18).

Biochemical Studies

The physiological and morphological studies clearly suggest that the medullary CD is important for K conservation. Two seminal reports indicated that the CD and the CNT possess a K-stimulated adenosinetriphosphatase (K-ATPase) that is a plausible candidate for active K absorption during K conservation (16, 30). Both reports support the assertion that the functional and structural changes during K deprivation represent changes caused by stimulation of an active K-absorbing mechanism (29). The inhibitory characteristics of this renal K-ATPase activity provide the primary pharmacological evidence suggesting that this activity represents an H-K-ATPase.

Doucet & Marsy (16) described a unique K-ATPase activity in the CNT (the DCT-granular segment, DCT_g), CCD, and OMCD of both rats and rabbits. This ATPase activity exhibited a high affinity for $K (K_m \sim 0.2$–0.4 mM), but was unaffected by either the Na-K-ATPase inhibitor, ouabain, or the mitochondrial $F_1 F_0$ ATPase inhibitor, azide. Importantly, the K-ATPase activity was sensitive to two known inhibitors of the gastric H-K-ATPase, vanadate and omeprazole. The effect of vanadate suggests that the renal K-ATPase possesses a phosphorylated intermediate (P-type ATPase). K depletion markedly increased K-ATPase in the OMCD and the CCD, which suggests that the enzyme is a plausible candidate for active K absorption.

Garg & Narang (30) provided further evidence suggesting that the renal K-ATPase activity might be an H-K-ATPase. They reported a similar nephronal distribution of K-ATPase activity as Doucet & Marsy (16) using a different enzyme assay. Additionally, the gastric H-K-ATPase inhibitor SCH28080 (100 μM) abolished K-ATPase activity. In the gastric mucosa the mechanism of action of SCH28080 has been extensively examined. This hydrophobic imidazopyridine is a potent inhibitor of gastric acid secretion (19), microsomal vesicular acidification (8, 39, 110), and K-stimulated ATP hydrolysis (3, 5, 8, 46, 90). SCH28080 inhibits the gastric H-K-ATPase by a reversible interaction with the enzyme that is competitive with respect to K (3, 5, 90, 110).

Subsequently, Cheval et al (11) demonstrated that SCH28080 appears to be a relatively specific inhibitor of K-ATPase activity in the CCD and the OMCD with an IC_{50} of 0.5 μM. Basal ATP hydrolysis was not inhibited by up to 100 μM SCH28080. Moreover, SCH28080 had no apparent effect on Na-K-ATPase activity or N-ethyl maleimide (NEM)-sensitive, vanadate-insensitive ATPase activity, an index of H-ATPase, at concentrations up to 100 μM. Rubidium (Rb) and K stimulated ATPase activity by quantitatively similar amounts, and ^{86}Rb uptake in both the cortical and medullary CD were inhibited by SCH28080. The effect of SCH28080 on Rb uptake was observed in the presence of 2.5 mM ouabain. Apparently, Rb uptake occurs by a mechanism that is distinct from Na-K-ATPase.

Thus the evidence from different experimental approaches indicates that during K conservation adaptive changes occur within the CD, particularly the OMCD. A portion of K secreted primarily in the CCD and ICT can be actively reabsorbed distally in the medullary CD. Hypertrophy of intercalated cells in the OMCD implies that K reabsorption may occur through intercalated cells. The activity of K-ATPase localized to the CNT and the CD is markedly stimulated during K-deprivation. Three structurally dissimilar inhibitors of the gastric H-K-ATPase are also potent inhibitors of this K-ATPase. Clearly, the pharmacology of the renal K-ATPase reflects the characteristics of the gastric H-K-ATPase and is not consistent with other known K transporters.

ION TRANSPORT BY H-K-ATPase IN THE COLLECTING DUCT

If an H-K-ATPase functions in the CD, then K absorption should be coupled to acidification of the urine. This simple statement has provided the basis for most of what is known about the function of H-K-ATPase in the kidney. Essentially, ion transport can be expected to obey a predictable and experimentally testable pattern. These principles have been used to examine the functional activity of H-K-ATPase in the segments of the CD.

Proton, K, and Rb Flux in the OMCD

We have concentrated much of our own efforts on the investigation of ion transport in the in vitro perfused $OMCD_i$ from rabbits adapted to a K-restricted diet. Studies of acidification and K transport have focused on the $OMCD_i$ for three reasons: (a) the $OMCD_i$ represents a major site for distal acidification (54, 103); (b) K restriction enhances absorptive K flux in the $OMCD_i$ (115); and (c) K depletion produces striking morphological changes in the rat $OMCD_i$ (36, 94, 99). Luminal acidification was measured as net total CO_2 flux[4]

---

[4]The term total CO_2 flux and bicarbonate flux will be used interchangeably because at physiologic pH, the majority of total CO_2 content is due to bicarbonate.

(J_{TCO_2}, in pmol•mm^{-1}•min^{-1}) and K absorption as net K flux (J_K, in pmol•mm^{-1}•min^{-1}). The contribution of a functional H-K-ATPase in the OMCD$_i$ was assessed by examining the effect of the gastric H-K-ATPase inhibitor omeprazole on both J_{TCO_2}, and J_K flux. Omeprazole profoundly inhibited luminal acidification without an effect on transepithelial voltage (V_T) (16). These observations suggest that the effect of omeprazole on J_{TCO_2}, was electrically silent.

Similarly, the OMCD$_i$ exhibited significant net K absorption in tubules derived from animals fed a K-restricted diet (116). Some K absorption could be attributed to passive K efflux through a paracellular pathway because the V_T was lumen positive. However, using previous measurements of K efflux, an upper limit of paracellular K permeability can be determined. Using these empirical measurements less than one half of the observed net K absorptive flux could be attributed to passive driving forces. Importantly, omeprazole abolished K absorption without affecting V_T, which indicates an effect of this agent on a non-electrogenic mechanism of K transport. Thus K absorption appears to occur predominantly via a transcellular pathway and not by paracellular, voltage-mediated mechanism.

Although these studies indicate the presence of a functional H-K-ATPase in the OMCD$_i$, the use of inhibitors to discern the presence of a functional H-K-ATPase is not without limitations. In the gastric mucosa the specificity of omeprazole to inhibit H-K-ATPase is conferred by its activation to a highly reactive agent within an acidic environment in situ (4, 45, 109). Therefore, omeprazole may not be entirely specific for H-K-ATPase, but rather could possibly modify other ion transporters involved in luminal acidification. Although omeprazole does not inhibit Mg^{2+}-ATPase activity at concentrations that fully inhibit gastric H-K-ATPase (4, 26, 109, 111), demonstration that a structurally distinct gastric H-K-ATPase inhibitor also predictably affects ion transport in the CD would considerably strengthen the hypothesis that the renal enzyme contributing to urinary acidification is in fact a P-type H-K-ATPase.

Therefore, the effect of SCH28080 on K absorption and renal acidification was examined in the OMCD$_i$ using the perfused tubule approach (117). Studies were conducted using Rb as a qualitative marker of unidirectional lumen-to-bath K flux because Rb and K are handled similarly by the CCD (113), and the renal enzyme appears to transport Rb and K equally well (11). In the OMCD$_i$ from K-restricted rabbits, SCH28080 (10 μM) inhibited Rb efflux by 41% without significantly affecting V_T. Importantly, the experiments were conducted in the presence of the Na-K-ATPase inhibitor ouabain in the perfusate.

Inclusion of ouabain was essential to exclude the contribution of a luminal Na-K-ATPase to K absorption because both K-ATPase and Na-K-ATPase activity are stimulated in the OMCD during K depletion (16, 37). The increase in Na-K-ATPase during K-depletion led to the proposal that in the rat, K absorption is mediated in part by a luminal Na-K-ATPase (37). Additional studies in the CCD (see below) also indicate that the pharmacological characteristics of active K absorption are most consistent with an H-K-ATPase.

To further address the importance of the renal H-K-ATPase, studies of luminal acidification were conducted in the $OMCD_i$ dissected from rabbits adapted to a K-replete (normal), or a K-restricted diet (117). SCH28080 (10 μM) significantly inhibited bicarbonate absorption in the $OMCD_i$ by a similar extent under both dietary conditions, approximately 65–75%, without significantly affecting V_T (Figure 1). Gifford et al (32) demonstrated a comparable degree of inhibition of bicarbonate absorption by 10 μM SCH28080 in the OMCD of K-replete rats. Moreover, they observed approximately 50% inhibition of bicarbonate absorption in the IMCD by this agent. Thus two structurally dissimilar inhibitors of the gastric H-K-ATPase profoundly reduce proton secretion and net or unidirectional K/Rb absorption in the OMCD. Together these observations indicate a significant role for H-K-ATPase in urinary acidification under both normal and K-restricted conditions.

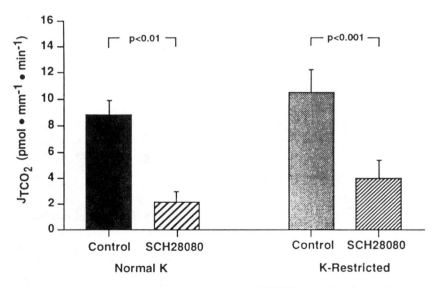

Figure 1 Effect of inhibition of H-K-ATPase by 10 μM SCH28080 on net bicarbonate absorption (J_{TCO_2}, in pmol•mm^{-1}•min^{-1}) in the $OMCD_i$ in rabbits on a normal diet (K-replete) (*left*) and on a low K diet (K-restricted) (*right*). In each case, bicarbonate absorption was inhibited to a similar extent (76% in K-replete animals and 65% in K-restricted animals, data adapted from 117).

K and Rb Flux in the CNT and CCD

Although the $OMCD_i$ appears to be an important site for K absorption, especially during K restriction, physiological studies (61) indirectly suggest that an apical K absorptive mechanism also exists in the cortex.

To determine whether H-K-ATPase contributes to net K transport in the CNT and CCD, investigators examined the effect of SCH28080 or omeprazole on net K transport in the in vivo perfused rat distal convolution (68) and the in vitro perfused rabbit CCD (119). The in vivo perfused CNT from K-deficient rats possessed significant SCH28080-inhibitable K absorption (68). Furthermore, the CCD from K-restricted animals exhibited small rates of K secretion during the control period, which significantly increased in the presence of luminal omeprazole. These observations suggest that a K absorptive mechanism exists in the CNT and CCD as well as the $OMCD_i$.

Further studies examined the mechanism of this K absorptive flux in the CCD of K-restricted rabbits. In order to determine whether the predominant pathway for active K absorptive flux is mediated by an H-K-ATPase or a luminal Na-K-ATPase, we contrasted the effect of 10 μM luminal SCH28080 with the effect of 0.1 mM luminal ouabain. It should be noted that 10 μM SCH28080 does not fully inhibit K-ATPase activity in the CD (11); therefore, the results undoubtedly underestimate the contribution of the H-K-ATPase. Nevertheless, SCH28080 inhibited Rb efflux by $39\pm8.0\%$, whereas a maximum pharmacologic concentration of ouabain did not significantly affect Rb efflux (124). The decrease in Rb efflux occurred without a change in V_T, which suggests that the mechanism of K/Rb transport was electroneutral. Similar to the studies of H-K-ATPase-mediated ion transport in the $OMCD_i$, these ion flux studies indicate that the K/Rb absorptive process exhibits pharmacological characteristics that are most consistent with an H-K-ATPase and not a Na-K-ATPase.

Intracellular pH Measurements in the OMCD and CCD

The role of the H-K-ATPase in the CCD has focused on K/Rb transport; however, the H-K-ATPase appears to exhibit electroneutral coupling of H and K transport. Therefore, urinary acidification is of equal concern. An electrogenic H-ATPase resident in the apical membrane has been thought to be the predominant mechanism for luminal acidification in the CD (10, 34, 103, 104). Although the physiological roles of these two pumps remain controversial, a growing body of evidence suggests that H-K-ATPase plays an important role in urinary acidification (see above).

Since H for K exchange normally results in cytoplasmic alkalinization, measurement of intracellular pH (pH_i) can be used to assess the role of plasma membrane proton pumps in the recovery from an acid load. If the renal

H-K-ATPase contributes significantly to intracellular pH recovery after induction of an acid load, then the rate of recovery of cellular pH should be significantly reduced by H-K-ATPase inhibitors. Hays & Alpern (38) tested this hypothesis in the $OMCD_i$ by examining the effect of SCH28080 on pH recovery to an acid load. Although the rates of pH recovery were small, no evidence for a SCH28080-inhibitable component of pH recovery was observed. The result appears to emphasize the role of H-ATPase in pH_i recovery by the $OMCD_i$ of K-replete animals.

However, in contrast, in two preliminary studies using fluorescent techniques for measuring pH_i, it was shown that intercalated cells of the CCD of K-replete animals express a SCH28080-inhibitable and K-dependent H extrusion mechanism in response to an acid load (49, 92). These experiments can be interpreted as compelling evidence for the presence of an H-K-ATPase in the interacalated cells of the CCD.

K-Dependent Acidification in Rabbit Medullary Membrane Vesicles

Presently, the biochemical analysis of the renal H-K-ATPase is in its formative stages. Preparation of appropriate quantities of pure enzyme for in depth study, such as has been performed on the gastric H-K-ATPase, may be impractical because of the relatively small abundance of the transporter in renal tissues. Therefore, the initial characterization of K-ATPase-dependent acidification has been performed in a rabbit renal medulla microsomal preparation enriched for plasma membrane (13). The microsomal preparation possessed both K-dependent ATPase activity and K-dependent acidification. SCH28080 and vanadate partially inhibited the latter, which suggests that H-K-ATPase is responsible for a component of the acidification. H-ATPase activity resident in the apical membrane and in lysosomes that contaminated the microsome preparation probably accounted for the remaining acidifying activity.

It should be noted that the animals used in preparation of the microsomes were K-replete (13). Therefore, significant H-K-ATPase apparently is present in CD cells even in the absence of K restriction. However, work of this nature cannot adequately address whether the H-K-ATPase is located in the apical membrane or in sub-apical intracellular vesicles. This is a point of considerable importance because stimulation of the gastric parietal cell for acid secretion involves mobilizing H-K-ATPase laden vesicles to the plasma (canalicular) membrane (23, 93).

Finally, the presence of K-ATPase activity in microdissected segments of the rabbit and rat CD was initially observed as ouabain- and azide-insensitive K-stimulated ATP hydrolysis (16, 30). This enzyme activity is pharmacologically distinct from NEM-sensitive ATPase activity (L. Garg, personal communication). Nevertheless, the observation that gastric H-K-ATPase is inhibited by approximately 100 μM NEM suggests that this agent may partially inhibit K-ATPase activity in the CD (42, 66). Therefore, until the renal H-K-ATPase has been fully characterized, results using NEM as an inhibitor of the vacuolar H-ATPase should be interpreted cautiously.

Summary

The pattern of ion transport in the CD is consistent with active K absorption via H-K-ATPase. Although the primary site of K absorption appears to be the OMCD, the CCD and CNT also possess ion transport characteristics of an H-K-ATPase. From a physiological point of view, probably the most interesting results are those suggesting a role of renal H-K-ATPase in K conservation. The enzyme appears to function in the CD of both K-replete and K-restricted animals. Logically, H-K-ATPase appears to be the primary urinary acidifying enzyme under conditions of K-restriction and may play a significant role in normal acid excretion.

IMMUNOREACTIVITY OF THE H-K-ATPase IN THE RAT AND RABBIT CD

The CD is a heterogeneous epithelium composed of two distinct cell types: principal cells and intercalated cells. In addition, within the CCD at least two types of intercalated cells can be distinguished (88, 108). Most of the studies previously discussed indicate that a functional H-K-ATPase is present at the apical membrane of the CCD. However, aside from the recent reports of pH_i measurements in individual cells of the CD, previous studies fail to provide evidence for the localization of this transporter to a specific cell type. In addition, such physiological studies do not preclude the possibility that a functional H-K-ATPase may represent an unusual mode of operation of the V-type H-ATPase, which is present in intercalated cells of the CD (9, 10).

The use of two different monoclonal antibodies that react with epitopes of the gastric H-K-ATPase and fail to recognize purified H-ATPase provides an approach toward the characterization of the proteins responsible for this H-K-ATPase activity. Murine monoclonal antibodies raised against hog gastric microsomes highly enriched in H-K-ATPase exhibited specific immunoreactivity with an antigen present in the intercalated cells of the CCD and OMCD of the rat and rabbit (120). When paraffin sections of rat and rabbit kidneys were processed for horseradish peroxidase immunohistochemistry, diffuse cytoplasmic staining of a sub-population of cells in the CCD and OMCD was apparent. In the rabbit 29.5% of the cells in the CCD, 31.9% of cells in the OMCD from the outer stripe ($OMCD_o$), and 19.8% of cells in the outer portion of the $OMCD_i$ exhibited H-K-ATPase immunoreactivity. Most of the immunoreactive cells could be identified as intercalated cells (120). Intercalated cells without H-K-ATPase immunoreactivity were not found in the rabbit, but in the CCD of the rat a few intercalated cells were without reaction product, which indicated either absence of H-K-ATPase immunoreactivity or too little immunoreactivity to be detected under the experimental conditions employed. Colocalization studies in the rat $OMCD_o$ demonstrated that H-K-ATPase and band 3 protein immunoreactivity were present in the same population of cells, further confirming that the immunoreactive cells were intercalated cells. The fact that two distinct monoclonal antibodies directed against the hog gastric H-K-ATPase exhibited immunoreactivity with both a rabbit and a rat intercalated cell antigen indicates, at the very least, that the antigen and the gastric H-K-ATPase share common epitopes. An obvious inference is that structural similarities probably exist between the gastric and renal H-K-ATPases.

Although no systematic immunohistochemical studies have been performed in the IMCD, preliminary observations indicate the presence of K-stimulated ATPase activity in the rabbit IMCD (31a). This observation suggests that H-K-ATPase may also be present in the IMCD cells because intercalated cells are absent in the IMCD of the rabbit.

REGULATION OF H-K-ATPase

Regulation of H-K-ATPase Enzymatic Activity (K-ATPase)

A complex pattern of regulation of the renal H-K-ATPase is beginning to emerge. The enzyme is apparently controlled by a number of factors. Dietary K intake is clearly one element modulating the renal H-K-ATPase as can be surmised from much of the work on K conservation. Hyperaldosteronism potentiates the degree of metabolic alkalosis induced by hypokalemia (40, 41, 44), which suggests a role for this hormone in distal acidification. Moreover, certain observations indicate that aldosterone stimulates the activity of this enzyme (28, 67). As might be expected from H-K-ATPase involvement in urinary acidification, the enzyme is also apparently affected by acid-base balance (48a).

Modulation of Enzymatic Activity by K Intake

K intake has been viewed as the central effector controlling K-ATPase activity. However, the signaling pathway for K-mediated regulation of the enzyme remains incompletely understood. Doucet & Marsy (16) clearly demonstrated that dietary K intake had a significant effect on K-ATPase activity in both the CCD and OMCD. After less than 96 hr, the activity of this enzyme had approximately doubled in both segments, and there was a continued increase in K-ATPase activity in the OMCD for up to five weeks in the rat.

Interestingly, after seven days on a low K diet, there was a significant increase in Na-K-ATPase activity in the medullary, but not the cortical, collecting duct. After five weeks of K depletion, CCD Na-K-ATPase activity continued to decline, whereas Na-K-ATPase activity in the OMCD increased approximately sevenfold. These observations suggest that adaptation to a low K diet involves not only increases in H-K-ATPase activity, but also Na-K-ATPase activity.

K-depletion results in striking changes in other enzymes as well. Imbert-Teboul et al (43) demonstrated alterations in specific adenylate cyclase activities during K depletion. The increase in adenylate cyclase is not a generalized phenomenon because adenylate cyclase response to vasopressin and glucagon decreased in the medullary thick ascending limb. Both Imbert-Teboul et al (43) and Hayashi & Katz (37) reported progressive hypertrophy of the OMCD during K depletion. Given the important role of cAMP in second messenger systems, changes in adenylate cyclase may be an important clue as to the cellular mechanism for H-K-ATPase control.

Hayashi & Katz (37) also reported that the increase in Na-K-ATPase activity was confined to the $OMCD_i$, which indicates an effect of K depletion on this nephron segment. The increase in Na-K-ATPase activity in the $OMCD_i$ was associated with a decrease in plasma aldosterone concentration during K-depletion. In contrast, during K-repletion the Na-K-ATPase activity decreased in the $OMCD_i$, whereas plasma aldosterone increased. Thus if aldosterone affects Na-K-ATPase activity in this segment, the role of aldosterone is not of the same quantitative importance or possibly does not act in the same manner as in the CCD, where aldosterone clearly stimulates Na-K-ATPase activity. Alternatively, these data may indicate that the effects of K-depletion on Na-K-ATPase activity in the OMCD are independent of plasma aldosterone.

In contrast to the relatively selective effects of K depletion on Na-K-ATPase activity in the medullary CD, K intake has a generalized effect on H-K-ATPase activity in the CNT, CCD, and OMCD. A low K intake stimulated and a high K intake suppressed K-ATPase activity (16, 31). This reciprocal relationship between K intake and H-K-ATPase activity may be pertinent to the effects of K depletion on bicarbonate transport in the CCD. In this segment, K depletion enhances bicarbonate absorption (63). Thus it is plausible that the increase in bicarbonate absorption is in part due to increased H-K-ATPase activity.

Modulation of Enzymatic Activity and Message Expression by Acid Base Balance

The effects of systemic acid base balance on H-K-ATPase activity are not yet fully characterized in all CD segments and during both metabolic and respiratory acid base disturbances. Nevertheless, the limited available data indicate that the enzyme is affected by systemic acid base balance.

Komatsu & Garg (48a) reported in preliminary observations that metabolic acidosis increases H-K-ATPase activity in the rat OMCD. This stimulatory effect of metabolic acidosis appears to be additive to the effect of K depletion. In contrast, metabolic alkalosis suppresses H-K-ATPase activity in the OMCD (48a).

A recent preliminary report also observed a sevenfold increase in mRNA for a putative rat H-K-ATPase after one week exposure to respiratory acidosis (33). This observation suggests that not only H-K-ATPase activity but also message expression is altered by systemic acid base changes.

Modulation of Enzyme Activity by Aldosterone

The effect of aldosterone on H-K-ATPase is incompletely understood. K depletion results in a marked increase in K-ATPase activity in both the CCD and OMCD commensurate with decreases in plasma aldosterone concentration. On the other hand, aldosterone stimulated K-ATPase activity in the rabbit CNT and CCD, but did not appear to affect significantly the activity of this enzyme in the OMCD or the IMCD (28). Whether the effect of aldosterone on H-K-ATPase is confined to the cortex or has different effects on H-K-ATPase in medullary segments will require further study.

Interestingly, in cultured Madin-Darby canine kidney (MDCK) cells, which exhibit certain characteristics of intercalated cells, Oberleithner and his colleagues (67) characterized a mechanism of acidification that appears similar to the H-K-ATPase observed in the CD. Apical acidification was stimulated by increasing apical K concentration and inhibited by apical barium (Ba) or omeprazole. Aldosterone stimulated apical acidification and short circuit current. The authors proposed a model of acidification in which electroneutral H-K exchange was functionally coupled to the operation of a Ba-sensitive channel. They hypothesized that omeprazole inhibited acidification by a direct effect on the H-K pump, whereas Ba acted indirectly to inhibit acidification by blocking the K channel. Thus, aldosterone may directly stimulate H-K-ATPase in certain cell types as suggested from chronic infusion studies (28). In view of the ability of the H-K-ATPase to transport Na on the luminal cation-binding site (see below), these observations may be relevant to the action of aldosterone on Na and K transport in the CCD (101, 118). Aldosterone stimulated Na efflux in the CCD in the presence of 0.1 mM amiloride, which suggests that aldosterone stimulated an amiloride-insensitive mechanism of Na absorption (101). Whether transport of Na via the H-K-ATPase could explain these observations awaits further study.

Regulation of H-K-ATPase-Mediated Ion Transport

Observations in the isolated perfused tubule indicate that peritubular pCO_2 (and pH) and luminal [Na] appear to influence the transport activity of the renal H-K-ATPase. The effect of 10% CO_2 on the activity of this pump suggests that acid-base disturbances may affect H-K-ATPase transport activity.

Effect of pCO_2 and pH on H-K-ATPase-Mediated Rb Efflux.

One of the consistent findings regarding renal K excretion is its reciprocal relationship with H secretion (22, 64, 107). On the basis of renal clearance experiments, Berliner proposed a competition between protons and K for secretion in exchange for Na absorption (6). A link between changes in acid-base balance and K transport in the CD appears plausible because the renal H-K-ATPase is also a proton-secreting pump. Studies of acute in vitro pH and pCO_2 changes on a related K-absorbing pump in the rat colon support such an assertion. In this system, decreasing ambient pH by increasing ambient pCO_2 from 1 to 10% CO_2 resulted in approximately a 15-fold enhancement of net Rb absorption due to enhancement of Rb absorptive flux (76).

In the CCD of K-restricted rabbits we observed that exposure to 10% CO_2 resulted in a dramatic increase in Rb tracer efflux (123). Acidosis typically inhibits conductance through K channels (71); thus it appears implausible that enhancement in Rb absorption is mediated by a Ba-sensitive K conductance. Nevertheless, to test whether the enhancement in Rb efflux is dependent on an H-K-ATPase, additional studies were conducted in the presence of luminal SCH28080. Under these conditions, 10% CO_2 failed to enhance Rb tracer efflux. Apparently, acidosis induced by 10% CO_2 enhances Rb efflux by an H-K-ATPase-dependent mechanism.

Although apical K/Rb uptake can be ascribed to H-K-ATPase, the mode of K/Rb exit was not certain. Intercalated cells studied under K-replete conditions exhibit little basolateral K conductance (65). However, for 10% CO_2 to stimulate transepithelial Rb efflux, a basolateral exit pathway must exist under K-restricted conditions. To examine the mechanism of Rb exit from the basolateral membrane during K-restriction, additional studies were conducted to examine the effect of CO_2 on Rb tracer efflux in the presence of 3 mM basolateral Ba. Although 10% CO_2 stimulated Rb efflux in the absence of basolateral Ba, in the presence of 3 mM basolateral Ba, 10% CO_2 failed to stimulate Rb efflux. These observations indicate that, at least during K restriction, basolateral Rb/K exit occurs by a Ba-sensitive pathway, presumably a K channel (125).

Effects of Luminal Na and K Concentration on H-K-ATPase-Mediated Ion Transport

Electroneutral transport contributes to tracer K/Rb flux in the CCD during K restriction. Under K-replete conditions it is well established that separate Na and K conductive pathways are present at the apical membrane of the CCD (42, 84, 100, 112). As a first step in the systematic examination of the pathways of K/Rb tracer efflux in K-restricted animals, we examined the effects of known inhibitors of conductive Na and K efflux . As before, we studied animals conditioned to a low K diet to enhance the H-K-ATPase component of K/Rb tracer efflux (126). Therefore, microperfusion studies were conducted in the presence and absence of Ba, an inhibitor of K channels (48, 84, 100, 112). Both luminal amiloride addition and luminal Na removal enhanced tracer Rb efflux. Interestingly, the effects were not mediated by identical pathways (126). Inhibition of the apical Na conductance with amiloride had no effect on Rb efflux in the presence of luminal Ba, which indicated that amiloride stimulated Rb efflux by a Ba-sensitive pathway, presumably via apical K channels. In contrast, enhancement of Rb efflux in response to luminal Na removal was only partially sensitive to either 2 or 4 mM Ba. However, the enhancement in Rb efflux by Na removal was abolished in the presence of both Ba and SCH28080, which indicates that luminal Na removal enhances Rb efflux in part via H-K-ATPase. Moreover, in contrast to studies conducted in K-replete animals, in which a Ba-sensitive pathway is the predominant mechanism for Rb efflux, Ba-sensitive Rb efflux represents a relatively small fraction of Rb efflux in tubules from K-restricted animals (126). Two plausible mechanisms could explain the stimulation of H-K-ATPase in the preceding experiments.

Possibly a decrease in intracellular K concentration ($[K]_i$) attendant to inhibition of the basolateral Na-K-ATPase could stimulate cellular Rb/K uptake mediated by H-K-ATPase. Observations on the gastric H-K-ATPase lend support for this viewpoint. Ouabain stimulated K absorption in gastric gland via H-K-ATPase (80). Moreover, gastric H-K-ATPase is stimulated as $[K]_i$ decreases to 60 mM (47) and a decrease in $[K]_i$ stimulates phosphoenzyme formation increasing enzyme activity (55). Thus maneuvers that result in a decrease in $[K]_i$ such as inhibition of basolateral Na-K-ATPase should stimulate K absorption via the H-K-ATPase. In support of this hypothesis we observed that inhibition of Na-K-ATPase by ouabain stimulates Rb efflux via H-K-ATPase (124). Apparently, inhibition of basolateral Na-K-ATPase stimulates apical H-K-ATPase in both the gastric gland and the CD.

Alternatively, the cation absorptive site of the renal H-K-ATPase may not be exclusively selective for K. Such a hypothesis does not preclude effects of $[K]_i$ on H-K-ATPase activity. If Na can bind to the K-binding site of the renal H-K-ATPase with less efficient transport via this pump, then the presence of a large luminal [Na] would reduce the tracer Rb efflux via H-K-ATPase. An experiment performed in our laboratory addresses this issue (124). SCH28080 significantly inhibited Rb efflux both in the presence and absence of luminal Na. However, the degree of inhibition of Rb efflux was significantly greater in the absence of luminal Na ($48.2\pm8.2\%$) than in the presence of luminal Na ($14.7\pm5.0\%$, $p<0.01$, Figure 2).

Therefore two pertinent observations can be made. First, the increase in Rb efflux observed upon luminal Na removal can only be fully abolished by the presence of both luminal Ba and luminal SCH28080. Second, the percentage inhibition of Rb tracer efflux by SCH28080 is greater in the absence of luminal Na compared to similar studies performed in the presence of luminal Na. Both observations suggest a possible interaction between the H-K-ATPase and luminal Na concentration. A plausible hypothesis for the nature of this interaction is that Na may be a partial agonist at the luminal cation-binding site of the renal H-K-ATPase and decreases H-K-ATPase-de-

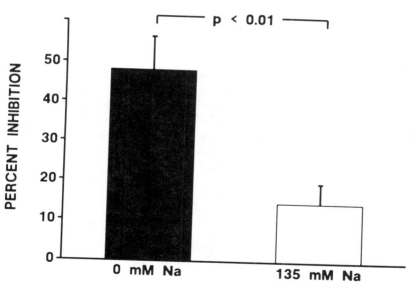

Figure 2   Effect of inhibition of H-K-ATPase by 10 μM SCH28080 on tracer Rb efflux, used as a marker of unidirectional K efflux, in the CCD. Rabbits were adapted to a low K diet in order to enhance the component of tracer efflux mediated by H-K-ATPase. The percent inhibition of Rb efflux was examined at two luminal [Na] as listed. In each case inhibition of H-K-ATPase significantly reduced Rb efflux; however, the percent inhibition of Rb efflux was significantly greater in the nominal absence of luminal Na than when luminal [Na] was 135 mM (data adapted from 124).

pendent Rb efflux. In other words, Na may compete with K for uptake across the apical membrane via the H-K-ATPase.

Indeed, evidence exists that a related H-K-ATPase in the rat colonic epithelium possesses the capacity to transport Na, albeit with a lower affinity than K (105). Like K absorptive flux, Na absorptive flux was inhibited by orthovanadate and mucosal ouabain when mucosal K concentration was 0.6 mM. However, increasing K concentration reduced the component of Na absorptive flux inhibited by either drug. The authors suggested that mucosal Na can compete with mucosal K for uptake at the apical membrane.

Work in several other systems provides evidence to support an apparent promiscuous nature of certain ATP-driven cation transporters. For example, the hog gastric H-K-ATPase has been shown to substitute Na for H on the cytosolic cation-binding site (78). Similarly, H may substitute for Na transport through the Na-K-ATPase in vesicles derived from red blood cells and in purified kidney Na-K-ATPase reconstituted into artificial membranes (7, 77). An unrelated F-type H-ATPase, the F_1F_0 ATP synthase of the bacterium *Propriogenium modestum,* has also been shown to transport Na rather than H (50, 51).

A direct test was devised to determine if Na acts as a partial agonist for cation efflux via the renal H-K-ATPase (126). Studies were conducted in the CCD of K-restricted rabbits in the presence of 0.1 mM luminal amiloride to block fully apical conductive Na efflux, and the effect of SCH28080 on lumen-to-bath ^{22}Na efflux was examined as a function of K concentration (126). In the presence of 0.5 mM luminal [K], SCH28080 significantly inhibited ^{22}Na efflux. In contrast, when similar studies were conducted in the presence of 20 mM luminal [K], SCH28080 had no significant effect on Na efflux, although under these conditions, SCH28080 inhibited Rb efflux. The most plausible explanation for these results is that Na can compete with K for transport via the renal H-K-ATPase (126).

PHYSIOLOGICAL SIGNIFICANCE

At present our knowledge of the physiologic regulation of the renal H-K-ATPase is limited. Thus the full implications of this pump with respect to K intake, acid base balance, and mineralocorticoid regulation are incompletely understood. However, certain consistent findings have emerged. It is apparent that K intake or some factor related to K intake profoundly affects the activity of this enzyme in all segments where it has been studied; namely, the CNT, the CCD, and the OMCD. Acid base balance also appears to influence the activity or the expression of this enzyme. Aldosterone affects H-K-ATPase activity, but the action of this hormone appears to be relatively selective on the cortex. These facts suggest that part of the potentiation of the metabolic alkalosis induced by mineralocorticoids during K-depletion is the more pronounced increase in H-K-ATPase activity when both stimuli are present. Alternatively, aldosterone may enhance the capacity for CD acidification by enhancing K secretion in the CCD to provide increased substrate in the form of luminal K for maximum operation of the H-K-ATPase. Observations in ion-tight renal medullary membrane vesicles by Curran et al (13) support this assertion. These investigators demonstrated that acidification in renal medullary microsomal membrane vesicles is enhanced by increasing intravesicular K concentration.

Finally, in view of the significant effect of two relatively specific gastric H-K-ATPase inhibitors, omeprazole and SCH28080, on acidification by the OMCD$_i$, it is possible that defects in the expression or regulation of H-K-ATPase may explain certain forms of distal renal tubular acidosis. Recent observations with a third known gastric H-K-ATPase inhibitor, vanadate, are also consistent with this hypothesis (13, 14).

INFERENCES FROM THE GASTRIC H-K-ATPase

A considerable portion of work on the renal H-K-ATPase has been guided by observations of the well-known gastric enzyme (for review see 15, 83). For example, ion transport characteristics and the effects of specific gastric H-K-ATPase inhibitors, such as omeprazole and SCH28080, have been central to identifying H-K-ATPase activity in the kidney. Similarly, antibodies raised against gastric enzyme label renal tissues. Therefore, recent advances on the study of the structure and function of the gastric H-K-ATPase as a model for work on the renal enzyme are briefly discussed below.

The gastric H-K-ATPase is a classical P-type ATPase consisting of two dissimilar subunits referred to as α and β. The α subunit possesses both the catalytic site and the ion translocation activity. Radiation inactivation experiments suggest that it may function as an oligomer of heterodimers (83) that have been visualized in two-dimensional arrays (83). One might expect the structural characteristics of the renal H-K-ATPase to closely resemble the gastric enzyme.

Study of the gastric H-K-ATPase using molecular biology methods is advancing rapidly. cDNA clones have been obtained for both subunits of the stomach H-K-ATPase from several species (57, 81, 87, 91). Furthermore, genes for both the α and β subunits have been obtained (58, 59).

Recently, a cDNA for a divergent colonic form of the α subunit has been identified for the rat (12). The latter is most intriguing because, unlike probes from previous cDNA clones, probes generated from the colonic H-K-ATPase yield a signal in Northern analyses that indicates a homologous mRNA is present in the kidney. This observation suggests that the colonic version will likely provide sufficient nucleotide sequence information to facilitate cloning of a cDNA for a renal H-K-ATPase α subunit in the very near future. We have also obtained a partial cDNA clone of a β-like subunit from rabbit kidney using the polymerase chain reaction (PCR) with oligonucleotide primers designed from the rabbit stomach β subunit cDNA sequence (K. Curran et al, unpublished observation). The PCR product has been used to obtain a complete cDNA clone of the H-K-ATPase β subunit from a rabbit renal medullary cDNA library.

THE FUTURE

Research on the H-K-ATPase can be expected to move into a very exciting phase within the next few years. Efforts are likely to proceed along three converging paths. The study of the physiological role will continue to exploit the breakthroughs provided by the now established approaches detailed in this review. A tremendous amount of work remains to characterize fully ion transport in the CD. Particular attention must be placed on the respective roles of the H-ATPase and the H-K-ATPase in urinary acidification. The possibility that H-K-ATPase may act as a Na transporter deserves careful examination. Importantly, the regulation of the renal H-K-ATPase subunits will require study at the cellular and subcellular levels. Finally, molecular biology is poised to supply the tools necessary to characterize the nature of the regulation of H-K-ATPase and may provide a source of enzymes for detailed enzymological description.

Literature Cited

1. Aithal, H. N., Toback, F. G., Dube, S., Getz, G. S., Spargo, B. H. 1977. Formation of renal medullary lysosomes during potassium-depletion nephropathy. *Lab. Invest.* 36:107–13
2. Backman, K. A., Hayslett, J. P. 1983. Role of the medullary collecting duct in potassium conservation. *Pflügers Arch.* 396:297–300
3. Beil, W., Hackbarth, I., Sewing, K. F. 1986. Mechanism of gastric antisecretory effect of SCH28080. *Br. J. Pharmacol.* 88:19–23
4. Beil, W., Hannemann, H., Madge, S., Sewing, K. F. 1987. Inhibition of gastric K^+/H^+-ATPase by acid-activated 2-((2-pyridylmethyl)sulphinyl) benzimidazole products. *Eur. J Pharmacol.* 133:37–45
5. Beil, W., Staar, U., Sewing, K. F.

1987. SCH28080 is a more selective inhibitor than SCH32651 at the K^+ site of gastric K^+/H^+-ATPase. *Eur. J. Pharmacol.* 139:349–52
6. Berliner, R. W. 1952. Renal secretion of potassium and hydrogen ions. *Fed. Proc.* 11:695–700
7. Blostein, R. 1985. Proton-activated rubidium transport catalyzed by the sodium pump. *J. Biol. Chem.* 260:829–33
8. Briving, C., Andersson, B. M., Nordberg, P., Wallmark, B. 1988. Inhibition of gastric H^+/K^+-ATPase by substituted imidazo[1,2-a]pyridines. *Biochim. Biophys. Acta* 946: 185–92
9. Brown, D., Gluck, S., Hartwig, J. 1987. Structure of the novel membrane-coating material in proton-secreting epithelial cells in identification as

an H^+ ATPase. *J. Cell Biol.* 105:1637–48

10. Brown, D., Hirsch, S., Gluck, S. 1988. Localization of a proton-pumping ATPase in rat kidney. *J. Clin. Invest.* 82:2114–26

11. Cheval, L., Barlet-Bas, C., Khodouri, C., Feraille, K. E., Marsky, S., Doucet, A. 1991. K^+-ATPase-mediated Rb^+ transport in rat collecting tubule: modulation during K^+ deprivation. *Am. J. Physiol.* (29):F800–5

12. Crowson, M. S., Shull, G. E. 1992. Isolation and characterization of a cDNA encoding the putative distal colon H^+,K^+-ATPase. *J. Biol. Chem.* 267:13740–48

13. Curran, K. A., Hebert, M. J., Cain, B. D., Wingo, C. S. 1992. Evidence for the presence of a K-dependent acidifying adenosine triphosphatase in the rabbit renal medulla. *Kidney Int.* In press

14. Dafnis, E., Spohn, M., Lonis, B., Kurtzman, N. A., Sabatini, S. 1992. Vanadate causes hypokalemic distal renal tubular acidosis. *Am. J. Physiol.* 262(31):F449–53

15. De Pont, J. J. H. H. M., de-Jong, H., Skrabanja, A. T. P., van der Hijden, H. T. W. M. 1988. Overview: H,K-ATPase: Na,K-ATPase's stepsister. In *The Na^+,K^+-Pump, Part A: Molecular Aspects*, pp. 585–602. New York: Liss

16. Doucet, A., Marsy, S. 1987. Characterization of K-ATPase activity in distal nephron: Stimulation by potassium depletion. *Am. J. Physiol.* 253(22):F418–23

17. Durlacher, S. H., Darrow, D. C., Winternitz, M. C. 1942. The effect of low potassium diet and of deoxycorticosterone acetate upon renal size. *Am. J. Physiol.* 136:346–49

18. Elger, M., Bankir, L., Kriz, W. 1992. Morphometric analysis of kidney hypertrophy in rats after chronic potassium depletion. *Am. J. Physiol.* 262(31):F656–67

19. Ene, M. D., Khan-Daneshmend, T., Roberts, C. J. C. 1982. A study of the inhibitory effects of SCH28080 on gastric secretion in man. *Br. J. Pharacol.* 76:389–91

20. Evan, A., Huser, J., Bengele, H. H., Alexander, E. A. 1980. The effect of alterations in dietary potassium on collecting system morphology in the rat. *Lab. Invest.* 42:668–75

21. Deleted in proof

22. Evans, B. M., Jones, N. C. H., Steiner, S., Steiner, M. 1954. Electrolyte excretion during experimental potassium depletion in man. *Clin. Sci.* 3:305–16

23. Forte, J. G., Black, J. A., Forte, T. M., Machen, T. E., Wolosin, J. M. 1981. Ultrastructural changes related to functional activity in gastric oxyntic cells. *Am. J. Physiol.* 241(4):G349–58

24. Fourman, P. 1952. The ability of the normal kidney to conserve potassium. *Lancet* 1:1042–44

25. Fowler, N., Giebisch, G., Whittembury, G. 1975. Distal tubular tracer microinjection study of renal tubular potassium transport. *Am. J. Physiol.* 229:1227–33

26. Fryklund, J., Helander, H. F., Elander, B., Wallmark, B. 1988. Function and structure of parietal cells after H^+-K^+-ATPase blockade. *Am. J. Physiol.* 254(17):G399–407

27. Ganser, A. L., Forte, J. G. 1973. K^+-stimulated ATPase in purified microsomes of bullfrog oxyntic cells. *Biochim. Biophys. Acta* 307:169–80

28. Garg, L. C. 1991. Effects of aldosterone on H-K-ATPase activity in rabbit nephron segments. In *Aldosterone: Fundamental Aspects*, ed. J. P. Bonvalet, N. Farman, M. Lombes, M. E. Rafestin-Oblin, p. 328. Paris: Libby

29. Garg, L. C. 1991. Respective roles of H-ATPase and H-K-ATPase in ion transport in the kidney. *J. Am. Soc. Nephrol.* 2:949–60

30. Garg, L. C., Narang, N. 1988. Ouabain-insensitive K-adenosine triphosphatase in distal nephron segments of the rabbit. *J.Clin. Invest.* 81(4):1204–8

31. Garg, L. C., Narang, N. 1989. Suppression of ouabain-insensitive K-ATPase activity in rabbit nephron segments during chronic hyperkalemia. *Physiol. Biochem.* 12:295–301

31a. Garg, L. C., Narang, N. 1990. Heterogeneity of ouabain-insensitive K-ATPase along the inner medullary collecting duct (IMCD). *Physiologist* 33:A104 (Abstr.)

32. Gifford, J. D., Rome, L., Galla, J. H. 1992. H^+-K^+-ATPase activity in rat collecting duct segments. *Am. J. Physiol.* 31:F692–95

33. Gifford, J. D., Ware, M. W., Crowson, S., Shull, G. E. 1991. Expression of a putative rat distal colonic H^+,K^+-ATPase mRNA in rat kidney: effect of respiratory acidosis. *J. Am. Soc. Nephrol.* 2:700 (Abstr.)

34. Gluck, S., Al-Awqati, Q. 1984. An electrogenic proton translocating adenosine triphosphatase from bovine kidney medulla. *J. Clin. Invest.* 73:1704–10

35. Halperin, M. L., Honrath, U., Wilson,

D. R., Sonnenberg, H. 1989. Effects of chronic hypokalaemia and adrenalectomy on potassium transport by the medullary collecting duct of the rat. *Clin. Sci.* 76:189–94

36. Hansen, G. T., Tisher, C. C., Robinson, R. R. 1980. Response of the collecting duct to disturbances of acid base and potassium balance. *Kidney Int.* 17:326–37

37. Hayashi, M., Katz, A. I. 1987. The kidney in potassium depletion. I. Na^+-K^+-ATPase activity and [^3H] ouabain-binding in the MCT. *Am. J. Physiol.* 252(21):F437–46

38. Hays, S. R., Alpern, R. J. 1990. Apical and basolateral membrane H^+ extrusion mechanisms in the inner stripe of the rabbit outer medullary collecting duct. *Am. J. Physiol.* 259(28):F628–35

39. Hersey, S. J., Steiner, L., Mendlein, J., Rabon, E. C., Sachs, G. 1988. SCH28080 prevents omeprazole inhibition of gastric H^+/K^+-ATPase. *Biochim. Biophys. Acta* 956:49–57

40. Hulter, H. N., Licht, J. H., Sebastian, A. 1979. K^+ deprivation potentiates the renal acid excretory effect of mineralocorticoid: obliteration by amiloride. *Am. J. Physiol.* 236(5):F48–57

41. Hulter, H. N., Sigala, J. F., Sebastian, A. 1978. K^+ deprivation potentiates the renal alkalosis-producing effect of mineralocorticoid. *Am. J. Physiol.* 235(4):F298–309

42. Im, W. B., Blakeman, D. P., Davis, J. P. 1986. Finding of a KCl-independent, electrogenic, ATP-driven H^+-pumping activity in rat light gastric membranes and its effect on the membrane K^+ transport activity. *J. Biol. Chem.* 261:11686–92

43. Imbert-Teboul, M., Doucet, A., Marsy, S., Siaume-Perez, S. 1987. Alterations in enzymatic activity along rat cortical tubule in potassium depletion. *Am. J. Physiol.* 253(22):F408–17

44. Kassirer, J. P., London, A. M., Goldman, D. M., Schwartz, W. B. 1970. On the pathogenesis of metabolic alkalosis in hyperaldosteronism. *Am. J. Med.* 49:306–15

45. Keeling, D. J., Fallowfield, C., Underwood, A. H. 1987. The specificity of omeprazole as an H^+-K^+-ATPase inhibitor depends upon the means of its activation. *Biochem. Pharmacol.* 36:339–44

46. Keeling, D. J., Laing, S. M., Senn-Bilfinger, J. 1988. Interactions of SCH28080 with the gastric (H^+-K^+)-ATPase. In *The Ion Pumps: Structure,*

Function, Regulation, pp. 255–60. New York: Liss

47. Koelz, H. R., Sachs, G., Berglindh, T. 1981. Cation effects on acid secretion in rabbit gastric glands. *Am. J. Physiol.* 241(4):G431–42

48. Koeppen, B. M., Biagi, B. A., Giebisch, G. 1983. Intracellular microelectrode characterization of the rabbit cortical collecting duct. *Am. J. Physiol.* 244(13):F35–47

48a. Komatsu, Y., Garg, L. C. 1991. Stimulation of ouabain-insensitive K-ATPase in rat medullary collecting duct by potassium depletion and metabolic acidosis. *FASEB J.* 5:A752

49. Laski, M. E. 1991. Luminal K removal inhibits pH_i recovery in type A intercalated cells (IC) of the rabbit cortical collecting tubule (CCT). *J. Am. Soc. Nephrol.* 2:704

50. Laubinger, W., Dimroth, P. 1988. Characterization of the ATP synthase of *Propionigenium modestum* as a primary sodium pump. *Biochemistry* 27:7531–37

51. Laubinger, W., Dimroth, P. 1989. The sodium ion translocating adenosine-triphosphatase of *Propionigenium modestum* pumps protons at low sodium ion concentrations. *Biochemistry* 28:7194–98

52. Lepke, S., Becker, A., Passow, H. 1992. Mediation of inorganic anion transport by the hydrophobic domain of mouse erythroid band 3 protein expressed in oocytes of *Xenopus laevis*. *Biochim. Biophys. Acta Biol. Membr.* 1106:13–16

53. Linas, S. L., Peterson, L. N., Anderson, R. J., Aisenbery, G. A., Simon, F. R., Berl, T. 1979. Mechanism of renal potassium conservation in the rat. *Kidney Int.* 15:601–11

54. Lombard, W. E., J. P. Kokko, H. R. Jacobson. 1983. Bicarbonate transport in cortical and outer medullary collecting tubules. *Am. J. Physiol.* 244(13):F289–96

55. Lorentzon, P., Sachs, G., Wallmark, B. 1988. Inhibitory effects of cations in the gastric H^+,K^+-ATPase: a potential-sensitive step in the K^+ limb of the pump cycle. *J. Biol. Chem.* 263:10705–10

56. Deleted in proof

57. Maeda, M., Ishizaki, J., Futai, M. 1988. cDNA cloning and sequence determination of pig gastric H-K-ATPase. *Biochem. Biophys. Res. Commun.* 157:203–9

58. Maeda, M., Oshiman, K., Tamura, S., Futai, M. 1990. Human gastric

H^+/K^+-ATPase gene. *J. Biol. Chem.* 265:9027–32

59. Maeda, M., Oshiman, K. I., Tamura, S., Kaya, S., Mahmood, S., et al. 1991. The rat H^+/K^+-ATPase beta subunit gene and recognition of its control region by gastric DNA binding protein. *J. Biol. Chem.* 266: 21584–88

60. Malnic, G., Klose, R. M., Giebisch, G. 1964. Micropuncture study of renal potassium excretion in the rat. *Am. J. Physiol.* 206:674–86

61. Malnic, G., Klose, R. M., Giebisch, G. 1966. Microperfusion study of distal tubular potassium and sodium transfer in the rat kidney. *Am. J. Physiol.* 211:548–59

62. Malnic, G., Klose, R. M., Giebisch, G. 1966. Micropuncture study of distal tubular potassium and sodium transport in the rat nephron. *Am. J. Physiol.* 211:529–47

63. McKinney, T. D., Davidson, K. K. 1987. Effect of potassium depletion and protein intake in vivo on renal tubular bicarbonate transport in vitro. *Am. J. Physiol.* 252(21):F509–16

64. Mills, J. N., Stanbury, S. W. 1954. A reciprocal relationship between K^+ and H^+ excretion in the diurnal excretory rhythm in man. *Clin. Sci.* 13: 177–86

65. Muto, S., Giebisch, G., Sansom, S. C. 1987. Effects of adrenalectomy on CCD: evidence for differential response of two cell types. *Am. J. Physiol.* 253(22):F742–52

66. Nagaya, H., Satoh, H., Kubo, K., Maki, Y. 1989. Possible mechanism for the inhibition of gastric (H^+/K^+)-adenosine triphosphatase by the proton pump inhibitor AG-1749. *J. Pharmacol. Exp. Ther.* 248(2):799–805

67. Oberleithner, H., Steigner, W., Silbernagl, S., Vogel, U., Gstraunthaler, G., Pfaller, W. 1990. Madin-Darby canine kidney cells III. Aldosterone stimulates an apical H^+/K^+ pump. *Pflügers Arch.* 416:540–47

68. Okusa, M. D., Unwin, R. J,. Velazquez, H., Giebisch, G., Wright, F. S. 1992. Active potassium absorption by the renal distal tubule. *Am. J. Physiol.* 262(31):F488–93

69. Oliver, J., MacDowell, M., Welt, L. G., Holliday, M. A., Hollander, W., Winters, R. W. 1957. The renal lesions of electrolyte imbalance. 1. The structural alterations in potassium-depleted rats. *J. Exp. Med.* 106:563–74

70. O'Neil, R. G., Helman, S. I. 1977. Transport characteristics of renal col-

lecting tubules: influence of DOCA and diet. *Am. J. Physiol.* 233(2):F544–58

71. O'Neil, R. G., Sansom, S. C. 1984. Electrophysiological properties of cellular and paracellular conductive pathways of the rabbit cortical collecting duct. *J. Membr. Biol.* 82:281–95

72. Ordonez, N. G., Spargo, B. H. 1976. The morphologic relationship of light and dark cells of the collecting tubule in potassium-depleted rats. *Am. J. Pathol.* 84:317–22

73. Ordonez, N. G., Toback, F. G., Aithal, H. N., Spargo, B. H 1977. Zonal changes in renal structure and phospholipid metabolism during reversal of potassium depletion nephropathy. *Lab. Invest.* 36:33–37

74. Ornt, D. B. 1986. Effect of potassium concentration and ouabain on the renal adaptation to potassium depletion in isolated perfused rat kidney. *Can. J. Physiol. Pharmacol.* 64:1427–33

75. Ornt, D. B., Tannen, R. L. 1983. Demonstration on intrinsic renal adaptation for K^+ conservation in short-term K^+ depletion. *Am. J. Physiol.* 245(14): F329–38

76. Perrone, R. D., McBride, D. E. 1988. Aldosterone and PCO_2 enhance rubidium absorption in rat distal colon. *Am. J. Physiol.* 254(17):G898–906

77. Polvani, C., Blostein, R. 1988. Protons as substitutes for sodium and potassium in the sodium pump reaction. *J. Biol. Chem.* 263(32):16757–63

78. Polvani, C., Sachs, G., Blostein, R. 1989. Sodium ions as substitutes for protons in gastric H,K-ATPase. *J. Biol. Chem.* 264(30):17854–59

79. Deleted in proof

80. Reenstra, W. W., Bettencourt, J. D., Forte, J. G. 1986. Active K^+ absorption by the gastric mucosa: inhibition by omeprazole. *Am. J. Physiol.* 250(13): G455–60

81. Reuben, M. A., Lasater, L. S., Sachs, G. S. 1990. Characterization of a β subunit of the gastric H^+-/K^+-transporting ATPase. *Proc. Natl. Acad. Sci. USA* 87:6767–71

82. Sachs, G., Chang, H. H., Rabon, E. C., Schackman, R., Lewin, M., Saccomani, G. 1976. A nonelectrogenic H^+ pump in plasma membranes of hog stomach. *J. Biol. Chem.* 251:7690–98

83. Sachs, G., Munson, K., Balaji, V. N., Aures-Fischer, D., Hersey, S. J., Hall, K. 1989. Functional domains of the gastric H-K-ATPase. *J. Bioeng. Biomembr.* 21:573–88

84. Sansom, S. C., O'Neil, R. G. 1985.

Mineralocorticoid regulation of apical cell membrane Na^+ K^+ transport of the cortical collecting duct. *Am. J. Physiol.* 248(17):F858–68

85. Schackmann, R., Schwartz, A., Saccomani, G., Sachs, G. 1977. Cation transport by gastric H^+:K^+ATPase. *J. Membr. Biol.* 32:361–81

86. Schrader, G. A., Prickett, C. O., Salmon, W. D. 1937. Symptomatology and pathology of potassium and magnesium deficiencies in the rat. *J. Nutr.* 14:85–104

87. Shull, G. E., Lingrel, J. B. 1986. Molecular cloning of the rat stomach H-K-ATPase. *J. Biol. Chem.* 261:16788

88. Schwartz, G. J., Barasch, J., Al-Awqati, Q. 1985. Plasticity of functional epithelial polarity. *Nature* 318:368–71

89. Schwartz, G. J., Burg, M. B. 1978. Mineralocorticoid effects on cation transport by cortical collecting tubules in vitro. *Am. J. Physiol.* 235(4):F576–85

90. Scott, C. K., Sundell, E., Castrovilly, L. 1987. Studies on the mechanism of action of the gastric microsomal $(H^+ + K^+)$-ATPase inhibitors SCH32651 and SCH28080. *Biochem. Pharmacol.* 36:97–104

91. Shull, G. E. 1990. cDNA cloning of the beta subunit of the rat gastric H,K-ATPase. *J. Biol. Chem.* 265:12123–26

92. Silver, R. B., Frindt, G., Palmer, L. G. 1991. Functional identification of an H-K-ATPase in mammalian cortical collecting tubule. *J. Am. Soc. Nephrol.* 2:751 (Abstr.)

93. Smolka, A., Helander, H. F., Sachs, G. 1983. Monoclonal antibodies against the gastric H,K-ATPase. *Am. J. Physiol.* 245(8):G589–96

94. Spargo, B. 1954. Kidney changes in hypokalemic alkalosis in the rat. *J. Lab. Clin. Med.* 43:802–14

95. Squires, R. D., Huth, E. J. 1959. Experimental potassium depletion in normal human subjects 1. Relationship of ionic intake to renal conservation of potassium. *J. Clin. Invest.* 38:1134–48

95a. Stanton, B. A., Biemesderfer, D., Wade, J. B., Giebisch, G. 1981. Structural and functional study of the rat distal nephron: effects of potassium adaptation and depletion. *Kidney Int.* 19:36–48

96. Stanton, B. A., Kaissling, B. 1988. Adaptation of distal tubule and collecting duct to increased Na delivery. II.

Na^+ K^+ transport. *Am. J. Physiol.* 255(24):F1269–75

97. Stanton, B. A., Pan, L., Deetjen, H., Guckian, V., Giebisch, G. 1987. Independent effects of aldosterone and potassium on induction of potassium adaptation in rat kidney. *J. Clin. Invest.* 79:198–206

98. Deleted in proof

99. Stetson, D. L., Wade, J. B., Giebisch, G. 1980. Morphologic alterations in the rat medullary collecting duct following potassium depletion. *Kidney Int.* 17:45–56

100. Stokes, J. B. 1984. Pathways of K^+ permeation across the rabbit cortical collecting tubule: effect of amiloride. *Am. J. Physiol.* 246(15):F457–66

101. Stokes, J. B. 1985. Mineralocorticoid effect on K^+ permeability of the rabbit cortical collecting tubule. *Kidney Int.* 28:640–45

102. Stokes, J. B., Ingram, M. J., Williams, A. D., Ingram, D. 1981. Heterogeneity of the rabbit collecting tubule: Localization of mineralocorticoid hormone action to the cortical portion. *Kidney Int.* 20:340–47

103. Stone, D. K., Seldin, D. W., Kokko, J. P., Jacobson, H. R. 1983. Mineralocorticoid modulation of rabbit medullary collecting duct acidification. *J. Clin. Invest.* 72:77–83

104. Stone, D. K., Seldin, D. W., Kokko, J. P., Jacobson, H. R. 1983. Anion dependence of rabbit medullary collecting duct acidification. *J. Clin. Invest.* 71:1505–8

105. Sweiry, J. H., Binder, H. J. 1990. Active potassium absorption in rat distal colon. *J. Physiol.* 423:155–70

106. Toback, F. G., Ordonez, N. G., Bortz, S. L., Spargo, B. H. 1976. Zonal changes in renal structure and phospholipid metabolism in potassium-deficient rats. *Lab. Invest.* 34:115–24

107. Toussaint, C., Vereerstraeten, P. 1962. Effects of blood pH changes on potassium excretion in the dog. *Am. J. Physiol.* 202:768–72

108. Verlander, J. W., Madsen, K. M., Tisher, C. C. 1987. Effect of acute respiratory acidosis on two populations of intercalated cells in the rat cortical collecting duct. *Am. J. Physiol.* 253(22):F1142–56

109. Wallmark, B., Brandstrom, A., Larsson, H. 1984. Evidence for acid-induced transformation of omeprazole into an active inhibitor of $(H^+ + K^+)$-ATPase within the parietal cell. *Biochim. Biophys. Acta* 778:549–58

110. Wallmark, B., Briving, C., Fryklund,

J., Munson, K., Jackson, R., et al. 1987. Inhibition of gastric H^+,K^+-ATPase and acid secretion by SCH 28080, a substituted pyridyl (1,2a)imidazole. *J. Biol. Chem.* 262(5):2077–84

111. Wallmark, B., Larsson, H., Humble, L. 1985. The relationship between gastric acid secretion and gastric H^+,K^+-ATPase activity. *J. Biol. Chem.* 260(25):13681–84

112. Wang, W., Giebisch, G. 1991. Dual modulation of renal ATP-sensitive K^+ channel by protein kinases A and C. *Proc. Natl. Acad. Sci. USA* 88:9722–25

113. Warden, D. H., Hayashi, M., Schuster, V. L., Stokes, J. B. 1989. K^+ and Rb^+ transport by the rabbit CCD: Rb^+ reduces K^+ conductance Na^+ transport. *Am. J. Physiol.* 257(26):F43–52

114. Wingo, C. S. 1984. Effect of ouabain on K secretion in cortical collecting tubules from adrenalectomized rabbits. *Am. J. Physiol.* 247(17):F588–95

115. Wingo, C. S. 1987. Potassium transport by the medullary collecting tubule of rabbit: effects of variation in K intake. *Am. J. Physiol.* 253(22):F1136–41

116. Wingo, C. S. 1989. Active proton secretion and potassium absorption in the rabbit outer medullary collecting duct—functional evidence for proton-potassium activated adenosine triphosphatase. *J. Clin. Invest.* 84:361–65

117. Wingo, C. S., Armitage, F. E. 1992. Rubidium absorption and proton secretion by rabbit outer medullary collecting duct via H-K-ATPase. *Am. J. Physiol.* 263(32):849–57

118. Wingo, C. S., Kokko, J. P., Jacobson, H. R. 1985. Effects of in vitro aldosterone on the rabbit cortical collecting tubule. *Kidney Int.* 28:51–57

119. Wingo, C. S., Madsen, K. M., Smolka, A., Tisher, C. C. 1989. Evidence for H-K-ATPase in intercalated cells of the rabbit cortical collecting duct. *Clin. Res.* 37:504A (Abstr.)

120. Wingo, C. S., Madsen, K. M., Smolka, A., Tisher, C. C. 1990. H-K-ATPase immunoreactivity in cortical and outer medullary collecting duct. *Kidney Int.* 38:985–90

121. Womersley, R. A., Darragh, J. H. 1955. Potassium and sodium restriction in the normal human. *J. Clin. Invest.* 34:456–61

122. Deleted in proof

123. Zhou, X., Wingo, C. S. 1990. H-K-ATPase mediates the enhancement of Rb absorption induced by 10% CO_2 in the cortical collecting duct (CCD). *Clin. Res.* 38:985A

124. Zhou, X., Wingo, C. S. 1992. H-K-ATPase enhancement by cortical collecting duct. *Am. J. Physiol.* 263(32):F43–48

125. Zhou, X., Wingo, C. S. 1992. Mechanisms for enhancement of Rb efflux by 10% CO_2 in cortical collecting duct (CCD). *Clin. Res.* 40(2):179A (Abstr.)

126. Zhou, X., Wingo, C. S. 1992. Mechanisms of rubidium permeation by rabbit cortical collecting duct during potassium restriction. *Am. J. Physiol.* 263(32):

Annu. Rev. Physiol. 1993. 55:349–74

SYNCHRONIZATION OF CORTICAL ACTIVITY AND ITS PUTATIVE ROLE IN INFORMATION PROCESSING AND LEARNING

Wolf Singer

Max Planck Institute for Brain Research, Deutschordenstr. 46, D-6000 Frankfurt/Main 71, Germany

KEY WORDS: synchronization, oscillation, assembly

INTRODUCTION

The first measurements of the electrical activity of the brain, performed more than 60 years ago with recordings from the scalp, revealed prominent oscillatory activity (19), and until more recently the analysis of oscillatory patterns in the electroencephalogram and in field potentials recorded with intracerebral macroelectrodes has remained a major research tool of neurophysiology. Analyzing the time structure of these wave patterns has established close correlations between the frequency spectrum of the oscillations and changes in the central state of the brain. Different stages of sleep and arousal and also abnormal states such as coma and anesthesia could be identified by relying exclusively on the spectral composition of frequencies in the EEG (for review see 14). However, once it became possible to record the activity of individual nerve cells, interest in field potentials and temporal structures declined. The discovery that the firing rate of neurons in peripheral structures of the nervous system reflected the intensity of sensory stimuli and the speed and force of muscle contractions introduced the notion of rate coding. The evidence of a close relation between the position of a neuron in the brain and its functional properties led to the concept of place coding. The

349

message conveyed by a neuron was thought to be defined entirely by the amplitude of the response and its provenance. As a consequence, in single unit studies, time received relatively little attention as a dimension for coding. This is reflected by the fact that neuronal responses to sensory stimuli or activities occurring in relation to motor acts are commonly averaged over successive trials in order to improve the signal-to-noise ratio. This averaging procedure destroys any temporal structure in the activation pattern that is not precisely locked to the stimulus or the motor response. Thus temporal codes were either ignored or undiscovered with the commonly applied methods of single unit analysis.

Recently, however, we have witnessed a dramatic change in attitude and interest. Attention has shifted again towards time as a coding dimension and many think that temporal relations between the responses of distributed neurons are as important a code as relations between response amplitudes. This renaissance of interest in the temporal aspects of nervous activity has several roots, some of which are elaborated in detail below.

Herein recent developments in this rapidly expanding field of research are reviewed with emphasis on the putative significance of self-generated temporal codes in cortical processing. The reason for this restriction is that there are numerous studies on the mechanisms of pattern generation in motor systems, especially in simple organisms, that demonstrate that neuronal processes are highly dynamic and that temporal codes matter (for review see 67). Inclusion of such a large field of research in this review would impose too much selection and arbitrariness.

OSCILLATIONS AND SYNCHRONY

The fact that fluctuations of field potentials can be recorded with macroelectrodes from the scalp or the dura or from within the brain indicates that a large number of neurons must be engaged in synchronized rhythmic discharges at the respective oscillation frequency. Otherwise, the weak currents associated with synaptic activity and action potentials of individual neurons would not result in recordable macropotentials. The occurrence of recordable amplitude fluctuations in macropotential recordings is thus always an indication for coherent activation of a large number of neurons. Such synchronized discharges can occur as a single event in which case they lead to a large, solitary potential. Examples are the ponto-geniculo-occipital waves that are generated in the brainstem in association with saccadic eye movements (82) and REM-sleep episodes (24, 83), or the potentials evoked by sensory stimulation (15). But synchronous discharges can also occur in a repetitive way in which case they give rise to oscillatory field potentials. The intervals between successive bursts can be more or less regular and lead to narrow or broad band oscillations. The spontaneously occurring field potential oscillations appear to follow the rule that the amplitude of the fluctuations decreases with increasing frequency of the oscillation. This indicates that rapidly oscillating cell assemblies comprise fewer neurons than slowly oscillating cell assemblies.

Particularly low frequency oscillations in the delta range (0.5 to 4 Hz) are observed during slow wave sleep, but also during pathological stages such as anesthesia or coma. Oscillatory activity in the theta range, around 6–7 Hz, is prominent in limbic structures such as the septum, the hippocampus, and the entorhinal cortex during states of attentive arousal. Oscillatory activity in the 10 Hz range, also known as α-activity, occurs during drowsiness or states of relaxation and is particularly pronounced over occipital cortical areas (for a review of the extensive literature see 14, 15). Up to this frequency range, oscillatory activity is of large amplitude and can readily be recorded with macroelectrodes, which indicates that the discharges of a large number of neurons are synchronized and phase-locked to these frequencies. This contrasts with the low amplitude, high frequency fluctuations in the EEG, which characterize high levels of arousal and attention. During these states, the Fourier spectrum of the EEG covers a broad range of frequencies extending from 10 up to 60 Hz. This pattern is commonly referred to as desynchronized EEG and is thought to reflect temporally incoherent activity of spatially distributed neurons. However, analysis with refined methods including digital filtering and intracerebral recording with microelectrodes has revealed the presence of rather regular oscillatory activity also under conditions characterized by desynchronized EEG. These investigations have disclosed oscillatory activity in the β and γ range, i.e. at frequencies between 15 to 30 Hz and 30 to 60 Hz, respectively. These high frequency oscillations occur spontaneously both in humans and higher mammals such as cats and monkeys when the subjects are in a state of focused attention (21, 105, 123, 125, 132, 133, 143), or when they are performing new and complicated motor acts (107). Oscillatory components in the γ-frequency range are also contained in field potential responses evoked by sensory stimuli. This has been shown to be the case for the cortical responses following acoustic (15, 16, 17, 54, 55, 56, 101, 116) and visual stimulation (40, 53, 59, 64, 65), for visual responses in the optic tectum of pigeons (110) and for the event-related P-300-wave that is thought to reflect high level cognitive processes related to selective attention (17). Particularly regular and prominent field potential oscillations in the range of 40 Hz also occur in the olfactory bulb during the inspiration phase of the respiratory cycle (3, 51, 52).

There is thus ample evidence from a variety of brain structures, especially those showing a laminar organization such as the neocortex, the tectum and the olfactory bulb, that groups of cells engage in high frequency synchronous activity even during states when the EEG is desynchronized. With the exception of the olfactory bulb, however, the amplitudes of these high frequency oscillations are usually small, thus indicating that the groups of neurons engaged in such synchronous activity are small or dissipated.

These observations indicate that neurons in cortical networks have the tendency to engage in synchronous activity in different distinct frequency bands whereby the probability of occurrence of synchronous activity in a particular frequency range depends on the central state of the brain, on the presence of sensory signals, and on the occurrence of motor acts. This raises the question as to the functional significance of these synchronization phenomena. As far as synchronization in the low frequency band up to 4 Hz is concerned, it is commonly held that such states of global synchrony are inappropriate for information processing. At these low frequencies very large populations of cells discharge in unison, and these self-generated rhythmic discharges are scarely influenced by sensory stimuli. The fact that such large scale synchronization in the low frequency band occurs during sleep and in coma and anesthesia seems to support this notion. It should be emphasized, however, that there have been proposals for a functional significance of low frequency oscillations in natural sleep in relation to processes of memory management and consolidation (75). The situation is different for the high frequency oscillations in the β- and γ-band because these are particularly pronounced in awake performing brains, appear to occur on a less global scale, and show close relations with sensory and motor processes (see below).

THE ORIGIN OF OSCILLATIONS

Oscillatory activity usually results from reciprocal interactions between excitatory and inhibitory mechanisms. Such interactions are realized either by coupling between excitatory and inhibitory membrane conductances within the same neuron or by network architectures comprising inhibitory interneurons and feedback connections (for review see 94, 95). In the former case, neurons tend to exhibit oscillatory firing patterns even if isolated, and therefore cells with such membrane properties are addressed as pacemaker cells. In the latter case, the oscillatory behavior is an emergent property of the network architecture. But in most cases, a combination of both mechanisms occurs. This has been demonstrated for thalamic oscillators where recurrent inhibition is implemented together with pacemaker neurons (for reviews see 103, 146). Less data are available on neocortical oscillations. Experiments in slices have revealed the existence of cells with pacemaker currents tuned to different oscillation frequencies including the γ-band (96, 134). Moreover, there is evidence from in vivo studies that cortical networks have a tendency to engage in rhythmic activity at various preferred frequencies between 10 and 40 Hz

(122). However, it is still unknown to what extent these preferences for distinct resonance frequencies are determined by pacemaker neurons and network properties, respectively. Detailed simulations of cortical networks with oscillatory behavior have been performed for the hippocampus (152) and recently also for the neocortex (26, 100, 161, 162).

THE BINDING PROBLEM, ASSEMBLIES, AND TEMPORAL CODES

In order to appreciate the putative functional role of synchrony and oscillations in the neocortex, current concepts on the nature of cortical representations need to be considered. There is growing evidence that both perceptual and motor functions of the neocortex are based on distributed processes. These occur in parallel at different sites and always involve vast numbers of neurons that, depending on the complexity of the task, may be disseminated throughout the whole cortical sheath. In the visual system, for example, even simple sensory stimuli evoke highly fragmented and widely distributed activity patterns. Because of the columnar organization of cortical areas, neurons preferring the same features or coding for adjacent points in visual space are often segregated from one another by groups of cells preferring different features. In addition, different features such as contours, color, depth, and motion are often processed in separate, non-contiguous cortical areas (38, 50, 112, 156, 163, 165, 166). Thus a particular visual object elicits responses in a large number of spatially distributed neurons each of which encodes only a partial aspect of the object. This raises the intriguing question, commonly addressed as the binding problem, of how these distributed activities are reintegrated in order to generate unambiguous representations of objects in the brain. One widely accepted proposal is that there are areas in the brain where all these distributed activities reconverge onto neurons that respond in a highly selective manner only to those constellations of features that characterize a particular natural object (13). However, this concept faces several problems. First, cells in areas occupying higher levels in the processing hierarchy are often less selective for particular features than those at earlier stages. Second, apart from cells responding preferentially to features of faces and hands (18, 37, 68, 117, 124), no other object-specific cells have been found so far. Third, it has been argued that there would probably not be enough cells in the brain if all distinguishable objects including their many different views would each have to be represented by a specialized neuron. Fourth, even if objects and their different views are represented in a more economical way by interpolation in small groups of neurons (118), no single area in the visual processing stream has been identified so far that could serve as the ultimate site of convergence and that would be large enough to accommodate the still exceedingly large number of required neurons. Fifth, one would have to postulate a large reservoir of uncommitted cells in order to allow for the representation of new, hitherto unknown objects. These neurons would have to maintain latent input connections from all feature-selective neurons at lower processing stages. For the representation of new objects, the subsets of these connections, which are activated by the unique feature constellation of the new object, would have to be selected and consolidated instantaneously.

Alternative concepts have therefore been developed. They are all based on the assumption that representations consist of assemblies of a large number of simultaneously active neurons that are distributed over many cortical areas (1, 22, 33, 42, 43, 44, 69, 73, 114, 115, 136, 137, 158). The essential advantage of assembly coding is that individual cells can participate at different times in the representation of different objects. The assumption is that just as a particular feature can be shared by many different patterns, a particular neuron can be shared by many different representations in that it participates at different times in different "assemblies" of co-active neurons. The code is thus relational, the significance of an individual response depends entirely on the context set by the other members of the assembly.

A basic requirement for representing objects by such assemblies is, of course, that neuronal elements that have joined a particular assembly are identifiable as members of this very assembly and distinguishable from members of other assemblies. Their responses have to be labeled so that they can be recognized as being related. This labeling is thought to be achieved by selective reciprocal connections between the neurons constituting an assembly. It is further assumed that these connections are endowed with adaptive synapses, the efficiency of which can change in a use-dependent way according to some kind of associative learning algorithm. Such adaptivity is required in order to allow for the modification of assemblies and hence for the representation of new objects and patterns. Several proposals have been made concerning the mechanisms by which these connections could serve to label the responses of neurons that have joined into the same assembly. The proposal that is most pertinent to the experiments on response synchronization in the visual cortex was formulated a decade ago by von der Malsburg (158, 159), who suggested that the selective connections should establish temporal coherence on a millisecond time scale between the responses of the coupled cells, thereby making these responses distinguishable as coming from the same assembly. Thus neurons joining into an assembly should synchronize their discharges. Expressing relations between members of an assembly by such a temporal code has the additional advantage that several assemblies can be active simultaneously in the same cortical area without becoming confounded. Assemblies that code for different figures in a scene could each engage in their own rhythm. Consequently, even if responses of neurons overlap on a coarse time scale they remain distinguishable as members of a particular assembly because their responses are correlated at a millisecond time scale with the responses of other cells of the same assembly, but not with cells of other assemblies. This concept of binding by synchrony has been developed further and generalized to intermodal integration (35) and even to integrative processes underlying phenomena such as attention (33) and consciousness (34). The implementation of this temporal coding principle in artificial neuronal networks has proven, that it is indeed very effective. It offers new solutions to segmentation problems that have been notoriously difficult to resolve with amplitude and position codes alone (12, 36, 41, 70, 85, 87, 88, 129, 130, 139, 140, 141, 148, 155, 159, 162).

EXPERIMENTAL SEARCH FOR SYNCHRONIZATION

Since assemblies are solely defined by relations between the responses of their constituting elements, they can only be identified by recording simultaneously from spatially distributed neurons in the brain and by evaluating relations between these responses (1, 4). Such correlation studies have been performed, but until recently they failed to disclose interactions of the kind postulated by the temporal binding hypothesis. The main reason is probably that most of these cross-correlation analyses had been performed to identify anatomical connections rather than to test the concept of temporally coded assemblies. Hence, stimulation and evaluation procedures were not designed to disclose dynamic interactions that depend on stimulus configuration. Many of the cross-correlation studies have actually been based on the analysis of spontaneous activity, which is appropriate for disclosing anatomical connectivity but not stimulus-induced dynamic coupling. Most of the interactions revealed by these analyses occurred only over very short distances and could be accounted for by assuming that the considered cell pairs receive either common excitatory or inhibitory input, or excite or inhibit one another, or have their firing probability influenced by common modulatory input (2, 7, 60, 92, 104, 109, 131, 150, 151, 153, 154).

A new motivation to reinvestigate the hypothesis of temporal coding by cross-correlation analysis came from the observation that spatially adjacent neurons in the cat visual cortex have a strong tendency to engage in highly synchronous oscillatory discharges (64, 65). This observation indicated that responses of feature-specific neurons have a distinct temporal patterning that could, in principle, be used for the labeling of assemblies by a temporal code. Moreover, it proved that groups of neurons can temporarily synchronize their responses as postulated by the hypothesis of temporal coding. This opened the possibility to investigate synchronization phenomena at the single cell level in the visual cortex, one of the best explored structures of the brain, whose putative functions are well defined by a large body of psychophysical data and theoretical concepts.

The phenomenon of local response synchronization has since then been observed at the multi-unit level in several areas of the visual cortex of anesthetized (40, 49) and awake cats (121), in the optic tectum of awake pigeons (110), and recently also in the visual cortex of anesthetized (93) and awake behaving monkeys (91). When presented with their preferred stimulus, neurons spaced close enough to be recorded simultaneously with a single electrode tend to engage in synchronous discharges. These are grouped in bursts that follow each other at intervals of 15–30 ms and hence appear as oscillations in the γ-frequency band. Each of these bursts is associated with a large negativity in the field potential, which is recorded from the same electrode (61, 65). Hence, the local field potential (LFP) exhibits pronounced oscillations in the range of 30 to 60 Hz. The frequency of these oscillations usually fluctuates over a range of 5 to 10 Hz even within a single oscillatory response. Episodes with constant frequency last only for 100–300 ms and can recover several times throughout the response to a continuously moving stimulus (61, 62, 91). Neither the time of occurrence of these synchronized response episodes nor the phase of the oscillations are related to the position of the stimulus within the neuron's receptive field. When cross-correlation functions are computed between responses to subsequently presented identical stimuli, these shift predictors reveal no relation between the respective time series (61, 65). It has further been shown in anesthetized and awake cats (45, 63, 90, 91, 121) and anesthetized and awake monkeys (90, 91) that similar response synchronization can occur also between spatially segregated cell groups recorded with different electrodes within the same visual area. These episodes of synchronization usually occur at times when the local groups of neurons are also engaged in synchronous repetitive bursting. Hence, the cross-correlograms typically show a broad peak centered around zero delay, which is flanked on either side by troughs reflecting the synchronous bursts and the pauses between the bursts. When the duration of these pauses is sufficiently constant throughout the episode of synchronization, the cross-correlograms show a modulation with multiple peaks and troughs.

The Feature Dependence of Response Synchronization

Detailed studies in anesthetized cats and recently in monkeys have revealed that synchronization probability for remote groups of cells depends on the spatial segregation and the feature preference of the respective cell groups as well as on the configuration of the stimuli (45, 38, 63, 90). Stimuli, which according to common Gestalt criteria appear as single figures, lead to synchronization among the responding groups, while stimuli appearing as independent figures or as parts of different figures fail to establish synchrony among the groups they excite (48, 63). Gestalt criteria investigated so far comprise continuity, vicinity, and common motion.

In agreement with a central prediction of the assembly hypothesis is the recent demonstration that two different, spatially overlapping stimuli can be represented by two independently synchronized assemblies of cells and that individual groups can switch between different assemblies depending on stimulus configuration (48). If groups of cells with overlapping receptive fields but different orientation preferences are activated with a single moving light bar, they synchronize their responses even if some of these groups are suboptimally activated (48). However, if such a set of groups is stimulated with two independent stimuli that move in different directions, they no longer form one coherently active assembly, but split into two independently synchronized assemblies; those groups join the same synchronously active assembly that shows a preference for the same stimulus. Thus the two stimuli become represented by two spatially interleaved but temporally segregated assemblies. Groups representing the same stimulus synchronize their responses, while no consistent correlations exist between the activities of assemblies representing different stimuli. Local response parameters of the individual groups such as the amplitude or the oscillatory patterning of the responses are unaffected by changes in the global configuration of the stimuli. Thus it is not possible to tell from the responses of individual groups whether they were activated by one coherent stimulus or by two different stimuli. The only clue for this distinction is provided by the evaluation of synchronicity of the responses of the activated groups. These results indicate that response synchronization between simultaneously activated groups depends not only on the feature preference of the respective groups but also and, to a crucial extent, on stimulus configuration. One methodological caveat following from this is that cross-correlation analysis does not reliably reflect anatomical connectivity (see also 4). The conclusion is that the coupling between distributed cell groups is dynamical and can change in a stimulus-dependent way.

Synchronization Between Areas

The hypothesis of assembly coding further implies that assemblies should be distributed entities extending across different cortical areas. In agreement with this prediction, response synchronization in the γ-frequency range has also been found between groups located in different cortical areas. In the cat, interareal synchronization has been observed between cells in areas 17 and 18 (40, 109), between cells in area 17 and area PLMS, an area specialized for motion processing (49), and even between neurons in A 17 of the two hemispheres (47). In all of these cases, synchronization depended on receptive field constellations and stimulus configurations, similar to the intraareal synchronization (49, 47). Assemblies of neurons with temporally coherent responses can thus be widely distributed and comprise cell groups located in different cortical areas.

The Substrate for Response Synchronization

It is commonly assumed in cross-correlation studies that synchronization of neuronal responses with zero-phase lag is indicative of common input (57). It has been proposed, therefore, that the observed synchronization phenomena in the visual cortex are due to common oscillatory input from subcortical centers. This notion has received support by the discovery of oscillatory activity in the 40 Hz range in thalamic neurons (58, 59, 145). However, synchronization by common subcortical input would alone be incompatible with the postulated role of synchronization in binding because it would neither allow for the required combinatorial flexibility nor for the dependency on feature constellations. The concept of assembly coding requires that the binding together of elements constituting an assembly is achieved through reciprocal connections between the elements of an assembly and not only by common input. This, however, was thought to be unlikely because it seemed difficult to establish synchronization with zero-phase lag by reciprocal interactions between spatially distributed neurons given the rather long conduction delays in the coupling connections. Recently, however, evidence has been obtained that response synchronization with zero-phase lag can indeed be achieved by cortico-cortical connections despite considerable conduction delays. It has been demonstrated that the response synchronization between cell groups in area 17 of the two hemispheres is abolished by severing the corpus callosum and hence is brought about by this reciprocal cortico-cortical projection (47). Response synchronization between the two hemispheres follows the same rules as synchronization between cells in area 17 of the same hemisphere, i.e. synchrony is established only by stimuli that, according to Gestalt criteria, appear as components of a single object. This further emphasizes the putative significance of response synchronization for perceptual grouping because it agrees with the postulate that components of objects that extend across the vertical meridian of the visual field and are projected to different hemispheres need to be bound together in the same way as components of objects that are projected only to one hemisphere. In the meantime, simulation studies are available that confirm that it is possible to establish synchrony without phase lag in the absence of common input and despite variable conduction delays in the synchronizing connections (89, 126, 129, 130).

Experience-Dependent Development of Synchronizing Connections

The theory of assembly coding implies that assemblies are bound together by the coupling connections between the constituting elements. Therefore, the criteria according to which particular features are grouped together reside in the functional architecture of the connections. If this architecture is specified entirely by genetic instructions, perceptual grouping criteria will have to be regarded as genetically determined. If the architecture is modifiable by activity and hence experience, criteria for the segmentation of the visual scene into distinct figures could be acquired by learning. The numerous interindividual similarities in the layout of cortico-cortical connections indicate that basic principles of organization such as laminar termination patterns and maximal spatial extent are determined genetically. But there is also evidence for extensive epigenetic modifications. In mammals, cortico-cortical connections develop mainly postnatally (27, 78, 98, 119) and attain their final specificity through an activity-dependent selection process (28, 80, 99, 120).

Direct evidence that this selection is based on a correlation analysis and leads to disruption of connections between cells that exhibit mainly decorrelated activity comes from experiments with strabismic kittens (97). Raising kittens with artificially induced strabismus leads to changes in the connections between the two eyes and cortical neurons so that individual cortical neurons become connected to only one eye (77). Thus the population of cortical neurons splits into two subpopulations of about equal size, each responding rather selectively to stimulation of one eye only. This reorganization goes along with a modification of perceptual abilities. Strabismic subjects usually develop normal monocular vision in both eyes but they become unable to bind signals conveyed by different eyes into coherent percepts even if these signals are made retinotopically contiguous by optical compensation of the squint angle (160). This indicates that in strabismics, binding mechanisms are abnormal or missing between cells driven from different eyes. Recently, it was found that in strabismics, response synchronization does not occur between cell groups connected to different eyes, while it is normal between cell groups connected to the same eye (86). Moreover, it was found that cortico-cortical connections had reorganized and unlike in normal animals, no longer connected neurons receiving input from different eyes (97).

These results have several important implications. First, they corroborate the notion that tangential intracortical connections are the substrate for response synchronization. Second, they support the view that response synchronization serves perceptual binding. Third, they prove that the architecture of tangential connections is shaped by experience, and fourth, they suggest that this selection occurs according to a correlation rule in similar ways as experience-dependent circuit selection at other levels of the visual system (for reviews see 138, 147).

RESPONSE SYNCHRONIZATION OUTSIDE VISUAL CORTEX

Apart from the studies in the visual cortex, which have been reviewed above, only few investigations have addressed the question of stimulation or context-dependent synchronization across spatially segregated groups of neurons. So far data are available only for the somatosensory and motor cortex (107), the acoustic and the frontal cortex (5, 157), and the pigeon optic tectum (S. Neuenschwander & F. Varela, in preparation). In every case, evidence has been obtained for transient interactions between simultaneously recorded neurons. As in the visual cortex, these episodes of manifest interactions were usually of short duration. In the acoustic and frontal cortex, the type of interaction was variable, in the optic tectum and the somato-motor cortex the interactions resembled those in the visual cortex, i.e. the cells synchronized their responses with zero-phase lag. Some indications are available that these episodes of coupled discharges and synchrony are correlated with behavior. Synchronization between units in somatosensory and motor cortex is particularly pronounced while the monkey tries to solve a difficult reaching task, but prolonged oscillations vanish once the task is learned and reaching is executed without difficulty (107). Synchronization between units in the frontal cortex has been reported to occur in contiguity with certain behavioral sequences in a complex delayed matching to sample task (5). Finally, there is the evidence for γ-range field oscillations during the P-300 event related potential. This potential is considered a correlate of cognitive processes related to attention (54). Its association with γ-oscillations might indicate therefore that synchronicity in the γ-frequency range is functionally relevant.

OSCILLATIONS, SYNCHRONY, AND THE PROBLEM OF EPIPHENOMENA

While these experimental results are all fully compatible with the hypothesis that response synchronization serves as a binding mechanism, the possibility needs to be considered that synchrony and oscillations are epiphenomena of a system's properties that have evolved for a completely different purpose.

Before discussing possible functional roles of oscillations and synchrony in a broader context, it needs to be emphasized that the two phenomena, while apparently often occurring together, do not necessarily depend on one another. Individual neurons can engage in oscillatory activity without necessarily being synchronized with other cells, likewise different cells can exhibit synchronous discharges in the absence of narrow or broad band oscillations. One extreme case is that two cells always discharge simultaneously but at irregular intervals, which have a Poisson distribution. This condition is frequent for cells driven by common input, e.g. for neighboring cells in the lateral geniculate nucleus (8). Another case is the occurrence of simultaneous but nonrepetitive burst responses in several cells. This is seen, for example, during PGO waves (135).

Oscillations as a Prerequisite for Synchrony

As reviewed in the introduction, oscillatory activity frequently appears to be associated with synchrony, which raises the question of whether and if so how oscillatory processes are related to synchronization. One possibility is that oscillatory activity favors the occurrence of synchrony. In oscillatory responses, the occurrence of a burst predicts with some probability the occurrence of the next. It has been argued that this predictability is a necessary prerequisite to synchronize remote cell groups with zero-phase lag, despite considerable conduction delays in the coupling connections (46). This view is supported by simulation studies that have shown that zero-phase lag synchronization can be achieved despite considerable conduction delays and variation of conduction times in the synchronizing connections if the coupled cell groups have a tendency to oscillate (89, 126, 129, 130). Another feature of networks with oscillatory properties is that network elements that are not linked directly can be synchronized via intermediate oscillators (89). This may be important, for instance, to establish relationships between cell groups lacking direct reciprocal connections, as is the case for remote cell groups within the same cortical area, or for cells distributed across cortical areas that process different sensory modalities. In both cases, linkages either via intermediate cortical relays or even via subcortical centers must be considered. The latter possibility is supported by the occurrence of gamma oscillations in a variety of thalamic nuclei (58, 59, 106, 145). These considerations suggest that oscillations, while not conveying any stimulus-specific information per se, may be instrumental for the establishment of synchrony over large distances and hence for the formation of temporally coded assemblies.

Synchronization is particularly easily achieved in networks that are sharply tuned to a single resonant frequency. If it is the role of oscillatory activity to facilitate synchronization, the question arises, why are the observed oscillations so irregular and cover such a broad frequency range? The reason for this could be that cell groups can be desynchronized more easily if their oscillations are broad-banded, and thus the network can be prevented from entering global states of synchrony that would be inappropriate for information processing. Furthermore, the number of assemblies that can coexist in the same cortical region is increased if the oscillation frequencies are variable because spurious correlations due to aliasing effects will be rare and only of short duration. Thus a broad banded oscillatory signal appears as a reasonable compromise between several opposing constraints.

Why Should Oscillations Occur in the γ-Frequency Range?

The other question is why do the stimulus-induced synchronization events occur on the basis of oscillations in the γ-range and not on the basis of the more prominent low frequency oscillations? The following considerations suggest that there may be good reasons why mechanisms subserving perceptual grouping at low levels of visual processing should operate at such a rapid time scale.

Psychophysical studies show that segmentation of natural scenes can be accomplished within 100 to 200 ms (20, 25). If several simultaneously active assemblies have to be distinguished, a few successive synchronous bursts will have to be evaluated before such distinctions become possible. Thus oscillations in the α- and β-frequency range would be too slow to serve as carrier signal for binding at this level of processing. But much higher frequencies than those observed experimentally would not be tolerable because the conduction times of coupling connections do not allow establishment of synchrony at much higher frequencies. Simulation studies indicate that reciprocally coupled groups of neurons can only be synchronized if the coupling delays do not exceed about one third of the average period time. For much larger delays, temporal correlation with zero-phase lag cannot be established (89, 126, 129, 130). Transcallosal synchronization, for example, which has to cope with delays of at least 5 to 6 ms (79), requires a minimum period time of roughly 15 ms. Thus oscillatory activity in the γ-range appears as a good compromise between the opposing constraints to establish synchrony rapidly and with high temporal resolution on the one hand and over long distances on the other. The first requires rapid succession of short bursts, the latter sets an upper limit to the frequency of reverberation.

Oscillations as a Consequence of Synchrony

These considerations suggest that oscillatory activity might be instrumental for and causally related to synchrony. However, it is also conceivable that oscillations occur as a consequence of synchrony. Disregarding for a moment the difficult question of how an assembly of interconnected cells could reach a state where they emit a first synchronous burst, it is easy to see that once such a synchronous burst has occurred there will be a pause and most likely another synchronous burst, and so on. The reasons for the pause are twofold. First, a synchronous discharge in a population of cells generates strong and simultaneous inhibition in the same pool of cells due to recurrent inhibition (see e.g. 39). Second, the burst responses will activate Ca^{2+}-dependent K conductances, and these will contribute to the reduction of excitability (94,

95). Upon fading of these inhibitory events, firing probability will increase simultaneously for all cells and this, together with maintained excitatory input and nonlinear voltage-gated membrane conductances such as the low threshold Ca^{2+}-channels (95), will favor the occurrence of the next synchronous burst, and so on. Thus oscillations are a likely consequence of synchrony and it actually becomes an important issue to understand how cortical networks can be prevented from entering states of global oscillations and, if they do, how these can be terminated. This issue has recently been addressed in a number of simulation studies (72, 76, 87, 88, 127, 128, 142, 159).

DETECTABILITY AND FUNCTIONAL SIGNIFICANCE OF γ OSCILLATIONS IN SINGLE UNIT RECORDINGS

Independent of the question of whether oscillatory activity is instrumental for the establishment of synchrony or whether it is just a consequence, oscillatory activity is interesting because it may serve as an indicator of synchrony. On the other hand, not observing oscillatory activity does not imply that there is no synchrony. This is particularly true for single unit recordings. The results from the visual cortex (61) and in particular from the olfactory bulb (52) clearly indicate that individual discharges of single units may be precisely time-locked with the oscillating field potential, which proves that these discharges occurred in synchrony with those of many other cells, without, however, showing any sign of oscillatory activity in their autocorrelation function. The reasons for this apparent paradox are sampling problems and non-stationarity of the time series. If the single cell does not discharge at every cycle and if the oscillation frequency is not perfectly constant over a period of time sufficiently long to sample enough discharges for an interpretable autocorrelation function, the oscillatory rhythm to which the cell is actually locked will not be disclosable. Thus the less active a cell and the more variable the oscillation frequency, the less is it legitimate to infer from non-periodically modulated autocorrelograms that a cell is not oscillating, or even less, not synchronized with other cells. This sampling problem becomes more and more accentuated as the frequency of the oscillations increases. This explains why γ-band oscillations have been observed first with macroelectrodes and remain difficult to observe with microelectrodes unless one can record from several coupled cells simultaneously.

Accordingly, while there are numerous field potential studies indicating the presence of γ-oscillations in many different cortical and subcortical areas (see introduction,) single unit analyses designed specifically for the search of γ-oscillations have failed to disclose them in a number of cortical areas or have led to controversial results. At present, all investigators agree that oscillating unit activity in the γ-range occurs in the primary visual cortex of cats and monkeys, whether anesthetized or awake (40, 58, 59, 64, 65, 81, 121), in cat area 18 (40, 65), and in area PMLS of cat visual cortex (49). For area MT(V5) of the monkey visual cortex, there is one positive (91) and one negative report (164). No evidence was found in temporal visual areas of the monkey (149), but Nakamura et al (108) observed both low and high frequency oscillations associated with a recognition task in the temporal pole of macaca mulatta. High frequency oscillations in single cell activity have also been observed in somatosensory cortex where they were suppressed during sensory stimulation (6), and in the frontal cortex where they occurred in relation with particular behavioral sequences (5). Finally, oscillatory multi-unit responses similar to those occurring in the cat visual cortex have been observed in the optic tectum of awake pigeons (110). These data confirm at the single unit level the evidence from field potential and EEG recordings that oscillatory activity in the γ-range is a wide spread phenomenon.

However, it needs to be emphasized that the presence or absence of a regular oscillatory time structure in single cell responses neither proves nor disproves that spatially segregated cells discharge in synchrony. Oscillations per se are thus of little diagnostic value for the validation of the temporal coding concept. What really matters is synchrony and the dependence of synchronization probability on stimulus configuration. But these features can only be assessed by recording from several units simultaneously. Neverthe-less, oscillations are of interest because they indicate organized activity and can be used to guide the search for synchronous events.

The Role of Synchrony in Signal Transmission and Synaptic Plasticity

While it is debatable whether response synchronization is of functional relevance in the context of binding, there can be no doubt that synchronization of neuronal discharges is of eminent functional importance for signal transmission and neuronal plasticity. Because neurons have a firing threshold and because synaptic potentials have a finite duration, signal transmission probability depends critically on the temporal structure of afferent input activity, synchronous input being the most effective of all possible constella-tions. This is particularly important for structures such as the neocortex, which are characterized by sparse connectivity. Statistical considerations on cortical connectivity indicate that a single neuron contacts a particular target cell with only a few synapses (1). Thus a cell will only be able to drive a follower cell if it is active in synchrony with many other cells that contact the same follower cell. Moreover, it becomes increasingly clear that synchronization is of outstanding importance for all processes of use-dependent synaptic plasticity. This holds both for the activity-dependent shaping of neuronal connectivity during development and use-dependent changes of synaptic gain in the mature brain (for review see 32). The reason is that the processes that lead to modifications in synaptic connectivity and in synaptic gain have thresholds that are voltage-dependent. Thus it has been shown that experience-dependent modifications of connections in the developing visual cortex occur only if the target cells of the modifiable connections are activated beyond a critical threshold (66), and it was possible to relate this threshold with the activation of NMDA-receptor-gated Ca^{2+}-conductances (29, 31, 84, for review of the extensive literature see 138). For synaptic gain changes in the mature cortex, two thresholds have been identified. If neurons are driven above a first threshold, modifiable synapses undergo a long-term depression (LTD) and when a second threshold is reached, they undergo long-term potentiation (LTP) of their efficacy (9, 74). The first threshold appears to be related to the activation threshold of voltage-gated Ca^{2+}-channels (9, 23), while the second is related to the activation of NMDA-receptor-gated conductances (10, 11). Rather similar conditions are found for synaptic modifications in the hippocampus and a variety of other brain structures (for review see 71). Thus the probability of occurrence of a synaptic modification and its direction, increase or decrease of efficacy, depend on the level of postsynaptic depolarization and hence directly on the synchrony of discharges in the afferents converging onto a particular neuron. Synchronously active inputs are likely to become enhanced, while inputs that are active out-of-phase with other synchronous inputs are likely to undergo depression (see e.g. 144). Finally, if there is no synchrony between any of the converging afferents, modifications are unlikely to occur because the relatively high modification thresholds will not be reached. It follows from this that the temporal coordination of distributed neuronal responses is crucial not only for signal transmission, but also for synaptic plasticity.

The Role of Oscillations in Synaptic Plasticity

The fact that the temporal correlation between converging inputs to a cell is a criticial variable in use-dependent plasticity adds a further aspect to the putative functional significance of an oscillatory time structure in neuronal discharge patterns. The responses of neurons are usually rather long, extending over several 100 ms. Thus most of the responses evoked by a visual scene in the visual cortex are overlapping in time. According to the established synaptic modification rules, this would in the long run increase the gain of most of the coupling connections in the visual cortex and hence lead to unselective and meaningless association of neurons. This superposition problem can be avoided if the responses of the connected neurons have an oscillatory time structure. In that case, the membrane potential alternates rapidly between de- and hyperpolarizing phases (81). As a consequence, only those of the simultaneously active, oscillating inputs will have a chance to improve synaptic gain, which oscillate in precise synchrony with the target cell. Only then will the active synapses be able to activate voltage-sensitive NMDA-receptor-gated conductances (102, 113), which has been identified as a necessary prerequisite for homosynaptic potentiation of synaptic transmission in hippocampus (30) and neocortex (10, 11). Inputs whose oscillatory responses are out of phase with the oscillatory activity of the postsynaptic cell, or exhibit a fixed phase shift, will either become depressed or remain unchanged depending on their phase relation with the cell's activity. Direct support for this prediction comes from results obtained in the hippocampus (144). The coincidence criterion for synaptic gain changes is then determined by the frequency of the oscillation of a response rather than by the overall duration of a response. For oscillations in the γ-frequency range, this implies that the temporal window for cooperative interactions between converging inputs narrows down to 10 ms and less. Thus imposing an oscillatory burst and pause modulation on neuronal responses improves by an order of magnitude the temporal precision with which mechanisms that rely on coincidence detection and cooperativity can operate.

In a sense the functional role of temporally structured responses in synaptic plasticity is the same as that proposed for assembly coding. It serves to resolve superposition problems by providing a fine grain temporal code to express relations. Thus considerations on assembly coding and on synaptic plasticity both lead to the same postulate of a temporal code that relies on synchrony at a millisecond time scale. This convergence is, of course, not unexpected because both the formation of assemblies and use-dependent synaptic modifications are intimately related. In order to assure that a particular constellation of features always leads to the emergence of the same assembly of coherently active neurons, an architecture of synchronizing connections has to be developed that assures preferential coupling between the neurons constituting this assembly. Hence, connections between cells that have repeatedly been part of an assembly should strengthen and consolidate. According to the concept of temporal coding, the signature for cells belonging to an assembly is the synchronization of their temporally structured responses. As synchrony between pre- and postsynaptic activation is at the same time the condition that favors strengthening of synaptic connections, the same temporal code that serves to distinguish the neurons of an assembly can thus be used to distinguish the connections that need to be reinforced to stabilize an assembly.

In conclusion, several independent lines of argument concerning the nature of neuronal representations, the constraints for signal transmission, and conditions of use-dependent synaptic plasticity all lead to the postulate of a temporal code. All emphasize the significance of synchrony at a millisecond time scale. This in turn requires a temporal structure in neuronal responses that allows first for the distinction of synchronous from asynchronous states with high temporal resolution, and second for the establishment of synchrony over large distances. Both of these requirements appear to be met best by oscillatory discharge patterns in which bursts and pauses follow one another with a certain degree of regularity that should be neither too high nor too low. The fact that such rhythmic, synchronous activities are ubiquitous in the brain suggests that temporal codes may indeed be of similar importance as position and amplitude codes. The evidence that the average frequency of these rhythms changes in a state-dependent way and differs in different brain structures would then indicate that different states and different functions require integration at different temporal and spatial scales. As the rhythm slows down, the temporal window during which events can be distinguished as synchronous or asynchronous broadens, temporal discrimination becomes less precise, but binding by synchrony can be achieved over larger distances and between more cells. The consistent observation that the amplitude of field potential oscillations increases as oscillation frequency decreases underlines this inverse relation between oscillation frequency and size of synchronously active cell assemblies.

OUTLOOK

In order to obtain direct evidence in support of or against the hypothesis that response synchronization serves as a code for neuronal processing, experiments are needed in which causal relation can be established between the occurrence of response synchronization in defined subgroups of neurons and particular functions that need to be assessed at the behavioral level. This will require simultaneously recording from several selected areas in the brain of awake behaving animals with techniques that enable assessment of response synchronization with high temporal resolution. With the techniques that are currently available, the number of recording sites that can be examined simultaneously is bound to remain small. This poses a severe sampling problem. For the brain, one or two bursts may be a highly significant event if they occur simultaneously in a large number of cells. Hence, for non-ambiguous conditions, the episodes characterized by synchronization can be kept very short and in extremis can be restricted to one or two bursts. For the experimenter, however, who can only look at a few cells, such brief events of synchrony may pass undetected, and may be deemed significant only if they recur. Thus until new techniques become available, the relationship between synchronization and behavior will be detectable only for conditions where synchronization is maintained long enough to be observed, even if only a few cells can be looked at simultaneously. This may confine the behavioral conditions suitable for such analyses to problem-solving tasks that are difficult, fraught with ambiguity, and require long periods of sustained, focused attention. It might be rewarding in this context to reconsult the EEG literature for the identification of behavioral states that are likely to be associated with response synchronization in the γ-frequency band.

Literature Cited

1. Abeles, M., ed. 1991. *Corticonics.* Cambridge: Cambridge Univ. Press
2. Abeles, M., Gerstein, G. L. 1988. Detecting spatiotemporal firing patterns among simultaneously recorded single neurons. *J. Neurophysiol.* 60:909–24
3. Adrian, E. D. 1941. Afferent discharges to the cerebral cortex from peripheral sense organs. *J. Physiol.* 100:159–91
4. Aertsen, A. M. H. J., Gerstein, G. L. 1985. Evaluation of neuronal connectivity: Sensitivity of cross-correlation. *Brain Res.* 340:341–54
5. Aertsen, A., Vaadia, E., Abeles, M., Ahissar, E., Bergmann I. I., et al. 1992. Neural interactions in the frontal cortex of a behaving monkey: Signs of dependence on stimulus context and behavioral states. *J. Hirnforschung.* 32: 735–43
6. Ahissar, E., Vaadia, E. 1990. Oscillatory activity of single units in the somatosensory cortex of an awake monkey and their possible role in texture analysis. *Proc. Natl. Acad. Sci. USA* 87:8935–39
7. Aiple, F., Kruger, J. 1988. Neuronal synchrony in monkey striate cortex: Interocular signal flow and dependency on spike rates. *Exp. Brain Res.* 72:141–49
8. Arnett, D. W. 1975. Correlation analysis in the cat dorsal lateral geniculate nucleus. *Exp. Brain Res.* 24:111–30
9. Artola, A., Brocher, S., Singer, W. 1990. Different voltage-dependent thresholds for the induction of long-term depression and long-term potentiation in slices of the rat visual cortex. *Nature* 347:69–72
10. Artola, A., Singer, W. 1987. Long-term potentiation and NMDA receptors in rat visual cortex. *Nature* 330:649–52
11. Artola, A., Singer, W. 1990. The involvement of N-methyl-D-aspartate receptors in induction and maintenance of long-term potentiation in rat visual cortex. *Eur. J. Neurosci.* 2:254–69
12. Baldi, P., Meir, R. 1990. Computing with arrays of coupled oscillators: An application to preattentive texture discrimination. *Neural Comp.* 2:458–71
13. Barlow, H. B. 1972. Single units and cognition: A neurone doctrine for perceptual psychology. *Perception* 1:371–94
14. Basar, E., ed. 1980. *EEG-brain dynamics. Relation between EEG and Brain Evoked Potentials.* Amsterdam: Elsevier/North Holland. 411 pp.
15. Basar, E. 1988. EEG-dynamics and evoked potentials in sensory and cognitive processing by the brain. In *Dynamics of Sensory and Cognitive Processing by the Brain, Springer Series in Brain Dynamics*, ed. E. Basar, 1:30–55. Berlin/Heidelberg/New York: Springer
16. Basar, E., Rosen, B., Basar-Eroglu, C., Greitschus, F. 1987. The association between 40 Hz-EEG and the middle latency response of the auditory evoked potential. *Int. J. Neurosci.* 33: 103–17
17. Basar-Eroglu, C., Basar, E. 1991. A compound P300–40 Hz response of the cat hippocampus. *Int. J. Neurosci.* 60: 227–37
18. Baylis, G. C., Rolls, E. T., Leonard, C. M. 1985. Selectivity between faces in the responses of a population of neurons in the cortex in the superior temporal sulcus of the monkey. *Brain Res.* 342:91–102
19. Berger, H. 1929. Uber das Elektroencephalogramm des Menschen. *Arch. Psychiat. Nervenkr.* 87:527–70
20. Biedermann, J. 1990. Higher-level vision. In *Visual Cognition and Action,* ed. D. N. Osherson, S. M. Kosslyn, J. M. Hollerbach, pp. 41–72. Cambridge: MIT Press
21. Bouyer, J. J., Montaron, M. F., Rougeul, A. 1981. Fast fronto-parietal rhythms during combined focused attentive behaviour and immobility in cat: Cortical and thalamic localizations. *Electroenceph. Clin. Neurophysiol.* 51: 244–52
22. Braitenberg, V. 1978. Cell assemblies in the cerebral cortex. In *Lecture Notes in Biomathematics 21, Theoretical Approaches in Complex Systems,* ed. R. Heim, G. Palm, pp. 171–88. Berlin: Springer
23. Brocher, S., Artola, A., Singer, W.

1992. Intracellular injection of Ca^{2+} chelators blocks induction of long-term depression in rat visual cortex. *Proc. Natl. Acad. Sci. USA* 89: 123–27

24. Brooks, D. C. 1968. Waves associated with eye movement in the awake and sleeping cat. *Electroenceph. Clin. Neurophysiol.* 24:532–41

25. Burr, D. C. 1981. Temporal summation of moving images by the human visual system. *Proc. R. Soc. London Ser. B* 211:321–39

26. Bush, P., Douglas, R. J. 1991. Synchronization of bursting action potential discharge in a model network of neocortical neurons. *Neural Comp.* 3: 19–30

27. Callaway, E. M., Katz, L. C. 1990. Emergence and refinement of clustered horizontal connections in cat striate cortex. *J. Neurosci.* 10:1134–53

28. Callaway, E. M., Katz, L. C. 1991. Effects of binocular deprivation on the development of clustered horizontal connections in cat striate cortex. *Proc. Natl. Acad. Sci. USA* 88:745–49

29. Cline, H. T., Debski, E., Constantine-Paton, M. 1987. NMDA receptor antagonist desegregates eye specific strips. *Proc. Natl. Acad. Sci. USA* 84:4342–45

30. Collingridge, G. L., Kehl, S. J., McLennan, H. 1983. Excitatory amino acids in synaptic transmission in the Schaffer collateral commissural pathway of the rat hippocampus. *J. Physiol.* 334:33–46

31. Constantine-Paton, M. 1990. NMDA receptor as a mediator of activity-dependent synaptogenesis in the developing brain. *Cold Spring Harbor Symp. Quant. Biol.* 55:431–43

32. Cook, J. E. 1991. Correlated activity in the CNS: a role on every timescale. *Trends Neurosci.* 14:397–401

33. Crick, F. 1984. Function of the thalamic reticular complex: The searchlight hypothesis. *Proc. Natl. Acad. Sci. USA* 81:4586–90

34. Crick, F., Koch, C. 1990. Towards a neurobiological theory of consciousness. *Sem. Neurosci.* 2:263–75

35. Damasio, A. R. 1990. Synchronous activation in multiple cortical regions: a mechanism for recall. *Sem. Neurosci.* 2:287–96

36. DeLiang, W., Buhmann, J., von der Malsburg, C. 1990. Pattern segmentation in associative memory. *Neural Comp.* 2:94–106

37. Desimone, R., Albright, T. D., Gross, C. G., Bruce, C. 1984. Stimulus-selective properties of inferior temporal neurons in the macaque. *J. Neurosci.* 4:2051–62

38. Desimone, R., Schein, S. J., Moran, J., Ungerleider, L. G. 1985. Contour, color and shape analysis beyond the striate cortex. *Vision Res.* 24:441–52

39. Douglas, R. J., Martin, K. A. C. 1990. Neocortex. In *Synaptic Organization of the Brain,* ed. G. M. Shepherd, pp. 356–438. New York: Oxford Univ. Press. 3rd ed.

40. Eckhorn, R., Bauer, R., Jordan, W., Brosch, M., Kruse, W., et al. 1988. Coherent oscillations: A mechanism for feature linking in the visual cortex? *Biol. Cybern.* 60:121–30

41. Eckhorn, R., Reitboeck, H. J., Arndt, M., Dicke, P. 1990. Feature linking via synchronization among distributed assemblies: Simulations of results from cat visual cortex. *NetWork* 2:293–307

42. Edelmann, G. M. 1987. *Neural Darwinism: The Theory of Neuronal Group Selection.* New York: Basic Books. 371 pp.

43. Edelman, G. M. 1989. *The Remembered Present.* New York: Basic Books. 272 pp.

44. Edelman, G. M., Mountcastle, V. B. 1978. *The Mindful Brain.* Cambridge: MIT Press. 100 pp.

45. Engel, A. K., König, P., Gray, C. M., Singer, W. 1990. Stimulus-dependent neuronal oscillations in cat visual cortex: Inter-columnar interaction as determined by cross-correlation analysis. *Eur. J. Neurosci.* 2:588–606

46. Engel, A. K., König, P., Kreiter, A. K., Schillen, T. B., Singer, W. 1992. Temporal coding in the visual cortex: new vistas on integration in the nervous system. *Trends Neurosci.* 15: 218–26

47. Engel, A. K., König, P., Kreiter, A. K., Singer, W. 1991. Interhemispheric synchronization of oscillatory neuronal responses in cat visual cortex. *Science* 252:1177–79

48. Engel, A. K., König, P., Singer, W. 1991. Direct physiological evidence for scene segmentation by temporal coding. *Proc. Natl. Acad. Sci. USA* 88:9136–40

49. Engel, A. K., Kreiter, A. K., König, P., Singer, W. 1991. Synchronization of oscillatory neuronal responses between striate and extrastriate visual cortical areas of the cat. *Proc. Natl. Acad. Sci. USA* 88:6048–52

50. Felleman, D. J., van Essen, D. C. 1991. Distributed hierarchical processing in the primate cerebral cortex. *Cerebral Cortex* 1:1–47

51. Freeman, W. J., ed. 1975. *Mass Action*

in the Nervous System. New York: Academic. 489 pp.

52. Freeman, W. J., Skarda, C. A. 1985. Spatial EEG-patterns, non-linear dynamics and perception: the neo-Sherringtonian view. Brain Res. Rev. 10:147–75

53. Freeman, W. J., van Dijk, B. W. 1987. Spatial patterns of visual cortical fast EEG during conditioned reflex in a rhesus monkey. Brain Res. 422:267–76

54. Galambos, R., Hillyard, S. A. 1981. Electrophysiological approaches to human cognitive processing. Neurosci. Res. Progr. Bull. p. 202

55. Galambos, R., Makeig, S. 1988. In Dynamics of Sensory and Cognitive Processing by the Brain, ed. E. Basar, T. Bullock, pp. 103–22. Berlin: Springer

56. Galambos, R., Makeig, S., Talmachoff, P. J. 1981. A 40-Hz auditory potential recorded from the human scalp. Proc. Natl. Acad. Sci. USA 78:2643–47

57. Gerstein, G. L., Perkel, D. H. 1972. Mutual temporal relationship among neuronal spike trains. Statistical techniques for display and analysis. Biophys. J. 12:453–73

58. Ghose, G. M., Freeman, R. D. 1990. Origins of oscillatory activity in the cortex. Soc. Neurosci. Abstr. 16:523.4

59. Ghose, G. M., Freeman, R. D. 1992. Oscillatory discharge in the visual system: does it have a functional role? J. Neurophys. In press

60. Gochin, P. M., Miller, E. K., Gross, C. G., Gerstein, G. L. 1991. Functional interactions among neurones in inferior temporal cortex of the awake macaque. Exp. Brain Res. 84:505–16

61. Gray, C. M, Engel, A. K., König, P., Singer, W. 1990. Stimulus-dependent neuronal oscillations in cat visual cortex: Receptive field properties and feature dependence. Eur. J. Neurosci. 2:607–19

62. Gray, C. M., Engel, A. K., König, P., Singer, W. 1992. Synchronization of oscillatory neuronal responses in cat striate cortex: temporal properties. Visual Neurosci. 8:337–47

63. Gray, C. M., König, P., Engel, A. K., Singer, W. 1989. Oscillatory responses in cat visual cortex exhibit inter-columnar synchronization which reflects global stimulus properties. Nature 338:334–37

64. Gray, C. M., Singer, W. 1987. Stimulus-specific neuronal oscillations in the cat visual cortex: a cortical functional unit. Soc. Neurosci. Abstr. 13:404.3

65. Gray, C. M., Singer, W. 1989. Stimulus-specific neuronal oscillations in orientation columns of cat visual cortex. Proc. Natl. Acad. Sci. USA 86:1698–702

66. Greuel, J. M., Luhmann, H. J., Singer, W. 1988. Pharmacological induction of use-dependent receptive field-modifications in the visual cortex. Science 242:74–77

67. Grillner, S., Wallen, P., Vianna di Prisco, G. 1990. Cellular network underlying locomotion as revealed in a lower vertebrate model: Transmitters, membrane properties, circuitry, and simulation. Cold Spring Harbor Symp. Quant. Biol. 55:779–89

68. Gross, C. G., Rocha-Miranda, E. C., Bender, D. B. 1972. Visual properties of neurons in inferotemporal cortex of the macaque. J. Neurophysiol. 35:96–111

69. Grossberg, S. 1980. How does the brain build a cognitive code? Psychol. Rev. 87:1–51

70. Grossberg, S., Somers, D. 1991. Synchronized oscillators during cooperative feature linking in a cortical model of visual perception. Neural Networks 4:453–66

71. Gustafsson, B., Wigstrom, H. 1990. Associative long-lasting modifications in synaptic efficacy. Sem. Neurosci. 2:317–19

72. Hansel, D., Sompolinsky, H. 1992. Synchronization and computation in a chaotic neural network. Phys. Rev. Lett. 68:718–21

73. Hebb, D. O. 1949. The Organization of Behavior. New York: Wiley. 335 pp.

74. Hirsch, J. C., Crepel, F. 1990. Use-dependent changes in synaptic efficacy in rat prefrontal neurons in vitro. J. Physiol. 427:31–49

75. Hobson, J. A. 1988. The Dreaming Brain. New York: Basic Books. 336 pp.

76. Horn, D., Sagi, D., Usher, M. 1991. Segmentation, binding, and illusory conjunctions. Neural Comp. 3:510–25

77. Hubel, D. H., Wiesel, T. N. 1965. Binocular interaction in striate cortex of kittens reared with artificial squint. J. Neurophysiol. 28:1041–59

78. Innocenti, G. M. 1981. Growth and reshaping of axons in the establishment of visual callosal connections. Science 212:824–27

79. Innocenti, G. M. 1986. General organization of callosal connections in the

cerebral cortex. In *Cerebral Cortex*, ed. E. G. Jones, A. Peters, pp. 291–353. New York: Plenum

80. Innocenti, G. M., Frost, D. O. 1979. Effects of visual experience on the maturation of the efferent system to the corpus callosum. *Nature* 280:231–34

81. Jagadeesh, B., Ferster, D., Gray, C. M. 1991. Visually evoked oscillations of membrane potential in neurons of cat area 17. *Soc. Neurosci. Abstr.* 17:73.2

82. Jeannerod, M., Sakai, K. 1970. Occipital and geniculate potentials related to eye movements in the unanaesthetized cat. *Brain Res.* 19:361–77

83. Jouvet, M. 1972. The role of monoamines and acetylcholine-containing neurons in the regulation of the sleep. *Erg. Physiol.* 64:166–307

84. Kleinschmidt, A., Bear, M. F., Singer, W. 1987. Blockade of "NMDA" receptors disrupts experience-dependent plasticity of kitten striate cortex. *Science* 238:355–58

85. Koerner, E., Tsuda, I., Shimizu, H. 1987. Parallel in sequence—toward the architecture of an elementary cortical processor. In *Mathematical Research: Parallel Algorithms and Architectures*, ed. A. Albrecht, H. Jung, K. Mehlhorn, pp. 37–47. Berlin: Akademie-Verlag

86. König, P., Engel, A. K., Lowel, S., Singer, W. 1990. Squint affects occurrence and synchronization of oscillatory responses in cat visual cortex. *Soc. Neurosci. Abstr.* 16:523.2

87. König, P., Janosch, B., Schillen, T. B. 1992. Assembly formation and segregation by a self-organizing neuronal oscillator model. *Comp. Neural Syst.* In press

88. König, P., Schillen, T. B. 1990. Segregation of oscillatory responses by conflicting stimuli—desynchronizing connections in neural oscillator layers. In *Parallel Processing in Neural Systems and Computers*, ed. R. Eckmiller, pp. 117–20. Amsterdam: Elsevier

89. König, P., Schillen, T. B. 1991. Stimulus-dependent assembly formation of oscillatory responses: I. synchronization. *Neural Comp.* 3:155–66

90. Kreiter, A. K., Engel, A. K., Singer, W. 1992. Stimulus-dependent synchronization of oscillatory neuronal activity in the superior temporal sulcus of the macaque monkey. *Eur. Neurosci. Assoc. Abstr.* 75:1076

91. Kreiter, A. K., Singer, W. 1992. Oscillatory neuronal responses in the visual cortex of the awake macaque monkey. *Eur. J. Neurosci.* 4:369–75

92. Krüger, J., Aiple, F. 1988. Multimicroelectrode investigation of monkey striate cortex: spike train correlations in the infragranular layers. *J. Neurophysiol.* 60:798–828

93. Livingstone, M. S. 1991. Visually evoked oscillations in monkey striate cortex. *Soc. Neurosci. Abstr.* 17:73.3

94. Llinas, R. R. 1988. The intrinsic electrophysiological properties of mammalian neurons: Insights into central nervous system function. *Science* 242:1654–64

95. Llinas, R. R. 1990. Intrinsic electrical properties of nerve cells and their role in network oscillation. *Cold Spring Harbor Symp. Quant. Biol.* 55:933–38

96. Llinas, R. R., Grace, A. A., Yarom, Y. 1991. In vitro neurons in mammalian cortical layer 4 exhibit intrinsic oscillatory activity in the 10- to 50-Hz frequency range. *Proc. Natl. Acad. Sci. USA* 88:897–901

97. Lowel, S., Singer, W. 1992. Selection of intrinsic horizontal connections in the visual cortex by correlated neuronal activity. *Science* 255:209–12

98. Luhmann, H. J., Martinez-Millan, L., Singer, W. 1986. Development of horizontal intrinsic connections in cat striate cortex. *Exp. Brain Res.* 63:443–48

99. Luhmann, H. J., Singer, W., Martinez-Millan, L. 1990. Horizontal interactions in cat striate cortex: I. Anatomical substrate and postnatal development. *Eur. J. Neurosci.* 2:344–57

100. Lytton, W. W., Sejnowski, T. J. 1991. Simulations of cortical pyramidal neurons synchronized by inhibitory interneurons. *J. Neurophysiol.* 66:1059–79

101. Madler, C., Poppel, E. 1987. Auditory evoked potentials indicate the loss of neuronal oscillations during general anaesthesia. *Naturwissenschaften* 74:42–43

102. Mayer, M. L., Westbrook, G. L., Guthrie, P. B. 1984. Voltage-dependent block by Mg^{2+} of NMDA responses in spinal cord neurones. *Nature* 309:261–63

103. McMullen, T. A., Ly, N. 1988. Model of oscillatory activity in thalamic neurons: role of voltage- and calcium-dependent ionic currents. *Biol. Cybern.* 58:243–59

104. Michalski, A., Gerstein, G. L., Czarkowska, J., Tarnecki, R. 1983. Interactions between cat striate cortex neurons. *Exp. Brain Res.* 51:97–107

105. Montaron, M. P., Bouyer, J. J., Rougeul, A., Buser, P. 1982. Ventral

mesencephalic tegmentum (VMT) controls electrocortical beta rhythms and associated attentive behavior in cat. *Behav. Brain Res.* 6:129–45

106. Munemori, J., Hara, K., Kimura, M., Sato, R. 1984. Statistical features of impulse trains in cat's lateral geniculate neurons. *Biol. Cybern.* 50:167–72

107. Murthy, V. N., Fetz, E. E. 1992. Coherent 25- to 35-Hz oscillations in the sensorimotor cortex of awake behaving monkeys. *Proc. Natl. Acad. Sci. USA* 89:5670–74

108. Nakamura, K., Mikami, A., Kubota, K. 1992. Oscillatory neuronal activity related to visual short-term memory in monkey temporal pole. *NeuroReport* 3:117–20

109. Nelson, J. I., Salin, P. A., Munk, M. H. J., Arzi, M., Bullier, J. 1992. Spatial and temporal coherence in cortico-cortical connections: a cross-correlation study in areas 17 and 18 in the cat. *Visual Neurosci.* 9:21–38

110. Neuenschwander, S., Varela, F. J. 1990. Sensory-triggered oscillatory activity in the avian optic tectum. *Soc. Neurosci. Abstr.* 16:47.6

111. Deleted in proof

112. Newsome, W. T., Pare, E. B. 1988. A selective impairment of motion perception following lesions of the middle temporal visual area (MT). *J. Neurosci.* 8:2201–11

113. Nowak, L., Bregestovski, P., Ascher, P., Herbet, A., Prochiantz, A. 1984. Magnesium gates glutamate-activated channels in mouse central neurones. *Nature* 307:462–65

114. Palm, G. 1982. *Neural Assemblies*. Heidelberg: Springer. 244 pp.

115. Palm, G. 1990. Cell assemblies as a guideline for brain research. *Concepts Neurosci.* 1:133–37

116. Pantev, C., Makeig, S., Hoke, M., Galambos, R., Hampson, S., et al. 1991. Human auditory evoked gamma-band magnetic fields. *Proc. Natl. Acad. Sci. USA* 88:8996–9000

117. Perrett, D. I., Mistlin, A. J., Chitty, A. J. 1987. Visual neurones responsive to faces. *Trends Neurosci.* 10: 358–64

118. Poggio, T. 1990. A theory of how the brain might work. *Cold Spring Harbor Symp. Quant. Biol.* 55:899–910

119. Price, D. J., Blakemore, C. 1985. The postnatal development of the association projection from visual cortical area 17 to area 18 in the cat. *J. Neurosci.* 5:2443–52

120. Price, D. J., Blakemore, C. 1985. Regressive events in the postnatal development of association projections in the visual cortex. *Nature* 316:721–24

121. Raether, A., Gray, C. M., Singer, W. 1989. Intercolumnar interactions of oscillatory neuronal responses in the visual cortex of alert cats. *Eur. Neurosci. Assoc.* 12:72.5

122. Rager, G., Singer, W. 1992.. Modulation of oscillatory responses in cat visual cortex by flicker stimuli of variable frequency. *Eur. Neurosci. Assoc. Abstr.* 15:1077

123. Ribary, U., Joannides, A. A., Singh, K. D., Hasson, R., Bolton, J. P. R., et al. 1991. Magnetic field tomography of coherent thalamocortical 40 Hz oscillations in humans. *Proc. Natl. Acad. Sci. USA* 88:11037–41

124. Rolls, E. T. 1991. Neural organization of higher visual functions. *Curr. Opin. Neurobiol.* 1:274–78

125. Rougeul, A., Bouyer, J. J., Dedet, L., Debray, O. 1979. Fast somato-parietal rhythms during combined focal attention and immobility in baboon and squirrel monkey. *Electroenceph. Clin. Neurophysiol.* 46:310–19

126. Schillen, T. B., König, P. 1990. Coherency detection by coupled oscillatory responses—Synchronization connections in neural oscillator layers. See Ref. 88, pp. 139–42

127. Schillen, T. B., König, P. 1991. Stimulus-dependent assembly formation of oscillatory responses: II. desynchronization. *Network* 3:167–78

128. Schillen, T. B., König, P. 1992. Temporal structure can solve the binding problem for multiple feature domains. *Comp. Neural Syst.* In press

129. Schuster, H. G., Wagner, P. 1990. A model for neuronal oscillations in the visual cortex. 1. Mean-field theory and derivation of the phase equations. *Biol. Cybern.* 64:77–82

130. Schuster, H. G., Wagner, P. 1990. A model for neuronal oscillations in the visual cortex. 2. Phase description of the feature dependent synchronization. *Biol. Cybern.* 64:83–85

131. Schwarz, C., Bolz, J. 1991. Functional specificity of the long-range horizontal connections in cat visual cortex: a cross-correlation study. *J. Neurosci.* 11:2995–3007

132. Sheer, D. E. 1984. Focused arousal, 40 Hz EEG, and dysfunction. In *Self-Regulation of the Brain and Behavior*, ed. T. Elbert, B. Rockstroh, W. Lutzenberger, N. Birbaumer, pp. 66–84. Berlin/Heidelberg/New York: Springer

133. Sheer, D. E. 1989. Sensory and cognitive 40-Hz event-related potentials.

In *Brain Dynamics,* ed. E. Basar, T. H. Bullock, pp. 338–74. Berlin: Springer

134. Silva, L. R., Amitai, Y., Connors, B. W. 1991. Intrinsic oscillations of neocortex generated by layer 5 pyramidal neurons. *Science* 251:432–35

135. Singer, W. 1977. Control of thalamic transmission by cortico-fugal and ascending reticular pathways in the visual system. *Physiol. Rev.* 57:386–420

136. Singer, W. 1985. Activity-dependent self-organization of the mammalian visual cortex. In *Models of the Visual Cortex,* ed. D. Rose, V. G. Dobson, pp. 123–36. Chichester: Wiley

137. Singer, W. 1990. Search for coherence: A basic principle of cortical self-organization. *Concepts Neurosci.* 1:1–26

138. Singer, W. 1990. The formation of cooperative cell assemblies in the visual cortex. *J. Exp. Biol.* 153:177–97

139. Sompolinsky, H., Golomb, D., Kleinfeld, D. 1990. Global processing of visual stimuli in a neural network of coupled oscillators. *Proc. Natl. Acad. Sci. USA* 87:7200–4

140. Sompolinsky, H., Golomb, D., Kleinfeld, D. 1991. Cooperative dynamics in visual processing. *Phys. Rev. A* 43:6990–7011

141. Sporns, O., Gally, J. A., Reeke, G. N., Edelman, G. M. 1989. Reentrant signaling among simulated neuronal groups leads to coherency in their oscillatory activity. *Proc. Natl. Acad. Sci. USA* 86:7265–69

142. Sporns, O., Tononi, G., Edelman, G. M. 1991. Modeling perceptual grouping and figure-ground segregation by means of active reentrant connections. *Proc. Natl. Acad. Sci. USA* 88:129–33

143. Spydell, J. D., Ford, M. R., Sheer, D. E. 1979. Task dependent cerebral lateralization of the 40 Hertz EEG rhythm. *Psychophysiology* 16:347–50

144. Stanton, P. K., Sejnowski, T. J. 1989. Associative long-term depression in the hippocampus induced by Hebbian covariance. *Nature* 339:215–18

145. Steriade, M., Curro-Dossi, R., Pareacute, D., Oakson, G. 1991. Fast oscillations (20–40 Hz) in thalamocortical systems and their potentiation by mesopontine cholinergic nuclei in the cat. *Proc. Natl. Acad. Sci. USA* 88: 4396–400

146. Steriade, M., Llinas, R. R. 1988. The functional states of the thalamus and the associated neuronal interplay. *Physiol. Rev.* 68:649–742

147. Stryker, M. P. 1990. Activity-dependent reorganization of afferents in the developing mammalian visual system. In *Development of the Visual System,* ed. D. M. K. Lam, C. J. Shaz, p. 267. Cambridge: MIT Press

148. Taylor, J. G., Keverne, E. B. 1991. Accessory olfactory learning. *Biol. Cybern.* 64:301–5

149. Tovee, M. J., Rolls, E. T. 1992. Oscillatory activity is not evident in the primate temporal visual cortex with static stimuli. *NeuroReport.* 3:369–72

150. Toyama, K., Kimura, M., Tanaka, K. 1981. Cross-correlation analysis of interneuronal connectivity in cat visual cortex. *J. Neurophysiol.* 46: 191–201

151. Toyama, K., Kimura, M., Tanaka, K. 1981. Organization of cat visual cortex as investigated by cross-correlation techniques. *J. Neurophysiol.* 46:202–14

152. Traub, R. D., Miles, R., Wong, R. K. S. 1989. Model of the origin of rhythmic population oscillations in the hippocampal slice. *Science* 243:1319–24

153. Ts'o, D., Gilbert, C. 1988. The organization of chromatic and spatial interactions in the primate striate cortex. *J. Neurosci.* 8:1712–27

154. Ts'o, D., Gilbert, C., Wiesel, T. N. 1986. Relationship between horizontal interactions and functional architecture in cat striate cortex as revealed by cross-correlation analysis. *J. Neurosci.* 6:1160–70

155. Tsuda, I. 1992. Dynamic link of memory—chaotic memory map in nonequilibrium neural networks. *Neural Networks* 5:313–26

156. Ungerleider, L. G., Mishkin, M. 1982. Two cortical visual systems. In *Analysis of Visual Behavior,* ed. D. J. Ingle, M. A. Goodele, R. J. W. Mansfield, p. 549. Cambridge: MIT Press

157. Vaadia, E., Ahissar, E., Bergman, H., Lavner, Y. 1991. Correlated activity of neurons: A neural code for higher brain functions? In *Neuronal Cooperativity, Springer Series in Synergistics,* ed. J. Kruger, pp. 249–79. Berlin/Heidelberg: Springer-Verlag

158. von der Malsburg, C. 1985. Nervous structures with dynamical links. *Ber. Bunsenges. Phys. Chem.* 89:703–10

159. von der Malsburg, C., Schneider, W. 1986. A neural cocktail-party processor. *Biol. Cybern.* 54:29–40

160. von Noorden, G. K. 1990. *Binocular Vision and Ocular Motility, Theory and Management of Strabismus.* St. Louis/Baltimore: Mosby. 557 pp.

161. Wilson, M. A., Bower, J. M. 1989. The simulation of large-scale neural

networks. In *Methods in Neuronal Modeling,* ed. C. Koch, I. Segev, pp. 291–334. Cambridge: MIT Press

162. Wilson, W. A., Bower, J. A. 1991. A computer simulation of oscillatory behaviour in primary visual cortex. *Neural Comp.* 3:498–509

163. Wurtz, R. H., Yamasaki, D. S., Duffy, D. J., Roy, J.-P. 1990. Functional specialization for visual motion processing in primate cerebral cortex. *Cold Spring Harbor Symp. Quant. Biol.* 55:717–27

164. Young, M. P., Kanaka, K., Yamara, S. 1992. On oscillating neuronal responses in the visual cortex of the monkey. *J. Neurophysiol.* 6:1464–74

165. Zeki, S. M. 1973. Colour coding in the rhesus monkey prestriate cortex. *Brain Res.* 53:422–27

166. Zeki, S., Watson, J. D. G., Lueck, C. J., Friston, K. J., Kennard, C., Frackowiak, R. S. J. 1991. A direct demonstration of functional specialization in human visual cortex. *J. Neurosci.* 11:641–49

Annu. Rev. Physiol. 1993. 55:375–96

THE MECHANISM OF EXPRESSION OF LONG-TERM ENHANCEMENT OF HIPPOCAMPAL SYNAPSES:
Current Issues and Theoretical Implications

Bruce L. McNaughton

Division of Neural Systems, Memory and Aging, University of Arizona, Tucson
Arizona, 85724

KEY WORDS: AMPA, brain, EPSP, LTP, neurotransmitter, NMDA, postsynaptic,
           presynaptic, receptor, synaptogenesis

INTRODUCTION AND HISTORICAL OVERVIEW

At least since the time of Hebb (49) it has been an act of faith within the psychological, neuroscience, and theoretical neural network communities that some persistent form of synaptic modification must underlie memory. The principal reason for this faith is simply that other proposals (e.g. molecular storage, altered threshold, etc) have led to a theoretical impasse when confronted with the problems posed by both capacity requirements and associative recall. The theory of how information can be associatively stored and retrieved through a variety of hypothetical synaptic "weight"-change rules is now well developed. With such rules, rather remarkable results have been obtained in the fields of cognitive science and artificial neural networks, both in capturing essential features of human or animal psychological data, and in solving intractable problems involving complex, nonlinear input-output mappings (for review see 50). These modification rules have one element in common: the involvement of the postsynaptic neuron as an essential locus of control.

Beginning in the late 1950s and continuing through the 1960s, a few

375

0066–4278/93/0315–0375$02.00

theoretically motivated neurophysiologists (e.g. 3, 12, 13, 40, 41, 88, 99) began to search for evidence of such synaptic mechanisms in the mammalian central nervous system (CNS). This search was encouraged by the existence of the phenomenon of post-tetanic potentiation (PTP), which was seen at both neuromuscular and spinal cord synapses and, which, by the late 1950s, was already known to involve an increase in the probability of transmitter release from presynaptic terminals (68). The problem was partly that PTP at these synapses was not even remotely persistent enough to account for long-term memory, and partly that PTP could be induced in single presynaptic fibers, even when the response of the postsynaptic cell was almost completely blocked. It was recognized that such a mechanism would not fulfill any of the persistance, specificity, or associativity requirements of Hebb's memory mechanism.

The first unambiguous evidence of persistent synaptic strengthening was discovered in the hippocampal formation of the anesthetized rabbit (70), and subsequently characterized in both anesthetized and awake animals (14, 15). Because of the history of research on PTP, the phenomenon was referred to as long-lasting potentiation. Subsequently, Douglas & Goddard (29), who came from a background in Hebbian psychology, adopted the name long-term potentiation (LTP) to emphasize the possible theoretical significance of this phenomenon as Hebb's proposed mechanism for long-term associative memory. Although indications had been present in preceding studies, the first concrete evidence for the associative requirement of Hebb's theory came from the demonstration (85) that, unlike PTP, the persistent modification could not be induced when only small numbers of afferent fibers were stimulated. Because this requirement for cooperativity among coactive afferent fibers distinguished the phenomenon from any previous form of synaptic potentiation, the name long-term enhancement (LTE) was adopted.[1] That enhancement was indeed not a long-term form of potentiation was subsequently demonstrated by showing that both phenomena occurred at the same synapses, and could be dissociated on mechanistic grounds (82). Specifically, whereas PTP increased the magnitude of paired-pulse synaptic depression in a manner consistent with an increase in fractional release of neurotransmitter, no such change accompanied LTE. This dissociation serves as a strong constraint in the current debate, outlined below, regarding the biophysical mechanism through which LTE is expressed.

Implicit in Hebb's principle is also a high degree of specificity in the induction process. On a given receiving cell, only those synapses that were

---

[1]It is an interesting historical note that Hebb, who at the time was professor emeritus at the location where cooperativity was discovered, responded with modest pleasure, but little surprise, on being presented with the evidence that he had been essentially correct for the past 30 years.

active at the time the enhancement threshold is crossed should be modified. Conversely, for a given presynaptic axon, only synapses on strongly depolarized cells should be modified. Evidence for these properties was obtained in several early studies using both intact animals (66, 83) and in vitro preparations (1); however, more recent in vitro work has suggested that there may be conditions in which this specificity principle (and by inference Hebb's rule) is at least partly violated (18; D. Madison, personal communication; see below).

The modern era of our understanding of the LTE phenomenon began with the discovery of the NMDA-selective class of glutamate receptor (114) and the subsequent demonstration of its crucial role as a voltage-sensitive switch in the induction process (23, 48). This voltage dependence provided an explanation for the cooperativity phenomenon (59, 115, 116), and firmly established the postsynaptic cell as the critical locus of control.[2] What remains a matter of considerable debate is exactly what is the critical alteration that leads to the expression of enhanced synaptic efficacy. The following review addresses the current status of this issue, and the relevance of the expression mechanism to theoretical questions concerning learning in neural systems. The theoretical significance of this question is considered first, followed by an examination of the empirical issues. These issues relate to the general question of whether long-term enhancement of synaptic efficacy involves postsynaptic alterations, presynaptic alterations, or both.

THEORETICAL SIGNIFICANCE OF THE MECHANISM OF LTE EXPRESSION

Given the strong empirical support for the embodiment of Hebb's principle in LTE induction, it might seem that further inquiry into the details of exactly what changes in the transmission process itself is of little relevance to the question of how memory works. To illustrate why this is not the case requires consideration of some general properties of associative memory networks (e.g. 43, 50, 81, 86) . The general assumption is that information is encoded primarily as a pattern of activity over a population of neurons that is sufficiently interconnected so that the activity of any cell can be recorded by changing the strength of the connection between it and at least one coactive unit (Hebb's principle). Associative recall (i.e. reinstatement of a stored pattern) occurs when the network is presented with an input pattern that is sufficiently like the stored one that, for each unit active in the original pattern,

---

[2]It does appear, however, that NMDA receptor activation alone is not sufficient to produce the persistent enhancement that occurs when there is at least some correlated presynaptic activation (Kauer et al 1988).

most of its currently active inputs terminate in enhanced synapses. For the remaining neurons, most active inputs will not have previously been enhanced. Suitable global threshold adjusting mechanisms, possibly involving GABA$_A$-mediated shunting inhibition (81, 86), then insure that only those cells respond that have a large proportion of enhanced active inputs. Given certain assumptions about the overall proportion of synapses that have been previously used, the cells that respond turn out (with high probability) to be the ones that were active in the original event. This effect is often referred to as pattern completion.

There are several important practical ways in which the details of how LTE is expressed bear on the efficiency of pattern completion. One concerns the question of reliability. Hippocampal unitary EPSPs typically exhibit substantial variance, with a considerable numbers of outright transmission failures (36, 51, 84, 101, 112). An increase in postsynaptic sensitivity, by whatever means, can only increase the average EPSP amplitude; however, alterations in either the number of release sites, or the release probability, leads necessarily to a synapse that is both stronger, on average, and more reliable. Reliability is a particularly important consideration in systems (like the hippocampus) whose principal neurons have low firing rates, although it has been pointed out that there may be some computational benefits of noise in the transmission process (44).

Perhaps the main theoretical motivation for worrying about the expression mechanism concerns the problem of partial connectivity and its impact on storage capacity. Contact probability within or between hippocampal subfields is (at best) about 5% on average. Theoretical studies have suggested that this may be too low for the standard sort of associative network to work efficiently (43, 81, 111). On the other hand, the typical axonal trajectory of a hippocampal pyramidal cell is quite extensive, in some cases covering as much as 70% of the total area of the synaptic target field (55). This suggests that the number of potential synaptic contacts may be much greater than the number of existing, morphologically identifiable synapses if part of the LTE expression mechanism involves the formation of new contact sites. This would be logically equivalent to the enhancement of a synapse from a zero weight to a nonzero weight, and would require the sort of "neurobiotaxis" of the presynaptic axon originally assumed by Hebb. To preserve Hebb's principle and synapse specificity, the activated postsynaptic neuron would have to express its competence to form such new contacts by providing the necessary receptors and other molecular components of the complete synapse. It might also broadcast some retrograde signal to nearby active inputs (although, as discussed below, such a signal is by no means essential). Thus, the possibility that LTE expression may involve both presynaptic and postsynaptic changes is attractive for purely theoretical reasons.

HOW IS LTE EXPRESSED?

There is little or no dispute in the current literature that the initial induction events leading to the expression of LTE involve an essential postsynaptic component. The experimental support for this assertion has been the subject of numerous recent review articles and compendia (16, 45, 46, 64, 78) and is touched on only briefly here. It is generally agreed that the combination of depolarization and agonist binding to NMDA receptors leads to calcium entry into the postsynaptic spine region. This presumably sets in motion a cascade of events leading to synaptic enhancement. Editorials in *Science* notwithstanding (6), at present this cascade, particularly the presynaptic and or postsynaptic locus of its ultimate targets, is (at best) poorly understood. Indeed, it is probably fair to say that virtually every piece of experimental evidence for one or another class of mechanisms has been called into question by discrepant results in the hands of other investigators. At least part of the extensive contradiction in the current literature appears to arise directly from the fact that, so far, LTE has never been observed, let alone studied, under natural conditions. Synapses are exceedingly complex molecular systems, whose input-output relations can, in principle, be modified at any or all of a considerable number of loci (71). When such a system is studied under a wide variety of conditions, many of which are far from the normal physiological state, contradictory results may well be expected. Nevertheless, it is difficult to resist the suspicion that there exists some single crucial parameter whose identification and subsequent control may bring order to the current state of chaos in this field.

Increased Synaptic Release of Neurotransmitter

The postsynaptic nature of the induction process carried with it the implication that the expression mechanism must be similarly postsynaptic, given the assumed unidirectional nature of information transmission of chemical synapses. As early as 1981, however, there were reports of increased release of neurotransmitter into extracellular perfusates following LTE induction (104). Subsequently, Dolphin et al (28) reported an LTE-related increase in the evoked release of radioactive glutamate after local perfusion with labeled glutamine in the dentate gyrus in intact, anesthetized animals. This increase was blocked by treatments that block LTE, including NMDA receptor antagonism (32) and stimulation of the commissural projection to the dentate gyrus (30, 75). In all three principal hippocampal subfields, LTE was associated with an increase in Ca^{2+}-dependent, K^+-stimulated release of glutamate and aspartate, with no effects either on high affinity reuptake, or Ca^{2+}-dependent or independent ligand binding, measured in both ex vivo (i.e. removed from brain after LTE induction) or in vitro tissue slices (see 16).

Similar ex vivo studies revealed increased K^+ stimulated glutamate release in tissue taken from animals three days following LTE induction in vivo. LTE has also been associated with an increase in the amount of intracellular Ca^{2+}, and Ca^{2+} uptake into both whole slices and synaptosomes prepared from enhanced tissue (see 16). An increase in Ca^{2+}-dependent, K^+-stimulated release of glutamate has been corroborated by at least one other laboratory (42).

Given the weight of the foregoing evidence from biochemical studies, it is difficult not to conclude that some presynaptic alteration must accompany LTE; however, there are a few caveats that may be raised, not the least of which has been the failure by a third group (2) to detect any enhanced release of glutamate during LTE, under experimental conditions that differ only slightly from those used by Dolphin et al (28). This raises a serious question concerning the necessity of elevated release for LTE expression. In discussing the possible reasons for the discrepancy, Aniksztejn et al (2) suggest that their push-pull cannulation procedure may cause less local damage than the method used by Dolphin et al (28). This possibility is considered further in the discussion of the role of nitric oxide.

In the original studies by Dolphin et al (28) and subsequent work from that group, there is a curious inconsistency between the magnitude of the change in glutamate release and the magnitude of the physiologically measured synaptic enhancement. In most experiments, the relative change in apparent glutamate release was substantially greater than the observed EPSP enhancement. Under the normal assumption that multiple quanta can act at the same population of receptors, the discrepancy is more than can reasonably be accounted for by nonlinear summation effects because it is known that the relative degree of presynaptic EPSP facilitation during paired pulses does not change following LTE (82, 120). This would suggest that neither the postsynaptic receptors nor the synaptic driving force are saturated following LTE in these studies. Assuming that the increased release reflects normal, action potential-dependent vesicular release, one possible interpretation of the relatively excessive increase in measured release is that the increase occurs preferentially at sites that either lack or are deficient in functional AMPA-type glutamate receptors. It is also possible, however, that the usual assumptions are not valid and that multiple quanta act at relatively independent receptor populations, each of which is close to saturation by a single quantum. In this case, a large increase in the amount of transmitter contained in each quantal packet would result in a proportionally smaller increase in the measured response. As discussed below, such uncertainties concerning the nature of quantal transmission in hippocampal synapses cloud the interpretation of several other results related to the expression mechanism.

The fact that substantial LTE can be induced without changing the magnitude of paired-pulse facilitation and/or depression (82) raises another caveat. These presynaptic phenomena are markedly affected by both altered extracellular Ca^{2+} and PTP, which affects intraterminal Ca^{2+} (27). Moreover, recent experiments (100) using optical imaging of Ca^{2+} signals in CA1 terminals that had been selectively filled with fluorescent Ca^{2+} indicators have failed to reveal changes in either residual Ca^{2+} or stimulus-induced Ca^{2+} transients during LTE, although the expected residual Ca^{2+} during paired-pulse facilitation was observed. These results rather strongly suggest that if LTE is dependent upon increased transmitter release, then the mechanism of this increase comes into effect at some stage in the release sequence after the influx of Ca^{2+} and is not dependent on either residual increases in Ca^{2+}, or on increased Ca^{2+} currents.

One possible locus of such a nonclassical mechanism for increasing transmitter release has been suggested by studies of the less persistent synaptic enhancement that is observed in the dentate gyrus (but apparently not CA1) following exposure to either norepinephrine (NE) or the β-adrenergic agonist isoproterenol (24, 53, 63, 92, 105). Parfitt et al (94) found that these agents cause an increase in the phosphorylation of the vesicle-associated proteins synapsin I and II. Phosphorylation of synapsins is thought to increase transmitter release by facilitating the movement of synaptic vesicles to release sites on the presynaptic membrane (69). This might have the effect of increasing the number of sites from which transmitter can be released (as opposed to the release probability per se) and hence not require residual Ca^{2+} or increased Ca^{2+} transients once established. Conceivably, an LTE-related increase in transmitter release might arise from a similar mechanism. It is also possible that, in studies involving electrical stimulation, at least some of the observed EPSP change may reflect this NE-mediated effect. In this context it is of interest that nitrous oxide (NO) appears to increase NE release by a glutamate/NMDA receptor-dependent process (87).

Increased Postsynaptic Responsiveness to Selective Transmitter Agonists

Early attempts failed to detect any LTE related increase in responsiveness to iontophoretically applied glutamate (73). It is now apparent, however, that at least part of this failure resulted from the surprising fact that the depolarizing effects of exogenous glutamate are not mediated through either NMDA or AMPA receptors (35). Neither CNQX, a selective antagonist of both AMPA responses and the fast EPSP, nor APV, which blocks NMDA receptors, are able to block glutamate-induced depolarizations. More recently, it has also been shown that there is a substantial decline in AMPA responsiveness in CA1 of old rats, with no change in glutamate responsiveness (8). It is believed that electrogenic reuptake systems mediate glutamate depolarization and restrict access of exogenous glutamate to the synaptic receptors (35).

Two more recent studies have examined the responsiveness of CA1 cells to AMPA following LTE induction (26, 98). In both cases, AMPA responses increased by an amount sufficient to account for the enhanced EPSP; however, this increase developed slowly and required 30–45 min for full expression. The slowly developing increase in AMPA responsiveness can be blocked by the protein kinase antagonist K-252b, which leaves a residual, decremental enhancement. The authors conclude that, although a postsynaptic mechanism is involved in the expression of the persistent phase of LTE, the early, decremental component was probably presynaptic in origin. This conclusion is certainly rather compelling, although, at the risk of appearing desperate, a somewhat plausible devil's advocate position could be proposed. It is possible, for example, that AMPA receptors occur both synaptically and extrasynaptically and that the bulk of the response to AMPA is mediated by the latter. It is also conceivable that the postsynaptic component of LTE involves a rapid change in the number or characteristics of synaptic AMPA receptors, which then spreads slowly to the extrasynaptic population.

Independent Enhancement of AMPA and NMDA Receptor-Mediated Responses

Although the evoked EPSP in CA1 is mediated primarily by AMPA receptors, an NMDA-dependent component can be demonstrated under appropriate conditions (22). An increase in transmitter release should result in measurable increases in both components if it is assumed that neither receptor population is saturated and that the two populations are indeed colocalized at the synapses undergoing LTE. This line of investigation was first undertaken by Muller & Lynch (91) and by Kauer et al (58), who showed that whereas both components could be increased by paired pulse facilitation (i.e. increased transmitter release), only the AMPA component was increased following LTE induction. Although it was subsequently shown (9, 119) that NMDA-mediated responses could undergo enhancement, Muller et al (90) suggested that this enhancement is qualitatively different from that of the AMPA component and is not necessarily coupled to it. More recently, Asztely et al (5) showed that under conditions in which enhancement of both the AMPA and NMDA components can be observed simultaneously, the latter is typically only one third the magnitude of the former. The enhancement of both components appear to follow the same time course.

Unfortunately, the conclusion of a postsynaptic mechanism from the foregoing experiments must be tempered by uncertainty regarding the underlying assumptions. First, it is not established with certainty that AMPA and NMDA receptors are colocalized at the same synapses in these studies. At the very least, the extent of such colocalization is questionable. While there is evidence of colocalization in unitary responses in hippocampal cultures prepared from developing brain (10), this colocalization was variable. Indeed the case has been made by Radpour & Thomson (96) that a substantial fraction of the NMDA component of the electrically evoked population response in CA1 does not come from Schaffer collateral synapses, but rather from the simultaneous (inadvertent) activation of a small population of local circuit excitatory connections among pyramidal cells. These cells were shown to have a substantial NMDA-mediated component. Such inhomogeneity in the synaptic populations could lead to the differential expression of LTE in the AMPA and NMDA components of population responses, in spite of a presynaptic expression mechanism. Second, there is room for argument that NMDA receptors may, in fact, be closer to saturation, and hence less susceptible to increased transmitter output, in spite of the failure to observe differences in paired-pulse facilitation. The much higher affinity of the NMDA receptor for glutamate (95) could lead to saturation of the NMDA component at lower agonist concentrations than required to saturate the AMPA component. It is not yet known whether multiple quanta released from a single fiber normally act at the same or independent receptor sites (see 61). Release of two quanta at independent sites during facilitation would result in a larger NMDA-mediated response than a single release, even if the NMDA receptors at both sites were saturated, whereas enhanced release at single sites might increase the AMPA component with little measurable effect on the NMDA component.

Postsynaptic Mechanisms of LTE Expression

If LTE involves increased postsynaptic responsiveness, what is the nature of the change? There are at least three possible candidates: an increase in the number or affinity of AMPA receptors, an increase in their unitary charge transfer, or an increase in the effective spread of synaptic currents from dendritic spines into dendrites. An early report of an increase in glutamate binding following LTE induction (72) was followed by negative results from different investigators (74). These studies were conducted prior to the appreciation of the complexity and multiplicity of the glutamate receptor system. It was soon recognized that Cl-dependent glutamate binding did not accurately reflect binding to synaptic receptors. Kessler et al (60) attempted to detect increased binding of AMPA, or the selective AMPA antagonist CNQX, in CA1 of slices that had been subjected to LTE inducing stimuli at multiple sites in order to maximize the percentage of enhanced synapses. Binding was expressed relative to the molecular layer of the fascia dentata, which served as an internal standard. There was no evidence of increased binding of either ligand. More recently, an increased binding of AMPA was detected with in situ autoradiography in hippocampus of animals in which unilateral LTE of the perforant pathway was induced in vivo (110). The interpretation of these results, however, is rather complicated. Although there was no increase in AMPA binding in control animals, or in animals subjected to rather high intensity stimulation, which did not lead to EPSP enhancement, the LTE correlated increase in AMPA binding was not restricted to the tetanized pathway. Rather it was found bilaterally, widely distributed throughout the hippocampus and cortex. It was suggested that LTE may have propagated from the tetanized site; however, numerous studies in acute or chronically prepared animals have failed to demonstrate transfer of perforant path LTE to the hemisphere contralateral to the tetanus. On the other hand, LTE induction can result in an increase in hippocampal sharp waves (19), which consist of quasi synchronous high frequency burst discharges, and might result in the spread of enhancement to structures not involved in the initial event. It remains unclear whether increased AMPA binding is directly involved in LTE expression.

A strong indirect argument has been made for alteration of AMPA receptor currents following LTE. Aniracetam, one of a class of so-called cognitive enhancing drugs, selectively increases and prolongs AMPA currents (56, 109) by reducing desensitization. Staubli et al (107) found that this effect is altered by prior induction of LTE, which caused a reduction in the net potentiating effect of Aniracetam and a complex alteration in the manner in which it affects the EPSP wave shape (106). The change is not simply an occlusion effect because Aniracetam and LTE affect the wave shapes (i.e. the decay time constants) of synaptic currents (inferred from field potentials) in opposite ways, and may reflect an alteration in the subunit composition of the AMPA receptors during LTE. Although more work will be required to clarify the nature of these effects, it would be a challenge to account for them by increased transmitter release; indeed, they are not present with paired pulse facilitation or increased stimulus intensity, nor does the difference diminish with partial blockade of AMPA receptors, which indicates that it is not due to postsynaptic voltage saturation. Unfortunately, as with many results in this field, the differential Aniracetam effect is more robust in some hands than in others (4, 54).

With regard to the dendritic spine hypothesis, there are several lines of evidence that cast some doubt as to the direct involvement of spine alterations in LTE expression, although there is strong evidence that spine shape, as well as the morphology of the synapse in general, is altered in association with LTE. This literature has been thoroughly discussed in recent reviews (16, 113). For the present it is sufficient to note that spine shape changes are not a priori required for LTE induced by cooperativity, at least not in the dentate gyrus. During denervation-induced sprouting reactions, LTE can be induced in synapses terminating on short (stubby) spines, whereas it normally occurs on long spines (97). This observation also casts doubt on the possible role of the dendritic spine in compartmentalizing Ca^{2+} transients during LTE induction. Note, however, that these data do not rule out the possibility that shape changes might result in significant electrotonic effects, only that such changes are not necessary for LTE induced in perforant path synapses by the cooperativity method. Nor do morphologically observable changes in spine dimensions represent the only way that spine electrotonus might be modified.

Formation of New Connections

Clearly, one explanation that would accommodate the evidence for both increased transmitter release and increased AMPA responsiveness and binding would be that formation of new synapses represents at least part of the mechanism of LTE expression. At least two sets of studies (20, 21, 65) are in agreement that LTE in CA1 is accompanied by a substantial increase in the number of synapses formed on the dendritic shafts of pyramidal cells and on stubby (sessile) spines. There are two related sources of uncertainty in the interpretation of these findings. The first is that the overall proportion of sessile spine and shaft synapses is rather small, so that the overall increase in synaptic number is too small to account completely for the magnitude of LTE, unless it is assumed that such synapses are substantially stronger than typical spine synapses. Second, it is uncertain whether the observed increase reflects true synaptogenesis, or the collapse of normal, preexisting dendritic spines. The relatively small numbers involved have precluded a clear establishment that the number of normal spines does not decrease by an amount sufficient to account for the increase in shaft and sessile spine synapses. In favor of the synaptogenesis argument is the finding mentioned above, that during reactive synaptogenesis, new contacts appear first on shafts and sessile spines. This leads to the proposal of a general hypothesis that may account for some of the conflicting findings with regard to presynaptic vs postsynaptic expression mechanisms.

Many axonal systems within the hippocampus are capable of intense reactive synaptogenesis in response to denervation (for review, see 108), and it is not the least implausible to suppose that the capacity for synaptogenesis might also account for at least part of the expression of LTE. As mentioned above, a wide variety of experimental paradigms and conditions, none of them physiological, have been employed in the search for the mechanism of LTE expression. Certainly the hippocampal slice preparation constitutes a case of acute denervation for the majority of surviving cells, and it is well established that extensive synaptogenesis occurs during the development of hippocampal cell and slice cultures (37, 38). The possibility thus exists that the variability of results concerning the locus of LTE expression is caused, at least partly, by the differential activation of a branch point in the biochemical cascade that is initiated by NMDA receptor activation; one leading to the formation of new release sites for transmitter and the attraction of new synapses to available postsynaptic sites, and one leading to enhancement of existing synapses through purely postsynaptic mechanisms. This hypothesis is pursued in the following discussion of the literature on quantal analysis of LTE, and of the existence and nature of retrograde messengers.

Retrograde Messengers

The evidence that, at least under some conditions, postsynaptically initiated, NMDA receptor-dependent LTE is expressed by presynaptic alterations led naturally to the hypothesis that there must be some retrograde chemical signal passed from the activated postsynaptic spine to the presynaptic terminal. Before entering into a discussion of the relevant evidence, it is worth noting that a retrograde message, in the sense of the physical transfer of a messenger substance, is not a priori necessary to link a postsynaptic induction mechanism with putative alterations in presynaptic release. It is entirely conceivable, for example, that changes in the expression or conformation of postsynaptic membrane constituents could induce, or at least permit, either synaptogenesis or increased transmitter release at existing synapses. This having been said, there is presently evidence for a role of at least two different diffusable substances as retrograde transmitters in the LTE induction pathway (see review 33): arachidonic acid (AA) and nitric oxide (NO). AA has been found, at least by some investigators, to fulfill many of the obvious criteria for a retrograde messenger, which include release from postsynaptic neurons in response to NMDA receptor activation (31), short half-life, induction of increased transmitter release (76, 77), and occlusion with tetanus induced LTE (118). However, the effects of exogenously applied AA are quite slow to onset, and this has led to doubts as to its role in the initial expression of LTE. Nevertheless, NDGA (nordihydroguaiateric acid), which inhibits AA synthesis or release, appears to block previously induced LTE (117), and thus a role of AA in the maintenance of LTE expression is possible.

The currently more popular candidate for a retrograde messenger is nitric oxide (NO). Following the discovery (39) of an NMDA receptor-dependent release of NO from cerebellar slices, and the suggestion that this might lead to functional modification in neighboring presynaptic terminals, the possible role of NO as the hypothetical retrograde messenger in LTE has been intensely investigated and a substantial case developed independently in several laboratories (17, 47, 93, 103). In experiments performed in vitro in CA1, it has been shown that LTE can be blocked by the active stereoisomers of competitive inhibitors of nitric oxide synthase (NOS), but not by the inactive isomers. The blockade is partly reversible by adding excess arginine, the normal NOS substrate. Hemoglobin, which binds NO with high affinity, also blocked LTE when added to the extracellular medium. Nitroprusside, which causes endogenous release of NO, caused an EPSP enhancement that was not additive with stimulus-induced LTE and, in hippocampal cell cultures, direct application of NO resulted in a long lasting increase in the frequency of spontaneous quantal EPSPs.

It thus appears that NO may perform the postulated function as a retrograde messenger to terminals contacting the activated postsynaptic neuron; moreover, the presynaptic facilitating effects of NO appear to lead to partial violation of the specificity principle inherent in Hebb's rule. Using hippocampal slice cultures prepared from 3–7 day old rats, Bonhoeffer et al (18) provided the first evidence that when LTE was induced by pairing low-frequency stimulation of afferent fibers with postsynaptic depolarization, synapses in neighboring neurons that were not subjected to depolarization also were enhanced. A similar effect was found in neocortical tissue, where it was shown that the spread of enhancement to nearby cells was restricted to synapses that had been activated during paired depolarization of the primary cell. Synapses made by unstimulated axons were not subject to the spread of LTE. These results have been confirmed by D. Madison and his co-workers (personal communication), who have also reported that the intercellular spread of LTE, which is restricted to cells at a distance of less than 100 μm, is blocked by interfering with NO. According to most theoretical models, such lack of specificity would have a disruptive effect on associative memory. One wonders why evolution would go to the trouble of building such exquisite specificity into the NMDA receptor mechanism only to throw it away in subsequent stages of the process.

The overall conclusion from these studies is thus that, at least under some conditions, an NMDA receptor-dependent release of NO from postsynaptic neurons results in the enhancement of transmitter release from any recently active presynaptic terminals within the short distance that NO is able to travel extracellularly. This distance is limited by the very short half-life of the highly reactive NO molecule, although the limit can be expected to vary with experimental conditions such as temperature or other conditions that may affect the balance between diffusion and chemical reaction rates. It would be a serious break with an established tradition in this field, however, if the NO story were allowed to stand without conflicting evidence. Accordingly, Barnes et al (7) have shown that in intact, alert animals with chronically implanted electrodes, virtually complete blockade of hippocampal NOS (confirmed by postmortem enzymatic assay) with the irreversible noncompetitive antagonist L-nitroarginine (L-NARG), had no detectable effect on perforant path LTE induced by electrical stimulation, nor was there any effect on spatial learning in the Morris water task. Spatial learning on this task is disrupted by doses of NMDA antagonists sufficient to block LTE (25, 89). To add to the confusion, recent results from Bliss and colleagues (67) have indicated that LTE blockade by L-NARG or hemoglobin in CA1 in vitro occurs at 23°C, but not at 29°C. This is consistent with an apparent temperature dependence of increased quantal release in LTE (see below). They also failed to block LTE in dentate gyrus with intrahippocampal infusions of L-NARG in vivo in anesthetized animals, although infusions of hemoglobin did result in blockade. Clearly, the universality of the role of NO in the LTE expression pathway is questionable and appears to depend on some, as yet undetermined, variable of the experimental preparation or protocol.

Recently Gribkoff & Lum-Ragan (44a) reported that, at 32°C, inhibition of nitric oxide synthase (NOS) had no effect on LTE induced in CA1 field potentials with a single 100 Hz/1 sec stimulus train of moderate current strength; however, when two such trains were delivered at high current strength, the additional LTE that occurred could be blocked by NOS inhibition. NMDA receptor antagonism blocked or reduced LTE under both conditions. These results support the idea that the biochemical cascade that is induced by NMDA receptor activation may have two, independently regulated branches, one leading to postsynaptic expression mechanisms, and one to NO release and presynaptic alterations.

QUANTAL ANALYSIS

Before beginning a discussion of the results from experiments involving quantal analysis, it is worth remarking that such experiments cannot by themselves, even in principle, unambiguously assign the locus of a change in synaptic efficacy to the presynaptic or postsynaptic zones. They can only place constraints on the kinds of pre- and postsynaptic hypotheses that can be entertained. Moreover, these constraints depend strongly on the ultimate physical basis of the quantal parameters, n and p , which have not been established with any degree of certainty in hippocampal synapses. Two hypothetical possibilities serve to illustrate this point. First, there may be release sites that are not associated with postsynaptic receptors. Addition of receptors, a postsynaptic change, would be spuriously interpreted as an increase in quantal content. Second, because the physical basis of the quantum of transmitter is also unknown, there remains a variety of possible ways in which the amount of transmitter per quantum could be increased (a presynaptic effect), with the result of an apparent increase in the size of the electrophys-iologically measured quantum.

The various conflicting opinions as to the reliability or validity of quantal analysis in mammalian CNS have been discussed recently by Korn & Faber (61). Such arguments notwithstanding, in CA1 Schaffer collateral and dentate gyrus perforant path synapses, the standard methods of quantal analysis, employing the simple binomial or Poisson assumptions, reveal the appropriate changes in m or q under conditions such as paired pulse facilitation or receptor blockade (respectively) in which the outcome can be predicted confidently in advance (8, 34, 79). In addition, by using a signal enhancement procedure involving template matching methods to remove potentials whose amplitude-normalized shapes deviate excessively from the mean shape, R. Malinow (personal communication) has demonstrated quite convincing quantal peaks with amplitudes within the range of previous estimates. It is thus unlikely that the discrepant findings described below are due in essence to either differences or inadequacies of the experimental procedures or analysis.

Based on one or more of the standard analysis methods, there is evidence for robust changes in either quantal size q (34, 80), number of quanta released per impulse (quantal content of EPSP), m (11, 52), or both (79). Two other studies (62, 112) also conclude in favor of either increased m or independent variation in both m and q (i.e. two expression mechanisms); however, these conclusion were based at least partly on an inappropriate preselection of data that almost certainly biased the outcome towards finding increased m (see 34). The bias was introduced by rejecting cases in which less than 30% LTE was observed. The observed magnitude of m can fluctuate either positively or negatively over the course of an experiment, sometimes in conjunction with the enhancement treatment, even though the mean change across experiments may not differ from zero (34). Because random reductions in m reduce the overall apparent LTE, removing those cases from the analysis would lead to a spurious conclusion that the LTE induction procedure, when successful, increases m.

In a recent series of experiments (B. McNaughton et al, unpublished observations) light has been shed on at least some of the remaining sources of discrepancy. Many of the reports of increased m have been based on experiments using the minimal stimulation procedure, in which the stimulus intensity is reduced to the point of intermittent response failure, at which point it is assumed that at most a small number of fibers is activated having contacts on the postsynaptic neuron in question (84). In addition, most (although not all, e.g. 57) experiments reporting increased m have been conducted at a temperature substantially below normal (i.e. 22–23°C). With the suspicion that temperature may in some way alter the balance between a presynaptic expression mechanism and a postsynaptic one, two studies were carried out in which the induction conditions originally used by Malinow & Tsien (79) were mimicked as closely as possible (with the exception that conventional, sharp-electrode current clamp recording was used instead of patch clamping). LTE was induced by pairing 40 stimuli delivered at 2.0 Hz with postsynaptically applied depolarizing current. Consistent with the results of Malinow & Tsien (79), substantially more EPSP increase was observed with this procedure at 22 than at 32°C. The additional enhancement was accounted for by an apparent increase in quantal content, which appeared only at low temperature. The same increase in quantal size was seen at both temperatures. This was replicated in two separate series of experiments. Curiously, however, omitting the postsynaptically applied current prevented the increase in quantal size, but not the increase in quantal content. The results of a small number of experiments involving NMDA receptor antagonism with 100 μM APV produced the expected block in the rise in quantal size with some residual change in quantal content, although the latter is not statistically significant, and as discussed below, is probably spurious. Our initial interpretation of these findings was that there might be a dramatic increase in the time course of post-tetanic potentiation at low temperature. There is a precedent for this interpretation in the early studies of Schlapfer et al (102), which demonstrated a pronounced temperature transition in the decay rate of PTP in *Aplysia* synapses. Subsequent studies, however, have proved this not to be the explanation.

In attempting to analyze the presumed prolonged PTP, we conducted a study using normal population field potentials and the high-frequency/cooperativity method of LTE induction. Surprisingly, although PTP was slightly prolonged at low temperature, there were no differences in the induction of lasting synaptic enhancement (>30 min).

Why should one method of induction lead to pronounced temperature dependencies in the magnitude of apparent enhancement and another not? In considering this question, we decided to reevaluate the assumption that the minimal stimulation method led to reliable activation of single axons. The minimal stimulation method selects the afferent axon with the lowest effective threshold for a given location of the stimulating electrode. Because the threshold function for electrical activation rises steeply, but not instantaneously (see 84), it is possible that a very slight change in the excitability of the Schaffer collateral fibers close to the stimulating electrode could lead to a substantial change in successful activation if the baseline were collected below the asymptote of the threshold function. We had previously found good agreement at 32°C between the quantal analysis results obtained with this method and with dual intracellularly recording of synaptically coupled cells, which suggests that this potential artifact was not a problem; however, it was decided to examine whether this was also true at low temperature. To test this, a series of studies were conducted in which well isolated single units in CA3 were antidromically activated from CA1. The initial intensity was intentionally adjusted to give about 70% failures in the antidromic record. Using the Malinow & Tsien (79) stimulation protocol for LTE induction (40 pulses, 2 Hz), this resulted in a robust increase (80–100%) in the success rate for antidromic activation. This occurred at low temperature only. This temperature-dependent enhancement of presynaptic excitability appears to be blocked by both APV, and the nitric oxide synthase inhibitor L-nitroarginine.

At present, we are somewhat uncertain of how to interpret these findings. On one hand, it is almost certainly the case that many of the published results involving minimal stimulation protocols at low temperature have been contaminated to some degree by this artifactual decrease in failure rate (i.e. the decreased failures seen during LTE are likely to reflect decreased failures of excitation, not of release). This is quite consistent, for example, with recent reports (R. Malinow, personal communication) that, in such experiments, the increase observed in apparent quantal content is inversely related to the initial value. On the other hand, the results do show that a localized change in stimulus rate can lead to a lasting presynaptic alteration, one that seems to be dependent on both NMDA receptor activation and nitric oxide synthesis. It is possible that this altered electrical excitability is a secondary consequence of a set of temperature-dependent changes that are principally related to increasing transmitter release. It is even possible that increased intrinsic excitability might itself lead to increased evoked release; however, until increased quantal release is shown to be reliable at physiological temperatures, with the appropriate controls for altered excitability (e.g. dual recording), its acceptability as a reflection of a normal plasticity mechanism must be questioned.

CONCLUSIONS

The mechanism of expression of long-term enhancement of hippocampal synapses under normal physiological circumstances is presently unresolved. There is little doubt that an increase in quantal size (probably of postsynaptic origin) contributes substantially to the most persistent component of the process. Under some conditions, there is likely to be enhanced transmitter release, although the extent to which this reflects an artifact of altered presynaptic excitability should be thoroughly reexamined. Assuming that these effects are triggered by a retrograde message involving the nitric oxide system, the possibility should also be considered that they reflect not normal plasticity, but rather a redirection or elaboration of the NMDA cascade to serve the needs of synaptic sprouting reactions that are known to accompany various types of acute denervation in the hippocampus.

ACKNOWLEDGMENTS

Supported by grants from the Office of Naval Research and the National Institute of Mental Health (MH46823). I am grateful to G. Rao for assistance with the literature survey, and to C. A. Barnes and W. E. Skaggs for helpful comments on the manuscript.

Literature Cited

1. Andersen, P., Sundberg, S. H., Sveen, O., Wigström, H. 1977. Specific long-lasting potentiation of synaptic transmission in hippocampal slices. *Nature* 266:736–37
2. Aniksztejn, L., Roisin, M. P., Amsellem, R., Ben-Ari, Y. 1989. Long-term potentiation in the hippocampus of the anaesthetized rat is not associated with a sustained enhanced release of endogenous excitatory amino acids. *Neuroscience* 28:387–92
3. April, R. S., Spencer, W. A. 1969. Enhanced synaptic effectiveness after prolonged changes in synaptic use. *Experentia* 25:1272–73
4. Asztely, F., Hanse, E., Wigström, H., Gustafsson, B. 1992. Aniracetam-evoked potentiation does not interact with long-term potentiation in the CA1 region of the hippocampus. *Synapse* 11:342–45
5. Asztely, F., Wigström, H., Gustafsson, B. 1992. The relative contribution of NMDA receptor channels in the expression of long-term potentiation in the hippocampal CA1 region. *Eur. J. Neurosci.* 4:681–90
6. Barinaga, M. 1990. The tide of memory, turning. *Science* 248:1603–5
7. Barnes, C. A., McNaughton, B. L., Bredt, D. S., Ferris, C. D., Snyder, S. H. 1992. Nitric oxide synthase inhibition in vivo has no effect on hippocampal synaptic enhancement or spatial memory. *Soc. Neurosci. Abstr.* 18:1215
8. Barnes, C. A., Rao, G., Foster, T. C., McNaughton, B. L. 1992. Region-specific age effects on AMPA sensitivity: Electrophysiological evidence for loss of synaptic contacts in hippocampal field CA1. *Hippocampus.* 2:457–68
9. Bashir, Z. I., Alford, S., Davies, S. N., Randall, A. D., Collingridge, G. L. 1991. Long-term potentiation of NMDA receptor-mediated synaptic transmission in the hippocampus. *Nature* 349:156–58
10. Bekkers, J. M., Stevens, C. F. 1989. NMDA and non-NMDA receptors are co-localized at individual excitatory synapses in cultured rat hippocampus. *Nature* 341:230–33
11. Bekkers, J. M., Stevens, C. F. 1990. Presynaptic mechanism for long-term potentiation in the hippocampus. *Nature* 346:724–27
12. Bindman, L. J., Lippold, O. C. J., Redfearn, J. W. T. 1964. The action of brief polarizing currents on the cerebral cortex of the rat (1) during current flow and (2) in the production of long-lasting after effects. *J. Physiol.* 172:369–82
13. Bliss, T. V. P., Burns, B. D., Uttley, A. M. 1968. Factors affecting the conductivity of pathways in the cerebral cortex. *J. Physiol.* 195:339–67
14. Bliss, T. V. P., Gardner-Medwin, A. R. 1973. Long-lasting potentiation of synaptic transmission in the dentate area of the anaesthetised rabbit following stimulation of perforant path. *J. Physiol.* 232:357–74
15. Bliss, T. V. P., Lømo, T. 1973. Long-lasting potentiation of synaptic transmission in the dentate area of the anaesthetised rabbit following stimulation of perforant path. *J. Physiol.* 232:331–56
16. Bliss, T. V. P., Lynch, M. A. 1988. Long-term potentiation of synaptic transmission in the hippocampus: Properties and mechanisms. In *Long-Term Potentiation: From Biophysics to Behavior*, ed. P. Landfield, S. Deadwyler, pp. 3–72. New York: Liss
17. Böhme, G. A., Bon, C., Stutzmann, J.-M., Doble, A., Blanchard, J.-C. 1991. Possible involvement of nitric oxide in long-term potentiation. *Eur. J. Pharmacol.* 199:379–81
18. Bonhoeffer, T., Staiger, V., Aertsen, A. 1989. Synaptic plasticity in rat hippocampal slice cultures: Local "Hebbian" conjuction of pre- and postsynaptic stimulation leads to distributed synaptic enhancement. *Proc. Natl. Acad. Sci. USA* 86:8113–17
19. Buzsaki, G. 1984. Long-term changes in hippocampal sharp-waves following high frequency afferent activation. *Brain Res.* 300:179–82
20. Chang, F.-L. F., Greenough, W. T. 1984. Transient and enduring morphological correlates of synaptic activity and efficacy change in the rat hippocampal slice. *Brain Res.* 309:35–46
21. Chang, F.-L. F., Isaacs, K. R., Greenough, W. T. 1991. Synapse formation occurs in association with the induction of long-term potentiation in two-year-old rat hippocampus in vitro. *Neurobiol. Aging* 12:517–22
22. Coan, E. J., Collingridge, G. L., Herron, C. E., Lester, R. A. J. 1985. Demonstration of a phencyclidine-sensitive *N*-methyl-d-aspartate-receptor-mediated component of an e.p.s.p. in

rat hippocampal slices. *J. Physiol.* 365:45P

23. Collingridge, G., Kehl, S., McLennan, H. 1983. Excitatory amino acids in synaptic transmission in the Schaffer collateral-commissural pathway of the rat hippocampus. *J. Physiol.* 334:3–46

24. Dahl, D., Sarvey, J. M. 1989. Norepinephrine induces pathway specific long-term potentiation and depression in the hippocampal dentate gyrus. *Proc. Natl. Acad. Sci. USA* 86:4776–80

25. Davis, S., Butcher, S. P., Morris, R. G. M. 1992. The NMDA receptor antagonist D-2-amino-5-phosphonopentanoate (D-AP5) impairs spatial learning and LTP in vivo at intracerebral concentrations comparable to those that block LTP in vitro. *J. Neurosci.* 12:21–34

26. Davies, S. N., Lester, R. A. J., Reymann, K. G., Collingridge, G. L. 1989. Temporally distinct pre- and postsynaptic mechanisms maintain long-term potentiation. *Nature* 338:500–3

27. Delaney, K. R., Zucker, R. S., Tank, D. W. 1989. Calcium in motor nerve terminals associated with posttetanic potentiation. *J. Neurosci.* 9:3558–67

28. Dolphin, A. C., Errington, M. L., Bliss, T. V. P. 1982. Long-term potentiation of the perforant path in vivo is associated with increased glutamate release. *Nature* 297:496–98

29. Douglas, R. M., Goddard, G. V. 1975. Long-term potentiation of the perforant path-granule cell synapse in the rat hippocampus. *Brain Res.* 86:205–15

30. Douglas, R. M., Goddard, G. V., Riives, M. 1982. Inhibitory modulation of long-term potentiation: Evidence for a postsynaptic locus of control. *Brain Res.* 240:259–72

31. Dumuis, A., Sebben, L., Haynes, L., Bockaert, J.-P. 1988. NMDA receptors activate the arachidonic acid cascade system in striatal neurons. *Nature* 336:68

32. Errington, M. L., Lynch, M. A., Bliss, T. V. P. 1987. Long-term potentiation in the dentate gyrus: Induction and increased glutamate release are blocked by D(-)aminophosphonovalerate. *Neuroscience* 20:279–84

33. Fazeli, M. S. 1992. Synaptic plasticity: on the trail of the retrograde messenger. *Trends Neurosci.* 15:115–17

34. Foster, T. C., McNaughton, B. L. 1991. Long-term synaptic enhancement in hippocampal field CA1 is due to increased quantal size, not quantal content. *Hippocampus* 1:79–91

35. Frenguelli, B. G., Blake, J. F., Brown, M. W., Collingridge, G. L. 1991. Electrogenic uptake contributes a major component of the depolarizing action of L-glutamate in rat hippocampal slices. *Br. J. Pharmacol.* 102:355–62

36. Friedlander, M. J., Sayer, R. J., Redman, S. J. 1990. Evaluation of long-term potentiation of small compound and unitary EPSPs at the hippocampal CA3-CA1 synapse. *J. Neurosci.* 10:814–25

37. Frotcher, M., Gähwiler, B. H. 1988. Synaptic organization of intracellularly stained CA3 pyramidal neurons in slice cultures of rat hippocampus. *Neuroscience* 24:541–61

38. Gähwiler, B. H. 1984. Development of the hippocampus in vitro. *Neuroscience* 11:751–60

39. Garthwaite, J., Charles, S. L., Chess-Williams, R. 1988. Endothelium-derived relaxing factor release on activation of NMDA receptors suggests a role as intercellular messenger in the brain. *Nature* 336:385–88

40. Gartside, I. B. 1968. Mechanisms of sustained increases in firing rate of neurons in the rat cerebral cortex after polarization: reverberating circuits or modification of synaptic conductance. *Nature* 220:382–83

41. Gartside, I. B. 1968. Mechanisms of sustained increases in firing rate of neurons in the rat cerebral cortex after polarization: role of protein synthesis. *Nature* 220:382–83

42. Ghijsen, W. E. J. M., Lopes Da Silva, F. H. 1991. Increase in endogenous amino acid release in long-term potentiation. In *Long-Term Potentiation: A Debate of Current Issues*, ed. M. Baudry, J. Davis, pp. 45–55. Cambridge: MIT Press

43. Gibson, W. G., Robinson, J. 1992. Statistical analysis of the dynamics of a sparse associative memory. *Neural Networks* 5:645–61

44. Gibson, W. G., Robinson, J. 1991. Probabilistic secretion of quanta in the central nervous system: granule cell synaptic control of pattern separation and activity regulation. *Philos. Trans. R. Soc. London Ser. B* 332:199–220

44a. Gribkoff, V. K., Lum-Ragan, J. T. 1992. Evidence for nitric oxide synthase inhibitor-sensitive and -insensitive hippocampal synaptic potentiation. *J. Neurophysiol.* 68:639–42

45. Gustafsson, B., Wigström, H. 1988. Physiological mechanisms underlying long-term potentiation. *Trends Neurosci.* 11:156–62

46. Gustafsson, B., Wigström, H. 1990.

Introduction: Associative long-lasting modifications in synaptic efficacy. *Sem. Neurosci.* 2:317–19

47. Haley, J. E., Wilcox, G. L., Chapman, P. F. 1992. The role of nitric oxide in hippocampal long-term potentiation. *Neuron* 8:211–16

48. Harris, E. W., Ganong, A. H., Cotman, C. W. 1984. Long-term potentiation in the hippocampus involves activation of N-methyl-D-aspartate receptors. *Brain Res.* 323:132–37

49. Hebb, D. O. 1949. *The Organization of Behavior.* New York: Wiley. 335 pp.

50. Hertz, J., Krogh, A., Palmer, R. G. 1991. *Introduction to the Theory of Neural Computation.* New York: Addison-Wesley. 327 pp.

51. Hess, G., Khunt, U., Voronin, L. L. 1987. Quantal analysis of paired-pulse facilitation in guinea pig hippocampal slices. *Neurosci. Lett.* 77:187–92

52. Hirata, K., Sawanda, S., Yamamoto, C. 1991. Enhancement of transmitter release accompanying with long-term potentiation in synapses between mossy fibers and CA3 neurons in hippocampus. *Neurosci. Lett.* 123:73–76

53. Hopkins, W. F., Johnston, D. 1984. Frequency-dependent noradrenergic modulation of long-term potentiation in the hippocampus. *Science* 226:350–52

54. Isaacson, J. S., Nicoll, R. A. 1992. Aniracetam reduces glutamate receptor desensitization and slows the decay of fast excitatory synaptic currents in the hippocampus. *Proc. Natl. Acad. Sci. USA* 88:10936–40

55. Ishizuka, N., Weber, J., Amaral, D. G. 1990. Organization of intrahippocampal projections originating from CA3 pyramidal cells in the rat. *J. Comp. Neurol.* 295:580–623

56. Ito, I., Tanabe, S., Khoda, A., Sugiyama, H. 1990. Allosteric potentiation of quisqalate receptors by a nootropic drug aniracetam. *J. Physiol.* 424:533–43

57. Kamiya, H., Sawada, S., Yamamoto, C. 1991. Persistent enhancement of transmitter release accompanying long-term potentiation in the guinea-pig hippocampus. *Neurosci. Lett.* 130:259–62

58. Kauer, J. A., Malenka, R. C., Nicoll, R. A. 1988. NMDA application potentiates synaptic transmission in the hippocampus. *Nature* 334:250–53

59. Kelso, S. R., Ganong, A. H., Brown, T. H. 1986. Hebbian synapses in hippocampus. *Proc. Natl. Acad. Sci. USA* 83:5326–30

60. Kessler, M., Arai, A., Vanderklish, P., Lynch, G. 1991. Failure to detect changes in AMPA receptor binding after long-term potentiation. *Brain Res.* 560:337–41

61. Korn, H., Faber, D. S. 1991. Quantal analysis and synaptic efficacy in the CNS. *Trends Neurosci.* 14:439–45

62. Kullman, D. M., Nicoll, R. A. 1992. Long-term potentiation is associated with increases in quantal content and quantal amplitude. *Nature* 357:240–44

63. Lacaille, J.-C., Harley, C. W. 1985. The action of norepinephrine in the dentate gyrus: Beta-mediated facilitation of evoked potentials in vitro. *Brain Res.* 258:210–20

64. Landfield, P. W., Deadwyler, S. A., eds. 1987. *Long-term Potentiation: From Biophysics to Behavior.* New York: Liss. 548 pp.

65. Lee, K. S., Oliver, M., Schottler, F., Lynch, G. 1980. Brief bursts of high-frequency produce two types of structural change in rat hippocampus. *J. Neurophysiol.* 44:247–58

66. Levy, W. B., Steward, O. 1979. Synapses as associative memory elements in the hippocampal formation. *Brain Res.* 175:233–45

67. Li, Y.-G., Errington, M. L., Williams, J. H., Bliss, T. V. P. 1992. Termperature-dependent block of LTP by the no synthase inhibitor L-nitroarginine. *Soc. Neurosci. Abstr.* 18:343

68. Liley, A. W. 1956. An investigation of spontaneous activity at the neuromuscular junction of the rat. *J. Physiol.* 132:650–66

69. Llinás, R. R., McGuinness, T. L., Leonard, C. S., Sugimori, M., Greengard, P. 1985. Intraterminal injection of synapsin I or of calcium/calmodulin dependent protein kinase II alters neurotransmitter release at the squid giant synapse. *Proc. Natl. Acad. Sci. USA* 82:3035–39

70. Lømo, T. 1966. Frequency potentiation of excitatory synaptic activity in the dentate area of the hippocampal formation. *Acta Physiol. Scand.* 68(Suppl. 277):28

71. Lynch, G., Baudry, M. 1991. Reevaluating the constraints on hypotheses regarding LTP expression. *Hippocampus* 1:9–14

72. Lynch, G., Halpain, S., Baudry, M. 1982. Effects of high-frequency synaptic stimulation on glumate receptor binding studied with a modified in vitro hippocampal slice preparation. *Brain Res.* 244:101–11

73. Lynch, G. S., Gribkoff, V. K., Deadwyler, S. A. 1976. Long term potentiation is accompanied by a re-

duction in dendritic responsiveness to glutamic acid. *Nature* 263:151–53

74. Lynch, M. A., Errington, M. L., Bliss, T. V. P. 1985. Long-term potentiation of synaptic transmission in the dentate gyrus: increased release of [^{14}C]glutamate without increase in receptor binding. *Neurosci. Lett.* 62:123–29

75. Lynch, M. A., Errington, M. L., Bliss, T. V. P. 1989. The increase in [^{3}H]glutamate release associated with long-term potentiation in the dentate gyrus is blocked by commissural stimulation. *Neurosci. Lett.* 103:191–96

76. Lynch, M. A., Errington, M. L., Bliss, T. V. P. 1989. Nordihydroguaiaretic acid blocks the synaptic component of long-term potentiation and the associated increases in release of glutamate and arachidonate: an in vivo study in the dentate gyrus of the rat. *Neuroscience* 30:693–701

77. Lynch, M. A., Voss, K. 1990. Arachiodonic acid increased inositol phospholipid metabolism and glutamate release in synaptosome prepared from hippocampal tissue. *J. Neurochem.* 55: 215–21

78. Madison, D. V., Malenka, R. C., Nicoll, R. A. 1991. Mechanisms underlying long-term potentiation of synaptic transmission. *Annu. Rev. Neurosci.* 14:479–97

79. Malinow, R., Tsien, R. W. 1990. Presynaptic changes revealed by whole-cell recordings of long-term potentiation in rat hippocampal slices. *Nature* 346: 177–80

80. Manabe, T., Renner, P., Nicoll, R. A. 1992. Postsynaptic contribution to long-term potentiation revealed by the analysis of miniature synaptic currents. *Nature* 355:50–55

81. Marr, D. 1971. Simple memory: A theory for archicortex. *Philos. Trans. R. Soc. London Ser. B* 262:23–81

82. McNaughton, B. L. 1982. Long-term synaptic enhancement and short-term potentiation in rat fascia dentata act through different mechanisms. *J. Physiol.* 324:249–62

83. McNaughton, B. L., Barnes, C. A. 1977. Physiological identification and analysis of dentate granule cell responses to stimulation of the medial and lateral perforant pathways in the rat. *J. Comp. Neurol.* 175:439–54

84. McNaughton, B. L., Barnes, C. A., Andersen, P. 1981. Synaptic efficacy and EPSP summation in granule cells of rat fascia dentata studied in vitro. *J. Neurophysiol.* 46:952–66

85. McNaughton, B. L., Douglas, R. M., Goddard, G. V. 1978. Synaptic enhancement in fascia dentata: Cooperativity among coactive afferents. *Brain Res.* 157:277–93

86. McNaughton, B. L., Nadel, L. 1990. Hebb-Marr networks and the neurobiological representation of action in space. In *Neuroscience and Connectionist Theory*, ed. M. A. Gluck, D. E. Rumelhart, pp. 1–63. New York: Erlbaum

87. Montague, P. R., Gancayco, C. D., Marchase, R. B., Friedlander, M. J. 1992. Possible role of NMDA-dependent nitric oxide production in neurotransmitter release. *Nature* In press

88. Morrell, F. 1961. Electrophysiological contributions to the neural basis of learning. *Physiol. Rev.* 41:443–94

89. Morris, R. G. M., Davis, S., Butcher, S. P. 1990. Hippocampal synaptic plasticity and NMDA receptors: a role in information storage? *Philos. Trans. R. Soc. London Ser. B* 329:187–204

90. Muller, D., Arai, A., Lynch, G. 1992. Factors governing the potentiation of NMDA receptor-mediated responses in hippocampus. *Hippocampus* 2:29–38

91. Muller, D., Lynch, G. 1988. Long-term potentiation differentially affects two components of synaptic responses in hippocampus. *Proc. Natl. Acad. Sci. USA* 85:9346–50

92. Neuman, R. S., Harley, C. W. 1983. Long-lasting potentiation of the dentate gyrus population spike by norepinephrine. *Brain Res.* 273:162–65

93. O'Dell, T. J., Hawkins, R., Kandel, E. R., Arancio, O. 1991. Tests of the roles of two diffusible substances in long-term potentiation: Evidence for nitric oxide as a possible early retrograde messenger. *Proc. Natl. Acad. Sci. USA* 88:11285–89

94. Parfitt, K. D., Hoffer, B. J., Browning, M. D. 1991. Norepinephrine and isoproterenol increase the phosphorylation of synapsin-I and synapsin-II in dentate slices of young but not aged Fisher-344 rats. *Proc. Natl. Acad. Sci. USA* 88:2361–65

95. Patneau, D. K., Mayer, M. L. 1990. Structure-activity relationships for amino acid transmitter candidates acting at N-methyl-D-aspartate and quisqualate receptors. *J. Neurosci.* 10:2385–99

96. Radpour, S., Thomson, A. M. 1991. Coactivation of local circuit NMDA receptor mediated epsps induces lasting enhancement of minimal Schaffer collateral EPSPs in slices of rat hippocampus. *Eur. J. Neurosci.* 3:602–13

97. Reeves, T., Steward, O. 1985. Time course of emergence of LTP during

reinervation of the dentate gyrus. *Soc. Neurosci. Abstr.* 11:779

98. Reymann, K. G., Davies, S. N., Matthies, H., Kase, H., Collingridge, G. L. 1990. Activation of a K-252b-sensitive protein kinase is necessary for a post-synaptic phase of long-term potentiation in area CA1 of rat hippocampus. *Eur. J. Neurosci.* 2:481–86

99. Rutledge, L. T. 1965. Facilitation: electrical response enhanced by conditional excitation of cerebral cortex. *Science* 148:1246–48

100. Saggau, P., Wu, L. G. 1992. The expression of long-term potentiation in hippocampal area CA1 does not change presynaptic calcium. *Soc. Neurosci. Abstr.* 18:429

101. Sayer, R. J., Redman, S. J., Andersen, P. 1989. Amplitude fluctuations in small EPSPs recorded from CA1 pyramidal cells in the guinea pig hippocampal slice. *J. Neurosci.* 9:840–50

102. Schlapfer, W. T., Tremblay, J. P., Woodson, P. B. J., Barondes, S. H., Smith, G. A. 1975. Marked prolongation of post-tetanic potentiation at a transition temperature and its adaptation. *Nature* 258:623–25

103. Schuman, E. M., Madison, D. V. 1991. A requirement for the intercellular messenger nitric oxide in long-term potentiation. *Science* 254:1503–6

104. Skrede, K. K., Malthe-Sørenssen, D. 1981. Increased resting and evoked release of transmitter following repetitive electrical tetanization in hippocampus: a biochemical correlate to long-lasting synaptic potentiation. *Brain Res.* 208:436–41

105. Stanton, P. K., Sarvey, J. M. 1987. Norepinephrine regulates long-term potentiation of both the population spike and dendritic EPSP in hippocampal dentate gyrus. *Brain Res. Bull.* 18:115–19

106. Staubli, U., Ambros-Ingerson, J., Lynch, G. 1992. Receptor changes and LTP: An analysis using aniracetam, a drug that reversibly modifies glutamate (AMPA) receptors. *Hippocampus* 2:49–58

107. Staubli, U., Kessler, M., Lynch, G. 1990. Aniracetam has proportionately smaller effects on synapses expressing long-term potentiation: Evidence that receptor changes subserve LTP. *Psychobiology* 18:377–81

108. Steward, O. 1986. Lesion-induced synapse growth in the hippocampus; In search of cellular and molecular mechanisms. In *The Hippocampus,* ed. R.

L. Isaacson, K. H. Pribram, 3:65–111. New York: Plenum

109. Tang, C.-M., Shi, Q.-Y., Katchman, A., Lynch, G. 1991. Modulation of the time course of fast EPSCs and glutamate channel kinetics by aniracetam. *Science* 254:288–90

110. Tocco, G., Maren, S., Shors, T. J., Baudry, M., Thompson, R. F. 1992. Long-term potentiation is associated with increased [^{3}H]AMPA binding in rat hippocampus. *Brain Res.* 573:228–34

111. Treves, A., Rolls, E. T. 1991. What determines the capacity of autoassociative memories in the brain? *Network* 2:371–98

112. Voronin, L. L. 1988. Quantal analysis of long-term potentiation. In *Synaptic Plasticity in the Hippocampus,* ed. H. L. Haas, G. Buzsáki, pp. 27–30. Berlin: Springer-Verlag

113. Wallace, C. S., Hawrylak, N., Greenough, W. T. 1991. Studies of synaptic structural modifications after long-term potentiation and kindling: Context for a molecular morphology. See Ref. 42, pp. 189–232

114. Watkins, J. C., Evans, R. H. 1981. Excitatory amino acid transmitters. *Annu. Rev. Pharmacol. Toxicol.* 21:165–204

115. Wigström, H., Gustaffson, B. 1985. Facilitation of hippocampal long-lasting potentiation by GABA antagonists. *Acta Physiol. Scand.* 125:159–72

116. Wigström, H., Gustaffson, B., Huang, Y.-Y. 1986. Mode of action of excitatory amino acid receptor antagonists on hippocampal long-lasting potentiation. *Neuroscience* 17:1105–15

117. Williams, J. H., Bliss, T. V. P. 1988. Induction but not maintenance of calcium-induced long-term potentiation in dentate gyrus and area CA1 of the hippocampal slice is blocked by nordihydroguaiaretic acid. *Neurosci. Lett.* 88:81

118. Williams, J. H., Errington, M. L., Lynch, M. A., Bliss, T. V. P. 1989. Arachidonic acid induces a long-term activity-dependent enhancement of synaptic transmission in the hippocampus. *Nature* 341:739–42

119. Xie, X., Berger, T. W., Barrionuevo, G. 1992. Isolated NMDA receptor-mediated synaptic responses express both LTP and LTD. *J. Neurophysiol.* 67:1009–13

120. Zalutsky, R. A., Nicoll, R. A. 1990. Comparison of two forms of long-term potentiation in single hippocampal neurons. *Science* 248:1619–24

Annu. Rev. Physiol. 1993. 55:397–426

STRUCTURAL CHANGES ACCOMPANYING MEMORY STORAGE

Craig H. Bailey

Center for Neurobiology and Behavior, College of Physicians and Surgeons of Columbia University, and The New York State Psychiatric Institute, 722 West 168th Street, New York, New York 10032

Eric R. Kandel

Howard Hughes Medical Institute, Center for Neurobiology and Behavior, College of Physicians and Surgeons of Columbia University, and The New York State Psychiatric Institute, 722 West 168th Street, New York, New York 10032

KEY WORDS: learning, synaptic plasticity, active zone, synapse formation, NCAM modulation

INTRODUCTION

Perhaps the most striking finding in the biology of memory is that long-term memory involves structural changes. A variety of memory processes ranging in complexity from those produced by elementary forms of nonassociative learning in invertebrates to those produced by higher order associative tasks in mammals are accompanied by alterations in the structure of synaptic connections. This finding raises three interesting conceptual issues. First, how does short-term memory, which involves only covalent modification of pre-existing proteins and an alteration of pre-existing connections, become transformed into a structural change? Second, is the stability of long-term memory achieved because of the stability of synaptic structures? If so, is loss of memory with time reflected in loss of synaptic connections? Finally, how do the structural changes that accompany long-term memory compare with the de novo synapse formation and synaptic pruning that occur during development? In this review we consider the recent evidence for structural changes in learning by focusing on these three issues. We begin by examining

397

0066–4278/93/0315–0397$02.00

the types of structural changes that accompany various forms of activity-dependent changes in both vertebrates and invertebrates. We then consider the
cellular and molecular mechanisms that might give rise to these structural
changes.

EVIDENCE FOR SYNAPSE FORMATION DURING LONG-TERM MEMORY

The structural modifications accompanying learning and memory can be
grouped into two major categories: changes in pre-exisiting synapses; and
changes in the number of synapses (91–93). Of the changes in pre-existing
synapses, the most reliable and potentially best-suited for correlation with
synaptic effectiveness are those that involve reorganization of the active zone
(53, 108, 131), a focal and specialized region of synaptic contacts that is
modified for the release of neurotransmitters. Experience-related manipulations produce changes in the size and vesicle complement of the active zone
(5, 6, 10, 14, 15, 17, 46, 62, 107, 203), in the total number of vesicles per
presynaptic terminal (65, 71, 79, 150, 182, 189, 190, 204, 205), in the
geometry of apposition between pre- and postsynaptic components (25, 26,
59–62, 139, 171, 179, 195, 196, 208), and in the extent and continuity of
the postsynaptic specialization (34, 52, 61, 80–84, 101, 105, 110, 189, 190,
203, 208, 209, 211). In addition, experience can produce various structural
modifications in postsynaptic dendritic spines (35, 44, 50, 51, 59–64, 70, 71,
95, 128, 132, 133, 154, 164, 165, 187, 188, 196a, 201).

   Although a change in the morphology of the active zone occurs frequently,
the most consistent structural feature to emerge as a potential substrate for
the storage of long-term memory appears to be an alteration in the number
or pattern of synaptic connections (91–94, 102, 206). We therefore limit this
review to alterations in synapse number produced by experience.

Activity Is Critical for the Synaptic Rearrangement that Establishes Ocular Dominance Columns

Some of the earliest evidence for structural changes with experience came
from studies of sensory deprivation during early critical periods of postnatal
development. Here, Hubel & Wiesel found that formation of synaptic
connections in the visual cortex requires appropriately patterned activity in
neurons. Using monocular deprivation they found that lack of visual experience during early development leads to permanent alterations in perceptual
capabilities later in life. These behavioral modifications are accompanied by
morphological and physiological changes consistent with an alteration in the
number and pattern of synaptic connections (112–114, 136).

   Subsequent studies by Stryker and others illustrated that the development of ocular dominance columns requires activity-dependent cooperation on a common target cell between afferent fibers from the same eye, while simultaneously there is competition between afferent fibers from the two eyes. Stryker & Harris (192) found that ocular dominance columns do not form in kittens when all impulse activity in retinal ganglion cells and optic nerves is blocked by injections of tetrodotoxin into each eye. With all activity blocked, synchronous stimulation of both optic nerves prevented the formation of ocular dominance columns, whereas asynchronous stimulation of the two optic nerves permitted their formation (191, 193). Thus, the segregation of afferent fibers and the establishment of ocular dominance columns can be altered by changing the balance of input activity from the two eyes during this critical period.

Labeling of afferent fibers at different developmental stages has allowed this segregation to be followed in populations of cells and more recently at the level of individual neurons (76, 120, 134–136). Early in development, single afferent fibers from the lateral geniculate nucleus have an extensive terminal arbor that covers several future ocular dominance columns for each eye. As a geniculate neuron matures, there is a gradual remodeling of its afferent axon that results in the pruning of those branches that traverse inappropriate territories and an expansion and strengthening of branches that course within appropriate territories. As a result, each neuron now connects only to cells of the ocular dominance columns for one eye. Shatz and her co-workers (38, 143, 180, 181, 185) found a similar activity-dependent pattern of selective retraction and directed growth underlying the development of the eye-specific layers in the lateral geniculate nucleus. A number of studies have further demonstrated that a wide range of sensory manipulations during development can lead to changes in the incidence of dendritic spines and synapses (54, 67–69, 74, 88, 163, 177, 195, 199, 200).

Variations in Environmental Complexity Are Reflected in Anatomical Changes

More global manipulations such as those in environmental complexity have shown that the morphology of the brain can be altered throughout a significant portion of the animal's life span. The initial reports by Rosenzweig, Bennett, Diamond, and their colleagues (31, 175, 176) provided the first evidence that enrichment of the environment could lead to structural changes in the brain. They found that when rats were placed together in enriched environments (large, toy-filled cages) their occipital cortex was thicker and heavier than the cortex of rats reared individually or in standard cages.

Over the past two decades, a comprehensive series of studies by Greenough and his colleagues, using either animals of weaning age or adults, demonstrated that the gross changes in the thickness of the occipital cortex actually reflect a 25–40% increase in the extent and branching of dendrites and a parallel increase in the number of synapses per neuron (73, 78, 90, 98–100, 118, 126, 127, 197, 202). Qualitatively similar synaptic and dendritic changes also have been reported in cats (30) and monkeys (73), and in other regions of the brain including subcortical structures and the cerebellum (78, 98, 116, 117, 170). These changes are often accompanied by alterations in nonneuronal elements that might support the increased metabolic demand placed on neuronal growth. For example, enriched experience that leads to increases in the number of synapses also leads to an increase in the volume and branching of capillaries (33) as well as in the size and surface density of glial cells (183).

Motor Learning

Changes in the number or pattern of synaptic connections have also been shown to accompany various learning paradigms. These include increases in the dendritic fields of pyramidal cells in the visual cortex following maze training (43, 96), and in the forelimb sensorimotor cortex following a handedness-reversal task (97, 210). Black et al (32) compared the effect on synaptic connectivity in the paramedian lobule of the cerebellar cortex of neuronal activity associated with motor learning and stereotypic activity arising from repetitive exercise. They placed adult rats in one of four experimental conditions: acrobatic conditioning, in which they were required to traverse an increasingly difficult series of elevated obstacles for food reward over a 30-day period; forced exercise on a treadmill; voluntary exercise on a running wheel to which the animals had free access; and inactivity conditioning, in which rats were kept in standard laboratory cages. The number of synapses per Purkinje cell was elevated by acrobatic motor learning and was unaffected by exercise. These results suggest that only those aspects of activity that are related to the acquisition of a particular learning task lead to changes in synaptic organization.

Additional evidence for structural plasticity in the cerebellum has come from a recent study by Anderson et al (3) examining the effects of eyeblink conditioning on the morphology of Purkinje cell dendrites in lobule six of the cerebellar hemisphere (HVI) of the rabbit. Conditioned animals were trained unilaterally using electrical stimulation to the dorsolateral pontine nucleus as the conditioned stimulus (CS) paired with a coterminating corneal air puff as the unconditioned stimulus (US). Rabbits that received unpaired training received the same number of pontine stimuli and air puff presentations, but at random intervals. The contralateral hemispheres served as controls in each group. Anderson et al found a significant decrease (15%) in the number of spiny dendritic branches of Purkinje cells in the hemisphere receiving paired conditioning trials compared to the contralateral untrained hemisphere. Since these branches are a major postsynaptic target for the parallel fibers, associative memory in the cerebellum may also be accompanied by a selective reduction in the presynaptic input onto Purkinje neurons.

Learning in the Adult Also Affects the Cortical Representation of Body Form

A fascinating series of studies by Merzenich and colleagues has demonstrated that the somatotopic maps in the brain can also be modified by experience (144–149). Electrophysiological mapping of the cortex in both normal animals and in animals exposed to either selective denervation or differential stimulation has shown that cortical somatic sensory maps differ systematically among individuals in a manner that reflects their use. Thus just as the structure of ocular dominance columns can be altered by experience during critical early periods of development, altered sensory experience in later life can also produce changes in the functional architecture of the brain. The extent to which this topographic reorganization might involve changes in the number or pattern of synaptic connections is not known.

Long-Term Potentiation and Kindling in the Hippocampus

Long-term potentiation (LTP) in the hippocampus is a form of synaptic plasticity that is thought to be involved in the storage of long-term memory for explicit forms of learning, forms of learning concerned with acquiring information of places, objects, and other living beings (29). Evidence for changes in synapse number with LTP in the CA1 region first came from studies by Lynch and his co-workers (132, 133), who reported that electrical stimulation that produced LTP either in vivo or in vitro also led to a rapid increase in the number of synapses onto dendritic shafts.

This observation was confirmed and extended in the slice by Chang & Greenough (44), who also found a rapid (within 10–15 min after stimulation) increase in the number of shaft synapses per unit area and, in addition, an increase in the number of sessile spine synapses (presumed to be immature or transitional synaptic contacts) in slices exposed to LTP compared to equivalent low-frequency stimulated control groups. Both spine and shaft synapses were found to be present on small dendrites, which may be pyramidal in origin. By contrast, only shaft synapses were found on large dendrites thought to arise from interneurons. These results could represent the selective formation of the two types of synapses or a process by which shaft synapses formed on pyramidal cells and then are transformed via an intermediate sessile spine shape to spine synapses. This stimulus-induced synaptogenesis in the hippocampus seems tightly correlated with LTP. Continuous high-frequency activation that did not produce LTP did not evoke any changes in synapse number. Although the relative number of both shaft and sessile spine synapses was approximately doubled following stimulation, this change represents only about a 5% increase in the total number of synapses. It is not known if this small change might be sufficient to account for the approximately 300% enhancement in the amplitude of the physiological response, but conceivably it could. LTP might affect only a small fraction, perhaps only 10%, of all the synapses in a given region of the hippocampus. Qualitatively similar, but smaller, effects have been described following the induction of LTP in hippocampal slices from older rats (45).

Recent studies by Geinisman and his co-workers (82) have also demonstrated changes in synapse number during the induction of LTP in the dentate gyrus. Previous studies, which suggested that LTP led to increases in the numerical density of synapses in the dentate gyrus (59, 60, 207), were based on random, nonserial sections and on biased methods for synapse quantitation. The interpretation of changes in synapse number obtained with these approaches may be influenced by several biases, the direction and magnitude of which could be different in control and experimental populations. Utilizing serial sections and unbiased stereological techniques, Geinisman et al assessed quantitatively the number of synapses per neuron for several morphologically distinct types of synaptic contacts. They elicited LTP with high-frequency stimulation of the medial perforant pathway in young adult rats on each of four consecutive days. Animals that received LTP were sacrificed 1 hr after the fourth stimulation. Rats that were stimulated, but not potentiated, and rats that were only implanted, but not stimulated, served as controls. Synapses were examined in the middle and inner molecular layers of the dentate gyrus. Geinisman et al found that the induction of LTP was accompanied by a highly selective increase in a single morphological subtype of synaptic contact—perforated axospinous synapses with a segmented postsynaptic density. Moreover, this change was found only in the synaptic region of the dentate gyrus that was physiologically-potentiated. The changes were not found in an immediately adjacent synaptic region that was not exposed to LTP. As with the studies in subfield CA1 (44, 132, 133) and previous studies in the dentate gyrus (59, 60, 63), these data could represent the selective formation of a particular class of synapse or a dynamic transformation of one synaptic form into another (41, 52, 66, 157) (Figure 1).

Long-term potentiation is not the only long-lasting change in neuronal function known to occur in the hippocampus. Another is kindling, an animal model of epilepsy in which an epileptiform discharge is induced by repetitive subthreshold stimulation. Kindling is often considered as a model of long-term memory since it evokes a virtually permanent augmentation of synaptic responsiveness in the stimulated circuit and seems to share some features in common with LTP. Although initial structural studies of kindling in the dentate gyrus (84) reported no change in the absolute number of axodendritic or axospinous contacts, the ratio of perforated to nonperforated synapses was

A

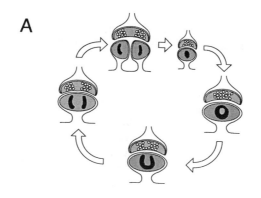

B

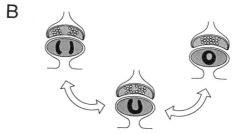

Figure 1 LTP in the dentate gyrus is associated with an increase in the number of axospinous synapses with segmented postsynaptic densities (PSD). It is not known if these additional synapses evolve from pre-existing synaptic junctions or are newly formed during LTP induction. The diagrams present two models of synapse turnover (*A*) and interconversion (*B*). In each case, presynaptic terminals are shown in cross section, whereas postsynaptic spines display an en face view of the PSD. The sequence of steps outlined in *A* has been suggested by earlier models of constant synapse turnover (41, 52, 66, 157) and includes (*a*) enlargement and initial splitting of a non-perforated axospinous synaptic contact into one with a large, fenestrated PSD; (*b*) tearing of the perforated PSD, which now appears horseshoe-shaped; (*c*) division of a single, horse-shoe-like PSD into separate segments; and (*d*) final splitting of a large axospinous synapse with segmented PSD into smaller, non-perforated synaptic contacts. Initially, both dendritic spines are in register with the same presynaptic terminal. Continuation of this process would presumably lead to two completely separate, non-perforated axospinous synapses. Another possibility, suggested in *B*, is that the interconversion does not involve non-perforated synapses and is limited to the various perforated subtypes (redrawn from 82).

found to increase by 45% in experimental groups. Recently, Morrell et al (153) re-examined the structural plasticity associated with kindling more closely and found an increase in synapse number. This increase again is highly selective and involves only one particular morphological subtype—perforated axospinous synapses with a segmented postsynaptic density. Thus the increase in the number of synapses found to accompany LTP and kindling in the dentate gyrus involves the same morphological subclass. This selective modification of connectivity with both LTP and kindling suggests that the increases in synapse number may share a common mechanism. Additional support for this notion comes from studies by Hawrylak et al (106), who examined the early structural events associated with the initial expression of kindling within CA1 of hippocampal slice preparations. They fixed tissue within 15 min after inducing a limited number of afterdischarges and found a 73% increase in the density of dendritic shaft synapses and a 103% increase in the density of sessile spine synapses, the same classes of synaptic contacts that were found to increase in number following LTP in CA1.

The increases in synapse number observed following LTP and kindling in the hippocampus and dentate gyrus are accompanied by a parallel increase in nonneuronal elements. As is the case in the studies of environmental complexity, one component of this change is in glial cells. Isaacs et al (115) explored the response of astrocytes to the induction of LTP in the dentate gyrus by using monoclonal antibodies to glial fibrillary acidic protein (GFAP) and examining differences in the size of astrocytes. Both the size and surface density of GFAP-positive cell processes were found to increase in the LTP groups when compared to controls receiving equivalent stimulation at lower frequencies. The astrocytic hypertrophy may reflect a plastic response of glial cells related to the changes in synapse number. This notion would be consistent with previous studies, which suggest a role for glial involvement in synaptogenesis (151, 198).

One-Trial Passive Avoidance Learning in the Chick

Certain avian species have provided important vertebrate model systems for cellular studies of learning. The work of Bateson (28a), Horn (109), Rose (173, 174), and their colleagues has focused on the domestic chick (*Gallus domesticus*), which is precocious when hatched and displays a number of interesting behavioral modifications that include imprinting and passive avoidance learning (for review, see 4). The training procedure for passive avoidance takes advantage of the fact that to survive, newly hatched chicks must learn a number of events within a short period of time. For example, chicks peck indiscriminately at small objects in their field of vision, but learn quickly to distinguish between food and nonfood objects. Thus in a paradigm known as one-trial passive avoidance learning, chicks learn to avoid pecking at beads coated with unpleasant tasting substances, such as methylanthranilate, Trained birds will reject an identical but dry or water-coated bead subsequently, whereas water-trained chicks will continue to peck at a water-coated or dry bead.

Stewart and his colleagues examined the structural correlates of passive avoidance learning (164, 165, 187–190). Previous biochemical and lesion studies had implicated loci within the chick forebrain as important for memory storage. These forebrain sites include the intermediate and medial hyperstriatum ventrale (IMHV), which is thought to be analogous to the associative cortex in mammals, and part of the paleostriatal complex, the lobus paralfactorus (LPO). A variety of physiological and biochemical studies indicate that the IMHV is necessary for the induction (or formation) of long-term memory, but not for its storage, whereas LPO seems to be required for the storage of long-term memory (173, 174). Many of the biochemical changes that accompany passive avoidance learning are transient and disappear after 3 hr, but the morphological changes are more enduring and are present 24 hr after training. Alterations at 24 hr post-training result in significant increases in various aspects of synaptic morphology as well as in the number of synapses and dendritic spines. These include potential structural correlates of altered synaptic efficacy in both IMHV and LPO as manifested by increases in active zone size and in the number of synaptic vesicles in presynaptic boutons (187–190). The most dramatic morphological changes, however, are increases in synapse number in LPO coupled with alterations in dendritic spine number (164, 165, 188, 189). These data suggest that a key morphological feature for the representation and storage of long-term memory in the chick is an increase in the number of synapses. Moreover, examination of the time course of these changes in LPO at different intervals from 1 to 48 hr following avoidance learning has demonstrated that the increase in synapse number is first detected at 24 hr. This delay in appearance suggests the increase may reflect the addition of newly formed synapses rather than the rapid splitting or conversion of synapses of the sort proposed for LTP and kindling in the hippocampus.

Birdsong

A novel approach to the neurobiological analysis of early postnatal learning has been taken by Konishi, Marler, Nottebohm, and their colleagues in the study of bird song (129, 140, 160). The development of the avian song center and the timing of the critical sensitive period for song learning depends on the interplay of genetic and environmental cues. In some species, the song structure can be modified and embellished in adulthood, long after the critical developmental period has passed. Neuroanatomical tracing and lesion studies have defined the location and connections of specific vocal control areas within the brains of songbirds (158, 161, 162). The morphology of these nuclei is correlated with various aspects of the song repertoire. Thus song centers are larger in males (which sing) than in females (which do not), as well as in males with more complex song repertoires (36, 159). There is also a positive correlation between the size of song nuclei and seasonal variations in this song repertoire (103, 159). Most of these changes can be mimicked by differential levels of sex hormones (7) and appear to represent underlying changes in neuronal number and synaptic connectivity.

Nonassociative and Associative Learning in Aplysia

Structural plasticity also has been studied at identified synapses of higher invertebrates. In many cases these alterations in structure can be correlated with learning and memory (for review, see 13).

One such model system has been the gill- and siphon-withdrawal reflex of the marine mollusc *Aplysia californica,* which can be modified by two elementary forms of nonassociative learning—habituation and sensitization—each capable of giving rise to a short-term memory lasting minutes to hours (39, 168) and a long-term memory persisting for several weeks (40, 77, 167).

A particularly well-studied component of this reflex is the monosynaptic connection between identified mechanoreceptor sensory neurons and their follower cells. Although this component accounts for only part of the behavioral modification measured in the intact animal, its simplicity has allowed reduction of the analysis of the long-term memory for both habituation and sensitization to the cellular and molecular level. Several aspects of the biophysical and biochemical mechanisms that underlie habituation and sensitization have now been analyzed in some detail and involve changes in synaptic effectiveness produced by modulation of transmitter release at the sensory-to-motor neuron synapse (for review, see 119).

To study the structural transformations underlying the transition from short- to long-term memory, Bailey & Chen combined selective intracellular labeling techniques with the analysis of serial sections to study complete reconstructions of identified sensory neuron synapses from both control and behaviorally modified animals (for review see 12, 13, 19–22). Their results indicate that long-term memory (lasting several weeks) is accompanied by a family of alterations at identified sensory neuron synapses. These changes reflect structural modifications at two different levels of synaptic organization: (*a*) alterations in focal regions of membrane specialization of the synapse—the number, size, and vesicle complement of sensory neuron active zones are larger in sensitized animals than controls and smaller in habituated animals (14, 17) and (*b*) a parallel but more pronounced and widespread effect involving modulation of the total number of presynaptic varicosities per sensory neuron (16). Sensory neurons from long-term habituated animals had on average 35% fewer varicosities (compared to their controls). By contrast, the morphological changes that accompany long-term sensitization involve a doubling in the total number of synaptic varicosities, as well as an increase in the size of each neuron's axonal arbor. Quantitative analysis of the time course over which these anatomical changes occur during long-term sensitization has further demonstrated that only alterations in the number of sensory neuron varicosities and active zones persist in parallel with the behavioral retention of memory (18). The relative permanence of these changes and their similarity in duration to the behavioral time course of the memory suggest that an increase in the number of sensory neuron synapses is the most likely of the structural candidates to contribute to the maintenance of long-term sensitization.

The increase in sensory neuron varicosities and the enlarged neuropil arbor following behavioral training for long-term sensitization can also be induced by cAMP, a second messenger activated by the modulatory neurotransmitter serotonin (5-HT), which is normally released by sensitizing stimuli in the intact animal. Thus Nazif et al (155) found that 24 hr after the intracellular injection of cAMP, pleural sensory neurons display approximately twice as many varicosities and 1.5 times as many branch points as compared to control cells injected with 5'-AMP, the immediate breakdown product of cAMP. A similar role for the cAMP cascade in shaping neuronal connectivity in *Drosophila* is suggested by the work of Corfas & Dudai (49), who examined the effects of the specific memory mutations *dunce* and *rutabaga* on the number of side branches and varicosities of an identified mechanoreceptor sensory neuron.

By contrast to these alterations in synapse number that accompany long-term memory, Bailey & Chen (15) found that the morphological correlates of short-term memory in *Aplysia* (lasting minutes to hours rather than days to weeks) are far less pronounced and are restricted to shifts in the proximity of synaptic vesicles adjacent to sensory neuron active zones, a phenomenon that may reflect altered levels of transmitter mobilization. These studies in *Aplysia* suggest a clear difference in the sequelae of structural events that underlie memories of differing durations. The transient duration of short-term memories involves the covalent modification of preexisting proteins (proteins that turn over slowly) and is accompanied by modest and rapid structural remodeling in the vicinity of the active zone such as the translocation of synaptic vesicles near the release site. The more prolonged duration of long-term memories is dependent upon new macromolecular synthesis and is accompanied by substantial and potentially more enduring morphological transformations that are reflected primarily by changes in the number and pattern of synaptic contacts.

RECONSTRUCTION OF GROWTH CHANGES IN CULTURE   The long-lasting growth of new synaptic connections between sensory neurons and their follower cells during long-term sensitization has recently been reconstituted in dissociated cell cocultures of sensory neurons and the identified gill motor neuron L7. Using low-light-level video microscopy, Glanzman et al (87) visualized fluorescently-labeled sensory neuron processes before and after repeated exposure to serotonin that evoke long-term facilitation. Twenty-four hr after serotonin treatment there was a significant increase in the number of sensory neuron varicosities. This increase was correlated with the long-term enhancement in the amplitude of the synaptic potential generated by the sensory neuron in the motor cell. Interestingly, this learning-related growth depended on the presence of an appropriate target cell, a requirement similar to that which is needed for synapse formation during development (86). The nature of this interaction between the presynaptic cell, and its target is not known. The signal from the postsynaptic cell may be cell-associated, such as a constituent of the motor cell's membrane, or diffusible, perhaps being released locally from the motor cell's processes.

Associative Learning in Hermissenda

Alkon et al (2) have examined the effects of associative training on the macroscopic structure of a single identified neuron, the medial type B photoreceptor cell in the mollusc *Hermissenda crassicornis*. Previous studies had demonstrated that associative memory can be correlated with a variety of biochemical and biophysical changes in this neuron. Four to five days following training, cells were labeled and the terminal arborizations measured. The terminal branching volume of cells from conditioned animals was found to be reduced compared to either naive animals or animals trained with unpaired stimuli. This retraction of the neuritic arbor in *Hermissenda* photoreceptors is similar to the reduction of Purkinje cells dendrites following associative learning in the cerebellum (3), as well as the loss of sensory neuron varicosities and axonal branches that accompany long-term habituation in *Aplysia* (14, 16). These learning-related regressive changes in neuronal architecture may share features in common with pruning and synapse elimination described during the later stages of neuronal development (169).

Collin et al (47) have begun to examine the signal transduction pathway that may mediate the structural correlates of associative memory in *Hermissenda*. Previous work had shown that microinjection of a small GTP-binding protein related to ras (cp20), which is phosphorylated by conditioning, can regulate potassium currents and lead to the enhanced excitability of type B photoreceptors that accompanies associate learning. Collin et al next demonstrated that cp20 can also induce the structural changes. Within 2 hr of the introduction of cp20 into the photoreceptors, quantitative confocal microscopy revealed a reduction of the terminal branching volume in more than 70% of the injected cells.

Long-Term Synaptic Plasticity at the Crustacean Neuromuscular Junction

A particularly informative set of studies relating synaptic structure and function has been carried out at arthropod neuromuscular junctions by Atwood and his colleagues (9, 11). These junctions have proven well-suited for examining activity-dependent and growth-dependent modifications of the synapse. In particular, crustacean motor terminals have provided a set of experimentally accessible peripheral synapses that share several plastic properties in common with central synaptic connections. One of the forms of prolonged synaptic plasticity exhibited by these synapses is long-term facilitation (for review, see 8). Long-term facilitation can be produced by repetitive stimulation of a motor neuron axon and leads to a progressive increase in the amplitude of evoked synaptic potentials followed by a long-lasting (several hours to one day) enhancement of transmission. Mathematical models predict that this increase in synaptic response could be explained by the appearance of additional transmitter-responding units on the nerve terminal, and suggest that normally silent synapses are capable of being recruited to an active state by tetanic activity. Recent ultrastructural studies have provided some direct morphological support for these theoretical predictions (211). Complete serial sections of nerve terminals from preparations exhibiting long-term facilitation and from corresponding controls indicate an increase in the percentage of synapses exhibiting presynaptic active zones following training. This change in the number of release sites is accompanied by an increased proportion of synapses displaying discontinuities or perforations in the junctional specializations, a phenomenon similar to that reported during learning in the mammalian central nervous system.

Activity-dependent structural changes have also been found in studies of the phasic and tonic motor innervation of crayfish neuromuscular junctions. Tonic motor neurons typically display high levels of activity and are characterized by terminals with large and abundant synaptic varicosities. By contrast, phasic motor neurons, which have low levels of impulse activity, do not develop clear varicose expansions, but rather have thinner, more uniform terminals. Following repeated stimulation, tonic terminals show facilitation and no depression, whereas phasic terminals demonstrate synaptic fatigue. To determine the role that activity might play in this morphological differentiation, Lnenicka et al (137) tonically stimulated a relatively silent phasic motor neuron over a period of one to two weeks in vivo. As a result of this conditioning, the phasic terminals demonstrated both an increase in fatigue resistance as well as a change in structure to a more tonic phenotype.

These morphological changes included both an increase in the number of synaptic varicosities as well as an increase in the size of mitochondria and individual synapses. These results indicate that the increased transmitter-releasing capabilities of tonic terminals compared to their phasic counterparts may be due to the presence of larger and more frequent synaptic varicosities (138). Moreover, the formation of these varicosities appears to be dependent upon some critical ongoing pattern of nerve impulse activity.

TIME COURSE OF STRUCTURAL CHANGES

Bailey & Chen (18) examined the structural changes at sensory neuron synapses in *Aplysia* that accompany long-term sensitization at 1 to 2 days, 1 week, and 3 weeks after the completion of behavioral training. They found that not all structural changes persist as long as the memory. The increase in the size and vesicle complement of sensory neuron active zones present 24 hr following the completion of training is back to control levels when tested 1 week later. These data indicate that, insofar as modulation of active zone size and associated vesicles is one of the structural mechanisms underlying long-term sensitization, it is associated with the initial phases and not with the persistence of the long-term process. By contrast, the duration of changes in varicosity and active zone number, which persist unchanged for at least 1 week and are only partially reversed at the end of 3 weeks, parallel the behavioral time course of memory, which suggests that only the changes in the number of sensory neuron synapses contribute to the maintenance of long-term sensitization.

The finding that some aspects of synaptic structure are transient while others endure suggests these changes are not all synchronously regulated. At the structural level, the cell appears to have several mechanisms of plasticity available to it. Independent support for this idea has recently been obtained by Ghirardi and her colleagues (151a). Repeated pulses of 5-HT lead to two types of changes in the sensory neurons of *Aplysia*: (*a*) a structural change outlined above, and (*b*) a persistent increase in the activity of cAMP-dependent protein kinase (194). To determine the role of the persistent kinase activity to the long-term functional change, Ghirardi et al applied an inhibitor of kinase A for 30 min, at various times during a 24 hr period, to sensory neurons that had previously been exposed to repeated pulses of 5-HT. She found that if the inhibitor was applied during the first 12 hr following the onset of facilitation, it blocked almost all of the facilitation. After 12 hr, however, the blockade became substantially less, and at 24 hr the inhibitors had essentially no effect. These findings indicate that some component, perhaps the growth of new synapses, once in place can carry the facilitation without requiring the continued persistent activity of protein kinase A and suggest that the structural changes may represent the final and perhaps most stable phase of long-term memory storage. Direct support for this idea comes from the studies of Bailey & Chen (18), which have shown that the loss of memory for sensitization (i.e. the gradual decrease in the retention of behavioral modification) is paralleled by a reduction of similar magnitude in the number of sensory neuron synapses. Combined, the findings of these two studies suggest that the stability of long-term memory storage may be achieved, in part, because of the relative stability of synaptic connections.

Comparable experiments have been done examining the time course of structural changes associated with LTP in CA1 of the rat hippocampal slice (44). By chemically arresting activity at different intervals after the completion of potentiating stimuli (10 to 15 min, 1 hr, and 8 hr), Chang & Greenough were able to distinguish between transient and more enduring structural changes during LTP. Similar to the earlier reports by Lee et al (132, 133), an overall change in the shape of dendritic spines was reported in this study; however, this effect was transient. The shape changes declined at 2 hr and were no longer observed at 8 hr when there was still a significant level of synaptic potentiation. By contrast, the increase in the density of shaft and sessile spine synapses was immediate and complete. These changes in synapse number first appeared at 10–15 min and persisted for 8 hr. Thus in the hippocampal subfield CA1, the duration of alterations in the shape of dendritic spines suggests that they may only represent a transient structural component of the increased responsiveness underlying LTP. Similar to the response of sensory neurons during long-term sensitization in *Aplysia*, the only morphological correlate of LTP in CA1 that endures in parallel with changes in synaptic effectiveness is an increase in synapse number.

MOLECULAR MECHANISMS CONTRIBUTING TO LEARNING-RELATED SYNAPTIC GROWTH

The finding that the number of synaptic connections is the most reliable anatomical measure of long-term memory raises the questions: What are the molecular mechanisms whereby learning modulates synapse formation? To what degree do these mechanisms in the mature animal resemble de novo synapse formation in the developing animal? Some early answers to these questions are beginning to emerge.

Signaling Events and Induction of the Structural Change

CELL ADHESION MOLECULES MAY HAVE A CRITICAL ROLE IN REGULATING SYNAPTIC REORGANIZATION   Beginning insights into the molecules that may contribute to the growth of synaptic connections has come from recent studies in *Aplysia*. Since the structural and functional changes underlying long-term memory require new protein synthesis, Barzilai et al (28) utilized quantitative two-dimensional gels to examine changes in specific proteins in the sensory neurons in response to 5-HT and found an increase in the expression of ten proteins and a decrease in the expression of five proteins. Six of these fifteen early proteins have now been identified. Strikingly, the two proteins that increase (clathrin and tubulin) and the four proteins that decrease their level of expression (NCAM-related cell adhesion molecules) all seem to relate to structural changes. We now consider these in turn.

Mayford et al (142) first focused on four proteins (D1 to D4) that decrease their expression following the application of 5-HT or cAMP. Cloning and sequencing of their cDNAs indicate that they encode different isoforms of an immunoglobulin-related cell adhesion molecule, now named apCAM, which is homologous to NCAM in vertebrates and fasciclin II in *Drosophila*. Moreover, imaging of fluorescently-labeled monoclonal antibodies (mAb) to apCAM shows that not only is there a decrease in the level of expression, but even preexisting protein is lost from the surface membrane of the sensory neurons within 1 hr after the addition of 5-HT. The transient modulation by 5-HT of the cell adhesion molecules, therefore, may represent one of the early molecular steps required for initiating learning-related growth of synaptic connections. Indeed, blocking the expression of the antigen by mAb causes defasciculation, a step that appears to precede synapse formation (86, 121).

Bailey et al (23) examined the mechanisms by which 5-HT modulates apCAMs by combining thin-section electron microscopy with immunolabeling using a gold-conjugated mAb specific to apCAM. Within 1 hr of its application, 5-HT led to a 50% decrease in the density of gold-labeled apCAM complexes at the surface membrane of the sensory neuron. This down-regulation is particularly prominent at sites where the processes of the sensory neurons contact one another and is achieved by a heterologous, protein synthesis-dependent activation of the endocytic pathway, which leads to internalization and apparent degradation of apCAM. The 5-HT-induced internalization of apCAM is initiated at coated pits along the surface membrane. Indeed, concomitant with the down-regulation of apCAM is an increase in the expression of the light chain of clathrin (111), which along with tubulin (A. Barzilai & K. Inokuchi, personal communication) are two of the ten early proteins that increase in their level of expression in response to 5-HT.

These initial effects of 5-HT on the surface and internal membrane systems of sensory neurons in *Aplysia* bear a striking similarity to the morphological changes induced in nonneuronal systems by EGF and other well-characterized growth factors (37, 56), or by NGF in PC12 cells (48), which suggests that modulatory transmitters important for learning, such as serotonin, may serve a double function. In addition to producing a transient regulation of the excitability of neurons, repeated or prolonged exposure of a modulatory transmitter can also produce an action comparable to that of a growth factor, which results in a more persistent regulation of the architecture of the neuron.

Based on these findings, Bailey et al have suggested that the 5-HT-induced internalization of apCAM and consequent membrane remodeling may represent the first morphological steps in the structural program underlying long-term facilitation. According to this view (see Figure 2), learning-related synapse formation is preceded by and perhaps requires endocytic activation, which can then serve a double function. First, the removal of cell adhesion molecules from the neuronal surface at sites of membrane apposition may destabilize adhesive contacts and facilitate defasciculation, a process that may be important in disassembly. Second, the massive endocytic activation might lead to a redistribution of membrane components that favors synapse formation. The assembly of membrane components required for initial synaptic growth may involve insertion, by means of targeted exocytosis, of endocytic membrane retrieved from sites of adhesion and recycled to sites of new synapse formation. Synapse formation may require, in addition, the recruitment of new transport vesicles from the trans-Golgi network.

Stabilization and Maintenance of the Structural Change

EVIDENCE FOR ALTERED GENE EXPRESSION   Since most of the molecules present in the nervous system must be replaced at regular intervals, the persistent changes in neuronal function and structure thought to underlie the storage of long-term memory would seem to require some mechanism that can survive this molecular turnover (54a). One such mechanism is altered gene expression (1, 27, 55, 57, 58, 72, 75, 89, 141, 152, 184, 186).

Studies in *Aplysia* have addressed this issue directly by examining in parallel the effects of inhibitors of protein and RNA synthesis on the structural and functional changes that accompany long-term facilitation. The long-term functional changes in synaptic strength evoked by 5-HT in dissociated cell cocultures of sensory neurons and the identified gill motor neuron L7 are dependent upon new macromolecular synthesis during the period of transmitter application (152). Anisomycin and actinomycin-D block the long-lasting increases produced by 5-HT in both the synaptic potential and in varicosity number (24). These results indicate that macromolecular synthesis is required for the expression of the long-lasting structural changes in the sensory cell and that this synthesis is coupled with the long-term functional modulation of sensory-to-motor synapses. A similar dependence on new protein synthesis has been reported for the in vivo structural changes in pleural sensory neurons where the cAMP-mediated increase in varicosity number can also be blocked by anisomycin (156).

It is possible that the early and more transient aspects of synaptic structural plasticity, i.e. those that are less resistant to disruptive agents, may be limited to interactions involving pre-existing macromolecules and may not require altered gene expression. Some evidence for this notion comes from studies

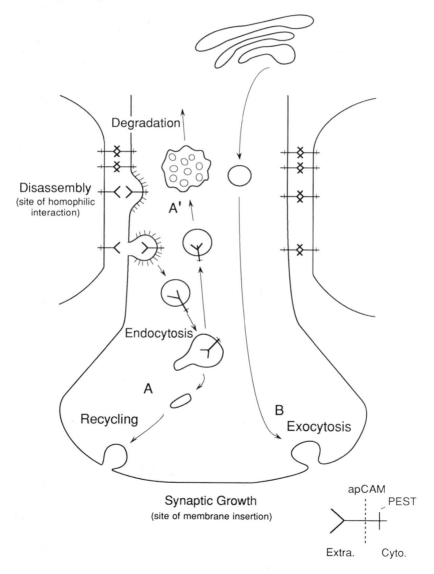

Degradation

Disassembly
(site of homophilic interaction)

A'

Endocytosis

A

Recycling

B
Exocytosis

Synaptic Growth
(site of membrane insertion)

apCAM
PEST

Extra.   Cyto.

of long-term facilitation at the crayfish neuromuscular junction, where it has been shown that rapid (0.5–1 hr) morphological transformations involving modifications of pre-existing active zones, as well as the insertion of new release sites, can occur in the absence of the neuronal cell body and protein synthesis (8, 211). Even more rapid changes (within 15 mins) have been described following the induction of long-term potentiation in the rat hippocampal slice (44, 133). Such rapid pre- and postsynaptic remodeling and resultant synaptogenesis might be triggered by a process of self-assembly from pre-existing components. This would permit the local control of synaptic morphology and allow the initial structural changes to take place in minutes rather than hours or days (see, for example, 104, 122). The stabilization of these initial, and perhaps local structural changes, might require an additional set of cellular processes, including altered macromolecular synthesis, which would then facilitate the further elaboration of the newly formed synaptic connections and allow them to persist for the duration of the long-term memory. An examination of structural changes at all stages of long-term memory—its induction and expression as well as its maintenance—would allow one to determine if each morphological state is equally dependent on new protein synthesis.

IDENTIFICATION OF LATE GENE PRODUCTS   To establish a more precise correlation between the inhibition of macromolecular synthesis and the changes in synaptic structure that accompany long-term memory requires a better understanding of the nature of the newly formed gene products and of how their altered expression affects the phenotypic properties of the partici-

←——————————————————————————————————

Figure 2   Internalization, disassembly and learning-related growth. The onset of synaptic growth in *Aplysia* is triggered by the facilitating transmitter 5-HT. Serotonin leads to a down-regulation of NCAM-related cell adhesion molecules (apCAMs). Part of this down-regulation occurs at the presynaptic membrane, where disassembly is achieved by a transient internalization involving the endosomal pathway. Internalization seems to be particularly active at sites of apposition (depicted here as stable, nongrowing regions where one neurite abuts and adheres to another), and is characterized there by intense endocytic activity. These focal endocytic bursts begin at coated pits and proceed through a series of endosomal precursors, including uncoupling (CURL) vesicles. Here, the internalized plasma membrane can follow one of two pathways. In pathway A, internalized endocytic membrane components are retrieved from sites of apparent adhesion in the tubular extension of the CURL and reinserted at the surface at sites of new synapse formation. In pathway A′, the apCAM molecules are targeted for degradation and become segregated within the swollen, vesicular portion of the CURL, which ultimately fuses with or matures into late endosomal compartments such as multivesicular bodies. Additional membrane inserted into the terminal for growth may also come by means of recruitment of new transport vesicles from the *trans*-Golgi network and the insertion of membrane by exocytosis (pathway B). The cytoplasmic domain of apCAM contains a prominent PEST sequence that may be proteolytically cleaved and lead to enhanced turnover of newly synthesized protein, as well as contribute to the rapid internalization that accounts for the altered expression of apCAM at the surface membrane (from 23).

pating neurons. Recent progress along this line has been made by a series of molecular studies focusing on long-term facilitation in *Aplysia*.

Kennedy, Kuhl, and their colleagues (123–125) have now cloned and identified two late proteins whose expression increases 24 hr after both behavioral training (42) and 5-HT application to isolated primary cultures of sensory neurons (28). One of these proteins is the *Aplysia* homologue of GRP78/BiP (124, 130), which is thought to chaperone the correct folding and assembly of secretory and transmembrane proteins in the lumen of the endoplasmic reticulum (166). The specific increase in *Aplysia* BiP expression occurs 3 hr following 5-HT application (124) and is coincident with the 3-hr increase in overall protein synthesis observed by Barzilai et al (28). This change in the specific expression of *Aplysia* BiP in sensory neurons suggests that BiP may serve as one of several rate-limiting steps in the assembly of protein necessary for the laying down of the structural changes characteristic of the long-term process.

Studies examining altered gene expression during learning in the vertebrate brain have primarily revealed transcriptional factors, such as *fos, jun,* and *Zif268,* whose specific regulatory roles in long-term synaptic plasticity have proven difficult to explore. By contrast, a recent study demonstrated that an effector gene, tissue-plasminogen activator (tPA), an extracellular serine protease, can be induced by seizure, kindling, and LTP in the rat hippocampus (Z. Qian et al, unpublished observations). Stimuli that evoke seizures, kindling, and LTP also induce the family of morphological changes described above. Since tPA is released from growth cones and this release is correlated with morphological differentiation, the increased expression of tPA may play a role in the structural changes that accompany activity-dependent synaptic plasticity in the adult.

CONCLUSIONS

Structural changes represent one of the key signatures of the long-term memory process. The morphological correspondence between the vertebrate and invertebrate studies indicates that learning may resemble a process of neuronal growth and differentiation across a broad segment of the animal kingdom and suggests that new synapse formation may be a highly conserved feature of long-lasting behavioral memory. Such changes could reflect the recruitment, by environmental stimuli, of developmental processes that are latent or inhibited in the fully differentiated neuron. Indeed, recent evidence suggests that the growth changes accompanying long-term memory storage share at least two features in common with synapse formation during development. First, in both cases the structural change exhibits a requirement for new protein and mRNA synthesis. These alterations in transcriptional and translational state can be initiated during the long-term process by repeated or prolonged exposure to modulatory neurotransmitters that, in this respect, appear to mimic the effects of growth factors and hormones during the cell cycle and differentiation. Second, the structural change is associated with a rapid and transient modulation of NCAM-related cell adhesion molecules that are present during the early development of the nervous system, where they appear to have a role in cell migration and process outgrowth. In the adult, the *Aplysia* NCAM seems to exert an inhibitory constraint on growth. Thus, aspects of the regulatory mechanisms underlying learning-related synaptic growth may eventually be understood in the context of the basic cell and molecular processes that govern synapse formation during development. Future studies are needed to inform us about how activity acts on the molecular machinery for structural changes to shape both the developing and the adult brain.

A particularly interesting feature of the structural changes revealed by molecular studies of learning-related growth is the ability of modulatory transmitters to regulate the expression of NCAM-related cell adhesion molecules. These findings potentially provide insight into the relationship between learning and development by illustrating how activity-dependent phenomena fine tune connections during development

Until recently, most neurobiologists believed that connections in the brain develop along the lines that Roger Sperry proposed for the visual systems of coldblooded vertebrates. According to Sperry's view, the precision in the connections between neurons is established independently of activity or experience and is specified completely by a set of labels or recognition molecules present on each pre- and postsynaptic neuron of the synapse. It is now clear that Sperry's conception only applies to pathway selection and target region selection, the first two of a three-step developmental program for synapse formation. The two molecularly guided targeting stages are followed by a third stage, cellular selection, whereby each presynaptic axon is matched to a specific postsynaptic target neuron through activity-dependent mechanisms to produce the point-to-point order required for the mature function of sensory relay regions. Moreover, there is now abundant evidence that activity is required to fine tune the patterns of connectivity underlying the neutral representations of many, perhaps all, sensory systems in the brain, including the representation of the retina in the lateral geniculate, superior colliculus, and cerebral cortex, and the representation of the tactile sensibilities of the body surface in the various relay stages of the somatic sensory system. Indeed, many of these connections continue to be capable of modification by activity throughout the adult life of the organism, thus illustrating a temporal continuity between development and learning.

As we have here described, by their ability to engage second-messenger systems that regulate gene expression, modulatory transmitters utilized for learning (such as glutamate acting through the NMDA receptor in vertebrates, or serotonin acting through G protein-coupled receptors in invertebrates) can initiate synaptic growth and regression resembling the programs of cellular differentiation normally associated with the actions of growth factors. These cellular programs can include alterations in the display of cell surface adhesion molecules. For example, serotonin released by activity from modulatory neurons in *Aplysia* activates the cAMP-dependent protein kinase to cause a transcriptionally-dependent down-regulation of NCAM-related cell adhesion molecules on the surface of sensory neurons. If this were generally the case, then in a sense, Sperry's idea that recognition determines connectivity could be reconciled with activity dependence. Activity initiated by experience could lead to the release of signaling molecules that engage transcriptional control mechanisms, which modulate cell surface receptors so as to regulate cell-cell interactions.

Literature Cited

1. Agranoff, B. W. 1967. Agents that block memory. In *The Neurosciences: A Study Program,* ed. G. C. Quarton, T. Melnechuk, F. O. Schmidt, pp. 756–64. New York: The Rockefeller Univ. Press
2. Alkon, D. L., Ikeno, H., Dworkin, J., McPhie, D. L., Olds, J. L., et al. 1990. Contraction of neuronal branching volume: An anatomic correlate of Pavlovian conditioning. *Proc. Natl. Acad. Sci. USA* 87:1611–14
3. Anderson, B., Relucio, K., Mohr, C., Logan, C., Knowlton, B., et al. 1991. Associated eye-blink conditioning, but not unpaired conditioning, causes morphological changes in Purkinje spiny branchlets. *Soc. Neurosci. Abstr.* 17: 869
4. Andrew, R. J. 1991. *Neural and Behavioral Plasticity. The Use of the Domestic Chick as a Model.* New York: Oxford Univ. Press
5. Applegate, M. D., Kerr, D. S., Landfield, P. N. 1987. Redistribution of synaptic vesicles during long-term potentiation in the hippocampus. *Brain Res.* 90:3401–6
6. Applegate, M. D., Landfield, P. N. 1988. Synaptic vesicle redistribution during hippocampal frequency potentiation and depression in young and aged rats. *J. Neurosci.* 8:1091–111
7. Arnold, A., Jordan, C. L. 1988. Hormonal organization of neural circuits.

In *Frontiers in Neuroendocrinology,* ed. L. Martini, W. F. Ganong, pp. 185–213. New York: Raven
8. Atwood, H. L., Dixon, D., Wojtowicz, J. M. 1989. Rapid introduction of long-lasting synaptic changes at crustacean neuromuscular junctions. *J. Neurobiol.* 20:373–85
9. Atwood, H. L., Govind, C. K. 1990. Activity-dependent and age-dependent recruitment and regulation of synapses in identified crustacean neurons. *J. Exp. Biol.* 153:105–27
10. Atwood, H. L., Lnenicka, G. A. 1986. Structure and function in synapses: Emerging correlations. *Trends Neurosci.* 9:248–50
11. Atwood, H. L., Wojtowicz, J. M. 1986. Short-term and long-term plasticity and physiological differentiation of crustacean motor synapses. *Int. Rev. Neurobiol.* 28:275–362
12. Bailey, C. H. 1991. Morphological basis of short- and long-term memory in *Aplysia.* In *Perspectives on Cognitive Neuroscience,* ed. H. Weingartner, R. Lister, pp. 76–92. New York: Oxford Univ. Press
13. Bailey, C. H. 1992. Morphological basis of learning and memory: Invertebrates. In *Encyclopedia of Learning and Memory,* ed. L. Squire. New York: Macmillan. In press
14. Bailey, C. H., Chen, M. 1983. Morphological basis of long-term habitua-

tion and sensitization in *Aplysia*. *Science* 220:91–93

15. Bailey, C. H., Chen, M. 1988. Morphological basis of short-term habituation in *Aplysia*. *J. Neurosci.* 8: 2452–59

16. Bailey, C. H., Chen, M. 1988. Long-term memory in *Aplysia* modulates the total number of varicosities of single identified sensory neurons. *Proc. Natl. Acad. Sci. USA* 85:2372–77

17. Bailey, C. H., Chen, M. 1988. Long-term sensitization in *Aplysia* increases the number of presynaptic contacts onto the identified gill motor neuron L7. *Proc. Natl. Acad. Sci. USA* 85:9356–59

18. Bailey, C. H., Chen, M. 1989. Time course of structural changes at identified sensory neuron synapses during long-term sensitization in *Aplysia*. *J. Neurosci.* 9:1774–80

19. Bailey, C. H., Chen, M. 1989. Structural plasticity at identified synapses during long-term memory in *Aplysia*. *J. Neurobiol.* 20:356–72

20. Bailey, C. H., Chen, M. 1990. Morphological alterations at identified sensory neuron synapses during long-term sensitization in *Aplysia*. See Ref. 184a, pp. 35–53

21. Bailey, C. H., Chen, M. 1991. Morphological aspects of synaptic plasticity in *Aplysia:* An anatomical substrate for long-term memory. *NY Acad. Sci.* 627: 181–96

22. Bailey, C. H., Chen, M. 1992. The anatomy of long-term sensitization in *Aplysia:* Morphological insights into learning and memory. In *Memory: Organization and Locus of Change*, ed. L. Squire, G. Lynch, N. Weinberger, J. McGaugh, pp. 273–300. New York: Oxford Univ. Press

23. Bailey, C. H., Chen, M., Keller, F., Kandel, E. R. 1992. Serotonin-mediated endocytosis of apCAM: An early step of learning-related synaptic growth in *Aplysia*. *Science* 256:645–49

24. Bailey, C. H., Montarolo, P. G., Chen, M., Kandel, E. R., Schacher, S. 1992. Inhibitors of protein and RNA synthesis block structural changes that accompany long-term heterosynaptic plasticity in *Aplysia*. *Neuron*. 9:749–58

25. Bailey, C. H., Thompson, E. B. 1979. Indented synapses in *Aplysia*. *Brain Res*. 173:13–20

26. Bailey, C. H., Thompson, E. B., Castellucci, V. F., Kandel, E. R. 1979. Ultrastructure of the synapses of sensory neurons that mediate the gill-withdrawal reflex in *Aplysia*. *J. Neurocytol.* 8:415–44

27. Barondes, S. H. 1975. Protein synthesis dependent and protein synthesis independent memory storage processes. In *Short-Term Memory*, ed. D. Deutsch, J. A. Deutsch, pp. 379–90. New York: Academic

28. Barzilai, A., Kennedy, T. E., Sweatt, J. D., Kandel, E. R. 1989. 5-HT modulates protein synthesis and the expression of specific proteins during long-term facilitation in *Aplysia* sensory neurons. *Neuron* 2:1577–86

28a. Bateson, P. P. G. 1966. The characteristics and context of imprinting. *Biol. Rev.* 41:177–220

29. Baudry, M., Davis, J. L., eds. 1991. *Long-term Potentiation: A Debate of Current Issues*. Cambridge, Mass: MIT Press

30. Beaulieu, C., Colonnier, M. 1987. Effect of the richness of the environment on the cat visual cortex. *J. Comp. Neurol.* 266:478–94

31. Bennett, E. L., Diamond, M. C., Krech, D., Rosenzweig, M. R. 1964. Chemical and anatomical plasticity of brain. *Science* 146:610–19

32. Black, J. E., Isaacs, K. R., Anderson, B. J., Alcantara, A. A., Greenough, W. T. 1990. Learning causes synaptogenesis, whereas motor activity causes angiogenesis in cerebellar cortex of adult rats. *Proc. Natl. Acad. Sci. USA* 87:5568–72

33. Black, J. E., Zelazny, A. M., Greenough, W. T. 1991. Capillary and mitochondrial support of neural plasticity in adult rat visual cortex. *Exp. Neurol.* 111:204–9

34. Bradley, P. M., Galal, K. M. 1987. The effects of protein synthesis inhibition on structural changes associated with learning in the chick. *Dev. Brain Res*. 37:267–76

35. Brandon, J. G., Coss, R. G. 1982. Rapid dendritic spine shortening during one-trial learning: The honeybee's first orientation flight. *Brain Res.* 252: 51–61

36. Brenowitz, E. A., Arnold, A. P. 1986. Interspecific comparison of the size of neural song control regions and song complexity in duetting birds: Evolutionary implications. *J. Neurosci.* 6: 2875–79

37. Bretscher, A. 1989. Rapid phosphorylation and reorganization of ezrin and spectrin accompany morphological changes induced in A-431 cells by epidermal growth factor. *J. Cell Biol.* 108:921–30

38. Campbell, G., Shatz, C. J. 1992. Synapses formed by identified retrogenicul-

ate axons during the segregation of eye input. *J. Neurosci.* 12:1847–58

39. Carew, T. J., Castellucci, V. F., Kandel, E. R. 1971. An analysis of dishabituation and sensitization of the gill-withdrawal reflex in *Aplysia. Int. J. Neurosci.* 2:79–98

40. Carew, T. J., Pinsker, H. M., Kandel, E. R. 1972. Long-term habituation of a defensive withdrawal reflex in *Aplysia. Science* 175:451–54

41. Carlin, P. K., Siekevitz, P. 1983. Plasticity in the central nervous system: Do synapses divide? *Proc. Natl. Acad. Sci. USA* 80:3517–21

42. Castellucci, V. F., Kennedy, T. E., Kandel, E. R., Goelet, P. 1988. A quantitative analysis of 2-D gels identifies proteins in which labeling is increased following long-term sensitization in *Aplysia. Neuron* 1:321–28

43. Chang, F.-L. F., Greenough, W. T. 1982. Lateralized effects of monocular training on dendritic branching in adult split-brain rats. *Brain Res.* 232:283

44. Chang, F.-L. F., Greenough, W. T. 1984. Transient and enduring morphological correlates of synaptic activity and efficacy change in the rat hippocampal slice. *Brain Res.* 309:35–46

45. Chang, P. L., Isaacs, K. R., Greenough, W. T. 1991. Synapse formation occurs in association with the induction of long-term potentiation in two-year-old rat hippocampus in vitro. *Neurobiol. Aging* 12:517–22

46. Chang, R. G., Govind, C. K. 1986. Reorganization of synaptic ultrastructure at facilitated lobster neuromuscular terminals. *J. Neurocytol.* 15:63–74

47. Collin, C., Sakakibara, M., McPhie, D., Sanchez-Andres, J. V., Nelson, T. J., Alkon, D. L. 1991. Structural correlates of associative memory in *Hermissenda* neurons: The role of small G-proteins. *Soc. Neurosci. Abstr.* 17: 536

48. Connolly, J. L., Green, S. A., Greene, L. A. 1984. Comparison of rapid changes in surface morphology and coated pit formation of PC12 cells in response to nerve growth factor, epidermal growth factor and dibutyryl cyclic AMP. *J. Cell Biol.* 98:457–65

49. Corfas, G., Dudai, Y. 1991. Morphology of a sensory neuron in *Drosophila* is abnormal in memory mutants and changes during aging. *Proc. Natl. Acad. Sci. USA* 88:7252–56

50. Coss, R. G., Brandon, J. G., Globus, A. 1980. Changes in the morphology of dendritic spines on honeybee calycal interneurons associated with cumulative nursing and foraging experiences. *Brain Res.* 192:49–59

51. Coss, R. G., Globus, A. 1978. Spine stems on tectal interneurons in jewel fish are shortened by social stimulation. *Science* 200:787–90

52. Cotman, C. W., Nieto-Sampedro, M. 1982. Brain function, synapse renewal, and plasticity. *Annu. Rev. Psychol.* 33:371–401

53. Couteaux, R., Pecot-Dechavassine, M. 1970. Vesicules synaptiques et poches au niveau des zones actives de la jonction neuromusculaire. *C. R. Acad. Sci.* 271:2346–49

54. Cragg, B. G. 1975. The development of synapses in kitten visual cortex during visual deprivation. *Exp. Neurol.* 46:445–51

54a. Crick, F. 1984. Memory and molecular turnover. *Nature* 312:101–2

55. Crow, T. J., Forrester, J. F. 1987. Inhibition of protein synthesis blocks long-term plasticity in identified B-photoreceptors in *Hermissenda. Soc. Neurosci. Abstr.* 13:389

56. Dadabay, C. Y., Patton, E., Copper, J. A., Pike, L. J. 1991. Lack of correlation between changes in polyphosphoinositide levels and actin/gelsolin complexes in A431 cells treated with epidermal growth factor. *J. Cell Biol.* 112:1151–56

57. Davis, H. P., Squire, L. R. 1984. Protein synthesis and memory: A review. *Physiol. Bull.* 96:518–59

58. Deadwyler, S. A., Dunwiddie, T., Lynch, E. 1988. A critical period of protein synthesis is required for long-term potentiation. *Synapse* 1:90–95

59. Desmond, N. L., Levy, W. B. 1983. Synaptic correlates of associative potentiation/depression: An ultrastructural study in the hippocampus. *Brain Res.* 265:21–30

60. Desmond, N. L., Levy, W. B. 1986. Changes in the numerical density of synaptic contacts with long-term potentiation in the hippocampal dentate gyrus. *J. Comp. Neurol.* 253:466–75

61. Desmond, N. L., Levy, W. B. 1986. Changes in the postsynaptic density with long-term potentiation in the dentate gyrus. *J. Comp. Neurol.* 253:476–82

62. Desmond, N. L., Levy, W. B. 1986. More front-line synaptic vesicles with long-term synaptic potentiation in the hippocampal dentate gyrus. *Soc. Neurosci. Abstr.* 12:504

63. Desmond, N. L., Levy, W. B. 1988. Synaptic interface surface area increases with long-term potentiation in the hip-

pocampal dentate gyrus. *Brain Res.* 453:308–14

64. Desmond, N. L., Levy, W. B. 1990. Morphological correlates of long-term potentiation imply the modification of existing synapses, not synaptogenesis in the hippocampal dentate gyrus. *Synapse* 5:139–43

65. DeVoogd, J. J., Nixdorf, B., Nottebohm, F. 1985. Synaptogenesis and changes in synaptic morphology related to acquisition of new behavior. *Brain. Res.* 329:304–8

66. Dyson, S. E., Jones, D. G. 1984. Synaptic remodeling during development and maturation: Function differentiation and splitting as a mechanism of modifying connectivity. *Dev. Brain Res.* 13:125–37

67. Fifkova, E. 1968. Changes in the visual cortex of rats after unilateral deprivation. *Nature* 220:379–81

68. Fifkova, E. 1970. Changes of axosomatic synapses in the visual cortex of monocularly deprived rats. *J. Neurobiol.* 1:61–71

69. Fifkova, E. 1970. The effect of monocular deprivation on the synaptic contacts of the visual cortex. *J. Neurobiol.* 1:285–94

70. Fifkova, E., Anderson, C. L. 1981. Stimulation-induced changes in dimensions of stalks of dendritic spines in the dentate molecular layer. *Exp. Neurol.* 74:621–27

71. Fifkova, E., van Harreveld, A. 1977. Long-lasting morphological changes in dendritic spines of dentate granular cells following stimulation of the entorhinal area. *J. Neurocytol.* 6:211–30

72. Flexner, J. B., Flexner, L. B., Stellar, E. 1963. Memory in mice as affected by intracerebral puromycin. *Science* 141:567–69

73. Floeter, M. K., Greenough, W. T. 1979. Cerebellar plasticity: Modification of Purkinje cell structure by differential rearing in monkeys. *Science* 206:227–29

74. Freire, M. 1979. Effects of dark rearing on dendritic spines in layer IV of the mouse visual cortex. A quantitative electron microscopical study. *J. Anat.* 126:193–201

75. Frey, U., Krug, M., Reymann, K. G., Matthies, H. 1988. Anisomycin, an inhibitor of protein synthesis, blocks late phases of LTP phenomena in the hippocampal CA1 region *in vitro*. *Brain Res.* 452:57–65

76. Friedlander, M. J., Martin, K. A. C., Wassenhove-McCarthy, D. 1991. Effects of monocular visual deprivation on geniculocortical innervation of area 18 in cat. *J. Neurosci.* 11:3268–88

77. Frost, W. N., Castellucci, V. F., Hawkins, R. D., Kandel, E. R. 1985. Monosynaptic connections made by the sensory neurons of the gill-withdrawal and siphon-withdrawal reflex in *Aplysia* participate in the storage of long-term memory for sensitization. *Proc. Natl. Acad. Sci. USA* 82:8266–69

78. Fuchs, J. L., Montemayer, M., Greenough, W. T. 1990. Effect of environmental complexity on size of the superior colliculus. *Behav. Neural Biol.* 54:198–203

79. Garey, L. J., Pettigrew, J. D. 1974. Ultrastructural changes in kitten visual cortex after environmental modification. *Brain Res.* 66:165–72

80. Geinisman, Y., de Toledo-Morrell, L., Morrell, F. 1986. Loss of perforated synapses in the dentate gyrus: Morphological substrate of memory deficit in aged rats. *Proc. Natl. Acad. Sci. USA* 83:3027–31

81. Geinisman, Y., de Toledo-Morrell, L., Morrell, F. 1990. The brain's record of experience: Kindling-induced enlargement of the active zone in hippocampal perforated synapses. *Brain Res.* 513:175–79

82. Geinisman, Y., de Toledo-Morrell, L., Morrell, F. 1991. Induction of long-term potentiation is associated with an increase in the number of axospinous synapses with segmented postsynaptic densities. *Brain Res.* 566:77–88

83. Geinisman, Y., Morrell, F., de Toledo-Morrell, L. 1988. Remodelling of synaptic architecture during hippocampal "kindling." *Proc. Natl. Acad. Sci. USA* 85:3260–64

84. Geinisman, Y., Morrell, F., de Toledo-Morrell, L. 1990. Increase in the relative proportion of perforated axospinous synapses following hippocampal kindling is specific for the synaptic field of stimulated axons. *Brain Res.* 507:325–31

85. Deleted in proof

86. Glanzman, D. L., Kandel, E. R., Schacher, S. 1989. Identified target motor neuron regulates neurite outgrowth and synapse formation of *Aplysia* sensory neurons in vitro. *Neuron* 3:441–50

87. Glanzman, D. L., Kandel, E. R., Schacher, S. 1990. Target-dependent structural changes accompanying long-term synaptic facilitation in *Aplysia* neurons. *Science* 249:799–802

88. Globus, A., Rosenzweig, M. R., Bennett, E. L., Diamond, M. C. 1973.

Effects of differential experience on dendritic spine counts in rat cerebral cortex. *J. Comp. Physiol. Psychol.* 82:175–81

89. Goelet, P., Castellucci, V. F., Schacher, S., Kandel, E. R. 1986. The long and short of long-term memory— a molecular framework. *Nature* 322:419–22

90. Green, E. J., Greenough, W. T., Schlumpf, B. E. 1983. Effects of complex or isolated environments on cortical dendrites of middle-aged rats. *Brain Res.* 264:233–40

91. Greenough, W. T. 1984. Structural correlates of information storage in the mammalian brain: A review and hypothesis. *Trends Neurosci.* 7:229–33

92. Greenough, W. T., Bailey, C. H. 1988. The anatomy of memory: Convergence of results across a diversity of tests. *Trends Neurosci.* 11:142–47

93. Greenough, W. T., Chang, F.-L. F. 1985. Synaptic structural correlates of information storage in mammalian nervous systems. In *Synaptic Plasticity,* ed. C. W. Cotman, pp. 335–72. New York: Guilford

94. Greenough, W. T., Chang, F.-L. F. 1988. Plasticity of synapse structure and pattern in the cerebral cortex. In *Cerebral Cortex,* ed. A. Peters, E. G. Jones, pp. 391–40. New York: Plenum

95. Greenough, W. T., Hwang, H.-M., Gorman, C. 1985. Evidence for active synapse formation, or altered postsynaptic metabolism, in visual cortex of rats reared in complex environments. *Proc. Natl. Acad. Sci. USA* 82:4549–52

96. Greenough, W. T., Juraska, J. M., Volkmar, F. R. 1979. Maze training effects on dendritic branching in occipital cortex of adult rats. *Behav. Neural Biol.* 26:287–97

97. Greenough, W. T., Larson, J. R., Withers, G. S. 1985. Effects of unilateral and bilateral training on dendritic branching in occipital cortex of adult rats. *Behav. Neural Biol.* 44:301–14

98. Greenough, W. T., McDonald, J. W., Parnisari, R. M., Camel, J. E. 1986. Environmental conditions modulate degeneration and new dendritic growth in cerebellum of senescent rats. *Brain Res.* 380:136–43

99. Greenough, W. T., Volkmar, F. R. 1973. Pattern of dendritic branching in occipital cortex of rats reared in complex environments. *Exp. Neurol.* 40:491–504

100. Greenough, W. T., Volkmar, F. R., Juraska, J. M. 1973. Effects of rearing complexity on dendritic branching in frontolateral and temporal cortex of the rat. *Exp. Neurol.* 41:371–78

101. Greenough, W. T., West, R. W., DeVoogd, T. J. 1978. Subsynaptic plate perforations: Changes with age and experience in the rat. *Science* 202:1096–98

102. Greenough, W. T., Withers, G. S., Wallace, C. S. 1990. Morphological changes in the nervous system arising from behavioral experience: What is the evidence that they are involved in learning and memory. See Ref. 184a, pp. 159–85

103. Gurney, M. E., Konishi, M. 1980. Hormone-induced sexual differentiation of brain and behavior in zebra finches. *Science* 208:1380–83

104. Han, H.-Q., Nichols, R. A., Rubin, M. R., Bähler, M., Greengard, P. 1991. Induction of formation of presynaptic terminals in neuroblastoma cells by Synapsin-IIb. *Nature* 349:697–700

105. Hatton, J. D., Ellisman, M. H. 1982. A restructuring of hypothalamic synapses is associated with motherhood. *J. Neurosci.* 2:704–7

106. Hawrylak, N., Chang, F.-L. F., Greenough, W. T. 1988. Synaptogenesis in kindling. *Soc. Neurosci. Abstr.* 14:881

107. Herrera, A. A., Grinnell, A. D., Wolowske, B. 1985. Ultrastructural correlates of experimentally altered transmitter release efficacy in frog motor-nerve terminals. *Neuroscience* 16:491–500

108. Heuser, J. E., Reese, T. S., Dennis, M. J., Jan, Y., Jan, L., Evans, L. 1979. Synaptic vesicle exocytosis captured by quick freezing and correlated with quantal transmitter release. *J. Cell Biol.* 81:275–300

109. Horn, G. 1985. *Memory, Imprinting and the Brain, an Inquiry into Mechanisms.* Oxford: Clarendon

110. Horn, G., Bradley, P., McCabe, B. J. 1985. Changes in the structure of synapse associated with learning. *J. Neurosci.* 5:3161–68

111. Hu, Y., Bailey, C. H., Chen, M., Barzilai, A. 1992. Long-term facilitation in *Aplysia* sensory neurons is associated with an increase in the light chain of clathrin and coated vesicles. *Soc. Neurosci. Abstr.* 18:941

112. Hubel, D. H., Wiesel, T. W. 1963. Reception fields in striate cortex of very young, visually inexperienced kittens. *J. Neurophysiol.* 26:994–1002

113. Hubel, D. H., Wiesel, T. W. 1970. The period of susceptibility to the physiological effects of unilateral eye closure in kittens. *J. Physiol.* 206:419–36

114. Hubel, D. H., Wiesel, T. W., LeVay, S. 1979. Plasticity of ocular dominance columns in monkey striate cortex. *Philos. Trans. R. Soc. London Ser. B* 278:377–409

115. Isaacs, K. R., Marks, A., Sirevaag, A. M., Chang, F.-L. F., Greenough, W. T. 1989. Long-term potentiation alters glial process in the dentate gyrus. *Soc. Neurosci. Abstr.* 15:610

116. Juraska, J. M., Fitch, J. M., Henderson, C., Rivers, N. 1985. Sex differences in dendritic branching of dentate granule cells following differential experience. *Brain Res.* 333:73–80

117. Juraska, J. M., Fitch, J. M., Washburne, D. L. 1989. The dendritic morphology of pyramidal neurons in the rat hippocampus CA3 area. II. Effects of gender and the environment. *Brain Res.* 479:115–19

118. Juraska, J. M., Greenough, W. T., Elliott, C., Mack, K., Berkowitz, R. 1980. Plasticity in adult rat visual cortex: An examination of several cell populations after differential rearing. *Behav. Neural Biol.* 29:157–67

119. Kandel, E. R., Schwartz, J. H. 1982. Molecular biology of learning: Modulation of transmitter release. *Science* 218:433–43

120. Katz, L. C., Gilbert, C. D., Wiesel, T. N. 1989. Local circuits and ocular dominance columns in monkey striate cortex. *J. Neurosci.* 9:1389–99

121. Keller, F., Schacher, S. 1990. Neuron-specific membrane glycoproteins promoting neurite fasciculation in *Aplysia californica. J. Cell Biol.* 111:2637–50

122. Kelly, R. B. 1991. A system for synapse control. *Nature* 349:650–51

123. Kennedy, T. E., Gawinowicz, M. A., Barzilai, A., Kandel, E. R., Sweatt, J. D. 1988. Sequencing of proteins from two-dimensional gels using in situ digestion and transfer of peptides to polyvinylidene difluoride membranes: Application to proteins associated with sensitization in *Aplysia. Proc. Natl. Acad. Sci. USA* 85:7008–12

124. Kennedy, T. E., Kuhl, D., Barzilai, A., Kandel, E. R., Sweatt, J. D. 1989. Characterization of changes in late protein and mRNA expression during the maintenance phase of long-term sensitization. *Soc. Neurosci. Abstr.* 15:1117

125. Kennedy, T. E., Wager-Smith, K., Barzilai, A., Kandel, E. R., Sweatt, J. D. 1988. Sequencing proteins from acrylamide gels. *Nature* 336:499–500

126. Kilman, V. L., Sirevaag, A. M., Greenough, W. T. 1991. Adult rats exposed to complex environments have a greater number of synapses per neuron than individually housed rats. *Soc. Neurosci. Abstr.* 17:535

127. Kilman, V. L., Wallace, C. S., Withers, G. S., Greenough, W. T. 1988. Four days of differential housing alters dendritic morphology of weaning rats. *Soc. Neurosci. Abstr.* 14:1135

128. Koch, C., Zador, A., Brown, T. H. 1992. Dendritic spines: Convergence of theory and experiment. *Science* 256:973–74

129. Konishi, M. 1989. Birdsong for neurobiologists. *Neuron* 3:541–49

130. Kuhl, D., Kennedy, T. E., Barzilai, A., Kandel, E. R. 1993. Long-term sensitization training in *Aplysia* leads to an increase in the expression of BiP, the major protein chaperon of the endoplasmic reticulum. *J. Cell Biol.* In press

131. Landis, D. M. D., Hall, A. K., Weinstein, L. A., Reese, T. S. 1988. The organization of cytoplasm at the presynaptic active zone of a central nervous system synapse. *Neuron* 1:201–9

132. Lee, K., Oliver, M., Schottler, F., Lynch, G. 1981. Electron microscopic studies of brain slices: The effects of high-frequency stimulation on dendritic ultrastructure. In *Electrophysiology of Isolated Mammalian CNS Properties,* ed. G. A. Kerkut, H. V. Wheal, pp. 189–211. New York: Academic

133. Lee, K., Schottler, F., Oliver, M., Lynch, G. 1980. Brief bursts of high-frequency stimulation produce two types of structural change in rat hippocampus. *J. Neurophysiol.* 4:247–58

134. LeVay, S., Stryker, M. P. 1979. The development of ocular dominance columns in the cat. In *Aspects of Developmental Neurobiology, Society for Neuroscience Symposia,* ed. J. A. Ferrendelli, 4:83–98. Bethesda, Md: Soc. Neurosci.

135. LeVay, S., Stryker, M. P., Shatz, C. J. 1978. Ocular dominance columns and their development in layer IV of the cat's visual cortex: A quantitative study. *J. Comp. Neurol.* 179:223–44

136. LeVay, S., Wiesel, T. W., Hubel, D. H. 1980. The development of ocular dominance columns in normal and visually deprived monkeys. *J. Comp. Neurol.* 191:1–51

137. Lnenicka, G. A., Atwood, H. L., Marin, L. 1986. Morphological transformation of synaptic terminals of a phasic motoneuron by long-term tonic stimulation. *J. Neurosci.* 6:2252–58

138. Lnenicka, G. A., Hong, S. J., Combatti, M., LePage, S. 1988. Activity-dependent development of synaptic varicosities at crayfish motor terminals. *J. Neurosci.* 11:1040–48

139. Markus, E. J., Petit, T. L. 1989. Synaptic structural plasticity: Role of synaptic shape. *Synapse* 3:1–11

140. Marler, P. 1991. Song-learning behavior: The interface with neuroethology. *Trends Neurosci.* 14:199–206

141. Matthies, H. 1991. Long-lasting maintenance of long-term potentiation and macromolecular synthesis. See Ref. 29, pp. 233–43

142. Mayford, M., Barzilai, A., Keller, F., Schacher, S., Kandel, E. R. 1992. Modulation of an NCAM-related cell adhesion molecule with long-term synaptic plasticity in *Aplysia*. *Science* 256: 638–44

143. Meister, M., Wong, R. O. L., Baylor, D. A., Shatz, C. J. 1991. Synchronous bursts of action potentials in ganglion cells of the developing mammalian retina. *Science* 252:939–43

144. Merzenich, M. M. 1984. Functional "maps" of skin sensations. In *The Many Facets of Touch. The summary publication of Johnson & Johnson Pediatric Roundtable #10 —Touch*, ed. C. C. Brown, pp. 15–22. Skillman, NJ: Johnson & Johnson Baby Products Co.

145. Merzenich, M. M. 1985. Sources of intraspecies and interspecies cortical map variability in mammals: Conclusions and hypotheses. In *Comparative Neurobiology: Modes of Communication in the Nervous System*, ed. M. J. Cohen, F. Strumwasser, pp. 105–16. New York: Wiley

146. Merzenich, M. M., Kaas, J. H., Wall, J., Nelson, R. J., Sur, M., Felleman, D. 1983. Topographic reorganization of somatosensory cortical areas 3B and 1 in adult monkeys following restricted deafferentation. *Neuroscience* 8:33–35

147. Merzenich, M. M., Kaas, J. H., Wall, J. T., Sur, M., Nelson, R. J., Felleman, D. 1983. Progression of change following median nerve section in the cortical representation of the hand in areas 3b and 1 in adult owl and squirrel monkey. *Neuroscience* 10:639–65

148. Merzenich, M. M., Nelson, R. J., Stryker, M. P., Cyander, M. S., Schoppman, A., Zook, J. M. 1984. Somatosensory cortical map changes following digit amputation in adult monkeys. *J. Comp. Neurol.* 224:591–605

149. Merzenich, M. M., Recanzone, E. G., Jenkins, W. M., Allard, T. T., Nudo,

R. J. 1988. Cortical representational plasticity. In *Neurobiology of Neocortex,* ed. P. Rakic, W. Singer, pp. 41–67. New York: Wiley

150. Meshul, C. K., Hopkins, W. F. 1990. Presynaptic ultrastructural correlates of long-term potentiation in the CA1 subfield of the hippocampus. *Brain Res.* 514:310–19

151. Meshul, C. K., Seil, F. J., Herndon, R. M. 1987. Astrocytes play a role in regulation of synaptic density. *Brain Res.* 402:139–45

151a. Montarolo, P. G., Ghirardi, M., Kandel, E. R. 1992. Contribution of persistent protein kinase A to serotonin-induced long-term facilitation of *Aplysia* sensory-motor synapses in culture. *Soc. Neurosci. Abstr.* 18:712

152. Montarolo, P. G., Goelet, P., Castellucci, V. F., Morgan, J., Kandel, E. R., Schacher, S. 1986. A critical period for macromolecular synthesis in long-term heterosynaptic facilitation in *Aplysia*. *Science* 234:1249–54

153. Morrell, F., Geinisman, Y., de Toledo-Morrell, L. 1991. Kindling-induced increase in the number of axospinous synapses with segmented postsynaptic densities. *Soc. Neurosci. Abstr.* 17:875

154. Muller, W., Connor, J. A. 1991. Dendritic spines as individual neuronal compartments for synaptic Ca^{2+} responses. *Nature* 354:73–76

155. Nazif, F. A., Byrne, J. H., Cleary, L. J. 1991. cAMP induces long-term morphological changes in sensory neurons of *Aplysia*. *Brain Res.* 539:324–27

156. Nazif, F. A., Byrne, J. H., Cleary, L. J. 1991. Long-term (24 hr) morphological changes induced by cAMP in pleural sensory neurons of *Aplysia* are dependent on de novo protein synthesis. *Soc. Neurosci. Abstr.* 17:1589

157. Nieto-Sampedro, M., Hoff, S. W., Cotman, C. W. 1982. Perforated postsynaptic densities: Probable intermediates in synapse turnover. *Proc. Natl. Acad. Sci. USA* 79:5718–22

158. Nottebohm, F. 1980. Brain pathways for vocal learning in birds: A review of the first 10 years. *Prog. Psychobiol. Physiol.* 9:85–124

159. Nottebohm, F. 1981. A brain for all seasons: Cyclical anatomical changes in song control nuclei of the canary brain. *Science* 214:1368–70

160. Nottebohm, F. 1991. Reassessing the mechanisms and origins of vocal learning in birds. *Trends Neurosci.* 14:206–11

161. Nottebohm, F., Kelley, P. B., Paton, J. A. 1982. Connections of vocal con-

trol nuclei in the canary telencephalon. *J. Comp. Neurol.* 207:344–57

162. Nottebohm, F., Stokes, T. M., Leonard, C. M. 1976. Central control of song in the canary, *Serinus canarius. J. Comp. Neurol.* 165:457–86

163. Parnavelas, J. G., Globus, A., Kaups, P. 1973. Continuous illumination from birth affects spine density of neurons in the visual cortex of the rat. *Exp. Neurol.* 40:742–47

164. Patel, S. N., Rose, S. P. R., Stewart, M. G. 1988. Training-induced spine density changes are specifically related to memory formation processes in the chick, *Gallus domesticus. Brain Res.* 463:168–73

165. Patel, S. N., Stewart, M. G. 1988. Changes in the number and structure of dendritic spines, 25 hrs after passive avoidance training in the domestic chick, *Gallus domesticus. Brain Res.* 449:34–46

166. Pelham, H. 1988. Heat shock proteins: Coming in from the cold. *Nature* 332:776–77

167. Pinsker, H. M., Hening, W. A., Carew, T. J., Kandel, E. R. 1973. Long-term sensitization of a defensive withdrawal reflex in *Aplysia. Science* 182:1039–42

168. Pinsker, H. M., Kupfermann, I., Castellucci, V. F., Kandel, E. R. 1970. Habituation and dishabituation of the gill-withdrawal reflex in *Aplysia. Science* 167:1740–42

169. Purves, D., Lichtman, J. W. 1985. *Principles of Neural Development.* Sunderland, Mass: Sinauer

170. Pysh, J. J., Weiss, M. 1979. Exercise during development induces an increase in Purkinje cell dendritic tree size. *Science* 206:230–32

171. Pysh, J. J., Wiley, R. G. 1972. Morphologic alterations of synapses in electrically stimulated superior cervical ganglia of the cat. *Science* 176:191–93

172. Deleted in proof

173. Rose, S. P. R. 1991. How chicks make memories: The cellular cascade from c-fos to dendritic remodelling. *Trends Neurosci.* 14:390–97

174. Rose, S. P. R. 1991. Biochemical mechanisms involved in memory formation in the chick. See Ref. 4, pp. 277–304

175. Rosenzweig, M. R., Bennett, E. L. 1978. Experiential influences on the brain anatomy and brain chemistry in rodents. In *Studies on the Development of Behavior and the Nervous System,* ed. G. Gottlieb, 4:289–327. New York: Academic

176. Rosenzweig, M. R., Bennett, E. L., Diamond, M. C. 1972. Chemical and anatomical plasticity of brain: Replication and extensions. In *Macromolecules and Behavior,* ed. J. Gaito, 2:205–78. New York: Appleton-Century-Crofts

177. Rothblat, L. A., Schwartz, M. 1979. The effect of monocular deprivation on dendritic spines in visual cortex of young and adult albino rats: Evidence for a sensitive period. *Brain. Res.* 161:156–61

178. Schneider, W. D., Johnson, E. M. Jr. 1989. Neurotrophic molecules. *Ann. Neurol.* 26:489

179. Schuster, T., Krug, M., Wenzel, J. 1990. Spinules in axospinous synapses of the rat dentate gyrus: Changes in density following long-term potentiation. *Brain Res.* 523:171–74

180. Shatz, C. J. 1990. Competitive interactions between retinal ganglion cells during prenatal development. *J. Neurobiol.* 21:197–211

181. Shatz, C. J. 1990. Impulse activity and the patterning of connections during CNS development. *Neuron* 5:745–56

182. Sirevaag, A. M., Greenough, W. T. 1987. Differential rearing effects on rat visual cortex synapses. III. Neuronal and glial nuclei, boutons, dendrites and capillaries. *Brain. Res.* 424:320–32

183. Sirevaag, A. M., Greenough, W. T. 1991. Plasticity of GFAP-immunoreactive astrocyte size and number in visual cortex of rats reared in complex environments. *Brain Res.* 540:273–78

184. Squire, L. R. 1987. *Memory and Brain.* New York: Oxford Univ. Press

184a. Squire, L. R., Lindenlaub, E., eds. 1990. *The Biology of Memory,* Vol. 23. Stuttgart/New York: Shattauer Verlag

185. Sretavan, D. W., Shatz, C. J. 1986. Prenatal development of retinal ganglion cell axons: Segregation into eye-specific layers. *J. Neurosci.* 6: 234–51

186. Stanton, P. K., Sarvey, J. M. 1984. Blockade of long-term potentiation in rat hippocampal CA1 region by inhibitors of protein synthesis. *J. Neurosci.* 4:3080–88

187. Stewart, M. G. 1990. Morphological correlates of long-term memory in the chick forebrain consequent on passive-avoidance learning. See Ref. 184a, pp. 93–220

188. Stewart, M. G. 1991. Changes in dendritic and synaptic structure in chick forebrain consequent on passive avoidance learning. See Ref. 4, pp. 305–20

189. Stewart, M. G., Csillag, A., Rose, S. P. R. 1987. Alterations in synaptic structure in the paleostriatal complex of the domestic chick, *Gallus domesti-*

cus, following passive avoidance training. *Brain Res.* 426:69–81

190. Stewart, M. G., Rose, S. P. R., King, T. S., Gabbott, P. L. A., Bourne, R. 1984. Hemispheric asymmetry of synapses in chick medial hyperstriatum ventrale following passive avoidance training: A stereological investigation. *Dev. Brain Res.* 12:261–69

191. Stryker, M. P. 1991. Activity-dependent reorganization of afferents in the developing mammalian visual system. In *Development of the Visual System,* ed. D. M.-K. Lam, C. J. Shatz, pp. 267–87. Cambridge, Mass: MIT Press

192. Stryker, M. P., Harris, W. A. 1986. Binocular impulse blockade prevents the formation of ocular dominance columns in cat visual cortex. *J. Neurosci.* 6:2117–33

193. Stryker, M. P., Strickland, S. L. 1984. Physiological segregation of ocular dominance columns depends on the pattern of afferent electrical activity. *Invest. Ophthalmol. Visual Sci.* 25:278 (Suppl.) (ARVO Abstr.)

194. Sweatt, D., Kandel, E. R. 1989. Persistent and transcriptionally-dependent increase in protein phosphorylation in long-term facilitation of *Aplysia* sensory neurons. *Nature* 339:51–54

195. Tieman, S. B. 1984. Effects of monocular deprivation on geniculocortical synapses in the cat. *J. Comp. Neurol.* 222:166–76

196. Tieman, S. B. 1985. The anatomy of geniculocortical connections in monocularly deprived cats. *Cell Mol. Neurobiol.* 5:35–45

196a. Trommald, M., Vaaland, J. L., Blackstad, T. W., Andersen, P. 1990. Dendritic spine changes in rat dentate granule cells associated with long-term potentiation. In *Neurotoxicity of Excitatory Amino Acids,* ed. A. Guidotti, pp. 163–79. New York: Raven

197. Turner, A. M., Greenough, W. T. 1985. Differential rearing effects on rat visual cortex synapses. I. Synaptic and neuronal density and synapses per neuron. *Brain Res.* 329:195–203

198. Tweedle, C. D., Hatton, G. I. 1984 Synaptic formation and disappearance in adult rat supraoptic nucleus during different hydration states. *Brain Res.* 309:373–76

199. Valverde, F. 1967. Apical dendritic spines of the visual cortex and light deprivation in the mouse. *Exp. Brain Res.* 3:337–52

200. Valverde, F. 1971. Rate and extent of recovery from dark rearing in the mouse. *Brain. Res.* 33:1–11

201. van Harreveld, A., Fifkova, E. 1975. Swelling of dendritic spines in the fascia dentata after stimulation of the perforant fibers as a mechanism of post-tetanic potentiation. *Exp. Neurol.* 49:736–49

202. Volkmar, F. R., Greenough, W. T. 1972. Rearing complexity affects branching of dendrites in the visual cortex of the rat. *Science* 176:1445–47

203. Vrensen, G., Cardozo, J. N. 1981. Changes in size and shape of synaptic connections after visual training: An ultrastructural approach of synaptic plasticity. *Brain Res.* 218:79–97

204. Vrensen, G., DeGroot, D. 1974. The effect of dark-rearing and its recovery on synaptic terminals in the visual cortex of rabbits: A quantitative electron microscopic study. *Brain Res.* 78:263–78

205. Vrensen, G., DeGroot, D. 1975. The effect of monocular deprivation on synaptic terminals in the visual cortex of rabbits: A quantitative electron microscopic study. *Brain Res.* 93:15–24

206. Wallace, C. S., Hawrylak, N., Greenough, W. T. 1991. Studies of synaptic structural modifications after long-term potentiation and kindling: Context for a molecular morphology. See Ref. 29, pp. 189–232

207. Wenzel, J., Matthies, H. 1985. Morphological changes in the hippocampal formation accompanying memory function and long-term potentiation. In *Memory Systems of the Brain,* ed. N. M. Weinberger, J. L. McGaugh, G. Lynch, pp. 151–70. New York: Guilford

208. Wesa, J. M., Chang, F.-L. F., Greenough, W. T., West, R. W. 1982. Synaptic contact curvature: Effects of differential rearing on rat occipital cortex. *Dev. Brain Res.* 4:253–57

209. West, R. W., Greenough, W. T. 1972. Effect of environmental complexity on cortical synapses of rats: Preliminary results. *Behav. Biol.* 7:279–84

210. Withers, G. S., Greenough, W. T. 1989. Reach training selectively alters dendritic branching in subpopulations of layer II-III pyramids in rat motor-somatosensory forelimb cortex. *Neuropsychologia* 27:61–69

211. Wojtowicz, J. M., Marin, L., Atwood, H. L. 1989. Synaptic restructuring during long-term facilitation at the crayfish neuromuscular junction. *Can. J. Physiol. Pharmacol.* 67:167–71

Annu. Rev. Physiol. 1993. 55:427–54

Ca²⁺ OSCILLATIONS IN NON-EXCITABLE CELLS

Clare Fewtrell

Department of Pharmacology, Cornell University, Ithaca, New York 14853

KEY WORDS: calcium gradients, calcium stores, channels, fura-2, inositol trisphosphate

INTRODUCTION

Oscillatory behavior in numerous biological systems has been recognized for many years. Some of the most striking examples are the oscillations in membrane potential seen in neuronal and cardiac cells, but similar oscillations are also seen in a number of secretory cells such as pancreatic β-cells. Furthermore, it is now clear that in many instances these fluctuations in membrane potential are accompanied by oscillations in the concentration of intracellular free ionized calcium ($[Ca^{2+}]_i$) resulting from Ca^{2+} influx via voltage-sensitive Ca^{2+} channels.

In contrast, Ca^{2+} responses in non-excitable cells are generated via very different mechanisms and, until recently, were not thought to oscillate. In response to a stimulus there is usually an initial increase in $[Ca^{2+}]_i$ resulting from release of Ca^{2+} from intracellular stores. $[Ca^{2+}]_i$ then falls to a lower but still elevated level that can be sustained for many minutes provided that extracellular Ca^{2+} is present. One of the first demonstrations that Ca^{2+} oscillations can occur in non-excitable cells was a study by Cobbold and colleagues using hepatocytes injected with the Ca^{2+}-sensitive photoprotein aequorin (163). In the same year Yada et al (166) showed, using Ca^{2+}-selective microelectrodes, that $[Ca^{2+}]_i$ oscillates in cultured epithelial cells. This raised the intriguing possibility that Ca^{2+} signals in non-excitable cells could be frequency, rather than simply amplitude, encoded as had been assumed up until then. With the advent of fluorescent probes for intracellular Ca^{2+} [in particular the ratiometric dye fura-2 (48)] and techniques for monitoring $[Ca^{2+}]_i$ at the single-cell level, it is now apparent that fluctuations or

427

0066–4278/93/0315–0427$02.00

oscillations in $[Ca^{2+}]_i$ are seen in many, if not all, types of cell in response to Ca^{2+}-mobilizing stimuli.

The discovery of voltage-sensitive channels in a wide variety of cells has led to some blurring of the distinction between excitable and non-excitable cells. However, it is generally agreed that excitable cells have a threshold potential at which voltage-dependent Na^+ or Ca^{2+} channels are activated, which in turn leads to the generation of one or more action potentials. Although this definition encompasses a number of secretory cells including pituitary gonadotropes (137, 138), chromaffin cells (84), and pancreatic β-cells (134), all of which show interesting Ca^{2+} oscillatory behavior, this review is confined to a discussion of Ca^{2+} oscillations in non-excitable cells. The multiplicity of oscillatory patterns that can be seen are described, and models for the generation of Ca^{2+} oscillations are reviewed. The various sites within the cell that are able to store and release Ca^{2+} are described briefly, together with their possible roles in the generation of Ca^{2+} oscillations. Although the Ca^{2+} influx pathway(s) or channels in non-excitable cells are not nearly as well-characterized as those in excitable cells, a number of candidates have been tentatively identified and are beginning to be characterized. Finally, Ca^{2+} gradients and waves associated with oscillations in Ca^{2+} and the relationship between Ca^{2+} signals and cell function are discussed.

While every effort has been made to cover the major developments in this rapidly moving field, this review necessarily reflects a somewhat personal view from the perspective of a mast cell physiologist. I therefore refer you to a number of excellent reviews on the subject that have appeared in recent years (6, 19, 64, 92, 126, 153) and to an issue of *Cell Calcium* that was devoted to Ca^{2+} oscillations (26).

PROPERTIES OF Ca^{2+} OSCILLATIONS

Although generally referred to as Ca^{2+} oscillations, the fluctuations in $[Ca^{2+}]_i$ in non-excitable cells rarely display the regular sinusoidal pattern of a true oscillation (Figure 1A), and only a few cell types show the rhythmic spiking activity commonly found in excitable cells (Figure 1B). Indeed, in a number cases one would be hard-put to distinguish the Ca^{2+} transients from completely random fluctuations in Ca^{2+}. However, certain patterns do emerge, and a number of features of Ca^{2+} oscillations in non-excitable cells can be recognized.

Probably the best example of repetitive Ca^{2+} spiking behavior is that first seen by Cobbold and his colleagues in hepatocytes (163). What they found was that stimulation with vasopressin or an α₁-adrenergic agonist resulted in brief increases or Ca^{2+} spikes, separated by longer periods at the resting level of $[Ca^{2+}]_i$. This type of spiking activity is shown in Figure 1B and D (Cell

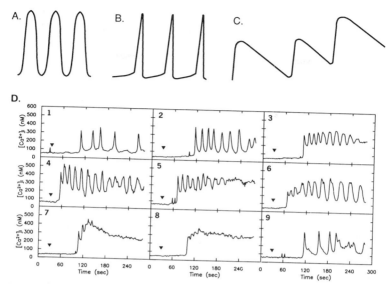

Figure 1   Typical oscillatory patterns. (*A*) Sinusoidal oscillations. (*B*) Transient oscillations or spikes. (*C*) Asymmetric oscillations. (*D*) Ca^{2+} responses in individual cells from a mucosal mast cell line illustrating the range of different oscillatory patterns that can be elicited in a single population of cells on the same day. Antigen (0.01–1 µg/ml) was added at the arrow. (P. Millard & C. Fewtrell, unpublished).

1). As the agonist concentration was increased, the amplitude of the [Ca^{2+}]$_i$ responses in hepatocytes remained the same, but the spiking frequency increased (163). Subsequent studies showed that the shape of each Ca^{2+} transient or spike varied with the stimulus used; those elicited by angiotensin were approximately twice as long (15 sec) as those seen in response to vasopressin (165), while those seen with ATP lasted about a minute (18). Such regular spiking behavior is relatively uncommon in non-excitable cells, and it was originally suggested that it might be because Ca^{2+} measurements were made with the photoprotein aequorin, rather than with the more commonly-used fluorescent indicator fura-2 (101). However, it is now clear that Ca^{2+} spiking activity can also be observed in fura-2-loaded hepatocytes (72, 124). Other cell types in which fairly regular spiking activity from a basal level of Ca^{2+} is also seen include histamine-stimulated endothelial cells (67), gastric chief cells (155) and pancreatic acinar cells (154, 169) stimulated with cholecystokinin or carbachol, fertilized oocytes (25), and carbachol-stimulated secretory cells from the avian salt gland (23). An interesting feature of this type of oscillation is that it is sometimes preceded by a gradual increase in [Ca^{2+}]$_i$ that is reminiscent of a pacemaker potential. This pattern was first observed in endothelial cells (67) and has since been demonstrated in hepatocytes (124). It is never as prominent as the pacemaker activity seen in many excitable cells and is more obvious in some records than in others. Nevertheless, it suggests that $[Ca^{2+}]_i$ may be involved in a regenerative process that triggers the Ca^{2+} spike.

Oscillations that are more sinusoidal in shape (Figure 1A) are frequently observed in non-excitable cells, but their amplitude and frequency are rarely constant. In mucosal mast cells such oscillations sometimes occur from resting levels of $[Ca^{2+}]_i$ (Figure 1D, Cell 2), but more commonly they are superimposed on an elevated $[Ca^{2+}]_i$ level (Figure 1D, Cell 3). Both the frequency and amplitude of Ca^{2+} oscillations are often greatest early in the response to a stimulus and decrease (Figure 1D, Cell 4), or even disappear (Figure 1D, Cell 5), after a few minutes. Occasionally oscillations develop slowly and are more apparent later in the response (Figure 1D, Cell 6). In a few cells a sustained or gradually decaying Ca^{2+} response is seen with little (Figure 1D, Cell 7) or no (Figure 1D, Cell 8) oscillation in $[Ca^{2+}]_i$. All of the patterns shown in Figure 1D were observed in cells of the RBL-2H3 mucosal mast cell line in response to crosslinking of immunoglobulin E (IgE) receptors with antigen (35, 96). However, similar responses are seen in a wide variety of other cell types including parotid acinar cells stimulated with cholinergic and adrenergic agonists (47), acetylcholine-stimulated pancreatic acinar cells (167), histamine- and carbachol-stimulated epithelial cells (29, 136), bradykinin-stimulated endothelial cells (131), serotonin-stimulated platelets (105), neutrophils undergoing chemotaxis and phagocytosis (85), antigen-stimulated B lymphocytes (162), and mitogen-activated leukemic T lymphocytes (81). Furthermore, a number of cell types exhibit both Ca^{2+} spiking behavior and this more sinusoidal type of Ca^{2+} oscillation (Figure 1D). These include, but are probably not limited to, pancreatic acinar cells (109, 168), gastric chief cells (155), mucosal mast cells (96), endothelial cells (66), and secretory cells from the avian salt gland (23).

A less common Ca^{2+} oscillatory pattern that seems to be distinct from the spiking and sinusoidal patterns already described (126) is illustrated in Figure 1C. The oscillations are highly asymmetric, consisting of a rapid increase in $[Ca^{2+}]_i$ followed by a slow decline during which the next asymmetric oscillation is initiated. Such a pattern is extremely prominent in angiotensin II-stimulated adrenal glomerulosa cells (121), but is also seen in neutrophils (68) and in mucosal mast cells (Figure 1D, Cell 9).

The frequency of Ca^{2+} oscillations varies considerably between cell types (see Table 1 in Reference 8). In non-excitable cells, oscillations generally occur every few seconds, although periods of a minute or more have been reported, particularly in oocytes and hepatocytes. Substantial variations in oscillation frequency are often seen within the same cell type, sometimes even in response to the same agonist. For example, the period of oscillations in hepatocytes ranges from less than 20 sec to several minutes (165).

Although individual cell responses, even to the same stimulus, are often extremely heterogeneous, the response of the same cell to successive exposures to the same agonist is sometimes remarkably similar. This was first observed in insulinoma cells, where the cell-specific pattern was termed a Ca^{2+} fingerprint (117), but it has also been dramatically demonstrated in hepatocytes (124). In a mucosal mast cell line stimulated sequentially via two populations of antigen-specific IgE-receptor complexes, this cellular fingerprint was not as pronounced. While some cells showed very similar [Ca^{2+}]$_i$ responses to the two antigens used, a significant fraction failed to exhibit a characteristic cell-specific response (P. Millard et al, unpublished observations). The reason for the wide variability between the Ca^{2+} responses of individual cells is not known, although it seems unlikely that it is related to cell cycle differences or to the presence of multiple cell clones within a population (2, 15, 35). Similarly, the basis for the cell-specific patterns, when these are seen, is unclear. However, any models for the generation of Ca^{2+} oscillations in non-excitable cells must be able to account for these phenomena.

MODULATION OF Ca^{2+} OSCILLATIONS

A correlation between agonist concentration and oscillation frequency has been noted in several cell types exhibiting Ca^{2+} spiking activity (5, 23, 67, 163), which suggests a role for frequency-encoded signaling in cell responses (122). However, a similar correlation has not been reported in cells showing the more sinusoidal type of Ca^{2+} oscillation. This may be because the responses of individual cells within a population are so variable; indeed, even within a single cell the oscillation frequency is rarely constant (Figure 1D). However, it seems clear that oscillation frequency is independent of agonist concentration in parotid (47) and pancreatic (167) acinar cells stimulated with cholinergic agonists and in bradykinin-stimulated endothelial cells (131). Instead, it appears that the mean amplitude of the Ca^{2+} response increases with agonist dose.

Of considerable concern is the possibility that the Ca^{2+} indicator used (usually fura-2) may affect the oscillatory pattern. This has been carefully examined by Thomas and his colleagues in hepatocytes (124). Initially, there appeared to be no correlation between the fura-2 load of a cell and either the height or the frequency of the Ca^{2+} oscillations. However, after additional fura-2-loading, a significant reduction in oscillation frequency was observed in the subsequent response of each cell, with only a twofold increase in intracellular fura-2 load (124). Apparently the marked heterogeneity in oscillation frequency between individual cells had masked the effect of Ca^{2+} buffering by fura-2. Although the intracellular fura-2 loads were not given for the latter experiment, the average load in the initial experiment was 20 μM, which is considerably lower than that used in many other studies (values between 40 and 400 μM have often been reported). Clearly, the possibility that fura-2 is affecting Ca^{2+} oscillations in other non-excitable cells should not be ignored. A useful model for predicting the effect of exogenous buffers, such as fura-2, on Ca^{2+} transients has been developed (132). However, little is known about the buffering characteristics and capacity of the cytoplasm, and this is clearly of major importance in assessing the relative contribution of an exogenous buffer. An estimate of binding sites with an average K_d of 0.55 μM and an intracellular concentration in the region of 0.76 mM has been reported for neutrophils (157), but similar estimates have not been made in other cell types. Ca^{2+} buffering is much less of a problem when using the Ca^{2+}-sensitive photoprotein aequorin, since the affinity of aequorin for Ca^{2+} is much lower, and it is also used at lower intracellular concentrations (20). However, while it has both advantages and disadvantages over fura-2 (20), aequorin is more difficult to work with and is not often used in studies with non-excitable cells.

A marked temperature-dependence of Ca^{2+} oscillation frequency (Q_{10} 2.8) was seen in carbachol-stimulated parotid acinar cells (47). Furthermore, the amplitude of the oscillations, relative to the overall Ca^{2+} response of the cell, decreased with increasing temperature. Indeed, Ca^{2+} oscillations were not even detected in this study at temperatures above 33°C. It is clear that oscillations are seen in other cell types (e.g. 96) at a more physiological temperature (37°C), and Ca^{2+} oscillations have since been reported at 37°C in parotid acinar cells (38). However, their frequency was much lower (one oscillation every 5 min) than that observed in the earlier study ($\sim$ one oscillation every 5 sec at 22°C) (47), and they were only seen in one third of the cells (38).

As is clear from this discussion, the shapes of Ca^{2+} oscillations can also vary considerably. There may be variations in oscillation shape between cell types and even differences between the responses of individual cells in a population to the same stimulus. As has already been mentioned, different agonists produce Ca^{2+} oscillations of various shapes in hepatocytes (see Figure 5 in Reference 8). In this instance, the rising phase of the Ca^{2+} spike and its magnitude are similar in all cases, but the rate of fall varies considerably and is often slightly erratic (21).

An interesting property of the responses of non-excitable cells to Ca^{2+}-mobilizing stimuli is that they often occur after a very pronounced latent period or lag time. In mucosal mast cells, the lag time varies considerably from cell to cell, even at an optimum concentration of stimulating antigen, and this variability is even more pronounced as the antigen concentration is decreased (95). A correlation between agonist dose and the latency of $[Ca^{2+}]_i$ responses is also seen in other cell types including adrenal glomerulosa cells (121), endothelial cells (67), and hepatocytes (101, 124). Of particular interest is the finding that in hepatocytes there is a correlation between the latency and the frequency of subsequent oscillations in Ca^{2+} (124). This observation has now been incorporated into a model for signal-induced Ca^{2+} oscillations that is based on Ca^{2+}-induced Ca^{2+} release (31). However, in leukemic T lymphocytes (Jurkat cells) there appeared to be no correlation between the latency and the period of the oscillations (81).

MODELS FOR THE GENERATION OF Ca^{2+} OSCILLATIONS

The range of different patterns exhibited by Ca^{2+} oscillations in non-excitable cells presents a challenge when trying to develop models for the generation of these oscillations. Indeed, this variety suggests that a number of different mechanisms exist. However, since a single cell type may exhibit most, if not all, of the different types of oscillatory patterns (see Figure 1D), it seems unlikely that each cell type has developed its own specific mechanism for the generation of Ca^{2+} oscillations. Instead, each cell may either contain a number of different mechanisms or a single, rather complex mechanism that is capable of generating the full range of oscillatory patterns. Agonist-stimulation of a wide variety of receptors in non-excitable cells leads to the activation of phospholipase C and the breakdown of phosphatidylinositol 4,5-bisphosphate into two important second messengers, inositol 1,4,5-trisphosphate (IP$_3$) and diacylglycerol (10, 11). Diacylglycerol activates protein kinase C (106), while IP$_3$ binds to a receptor that acts as a channel in the membrane of certain Ca^{2+} stores and releases intracellular Ca^{2+} (34). In most non-excitable cells it is possible to elicit a few (usually two or three) Ca^{2+} oscillations even in the absence of extracellular Ca^{2+}, although Ca^{2+} influx is generally required to sustain these oscillations (47, 67, 72, 96). This suggests that the source of Ca^{2+} for these oscillations is intracellular, but that influx across the plasma membrane is ultimately required to replenish intracellular stores of Ca^{2+}. Therefore, most of the models described below concentrate on mechanisms for the oscillatory release of Ca^{2+} from one or more intracellular stores. The first group contains models in which IP$_3$ oscillates, in the second group IP$_3$ is elevated but does not oscillate, while the third group includes models that do not necessarily require any increase in IP$_3$ levels.

IP3 *Levels Oscillate*

RECEPTOR-CONTROLLED OSCILLATOR MODEL   This has been proposed by Cobbold and Cuthbertson and their colleagues and was recently reviewed (21) and mathematically modeled (24) by them. Its central theme is that since the shape of the falling phase of a Ca^{2+} transient in hepatocytes depends on the agonist used, receptor-specific information must also be retained during the response itself. Essentially, this model proposes that when receptors are stimulated, associated GTP-binding proteins (G proteins) become activated and, once a certain threshold is reached, phospholipase C is activated and there is a burst of IP3 and diacylglycerol production. IP3 causes a massive release of Ca^{2+} from stores and a Ca^{2+} spike is initiated. Termination of this spike is thought to result from activation of protein kinase C by Ca^{2+} and diacylglycerol, which then exerts negative feedback on the earlier activation steps. The agonist specificity of the falling phase of the Ca^{2+} spike is thus envisaged as resulting from the different dynamics with which protein kinase C inactivates the specific receptors and/or their associated G proteins.

Evidence in support of this model comes from the finding that protein kinase C inhibitors prolong the falling phase of Ca^{2+} spikes induced by phenylephrine or vasopressin (133). Therefore, one might predict that a phorbol ester that activates protein kinase C would shorten the falling phase, but what is actually seen is that the spiking frequency is decreased, while at higher concentrations phorbol esters prevent Ca^{2+} spiking altogether (164). However, phorbol esters activate protein kinase C continuously, while the effect of the physiological activator diacylglycerol is of relatively short duration and, according to the model, its levels are only transiently increased. Sustained activation of protein kinase C is thought to drive the receptors and/or their associated G proteins into a more permanently inhibited state, thus making it difficult to induce Ca^{2+} spiking activity (21). This would explain why the frequency of spiking is decreased by phorbol esters. Furthermore, it is proposed that concentrations sufficient to affect the falling phase of the Ca^{2+} spike will already have prevented spike generation altogether (21).

IP3-CA^{2+} CROSSCOUPLING MODEL   Meyer & Stryer have proposed a model (91) in which the cooperative release of Ca^{2+} from an IP3-sensitive store (90, 93) results in positive feedback by Ca^{2+} on phospholipase C. This then results in a surge of IP3 production and further release of Ca^{2+}. The crosscoupling between the cooperative effects of IP3 and the positive feedback by Ca^{2+} leads to a bistable system with an extremely sharp threshold between the basal and activated states (91, 92). This is consistent with the finding that although there may be a significant lag prior to the initiation of a Ca^{2+} response, the increase in $[Ca^{2+}]_i$ usually occurs extremely rapidly once it has been initiated

(95). Termination of the Ca^{2+} spike was thought to occur when the IP3-sensitive stores became depleted and the Ca^{2+} that had been released was sequestered into an IP3-insensitive store. Subsequent Ca^{2+} spikes were initiated once the IP3-sensitive Ca^{2+} stores had been replenished to a critical threshold level. Originally the mitochondria were proposed as the site of Ca^{2+} sequestration since there was evidence for transient accumulation of Ca^{2+} by mitochondria in antigen-stimulated mucosal mast cells (see 100). However, inhibiting mitochondrial Ca^{2+} accumulation in these cells did not prevent Ca^{2+} oscillations (96) and thus another deactivation mechanism was proposed. Although Ca^{2+} accumulation by another IP3-insensitive store or extrusion across the plasma membrane could presumably serve this function, Meyer & Stryer instead suggested that elevated $[Ca^{2+}]_i$, itself, terminates IP3-induced Ca^{2+} release (92), perhaps by activating a protein, calmedin, which inhibits the binding of IP3 to its receptor (27). In this modified model, another Ca^{2+} spike is thought to begin when the proportion of activatable IP3-sensitive channels recovers to a threshold value that is set by the degree of receptor activation induced by agonist (92). This is somewhat akin to the model proposed by Payne et al (113), which is described below.

Intracellular infusion of Ca^{2+} in pancreatic acinar cells leads to Ca^{2+} oscillations (159), which would be consistent with Ca^{2+}-induced activation of phospholipase C as proposed in the Meyer & Stryer model. However, while heparin inhibited oscillations induced by IP3 or acetylcholine, it was unable to prevent those seen in response to Ca^{2+} infusion (159). This suggests that the ability of infused Ca^{2+} to produce Ca^{2+} oscillations is independent of IP3 generation (159). Furthermore, infusion of IP3, or its non-hydrolyzable analogue inositol (1,4,5)-trisphosphorothioate, led to oscillations in $[Ca^{2+}]_i$, which suggests that fluctuations in IP3 levels are not required for the generation of Ca^{2+} oscillations. Thus it seems unlikely that the Meyer & Stryer model can account for the oscillations in Ca^{2+} seen in pancreatic acinar cells (115). In contrast, the Meyer & Stryer model seems to be the only one that is consistent with the properties of the Ca^{2+} oscillations generated in fibroblasts (52) (see below).

IP3 IS METABOLIZED TO IP4, WHICH THEN PROMOTES REUPTAKE OF CA^{2+} INTO THE IP3-SENSITIVE POOL   This model is based on the finding by Hill et al that in permeabilized cells of the liver epithelial line 261B, the 2,4,5-isomer of IP3, which cannot be metabolized to inositol 1,3,4,5-tetrakisphosphate (IP4), was only able to induce release and not reuptake of Ca^{2+} (61). In contrast, when the normal 1,4,5-isomer of IP3 was added, both release and resequestering of Ca^{2+} by the IP3-sensitive stores occurred. If IP4 was added immediately before I(2,4,5)P3, the Ca^{2+} released was reaccumulated into the IP3-sensitive store (60), and the response was indistinguishable from that seen with the metabolizable analogue I(1,4,5)P3 (61). A model in which the levels of the releasing agent (IP3) fall as it is metabolized to the compound (IP4) that promotes reuptake into stores, could, in principle, give rise to oscillations in $[Ca^{2+}]_i$. However, to my knowledge, the findings of Hill et al (60, 61) have yet to be confirmed and extended to other cell types.

IP3 Is Elevated but Does Not Oscillate

The discovery that continuous internal perfusion with IP3 produced cyclical changes in a Ca^{2+}-sensitive Cl^- conductance in hepatocytes suggested that Ca^{2+} oscillations could be elicited without any fluctuations in intracellular IP3 levels (16). In agreement with this it was found that a single injection of IP3 into a *Limulus* photoreceptor (113) was able to induce multiple oscillations in $[Ca^{2+}]_i$. To exclude the possibility that the oscillations were caused by the metabolism of IP3, the non-metabolizable analogue inositol trisphosphorothioate was examined and was found to induce Ca^{2+} oscillations in pancreatic acinar cells (160). On the basis of these and other findings, two models have been proposed in which Ca^{2+} oscillations occur at a constant, but elevated, level of IP3.

NEGATIVE FEEDBACK BY CA^{2+} ON IP3-INDUCED CA^{2+} RELEASE   This model, which was first formulated by Payne et al (112, 113), proposes that IP3 causes an initial rapid release of Ca^{2+} from stores, but that as $[Ca^{2+}]_i$ increases, it inhibits further IP3-induced release. As Ca^{2+} is re-sequestered, this inhibition is removed, and IP3 is able to initiate another cycle of Ca^{2+} release. The model was based on the finding that Ca^{2+} was able to inhibit its own release in response to microinjection of IP3 in *Limulus* photoreceptors (113) or photolysis of caged IP3 in *Xenopus* oocytes (111). There is good evidence in a number of cell types for inhibition of IP3-induced Ca^{2+} release by micromolar concentrations of $[Ca^{2+}]_i$. It was also shown recently that the Ca^{2+}-dependence of the open probability of the IP3-sensitive channel displays a bell-shaped curve with a maximum at 0.2 μM Ca^{2+} and sharp decreases on either side of the peak (12). A similar bell-shaped dependence on Ca^{2+} has been demonstrated in synaptosome-derived microsomal vesicles (36). Negative feedback by Ca^{2+} would seem most appropriate as a mechanism for generating sinusoidal oscillations since IP3-induced release should resume as soon as the $[Ca^{2+}]_i$ drops below a certain level. It is less easy to explain how Ca^{2+} spikes separated by significant periods at resting $[Ca^{2+}]_i$ could be generated, and it is also not clear how dose-dependent modulation of oscillation frequency could occur.

CA^{2+}-INDUCED CA^{2+} RELEASE   This model is based on the process originally described in skeletal muscle, in which release of Ca^{2+} from sarcoplasmic reticulum can be triggered by calcium itself via a positive feedback loop. This model was first applied to non-excitable cells by Berridge and his colleagues (e.g. 9) and has since been placed on a more quantitative footing (32, 46). It is envisaged that a sustained increase in IP$_3$ causes a relatively constant release of Ca^{2+} from an IP$_3$-sensitive store and that this store is continuously replenished as a result of Ca^{2+} influx. The Ca^{2+} that is released fails to cause a significant increase in [Ca^{2+}]$_i$ since it is rapidly sequestered in a Ca^{2+}-sensitive (and IP$_3$-insensitive) store, which is presumably empty prior to stimulation. Once the Ca^{2+}-sensitive store is full, [Ca^{2+}]$_i$ finally begins to increase and the store is ultimately triggered to release its contents by Ca^{2+}-induced Ca^{2+} release. Release continues until the Ca^{2+}-sensitive store is empty and the next Ca^{2+} oscillation is not initiated until this store has refilled. Thus the period of the oscillations is set by the time taken to replenish the Ca^{2+}-sensitive store. This is dependent on the rate of release of Ca^{2+} from the IP$_3$-sensitive store which will, in turn, depend on the level of IP$_3$. Since the model invokes two types of Ca^{2+} stores, it is also called the two-pool model (7).

This model, or variants of it, seems to explain quite well the generation of Ca^{2+} oscillations in a number of cell types including pancreatic acinar cells (115), endothelial cells (66), and hepatocytes (151), although other models have also been proposed, particularly for hepatocytes. The slow "pacemaker" rise in [Ca^{2+}]$_i$ that is sometimes seen immediately before a Ca^{2+} oscillation (67, 124) is clearly consistent with this model. The model also explains the finding in some cell types that the initial latency and the subsequent frequency of Ca^{2+} oscillations are correlated and vary with agonist dose, since these parameters are both dependent on the amount of IP$_3$ produced in response to a stimulus (31). In contrast, the amplitude and the shape of the oscillations should not be affected by the dose of agonist since these properties are determined by the capacity and distribution of the Ca^{2+}-sensitive stores. This model therefore fails to explain why oscillation shape is often agonist-specific (21, 165).

IP$_3$-Independent Models

THAPSIGARGIN-INDUCED CA^{2+} OSCILLATIONS   In light of the above models, all of which involve IP$_3$-sensitive Ca^{2+} stores, the finding that thapsigargin and certain other Ca^{2+}-ATPase inhibitors are able to induce Ca^{2+} oscillations in parotid acinar cells (39, 41) came as a considerable surprise. Thapsigargin depletes IP$_3$-sensitive Ca^{2+} stores by specifically inhibiting the endoplasmic reticulum-type Ca^{2+}-ATPase of these stores (149). Thapsigargin also activates Ca^{2+} influx (145) and this has provided strong support for the capacitative model for Ca^{2+} entry proposed by Putney (119). In this model (see below), the stimulus for Ca^{2+} influx is thought to be the emptying of intracellular Ca^{2+} stores (120). The thapsigargin-induced Ca^{2+} oscillations in parotid acinar cells were dependent on extracellular Ca^{2+} and occurred while the IP3-sensitive stores were completely depleted of Ca^{2+} (39). Since these oscillations are sensitive to caffeine and ryanodine (40), it seems likely that they are caused by the release of Ca^{2+} from a sarcoplasmic reticulum-like store that is insensitive to both thapsigargin and IP3, rather than to a mechanism that directly affects Ca^{2+} influx across the plasma membrane. Furthermore, since the thapsigargin-induced Ca^{2+} oscillations closely resemble the slow oscillations seen in response to carbachol, this raises the possibility that the IP3-sensitive store is not involved in the generation of agonist-induced oscillations in parotid acinar cells (39).

CA^{2+} INFLUX AND FLUCTUATIONS IN MEMBRANE POTENTIAL   In excitable cells, $[Ca^{2+}]_i$ spiking activity is usually initiated when the cell is depolarized sufficiently to activate voltage-sensitive Ca^{2+} channels. The subsequent influx of Ca^{2+} depolarizes the cell further, which results in a Ca^{2+} spike. Since most non-excitable cells lack voltage-sensitive Ca^{2+} channels, depolarization has no effect in the absence of a stimulus and, in many instances, it actually inhibits agonist-stimulated Ca^{2+} influx. This was initially demonstrated in mucosal mast cells (70, 98) and in T lymphocytes (44, 107), but has since been observed in many other cell types including neutrophils (30), parotid acinar cells (89), hepatocytes (72), and endothelial cells (82). This inhibition of Ca^{2+} influx is thought to be due, at least in part, to the reduction or abolition of the electrical component of the electrochemical gradient for Ca^{2+} (98, 114).

Agonist-stimulation of mucosal mast cells also leads to a partial depolarization of the cells, probably as a direct consequence of Ca^{2+} influx (70, 99). The possibility that fluctuations in membrane potential, and consequently of Ca^{2+} influx, might account for Ca^{2+} oscillations in these cells was therefore attractive (35, 96). However, Ca^{2+} oscillations persisted even when the membrane potential was clamped at the potassium equilibrium potential, using the potassium ionophore, valinomycin. Furthermore, when the cells were completely depolarized in high potassium, stimulation with antigen still caused several marked oscillations in $[Ca^{2+}]_i$ (96). Although these results do not rule out the possibility that fluctuations in membrane potential affect $[Ca^{2+}]_i$, it is clear that they are not required for the initiation of Ca^{2+} oscillations in these cells.

Systematic changes in membrane potential have been shown to cause oscillations in $[Ca^{2+}]_i$ in peritoneal mast cells (114) and leukemic T lymphocytes (Jurkat cells) (81). This was done by varying the command potential using the whole-cell configuration of the patch-clamp technique and recording membrane current and $[Ca^{2+}]_i$ simultaneously. However, it is not clear whether similar fluctuations in $[Ca^{2+}]_i$ and membrane potential occur in these cells in response to physiological stimuli. Using the perforated patch recording configuration (to minimize loss of intracellular components that might be important for signal transduction, 62), it was possible to measure Ca^{2+} responses to phytohemagglutinin in Jurkat cells (81). These showed that oscillations in the Ca^{2+} current began slightly before oscillations in $[Ca^{2+}]_i$, and suggested that Ca^{2+} influx is the source of Ca^{2+} for the oscillations. However, since the membrane potential was clamped at $-80mV$ in these experiments, fluctuations in membrane potential cannot be the driving signal for the oscillations in Ca^{2+} current and $[Ca^{2+}]_i$ (81).

From the results presented so far, it seems likely that Ca^{2+} oscillations in most non-excitable cells occur as a result of release of Ca^{2+} from intracellular stores. However, in almost every case oscillations cannot be sustained for any length of time without Ca^{2+} influx across the plasma membrane. In mucosal mast cells, for example, only three or four oscillations in $[Ca^{2+}]_i$ can be elicited by antigen when Ca^{2+} influx is inhibited (e.g. with La^{3+}, or by depolarizing the cells in high potassium, or by removing extracellular Ca^{2+}), but oscillations are resumed as soon as Ca^{2+} influx is restored (96). Furthermore, varying the extracellular Ca^{2+} concentration has been shown to modulate the frequency of Ca^{2+} oscillations in a number of cell types, including hepatocytes (72) and the pancreatic acinar cell line AR42J (169). Thus Ca^{2+} influx, and perhaps also fluctuations in membrane potential, can affect Ca^{2+} oscillations in non-excitable cells, at least indirectly.

Testing the Validity of the Different Models

Distinguishing between the various models described above, and the many variants that have also been proposed, is not an easy task. In most instances, certain features of a particular model fit well with results from some cell types, but it is probably fair to say that no model fits all or even most of the data. Most models were developed to explain the results obtained in one or a few cell types, and there have been few systematic attempts to compare and test the various models rigorously. While it may be tempting to propose that each cell type has developed its own method of generating Ca^{2+} oscillations, the finding that a single cell type can often generate a wide variety of oscillatory patterns (see Figure 1D) would argue for a more general, if complicated, mechanism. Thus comparisons between models and attempts to generate a unifying model are clearly of considerable importance. Rigorous testing of predictions from various models is usually the most valuable way of testing the validity of a particular model, but before the response of a system to a specific perturbation can be examined, it is essential to establish a consistent and reproducible oscillatory response. This has not been easy because of the inherent variability and unpredictability of the Ca^{2+} oscillations in most non-excitable cells.

An attempt to overcome this problem has been made by Harootunian, R. Y. Tsien, and their colleagues, who have devised methods for obtaining reproducible patterns of oscillations in REF52 fibroblasts (51–53). Initially, this was achieved by depolarizing the cells with the pore-forming antibiotic, gramicidin, and then stimulating them with an agonist such as vasopressin, which elevates IP_3 levels (53), but two additional methods for generating reproducible oscillations in these cells have now been developed (51). This model system has been used to test the validity of a number of predictions from four of the models described above that have been proposed for the generation of Ca^{2+} oscillations. Various approaches were used to alter the ability of the cells to generate oscillations and/or to change the shape or phase of the Ca^{2+} oscillations. These included examining the effects of non-hydrolyzable IP_3 analogues, caged second messengers (IP_3, diacylglycerol, Ca^{2+}), protein kinase C inhibitors, changes in membrane potential, or depletion of Ca^{2+} stores with thapsigargin. From these studies it appeared that the only model that was consistent with the results obtained in fibroblasts was the IP_3-Ca^{2+} crosscoupling model proposed by Meyer & Stryer (91). The fibroblast model system does, however, have a number of drawbacks. In the first place, fibroblasts have voltage-sensitive Ca^{2+} channels, whereas the majority of other non-excitable cells do not. Thus Ca^{2+} oscillations in these cells may not be typical of those usually seen in non-excitable cells. Furthermore, as the authors themselves point out (51), the pharmacological manipulations used to obtain reproducible and prolonged trains of oscillations in fibroblasts raise concerns as to the physiological relevance of this mechanism for generating Ca^{2+} oscillations. Finally, there is no obvious cell function that can be correlated with the changes in $[Ca^{2+}]_i$ (51). Nevertheless, it is only by systematic approaches such as these that we are likely to unravel the complex mechanisms involved in the generation and modulation of Ca^{2+} oscillations.

Ca^{2+} STORES

In muscle cells there is a specialized Ca^{2+}-storing organelle, the sarcoplasmic reticulum, about which a significant amount is known. The corresponding organelle(s) in non-muscle cells have been less easy to identify, and there is still considerable controversy concerning the structure and intracellular location of Ca^{2+} stores in other cell types (75, 130). In the late 1970s, Henkart and her colleagues suggested that specialized regions or "subsurface cysterns" of endoplasmic reticulum in neurons might be Ca^{2+} stores (54, 56). They also showed that surface stimuli induce oscillations in membrane potential in a fibroblastic cell line, which are due to a K^+ conductance that is activated by the release of Ca^{2+} from intracellular stores (55, 104). Many of the findings and ideas in these early papers preempted work that has subsequently appeared in the literature, and it is now generally agreed that some or all of the endoplasmic reticulum acts as a Ca^{2+} store in non-muscle cells (130). More recently, Volpe and his colleagues proposed that the Ca^{2+} store is an entirely separate organelle, which they dubbed the calciosome (76, 156), but this remains controversial (130).

IP3-Sensitive Stores

Since the discovery that IP_3 was able to induce the release of Ca^{2+} from intracellular stores in pancreatic acinar cells (142), this process has been studied extensively in many different cell types using permeabilized cells and subcellular fractions (4). The IP_3 receptor has been isolated (143), cloned (42), and reconstituted into liposomes in a functional form (34). It has been shown to behave as a calcium channel (12, 33) and has some structural similarity to the ryanodine receptor of the sarcoplasmic reticulum (94). However, the intracellular location of IP_3 receptors and the identity of the IP_3-sensitive store are still highly controversial (130). In many instances the IP_3-sensitive pool appears to co-localize with the endoplasmic reticulum (69, 116, 141, 147). However, in a number of cell types there is evidence that the IP_3-sensitive pool is preferentially localized near the plasma membrane (37, 49, 57, 108, 129). The IP_3-binding activity in liver copurifies with a plasma membrane marker, but the two activities can be dissociated by freezing or treatment with cytochalasin B, which suggests that the IP_3-sensitive stores may be linked to the plasma membrane via actin microfilaments (128). There is also evidence that, as is the case in sarcoplasmic reticulum, the Ca^{2+} uptake and release sites may be spatially separated in the IP_3-sensitive store (28, 88, 128, 130).

IP3-Insensitive Stores

Many studies have shown that IP_3, or IP_3-mobilizing stimuli, are unable to release all of the non-mitochondrial pool of Ca^{2+} (e.g. 146, 150), which suggests that several different types of Ca^{2+} stores may exist. Indeed, several of the models described above for the generation of Ca^{2+} oscillations require more than one functionally distinct Ca^{2+} pool. In the Ca^{2+}-induced Ca^{2+} release model, the Ca^{2+} released in response to IP_3 is accumulated in a second, Ca^{2+}-sensitive pool (7), and it has been shown that direct infusion of Ca^{2+} into pancreatic acinar cells results in Ca^{2+} oscillations (109). The intracellular location of the Ca^{2+}-sensitive pool is not known, but evidence in support of its existence in non-muscle cells has been obtained (see 58). In contrast to the IP_3-sensitive store, the Ca^{2+}-sensitive store is affected by ryanodine and caffeine, both of which have effects on Ca^{2+} release from muscle sarcoplasmic reticulum. Caffeine-sensitive ryanodine binding has been reported in liver (139), and ryanodine also inhibited calcium sequestration in permeabilized hepatocytes (3), which suggests that there is indeed a Ca^{2+}-sensitive store in these cells.

Localization of Ca^{2+} Stores

In view of the intracellular gradients of Ca^{2+} that have been detected in a number of cell types (see below), the possibility that Ca^{2+} stores are preferentially located in specific regions of certain cells is an attractive one. An obvious example is the *Limulus* photoreceptor, where the IP3-sensitive store is restricted to the light-sensing R-lobe of the cell (113). Less extreme localization of endoplasmic reticulum Ca^{2+} stores has been reported in other cell types (14, 110), and the possibility that the IP3-releasable store may lie close to the plasma membrane has already been discussed. The finding that the IP3 receptor is also present on the nuclear and perinuclear membranes (127, 135, 161) is of particular interest since $[Ca^{2+}]_i$ gradients between the nucleus and cytoplasm have been reported in some excitable cells (59, 118) and in antigen-stimulated mucosal mast cells (35). IP3 receptors are not usually found in Golgi membranes (127), but it is clear that the Golgi region in a number of cell types (17), including mucosal mast cells (S. Chandra et al, unpublished observations), is particularly rich in calcium and might therefore act as an IP3-insensitive store.

Ca^{2+} INFLUX PATHWAY(S) IN NON-EXCITABLE CELLS

Although oscillations in most, if not all, non-excitable cells appear to involve the release of Ca^{2+} from intracellular stores, they can only be sustained for a short time in the absence of Ca^{2+} influx (47, 67, 72, 96) and occasionally they are abolished as soon as influx is inhibited (79, 167). Thus it is clear that Ca^{2+} influx plays an important, though perhaps indirect, role in the maintenance of Ca^{2+} oscillations. The voltage-sensitive Ca^{2+} channels found in most excitable cells have been classified and characterized using a variety of techniques including electrophysiological, biochemical, and molecular biological approaches (152). Although Ca^{2+} channels are assumed to exist in non-excitable cells, remarkably little is known about them (43, 87, 123, 153). It is clear that few if any non-excitable cells possess voltage-dependent Ca^{2+} channels, and there is little direct evidence that the Ca^{2+} influx pathways in non-excitable cells are actually channels and not carriers or exchangers of some sort.

Currently the most widely accepted model for receptor-regulated Ca^{2+} entry is the so-called capacitative model proposed by Putney (119, 120). This model was based on the observation that when intracellular stores were depleted of Ca^{2+} by activating receptors that led to the generation of IP_3, store refilling required extracellular Ca^{2+}, but did not depend on continued receptor activation. This suggested that Ca^{2+} influx was not receptor-activated, but was somehow triggered by the emptying of Ca^{2+} stores. Furthermore there appeared to be little or no increase in $[Ca^{2+}]_i$ even when the stores were rapidly refilling. Although a gap junction-like mechanism has been proposed (89), it now seems more likely that the empty stores are simply accumulating cytoplasmic Ca^{2+} extremely efficiently and/or are in close proximity to the site of Ca^{2+} influx (120, 153). When first proposed, this model seemed rather speculative and was not easy to test. However, it received a strong boost when it was shown that Ca^{2+} influx was also activated when stores were depleted by means other than IP_3 (120). Thus thapsigargin, a specific inhibitor of the endoplasmic reticulum Ca^{2+}-pumping ATPase (149), slowly depletes stores of Ca^{2+} and concomitantly stimulates Ca^{2+} influx. Since the original demonstration in parotid acinar cells (145), thapsigargin-induced Ca^{2+} influx has been observed in many different cell types (for a partial listing see Table 1 in Reference 148).

If the store does not communicate directly with the Ca^{2+} influx pathway, then presumably a second messenger of some sort is required to activate influx. Ca^{2+}-activated Ca^{2+} influx has been described in neutrophils (158), but it is unlikely to be a general mechanism since influx is often activated when cytoplasmic $[Ca^{2+}]_i$ is at, or close to, resting levels (e.g. 96). Both IP_3 and IP_4, either separately or in combination, have been proposed to activate influx, but this is still the subject of considerable controversy (reviewed in 153). More recently cytochrome P450 has been suggested to activate influx, but so far the evidence in support of this intriguing idea is largely pharmacological (1).

Electrophysiological studies on the Ca^{2+} influx pathway or channel(s) in non-excitable cells have been few and far between. Two Ca^{2+} conductances have been identified in stimulated peritoneal mast cells, and one of these was activated by IP_3 (114). A conductance with very similar properties has also been described in leukemic T cells (81). It now seems likely that this pathway is in fact stimulated by the emptying of Ca^{2+} stores (63), which lends further support to the capacitative model for Ca^{2+} entry. In both cell types, it was impossible to detect single channel events, either in patches or by noise analysis (81, 86), which suggests that the conductance of the channel, if indeed it is a channel, is less than 1pS and/or the openings are too brief to detect (81). Ca^{2+}-permeable channels activated by IP_3 (78) or IP_4 (83) have been reported in T lymphocytes and endothelial cells, respectively, but have yet to be identified in other cell types. Ca^{2+} influx pathways have also been characterized in various cell types using a variety of approaches, both direct and indirect. It remains to be seen whether these will turn out to be the same (or similar), or whether non-excitable cells have developed multiple Ca^{2+} influx mechanisms that can be activated in a variety of ways.

Ca^{2+} GRADIENTS AND WAVES ASSOCIATED WITH Ca^{2+} OSCILLATIONS

One of the most dramatic intracellular Ca^{2+} gradients is the fertilization wave that occurs when a sperm fuses with an egg. This wave, which was first measured in medaka eggs using the Ca^{2+}-sensitive photoprotein aequorin, originates at the site of fusion and is propagated by the release of Ca^{2+} from intracellular stores (45). In hamster oocytes, repetitive Ca^{2+} transients are seen; the first two or three occur as a wave originating from the site of fertilization, while subsequent increases occur almost synchronously throughout the entire egg (reviewed in 97). Both IP_3- and Ca^{2+}-induced Ca^{2+} release are involved, while extracellular Ca^{2+} is necessary to sustain the response. Confocal microscopy of fluo-3 in frog oocytes transfected with muscarinic acetylcholine receptors suggests that regenerative spiral waves of Ca^{2+} are produced in response to acetylcholine and that when two wavefronts collide they annihilate one another (80). Assuming that sperm utilize the same pathway as acetylcholine, this suggests that the fertilization wave is propagated through a regenerative excitable medium with an absolute refractory period of about 4.7 sec for the Ca^{2+} stores (80).

Intracellular gradients of Ca^{2+} are also associated with oscillations in $[Ca^{2+}]_i$ in hepatocytes (125) and endothelial cells (65) and originate as waves from a specific locus in each cell. In the hepatocyte, this locus is the same regardless of the stimulus used, which suggests that the signal transduction apparatus is also localized to this region. In contrast, the termination of each Ca^{2+} oscillation occurs synchronously throughout the cell, which suggests that Ca^{2+} sequestration mechanisms are more uniformly distributed (125).

Ca^{2+} gradients have been detected in pancreatic acinar cells (50, 71), but there is some disagreement as to their properties and site of origin. In small clusters of cells (71), acetylcholine was found to cause an initial rise in $[Ca^{2+}]_i$ at the luminal end of each cell, which then spread towards the basolateral side as $[Ca^{2+}]_i$ increased. This in turn led to activation of Ca^{2+}-dependent Cl^- channels. On the basis of these results a "push-pull" model for unidirectional Cl^- transport was proposed in which luminal Cl^- channels are activated initially, thereby allowing Cl^- secretion into the lumen. As the Ca^{2+} signal spreads, a Ca^{2+}-sensitive cation channel is activated, and the cell depolarizes beyond the Cl^- reversal potential. At this point Cl^- is "pulled" into the cells via basolateral Cl^- channels that have now opened in response to the wave of Ca^{2+} (71). Oscillations in Ca^{2+} would allow this mechanism to cycle continuously. However, a more recent study in intact acini, prepared using a more gentle isolation procedure, showed that the increase in $[Ca^{2+}]_i$ originated at the basolateral end and was somewhat damped during propagation to the luminal region (50).

In those non-excitable cells, where waves of Ca^{2+} are seen, the rate of propagation is usually in the region of 5–50 μm/sec, which suggests that there may be a common mechanism involved (11, 126). One possibility is that Ca^{2+} and IP_3 act as positive regulators of one another, with IP_3 releasing Ca^{2+} which then stimulates the production of more IP_3 (144). An alternative model is self-propagation via Ca^{2+}-induced Ca^{2+} release, with the rate of propagation being related to the proximity of neighboring Ca^{2+}-sensitive Ca^{2+} stores (32, 125). Since IP_3 diffuses more quickly than Ca^{2+} in the cytoplasm, the Ca^{2+} stores will need to be more closely spaced to obtain the same propagation rate via Ca^{2+}-induced release, as opposed to IP_3-induced Ca^{2+} release (92).

Transient standing gradients of Ca^{2+} were observed between the nuclear and cytoplasmic regions in antigen-stimulated tumor mast cells and were associated with oscillations in $[Ca^{2+}]_i$ (35). Both the frequency and the phase of the oscillations in the two regions were the same, but the amplitude was greater in the nucleus. The gradients were most obvious at the peaks of the oscillations and virtually disappeared in the troughs, or when oscillations ceased, even though $[Ca^{2+}]_i$ remained elevated. It seems unlikely that these gradients can be explained by any of the more obvious artifacts, but it is difficult to exclude this possibility altogether, particularly in the case of standing gradients (153). If such small cells are indeed able to maintain large standing gradients of Ca^{2+} for many seconds, this implies that there are substantial fluxes of calcium into and out of the cytoplasm (22). Although the subcellular location of Ca^{2+} stores is unknown, the higher Ca^{2+} signal in the nucleus during oscillations might be explained if the stores were concentrated in the perinuclear region, since it is known that stores are involved in the generation of Ca^{2+} oscillations in these cells (96).

ROLE OF Ca^{2+} OSCILLATIONS

Much has already been written about the advantages of frequency-encoded vs amplitude-dependent signaling (8, 9, 64, 122). These include the improved signal-to-noise ratio, particularly at low agonist concentrations. Thus a small increase in $[Ca^{2+}]_i$ may be difficult to distinguish from resting levels, whereas a large $[Ca^{2+}]_i$, transient even when it occurs relatively infrequently, is easily detected. This may be particularly important for the successful propagation of a wave of Ca^{2+} within (125) or between cells (50, 79). With a sustained increase in $[Ca^{2+}]_i$, there is also a danger that cells may become overloaded with Ca^{2+}, whereas limiting increases in $[Ca^{2+}]_i$ to brief spikes should reduce the likelihood of Ca^{2+}-induced cell damage and also decrease the utilization of energy by Ca^{2+}-pumping ATPases. Cellular responses often desensitize during prolonged stimulation; if $[Ca^{2+}]_i$ is involved in this phenomenon, desensitization might be avoided if $[Ca^{2+}]_i$ oscillates (64). Furthermore, the availability of both amplitude and frequency-encoded signaling provides the opportunity for multiple signals to be generated by Ca^{2+} in the same cell. Thus one response may be triggered by large but brief increases in Ca^{2+}, while another response may require a lower but more sustained increase in $[Ca^{2+}]_i$. For example, the presence of four Ca^{2+}- binding sites on calmodulin gives it an extremely steep activation curve (Hill coefficient of 3–4) (73), which makes calmodulin an attractive candidate as an intracellular "digital switch" for the detection of Ca^{2+} oscillations (64, 126). The doubly liganded form of calmodulin may also have signaling properties (74), which may be important at intermediate Ca2+ concentrations. Other possible trans- duction mechanisms include Ca^{2+}-dependent protein phosphorylation and dephosphorylation cycles, which could also be regulated by Ca^{2+} oscillations (64).

In some cells, such as hepatocytes (163), the frequency of Ca^{2+} oscillations appears to be tightly coupled to the strength of the stimulus (i.e. agonist concentration). However, in many other cell types the variability between individual cells in the population obscures any correlation between the oscillatory response and the nature and/or strength of the stimulus. In spite of the profusion of studies describing Ca^{2+} oscillations, relatively few attempts have been made to correlate the functional response of a particular cell with its individual Ca^{2+} response. In individual peritoneal mast cells, it was shown that exocytosis, as monitored by the increase in membrane capacitance, is significantly enhanced as a result of both transient and sustained increases in $[Ca^{2+}]_i$ (102, 103). This suggests that mast cells may not distinguish between frequency and amplitude-encoded signals. A clear inverse correlation between $[Ca^{2+}]_i$ and cell volume was seen during carbachol-induced oscillations in acinar cells from rat salivary gland, but similar correlations were also seen in response to sustained or biphasic increases in $[Ca^{2+}]_i$ (38). This again suggests that the cells are responding to the absolute level of $[Ca^{2+}]_i$ rather than the frequency of Ca^{2+} oscillations. A role for Ca^{2+} oscillations has, however, been proposed in the push-pull model (71) for unidirectional fluid secretion in pancreatic acinar cells (see above), and this is consistent with the suggestion that the transition from oscillations to a sustained increase in $[Ca^{2+}]_i$ in these cells may be associated with the inhibition of secretion (140).

Changes in $[Ca^{2+}]_i$ have been correlated with movement in a number of cell types. At least one $[Ca^{2+}]_i$ transient, and usually several, were seen during neutrophil migration, whereas transients were virtually never seen in stationary cells (85). Ca^{2+} oscillations were also frequently seen in macrophages during frustrated phagocytosis, although their role in this process is not clear (77). In newt eosinophils, both gradients and fluctuations in [Ca^{2+}]$_i$ were seen during chemotaxis, but temporal responses were not shown, so it is not clear whether Ca^{2+} oscillates (13).

Although thus far there has been no clear demonstration of a cell function that is regulated by the frequency of Ca^{2+} oscillations in non-excitable cells, this may reflect the difficulty of measuring function at the single-cell level, rather than the lack of such a mechanism. Furthermore, since the amplitude, duration, and shape of the Ca^{2+} oscillations may also vary, as may the plateau level of [Ca^{2+}]$_i$ from which oscillations occur, responses that are only sensitive to changes in oscillation frequency may be rare.

ACKNOWLEDGMENTS

I would like to thank Patricia Cleveland and William Weintraub for their comments and suggestions and Paul Millard for providing the data shown in Figure 1D. Support from the following National Science Foundation grants is gratefully acknowledged: DCB-8702584, DIR-8716854, and DCB-9105361.

Literature Cited

1. Alvarez, J., Montero, M., Garcia-Sancho, J. 1992. Cytochrome P450 may regulate plasma membrane Ca^{2+} permeability according to the filling state of the intracellular Ca^{2+} stores. *FASEB J.* 6:786–92

2. Ambler, S. K., Poenie, M., Tsien, R. Y., Taylor, P. 1988. Agonist-stimulated oscillations and cycling of intracellular free calcium in individual cultured muscle cells. *J. Biol. Chem.* 263:1952–59

3. Bazotte, R. B., Pereira, B., Higham, S., Shoshan-Barmatz, V., Kraus-Friedmann, N. 1991. Effects of ryanodine on calcium sequestration in the rat liver. *Biochem. Pharmacol.* 42:1799–1803

4. Berridge, M. J. 1987. Inositol trisphosphate and diacylglycerol: two interacting second messengers. *Annu. Rev. Biochem.* 56:159–93

5. Berridge, M. J. 1988. Inositol trisphosphate-induced membrane potential oscillations in *Xenopus* oocytes. *J. Physiol.* 403:589–99

6. Berridge, M. J. 1990. Calcium oscillations. *J. Biol. Chem.* 265:9583–86

7. Berridge, M. J. 1991. Cytoplasmic calcium oscillations: A two pool model. *Cell Calcium* 12:63–72

8. Berridge, M. J., Cobbold, P. H., Cuthbertson, K. S. R. 1988. Spatial and temporal aspects of cell signalling. *Philos. Trans. R. Soc. London Ser. B* 320:325–43

9. Berridge, M. J., Galione, A. 1988. Cytosolic calcium oscillators. *FASEB J.* 2:3074–82

10. Berridge, M. J., Irvine, R. F. 1984. Inositol trisphosphate, a novel second messenger in cellular signal transduction. *Nature* 312:315–21

11. Berridge, M. J., Irvine, R. F. 1989. Inositol phosphates and cell signalling. *Nature* 341:197–205

12. Bezprozvanny, I., Watras, J., Ehrlich, B. E. 1991. Bell-shaped calcium-response curves of Ins(1,4,5)P$_3$- and calcium-gated channels from endoplasmic reticulum of cerebellum. *Nature* 351:751–54

13. Brundage, R. A., Fogarty, K. E., Tuft, R. A., Fay, F. S. 1991. Calcium gradients underlying polarization and chemotaxis of eosinophils. *Science* 254:703–6

14. Busa, W. B., Ferguson, J. E., Joseph, S. K., Williamson, J. R., Nuccitelli, R. 1985. Activation of frog *(Xenopus laevis)* eggs by inositol trisphosphate. I. Characterization of Ca^{2+} release from

intracellular stores. *J. Cell Biol.* 101:
677–82

15. Byron, K. L., Villereal, M. L. 1989.
Mitogen-induced $[Ca^{2+}]_i$ changes in
individual human fibroblasts. Image
analysis reveals asynchronous responses
which are characteristic for different
mitogens. *J. Biol. Chem.* 264:18234–39

16. Capiod, T., Field, A. C., Ogden, D.
C., Sandford, C. A. 1987. Internal
perfusion of guinea-pig hepatocytes
with buffered Ca^{2+} or inositol 1,4,5-
trisphosphate mimics noradrenaline activation of K^+ and Cl^- conductances.
FEBS Lett. 217:247–52

17. Chandra, S., Kable, E. P. W., Mor-
rison, G. H., Webb, W. W. 1991.
Calcium sequestration in the Golgi apparatus of cultured mammalian cells
revealed by laser scanning confocal
microscopy and ion microscopy. *J.
Cell Sci.* 100:747–52

18. Cobbold, P., Woods, N., Wainwright,
J., Cuthbertson, R. 1988. Single cell
measurements in research on calcium-
mobilizing purinoceptors. *J. Recept.
Res.* 8:481–91

19. Cobbold, P. H., Cuthbertson, K. S.
R. 1990. Calcium oscillations: phe-
nomena, mechanisms and significance.
Semin. Cell Biol. 1:311–21

20. Cobbold, P. H., Rink, T. J. 1987.
Fluorescence and bioluminescence mea-
surement of cytoplasmic free calcium.
Biochem. J. 248:313–28

21. Cobbold, P. H., Sanchez-Bueno, A.,
Dixon, C. J. 1991. The hepatocyte
calcium oscillator. *Cell Calcium* 12:87–
95

22. Connor, J. A., Wadman, W. J.,
Hockberger, P. E., Wong, R. K. S.
1988. Sustained dendritic gradients of
Ca^{2+} induced by excitatory amino acids
in CA1 hippocampal neurons. *Science*
240:649–53

23. Crawford, K. M., Stuenkel, E. L.,
Ernst, S. A. 1991. Agonist-induced
frequency modulation of Ca^{2+} oscillations in salt gland secretory cells. *Am.
J. Physiol.* 261:C177–84

24. Cuthbertson, K. S. R., Chay, T. R.
1991. Modelling receptor-controlled intracellular calcium oscillators. *Cell Calcium* 12:97–109

25. Cuthbertson, K. S. R., Cobbold, P.
H. 1985. Phorbol ester and sperm
activate mouse oocytes by inducing
sustained oscillations in cell Ca^{2+}. *Nature* 316:541–42

26. Cuthbertson, K. S. R., Cobbold, P.
H. 1991. Preface to "Oscillations in
Cell Calcium" issue. *Cell Calcium* 12:
61–62

27. Danoff, S. K., Supattapone, S., Snyder, S. H. 1988. Characterization of
a membrane protein from brain mediating the inhibition of inositol 1,4,5-
trisphosphate receptor binding by
calcium. *Biochem. J.* 254:701–5

28. Dawson, A. P., Comerford, J. G.
1989. Effects of GTP on Ca^{2+} movements across endoplasmic reticulum
membranes. *Cell Calcium* 10:343–50

29. Devor, D. C., Ahmed, Z., Duffey,
M. E. 1991. Cholinergic stimulation
produces oscillations of cytosolic Ca^{2+}
in a secretory epithelial cell line, T84.
Am. J. Physiol. 260:C598–C608

30. Di Virgilio, F., Lew, P. D., Andersson,
T., Pozzan, T. 1987. Plasma membrane
potential modulates chemotactic pep-
tide-stimulated cytosolic free Ca^{2+}
changes in human neutrophils. *J. Biol.
Chem.* 262:4574–79

31. Dupont, G., Berridge, M. J., Goldbeter, A. 1990. Latency correlates with
period in a model for signal-induced
Ca^{2+} oscillations based on Ca^{2+}-in-
duced Ca^{2+} release. *Cell Regul.* 1:853–
61

32. Dupont, G., Berridge, M. J., Goldbeter, A. 1991. Signal-induced Ca^{2+} oscillations: Properties of a model based
on Ca^{2+}-induced Ca^{2+} release. *Cell
Calcium* 12:73–85

33. Ehrlich, B. E., Watras, J. 1988. Inositol
1,4,5-trisphosphate activates a channel
from smooth muscle sarcoplasmic reticulum. *Nature* 336:583–86

34. Ferris, C. D., Huganir, R. L.,
Supattapone, S., Snyder, S. H. 1989.
Purified inositol 1,4,5-trisphosphate receptor mediates calcium flux in reconstituted lipid vesicles. *Nature* 342:
87–89

35. Fewtrell, C., Mohr, F. C., Ryan,
T. A., Millard, P. J. 1989. Calcium:
an important second messenger in
mast cells. *Ciba Found. Symp.* 147:
114–32

36. Finch, E. A., Turner, T. J., Goldin,
S. M. 1991. Calcium as a coagonist
of inositol 1,4,5-trisphosphate-induced
calcium release. *Science* 252:443–46

37. Foskett, J. K., Gunter-Smith, P. J.,
Melvin, J. E., Turner, R. J. 1989.
Physiological localization of an ago-
nist-sensitive pool of Ca^{2+} in parotid
acinar cells. *Proc. Natl. Acad. Sci.
USA* 86:167–71

38. Foskett, J. K., Melvin, J. E. 1989.
Activation of salivary secretion: coupling of cell volume and $[Ca^{2+}]_i$ in
single cells. *Science* 244:1582–85

39. Foskett, J. K., Roifman, C. M., Wong,
D. 1991. Activation of calcium oscil-

lations by thapsigargin in parotid acinar cells. *J. Biol. Chem.* 266:2778–82

40. Foskett, J. K., Wong, D. 1991. Free cytoplasmic Ca^{2+} concentration oscillations in thapsigargin-treated parotid acinar cells are caffeine- and ryanodine-sensitive. *J. Biol. Chem.* 266: 14535–38

41. Foskett, J. K., Wong, D. 1992. Calcium oscillations in parotid acinar cells induced by microsomal Ca^{2+}-ATPase inhibition. *Am. J. Physiol.* 262:C656–63

42. Furuichi, T., Yoshikawa, S., Miyawaki, A., Wada, K., Maeda, N., Mikoshiba, K. 1989. Primary structure and functional expression of the inositol 1,4,5-trisphosphate-binding protein P_{400}. *Nature* 342:32–38

43. Gallacher, D. V. 1988. Control of calcium influx in cells without action potentials. *News Physiol. Sci.* 3:244–49

44. Gelfand, E. W., Cheung, R. K., Grinstein, S. 1984. Role of membrane potential in the regulation of lectin-induced calcium uptake. *J. Cell. Physiol.* 121:533–39

45. Gilkey, J. C., Jaffe, L. F., Ridgway, E. B., Reynolds, G. T. 1978. A free calcium wave traverses the activating egg of the medaka, *Oryzias latipes*. *J. Cell Biol.* 76:448–66

46. Goldbeter, A., Dupont, G., Berridge, M. J. 1990. Minimal model for signal-induced Ca^{2+} oscillations and for their frequency encoding through protein phosphorylation. *Proc. Natl. Acad. Sci. USA* 87:1461–65

47. Gray, P. T. A. 1988. Oscillations of free cytosolic calcium evoked by cholinergic and catecholaminergic agonists in rat parotid acinar cells. *J. Physiol.* 406:35–53

48. Grynkiewicz, G., Poenie, M., Tsien, R. Y. 1985. A new generation of Ca^{2+} indicators with greatly improved fluorescence properties. *J. Biol. Chem.* 260:3440–50

49. Guillemette, G., Balla, T., Baukal, A. J., Catt, K. J. 1988. Characterization of inositol 1,4,5-trisphosphate receptors and calcium mobilization in a hepatic plasma membrane fraction. *J. Biol. Chem.* 263:4541–48

50. Habara, Y., Kanno, T. 1991. Dose-dependency in spatial dynamics of $[Ca^{2+}]_c$ in pancreatic acinar cells. *Cell Calcium* 12:533–42

51. Harootunian, A. T., Kao, J. P. Y., Paranjape, S., Adams, S. R., Potter, B. V. L., Tsien, R. Y. 1991. Cytosolic Ca^{2+} oscillations in REF52 fibroblasts: Ca^{2+}-stimulated IP$_3$ production or volt-age-dependent Ca^{2+} channels as key positive feedback elements. *Cell Calcium* 12:153–64

52. Harootunian, A. T., Kao, J. P. Y., Paranjape, S., Tsien, R. Y. 1991. Generation of calcium oscillations in fibroblasts by positive feedback between calcium and IP$_3$. *Science* 251:75–78

53. Harootunian, A. T., Kao, J. P. Y., Tsien, R. Y. 1988. Agonist-induced calcium oscillations in depolarized fibroblasts and their manipulation by photoreleased Ins(1,4,5)P$_3$, Ca^{2+}, and Ca^{2+} buffer. *Cold Spring Harbor Symp. Quant. Biol.* 53:935–43

54. Henkart, M., Landis, D. M. D., Reese, T. S. 1976. Similarity of junctions between plasma membranes and endoplasmic reticulum in muscle and neurons. *J. Cell Biol.* 70:338–47

55. Henkart, M. P., Nelson, P. G. 1979. Evidence for an intracellular calcium store releasable by surface stimuli in fibroblasts (L cells). *J. Gen. Physiol.* 73:655–73

56. Henkart, M. P., Reese, T. S., Brinley, F. J. Jr. 1978. Endoplasmic reticulum sequesters calcium in the squid giant axon. *Science* 202:1300–3

57. Henne, V., Piiper, A., Soling, H.-D. 1987. Inositol 1,4,5-trisphosphate and 5′-GTP induce calcium release from different intracellular pools. *FEBS Lett.* 218:153–58

58. Henzi, V., MacDermott, A. B. 1992. Characteristics and function of Ca^{2+}- and inositol 1,4,5-trisphosphate-releasable stores of Ca^{2+} in neurons. *Neuroscience* 46:251–73

59. Hernández-Cruz, A., Sala, F., Adams, P. R. 1990. Subcellular calcium transients visualized by confocal microscopy in a voltage-clamped vertebrate neuron. *Science* 247:858–62

60. Hill, T. D., Boynton, A. L. 1990. Inositol tetrakisphosphate-induced sequestration of Ca^{2+} replenishes an intracellular pool sensitive to inositol trisphosphate. *J. Cell. Physiol.* 142:163–69

61. Hill, T. D., Dean, N. M., Boynton, A. L. 1988. Inositol 1,3,4,5-tetrakisphosphate induces Ca^{2+} sequestration in rat liver cells. *Science* 242:1176–78

62. Horn, R., Marty, A. 1988. Muscarinic activation of ionic currents measured by a new whole-cell recording method. *J. Gen. Physiol.* 92:145–59

63. Hoth, M., Penner, R. 1992. Depletion of intracellular calcium stores activates a calcium current in mast cells. *Nature* 355:353–56

64. Jacob, R. 1990. Calcium oscillations in electrically non-excitable cells. *Biochim. Biophys. Acta* 1052:427–38

65. Jacob, R. 1990. Imaging cytoplasmic free calcium in histamine stimulated endothelial cells and in fMet-Leu-Phe stimulated neutrophils. *Cell Calcium* 11:241–49

66. Jacob, R. 1991. Calcium oscillations in endothelial cells. *Cell Calcium* 12:127–34

67. Jacob, R., Merritt, J. E., Hallam, T. J., Rink, T. J. 1988. Repetitive spikes in cytoplasmic calcium evoked by histamine in human endothelial cells. *Nature* 335:40–45

68. Jaconi, M. E. E., Rivest, R. W., Schlegel, W., Wollheim, C. B., Pittet, D., Lew, P. D. 1988. Spontaneous and chemoattractant-induced oscillations of cytosolic free calcium in single adherent human neutrophils. *J. Biol. Chem.* 263:10557–60

69. Joseph, S. K., Williams, R. J., Corkey, B. E., Matschinsky, F. M., Williamson, J. R. 1984. The effect of inositol trisphosphate on Ca^{2+} fluxes in insulin-secreting tumor cells. *J. Biol. Chem.* 259:12952–55

70. Kanner, B. I., Metzger, H. 1984. Initial characterization of the calcium channel activated by the cross-linking of the receptors for immunoglobulin E. *J. Biol. Chem.* 259:10188–93

71. Kasai, H., Augustine, G. J. 1990. Cytosolic Ca^{2+} gradients triggering unidirectional fluid secretion from exocrine pancreas. *Nature* 348:735–38

72. Kawanishi, T., Blank, L. M., Harootunian, A. T., Smith, M. T., Tsien, R. Y. 1989. Ca^{2+} oscillations induced by hormonal stimulation of individual fura-2-loaded hepatocytes. *J. Biol. Chem.* 264:12859–66

73. Klee, C. B., Crouch, T. H., Richman, P. G. 1980. Calmodulin. *Annu. Rev. Biochem.* 49:489–515

74. Klee, C. B., Newton, D. L. 1985. Calmodulin: An overview. In *Control and Manipulation of Calcium Movement*, ed. J. R. Parratt, pp. 131–46. New York: Raven

75. Krause, K.-H. 1991. Ca^{2+}-storage organelles. *FEBS Lett.* 285:225–29

76. Krause, K.-H., Pittet, D., Volpe, P., Pozzan, T., Meldolesi, J., Lew, D. P. 1989. Calciosome, a sarcoplasmic reticulum-like organelle involved in intracellular Ca^{2+}-handling by non-muscle cells: Studies in human neutrophils and HL-60 cells. *Cell Calcium* 10:351–61

77. Kruskal, B. A., Maxfield, F. R. 1987. Cytosolic-free calcium increases before and oscillates during frustrated phagocytosis in macrophages. *J. Cell Biol.* 105:2685–93

78. Kuno, M., Gardner, P. 1987. Ion channels activated by inositol 1,4,5-trisphosphate in plasma membrane of human T-lymphocytes. *Nature* 326:301–4

79. Laskey, R. E., Adams, D. J., Cannell, M., van Breemen, C. 1992. Calcium entry-dependent oscillations of cytoplasmic calcium concentration in cultured endothelial cell monolayers. *Proc. Natl. Acad. Sci. USA* 89:1690–94

80. Lechleiter, J., Girard, S., Peralta, E., Clapham, D. 1991. Spiral calcium wave propagation and annihilation in *Xenopus laevis* oocytes. *Science* 252:123–26

81. Lewis, R. S., Cahalan, M. D. 1989. Mitogen-induced oscillations of cytosolic Ca^{2+} and transmembrane Ca^{2+} current in human leukemic T cells. *Cell Regul.* 1:99–112

82. Lückhoff, A., Busse, R. 1990. Calcium influx into endothelial cells and formation of endothelium-derived relaxing factor is controlled by the membrane potential. *Pflügers Arch.* 416:305–11

83. Lückhoff, A., Clapham, D. E. 1992. Inositol 1,3,4,5-tetrakisphosphate activates an endothelial Ca^{2+}-permeable channel. *Nature* 355:356–58

84. Malgaroli, A., Fesce, R., Meldolesi, J. 1990. Spontaneous $[Ca^{2+}]_i$ fluctuations in rat chromaffin cells do not require inositol 1,4,5-trisphosphate elevations but are generated by a caffeine- and ryanodine-sensitive intracellular Ca^{2+} store. *J. Biol. Chem.* 265:3005–8

85. Marks, P. W., Maxfield, F. R. 1990. Transient increases in cytosolic free calcium appear to be required for the migration of adherent human neutrophils. *J. Cell Biol.* 110:43–52

86. Matthews, G., Neher, E., Penner, R. 1989. Second messenger-activated calcium influx in rat peritoneal mast cells. *J. Physiol.* 418:105–30

87. Meldolesi, J., Pozzan, T. 1987. Pathways of Ca^{2+} influx at the plasma membrane: voltage-, receptor-, and second messenger-operated channels. *Exp. Cell Res.* 171:271–83

88. Menniti, F. S., Bird, G. St. J., Takemura, H., Thastrup, O., Potter, B. V. L., Putney, J. W. Jr. 1990. Mobilization of calcium by inositol trisphosphates from permeabilized rat parotid acinar cells. Evidence for translocation of calcium from uptake to release sites within the inositol 1,4,5-trisphosphate- and thapsigargin-sensi-

tive calcium pool. *J. Biol. Chem.* 266: 13646–53

89. Merritt, J. E., Rink, T. J. 1987. Regulation of cytosolic free calcium in fura-2-loaded rat parotid acinar cells. *J. Biol. Chem.* 262:17362–69

90. Meyer, T., Holowka, D., Stryer, L. 1988. Highly cooperative opening of calcium channels by inositol 1,4,5-trisphosphate. *Science* 240:653–56

91. Meyer, T., Stryer, L. 1988. Molecular model for receptor-stimulated calcium spiking. *Proc. Natl. Acad. Sci. USA* 85:5051–55

92. Meyer, T., Stryer, L. 1991. Calcium spiking. *Annu. Rev. Biophys. Biophys. Chem.* 20:153–74

93. Meyer, T., Wensel, T., Stryer, L. 1990. Kinetics of calcium channel opening by inositol 1,4,5-trisphosphate. *Biochemistry* 29:32–37

94. Mignery, G. A., Südhof, T. C., Takei, K., De Camilli, P. 1989. Putative receptor for inositol 1,4,5-trisphosphate similar to ryanodine receptor. *Nature* 342:192–95

95. Millard, P. J., Gross, D., Webb, W. W., Fewtrell, C. 1988. Imaging asynchronous changes in intracellular Ca^{2+} in individual stimulated tumor cells. *Proc. Natl. Acad. Sci. USA* 85:1854–58

96. Millard, P. J., Ryan, T. A., Webb, W. W., Fewtrell, C. 1989. Immunoglobulin E receptor cross-linking induces oscillations in intracellular free ionized calcium in individual tumor mast cells. *J. Biol. Chem.* 264:19730–39

97. Miyazaki, S. 1991. Repetitive calcium transients in hamster oocytes. *Cell Calcium* 12:205–16

98. Mohr, F. C., Fewtrell, C. 1987. Depolarization of rat basophilic leukemia cells inhibits calcium uptake and exocytosis. *J. Cell Biol.* 104:783–92

99. Mohr, F. C., Fewtrell, C. 1987. IgE receptor-mediated depolarization of rat basophilic leukemia cells measured with the fluorescent probe bis-oxonol. *J. Immunol.* 138:1564–70

100. Mohr, F. C., Fewtrell, C. 1990. The effect of mitochondrial inhibitors on calcium homeostasis in tumor mast cells. *Am. J. Physiol.* 258:C217–26

101. Monck, J. R., Reynolds, E. E., Thomas, A. P., Williamson, J. R. 1988. Novel kinetics of single cell Ca^{2+} transients in stimulated hepatocytes and A10 cells measured using fura-2 and fluorescent videomicroscopy. *J. Biol. Chem.* 263:4569–75

102. Neher, E. 1988. The influence of intracellular calcium concentration on degranulation of dialysed mast cells from rat peritoneum. *J. Physiol.* 395:193–214

103. Neher, E. 1991. Ion influx as a transduction signal in mast cells. *Int. Arch. Allergy Appl. Immunol.* 94:47–50

104. Nelson, P. G., Henkart, M. P. 1979. Oscillatory membrane potential changes in cells of mesenchymal origin: The role of an intracellular calcium system. *J. Exp. Biol.* 81:49–61

105. Nishio, H., Ikegami, Y., Segawa, T. 1991. Fluorescence digital image analysis of serotonin-induced calcium oscillations in single blood platelets. *Cell Calcium* 12:177–84

106. Nishizuka, Y. 1984. The role of protein kinase C in cell surface signal transduction and tumour promotion. *Nature* 308:693–97

107. Oettgen, H. C., Terhorst, C., Cantley, L. C., Rosoff, P. M. 1985. Stimulation of the T3-T cell receptor complex induces a membrane-potential-sensitive calcium influx. *Cell* 40:583–90

108. O'Rourke, F. A., Halenda, S. P., Zavoico, G. B., Feinstein, M. B. 1985. Inositol 1,4,5,-trisphosphate releases Ca^{2+} from a Ca^{2+}-transporting membrane vesicle fraction derived from human platelets. *J. Biol. Chem.* 260:956–62

109. Osipchuk, Y. V., Wakui, M., Yule, D. I., Gallacher, D. V., Petersen, O. H. 1990. Cytoplasmic Ca^{2+} oscillations evoked by receptor stimulation, G-protein activation, internal application of inositol trisphosphate or Ca^{2+}: Simultaneous microfluorimetry and Ca^{2+} dependent Cl$^-$ current recording in single pancreatic acinar cells. *EMBO J.* 9:697–704

110. O'Sullivan, A. J., Cheek, T. R., Moreton, R. B., Berridge, M. J., Burgoyne, R. D. 1989. Localization and heterogeneity of agonist-induced changes in cytosolic calcium concentration in single bovine adrenal chromaffin cells from video imaging of fura-2. *EMBO J.* 8:401–11

111. Parker, I., Ivorra, I. 1990. Inhibition by Ca^{2+} of inositol trisphosphate-mediated Ca^{2+} liberation: A possible mechanism for oscillatory release of Ca^{2+}. *Proc. Natl. Acad. Sci. USA* 87:260–64

112. Payne, R., Flores, T. M., Fein, A. 1990. Feedback inhibition by calcium limits the release of calcium by inositol trisphosphate in *Limulus* ventral photoreceptors. *Neuron* 4:547–55

113. Payne, R., Walz, B., Levy, S., Fein,

452   FEWTRELL

A. 1988. The localization of calcium release by inositol trisphosphate in *Limulus* photoreceptors and its control by negative feedback. *Philos. Trans. R. Soc. London Ser. B* 320:359–79

114. Penner, R., Matthews, G., Neher, E. 1988. Regulation of calcium influx by second messengers in rat mast cells. *Nature* 334:499–504

115. Petersen, O. H., Gallacher, D. V., Wakui, M., Yule, D. I., Petersen, C. C. H., Toescu, E. C. 1991. Receptor-activated cytoplasmic Ca^{2+} oscillations in pancreatic acinar cells: Generation and spreading of Ca^{2+} signals. *Cell Calcium* 12:135–44

116. Prentki, M., Biden, T. J., Janjic, D., Irvine, R. F., Berridge, M. J., Wollheim, C. B. 1984. Rapid mobilization of Ca^{2+} from rat insulinoma microsomes by inositol-1,4,5-trisphosphate. *Nature* 309:562–64

117. Prentki, M., Glennon, M. C., Thomas, A. P., Morris, R. L., Matschinsky, F. M., Corkey, B. E. 1988. Cell-specific patterns of oscillating free Ca^{2+} in carbamylcholine-stimulated insulinoma cells. *J. Biol. Chem.* 263:11044–47

118. Przywara, D. A., Bhave, S. V., Bhave, A., Wakade, T. D., Wakade, A. R. 1991. Stimulated rise in neuronal calcium is faster and greater in the nucleus than the cytosol. *FASEB J.* 5:217–22

119. Putney, J. W. Jr. 1986. A model for receptor-regulated calcium entry. *Cell Calcium* 7:1–12

120. Putney, J. W. Jr. 1990. Capacitative calcium entry revisited. *Cell Calcium* 11:611–24

121. Quinn, S. J., Williams, G. H., Tillotson, D. L. 1988. Calcium oscillations in single adrenal glomerulosa cells stimulated by angiotensin II. *Proc. Natl. Acad. Sci. USA* 85:5754–58

122. Rapp, P. E., Berridge, M. J. 1981. The control of transepithelial potential oscillations in the salivary glands of *Calliphora erythrocephala. J. Exp. Biol.* 93:119–32

123. Rink, T. J. 1990. Receptor-mediated calcium entry. *FEBS Lett.* 268:381–85

124. Rooney, T. A., Sass, E. J., Thomas, A. P. 1989. Characterization of cytosolic calcium oscillations induced by phenylephrine and vasopressin in single fura-2-loaded hepatocytes. *J. Biol. Chem.* 264:17131–41

125. Rooney, T. A., Sass, E. J., Thomas, A. P. 1990. Agonist-induced cytosolic calcium oscillations originate from a specific locus in single hepatocytes. *J. Biol. Chem.* 265:10792–96

126. Rooney, T. A., Thomas, A. P. 1991. Organization of intracellular calcium signals generated by inositol lipid-dependent hormones. *Pharmacol. Ther.* 49:223–37

127. Ross, C. A., Meldolesi, J., Milner, T. A., Satoh, T., Supattapone, S., Snyder, S. H. 1989. Inositol 1,4,5,-trisphosphate receptor localized to endoplasmic reticulum in cerebellar Purkinje neurons. *Nature* 339:468–70

128. Rossier, M. F., Bird, G. St. J., Putney, J. W. Jr. 1991. Subcellular distribution of the calcium-storing inositol 1,4,5-trisphosphate-sensitive organelle in rat liver. Possible linkage to the plasma membrane through the actin microfilaments. *Biochem. J.* 274:643–50

129. Rossier, M. F., Capponi, A. M., Vallotton, M. B. 1989. The inositol 1,4,5-trisphosphate-binding site in adrenal cortical cells is distinct from the endoplasmic reticulum. *J. Biol. Chem.* 264:14078–84

130. Rossier, M. F., Putney, J. W. Jr. 1991. The identity of the calcium-storing, inositol 1,4,5-trisphosphate-sensitive organelle in non-muscle cells: Calciosome, endoplasmic reticulum... or both? *Trends Neurosci.* 14:310–14

131. Sage, S. O., Adams, D. J., van Breemen, C. 1989. Synchronized oscillations in cytoplasmic free calcium concentration in confluent bradykinin-stimulated bovine pulmonary artery endothelial cell monolayers. *J. Biol. Chem.* 264:6–9

132. Sala, F., Hernández-Cruz, A. 1990. Calcium diffusion modeling in a spherical neuron. Relevance of buffering properties. *Biophys. J.* 57:313–24

133. Sanchez-Bueno, A., Dixon, C. J., Woods, N. M., Cuthbertson, K. S. R., Cobbold, P. H. 1990. Inhibitors of protein kinase C prolong the falling phase of each free-calcium transient in a hormone-stimulated hepatocyte. *Biochem. J.* 268:627–32

134. Santos, R. M., Rosario, L. M., Nadal, A., Garcia-Sancho, J., Soria, B., Valdeolmillos, M. 1991. Widespread synchronous $[Ca^{2+}]_i$ oscillations due to bursting electrical activity in single pancreatic islets. *Pflügers Arch.* 418:417–22

135. Satoh, T., Ross, C. A., Villa, A., Supattapone, S., Pozzan, T., et al. 1990. The inositol 1,4,5-trisphosphate receptor in cerebellar Purkinje cells: Quantitative immunogold labeling reveals concentration in an ER subcompartment. *J. Cell Biol.* 111:615–24

136. Sauvé, R., Diarra, A., Chahine, M.,

Simoneau, C., Garneau, L., Roy, G. 1990. Single-channel and Fura-2 analysis of internal Ca^{2+} oscillations in HeLa cells: Contribution of the receptor-evoked Ca^{2+} influx and effect of internal pH. *Pflügers Arch.* 416:43–52

137. Schlegel, W., Winiger, B. P., Mollard, P., Vacher, P., Wuarin, F., et al. 1987. Oscillations of cytosolic Ca^{2+} in pituitary cells due to action potentials. *Nature* 329:719–21

138. Shangold, G. A., Murphy, S. N., Miller, R. J. 1988. Gonadotropin-releasing hormone-induced Ca^{2+} transients in single identified gonadotropes require both intracellular Ca^{2+} mobilization and Ca^{2+} influx. *Proc. Natl. Acad. Sci. USA* 85:6566–70

139. Shoshan-Barmatz, V., Pressley, T. A., Higham, S., Kraus-Friedmann, N. 1991. Characterization of high-affinity ryanodine-binding sites of rat liver endoplasmic reticulum. Differences between liver and skeletal muscle. *Biochem. J.* 276:41–46

140. Sjödin, L., Dahlén, H. G., Gylfe, E. 1991. Calcium oscillations in guinea-pig pancreatic acinar cells exposed to carbachol, cholecystokinin and substance P. *J. Physiol.* 444:763–76

141. Streb, H., Bayerdorffer, E., Haase, W., Irvine, R. F., Schulz, I. 1984. Effect of inositol-1,4,5-trisphosphate on isolated subcellular fractions of rat pancreas. *J. Membr. Biol.* 81:241–53

142. Streb, H., Irvine, R. F., Berridge, M. J., Schulz, I. 1983. Release of Ca^{2+} from a nonmitochondrial intracellular store in pancreatic acinar cells by inositol-1,4,5-trisphosphate. *Nature* 306:67–69

143. Supattapone, S., Worley, P. F., Baraban, J. M., Snyder, S. H. 1988. Solubilization, purification, and characterization of an inositol trisphosphate receptor. *J. Biol. Chem.* 263:1530–34

144. Swann, K., Whitaker, M. 1986. The part played by inositol trisphosphate and calcium in the propagation of the fertilization wave in sea urchin eggs. *J. Cell Biol.* 103:2333–42

145. Takemura, H., Hughes, A. R., Thastrup, O., Putney, J. W. Jr. 1989. Activation of calcium entry by the tumor promoter thapsigargin in parotid acinar cells. Evidence that an intracellular calcium pool, and not an inositol phosphate, regulates calcium fluxes at the plasma membrane. *J. Biol. Chem.* 264:12266–71

146. Taylor, C. W., Putney, J. W. Jr. 1985. Size of the inositol 1,4,5-trisphosph-

ate-sensitive calcium pool in guinea-pig hepatocytes. *Biochem. J.* 232:435–38

147. Terasaki, M., Sardet, C. 1991. Demonstration of calcium uptake and release by sea urchin egg cortical endoplasmic reticulum. *J. Cell Biol.* 115:1031–37

148. Thastrup, O. 1990. Role of Ca^{2+}-ATPases in regulation of cellular Ca^{2+} signalling, as studied with the selective microsomal Ca^{2+}-ATPase inhibitor, thapsigargin. *Agents Actions* 29:8–15

149. Thastrup, O., Cullen, P. J., Drobak, B. K., Hanley, M. R., Dawson, A. P. 1990. Thapsigargin, a tumor promoter, discharges intracellular Ca^{2+} stores by specific inhibition of the endoplasmic reticulum Ca^{2+}-ATPase. *Proc. Natl. Acad. Sci. USA* 87:2466–70

150. Thévenod, F., Dehlinger-Kremer, M., Kemmer, T. P., Christian, A.-L., Potter, B. V. L., Schulz, I. 1989. Characterization of inositol 1,4,5-trisphosphate-sensitive (IsCaP) and -insensitive (IisCaP) nonmitochondrial Ca^{2+} pools in rat pancreatic acinar cells. *J. Membr. Biol.* 109:173–86

151. Thomas, A. P., Renard, D. C., Rooney, T. A. 1991. Spatial and temporal organization of calcium signalling in hepatocytes. *Cell Calcium* 12:111–26

152. Tsien, R. W., Ellinor, P. T., Horne, W. A. 1991. Molecular diversity of voltage-dependent Ca^{2+} channels. *Trends Pharmacol. Sci.* 12:349–54

153. Tsien, R. W., Tsien, R. Y. 1990. Calcium channels, stores, and oscillations. *Annu. Rev. Cell Biol.* 6:715–60

154. Tsunoda, Y., Stuenkel, E. L., Williams, J. A. 1990. Oscillatory mode of calcium signaling in rat pancreatic acinar cells. *Am. J. Physiol.* 258:C147–55

155. Tsunoda, Y., Williams, J. A., DelValle, J. 1991. Secretagogue-induced Ca^{2+} oscillations in isolated canine gastric chief cells. *Biochim. Biophys. Acta Mol. Cell Res.* 1091:251–54

156. Volpe, P., Krause, K.-H., Hashimoto, S., Zorzato, F., Pozzan, T., et al. 1988. "Calciosome," a cytoplasmic organelle: The inositol 1,4,5-trisphosphate-sensitive Ca^{2+} store of nonmuscle cells? *Proc. Natl. Acad. Sci. USA* 85:1091–95

157. von Tscharner, V., Deranleau, D. A., Baggiolini, M. 1986. Calcium fluxes and calcium buffering in human neutrophils. *J. Biol. Chem.* 261:10163–68

158. von Tscharner, V., Prod'Hom, B., Baggiolini, M., Reuter, H. 1986. Ion

channels in human neutrophils activated by a rise in free cytosolic calcium concentration. *Nature* 324:369–72

159. Wakui, M., Osipchuk, Y. V., Petersen, O. H. 1990. Receptor-activated cytoplasmic Ca^{2+} spiking mediated by inositol trisphosphate is due to Ca^{2+}-induced Ca^{2+} release. *Cell* 63:1025–32

160. Wakui, M., Potter, B. V. L., Petersen, O. H. 1989. Pulsatile intracellular calcium release does not depend on fluctuations in inositol trisphosphate concentration. *Nature* 339:317–20

161. Walton, P. D., Airey, J. A., Sutko, J. L., Beck, C. F., Mignery, G. A., et al. 1991. Ryanodine and inositol trisphosphate receptors coexist in avian cerebellar Purkinje neurons. *J. Cell Biol.* 113:1145–58

162. Wilson, H. A., Greenblatt, D., Poenie, M., Finkelman, F. D., Tsien, R. Y. 1987. Crosslinkage of B lymphocyte surface immunoglobulin by anti-Ig or antigen induces prolonged oscillation of intracellular ionized calcium. *J. Exp. Med.* 166:601–6

163. Woods, N. M., Cuthbertson, K. S. R., Cobbold, P. H. 1986. Repetitive transient rises in cytoplasmic free calcium in hormone-stimulated hepatocytes. *Nature* 319:600–2

164. Woods, N. M., Cuthbertson, K. S. R., Cobbold, P. H. 1987. Phorbolester-induced alterations of free calcium ion transients in single rat hepatocytes. *Biochem. J.* 246:619–23

165. Woods, N. M., Cuthbertson, K. S. R., Cobbold, P. H. 1987. Agonist-induced oscillations in cytoplasmic free calcium concentration in single rat hepatocytes. *Cell Calcium* 8:79–100

166. Yada, T., Oiki, S., Ueda, S., Okada, Y. 1986. Synchronous oscillation of the cytoplasmic Ca^{2+} concentration and membrane potential in cultured epithelial cells. *Biochim. Biophys. Acta* 887:105–12

167. Yule, D. I., Gallacher, D. V. 1988. Oscillations of cytosolic calcium in single pancreatic acinar cells stimulated by acetylcholine. *FEBS Lett.* 239:358–62

168. Yule, D. I., Lawrie, A. M., Gallacher, D. V. 1991. Acetylcholine and cholecystokinin induce different patterns of oscillating calcium signals in pancreatic acinar cells. *Cell Calcium* 12:145–51

169. Zhao, H., Loessberg, P. A., Sachs, G., Muallem, S. 1990. Regulation of intracellular Ca^{2+} oscillation in AR42J cells. *J. Biol. Chem.* 265:20856–62

Annu. Rev. Physiol. 55:455–72

PACEMAKER MECHANISMS IN CARDIAC TISSUE

Dario DiFrancesco

Dipartimento di Fisiologia e Biochimica Generali, Elettrofisiologia, Università di Milano, via Celoria 26, 20133 Milano, Italy

KEY WORDS: cardiac pacemaker, sinoatrial node, pacemaker current, i_f current, modulation

INTRODUCTION

The heartbeat is a sign of life, and not surprisingly it has attracted much interest and curiosity since the early stages of scientific investigation. Even Leonardo da Vinci, in his anatomical studies, realized that rhythmic, restless activity was an intrinsic property of cardiac muscle (92), "As to the heart: it moves itself, and doth never stop, except it be for eternity." In fact, a search for the basis of spontaneous cardiac activity could only be undertaken several centuries after these primitive observations with the development of techniques that allowed the study of the electrical properties of excitable tissues and particularly of cardiac muscle (18, 71, 77, 23).

Cardiac pacemaker activity originates in specialized myocytes located in restricted areas of the heart that are characterized by the ability to beat spontaneously even when separated from the rest of the cardiac muscle (24, 106, 103, 11, 81). Voltage-clamp investigation of pacemaker tissue opened the way to a better understanding of the ionic mechanisms promoting rhythmicity in pacemaker tissue (64, 6). In pacemaker cells of the mammalian sino-atrial (SA) node, spontaneous activity results from a typical phase of their action potential, the slow diastolic depolarization. The concept that a slow depolarization is an inherent property of spontaneously active myocardium is an old one that has been actively investigated since the first recordings of cardiac electrical activity revealed the existence of a slow depolarizing phase preceding the action potential onset in beating tissue (for a review, see 105). During this phase, corresponding to diastole of the cardiac contraction cycle, the membrane slowly depolarizes following termination of an action potential, until threshold for a new action potential is reached. Thus, the

455

0066–4278/93/0315–0455$02.00

diastolic depolarization is responsible for initiating rhythmic behavior and characterizes action potentials of SA node and other spontaneously active cardiocytes.

Besides generating rhythmic activity, the diastolic (or pacemaker) depolarization is involved in the control of firing frequency by the autonomic neurotransmitters. It is known that stimulation of the sympathetic and parasympathetic nervous systems leads to acceleration and slowing of cardiac rate, respectively. A main physiological mechanism by which low doses of autonomic transmitters modulate cardiac rate is the control of the steepness of pacemaker depolarization. An example of the way this is accomplished is illustrated in Figure 1. Here three traces, recorded from a sino-atrial node cell in normal Tyrode solution and in the presence of either isoprenaline 10 nM or acetylcholine 3 nM, are superimposed. Clearly, under these conditions neither drug significantly alters action potential shape or duration, and changes in the spontaneous frequency are entirely due to effects on the duration of diastolic depolarization. This means that, at least at these low neurotransmitter concentrations, autorhythmicity is controlled by the rate of development of the pacemaker phase. What is the ionic basis of the diastolic depolarization? As any depolarizing process requires a net inward ionic flow, we expect to find at least one inward current activated in the pacemaker range of voltages that is able to drive the diastolic depolarization. In this review we consider the current experimental evidence for the mechanisms underlying generation of autorhythmicity in cardiac cells and its control by β-adrenergic and muscarinic stimulation. As is discussed below, among the various components present in SA node cells, the hyperpolarization-activated (i_f) current appears to be most specifically designed to initiate the development of a slow depolarizing process in the diastolic range and to control its rate of rise in response to neurotransmitter-induced modulation.

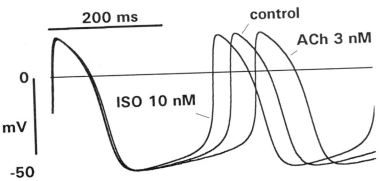

Figure 1 Acceleration and slowing of spontaneous activity induced by isoprenaline 10 nM and acetylcholine 3 nM, respectively, in a single sino-atrial node cell. Temperature was 35°C.

GENERATION OF PACEMAKER ACTIVITY

The Rise and Fall of the i_{K2} Current

First attempts at investigating the mechanisms underlying generation of the diastolic depolarization were made in Purkinje fibers by Weidmann (104), who measured a decrease in membrane conductance during diastolic depolarization. The simplest interpretation of this result was that the diastolic phase was associated with a decaying K^+ current. On the basis of similar conductance measurements in voltage-clamp conditions, Vassalle (103) proposed that the pacemaker depolarization in Purkinje fibers resulted from a decline of K^+ permeability. The view that a decay of a K^+ current could be responsible for generation of pacemaker activity later received substantial support from the work of Noble & Tsien (80) and others (87, 60, 22), who described a pacemaker current in Purkinje fibers in terms of a pure K^+ current (i_{K2}) outward and deactivating on hyperpolarization in the diastolic voltage range. The i_{K2} current was regarded for many years as perhaps the best analyzed cardiac ionic component, especially relevant to electrical behavior of Purkinje fibers, because it was involved not only in the generation of the pacemaker depolarization, but also in its control by catecholamines (59, 101). The view that pacemaker activity of cardiac Purkinje fibers was the result of i_{K2} deactivation held for over ten years and was, in Weidmann's words, "universally accepted" (105). However, in the late seventies new evidence revealed that the i_{K2} interpretation was deeply incorrect. Rather than an outward current activated on depolarization, the Purkinje fibers' i_{K2} was in fact shown to be an inward current, unselectively carried by K^+ and Na^+ and activated on hyperpolarization in the pacemaker range of voltages (27, 28): a falling i_{K2} was to be replaced by a rising i_f.

The i_{K2} Re-interpretation: Identification with the i_f Current

The i_{K2} re-interpretation was made possible by two independent findings: (a) K^+-depletion processes could distort the time-course of currents during voltage clamp in Purkinje fibers to the extent of inducing a fake current reversal near the K^+ equilibrium potential (40, 27); (b) a newly found pacemaker current carried by Na^+ and K^+, inward and activating on hyperpolarization in the SA node (i_f or i_h current) (10, 107) shared several properties in common with i_{K2} (41). The new interpretation (for reviews see 29, 78, 30) accommodated several results that could not be explained previously, such as the disappearance of the i_{K2} current in Na^+-free solutions (75), hardly a property of a pure K^+ current, and the fact that the reversal potential was too negative for a K^+ current (22). Interestingly, the re-interpretation was not only able to correctly account for the diastolic depolarization of Purkinje fibers, but also to explain the early conductance measurements that had led to the K^+ current decay hypothesis (37).

As in Purkinje fibers, involvement of a K^+ current decay mechanism in the generation of rhythmic activity had been proposed in depolarized frog atrium (7) and in the frog sinus venosus (11). In frog atrium, rhythmic behavior was not spontaneous, but was evoked by an externally applied depolarizing current (inward from the cell's point of view), and since no outward component can generate a depolarization, in this experimental arrangement, the applied current acted as the proper pacemaker current. In the frog sinus venosus an inward current activated on hyperpolarization was observed, but reported to have an activation range too negative to contribute to the pacemaker depolarization (11). This current was later found to have the same properties as i_f in the mammalian SA node, and its participation in pacemaking is still debated (2).

Hypotheses for Pacemaker Generation

The demonstration that i_{K2} and i_f were identical and that the Purkinje fibers' pacemaker depolarization was associated with activation of an inward current, not with inactivation of an outward current, lent support to the hypothesis that in the SA node (the natural pacemaker of mammalian heart) a similar process could be responsible for initiating pacemaker activity (i_f-activation hypothesis) (9, 74, 30). Arguments against this view, however, were based on observations that the range of i_f activation could be too negative relative to the range of pacemaker depolarization (108). Other possible mechanisms for pacing generation in SA node have been suggested (6, 78): the activation of the Ca^{2+} current (108), and the decay of the delayed K^+ current (i_K), which underlies action potential repolarization in this preparation (i_K-decay hypothesis) (12).

It is important to stress that no outward current can generate a depolarization. Thus it may be misleading to interpret the i_K-decay hypothesis in terms of i_K deactivation being the depolarization generating process itself, or i_K being the pacemaker current. Some degree of confusion may arise from the intuitive but incorrect assumption that changes in voltage are directly related to changes in current. This is not so. In fact, during activity, the relation $I_{ionic} = -C \, dV/dt$ holds, which means that voltage changes are directly proportional to the absolute value of net ionic current flowing through the membrane. A pacemaker-generating process thus requires an inward current mechanism able to supply a constant current flow during development of a depolarization of constant slope which is what, to a first approximation, the pacemaker depolarization is. For these reasons, the i_K-decay hypothesis above included the assumption that a background current, inward in the diastolic range, was unmasked by decay of i_K. It should also be noticed that the i_f-activation hypothesis does not exclude that i_K decays during the diastolic depolarization; it simply assumes that the diastolic depolarization is not initiated by the unmasking of a background inward current (passive mechanism), but by activation of i_f (active mechanism). In the following we outline the main properties of the ionic components of SA node myocytes that are activated within the range of diastolic potentials and discuss their possible role in pacemaker depolarization.

CURRENTS INVOLVED IN PACEMAKING

The Hyperpolarization-activated i_f Current

The i_f current of SA node is an unspecific cation current, normally carried by Na^+ and K^+, inward and slowly activating upon hyperpolarization in a voltage range comprising that of the diastolic depolarization. First studied in 1979 in relation to its role in the catecholamine-induced frequency acceleration (10), its properties were later described with some detail at the multicellular (9, 107, 74), single-cell (76, 36, 25, 33, 102) and single-channel level (31, 46). The i_f features are well suited for generating a depolarizing process in response to a hyperpolarization that enters the range of i_f activation (30). In order to assess the degree of i_f involvement in the generation of the nodal diastolic depolarization, it is essential to evaluate this range correctly. Uncertainty over the role of i_f may originate from the fact that reported values of i_f activation threshold show some variability. Variability of the activation range, however, appears to be a typical feature of the i_f current. As discussed below, i_f is directly modulated by cAMP, whose action is to shift, under the regulatory control of neurotransmitters, the i_f activation curve along the voltage axis. This affects the degree of current activation and consequently the rate of development of diastolic depolarization. Thus even in the same type of cell, variability of the position of the i_f curve may simply reflect variations in the intracellular cAMP levels.

In multicellular nodal preparations, i_f was originally reported to be activated on hyperpolarization from holding potentials of about -35 mV, well within the diastolic range (10, 9), although other reports indicated a threshold near –50mV, which suggests a limited contribution to diastolic depolarization (107). The i_f activation range has also been found to vary in single-cell preparations (36, 39, 25), with estimates of the i_f activation threshold going from -35 mV (32) or -40 mV (102) down to -60/-65 mV mV (25). It is possible that part of this variability is attributable to current run-down resulting from the wash-out through the patch pipette of a diffusible substance necessary for channel activity (36), although some variation can also originate from natural cell heterogeneity. The presence of run-down also suggests that measurement of the i_f threshold in single cells may yield values more negative than the real ones. This is because run-down quickly reduces the amount of i_f measurable on voltage clamp by first displacing the current activation curve to more negative voltages, and then by decreasing its fully activated amplitude (36). Together with run-down, other factors like incomplete series resistance compensation (33) may contribute to the underestimation of the size of i_f. Furthermore, i_f activation kinetics are slow at depolarized voltages (39) and require correspondingly long steps for complete activation, or proper I/V curve protocols. Measurement of the activation curve with steps of fixed 0.5 to 3 sec duration, for example (76, 25, 102), may lead to incomplete current activation at depolarized voltages and to a more negative estimate of activation threshold.

Another consideration relevant to the problem of the i_f contribution to normal pacemaking concerns the amount of net inward current required to drive the diastolic depolarization. Since SA node cells have a mean capacity of about 30 pF (31, 25), and the rate of diastolic depolarization is normally around 0.1 mV/sec, only a tiny net inward current of 3 pA is necessary to generate the pacemaker depolarization. It is therefore important that in relation to its contribution to pacemaker activity, i_f activation is studied on an adequately expanded current scale. Recent experimental analysis and numerical reconstruction have shown that the i_f size and kinetics are compatible with a contribution to diastolic depolarization and that, in fact, the process of i_f activation may be considered partly (102) or fully responsible for its generation (31). Detailed voltage-clamp investigation of the diastolic range has also shown that in pacing cells the net background (time-independent) current can be outward down to voltages as negative as –65 mV, thus indicating that in these cells no pacemaker depolarization would be possible without i_f activation (31).

A direct evaluation of the i_f contribution to diastolic depolarization would be possible if the current could be blocked by pharmacological means. Cs, a blocker of i_f, slows but does not arrest pacemaker activity in SA node cells at a concentration of 2 mM (83, 26), which may suggest that an i_f contribution is present, but not essential to pacemaker generation. It is unlikely, however, that full block of i_f is achieved during activity with Cs at the concentration of 2 mM. For example, even higher concentrations (5 mM) have been shown to leave a substantial fraction of fully activated i_f, ranging from approximately 23% at -65 mV to 38% at -45 mV (data from Reference 36, Figure 10). A more specific and efficient i_f blocker would thus be desirable for a quantitative analysis of the i_f contribution. On the other hand, as Cs in the range of 1–2 mM apparently does not affect other currents in SA node cells, the Cs-induced rate reduction indicates that i_f normally makes an important contribution to cardiac pacemaking (26).

If the bulk of evidence now points to i_f as a major component contributing to generation of the pacemaker depolarization, its role in mediating autonomic rate control, as discussed below, strengthens the view that i_f activation represents the most relevant mechanism involved in SA node rhythm control at low neurotransmitter concentrations.

The Slow Inward Currents and the Background Inward Current

Early measurements in multicellular SA nodes indicated that in this preparation a Ca^{2+}-dependent current was elicited upon depolarization beyond a threshold of about -50 mV (67). It was originally proposed that this current could participate in the development of the diastolic depolarization, and a numerical model for SA node activity was constructed on the assumption that the Ca^{2+} current was responsible for pacemaking generation (108, 109). However, this view was not supported by evidence from current-clamp experiments, which indicate that Ca^{2+} entry can give a contribution to only the last fraction of pacemaker depolarization (14). In a more recent analysis in single nodal myocytes, two Ca^{2+} inward components (L-type and T-type) have been reported (54). The largest, long lasting (L-) component ($i_{Ca,L}$) activates near -30 mV, while the transient (T-) component ($i_{Ca,T}$) is reported to activate at about -50 mV. As both these Ca^{2+} currents are activated on depolarization with fast activation and, for the T-component, inactivation kinetics, their properties are appropriate for generation of the rapid action potential depolarization and upstroke. Because of its more negative threshold, the T-component has also been proposed to contribute to the diastolic depolarization, on the basis of evidence that Ni, a blocker of $i_{Ca,T}$, slows the diastolic depolarization rate (54). This depends on the assumption that Ni acts specifically on $i_{Ca,T}$. However, Ni also has a moderate depressing action on i_f. In three cells, 40 μM Ni reversibly decreased i_f recorded during 2 sec steps at -65 mV by 18.2 $\pm$3.3% (D. DiFrancesco, unpublished data; see also 54, Figure 11). In view of the small values of net current flowing during the pacemaker phase, the slowing action of Ni cannot be taken as conclusive evidence for a contribution of $i_{Ca,T}$ to pacemaker depolarization.

Assessment of the degree of involvement of Ca^{2+} currents in pacemaker generation can also be done by measuring "window" Ca^{2+} components. Since Ca^{2+} currents are activated on depolarization and not on hyperpolarization, the presence of a window is a necessary condition for a current contribution to initiation of diastolic depolarization. While activation and inactivation curves for the L-component overlap over a relatively wide range at depolarized voltages, those for the T-component show either no obvious overlapping (54), or a substantial overlapping (49). However, evidence that a Ca^{2+}-dependent background component, as obtained by investigating the sensitivity of the instantaneous current to Ca^{2+}-channel blockers, can only be recorded positive to -45 mV (33) favors the view that a substantial T-type window component is lacking in SA node cells.

An unusual, incompletely understood property of the nodal slow inward current is its dependence upon external Na^+. This was clearly observed in multicellular SA nodes (85, 67) and, for the L-component, in single nodal myocytes (89). Although the Ca^{2+}-ionic nature of nodal slow inward currents is clearly apparent from their Ca^{2+} dependence (85, 67) and from the fact that in single cells both T- and L-type components can be recorded in Na^+-free solutions (54), the problem of the Na^+ dependence of these components remains to be clarified.

The nature of the net background (time-independent, instantaneous) current in SA node is still uncertain (26). In the absence of direct experimental evidence, a background component, inward in the pacemaker range and Na^+-dependent, has often been assumed and included in the reconstruction of nodal electrical activity, on the basis of indirect evidence extrapolated from data in other tissues and for consistency with previous models (38, 79, 13). As mentioned above, the presence of an inward background component is a necessary requirement of the i_K-decay hypothesis.

Recently, a Na^+-dependent current has been reported in SA node myocytes on the basis of ion-substitution experiments (66). According to these results, the Na^+-dependence of the background component would supply some 50 pA in the diastolic range. This value far exceeds the few pA required for the net diastolic current (see above). Furthermore, to reconcile these data with previous evidence that no net inward current is recorded down to about -65 mV in beating cells (33), an additional, nearly equivalent background K^+ conductance must also be assumed. This agrees with the fact that the same background conductance is reported to have a K^+ permeability much larger than that to Na^+ (55). The balance between inward and outward background components in the diastolic range might provide the conditions that facilitate initiation of the diastolic phase by activation of even small amounts of a time-dependent inward current like i_f.

CONTROL OF PACEMAKER ACTIVITY BY NEUROTRANSMITTERS

The modulation of mammalian heart rate by the autonomic nervous system originates in the SA node, the most densely innervated cardiac region: sympathetic stimulation leads to acceleration, and parasympathetic stimulation to slowing of the SA node cell spontaneous activity. We now discuss the major modifications induced by neurotransmitters on some of the ionic currents of pacemaker cells and how these modifications contribute to the nervous control of pacemaking.

Sympathetic Modulation

β-adrenergic stimulation has several actions on ionic currents participating in the generation of electrical activity of SA node cells. Stimulation of the Ca^{2+} current has been reported in multicellular preparations (10, 82) and in single myocytes, where only the L-component appears to be modulated (54). As in ventricular myocytes (86, 68), activation of adenylyl-cyclase and cAMP production are involved in this action. This is indicated, for example, by experiments where the L-component is increased by β-receptor-independent stimulation of adenylyl-cyclase by forskolin (D. DiFrancesco, unpublished observation).

Epinephrine increases the fully-activated Ca^{2+} current of SA node without apparently affecting its kinetics (82), in agreement with evidence in other cardiac preparations (91). Also in agreement with results in different cardiac cells (90, 20, 17), single-channel studies in nodal myocytes have shown that epinephrine increases the probability of L-channel opening without modification of its conductance (54). As the T-component is not modulated by β-adrenergic stimulation, and the L-component is activated at voltages more positive than - 30 mV (54), neither current is likely to play a major role in sympathetic rhythm modulation in pacemaker tissue. This does not exclude the possibility that modification of the Ca^{2+} current will affect the spontaneous rate, as implied by the finding that Ca^{2+} current activation occurs during the last fraction of the pacemaker depolarization (13).

A catecholamine-activated, cAMP-regulated current, inward near resting voltages, has been described in ventricular myocytes (47, 48) and attributed to chloride ions (58, 1, 73). Although a Cl⁻ background current has been described in the SA node (94), evidence for a catecholamine-activated component is lacking, which rules against a contribution of background components to the chronotropic action of sympathetic stimulation in SA node cells.

Catecholamines have also been reported to activate the i_K current in multicellular SA node preparations, although single-cell studies are still lacking (10, 82). Dependence upon β-adrenergic stimulation has been characterized for delayed K^+ currents in other cardiac cell types (16, 51, 113), where it appears to involve phosphorylation by protein kinases A and C (99, 110).

The i_K increase caused by β-stimulation provides a further, stringent element of discrimination between different hypotheses for pacing generation. Indeed, if decay of i_K and unmasking of a background inward current were the main mechanisms promoting pacemaker depolarization, β-adrenergic stimulation would be accompanied by a larger K^+ conductance and would thus give rise to slowing, rather than acceleration. This apparent paradox can only be resolved by assuming that the inward current promoting diastolic depolarization is itself stimulated by catecholamines (15). As discussed above, an increase of $i_{Ca,L}$ can only affect the last fraction of pacemaker depolarization. This consideration supports the view that the event leading to generation of diastolic depolarization under normal conditions is activation of the i_f current. By accelerating repolarization and thus shortening action potential duration, catecholamine-induced i_K increase may help keep the ratio of action potential duration to cycle length within an appropriate range during adrenergic stimulation.

Modulation of the hyperpolarization-activated current by epinephrine and the relevance of this mechanism to the sympathetic control of rhythm have been known since the current was first studied in the SA node (10). In the SA node (36) and Purkinje fibers (101), i_f activation by β-adrenergic stimulation occurs via a positive shift of the voltage dependence of the current activation curve and kinetics. This causes acceleration of spontaneous activity by increasing the slope of diastolic depolarization, which shortens the time required to reach the threshold for action potential generation (see Figure 1).

Although a detailed quantitative analysis of the action of catecholamines on i_f in SA node myocytes is still lacking, an i_f increase and a simultaneous frequency acceleration can be recorded at fairly low isoprenaline doses (0.001–0.003 μM) (A. Zaza et al, unpublished data). The comparison in Figure 1 of the activities recorded in a single SA node myocyte in control conditions and during perfusion with isoprenaline 0.01 μM shows that β-stimulation modifies the diastolic depolarization without significant change in action potential shape and duration, which rules against large variations of either Ca^{2+} or K^+ currents. This evidence supports the notion that the main process mediating chronotropic response of moderate β-activation is i_f modulation.

Parasympathetic Modulation

One of the first phenomena investigated by microelectrode recording in cardiac tissue, the action of vagal stimulation on heart rate, was shown in early studies to be associated with membrane hyperpolarization and an increased K^+ permeability (62, 19, 24, 63). A K^+ current activated by ACh ($i_{K,ACh}$) has been described in both amphibian and mammalian heart, and its properties have been characterized in detail in intact cardiac tissue (52, 98, 50, 84), single-cell (88, 4, 96), and single-channel experiments (93, 97, 70).

However, the well established notion that vagal stimulation slows heart rate by activating a K^+ current has been recently challenged by the finding that in SA node cells, ACh has an additional, strong inhibitory action on the i_f current (43). ACh inhibits i_f by a mechanism, opposite to that of catecholamines, that involves reduced cAMP production and a consequent shift of the current activation curve to more negative voltages (44, 45). The experimental evidence indicates that the i_f inhibition is the main process by which moderate ACh concentrations control cardiac rate (35). Although both actions are mediated by muscarinic receptors, activation of K^+ channels requires 20-fold higher doses of ACh than i_f inhibition. Thus, whereas half inhibition of i_f occurs at 0.013 µM ACh, a concentration of 0.26 µM ACh is required to half activate $i_{K,ACh}$. Measurement of the dose-response relationships for i_f inhibition and $i_{K,ACh}$ activation indicates that in the concentration range up to 0.01–0.03 µM, ACh acts selectively on i_f. Since at these doses ACh is indeed effective at slowing spontaneous rate, the i_f inhibition appears to play a key role in the vagal control of rhythm. The notion that slowing is caused by inhibition of the inward i_f current, rather than activation of a K^+ conductance, agrees with the evidence shown in Figure 1 that slowing caused by low ACh concentrations or moderate vagal stimulation occurs without membrane hyperpolarization (61).

There is substantial evidence that the Ca^{2+} current is inhibited by ACh in various cardiac preparations (57). The Ca^{2+} current of intact SA node has been reported to be "remarkably insensitive" to ACh (84), although a significant reduction of basal current can sometimes be observed in single cells (45, 8). In experiments where i_f and $i_{Ca,L}$ were recorded simultaneously, we have repeatedly observed that 0.03 µM ACh substantially inhibits i_f, but does not modify $i_{Ca,L}$ (34). In a study done in the range 0.01 to 300 µM, we have observed that the threshold ACh concentration, which reduces $i_{Ca,L}$ by a measurable amount, is 0.1 µM in single nodal myocytes. Even at 300 µM ACh, $i_{Ca,L}$ can be maximally reduced by about only 30% ((D. DiFrancesco et al, unpublished data). These data rule against a major role for Ca^{2+} currents in ACh-induced slowing, even at relatively high ACh doses.

MECHANISMS THAT REGULATE CURRENTS INVOLVED IN PACEMAKER ACTIVITY

Significant progress in understanding the cellular processes that regulate cardiac ion channels has come from the use of patch-clamp techniques (56) in isolated myocytes. Whereas the bulk of information concerning Ca^{2+} and K^+ currents comes from experimentation in ventricular and atrial tissues (for review, see 57, 6, 100, 65), relevant evidence on the i_f and $i_{K,ACh}$ currents has been derived from experiments on nodal cells.

Direct G protein-mediated channel activation was first demonstrated for the

$i_{K,ACh}$ current in atrial cells (88, 4, 70, 110, 72). This mechanism, in which channel regulation occurs across the membrane without the involvement of a diffusible intracellular second messenger, may be especially relevant to beat-to-beat regulation of cardiac performance. There seems to be general agreement that α subunits of the G protein controlling the ACh-activated channel (G_K) are directly involved in channel opening, and $\beta\gamma$ subunits may control channel performance via activation of phospholipase A2 (5, 69, 3). The presence of a fast, direct, G protein-mediated modulation of the Ca^{2+} current reported in other cardiac preparations (111, 95) has not been investigated in the SA node.

Activation by catecholamines and inhibition by ACh of the i_f current involve adenylyl-cyclase activity and cAMP, which is the second messenger in i_f modulation. This has been shown in Purkinje fibers (101, 21) and in SA node myocytes (36, 45). The chain of events leading to rhythm modulation by neurotransmitters through the i_f current may therefore be summarized as follows: by activating adenylyl-cyclase, catecholamines increase cAMP levels and induce a consequent rightward shift of the i_f activation curve, which leads to cardiac acceleration; the opposite mechanism, i.e. inhibition of adenylyl-cyclase, decrease of cAMP levels, and generation of a leftward shift of i_f activation curve, characterizes the slowing action of ACh. Modifications of i_f kinetics occur without effect on the fully activated I/V curve (36, 44). In agreement with these whole cell results, direct recording of single i_f-channels (31) has shown that β-stimulation increases the probability of i_f channel opening on hyperpolarization, but does not affect the single-channel conductance. A recent investigation of the interaction between cAMP and i_f channels has led to the unexpected result that cAMP controls i_f channels directly, rather than by phosphorylation through cAMP-dependent protein kinase, as occurs for all other cardiac cAMP-regulated channels (42). In this respect, i_f channels are similar to cyclic-nucleotide-dependent channels of sensory neurons.

In addition to cAMP, i_f channels have been reported to be directly controlled by G proteins (112). These results indicate that i_f channels can be activated by G_s and inhibited by G_o with a mechanism that would provide fast i_f channel control during beat-to-beat modulation. Control of i_f by cAMP and partial control by G protein are not mutually incompatible. However, several observations point to cAMP-mediated control as the main mechanism for i_f modulation. These include evidence of i_f modulation by maneuvers that alter the intracellular cAMP level independently of the interaction with membrane receptors (like direct stimulation of adenylyl-cyclase or inhibition of phosphodiesterase) (45), as well as evidence that i_f channels in cell-attached patches can be modulated by externally perfused epinephrine (31). Finally, a suggested direct role for intracellular Ca^{2+} ions in modulation of i_f channels (53) has not been confirmed in inside-out macro-patch experiments (114).

CONCLUSIONS

Elucidation of the mechanisms underlying cardiac pacemaking requires a detailed knowledge of the properties of ionic currents flowing during the diastolic depolarization. An ionic current apt to generate and control the slow depolarization of pacemaker cells should possess a few specific properties: (a) the current should activate on hyperpolarization at the termination of an action potential and should be substantially activated when the membrane potential approaches the MDP in the range -65–70 mV; (b) its kinetics should allow the generation of a slow voltage depolarization of approximately constant slope; (c) in order to mediate rhythm modulation by neurotransmitters, the inward current should increase during β-adrenergic stimulation and decrease during cholinergic stimulation.

The i_f current is the only current system displaying all the above features in SA node myocytes. Indeed, its peculiar property of being an inward current activated on hyperpolarization in the diastolic range is by itself clearly capable of generating a depolarizing process following action potential repolarization. Furthermore, the ability to generate a slow depolarizing process is best achieved by a slow time-dependent activation process, which allows the development of a constant current flow during a depolarization. Notice that inward currents activated on depolarization (e.g. Ca^{2+} and Na^+ currents) are apt to underlie regenerative, all-or-nothing depolarizing processes in a positive-feedback fashion, rather than slow, controlled depolarizations. For this reason these latter components are responsible for generation of the fast depolarizing phase of the action potential. Finally, i_f is modulated in opposite ways by β-adrenergic and cholinergic stimuli via a cAMP-dependent, phosphorylation-independent pathway that allows a fine rhythm control by the autonomic nervous system. The key element in the pacemaking process and its modulation by moderate neurotransmitter concentrations thus appears to be the position of the i_f activation curve on the voltage axis: the more this curve is shifted to the right, the more i_f current will be available for a faster diastolic depolarization. Since the position of the i_f activation curve is controlled by cAMP, the diastolic rate can be finely tuned by the opposite actions of β-adrenergic and cholinergic transmitters to achieve the desired autorhythmic rate.

ACKNOWLEDGMENTS

This work was supported by the Consiglio Nazionale delle Ricerche (CT90.03303) and the Ministero dell' Università e della Ricerca Scientifica e Tecnologica. I thank Dr. Richard B. Robinson for comments on the manuscript and Prof. Denis Noble for translating Leonardo into Shakespearean English.

Literature Cited

1. Bahinski, A., Nairn, A. C., Green-gard, P., Gadsby, D. C. 1989. Chloride conductance regulated by cyclic AMP-dependent protein kinase in cardiac myocytes. *Nature* 340: 718–21

2. Bois, P., Lenfant, J. 1990. Isolated cells of the frog sinus venosus: properties of the inward current activated during hyperpolarization. *Pflügers Arch.* 416: 339–46

3. Bourne, H. R. 1989. G-protein subunits: who carries what message? *Nature* 337: 504–5

4. Breitwieser, G. E., Szabo, G. 1985. Uncoupling of cardiac muscarinic and β-adrenergic receptors from ion channels by a guanine nucleotide analogue. *Nature* 317:538–40

5. Brown, A. M., Birnbaumer, L. 1990. Ionic channels and their regulation by G protein subunits. *Annu. Rev. Physiol.* 52:197–213

6. Brown, H. F. 1982. Electrophysiology of the sinoatrial node. *Physiol. Rev.* 62:505–30

7. Brown, H. F., Clark, A., Noble, S. J. 1976. Identification of the pacemaker current in frog atrium. *J. Physiol.* 258: 521–45

8. Brown, H. F., Denyer, J. C. 1989. Low-dose acetylcholine reduces calcium current in isolated sino-atrial node cells of rabbit. *J. Physiol.* 410:65P

9. Brown, H. F., DiFrancesco, D. 1980. Voltage-clamp investigations of membrane currents underlying pacemaker activity in rabbit sino-atrial node. *J. Physiol.* 308:331–51

10. Brown, H. F., DiFrancesco, D., Noble, S. J. 1979. How does adrenaline accelerate the heart? *Nature* 280:235–36

11. Brown, H. F., Giles, W., Noble, S. J. 1977. Membrane currents underlying activity in frog sinus venosus. *J. Physiol.* 271:783–816

12. Brown, H. F., Kimura, J., Noble, S. J. 1982. The relative contributions of various time-dependent membrane currents to pacemaker activity in the sino atrial node. In *Cardiac Rate and Rhythm*, ed. L. N. Boumann, H. J. Jongsma, pp. 53–68. The Hague: Nijhoff

13. Brown, H. F., Kimura, J., Noble, D., Noble S. J., Taupignon, A. 1984. The slow inward current, i_{si}, in the rabbit sino-atrial node investigated by voltage clamp and computer simulation. *Proc. R. Soc. London Ser. B* 222:305–28

14. Brown, H. F., Kimura, J., Noble, D., Noble S. J., Taupignon, A. 1984. The ionic currents underlying pacemaker activity in rabbit sino-atrial node: experimental results and computer simulations. *Proc. R. Soc. London Ser. B* 222:329–47

15. Brown, H. F., McNaughton, P. A., Noble, D., Noble, S. J. 1975. Adrenergic control of cardiac pacemaker currents. *Philos. Trans. R. Soc. London Ser. B* 270:527–37

16. Brown, H. F., Noble, S. J. 1974. Effects of adrenaline on membrane currents underlying pacemaker activity in frog atrial muscle. *J. Physiol.* 238: 51–53P

17. Brum, G., Osterrieder, W., Trautwein, W. 1984. β-adrenergic increase in the calcium conductance of cardiac myocytes studied with the patch-clamp. *Pflügers Arch.* 401:111–18

18. Burdon-Sanderson, J., Page, F. J. M. 1883. On the electrical phenomena of the excitatory process in the heart of the frog and of the tortoise, as investigated photographically. *J. Physiol.* 4:327–38

19. Burgen, A. S. V., Terroux, K. G. 1953. On the negative inotropic effect in the cat's auricle. *J. Physiol.* 120:449–64

20. Cachelin, A. B., De Peyer, J. E., Kokubun, S., Reuter, H. 1983. Calcium channel modulation by 8-bromo-cyclic AMP in cultured heart cells. *Nature* 304:462–64

21. Chang, F., Gao, J., Tromba, C., Cohen, I. S., DiFrancesco, D. 1990. Acetylcholine reverses the effects of β-agonists on the pacemaker current in canine Purkinje fibres but has no direct action. A difference between primary and secondary pacemakers. *Circ. Res.* 66:633–36

22. Cohen I., Daut J., Noble D. 1976. The effects of potassium and temperature on the pacemaker current i_{K2} in Purkinje fibres. *J. Physiol.* 260:55–74

23. Coraboeuf, E., Weidmann, S. 1949. Potentiels d' action du muscle cardiaque obtenus à l' aide de microélectrodes intracellulaires. Présence d' une inversion de potentiel. *C. R. Soc. Biol.* 143:1360–61

24. del Castillo, J., Katz, B. 1955. Production of membrane potential changes in the frog's heart by inhibitory nerve impulses. *Nature* 175:1035

25. Denyer, J. C., Brown, H. F. 1990. Rabbit isolated sino-atrial node cells: isolation and electrophysiological properties. *J. Physiol.* 428:405–24

26. Denyer J. C., Brown H. F. 1990. Pacemaking in rabbit isolated sino-atrial node cells during Cs block of the hyperpolarization-activated current i_f. *J. Physiol.* 429:401–9

27. DiFrancesco, D. 1981. A new interpretation of the pacemaker current in calf Purkinje fibres. *J. Physiol.* 314: 359–76

28. DiFrancesco, D. 1981. A study of the ionic nature of the pacemaker current in calf Purkinje fibres. *J. Physiol.* 314:377–93

29. DiFrancesco, D. 1982. The pacemaker current i_{K2} in Purkinje fibres re-interpreted and identified with the current i_f in the SA node. See Ref. 12, pp. 69–91

30. DiFrancesco, D. 1985. The cardiac hyperpolarizing-activated current, i_f. Origins and developments. *Prog. Biophys. Mol. Biol.* 46:163–83

31. DiFrancesco, D. 1986. Characterization of single pacemaker channels in cardiac sino-atrial node cells. *Nature* 324:470–73

32. DiFrancesco, D. 1990. The hyperpolarization-activated current, i_f, and cardiac pacemaking. In *Cardiac Electrophysiology: a Textbook*, ed. M. R. Rosen, M. J. Janse, A. L. Wit, pp. 117–32. New York: Futura

33. DiFrancesco, D. 1991. The contribution of the hyperpolarization-activated current (i_f) to the generation of spontaneous activity in rabbit sino-atrial node myocytes. *J. Physiol.* 434:23–40

34. DiFrancesco, D. 1992. Regulation of the pacemaker current and pacemaker activity by acetylcholine. In *Vagal Control of the Heart— Experimental Basis and Clinical Implications*, ed. M. N. Levy, P. J. Schwartz. New York: Futura. In press

35. DiFrancesco, D., Ducouret, P., Robinson, R. B. 1989. Muscarinic modulation of cardiac rate at low acetylcholine concentrations. *Science* 243:669–71

36. DiFrancesco, D., Ferroni, A., Mazzanti, M., Tromba, C. 1986. Properties of the hyperpolarizing-activated current (i_f) in cells isolated from the rabbit sino-atrial node. *J. Physiol.* 377: 61–88

37. DiFrancesco, D., Noble, D. 1982. Implications of the reinterpretation of i_{K2} for the modelling of the electrical activity of the pacemaker

38. DiFrancesco, D., Noble, D. 1985. A model of cardiac electrical activity incorporating ionic pumps and concentration changes. *Philos. Trans. R. Soc. London Ser. B* 307:353–98

39. DiFrancesco, D., Noble, D. 1989. Current i_f and its contribution to cardiac pacemaking. In *Neuronal and Cellular Oscillators*, ed. J. W. Jacklet, pp. 31–57. New York: Dekker

40. DiFrancesco, D., Ohba, M., Ojeda, C. 1979. Measurement and significance of the reversal potential for the pacemaker current (i_{K2}) in sheep Purkinje fibres. *J. Physiol.* 297:135–62

41. DiFrancesco, D., Ojeda, C. 1980. Properties of the current i_f in the sino-atrial node of the rabbit compared with those of the current i_{K2} in Purkinje fibres. *J. Physiol.* 308:353–67

42. DiFrancesco, D., Tortora, P. 1991. Direct activation of cardiac pacemaker channels by intracellular cyclic AMP. *Nature* 351:145–47

43. DiFrancesco, D., Tromba, C. 1987. Acetylcholine inhibits activation of the cardiac pacemaker current, i_f. *Pflügers Arch.* 410:139–42

44. DiFrancesco, D., Tromba, C. 1988. Inhibition of the hyperpolarizing-activated current, i_f, induced by acetylcholine in rabbit sino-atrial node myocytes. *J. Physiol.* 405:477–91

45. DiFrancesco, D., Tromba, C. 1988. Muscarinic control of the hyperpolarizing-activated current i_f in rabbit sino-atrial node myocytes. *J. Physiol.* 405: 493–510

46. DiFrancesco, D., Tromba, C. 1989. Channel activity related to pacemaking. In *Isolated Adult Cardiomyocytes*, ed. G. Isenberg, H. M. Piper, 2:97–115. Boca Raton:CRC

47. Egan, T. M., Noble, D., Noble, S. J., Powell, T., Twist, V. W. 1987. An isoprenaline activated sodium-dependent inward current in ventricular myocytes. *Nature* 328:634–37

48. Egan, T. M., Noble, D., Noble, S. J., Powell, T., Twist, V. W., Yamaoka, K. 1988. On the mechanism of isoprenaline- and forskolin-induced depolarization of single guinea-pig ventricular myocytes. *J. Physiol.* 400:299–320

49. Fermini, B., Nathan, R. D. 1991. Removal of sialic acid alters both T- and L-type calcium currents in cardiac myocytes. *Am. J. Physiol.* 260:H735–43

50. Garnier, D., Nargeot, J., Ojeda, C.,

Rougier, O. 1978. The action of acetylcholine on background conductance in frog atrial trabeculae. *J. Physiol.* 274:381–96

51. Giles, W., Nakajima, T., Ono, K., Shibata, E. F. 1989. Modulation of the delayed rectifier K+current by isoprenaline in bull-frog atrial myocytes. *J. Physiol.* 415:233–49

52. Giles, W., Noble, S. J. 1976. Changes in membrane currents in bullfrog atrium produced by acetylcholine. *J. Physiol.* 261:103–23

53. Hagiwara, N., Irisawa, H. 1989. Modulation by intracellular Ca^{2+} of the hyperpolarization-activated inward current in rabbit single sino-atrial node cells. *J. Physiol.* 409:121–41

54. Hagiwara, N., Irisawa, H., Kameyama, M. 1988. Contribution of two types of calcium currents to the pacemaker potential of rabbit sino-atrial node cells. *J. Physiol.* 395:233–53

55. Hagiwara, N., Irisawa, H., Kasanuki, H., Hosoda, S. 1992. Background current in sinoatrial node cells of the rabbit heart. *J. Physiol.* 448:53–72

56. Hamill, O. P., Marty, A., Neher, E., Sakmann, B., Sigworth, F. J. 1981. Improved patch-clamp techniques for high-resolution current recording from cells and cell-free membrane patches. *Pflügers Arch.* 391:85–100

57. Hartzell, H. C. 1988. Regulation of cardiac ion channels by catecholamines, acetylcholine and second messenger systems. *Prog. Biophys. Mol. Biol.* 52:165–247

58. Harvey, R. D., Hume, J. R. 1989. Autonomic regulation of a chloride current in heart. *Science* 244:983–85

59. Hauswirth, O., Noble, D., Tsien, R. W. 1968. Adrenaline: mechanism of action on the pacemaker potential in cardiac Purkinje fibers. *Science* 162:916–17

60. Hauswirth, O., Noble, D., Tsien, R. W. 1972. Separation of the pacemaker and plateau components of delayed rectification in cardiac Purkinje fibres. *J. Physiol.* 225:211–35

61. Hirst, G. D. S., Bramich, N. J., Edwards, F. R., Klemm, M. 1992. Transmission of autonomic neuroeffector junctions. *Trends Neurosci.* 145:40–46

62. Hoffman, B. F., Suckling, E. E. 1953. Cardiac cellular potentials. Effect of vagal stimulation and acetylcholine. *Am. J. Physiol.* 173:312–20

63. Hutter, O., Trautwein, W. 1956. Vagal and sympathetic effects on the pacemaker fibers in the sinus venosus of the heart. *J. Gen. Physiol.* 39:715–33

64. Irisawa, H. 1978. Comparative physiology of the cardiac pacemaker mechanism. *Physiol. Rev.* 58:461–98

65. Irisawa, H., Brown, H. F., Giles, W. 1992. Cardiac pacemaker mechanisms. *Physiol. Rev.* In press

66. Irisawa, H., Hagiwara, N. 1991. Ionic currents in sinoatrial node cells. *J. Cardiovasc. Electrophysiol.* 2:531–40

67. Irisawa, H., Yanagihara, K. 1980. The slow inward current of the rabbit sinoatrial nodal cell. In *The Slow Inward Current and Cardiac Arrhythmias*, ed. D. P. Zipes, J. C. Bailey, V. Elharrar, pp. 265–84. The Hague:Nijhoff

68. Kameyama, M., Hescheler, J., Hofmann, F., Trautwein, W. 1986. Modulation of Ca current during the phosphorylation cycle in the guinea-pig heart. *Pflügers Arch.* 407:123–28

69. Kim, D., Lewis, D. L., Graziadei, L., Neer, E. J., Bar-Sagi, D., Clapham, D. E. 1989. G-protein βγ subunits activate the cardiac muscarinic K channel via phospholipase A2. *Nature* 337:557–60

70. Kurachi, Y., Nakajima, T., Sugimoto, T. 1986. Acetylcholine activation of K channel in cell-free membrane of atrial cells. *Am. J. Physiol.* 251:H681–84

71. Ling, G., Gerard, R. W. 1949. The normal membrane potential of frog sartorius muscle. *J. Cell. Comp. Physiol.* 34:383–96

72. Logothetis, D. E., Kurachi, Y., Galper, J., Neer, E. J., Clapham, D. E. 1987. The βγ subunits of GTP-binding proteins activate the muscarinic K channels in heart. *Nature* 325:321–26

73. Matsuoka, S., Ehara, T., Noma, A. 1990. Chloride-sensitive nature of the adrenaline-induced current in guinea-pig cardiac myocytes. *J. Physiol.* 425:579–98

74. Maylie, J., Morad, M. 1984. Ionic currents responsible for the generation of pacemaker current in the rabbit sino-atrial node. *J. Physiol.* 355:215–35

75. McAllister, R. E., Noble, D. 1966. The time and voltage dependence of the slow outward current in cardiac Purkinje fibres. *J. Physiol.* 186:632–62

76. Nakayama, T., Kuraki, Y., Noma, A., Irisawa, H. 1984. Action potential and membrane currents of single pacemaker cells of the rabbit heart. *Pflügers Arch.* 402:248–57

77. Nastuk, W. L., Hodgkin, A. L. 1950. The electrical activity of single muscle

fibres. *J. Cell. Comp. Physiol.* 35:39–73

78. Noble, D. 1984. The surprising heart: a review of recent progress in cardiac electrophysiology. *J. Physiol.* 353:1–50

79. Noble, D., Noble, S. 1984. A model of sino-atrial node electrical activity based on a modification of the DiFrancesco-Noble (1984) equations. *Proc. R. Soc. London Ser. B* 222:295–304

80. Noble, D., Tsien, R. W. 1968. The kinetics and rectifier properties of the slow potassium current in calf Purkinje fibres. *J. Physiol.* 195:185–214

81. Noma, A., Irisawa, H. 1976. Membrane currents in the rabbit sinoatrial node cell as studied by the double microelectrode method. *Pflügers Arch.* 366:45–52

82. Noma, A., Kotake, H., Irisawa, H. 1980. Slow inward current and its role in mediating the chronotropic effect of epinephrine in the rabbit sinoatrial node. *Pflügers Arch.* 388:1–9

83. Noma, A., Morad, M., Irisawa, H. 1983. Does the "pacemaker current" generate the diastolic depolarization in the rabbit SA node cells? *Pflügers Arch.* 397: 190–94

84. Noma, A., Trautwein, W. 1978. Relaxation of the ACh-induced potassium current in the rabbit sino-atrial node. *Pflügers Arch.* 377:193–200

85. Noma, A., Yanagihara, K., Irisawa, H. 1977. Inward membrane currents in the rabbit sino-atrial node cell. *Pflügers Arch.* 372:43–51

86. Osterrieder, W., Brum, G., Hescheler J., Trautwein, W., Hofmann, F., Flockerzi, V. 1982. Injection of sub-units of cyclic AMP-dependent protein kinase into cardiac myocytes modulates Ca current. *Nature* 298:576–78

87. Peper, K., Trautwein, W. 1969. A note on the pacemaker current in Purkinje fibres. *Pflügers Arch.* 309:356–61

88. Pfaffinger, P. J., Martin, J. M., Hunter, D. D., Nathanson, N. M., Hille, B. 1985. GTP-binding proteins couple cardiac muscarinic receptors to a K channel. *Nature* 317:536–38

89. Porciatti, F., DiFrancesco, D. 1990. High Na permeability of L-type Ca channels in isolated rabbit SA node cells. *J. Physiol.* 426:18P

90. Reuter, H. 1983. Calcium channel modulation by neurotransmitters, enzymes and drugs. *Nature* 301:569–74

91. Reuter, H., Scholz, H. 1977. The regulation of Ca conductance of cardiac muscle by adrenaline. *J. Physiol.* 264: 49–62

92. Sabachnikoff, T. 1901. I manoscritti di Leonardo da Vinci della Reale Biblioteca di Windsor. Dell' Anatomia. Fogli B- folio 13-recto. Torino:Roux e Viarengo

93. Sakmann, B., Noma, A., Trautwein, W. 1983. Acetylcholine activation of single muscarinic K channels in isolated pacemaker cells of the mammalian heart. *Nature* 303:250–53

94. Seyama, I. 1976. Characteristics of the anion channel in sino-atrial node cell of the rabbit. *J. Physiol.* 294:447–60

95. Shuba, Y. M., Hesslinger, B., Trautwein, W., McDonald, T. F., Pelzer, D. 1990. Whole-cell calcium current in guinea-pig ventricular myocytes dyalised with guanine nucleotides. *J. Physiol.* 424: 205–28

96. Simmons, M. A., Hartzell, H. C. 1987. A quantitative analysis of the acetylcholine-activated potassium current in single cells from frog atrium. *Pflügers Arch.* 409:454–61

97. Soejima, M., Noma, A. 1984. Mode of regulation of the ACh- sensitive K channel by the muscarinic receptors in the rabbit atrial cells. *Pflügers Arch.* 400:424–31

98. Ten Eick, R., Nawrath, H., McDonald, T. F., Trautwein, W. 1976. On the mechanism of the negative inotropic effect of acetylcholine. *Pflügers Arch.* 361:207–13

99. Toshe, N., Kameyama, M., Irisawa, H. 1987. Intracellular Ca^{2+} and protein kinase C modulate K current in guinea-pig heart cell. *Am. J. Physiol.* 253: H1321–24

100. Trautwein, W., Hescheler, J. 1990. Regulation of cardiac L- type calcium current by phosphorylation and G proteins. *Annu. Rev. Physiol.* 52:257–74

101. Tsien, R. W. 1974. Effect of epinephrine on the pacemaker potassium current of cardiac Purkinje fibers. *J. Gen. Physiol.* 64:293–319

102. van Ginneken, A. C. G., Giles, W. 1991. Voltage clamp measurements of the hyperpolarization-activated inward current i_f in single cells from rabbit sino-atrial node. *J. Physiol.* 434:57–83

103. Vassalle, M. 1966. Analysis of cardiac pacemaker potential using a voltage clamp technique. *Am. J. Physiol.* 210:1335–41

104. Weidmann, S. 1951. Effect of current flow on membrane potential of cardiac muscle. *J. Physiol.* 115:227–36

105. Weidmann, S. 1980. Historical perspective. See Ref. 67, pp. 3–9

106. West, T. C. 1955. Ultramicroelectrode recording from the cardiac pacemaker. *J. Pharm. Exp. Ther.* 115:283–90

107. Yanagihara, K., Irisawa, H. 1980. Inward current activated during hyperpolarization in the rabbit sinoatrial node cell. *Pflügers Arch.* 385:11–19

108. Yanagihara, K., Irisawa, H. 1980. Potassium current during the pacemaker depolarization in rabbit sinoatrial node cell. *Pflügers Arch.* 388:255–60

109. Yanagihara, K., Noma, A., Irisawa, H. 1980. Reconstruction of sinoatrial node pacemaker potential based on voltage clamp experiments. *Jpn. J. Physiol.* 30:841–57

110. Yatani, A., Codina, J., Brown, A. M., Birnbaumer, L. 1987. Direct activation of mammalian atrial muscarinic potassium channels by GTP regulatory protein GK. *Science* 235:207–11

111. Yatani, A., Codina, J., Imoto, Y. Reeves, J. P., Birnbaumer, L., Brown, A. M. 1987. Direct regulation of mammalian cardiac calcium channels by a G-protein. *Science* 238:1288–92

112. Yatani, A., Okabe, K., Codina, J., Birnbaumer, A., Brown, A. M. 1990. Heart rate regulation by G protein acting on the cardiac pacemaker channel. *Science* 249:1163–66

113. Yazawa, K., Kameyama, M. 1990. Mechanism of receptor-mediated modulation of the delayed outward potassium current in guinea-pig ventricular myocytes. *J. Physiol.* 421:135–50

114. Zaza, A., Maccaferri, G., Mangoni, M., DiFrancesco, D. 1991. Intracellular calcium does not directly modulate cardiac pacemaker (i_f) channels. *Pflügers Arch.* 419:662–64

Annu. Rev. Physiol. 1993. 55:473–501

THE USE OF PHYSICAL METHODS IN DETERMINING GRAMICIDIN CHANNEL STRUCTURE AND FUNCTION

David D. Busath

Department of Physiology, Brown University School of Medicine, Providence, Rhode Island 02912

KEY WORDS: membrane, channel

INTRODUCTION

Various membrane proteins have been sequenced and their topology relative to the membrane identified using biochemical clues. It is desirable to identify their atomic structures to allow the mechanism of function to be determined, but membrane proteins do not yield readily to X-ray crystallography and two-dimensional NMR, so physiologists presently use other physical methods to infer membrane protein structure. The gramicidin channel provides an instructive model probably because it is the best characterized membrane protein.

The gramicidin peptide dimerizes spontaneously in lipid bilayers to form single-file cation channels that last a random duration and then dissociate again. Voltage or agonist dependence of the formation rate and channel lifetime are limited to subtle effects attributed primarily to membrane thinning by electrostriction and to interactions between the peptide and the permeating ions. Therefore, the main function of the channel as a membrane protein is its selective permeability to monovalent alkali metal cations, ammonium, formamidinium, hydrazine, and methylammonium, with the exclusion of all anions, multivalent cations, and larger organic cations. This is thought to be

473

0066-4278/93/0315–0473$02.00

accomplished by the limited and effectively rigid diameter of the pore formed by the peptide backbone. The side chains project outward and modulate the channel conductance. They strongly affect the dimer stability, presumably through specific (hydrogen bonding) and nonspecific (hydrophobic) interactions.

This article reviews the determination of the molecular structure (secondary, tertiary, and quarternary) starting from the point where only the primary sequence was known. We first discuss the basis for early modeling as a β structure, the physical methods used to test the models, and the advantages and limitations of these older methods, and then review the most recent progress on structure and function.

Previous reviews have addressed the experimentally observed permeability properties of gramicidin channels (1, 10, 48, 54), the analysis of peptide backbone structures (141, 177), the use of NMR to estimate ion association and dissociation rates (169), the effect of gramicidin on lipids (40, 44), and progress on modeling the energetics of cation transport (80, 81, 118). Some of these topics are revisited with emphasis on subsequent work and new interpretations of older results. The effects of the peptide on lipid structure are not considered here.

INITIAL MODELS

The gramicidin sequence is unusual in that D- amino acids are located at all even-numbered positions except position two, which is a (non-chiral) Gly. Urry and colleagues proposed a single-stranded π(L,D)- or β- helix as a likely conformation for the peptide channel because it optimizes the number of intrapeptide hydrogen bonds as would be expected in the lipid environment, and because such a helix would have about the right diameter to allow passage of the then known permeant ions (160, 165). The intramonomer hydrogen bonds follow a parallel β-pleated sheet pattern. One helix is too short to span the bilayer, but two monomers of the same pitch and helicity can associate end-to-end with six antiparallel β-sheet hydrogen bonds. Intra- and intermonomer hydrogen bonding are optimized when there are (approximately) an even number of amino acids per turn. The length of a dimer with 6.3 amino acids per turn is 25 Å, sufficient to span the hydrophobic portion of di- and monoglyceride bilayers.

The single-stranded β-helix represents a special case of the β-barrel family. Other members include six- and eight-stranded antiparallel β-barrels, eight-stranded parallel α/β-barrels (24, 121), and large antiparallel β-barrels (12–20 strands) (e.g. 76, 181). This relationship is pertinent because an eight-stranded antiparallel β-barrel structure has been proposed as the pore-lining region of the voltage-gated potassium channel (19, 20, 46) and of an epithelial anion channel (113) on the basis of arguments similar to those Urry used to predict the gramicidin structure.

Shortly after the single-stranded β-helix was proposed for gramicidin channels, it was noted that a double-stranded helix would also be possible (171) in either parallel or antiparallel conformation. Higher level oligomers of gramicidin (i.e. barrels), although plausible, have not been discussed in the literature. In general, antiparallel barrels must have an even number of strands to form a regular hydrogen-bond pattern. Parallel barrels could be formed with either an even or an odd number of strands, although in the latter, slight distortions in the hydrogen-bond pattern would result. Except for side chain crowding, there is no obvious reason to exclude barrels with three or more strands from consideration. Double-stranded helices of gramicidin have been shown to exist in organic solvents and, under exceptional circumstances, to form channels in lipid bilayers, but the most-studied ion channel is now well-established to be the single-stranded helix dimer formed from monomers floating in each leaflet of the lipid bilayer (107).

Because even-numbered amino-acids in gramicidin have D- chirality, the side chains all project on one side of the β-structure instead of on alternating sides as found in all-L proteins. Therefore, the single- and double-stranded gramicidin structures could have all side-chains projecting either into or out of the helix. Urry proposed outward pointing side chains, allowing the hydrophobic side chains to project into the lipid, a hydrophilic peptide backbone to form the channel, and the number of amino acids per turn to be small so that a dimer of single helices could span the bilayer.

MUTATIONS

Channel structure models have been tested with mutations, analogous to the process of site-directed mutagenesis. Dimers covalently linked at their N-termini with malonyl (14, 165) or related (111) connectors, or with variants of tartaric acid (144, 145) had conductances similar to that of gramicidin A, but exhibited prolonged channel lifetimes. If the conformation of the connector is photosensitive, channel conductance may be switched between two states by light exposure (146, 147). On the other hand, methylation of the N-terminal formyl residue reduces channel lifetime (154). Charged groups at the normally neutral N-terminus prevent channel formation (3, 11, 12), whereas at the normally neutral C-terminus, they do not (4, 13), which suggests that the C-terminus falls near the aqueous boundary. If the charged C-terminus peptide was placed only on one side of the membrane, channels did not form (e.g. 123), whereas when placed on both sides, channels formed readily, which indicates that parallel double-helices or higher order β-barrels do not form. The formation of channels with charged C-terminus peptide added to both sides of the bilayer is consistent with the antiparallel double-helix model, but the failure of charged N-terminal peptides to form channels is not. Taken together with the demonstration of head-to-head covalently linked dimers, these results yielded convincing proof that the gramicidin channel is formed from dimers with the N-termini in the hydrophobic bilayer.

Other backbone alterations include the appendage of a titratable acidic group of variable length at the N-terminus (3), which produces pH-sensitive channels, a lipid group at the C-terminus (89), which stabilizes the channel, and various changes in the length of the peptide (95, 103, 124, 153, 163). The structurally conservative deletion mutant, des-L-Val^7-D-Val^8 gramicidin A, had a decreased channel lifetime as expected for a mismatch between channel length, and bilayer thickness, but unexpectedly a 35% lower conductance in 1 M KCl, which was ascribed to a decrease in the rate of second ion entry (measured by NMR) and thus of the quasi-knockoff kinetics (163).

Recently, additional charged C-terminal peptides have been tested. Desethanolamine gramicidin A forms two conductance populations whose conductance, but not relative frequency of occurrence is affected by pH, as is expected for channels of two different conformations, each with titratable end-groups (120). O-pyromellityl gramicidin produces a single conductance when pure, but when mixed with another analogue, forms homodimers and two types of heterodimers, which indicates that the conducting channel is a dimer (39). Taurine^{16}-gramicidin A has the same conductance as gramicidin A at high (1 M) ionic strength, but higher conductance at low (0.1 M) ionic strength (123). Heterodimers with gramicidin A in 0.1 M NaCl yield a current-voltage relation with increased conductance in both limbs (77). This indicates that facilitation of ion entry into the channel has more impact on conductance than slowing of ion translocation and that slowing exit has less impact than facilitating translocation, which suggests that at moderate membrane potentials and Na$^+$ concentrations, entry is the most rate limiting factor, followed by translocation and exit.

The effects of side chain mutations on channel permeability and conductance heterogeneity have been studied. Mutations of L-Val^1 in the center of the bilayer to various polar amino acids (2, 16) reduced the maximum channel Na$^+$ conductance without much effect on the apparent affinity for Na$^+$. The effect did not correlate with electron withdrawing power of the side chains, which indicates that their electric dipole potential was primarily responsible (88). Mutation of one or more of the four Trps to Phe (15, 17, 61, 63, 116) or naphtylalanine (43) lowered the channel conductance, presumably because of the reduced dipole potential of the side chain. Dramatic effects on channel lifetime suggest that side chain-lipid interactions stabilize the channel (17). Several uncoded side chains (e.g. naphthyalanine) differing from Trp in the direction of their dipole and in hydrophobicity also had marked effects on conductance, but the correlation with the dipole moment was weak, which suggests that the effects come from multiple factors, possibly including orientation of the side chain dipole produced by local hydrogen bond, electrostatic, and lipid interactions (42). A5L (164) and L7A (115) analogues reduce the heterogeneity in conductance states observed in single channel conductance, possibly by modifying the population of Trp^{11} (172) and Trp^{13} orientations.

The helix handedness for several gramicidin analogues has been defined by their ability to form heterodimers with gramicidin A^+ (right-handed, in which L- and D-amino acids alternate starting with L-) or gramicidin A^- (left-handed, starting with D-) (47, 77, 90, 131). Positive sequences are found only to yield right-handed helices, whereas negative sequences yield only left-handed helices (90), irrespective of side chains and terminators. Preliminary potential energy calculations predicted only slight energy differences between right- and left-handed helices for the positive sequence, but computations were not done for the negative sequence (173). The comparison ought to be a sensitive test for modern peptide backbone force computations.

SINGLE CHANNEL NOISE AND CURRENT FLUCTUATIONS

Spontaneous brief closures or flicker blocks have been found in analogues of gramicidin A (128, 154) and, although shorter, have been found in gramicidin A itself (122, 138, 137). Similar blocks can be induced by the addition of iminium ions to the bath (65), although the mechanism is presumably different, namely the slow passage of the iminium ion through the channel, as suggested by the reduction in block duration with voltage. Between the spontaneous flicker blocks, the single channel noise is white to attainable frequencies and has been found to differ from the expected shot noise, being lower or higher depending on the permeant ion, the voltage, the bilayer thickness, and the solvent (58, 59, 138). Lower noise was attributed to single-filing of the ions in the channels, whereas excess noise appears to reflect conformational fluctuations that occur primarily in the unoccupied channel, last ~ 1 μs, and are associated with a reduced rate of ion entry (60). The more conductive conformation may have several inwardly rotated carbonyl oxygens that could facilitate cation binding, as was suggested to explain selectivity (165) and temperature effects on single channel conductance (162).

FLUORESCENCE, ENERGY TRANSFER, AND SURFACE POTENTIAL

Trps 9, 11, 13, and 15 appear to play a significant role in the behavior of the peptide. As mentioned above, when they are mutated to apolar side chains, the channel conductance is decreased. They may also help to orient the monomer with respect to the lipid-water interface. Analysis of the energy transfer between Trp side chains and n-(9-anthroyloxy) fatty acid membrane probes demonstrated that the Trp side chains are located near the lipid-water interface (21). This model study demonstrated the usefulness of energy transfer studies for locating the Trp side chains in other membrane proteins.

The surface potential of a lipid-gramicidin monolayer at an air-water interface in a Langmuir trough can be measured with a matched pair of Americium 241 electrodes placed above the interface on either side of the teflon barrier used to compress the monolayer. The electrodes measure the difference in electric potential in the air directly, which is equal to the difference in the electric potential drops across the two interfaces. Lipid monolayers generally yield a positive potential (acyl tail relative to polar head group) of a few tenths of a volt, independent of head group structure. Tryptophan dipoles are expected to align with this head group field and produce a contrary field that reduces the surface potential. Measurements of surface potential at lipid/peptide mole ratios and surface pressures where gramicidin is thought to form monomeric β-helices with the helix axis perpendicular to the interface yielded a potential lower by about 80 mV with gramicidin A than with gramicidin M^- (in which all four tryptophans have been replaced with phenylalanine) (64). This helps explain how tryptophan side chains enhance conductance: they reduce a surface potential that normally inhibits ion entry into the bilayer region.

CIRCULAR DICHROISM

The double-helix conformation of gramicidin A can be distinguished from the single-helix channel form by the circular dichroism (CD) spectrum, which is positive from 190–210 nm and negative from 210–260 nm for the double helix and vice versa for the single helix (99, 175). In liposomes, the double helix form is converted to single helix by heating at 75°C for 24 hr; alternatively, the single helix form is obtained immediately when the peptide is added from very polar solvents such as trifluoroethanol (99). This result has been nicely confirmed with high performance liquid chromatography (HPLC) methods (see below). The ellipticity in the region from 230–260 nm is strongly affected by the Trp side chains, but replacement by Phe (which doesn't absorb in the same region) allows the determination of the helical handedness. The ellipticity is positive for gramicidin M^-, which is appropriate for a left-handed helix (62), consistent with gramicidin A^+ forming a right-handed helix.

HIGH-PERFORMANCE LIQUID CHROMATOGRAPHY

HPLC, both analytical and preparative, has been used to purify the peptide (91, 143), and thin layer chromatography (TLC) has been used to separate conformational species (171). Recently, size-exclusion HPLC has replaced TLC in careful studies of the rate and lipid-dependence of interconversion between single- and double-helical forms (e.g. 9, 23). In this technique, gramicidin molecules are first incubated in organic solvents with different concentrations of phosphatidylcholines and then separated on a column according to the size of the peptide aggregate. The peptides can be assumed not to change aggregation state during passage through the column. In tetrahydrofuran, lipid was found to increase the apparent dimer dissociation constant by four to five orders of magnitude. The lipid:peptide mole fraction dependence suggested that one to two lipid molecules were sufficient to induce monomerization (22). Alkanes and triacylglycerols do not alter the conformational equilibrium, which indicates that the diglyceride phosphate is responsible for inducing the monomeric state (23). The technique has been extended to small unilamelar vesicles and lysolecithin micelles (8, 9) where it was clearly demonstrated that the ratio of double helix to single helix remains quite stable as the peptide is incorporated into lipid vesicles, sonicated on ice, and then injected into the lipid-stripping (22) size-exclusion HPLC column. The conformations were confirmed with circular dichroism. Conversion to the monomer form by overnight incubation at 68°C in lysolecithin micelles was also demonstrated by the same technique. This approach provides a quantitative new assay for the conformation ratio and confirms earlier findings that the minimal inter-conversion between states takes place in the bilayer (85).

NUCLEAR MAGNETIC RESONANCE

NMR has been used to (a) locate the cation-binding sites, (b) measure cation-binding affinity and rate constants for entry and exit, (c) determine the conformation of the backbone and Trp side chains, and (d) measure the backbone torsion angles and libration kinetics. The first was done with ^{13}C NMR in lysolecithin micelles; the second with quadrupolar ion resonance in lysolecithin micelles, with ^{205}Tl competition studies in dimyristoyl-phosphatidylcholine (DMPC) vesicles, and with Mg^{2+} induced paramagnetic proton relaxation in SDS micelles; the third with two dimensional- and proton exchange ^{1}H NMR in SDS micelles; and the fourth with solid state and oriented multilayer ^{15}N NMR. These topics will be addressed separately.

Ion-Binding Site

Before the locations of the cation binding sites in the channel were determined with X-ray diffraction (see below), Urry and colleagues identified the approximate locations using ^{13}C NMR with peptides labeled at the carbonyl carbons of individual residues (166, 168). When Na^+, Tl^+, or Ba^{2+} bind to the carbonyl oxygen of the labeled carbon, they cause a chemical shift by electrostatic interaction with the carbonyl oxygen. It was found that the largest effects were in residues 11 and 13, with lesser effects in residues 9, 14, and 15, and no effects in residues 1, 3, 5, 7, and 8. Carbonyl 14 was strongly affected by Ba^{2+} binding. These results were originally interpreted in terms of the left-handed β-helix to indicate that the binding sites were separated by approximately 20 Å. In the right-handed helix, the C-O vectors of carbonyls 11 and 13 point toward the center of the bilayer and that of carbonyl 14 points toward the water rather than vice-versa as in the left-handed helix. In the context of the right-handed helix, subsequently shown to be the correct structure (see below), the binding sites are therefore farther into the channel.

Roux (125) gives the positions of the probable Na^+-binding sites in the right-handed helix based on free energy calculations. The one nearest the position measured with X-ray diffraction is site 6 at 9.3 Å from the center of the channel, where Na^+ interacts with carbonyls 10, 15, 8, and 13. Because site 6 does not include carbonyl 11, this position does not fit as well with the carbonyl chemical shift data as site 5 at 7.75 Å, where the ion interacts with carbonyls 8, 13, 6, and 11. Yet both site 5 and site 6 contain carbonyl 8, which showed no chemical shift. These conflicting details cannot be immediately rationalized. Nevertheless, the carbonyl carbon chemical shift data point to a binding site near the channel entrance and, moreover, demonstrate that the ion dwell-time in the center of the channel is small under equilibrium conditions, consistent with the notion that there is a broad energy barrier separating the binding sites at the entrances.

At a concentration of Tl^+ (83 mM) sufficient to assure double occupancy of the channel, the chemical shift profile was similar to that obtained in conditions favoring single occupancy (3 mM Tl^+ or 100 mM Na^+), which suggests that the binding positions are unaffected by the binding of a second ion at the opposite site (166). However, more recent results indicate an outward shift of the bound cations with double occupancy (D. W. Urry, personal communication).

The location of divalent cation-binding sites has been determined in SDS micelles by means of induced paramagnetic proton relaxation to provide estimates of the distances from several peptide protons and bound Mn^{2+} (56). The cation binds 17.5 Å from the center of the channel. At this distance ($\sim$5 Å) from the entrance, the ion must remain surrounded by one hydration shell, which renders it too large to enter the channel.

Ion-Binding Affinity, Entry, and Exit Rate Constants

Urry and colleagues have also characterized the first and second ion-binding affinities and entry and exit rate constants for the alkali metal cations using ion chemical shift and NMR relaxation methods. The exit rate constants at high concentrations (for the doubly-occupied channel) were particularly accessible. In addition, the exit rate constant for Na^+ from the singly-occupied channel, measured from the concentration dependence of the line-width at half-intensity, was found to be lower ($\sim 3 \times 10^5$/s) than the rate constant for exit from the doubly occupied channel ($\sim 2 \times 10^7$/s). For this reason, the first ion-binding parameters are referred to as tight-site parameters, and those of second-ion binding as weak-site parameters. These results have been summarized thoroughly in two reviews (161, 166). The tight- and weak-site binding constants and the weak-site exit rate constants for the alkali metal cations are shown in Table 1.

The conclusion that it is possible to measure both tight- and weak-binding affinities is based upon observed curvature in the plot of excess longitudinal relaxation rate for Na^+ and plateaus in the semilog plot of ion-induced chemical shifts in ^{13}C-labeled carbonyl carbons vs concentration for K^+, Rb^+, and Tl^+. Monoi confirmed the finding for the excess longitudinal relaxation rate for Na^+ (101) and measured Na^+ binding and rate constants consistent with those in Table 1. The observation of a weak-site affinity is important because it explains channel conductance. The entry rate is diffusion limited and similar to the ion passage rate. To the extent that the exit rate constant is smaller than that for entry yielding a binding constant of >1 M^{-1}, the channel throughput should be limited by exit, and smaller than actually observed ($>10^7$ ions/s). Urry has argued (166) that for the alkali metal cations at moderate concentrations (e.g. above ~ 50 mM), conductance occurs by what is referred to above as a quasi-knockoff mechanism: binding of a second ion raises the exit rate constant (for both ions) to the weak-site value, which is similar to the diffusion-limited entry rate (166).

Hinton and colleagues have measured the Tl^+ binding affinity with ^{205}Tl

Table 1 Binding constants and exit rate constants for alkali metal cations

Ion	$k_{b,tight}$ (M^{-1})	$k_{b,weak}$ (M^{-1})	$k_{off,weak}$ $(\times 10^7$/s)
Li^+	25	0.77	1.7
Na^+	30	2.6	2.1
K^+	~ 50	8.3	2.6
Rb^+	~ 60	4.	6.6
Cs^+	60	4.	5.9

(Taken with permission from 166.)

NMR (71, 136) and have estimated the thermodynamic parameters for the binding of NH_4^+, Ag^+, and the alkali metal cations, (72, 70) and the major divalent cations (69) using Tl^+-competition binding. They found evidence of double occupancy for Tl^+ in DMPC vesicles (136) in that the Tl^+ chemical shift was positive at low concentrations, but negative at high concentrations. The competition studies (72) were performed with low Tl^+ concentrations and were analyzed in terms of a one-site-per-channel model. They give estimates for the alkali metal affinities of the gramicidin monomer in lysolecithin micelles, which are similar to the tight-site affinities in Table 1. The enthalpy and entropy of binding (70) are both negative and increase with the sequence $K^+ < Cs^+ < Rb^+ < Na^+$ Li^+, in a pattern consistent with the enthalpy and entropy of transfer between water and dimethylformamide, a model of the peptide carbonyl. The enthalpy of binding ranges from -4.9 to -3.1 kcal/M and the entropy from -7.8 to -3.3 cal/deg M. Ag^+, Tl^+, and NH_4^+ have higher binding affinities than the alkali metal cations. The divalent cations bind with affinities that are similar to or higher than the alkali metal cations (69). As stated above, they bind outside of the channel rather than in the Tl^+ site, but nevertheless compete with Tl^+ for binding.

Channel Structure

Early ^1H-, ^{13}C-, and ^{19}F-NMR studies demonstrated that the channel form in phosphatidylcholine vesicles was the head-to-head dimer (e.g. 180). Subsequently, the internal and Cartesian coordinates for the channel form of the peptide in SDS micelles have been determined by analysis of nuclear Overhauser effect, spin-spin coupling constants, and amide proton solvent accessibility with ^1H NMR (e.g. 32). The refined structure for the right-handed $\beta^{6.3}$ helix dimer was first published in Russian (6) and is now available in English (7). This backbone structure has been confirmed independently using SDS micelles (157) and dodecylphosphocholine micelles, (D. W. Urry, personal communication), and does not differ significantly from previous models of the right-handed $\beta^{6.3}$ helix. The dihedral conformations were shown to be stable, except for those of the ethanolamine terminus, the Gly^2-Ala^3 peptide group, and the side chains of L-Val^7 and D-Leu^4 (7). It was suggested that the mobile sections explain the observed conductance dispersity.

Backbone Dihedrals and Kinetics

Additional resolution can be obtained with NMR of membrane proteins by using oriented phospholipid multilayers and examining anisotropy in the chemical shift, i.e. differences that result from rotating the planes of the bilayers in the magnetic field. Recent applications utilize ^{13}C-labeled carbonyl (139, 140) and Trp indole C2 (135) carbons, ^{2}H-labeled formyl (67) and Val-3 Cα (68) hydrogens, and ^{15}N-labeled backbone amide nitrogens (37, 105, 106, 156). A related method makes use of the axial symmetry of the electric field to put constraints on the orientation of the Cα-H bonds of ^{2}H-labeled backbone atoms deduced from quadrupolar splittings in unoriented DMPC dispersions (117). The channel has been demonstrated to be a right-handed helix (37, 67, 105, 117, 156), with C=O bonds aligned approximately parallel to the helix axis (37, 140, 156). Leu-4 carbonyl libration into the channel is limited to ~15° (106). The dynamics of the backbone motion should be accessible with this method. The outer turn of the helix (residues 10–15) is more mobile than the inner turns (residues 1–9) (140, 68) and rotates into the channel when Na$^+$ binds (139). The tryptophans were found to have the same orientation in phosphatidylcholine as had been found in SDS micelles by two-dimensional NMR (135).

X-RAY CRYSTALLOGRAPHY

Ideally, the crystal structure of the channel form of the peptide is needed. All solutions to date have been for the double-helical form, which has been dubbed the pore structure (see 177 for a review). Co-crystals of peptide and phospholipid have been prepared and found to diffract to 2 Å resolution (178). The unit cell appears to contain one gramicidin monomer and two lipid molecules, with the lipids apparently packed in a bilayer-like pattern. Atomic coordinates have not yet been reported, but it is hoped that the peptide will have the single-helix channel structure.

INFRARED SPECTROSCOPY AND NORMAL MODES ANALYSIS

Infrared absorption depends on the frequency of normal modes of bond stretching and bond angle bending. The amide I band reflects the peptide backbone hydrogen bond C=O stretching and differs according to secondary structure, occurring at 1650 (cm^{-1}) for alpha helix, and at 1630 (cm^{-1}) for parallel and antiparallel β-sheet. For gramicidin in DMPC or di-palmitoylphosphatidylcholine (DPPC) liposomes, the amide I band was found at 1635 (cm^{-1}), which was interpreted to be consistent with the single-stranded β-helix (41). However, the solvent from which the lipid-peptide mixture was freeze-dried prior to dispersement and vortexing was not re-ported, so the conformation of the gramicidin, now known to depend on this factor, may have been double-helix.

Polarized Fourier-transform infrared-attenuated total-reflection spectros-copy was used with gramicidin in DMPC, DPPC, and dipalmitoylphosphatidylethanolamine (DPPE) multibilayers to determine the orientation of the channel axis relative to the bilayer (108). For this purpose, the dichroic ratio of the amide band was measured as a function of incubation time at temperatures above that of the gel-liquid-crystalline phase transition. It was found to increase with time over the period of 1 hr for DMPC, consistent with a change in channel axis orientation from parallel to perpendicular to the bilayer. In DPPE it never changed, consistent with the known rigidity of such bilayers. The amide I peak was at 1639 cm^{-1} in DMPC bilayers. However, here again no evidence was provided that the channel structure was a single rather than double helix.

Other infrared absorption peaks can also be interpreted by comparison with predicted normal modes of vibration, computed using standard protein force fields. Naik & Krimm predicted Raman-active amide I bands at 1666 and 1668 cm^{-1} for double-helix structures, and at $\sim$ 1650 cm^{-1} for the single-stranded helix (104). After incubation of the peptide in lysolecithin vesicles at 68°C for 8–15 h, the absorption band shifted from 1665 to 1654 cm^{-1}. When the sample was dried out, a strong band returned at 1671 cm^{-1} with a small band remaining at 1650 cm^{-1}. The conversion during incubation (which has also been shown by CD to yield the single-helix conformation) was a remarkable validation of the force field used for the normal mode calculations and of the ability of Raman spectroscopy to distinguish between similar structures. However, the complexity of the predicted and observed bands, and the variety of conformations assumable by the peptide also demonstrated the need for great care in analyzing infrared spectra.

The vibrations referred to above are of high frequency and not likely to be cooperative with ion motions in the channel. On the basis of potential energy calculations, Venkatachalam & Urry proposed that coordinated inward rotations of carbonyl oxygens (peptide librations) might occur during cation passage, perhaps forming a metastable state that would facilitate ion passage by better coordination of the ions (174). If librations occur on a time scale comparable to that of ion passage, they could strongly affect ion kinetics (93). With this in mind, Roux & Karplus analyzed the slow normal modes of vibration of the peptide backbone using the CHARMM (chemistry at Harvard molecular mechanics) force field to evaluate the possibility of low-frequency librations of a meta-stable (inwardly-rotated) state, or of cooperative behavior between peptide carbonyls. They found no long range correlations between peptide librations, but they did observe normal modes of carbonyl librations as expected. These had the lowest of the frequencies computed for the channel (75–175 cm^{-1}). However, this wavelength corresponds to a vibration period of $\sim$0.5 ps, still three to four orders of magnitude faster than ion motions. It seems unlikely that vibrations would be slowed to this degree by lipids or waters, which were not included in the calculation. Computations of the effect of ions on the channel during molecular dynamics trajectories indicate that ion-induced peptide librations are localized to the neighborhood of the ion (125, 127). The high frequency of librational modes predicts that the channel would quickly relax back to its native structure and thus have no memory of ion passage. On the other hand, slower motions on the ns time scale have been postulated to account for solid state-oriented multilayer NMR results (T. Cross, personal communication).

Raman spectroscopy can also be used to evaluate the hydrophobicity of the tryptophan side chain environment and to measure χ_2, the dihedral angle of the Cβ-Cγ bond (155). This is important for determination of the conformation of the tryptophan side chains, a subject of considerable interest because of their demonstrated impact on channel conductance and lifetime (e.g. 17). The main questions are the orientation of the indole dipoles, which determine the contribution to the energy profile of the electric field (50, 129, A. Dorigo, D. Busath, unpublished observations), the extent of hydrogen-bonding with lipid head groups, and the motion and mobility of the Trp side chains upon ion binding. For these measurements, gramicidin was incorporated into phosphatidylcholine vesicles [DLPC (dilaurylphosphatidylcholine), DMPC, or DPPC] and verified by CD to be in the channel conformation (167, 176). Based on the relative position of one of the absorption bands for tryptophan, the χ_2 of the tryptophan side chains was determined to be $\pm 90°$. The peak was as narrow with all four Trps (9, 11, 13, and 15) as is typically found with only one, from which it was concluded that all have the same χ_2.

Tryptophan has another degree of freedom in that its χ_1 can assume approximate positions of ± 60, or $+180$. The ratio of absorption intensities for a doublet at 1360 and 1341 cm^{-1} was high in liposomes, which indicates that the tryptophan indole rings are located in the hydrophobic tail region of the liposomes. The ratio became large in thicker bilayers (DPPC>DMPC>DLPC), which demonstrates that some of the tryptophan side chains were exposed to water in the thinner bilayer, but the position of the 1549 cm^{-1} band did not shift, thus indicating that the χ_2 did not change.

The rate of deuterium exchange on the indole N-H was followed using the intensity of the 1385 cm^{-1} band as a measure of water accessibility. In DPPC bilayers, the kinetics of exchange for each of the four tryptophans was distinguishable. Upon Na$^+$ binding, the exchange kinetics in DMPC and DLPC bilayers changed in a way suggesting that the Trp indole rings move toward the bilayer center.

By combined analysis of the Raman results, it was possible to reduce the number of consistent models for Trp side chain positions from 6^4 (six position for each of four tryptophans) to six. Two were favorable because they featured W11 and W13 as the second and third most accessible to water, consistent with the deuterium exchange kinetics as well as the NMR results on the sensitivity of the chemical shifts of the carbonyl carbons 11 and 13 to Na^+ binding (166).

Thus Raman studies of the Trp absorption bands may allow direct measure of the Trp indole χ_2, environment hydrophobicity, and water accessibility. Because the four Trp side chains in gramicidin differ in indole position by no more than 11Å in their positions relative to the bilayer interface and yet are distinguishable in kinetics of deuteration, this approach provides an exquisite test of side-chain position.

X-RAY DIFFRACTION IN ORIENTED MULTILAYERS

Lipid multilayers containing gramicidin can be oriented in an X-ray beam. Because the channels are not ordered in the plane of the bilayer, resolution of individual atoms cannot be obtained in this way, but helical parameters and the depth of ion binding sites in the bilayer can be determined.

The gramicidin channel pitch was found to be 4.7 (±0.2) Å with 5 helical turns per channel in gel and liquid-crystalline phases. The pitch did not change upon addition of equimolar Na^+ or Tl^+ (84). These results are consistent with the predictions for the right-handed β-helical dimer with 6.3 amino acids per turn, 2.5 turns per 15-amino acid monomer.

Difference patterns upon addition of permeant (Tl^+, K^+) or impermeant cations (Ba^{2+}) demonstrated symmetrical cation binding sites for Tl^+ and K^+ at 9.6 (±0.3) Å from the center of the channel (7.6% in from the entrance), whereas Ba^{2+} binds at 13.0 (±0.2) Å from the center, outside the channel (109). The result for the permeant cations is an important confirmation that there is a binding site inside the channel, as has been long supposed by those modeling current-voltage-concentration data (e.g. 159) and had been inferred from ion-induced chemical shifts using NMR (166, 168). The fact that Ba^{2+} does not enter the channel is consistent with the NMR evidence mentioned above for the location of the Mn^{2+} binding site (56).

DIELECTRIC RELAXATION AND LASER DOPPLER VELOCIMETRY

The dielectric permittivity of a solution is increased by the addition of orientable dipoles. The frequency dependence of the permittivity reflects the relaxation rate of the dipole. Gramicidin packaged in liposomes and containing a permeant cation should behave as a dipole. The real portion of the complex permittivity was compared for lysolecithin/gramicidin/salt solutions where the cation was 10 mM Tl^+, Na^+, or K^+ (66). The gramicidin was demonstrated by CD to be in the channel form. The binding affinities of the gramicidin channel for Na^+ and K^+ are thought to be around 30–50 mM (72), whereas for Tl^+ the affinity is ~ 1 mM (71). Therefore, the Na^+ and K^+ cases served as controls where no dielectic dispersion would be expected. An increase in permittivity was observed with Tl^+ in the 0.1–10 MHz region, which was well-fit with a Cole-Cole function to yield an estimate of the relaxation time of 120 ns, i.e. a translocation rate constant of $\sim 4/\mu s$. It was argued that this was too fast for micelle or channel reorientation and therefore must represent the average time between two jumps in the channel. Unfortunately, the magnitude of the permittivity increase was ~ 10 times higher than expected for a single ion hopping between two Tl^+ binding sites at the channel concentration used, so the relaxation time must be viewed with caution. Nevertheless, this is the only direct measurement of the equilibrium rate of translocations between the two binding sites available.

Laser Doppler velocimetry is another way to measure ion motion within the channel. Using this approach, the translocation velocity of ions in the channel was measured to be 18.8 cm/s at 100 mV for Tl^+ (97). If the entry site is fully occupied and the exit site is effectively empty (i.e. translocation is rate limiting), the velocity is inversely related to the translocation rate constant, which was thus computed to be $\sim 70/\mu s$.

SCANNING TUNNELING MICROSCOPY

Atomic probe (scanning tunneling, STM, and atomic force, AFM) microscopy permits imaging of solid surfaces with atomic resolution. The techniques have been extended with success to the imaging of Langmuir-Blodgett films: one, two, or three lipid monolayers coating a solid surface. Lipid head groups, imaged this way, generally appear as a single mass of appropriate dimensions (e.g. 57). Not surprisingly, the first membrane protein to which scanning tunneling microscopy has been applied is the gramicidin channel (92). Gramicidin was packed into mono-olein and DPPC monolayers on an oxidized pyrolitic graphite substrate or into bilayers on a nonoxidized graphite substrate. Pure lipid monolayer images were used as controls. At low density, individual peaks corresponding to gramicidin channels were detected extending above the lipid head group background. At high density, chain-like clusters formed. Similar gramicidin chains had been observed earlier with electron microscopy (142). A central channel of 0.4 nm diameter was evident and the asymmetry in the cylindrical image gave the impression of tryptophan side chains projecting out from the channel. It is reasonable to expect that similar images could be obtained under water using STM or AFM.

FLUORESCENCE DEPOLARIZATION AND LIFETIME

Fluorescent molecules, whose orientation is fixed in space, emit polarized light when excited by it. Any depolarization in the emission is a measure of the rotation undergone by the molecule between adsorption and emission, characteristically a period of a few ns. In micelles, vesicles, and bilayers, gramicidin Trp fluorescence depolarization is small compared to that of the free amino acid in solution and comparable to that of immobile side chains in the interior of globular proteins (34, 132). The low depolarization is consistent with the narrow Trp χ_2 band in Raman and with the notion that Trp side chains are stable on a long time scale. There was increased mobility in the fluid phase of DMPC bilayers, which suggests that ring-stacking between Trp-9 and Trp-15 (which are near each other in the $\beta^{6.3}$ helix) is disrupted in this lipid when it is fluid, whereas DPPC and DPOC bilayers had stable depolarization through the gel-liquid phase transition (132). At high pressures (1000 Atm), gel phase DMPC had significantly increased depolarization, ascribed to pressure-induced bilayer thinning and disruption of hydrogen bonds between the lipid head group and the Trp side chains (133).

If the Trp side chain positions remain stable for seconds, heterogeneity in their orientation may give rise to the single-channel conductance variations observed for 5–50% of channels in single channel experiments (27). The low conductance channels have rectifying current-voltage relations (29), which suggest that the binding affinity is increased on one end of the channel (30). Detergents induce the low-conductance conformation, but apparently need not be in direct contact to maintain it (130), indicating that the low conductance is due to a variation in the channel conformation. Backbone variants cannot be ruled out, but side chain conformers would seem more likely. Although Trp side chain rotation times for peptides associated with membranes are normally measured in nanoseconds (179), the low depolarization and narrow Trp χ_2 band in Raman spectroscopy suggest that gramicidin side chain positions in lipid membranes are stable for long times.

RADIOLYSIS AND PHOTOLYSIS

The significance of the tryptophans in gramicidin was underlined by the observation that UV light inactivates gramicidin channels, a phenomenon also seen in Na channels. This rather nonspecific finding will not be dwelt on here, except for a few points. The inactivation by UV photolysis was ascribed to Trp photolysis because the action spectrum resembled the Trp adsorption spectrum (31) and because the rate of Trp fluorescence decay was similar to the rate of channel inactivation under similar conditions of UV illumination (78). The latter finding was enigmatic because the quantum yield calculated with such an assumption would be very high, and also because it suggested that all eight Trp side chains must be photolysed to destroy a channel, whereas initial observations had suggested that this could not be the case because there was no delay in the time course of inactivation (31). The point was tested with analogues of gramicidin containing, one, two, or three Trps rather than four (150). The UV-induced decay was a double exponential. The time constants for both exponentials varied approximately in proportion to the number of Trps present, consistent with the concept that photolysis of any one of the Trps inactivates the channel. Similar results were found with ionizing X-irradiation (149, 150), although the mechanism was shown to involve the reaction of free radicals with the Trps. Neither UV- nor X-irradiation are effective with gramicidin M$^-$, which contains Phe in place of each Trp. Flash photolysis with a 0.1 ms UV flash (28) demonstrated that channels terminate abruptly during the flash. A slow after-decay after the flash, followed by recovery suggested that the flash caused many monomers to exit the bilayer, followed by slow replacement from the aqueous bath.

PEPTIDE AGGREGATION

The gramicidin dimer has generally been thought to be the conducting channel, but aggregation of dimers has been shown to occur at high peptide densities (92, 142). Several experimental findings such as the similarity between relaxation kinetics of gramicidin monomers and covalently linked gramicidin dimers in temperature- and voltage-jump experiments (148), the high sensitivity to UV light (31), the high dielectric permittivity (66), and the effects of Trp photolysis or radiolysis on channel formation rate (150) are difficult to explain without invoking a required cooperativity between dimers for conduction (150). These experiments are all done with high densities of peptide, however, where aggregation would be expected to occur. The assertion that aggregation is necessary for channel conductance has been rebutted on the basis of heterodimer experiments (39).

Other molecules can inhibit gramicidin formation, presumably through effects on the pre-channel equilibria. Recently, for instance, local anesthetics were found to reduce the conductance of gramicidin-containing bilayers (110) by reducing the channel occurrence frequency (26). Presumably, the anesthetics reduce the density of peptide in the bilayer by stabilizing the aqueous state or by speeding the peptide bilayer-exit rate, because they do not affect single-channel lifetime or conductance.

MOLECULAR ENERGY CALCULATIONS

During the past decade, over fifty studies of gramicidin permeation using atomistic models have been published. As of 1987, studies had appeared on (a) the structure, energetics, and channel mobility (e.g. 173, 174); (b) the mobility, energetics, and diffusion of waters (e.g. 98) and alkali metal cations (e.g. 53, 55, 87, 94, 134) in the channel; (c) the electrostatic potential from the backbone (119) and the side chains (50); (d) the ion-ion interaction energy in the channel (119); (e) the potential energy of anions (151, 152) and divalent cations (52) in the channel; (f) the effect of an applied potential on the motions of a cation in the channel (86); and (g) the relative entropies of the monovalent cations in the channel (25). All were reasonably consistent with expectations. The $\beta^{6.3}$ helix (left- or right-handed) is predicted to be energetically stable and several side chain conformations are energetically feasible. The smaller cations like Na^+ can move off the channel axis and have higher entropy in the channel, whereas Cs^+ is constrained to the axis and therefore more mobile along the axis. Waters tend to align with oxygens facing the cation in the channel. The side chains contribute significantly to the potential energy profile for a cation in the channel. Anions are well coordinated in the channel, but are repelled from the entrance of the channel by the carbonyl oxygens interacting with the waters of hydration and the anion itself. The interaction of Ca^{2+} with the channel is strong, but much less so than that with water, which indicates that failure to dehydrate prevents entry into the channel. Applied potential causes ion motion as expected. In addition, continuum theory electrostatic calculations provided insight into the role of long-range electrostatic potentials from the bilayer, the electrolyte, and other factors normally left out of atomistic calculations (e.g. 79). These calculations demonstrate that the potentials resulting from the low dielectric of the bilayer and from the ions in the bath form a rounded barrier of height ~7.5 kcal/mole at the center of the channel. However, the calculated free energy barriers to monovalent cation passage predicted from molecular dynamics computations were impenetrably high and failed to display a binding site at the entrance (reviewed in 80). This was probably due to imbalance in the force fields for cation-water and cation-channel interactions.

Since 1987, free energy computations (5, 125, 126, 127) yielded energy barriers of ~6 kcal/mole for Na^+ passage through the channel, approximately consistent with the observed conductance. Binding sites were predicted at ±9.3 Å (125), the position where Na^+ was still in contact with multiple water oxygens from the bulk solution as well as two backbone carbonyl oxygens and one water oxygen from inside the channel. Deeper into the channel, the Na^+ interactions were restricted to the two backbone carbonyl oxygens, one water oxygen deeper in the pore, and just one water oxygen on the other side. In addition to this exciting progress in predicting the free energy profile for Na^+, recent studies have shown that the water permeability of the channel should depend on the channel flexibility, which is apparently somewhat reduced by the lipid environment judging by the high computed water mobility for the channel in vacuum (36). Cs^+ permeability is predicted to be higher than Na^+ permeability mainly because of the lower affinity of Cs^+ for water (51). Electroneutrality is expected to be violated near the entry to a channel (114).

Access resistance corrections to Brownian dynamics modeling of Na^+ conductance result in a small change in the transport energy profile required to fit the data (35). The waters in the channel, although generally aligned, can undergo coordinated configuration changes (38). High ionic strength in the bath shouldn't affect the image barrier, but should stabilize multiple occupancy in the channel (83). Ions in the channel should cause appreciable inward librations of peptide carbonyl oxygens in the vicinity (82, 127). The water dipolar susceptibility should be low in an ion-free channel because of interactions with the channel walls and could be further reduced 100-fold by saturation of the ordering effect when an ion is present in the channel (112). The apparent dielectric constant between two charges in the channel should depend strongly on the distance between them (102). Shielding of the positive end of Trp dipoles, which are expected to be nearer the bath electrolyte than the negative end, should favor cation occupancy of the channel by producing a broad negative potential over the length of the channel (129). The peptide carbonyls rotate into the channel by ~15 or 25° in the absence of ions according to both molecular dynamics and solid state NMR. The measured backbone ^{15}N chemical shifts are essentially identical with those predicted from the calculated dynamic average structure (37). The small iminium ions, guanidinium and acetamidinium, have a barrier to channel entry due to the outer turn of the helix (158).

KINETIC MODELS

Models of ion transport generally describe ion diffusion up to the entry of the channel and binding at the entry site, translocation through the channel to the exit site, and release from the exit and diffusion into the bulk. The three-barrier, two-site, single-filing double occupancy model (3B2S), first used to describe gramicidin conductance (73) has been successful in predicting many of the features of the conductance data. It has been enhanced in the three-barrier, four site (3B4S) model, which depicts the entry/exit process as a compound step (49), or by explicit inclusion of interfacial polarization and diffusion limitation effects on the entry rate constant (18, 74). The translocation step has also been further dissected as an electro-diffusion process modeled with both Brownian dynamics (a Monte-Carlo approach, 75), or Nernst-Planck continuum theory (an analytical approach, 96). However, the predictions of these different enhancements do not differ sufficiently to allow distinction between the methods. Present usage is determined by expediency as much as appropriateness. For instance, although the translocation step is best represented as a series of small steps or a diffusive process, it is more convenient for data fitting to lump it into a single kinetic step (18, 59, 77).

3B2S and 3B4S models have been used to reconcile current-voltage-concentration data with reversal potential data (159), low-concentration conductance-voltage data with flux-ratio data (49), zero-current conductance-concentration data with anomalous mole fraction conductance data (100), current-concentration data with NMR-determined rate constant data (170), high-voltage-current-concentration data for a series of Trp mutations (18), and current-voltage-concentration data with single-channel noise data (59, 60, 137). In general, multiple occupancy has been used to explain various features in the data such as flux ratio exponents greater than one, saturation and self-block in the current-concentration relation, inflections in the Eadie-Hofstee plot, and bends in the excess longitudinal relaxation rate-concentration plots. Generally, in 1 M salts, the models have kinetic steps with rate constants of $\sim 10^7$/s (except for exit from the singly occupied channel, which varies greatly between models), as they must to predict the observed pS conductances, but models differ in predictions of which steps are rate-limiting. Each attempt at unification puts new constraints on the relative values of the rate constants, but a grand unification is needed that accounts for all of these data, or at least, the most discriminating and reliable data, simultaneously. The simple three-step (3B2S) model is well known to be inadequate for predicting all of the current-voltage-concentration data simultaneously and may be misleading because of the oversimplification of each step. Nonetheless, given the X-ray diffraction and NMR observations that there are only two significant monovalent cation binding sites, the complexity of the noise-inducing gramicidin conformational fluctuations, and the feasibility of embellishing the entry and translocation rate equations to take Brownian motion and interfacial polarization into account, this simple model would seem the most prudent basis for such a grand unification at the present.

SUMMARY

The various details provided by physical methods have been integrated into a coherent picture of the cation transport process. The free energy profile describes simultaneously the thermodynamic and kinetic factors that govern conductance. Localization of ion binding sites near each end of the channel by NMR and X-ray crystallographic techniques demonstrates that there is an energy barrier separating the two ends. There is no a priori reason to suspect any barrier to ion entry into the channel, and recent molecular modeling computations confirm this intuition. Therefore, the channel is best described as a two-site, one-barrier channel. However, the movement of ions across the central barrier over a distance of 1.9 nm is really a multistep process best described as Brownian motion (even the short steps from one pair of carbonyls to the next is more diffusive than activated for ions as large as Na^+), the entry step is probably best considered as a compound step requiring correction for interfacial polarization and diffusion limitation, the binding sites in the channel ought not be considered to be in equilibrium with the bath, and quasi-knock off behavior (binding of a second ion at the entry facilitates release of a first ion from the exit) is probably the rule at physiological permeant ion concentrations and higher.

Progress will probably focus on channel kinetics. The channel backbone probably undergoes conformational changes as the ions pass which, according to solid state NMR results, may last long enough to provide the channel with a sort of memory and which may give rise to excess single channel noise. These conformational changes are further reflected in shifts in side chain positions which, in turn, may be partly responsible for changes in the single-channel lifetime, which appears to be exquisitely sensitive to side chain-lipid interactions. Reasonable explanations for the impermeance of divalent cations, anions, and medium-sized organic cations such as guanidinium have proven elusive at first, but it now appears that divalent cations bind water too tightly, anions bind water in an orientation that produces unfavorable contacts between water oxygens and peptide carbonyl oxygens at the channel entry, and iminium ions bind strongly to the flexible peptide carbonyls at the channel entry.

ACKNOWLEDGMENTS

The author wishes to thank O. S. Andersen, J. Hinton, D. W. Urry, and G. Szabo for many helpful conversations and D. W. Urry for access to unpublished data. Supported by National Institutes of Health R01 GM33361.

Note: The reference database used to compile this review contains approximately 725 articles on gramicidin spanning the last 53 years. It is available from the author on request in electronic or printed format.

Literature Cited

1. Andersen, O. S. 1984. Gramicidin channels. *Annu. Rev. Physiol.* 46:531–48
2. Andersen, O. S., Koeppe, R. E. II, Durkin, J. T., Mazet, J.-L. 1987. Structure-function studies on linear gramicidins. Site-specific modifications in a membrane channel. In *Ion Transport Across Membranes*, ed. K. Yagi, B. Pullman, pp. 295–314. Tokyo: Academic
3. Apell, H. J., Bamberg, E., Alpes, H. 1979. Dicarboxylic acid analogs of gramicidin A: dimerization kinetics and single channel properties. *J. Membr. Biol.* 50:271–85
4. Apell, H. J., Bamberg, E., Alpes, H., Lauger, P. 1977. Formation of ion channels by a negatively charged analog of gramicidin A. *J. Membr. Biol.* 31:171–88

5. Aqvist, J., Warshel, A. 1989. Energetics of ion permeation through membrane channels. Solvation of Na^+ by gramicidin A. *Biophys. J.* 56:171–82
6. Arseniev, A. S., Barsukov, I. L., Bystrov, V. F., Lomize, A. L. 1986. Gramicidin-A transmembrane ion-channel—3-dimensional structure reconstruction based on NMR-spectroscopy and energy refinement. *Biol. Membr.* 3:1077–4
7. Arseniev, A. S., Lomize, A. L., Barsukov, I. L., Bystrov, V. F. 1990. Gramicidin A transmembrane channel. Three-dimensional structural rearrangement based on NMR spectroscopy and energy refinement. *Biol. Membr.* 3:1723–78
8. Baño, M. C., Braco, L., Abad, C. 1989. HPLC study on the 'history' dependence of gramicidin A conformation

in phospholipid model membranes. *FEBS Lett.* 250:67–71.

9. Baño, M. C., Braco, L., Abad, C. 1991. Conformational transitions of gramicidin A in phospholipid model membranes. A high-performance liquid chromatography assessment. *Biochemistry* 30:886–94

10. Bamberg, E., Alpes, H., Apell, H. J., Benz, R., Janko, K., et al. 1977. Studies on the gramicidin channel. In *Biochemistry of Membrane Transport*, ed. G. Semenza, E. Carafoli, pp. 179–201. Berlin: Springer

11. Bamberg, E., Alpes, H., Apell, H. J., Bradley, R., Härter, B., et al. 1979. Formation of ionic channels in black lipid membranes by succinic derivatives of gramicidin A. *J. Membr. Biol.* 50:257–70

12. Bamberg, E., Apell, H. J., Alpes, H. 1977. Structure of the gramicidin A channel: discrimination between the πL,D and the beta helix by electrical measurements with lipid bilayer membranes. *Proc. Natl. Acad. Sci. USA* 74:2402–6

13. Bamberg, E., Apell, H. J., Alpes, H., Gross, E., Morell, J. L., et al. 1978. Ion channels formed by chemical analogs of gramicidin A. *Fed. Proc.* 37:2633–38

14. Bamberg, E., Janko, K. 1977. The action of a carbonsuboxide dimerized gramicidin A on lipid bilayer membranes. *Biochim. Biophys. Acta* 465:486–99

15. Bamberg, E., Noda, K., Gross, E., Läuger, P. 1976. Single-channel parameters of gramicidin A, B and C. *Biochim. Biophys. Acta* 419:223–28

16. Barrett Russell, E. W., Weiss, L. B., Navetta, F. I., Koeppe, R. E. II, Andersen, O. S. 1986. Single-channel studies on linear gramicidin with altered amino acid side chains. *Biophys. J.* 49:673–86

17. Becker, M. D., Greathouse, D. V., Koeppe, R. E., Andersen, O. S. 1991. Amino acid sequence modulation of gramicidin channel function: effects of tryptophan-to-phenylalanine substitutions on the single-channel conductance and duration. *Biochemistry* 30:8830–39

18. Becker, M. D., Koeppe, R. E. II, Andersen, O. S. 1992. Amino acid substitutions and ion channel function. Model-dependent conclusions. *Biophys. J.* 62:25–27

19. Bogusz, S., Boxer, A., Busath, D. D. 1992. An SS1-SS2 β-barrel structure for the voltage-activated potassium channel. *Protein Eng.* 5:285–93

20. Bogusz, S., Busath, D. D. 1992. Is a beta-barrel model of the K^+ channel energetically feasible? *Biophys. J.* 62:19–21

21. Boni, L. T., Connoly, A. J., Kleinfeld, A. M. 1986. Transmembrane distribution of gramicidin by tryptophan energy transfer. *Biophys. J.* 49:122–23

22. Braco, L., Abad, C., Campos, A., Figueruelo, J. E. 1986. Time-dependent monomerization of gramicidin A, enhanced by phosphatidylcholine in non-polar solvents. A high-performance liquid chromatographic and spectrofluorometric study. *J. Chromatog.* 353:181–92

23. Braco, L., Baño, M. C., Chillaron, F., Abad, C. 1986. Conformational species of gramicidin A in non-polar solvent. A kinetic and thermodynamic treatment in the absence and presence of phosphatidylcholine as studied by high-performance liquid chromatography. *Biophys. Chem.* 25:297–305

24. Branden, C., Tooze, J. 1991. *Introduction of Protein Structure*, pp. 43–84. New York/London: Garland

25. Brickmann, J., Fischer, W. 1983. Entropy effects on the ion-diffusion rate in transmembrane protein channels. *Biophys. Chem.* 17:245–58

26. Bridal, T. R., Busath, D. 1992. Inhibition of gramicidin channel activity by local anesthetics. *Biochim. Biophys. Acta.* 1107:31–38

27. Busath, D. D., Andersen, O. S., Koeppe, R. E. 1987. On the conductance heterogeneity in membrane channels formed by gramicidin A. A cooperative study. *Biophys. J.* 51:79–88

28. Busath, D. D., Hayon, E. 1988. Ultraviolet flash photolysis of gramicidin-doped lipid bilayers. *Biochim. Biophys. Acta* 944:73–78

29. Busath, D., Szabo, G. 1981. Gramicidin forms multi-state rectifying channels. *Nature* 294:371–73

30. Busath, D., Szabo, G. 1988. Permeation characteristics of gramicidin conformers. *Biophys. J.* 53:697–707

31. Busath, D. D., Waldbillig, R. C. 1983. Photolysis of gramicidin A channels in lipid bilayers. *Biochim. Biophys. Acta* 736:28–38

32. Bystrov, V. F., Arseniev, A. S. 1988. Diversity of the gramicidin A spatial structure: Two-dimensional ^{1}-H NMR study in solution. *Tetrahedron* 44:925–40

33. Bystrov, V. F., Arseniev, A. S., Barsukov, I. L., Golovanov, A. P., Maslennikov, I. V. 1990. The structure of the

transmembrane channel of gramicidin A—NMR-study of its conformational stability and interaction with divalent-cations. *Gazz. Chim. Ital.* 120:485–91

34. Camalenodelgado, J. M., Xiao, K. Z., Fendler, J. H. 1990. Intrinsic gramicidin fluorescence lifetimes in bilayer lipid-membranes and in vesicles. *Can. J. Chem.* 68:888–96

35. Chiu, S. W., Jakobsson, E. 1989. Stochastic theory of singly occupied ion channels. II. Effects of access resistance and potential gradients extending into the bath. *Biophys. J.* 55:147–57

36. Chiu, S. W., Jakobsson, E., Subramaniam, S., McCammon, J. A. 1991. Time-correlation analysis of simulated water motion in flexible and rigid gramicidin channels. *Biophys. J.* 60:273–85

37. Chiu, S. W., Nicholson, L. K., Brenneman, M. T., Subramaniam, S., Teng, Q., et al. 1991. Molecular dynamics computations and solid state nuclear magnetic resonance of the gramicidin cation channel. *Biophys. J.* 60:974–78

38. Chiu, S. W., Subramaniam, S., Jakobsson, E., McCammon, J. A. 1989. Water and polypeptide conformations in the gramicidin channel. A molecular dynamics study. *Biophys. J.* 56:253–61

39. Cifu, A. S., Koeppe, R. E., Andersen, O. S. 1992. On the supramolecular organization of gramicidin channels. The elementary conducting unit is a dimer. *Biophys. J.* 61:189–203

40. Cornell, B. 1987. Gramicidin A—phospholipid model systems. *J. Bioenerg. Biomembr.* 19:655–76

41. Cortijo, M., Alonso, A., Gomez-Fernandez, J. C., Chapman, D. 1982. Intrinsic protein-lipid interactions. Infrared spectroscopic studies of gramicidin A, bacteriorhodopsin and Ca^{2+}-ATPase in biomembranes and reconstituted systems. *J. Mol. Biol.* 157:597–618

42. Daumas, P., Benamar, D., Heitz, F., Ranjalahy-Rasoloarijao, L., Mouden, R., et al. 1991. How can the aromatic side-chains modulate the conductance of the gramicidin channel? A new approach using non-coded amino acids. *Int. J. Pept. Protein Res.* 38:218–28

43. Daumas, P., Heitz, F., Ranjalahy-Rasoloarijao, L., Lazaro, R. 1989. Gramicidin A analogs: influence of the substitution of the tryptophans by naphthylalanines. *Biochimie* 71:77–81

44. De Kruijff, B., Killian, J. A., Tournois, H. 1988. Influence of gramicidin on lipid organization and dynamics in membranes. In *Transport through Membranes: Carriers, Channels and Pumps*, ed. A. Pullman, J. Jortner, B. Pullman, pp. 267–87. Dordrecht/Boston/London: Kluwer

45. Deleted in proof

46. Durell, S. R., Robert Guy, H. 1992. Atomic scale structure and functional models of voltage-gated potassium channels. *Biophys. J.* 62:238–50

47. Durkin, J. T., Koeppe, R. E., Andersen, O. S. 1990. Energetics of gramicidin hybrid channel formation as a test for structural equivalence. Side-chain substitutions in the native sequence. *J. Mol. Biol.* 211:221–34

48. Eisenman, G., Horn, R. 1983. Ionic selectivity revisited: the role of kinetic and equilibrium processes in ion permeation through channels. *J. Membr. Biol.* 76:197–225

49. Eisenman, G., Sandblom, J. P. 1983. Energy barriers in ionic channels: data for gramicidin A interpreted using a single-file (3B4S) model having 3 barriers separating 4 sites. In *Physical Chemistry of Transmembrane Ion Motions*, ed. G. Spach, pp. 329–47. Amsterdam: Elsevier

50. Etchebest, C., Pullman, A. 1985. The effect of the amino-acid side chains on the energy profiles for ion transport in the gramicidin A channel. *J. Biomolec. Struct. Dyn.* 2:859–70

51. Etchebest, C., Pullman, A. 1988. Energy profile of Cs^+ in gramicidin A in the presence of water. Problem of the ion selectivity of the channel. *J. Biomolec. Struct. Dyn.* 5:1111–25

52. Etchebest, C., Pullman, A., Ranganathan, S. 1985. The gramicidin A channel: theoretical energy profile computed for single occupancy by a divalent cation, Ca^{2+}. *Biochim. Biophys. Acta* 818:23–30

53. Etchebest, C., Ranganathan, S., Pullman, A. 1984. The gramicidin A channel: comparison of the energy profiles of Na^+, K^+ and Cs^+. Influence of the flexibility of the ethanolamine end chain on the profiles. *FEBS Lett.* 173:301–6

54. Finkelstein, A., Andersen, O. S. 1981. The gramicidin A channel: a review of its permeability characteristics with special reference to the single-file aspect of transport. *J. Membr. Biol.* 59:155–71

55. Fischer, W., Brickmann, J., Läuger, P. 1981. Molecular dynamics study of ion transport in transmembrane protein channels. *Biophys. Chem.* 13:105–16

56. Golovanov, A. P., Barsukov, I. L., Arseniev, A. S., Bystrov, V. F., Sukhanov, S. V., et al. 1991. The divalent

cation-binding sites of gramicidin A transmembrane ion-channel. *Biopolymers* 31:425–34

57. Hansma, H. G., Gould, S. A. C., Hansma, P. K., Gaub, H. E., Long, M. L., et al. 1991. Imaging nanometer scale defects in Langmuir-Blodgett films with the atomic force microscope. *Langmuir* 7:1051–54

58. Heinemann, S. H., Sigworth, F. J. 1988. Open channel noise. IV. Estimation of rapid kinetics of formamide block in gramicidin A channels. *Biophys. J.* 54:757–64

59. Heinemann, S. H., Sigworth, F. J. 1990. Open channel noise. V. Fluctuating barriers to ion entry in gramicidin A channels. *Biophys. J.* 57:499–514

60. Heinemann, S. H., Sigworth, F. J. 1991. Open channel noise. VI. Analysis of amplitude histograms to determine rapid kinetic parameters. *Biophys. J.* 60:577–87

61. Heitz, F., Gavach, C., Spach, G., Trudelle, Y. 1986. Analysis of the ion transfer through the channel of 9,11,13,15-phenylalanyl-gramicidin A. *Biophys. Chem.* 24:143–48

62. Heitz, F., Heitz, A., Trudelle, Y. 1986. Conformations of gramicidin A and its 9,11,13,15-phenylalanyl analog in dimethyl sulfoxide and chloroform. *Biophys. Chem.* 24:149–60

63. Heitz, F., Spach, G., Trudelle, Y. 1982. Single channels of 9,11,13,15-destryptophyl-phenylalanyl-gramicidin A. *Biophys. J.* 40:87–89

64. Heitz, F., Van Mau, N., Bennes, R., Daumas, P., Trudelle, Y. 1989. Single channels and surface potential of linear gramicidins. *Biochimie* 71:83–88

65. Hemsley, G., Busath, D. 1991. Small iminium ions block gramicidin channels in lipid bilayers. *Biophys. J.* 59:901–7

66. Henze, R., Neher, E., Trapane, T. L., Urry, D. W. 1982. Dielectric relaxation studies of ionic processes in lysolecithin-packaged gramicidin channels. *J. Membr. Biol.* 64:233–39

67. Hing, A. W., Adams, S. P., Silbert, D. F., Norberg, R. E. 1990. Deuterium NMR of ^{2}HCO-Val^1 . . . gramicidin A and ^{2}HCO-Val^1-D-Leu^2 . . . gramicidin A in oriented DMPC bilayers. *Biochemistry* 29:4156–66

68. Hing, A. W., Adams, S. P., Silbert, D. F., Norberg, R. E. 1990. Deuterium NMR of Val^1 . . . (2-^{2}H)Ala^3 . . . gramicidin A in oriented DMPC bilayers. *Biochemistry* 29:4144–56

69. Hinton, J. F., Fernandez, J. Q., Shungu, D. C., Millett, F. S. 1989. Thermodynamic parameters for the binding of divalent cations to gramicidin A incorporated into a lipid environment by Tl-^{205} nuclear magnetic resonance. *Biophys. J.* 55:327–30

70. Hinton, J. F., Fernandez, J. Q., Shungu, D. C., Whaley, W. L., Koeppe, R. E., et al. 1988. Tl-^{205} nuclear magnetic resonance determination of the thermodynamic parameters for the binding of monovalent cations to gramicidins A and C. *Biophys. J.* 54:527–33

71. Hinton, J. F., Koeppe, R. E., Millett, F. S., Paczkowski, J. A., Shungu, D., et al. 1986. Equilibrium binding constants for Tl$^+$ with gramicidin-A, gramicidin-B, and gramicidin-C in a lysophosphatidylcholine environment determined by Tl-^{205} nuclear magnetic-resonance spectroscopy. *Biophys. J.* 49:571–77

72. Hinton, J. F., Whaley, W. L., Shungu, D., Koeppe, R. E., Millett, F. S. 1986. Equilibrium binding constants for the group I metal cations with gramicidin-A determined by competition studies and Tl$^+$-^{205} nuclear magnetic resonance spectroscopy. *Biophys. J.* 50:539–44

73. Hladky, S. B. 1972. *The mechanisms of ion conduction in thin lipid membranes containing gramicidin A.* PhD thesis. Cambridge Univ., England

74. Hladky, S. B. 1984. Ion currents through pores. The roles of diffusion and external access steps in determining the currents through narrow pores. *Biophys. J.* 46:293–97

75. Jakobsson, E., Chiu, S. W. 1987. Stochastic theory of ion movement in channels with single-ion occupancy. Application to sodium permeation of gramicidin channels. *Biophys. J.* 52:33–45

76. Jap, B. K., Walian, P. J., Gehring, K. 1991. Structural architecture of an outer membrane channel as determined by electron crystallography. *Nature* 350:167–70

77. Jin, X. Z. 1992. *The impact of the negative charge on cation permeation in the taurine 16-gramicidin A channel.* PhD thesis. Brown Univ. 132 pp.

78. Jones, D., Hayon, E., Busath, D. 1986. Tryptophan photolysis is responsible for gramicidin-channel inactivation by ultraviolet light. *Biochim. Biophys. Acta* 861:62–66

79. Jordan, P. C. 1984. The total electrostatic potential in a gramicidin channel. *J. Membr. Biol.* 78:91–102

80. Jordan, P. C. 1987. Microscopic approach to ion transport through transmembrane channels. The model system

gramicidin. *J. Phys. Chem.* 91:6582–91
81. Jordan, P. C. 1988. Ion transport through transmembrane channels: Ab initio perspectives. *Curr. Top. Membr. Transp.* 33:91–111
82. Jordan, P. C. 1990. Ion-water and ion-polypeptide correlations in a gramicidin-like channel. A molecular dynamics study. *Biophys. J.* 58:1133–56
83. Jordan, P. C., Bacquet, R. J., McCammon, J. A., Tran, P. 1989. How electrolyte shielding influences the electrical potential in transmembrane ion channels. *Biophys. J.* 55:1041–52
84. Katsaras, J., Prosser, R. S., Stinson, R. H., Davis, J. H. 1992. Content helical pitch of the gramicidin channel in phospholipid bilayers. *Biophys. J.* 61:827–30
85. Killian, J. A., Prasad, K. U., Hains, D., Urry, D. W. 1988. The membrane as an environment of minimal interconversion. A circular dichroism study on the solvent dependence of the conformational behavior of gramicidin in diacylphosphatidylcholine model membranes. *Biochemistry* 27:4848–55
86. Kim, K. S. 1985. Microscopic effect of an applied voltage on the solvated gramicidin A transmembrane channel in the presence of Na^+ and K^+ cations. *J. Comp. Chem.* 6(3):256–63
87. Kim, K. S., Clementi, E. 1985. Energetic and hydration structures of a solvated gramicidin A transmembrane channel for K^+ and Na^+ cations. *J. Am. Chem. Soc.* 107:5504–13
88. Koeppe, R. E. II, Mazet, J. L., Andersen, O. S. 1990. Distinction between dipolar and inductive effects in modulating the conductance of gramicidin channels. *Biochemistry* 29:512–20
89. Koeppe, R. E. II, Paczkowski, J. A., Whaley, W. L. 1985. Gramicidin K, a new linear channel-forming gramicidin from *Bacillus brevis*. *Biochemistry* 24:2822–26
90. Koeppe, R. E. II, Providence, L. L., Greathouse, D. V., Heitz, F., Trudelle, Y., et al. 1992. On the helix sense of gramicidin A single channels. *Proteins* 12:49–62
91. Koeppe, R. E. II, Weiss, L. B. 1981. Resolution of linear gramicidins by preparative reversed-phase high-performance liquid chromatography. *J. Chromatog.* 208:414–18
92. Kolomytkin, O. V., Golubok, A. O., Davydov, D. N., Timofeev, V. A., Vinogradova, S. A., et al. 1991. Ionic channels in Langmuir-Blodgett films imaged by a scanning tunneling microscope. *Biophys. J.* 59:889–93

93. Läuger, P. 1987. Ion movement through channels with conformational substates. In *Ion Transport Through Membranes*, ed. K. Yagi, B. Pullman, pp. 85–99. New York: Academic
94. Lee, W. K., Jordan, P. C. 1984. Molecular dynamics simulation of cation motion in water-filled gramicidinlike pores. *Biophys. J.* 46:805–19
95. Lelievre, D., Heitz, F., Trudelle, Y., Spach, G. 1989. Synthesis and characterization of retro gramicidin A-D-Ala-gramicidin-A, a 31-residue-long gramicidin analog. *Int. J. Pept. Protein Res.* 33:379–85
96. Levitt, D. G. 1982. Comparison of Nernst-Planck and reaction-rate models for multiple occupied channels. *Biophys. J.* 37:575–87
97. Macias, F., Starzak, M. E. 1992. Laser doppler scattering for the determination of ionic velocity distributions in channels and membranes. In *Biomembrane Electrochemistry*, ed. M. Blank, I. Vodyanoy, Washington, DC: Am. Chem. Soc. In press
98. Mackay, D. H., Berens, P. H., Wilson, K. R., Hagler, A. T. 1984. Structure and dynamics of ion transport through gramicidin A. *Biophys. J.* 229–48
99. Masotti, L., Spisni, A., Urry, D. W. 1980. Conformational studies on the gramicidin A transmembrane channel in lipid micelles and liposomes. *Cell. Biophys.* 2:241–51
100. McBride, D. W. 1981. *Anomalous mole fraction behavior, momentary block, and lifetimes of gramicidin A in silver and potassium flouride solutions.* PhD thesis. Univ. Calif., Los Angeles. 313 pp.
101. Monoi, H. 1985. Nuclear magnetic resonance of ^{23}Na ions interacting with the gramicidin channel. *Biophys. J.* 48:643–62
102. Monoi, H. 1991. Effective pore radius of the gramicidin channel. Electrostatic energies of ions calculated by a three-dielectric model. *Biophys. J.* 59:786–94
103. Morrow, J. S., Veatch, W. R., Stryer, L. 1979. Transmembrane channel activity of gramicidin A analogs: effects of modification and deletion of the amino-terminal residue. *J. Molec. Biol.* 132:733–38
104. Naik, V. M., Krimm, S. 1986. Vibrational analysis of the structure of gramicidin A. I. Normal mode analysis. *Biophys. J.* 49:1131–45
105. Nicholson, L. K., Cross, T. A. 1989. Gramicidin cation channel: an experimental determination of the right-

handed helix sense and verification of β-type hydrogen bonding. *Biochemistry* 28:9379–9385

106. Nicholson, L. K., Teng, Q., Cross, T. A. 1991. Solid-state nuclear magnetic resonance derived model for dynamics in the polypeptide backbone of the gramicidin A channel. *J. Molec. Biol.* 218:621–37

107. O'Connell, A. M., Koeppe, R. E., Andersen, O. S. 1990. Kinetics of gramicidin channel formation in lipid bilayers: transmembrane monomer association. *Science* 250:1256–59

108. Okamura, E., Umemura, J., Takenaka, T. 1986. Orientation of gramicidin D incorporated into phospholipid multibilayers: a Fourier transform infrared-attenuated total reflection spectroscopic study. *Biochim. Biophys. Acta* 856:68–75

109. Olah, G. A., Huang, H. W., Liu, W. H., Wu, Y. L. 1991. Location of ion-binding sites in the gramicidin channel by X-ray diffraction. *J. Molec. Biol.* 218:847–58

110. Ondriaš, K., Bérczi, A., Mîsik, V., Štolc, S. 1986. Influence of local anaesthetics on electrical conductivity of planar lipid membrane doped with gramicidin. *Stud. Biophys.* 115:17–22

111. Ovchinnikov, Y. A., Ivanov, V. T. 1983. Helical structures of gramicidin A and their role in ion channeling. In *Conformation in Biology, the Festschrift celebrating the Sixtieth Birthday of G. N. Ramachandran F. R. S.*, ed. R. Srinivasan, R. H. Sarma. pp. 155–74. New York: Adenine

112. Partenskii, M. B., Cai, M., Jordan, P. C. 1991. A dipolar chain model for the electrostatics of transmembrane ion channels. *Chem. Phys.* 153:125–31

113. Paulmichl, M., Li, Y., Wickman, K., Ackerman, M., Peralta, E., et al 1992. New mammalian chloride channel identified by expression cloning. *Biophys. J.* 356:238–41

114. Peskoff, A., Bers, D. M. 1988. Eletrodiffusion of ions approaching the mouth of a conducting membrane channel. *Biophys. J.* 53:863–75

115. Prasad, K. U., Alonsoromanowski, S., Trapane, T. L., Urry, D. W., Venkatachalam, C. M. 1986. Synthesis, characterization, and black lipid-membrane studies of [7-L-alanine] gramicidin A. *Biochemistry* 25:456–63

116. Prasad, K. U., Trapane, T. L., Busath, D., Szabo, G., Urry, D. W. 1983. Synthesis and characterization of $(1-^{13}C)$ Phe^9 gramicidin A. Effects of side chain

variations. *Int. J. Pept. Protein Res.* 22:341–47

117. Prosser, R. S., Davis, J. H., Dahlquist, F. W., Lindorfer, M. A. 1991. ^2H nuclear magnetic resonance of the gramicidin A backbone in a phospholipid bilayer. *Biochemistry* 30:4687–96

118. Pullman, A. 1987. Energy profiles in the gramicidin A channel. *Q. Rev. Biophys.* 20:173–200

119. Pullman, A., Etchebest, C. 1983. The gramicidin A channel: the energy profile for single and double occupancy in a head-to-head β (6.3 3,3)-helical dimer backbone. *FEBS Lett.* 163:199–202

120. Reinhardt, R., Janko, K., Bamberg, E. 1986. Single channel conductance changes of the desethanolamine-gramicidin through pH variations. In *Electrical Double Layer in Biology*, ed. M. Blank, pp. 91–102. New York: Plenum

121. Richardson, J. S., Richardson, D. C. 1989. Principles and patterns of protein conformation. In *Prediction of Protein Structure and the Principles of Protein Conformation*, ed. G. D. Fasman, pp. 34–41. New York/London: Plenum

122. Ring, A. 1986. Brief closures of gramicidin A channels in lipid bilayer membranes. *Biochim. Biophys. Acta* 856:646–53

123. Roeske, R. W., Hrinyo-Pavlina, T. P., Pottorf, R. S., Bridal, T., Jin, X. Z., et al. 1989. Synthesis and channel properties of [Tau 16] gramicidin A. *Biochim. Biophys. Acta* 982:223–27

124. Rottenberg, H., Koeppe, R. E. 1989. Stimulation of cation-transport in mitochondria by gramicidin and truncated derivatives. *Biochemistry* 28:4361–67

125. Roux, B. 1990. *Theoretical study of ion transport in the gramicidin A channel.* PhD thesis. Harvard Univ.

126. Roux, B., Karplus, M. 1991. Ion transport in a model gramicidin channel. Structure and thermodynamics. *Biophys. J.* 59:961–81

127. Roux, B., Karplus, M. 1991. Ion transport in a gramicidin-like channel: Dynamics and mobility. *J. Phys. Chem.* 95:4856–68

128. Rudnev, V. S., Ermishkin, L. N., Fonina, L. A., Rovin, Y. G. 1981. The dependence of the conductance and lifetime of gramicidin channels on the thickness and tension of lipid bilayers. *Biochim. Biophys. Acta* 642:196–202

129. Sancho, M., Martínez, G. 1991. Electrostatic modeling of dipole-ion in-

teractions in gramicidin-like channels. *Biophys. J.* 60:81–88

130. Sawyer, D. B., Koeppe, R. E., Andersen, O. S. 1989. Induction of conductance heterogeneity in gramicidin channels. *Biochemistry* 28:6571–83

131. Sawyer, D. B., Williams, L. P., Whaley, W. L., Koeppe, R. E., Andersen, O. S. 1990. Gramicidins A, B, and C form structurally equivalent ion channels. *Biophys. J.* 58:1207–12

132. Scarlata, S. F. 1988. The effects of viscosity on gramicidin tryptophan rotational motion. *Biophys. J.* 54:1149–57

133. Scarlata, S. F. 1991. Effect of increased chain packing on gramicidin-lipid interactions. *Biochemistry* 30:9853–59

134. Schröder, H. 1983. Transit time conception for ion diffusion through membrane channels. *J. Chem. Phys.* 79:1991–96

135. Separovic, F., Hayamizu, K., Smith, R., Cornell, B. A. 1991. C-^{13} chemical-shift tensor of L-tryptophan and its application to polypeptide structure determination. *Chem. Phys. Lett.* 181:157–62

136. Shungu, D. C., Hinton, J. F., Koeppe, R. E., Millett, F. S. 1986. Investigation of the interaction between thallous ions and gramicidin A in dimyristoylphosphatidylcholine vesicles: a thallium-^{205} NMR equilibrium study. *Biochemistry* 25:6103–8

137. Sigworth, F. J., Shenkel, S. 1988. Rapid gating events and current fluctuations in gramicidin-A channels. *Curr. Top. Membr. Transp.* 33:113–30

138. Sigworth, F. J., Urry, D. W., Prasad, K. U. 1987. Open channel noise. III. High-resolution recordings show rapid current fluctuations in gramicidin A and four chemical analogues. *Biophys. J.* 52:1055–64

139. Smith, R., Thomas, D. E., Atkins, A. R., Separovic, F., Cornell, B. A. 1990. Solid-state ^{13}C-NMR studies of the effects of sodium ions on the gramicidin A ion channel. *Biochim. Biophys. Acta* 1026:161–66

140. Smith, R., Thomas, D. E., Separovic, F., Atkins, A. R., Cornell, B. A. 1989. Determination of the structure of a membrane-incorporated ion channel. Solid-state nuclear magnetic resonance studies of gramicidin A. *Biophys. J.* 56:307–14

141. Spach, G., Duclohier, H., Molle, G., Valleton, J. M. 1989. Structure and supramolecular architecture of membrane channel-forming peptides. *Biochimie* 71:11–21

142. Spisni, A., Pasquali-Ronchetti, I., Casali, E., Lindner, L., Cavatorta, P., et al.

1983. Supramolecular organization of lysophosphatidylcholine-packaged gramicidin A. *Biochim. Biophys. Acta* 732:58–68

143. Stankovic, C. J., Delfino, J. M., Schreiber, S. L. 1990. Purification of gramicidin A. *Anal. Biochem.* 184:100–3

144. Stankovic, C. J., Heinemann, S. H., Delfino, J. M., Sigworth, F. J., Schreiber, S. L. 1989. Transmembrane channels based on tartaric acid-gramicidin A hybrids. *Science* 244:813–17

145. Stankovic, C. J., Heinemann, S. H., Schreiber, S. L. 1990. Immobilizing the gate of a tartaric acid gramicidin-A hybrid channel molecule by rational design. *J. Am. Chem. Soc.* 112:3702–4

146. Stankovic, C. J., Heinemann, S. H., Schreiber, S. L. 1991. Photo-modulated ion channels based on covalently linked gramicidins. *Biochim. Biophys. Acta* 1061:163–70

147. Stankovic, C. J., Schreiber, S. L. 1991. Molecular design of transmembrane ion channels. *Chemtracts Org. Chem.* 4:1–20

148. Stark, G., Strässle, M., Takácz, Z. 1986. Temperature-jump and voltage-jump experiments at planar lipid membranes support an aggregational (micellar) model of the gramicidin A ion channel. *J. Membr. Biol.* 89:23–37

149. Strässle, M., Stark, G., Wilhelm, M. 1987. Effects of ionizing radiation on artificial (planar) lipid membranes. I. Radiation inactivation of the ion channel gramicidin A. *Int. J. Rad. Biol. Relat. Studies Phys. Chem. Med.* 51:265–86

150. Strässle, M., Wilhelm, M., Heitz, F., Daumas, P., Lazaro, R., et al. 1989. Radiolysis and photolysis of ion channels formed by analogs of gramicidin-A with a varying number of tryptophan residues. *Biochim. Biophys. Acta* 980:305–14

151. Sung, S. S., Jordan, P. C. 1987. Why is gramicidin valence selective? A theoretical study. *Biophys. J.* 51:661–72

152. Sung, S. S., Jordan, P.C. 1987. The interaction of Cl^{-} with a gramicidin-like channel. *Biophys. Chem.* 27:1–6

153. Sychev, S. V., Nevskaya, N. A., Jordanov, St., Shepel, E. N., Miroshnikov, A. I., et al. 1980. The solution conformation of gramicidin A and its analogs. *Biorgan. Chem.* 9:121–51

154. Szabo, G., Urry, D. W. 1979. N-acetyl gramicidin: single-channel properties and implications for channel structure. *Science* 203:55–57

155. Takeuchi, H., Nemoto, Y., Harada, I. 1990. Environments and conformations

of tryptophan side chains of gramicidin A in phospholipid bilayers studied by Raman spectroscopy. *Biochemistry* 29: 1572–79

156. Teng, Q., Nicholson, L. K., Cross, T. A. 1991. Experimental determination of torsion angles in the polypeptide backbone of the gramicidin A channel by solid state nuclear magnetic resonance. *J. Mol. Biol.* 218:607–19

157. Tucker, W. A., Fletcher, T. G., Hinton, J. F., Harms, G. 1992. Three dimensional structure of gramicidin in SDS micelles. *Biophys. J.* 61:A525 (Abstr.)

158. Turano, B., Pear, M., Busath, D. 1992. Gramicidin channel selectivity. Molecular mechanics calculations for formamidinium, guanidinium, and acetamidinium. *Biophys. J.* 63:152–61

159. Urban, B. W., Hladky, S. B., Haydon, D. A. 1980. Ion movements in gramicidin pores. An example of single-file transport. *Biochim. Biophys. Acta* 602: 331–54

160. Urry, D. W. 1971. The gramicidin A transmembrane channel: a proposed $\pi_{(L,D)}$ helix. *Proc. Natl. Acad. Sci. USA* 68:672–76

161. Urry, D. W. 1987. NMR relaxation studies of alkali metal ion interactions with the gramicidin A transmembrane channel. *Bull. Mag. Res.* 9(4):109–31

162. Urry, D. W., Alonso-Romanowski, S., Venkatachalam, C. M., Bradley, R. J., Harris, R. D. 1984. Temperature dependence of single channel currents and the peptide libration mechanism for ion transport through the gramicidin A transmembrane channel. *J. Membr. Biol.* 81:205–17

163. Urry, D. W., Alonso-Romanowski, S., Venkatachalam, C. M., Trapane, T. L., Harris, R. D., et al. 1984. Shortened analog of the gramicidin A channel argues for the doubly occupied channel as the dominant conducting state. *Biochim. Biophys. Acta* 775:115–19

164. Urry, D. W., Alonso-Romanowski, S., Venkatachalam, C. M., Trapane, T. L., Prasad, K. U. 1984. The source of the dispersity of gramicidin A single-channel conductances. The L-Leu5-gramicidin A analog. *Biophys. J.* 46: 259–65

165. Urry, D. W., Goodall, M. C., Glickson, J. D., Mayers, D. F. 1971. The gramicidin A transmembrane channel: characteristics of head-to-head dimerized $\pi_{(L,D)}$ helices. *Proc. Natl. Acad. Sci. USA* 68:1907–11

166. Urry, D. W., Prasad, K. U., Trapane, T. L. 1982. Location of monovalent cation binding sites in the gramicidin channel. *Proc. Natl. Acad. Sci. USA* 79:390–94

167. Urry, D. W., Spisni, A., Khaled, A. 1979. Characterization of micellarpackaged gramicidin A channels. *Biochem. Biophys. Res. Commun.* 88: 940–49

168. Urry, D. W., Trapane, T. L., Prasad, K. U. 1983. Is the gramicidin A transmembrane channel single-stranded or doublestranded helix? A simple unequivocal determination. *Science* 221:1064–67

169. Urry, D. W., Trapane, T. L., Venkatachalam, C. M., McMichens, R. B. 1989. Ion interactions at membranous polypeptide sites using nuclear magnetic-resonance-determining rate and binding constants and site locations. *Meth. Enzymol.* 171:286–342

170. Urry, D. W., Venkatachalam, C. M., Spisni, A., Läuger, P., Khaled, M. A. 1980. Rate theory calculation of gramicidin single-channel currents using NMR-derived rate constants. *Proc. Natl. Acad. Sci. USA* 77:2028–32

171. Veatch, W. R., Fossel, E. T., Blout, E. R. 1974. The conformation of gramicidin A. *Biochemistry* 13:5249–56

172. Venkatachalam, C. M., Alonso-Romanowski, S., Prasad, K. U., Urry, D. W. 1984. The Leu-5 gramicidin A analog: Molecular mechanics calculations and analysis of single channel steps related to multiplicity of conducting states. *Int. J. Quantum Chem. Quantum Biol. Symp.* 11:315–26

173. Venkatachalam, C. M., Urry, D. W. 1983. Theoretical conformational analysis of the gramicidin A transmembrane channel. I. Helix sense and energetics of head-to-head dimerization. *J. Comp. Chem.* 4:461–69

174. Venkatachalam, C. M., Urry, D. W. 1984. Theoretical analysis of gramicidin A transmembrane channel. II. Energetics of helical librational states of the channel. *J. Comp. Chem.* 5:64–71

175. Wallace, B. A. 1983. Gramicidin A adopts distinctly different conformations in membranes and in organic solvents. *Biopolymers* 22:397–402

176. Wallace, B. A. 1986. Structure of gramicidin A. *Biophys. J.* 49:295–306

177. Wallace, B. A. 1990. Gramicidin channels and pores. *Annu. Rev. Biophys. Biophys. Chem.* 19:127–57

178. Wallace, B. A., Janes, R. W. 1991. Co-crystals of gramicidin A and phos-

pholipid. A system for studying the structure of a transmembrane channel. *J. Mol. Biol.* 217:625–27

179. Weaver, A. J., Kemple, M. D., Prendergast, F. G. 1988. Tryptophan sidechain dynamics in hydrophobic oligopeptides determined by use of ^{13}-C nuclear magnetic resonance spectroscopy. *Biophys. J.* 54:1–15

180. Weinstein, S., Durkin, J. T., Veatch, W. R., Blount, E. R. 1985. Conformation of the gramicidin A channel in phospholipid vesicles: a fluorine-^{19} nuclear magnetic resonance study. *Biochemistry* 24:4374–82

181. Weiss, M. S., Abele, U., Weckesser, J., Welte, W., Schiltz, E., et al. 1991. Molecular architecture and electrostatic properties of a bacterial porin. *Science* 254:1627–30

Annu. Rev. Physiol. 1993. 55:503–25

COMPARATIVE ASPECTS OF MUSCLE CAPILLARY SUPPLY

Odile Mathieu-Costello

Department of Medicine, University of California, San Diego, La Jolla, California 92093–0623

KEY WORDS: O_2 transport, morphometry, bird, bat, tuna

INTRODUCTION

Since the pioneering work of Krogh (29) on the modeling of O_2 supply to tissue, that of Schmidt-Nielsen & Pennycuik (59) on muscle capillary density in relation to animal size and oxygen consumption, and that of Romanul (57) on capillary supply and muscle fiber aerobic capacity , numerous studies have examined muscle capillarity in a variety of animals and experimental conditions. Comparative approaches are useful to investigate basic features and limits in the design of muscle capillary supply. They allow one to exploit large differences among muscles or animals in functional and metabolic characteristics, requirements, and constraints. Krogh (29) found a coarser capillary network in muscles of cold-blooded animals (cod and frog) than in warm-blooded animals of different size (horse, dog, guinea pig). Comparing capillary counts in muscles of mammals varying over a range of about 100,000-fold in body size (bat to cattle), Schmidt-Nielsen & Pennycuik (59) found a greater capillary density in the smallest animals (bat, mouse, rat), but no clear relation between capillarity and body size thereafter (rat to cattle).

This article reviews current knowledge on the size and geometry of the capillary network in various muscles, with particular emphasis on the comparison of highly aerobic muscles across species and animal groups (mammal, bird, and fish). Over the last decade, there has been a number of developments in the structural assessment of muscle capillarity, as well as functional aspects of vascular supply and blood-tissue exchange kinetics. First we briefly examine methodological aspects of muscle capillary-to-fiber morphometry. We summarize which measurements can be made and their significance in terms of muscle potential for blood-tissue exchange. Then we explore similarities and differences in muscle capillary supply across species.

503

0066–4278/93/0315–0503$02.00

We compare the most O_2 demanding skeletal muscles in mammal, bird, and fish, as well as mammalian heart and less aerobic muscles, and we examine functional implications in terms of O_2 delivery, fiber O_2 demand, and O_2 flux from capillary to muscle mitochondria in highly aerobic muscles.

METHODOLOGY

Structural Assessment of Muscle Capillarity

MORPHOMETRY   Historically, the most frequently used method to estimate muscle capillarity has been to use transverse sections to the muscle fiber axis and count the number of capillary profiles (i.e. sections) per unit cross-sectional area of muscle or per number of fiber. The first measurement, commonly called capillary density (or capillary per fiber square millimeter), was used by Krogh (29) in his classical study of muscle capillarity and O_2 supply. The second measurement is capillary-to-fiber ratio. Both estimates are still widely used in the literature. They present both advantages and disadvantages compared to one another. Capillary density incorporates fiber size, i.e. it accounts for differences in diffusion distances when comparing capillarity between muscles or experimental conditions. However, it is sensitive to any perturbation in fiber size, for example, as a result of animal growth, experimental procedure, or tissue preparation, in addition to changes in capillary number per se. Capillary-to-fiber ratio $N_N(c,f)$ is not affected by changes in fiber size due to preparation procedures, but it does not incorporate possible differences in fiber size between animals or experimental conditions in the estimate of muscle potential for blood-tissue exchange.

Plyley & Groom (49) introduced the idea of considering muscle capillary supply on an individual fiber basis by measuring the number of capillaries around a fiber, N_{CAF}, as well as the sharing factor, SF, which is the number of fibers sharing a capillary, $SF = N_{CAF}/N_N(c,f)$. Several methods have also been proposed to quantify capillary spatial heterogeneity and the distribution of diffusion distances in muscle transverse sections (see 8 for review). Appell & Hammersen (2) pointed out that capillary counts in muscle transverse sections do not fully account for capillary geometry. Unless capillaries are convoluted enough to be intercepted several times by the same plane of sectioning, counting capillary number in transverse sections is totally insensitive to capillary tortuosity. Stereological theory posits that if capillaries are perfectly oriented parallel to the muscle fiber axis (no tortuosity, no branching), capillary counts per unit cross-sectional area of muscle fibers are a direct estimate of capillary length per fiber volume. On the contrary, they underestimate the length of capillaries by 100% if those are randomly oriented relative to the muscle fiber axis. The morphometric assessment of capillary geometry in muscles is a difficult problem because of the partial orientation of vessels. Capillaries run mostly parallel to the muscle fibers with some degree of tortuosity and branching. We proposed a model-based method to estimate muscle capillary length density (31). Briefly, the more convoluted muscle capillaries are, the greater the probability of intercepting them in a section taken parallel to the muscle fiber axis (i.e. longitudinal section). Using the ratio of capillary density (i.e. number per fiber sectional area) in transverse and longitudinal sections, one can quantify the degree of capillary orientation and estimate capillary length per fiber volume. The method is based on the so-called spherical normal Fisher (or Dimroth-Watson; 6) axial distribution of capillary segments relative to the muscle fiber axis. Briefly, the distribution gives the probability density function of intercepting capillaries in transverse and longitudinal sections, depending on their degree of orientation. Thus knowing how many capillaries are found per fiber mm^2 in muscle transverse and longitudinal sections allows one to estimate their degree of orientation. Once capillary orientation is known, one can estimate capillary length per volume of muscle fiber and the percentage of capillary length added by tortuosity and branching (31). The systematic analysis of sections taken at various angles from 0 to 90° to the muscle fiber axis revealed that the Dimroth-Watson model provides quite a good fit to capillary orientation distribution in a variety of muscles with widely different capillary density and geometry such as cat extended soleus (31), rat solei fixed at different sarcomere lengths (32), rat heart (51), and pigeon pectoralis muscle (35). Indirect evidence that the Dimroth-Watson distribution closely describes capillary orientation was also recently obtained in muscles with extremely high O_2 demand and capillary density such as bat pectoralis, hummingbird flight muscle, and tuna red muscle (36). Unbiased estimates of capillary surface per fiber volume can be obtained using the vertical section method of Baddeley et al (4). Gokhale (15) recently proposed a method to obtain unbiased estimates of curve length density from the projection of vertical sections. Both methods are elegant and very powerful. They allow one to obtain estimates of capillary surface and length density without assumptions regarding their degree of orientation. However, to date, there has not been a nonmodel-based method available to estimate the degree of orientation of partially oriented structures, such as capillaries in muscles. As shown further in the text, using the Dimroth-Watson axial distribution allows quantification of capillary geometry and thus comparison between muscle and species.

POTENTIAL SOURCES OF ERRORS   Estimates of capillary density (i.e. number of capillaries per fiber cross-sectional area) are sensitive to factors that affect fiber size such as tissue preparation and changes in fiber girth with muscle shortening or extension. It is generally accepted that minimal dimensional changes occur in material prepared for histochemistry, while some shrinkage can occur during tissue fixation and preparation for electron microscopy, although the issue is not fully resolved (7, 47). Gray & Renkin (16) pointed out the importance of normalizing data to sarcomere length when comparing capillary density and fiber size in different muscles. Unfortunately, this source of variation is generally not taken into account, and sarcomere length is practically never reported when data on fiber size or capillarity are compared between muscles. This is particularly important in perfusion-fixed tissue where ranges in sarcomere length can be very large, for example 1.74–2.85 μm, depending on joint position during fixation. Even in muscle biopsies, where fibers are generally shortened when the tissue is prepared without fixation of length, as much as 30% difference in sarcomere length can be found between samples (40).

Estimation of capillary orientation and length density is best done after muscle vascular perfusion fixation in situ to avoid capillary collapsing and fiber kinking in immersion-fixed tissue. The degree of contraction or extension of the muscles, i.e. sarcomere length, must also be taken into consideration when capillary geometry is compared between muscles (52). It is known that capillary tortuosity is a direct function of sarcomere length. It can add as much as 70% to capillary length in shortened muscles (32, 41, 39), while capillaries straighten and then stretch during muscle extension (9). Because capillary geometry can vary between muscles and animals (e.g. mammalian hindlimb, heart and bird flight muscle; see below), it is not appropriate to compare muscle capillarity based on capillary density in transverse section only, even if all muscles are fixed at the same sarcomere length. Because the preservation of intercellular spaces during preparation for histology and electron microscopy is unreliable, estimates of capillarity are best determined relative to fiber volume as a reference space rather than muscle volume.

NEW DIRECTIONS   In recent years, an effort was made to find an index of capillarity in transverse sections that accounted for the three-dimensional arrangement of the capillary network. Considering capillary-to-fiber contact length in muscle transverse sections allows one to incorporate the increased surface area resulting from capillary tortuosity and anastomoses into the estimate of the muscle potential for blood-tissue exchange (62). This concept is particularly important considering the potential role of the capillary-to-fiber interface in determining O_2 flux rates in red muscles (22). We derived stereological equations that show how capillary-to-fiber perimeter ratio in transverse sections is related to other estimates of muscle capillarity (capillary density, capillary-to-fiber ratio, etc), capillary geometry, and fiber size. The effect of sarcomere length on these variables showed that while capillary density, capillary geometry, and fiber size vary substantially with fiber shortening, the ratio between capillary perimeter and fiber perimeter in transverse sections (i.e. capillary-to-fiber perimeter ratio) itself changes little with sarcomere length. This allows a direct comparison of the structural potential for blood-tissue exchange in muscles of different fiber size or examined at different sarcomere length (38). Considering not only mitochondrial volume density in the muscle fibers $V_V(mt,f)$, but also the product of $V_V(mt,f)$ and fiber cross-sectional area allows one to examine estimates of capillary supply (e.g. the number around a fiber N_{CAF} and capillary surface per fiber surface) on an individual fiber basis, i.e. relative to the volume of mitochondria per unit length of fiber. This is particularly useful when red muscles with widely differing fiber size are compared (43).

Correlation with Function

O_2 DELIVERY Morphometric estimates of muscle capillarity are indicators of the maximum structural potential for supply of the muscle fibers. They provide insights on the amount and distribution of capillary circuitry available for blood-tissue exchange into which functional variables such as blood flow, red cell velocity patterns, and oxygenation can be incorporated. Capillary density, fiber size, and the distribution of capillary distances permit comparison of structural diffusion distances among muscles, while capillary-to-fiber number ratio is an indicator of the potential for supply of the muscle fibers independently of their size. Looking at the number of capillaries around a fiber allows consideration of vascular supply on an individual fiber basis and the sharing factor accounts for the spatial distribution of capillaries relative to the muscle fibers. Capillary length per fiber volume influences transit time as well as the amount of capillary surface available for exchange per volume of muscle fiber and mitochondria. Capillary-to-fiber perimeter in transverse sections is an index of the amount of capillary surface per fiber surface, i.e. the size of the capillary-to-fiber interface, which is one of the determinants of O_2 flux rate. Fiber size influences practically every aspect of muscle capillary supply. It determines maximal diffusion distance to the center of the muscle fibers and affects capillary density and intercapillary distances and distribution, capillary length and surface per fiber volume, as well as capillary-to-fiber surface ratio and mitochondrial volume per fiber. The space between capillaries and muscle fibers is an important component of the diffusion path from capillary to muscle mitochondria. It does not contain O_2 carriers and thus can represent a major site of resistance to O_2 transport. Unfortunately, the preservation of intercellular spaces during tissue preparation is unreliable. Data on the size of the intercellular compartment in situ and comparison between muscles are not available.

O_2 DEMAND   Since the pioneering work of Krogh (29) and Romanul (57), muscle capillarity has traditionally been considered almost exclusively in relation to muscle aerobic capacity, although more recently evidence has emerged that the role of muscle capillaries for functions other than O_2 supply need also to be taken into account, especially in glycolytic muscles (26). In tissues prepared for electron microscopy, O_2 demand is assessed by estimating mitochondrial volume density. Again, this represents the maximum potential for O_2 consumption in the muscle fibers. The surface density of inner mitochondrial membrane per volume of mitochondria varied by as much as twofold, from 200,000 to 400,000 cm^2/cm^3 in skeletal muscles of mammals (mice to wildebeest), with no apparent relationship with body size or muscle aerobic capacity (24). Similarly, values in cardiac muscle (310,000–450,000 cm^2/cm^3) were not dependent on body size (mice to cattle; 25). However, in hummingbird flight muscle (61) and in tuna red muscle (45), the packing density of inner mitochondrial membranes was greater than in mammalian skeletal and cardiac muscles. It reached values of 600,000 (hummingbird) and 700,000 (tuna) cm^2/cm^3, which may represent upper limits to the packing of the electron transport chain enzymes (cristae), while allowing enough space for Krebs cycle enzymes (matrix) in mitochondria (61). Knowing animal maximal oxygen consumption, muscle mass, and mitochondrial volume, one can calculate average in situ mitochondrial respiratory rates in animals operating at their maximum aerobic capacity. Interestingly, this maximal O_2 consumption of a unit volume of mitochondria was invariant (close to 5 ml O_2 per min per ml mitochondria) in mammals varying in body size by more than five orders of magnitude (24). However, respiratory rates of muscle mitochondria in flying hummingbirds are approximately two times higher than in locomotory muscles of mammals running at $\dot{V}_{O_2}$ max (61). This suggests a greater capacity for O_2 flux from capillary to muscle mitochondria in the hummingbird.

LOOKING AT EXTREMES

In most muscles, the study of capillarity in relation to functional needs and fiber metabolism is difficult because of the complexity of fiber type distribution. The majority of skeletal muscles is composed of a mosaic of fiber types, and it is often difficult to assess specific vascular supply to surrounding fibers with widely differing functional and metabolic properties. Thus a number of studies have concentrated on relatively homogeneous red and white muscles and compared them with mixed muscles with different proportions of fiber types. Several generalizations have emerged: (a) the much greater capillary densities in red than white muscles are mainly due to differences in fiber size, while the number of capillaries around a fiber is relatively constant (3.2–4.0) over a wide range of muscle capillary densities (49); (*b*) relating capillary length and fiber mitochondrial volume in a variety of muscles (locomotory, diaphragm, and heart) in mammals (shrew to cattle) suggests that there is approximately 10 km of capillary length per ml of mitochondria in a muscle irrespective of its type (23); (*c*) contradictory to previous reports suggesting a more sinuous course of capillaries in red muscles (1, 56, 57), we found that in a variety of locomotory muscles of mammals (mouse to cattle) differing in capillary density by almost threefold, capillary tortuosity was a function of sarcomere length, not aerobic capacity (33); (*d*) in fact, capillary tortuosity and the effect of fiber shortening on capillary geometry were less in highly aerobic flight muscle of pigeon (35) and in rat myocardium (50) than in mammalian skeletal muscles.

The Most O_2-Demanding Skeletal Muscles

The comparative study of ultimate cases of muscles with extremely high aerobic capacity is of particular interest to explore upper limits as well as strategies and constraints in structural design(s) for high O_2 fluxes from capillary to muscle mitochondria. For example, the highly aerobic pectoralis muscle of pigeon shows not only a greater capillary density and a smaller fiber size than mammalian hindlimb muscles, but it also has a different capillary arrangement. Venular portions of the capillary bed are oriented perpendicular to the muscle fiber axis, forming manifolds around groups of muscle fibers (53). Such an arrangement may have several advantages. It could facilitate augmented capillary supply to and from the muscle fibers at the venular end of the network where substrates and O_2 content are lowest and metabolite concentration highest. It could also be related to other functional aspects of O_2 delivery such as heat dissipation and/or the blood pumping action of the muscle during flight (17), or it may compensate for the less favorable rheological properties of the avian blood cells (10, 11). Thus it is particularly intriguing to examine the geometry of the capillary network in the most highly aerobic skeletal muscle of bird (hummingbird flight muscle) in comparison to those in the flight muscle of a mammal (bat) and in a highly aerobic muscle of a very athletic fish (tuna). Ultimate cases of high O_2 demand in bird, mammal, and fish muscles are solely composed of one population of fibers (highly aerobic fast-twitch), which facilitates the analysis of vascular supply in relation to muscle fiber aerobic capacity. Fish red blood cells are nucleated, as in bird, but they can be much larger than bird red cells, and fishes operate at different body temperature than birds and mammals. Thus one can expect similarities in terms of high O_2 demand, but also different constraints on vascular supply and fiber metabolism in each animal group.

In this section, we examine the structural design for maximal O_2 flux in the hummingbird flight muscle, which is the most aerobic muscle among vertebrates. Then we investigate similarities and differences with the vascular supply of the flight muscle of a small bat, the red muscle of tuna, and the red but less aerobic hindlimb muscles of mammals such as rat and bat. Until recently little was known on capillary-to-fiber geometry in relation to O_2 demand in such muscles. We briefly summarize recently published data from our laboratory (37, 42, 43).

HUMMINGBIRD   Small fiber size, dense capillary network, and high aerobic capacity of muscle fibers are characteristic features of the hummingbird flight muscle (18, 30). They are illustrated in Figure 1, which shows the dramatic difference in fiber size and capillary density between hummingbird flight muscle and a mammalian limb muscle such as rat M. soleus. In 3–4 g hummingbirds (*Selaphorus rufus*) pectoralis and supracoracoideus muscles,

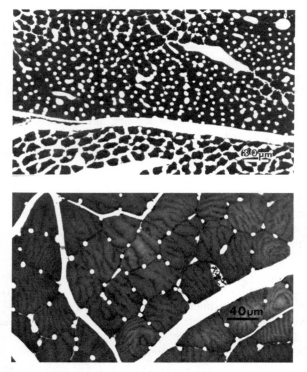

Figure 1   Light micrographs of portions of muscle bundles in transverse sections showing the large difference in fiber size and capillary density between hummingbird flight muscle (*top*) and rat soleus muscle (*bottom*). Capillaries are empty after vascular perfusion fixation (top micrograph is from Reference 42).

average fiber cross-sectional area was 201 ± 14 (SE) μm^2 at 2.1 μm sarcomere length (42). This is about one tenth that of the rat soleus muscle at the same sarcomere length (32). Comparable values for aerobic fibers in pigeon pectoralis muscle and for dog hindlimb are about two and eight times greater than in hummingbird (34, 35). Capillary density (i.e. number per fiber cross-sectional area) in hummingbird flight muscle was ~ 8000 mm^{-2}, which is about two, five, and six times greater than in pigeon pectoralis, dog hindlimb, and rat soleus muscle, respectively. The denser capillarity in hummingbird is mainly due to the smaller fiber size, rather than an increase in capillary number. In fact, the number of capillaries per fiber (i.e. capillary-to-fiber ratio) was lower in hummingbird flight muscles (group mean, 1.6 ± 0.1) than in other muscles (pigeon pectoralis, 2.0 ± 0.1; dog hindlimb, and rat M. soleus, 2.6 ± 0.3). The number of capillaries around a fiber (measured in muscle transverse sections) was 4.82 ± 0.15 in hummingbird flight muscle. This yields an average capillary sharing factor (i.e. number of fibers sharing one capillary) of about 3.1. It is in the upper range of sharing factor values in mammalian striated muscles (49).

Capillary geometry is similar to that in pectoralis muscle of pigeon (35, 53) in that capillaries running parallel to the muscle fibers as well as branches oriented perpendicular to the muscle fiber axis are found (Figure 2), which suggests the presence of capillary manifolds in hummingbird flight muscle. However, there is also a substantial amount of tortuosity in portions of capillaries in the hummingbird (Figure 2). Overall, the degree of orientation of capillaries was intermediate between that in pigeon and rat muscles at similar sarcomere length (see below). Because of the great capillary density,

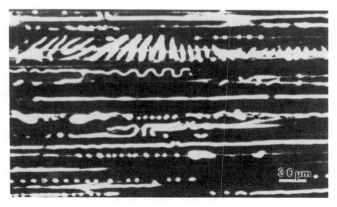

Figure 2 Light micrograph of a portion of muscle bundle in longitudinal section of hummingbird flight muscle that shows sections of straight and/or tortuous capillaries, as well as others cut in transverse or oblique sections, which suggests the presence of capillary manifolds in the muscle. Sarcomere length was 2.03 μm (from Reference 42).

the capillary length added by tortuosity and branching in hummingbird flight muscle is very large. It ranged from 1052 to 2122 mm per mm^3 of fiber volume, which is similar to the entire capillary length per fiber volume in rat soleus or dog gastrocnemius muscles.

Mitochondrial volume density (i.e. volume of mitochondria per volume of fiber) is about 35% in hummingbird flight muscles, with approximately one half to one third of total fractional volume of mitochondria being subsarcolemmal, i.e. located in close proximity to the muscle cell membrane. If we divide capillary length per fiber volume by mitochondrial volume density, we find that there is about 26 km of capillary length per ml of mitochondria in the muscle fibers of the hummingbird flight muscle. Capillary surface per fiber volume was 1170 ± 100 cm^2/cm^3 (group mean$\pm$SE) in the same samples, yielding a capillary surface of about 3400 cm^3 per ml of mitochondria. Both values of capillary length and surface per unit volume of mitochondria in the hummingbird are more than twice those estimated for mammalian muscles based on the study of limb, diaphragm, and heart samples in a series of animals ranging in size from shrew to cattle (23). In hummingbird, the aggregate surface area of inner and outer mitochondrial membranes is about 200 and 20 times greater than capillary surface area, respectively. On average, mitochondrial volume per μm length of fiber (i.e. the product of mitochondrial volume density and fiber cross-sectional area) is $\sim$75 μm^3. This volume is supplied by four to five capillaries running along each fiber and some capillary branches oriented perpendicular to the muscle fiber axis. Capillary-to-fiber perimeter ratio in transverse sections, a measure of capillarity that accounts for capillary geometry, but is relatively insensitive to sarcomere length is about 35% (42).

BAT   Small fiber size (13), high aerobic capacity (3) and high capillary density (48) are also found in the flight muscle of bats. In pectoralis muscle of 15–16 g big brown bats (*Eptesicus fuscus*; Figure 3), fiber cross-sectional area at 2.1 μm sarcomere length was 318 ± 10 μm^2 (43), a value comparable or smaller than that of aerobic fibers in pigeon pectoralis muscle (35). On average, this is about 50% greater than fiber size in hummingbird flight muscle.

Striking similarities between bat and hummingbird flight muscle morphometrics include the high values for capillary length density ($\sim$ 9000 mm/mm^3 fiber volume), capillary surface per fiber volume ($\sim$ 1200 cm^2/cm^3) and mitochondrial volume per volume of fiber ($\sim$ 35%). Thus as in hummingbird flight muscles, capillary length and surface per ml of fiber mitochondria in pectoralis muscle of bat are more than twofold greater than previously estimated for mammalian muscle, based on the study of various muscles including the highly aerobic diaphragm and heart muscles of the shrew, i.e. the smallest mammal (23). The similar capillary length and surface per fiber

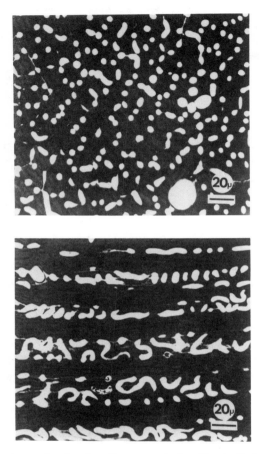

Figure 3 Light micrographs of portion of transverse (*top*) and longitudinal section (*bottom*) of bat pectoralis muscle. Note high capillary density, small fiber size, and substantial degree of capillary tortuosity. Sarcomere length was 2.17 μm (from Reference 43).

volume in bat and hummingbird flight muscles are achieved by different capillary geometries. We mentioned above the 50% greater fiber size in bat. Capillary-to-fiber ratio is about 30% greater in bat, and there is a greater contribution of capillary tortuosity in bat than hummingbird (compare Figures 3, 2). However, capillary length per fiber volume, i.e. capillary-to-fiber ratio times capillary orientation coefficient divided by fiber cross-sectional area, is remarkably similar in the two muscles. Similarly, capillary number around a fiber and capillary-to-fiber perimeter ratio are about 20% greater in bat than hummingbird. Because of the greater fiber size, the volume of mitochondria per μm length of fiber (i.e. the product of mitochondrial volume density and fiber cross-sectional area) is also greater in the bat. On average, there is about 105 μm^3 mitochondrial volume per μm length of fiber in bat pectoralis muscle. This volume is supplied by five to six capillaries running along each fiber. Capillary-to-fiber surface ratio is about 46%, a value 24% greater than in the hummingbird. However, the size of the capillary-to-fiber interface (i.e. capillary surface per fiber surface) per unit mitochondrial volume in the muscle fibers is about the same in the two muscles.

TUNA   In red muscle of tuna, similar to hummingbird and bat flight muscles, fiber size is small, and capillary density and mitochondrial volume density (5, 14, 27) are high. In the red muscle of 1.5 to 2 kg skipjack tuna (*Katsuwonus pelamis*), fiber cross-sectional area at 2.1 μm sarcomere length was 475±25 μm^2 (37), which is about eightfold smaller than in white muscle in the same animal. Compared with hummingbird and bat flight muscles, tuna red muscle fibers are 2.4 and 1.5 times greater, respectively. They are almost as small as aerobic fibers of pigeon flight muscle (35) and three to four times smaller than dog hindlimb or rat soleus muscle fibers. Capillary length density (∼ 4000 mm/mm^3 fiber volume) and capillary surface per fiber volume (∼ 500 cm^2/cm^3) are less than half those in hummingbird and bat flight muscle, while mitochondrial volume density (∼ 28%) is almost as high as in those muscles. Thus capillary length and surface per unit volume of mitochondria are smaller than in hummingbird and bat flight muscle. They are close to those seen in mammalian limb, diaphragm, and heart (see above). There is about 15 km of capillary length and 1800 cm^2 of capillary surface per ml of mitochondria in tuna red muscle.

Interestingly, capillary-to-fiber geometry in tuna red muscle shows similarities to both bird flight muscle and skeletal muscles of mammals. Longitudinal sections and corrosion casts show a large number of capillary branches oriented perpendicular to the muscle fibers (Figure 4), which suggests the presence of capillary manifolds in tuna red muscle. However, the contribution of those branches to capillary length is much greater than in bird flight muscle The percentage added to capillary length (compared with straight unbranched capillaries running strictly parallel to the muscle fibers) was 44±4% (group mean, ± SE) in tuna red muscle. This value is remarkably similar to that in rat limb muscles at the same sarcomere length, in spite of the dramatic difference in capillary geometry between the muscles (37, 41). The added capillary length in tuna red muscle (1300 mm per mm^3 of fiber) is almost as great as that in hummingbird flight muscle (group mean, 1400 mm/mm^3) with substantially greater capillary density.

In tuna red muscle, the aggregate surface of inner and outer mitochondrial membranes is about 400 and 40 times greater than capillary surface area,

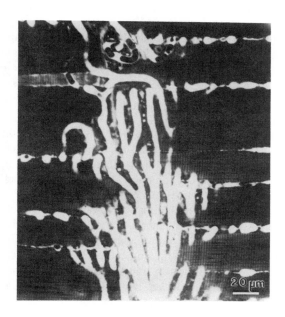

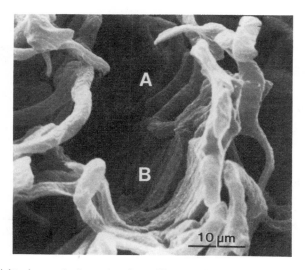

Figure 4 Light micrograph of a section of a capillary manifold in a longitudinal section of tuna red muscle (*top*). The scanning electron micrograph of a cross-sectional view of a corrosion cast from tuna red muscle (*bottom*) shows the dense envelope formed by capillaries around muscle fibers. Based on fiber dimensions, two muscle fibers (*A* and *B*) could be contained in the empty space (from Reference 37).

respectively. In other words, capillary surface per mitochondrial inner (and outer) membrane surface area in tuna red muscle is about half that in hummingbird flight muscle. Mitochondrial volume per μm length of muscle fiber is about 160 μm³. It is supplied by four to five capillaries running along each fiber. These capillaries and branches oriented perpendicular to the muscle fiber axis yield a capillary-to-fiber perimeter ratio of about 30%.

Comparison with Rat and Bat Limb Muscles

Figure 5 summarizes data on capillary geometry. We mentioned the substantial increase in capillary tortuosity with fiber shortening in hindlimb muscles of mammals. The solid line in Figure 5 shows that tortuosity and branching can add as much as 70% to capillary length in shortened limb muscles of rat. In pigeon flight muscle (broken line) this contribution is much less because of the different capillary geometry. In tuna where capillary manifolds are found (as in pigeon flight muscle), the contribution of tortuosity and branching to capillary length is similar to that in rat hindlimb, and it is much greater than in pigeon flight muscle at the same sarcomere length. This reflects differences in relative numbers of capillaries in transverse and longitudinal sections to the muscle fiber axis between muscles. It could be due to differences in length and/or number of branches in capillary manifolds in tuna compared with pigeon.

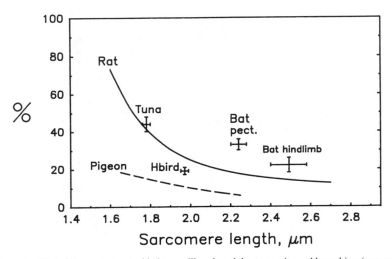

Figure 5   Plot of the percentage added to capillary length by tortuosity and branching (compared with straight, unbranched capillaries oriented parallel to the muscle fiber axis) against sarcomere length in various muscles. Values are mean±SE from (tuna) (37); (hummingbird) (42); (bat muscles) (43). Relationships in rat hindlimb (*solid line*) and pigeon pectoralis muscles (*broken line*) are from References 38 and 35, respectively.

There is a strong linear relationship between capillary length per fiber volume and fiber mitochondrial volume density in rat soleus and bat hindlimb and pectoralis muscles (Figure 6). The linear regression (r = 0.99) yields a capillary length per fiber volume of 8857 mm^{-2} at 35% mitochondrial volume density. This value is almost identical to that found in hummingbird flight muscle with the same mitochondrial volume density. The fact that there is a strong relationship between capillary length and fiber mitochondrial volume density was previously demonstrated in a variety of mammalian muscles (23). The examination of highly aerobic flight muscles of bat and hummingbird, as well as less aerobic bat hindlimbs, showed that capillary length per unit volume of mitochondria can be much greater than previously thought. It is also interesting to note that the capillary length per mitochondrial volume density is as great in tuna red muscle as in mammalian heart (Figure 6).

Looking at capillary supply on an individual fiber basis, we find that capillary-to-fiber ratio is linearly related to mitochondrial volume per unit length of fiber in hummingbird, bat and rat muscles (Figure 7), i.e. in muscles

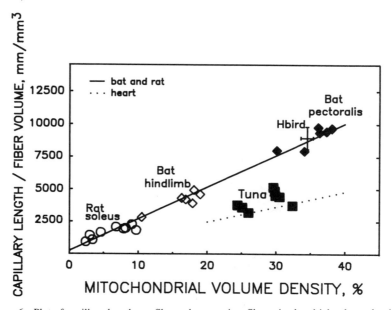

Figure 6 Plot of capillary length per fiber volume against fiber mitochondrial volume density in various muscles. Linear relationship in bat pectoralis (*filled diamond*); bat hindlimb (*open diamond*); and rat M. soleus (*open circle*). [y = (249 • x) + 142; r = 0.993] is from Reference 43. Values in tuna red muscle (*filled square*) and group mean ± SE in hummingbird flight muscle are from References 37 and 42, respectively. Relationship in mammalian heart [y = (118 • x) + 86; r = 0.85] is from Reference 23.

with extremely large differences in capillary and mitochondrial densities (Figure 6). The linear regression (r = 0.90) yields an average capillary-to-fiber ratio of 2.75 at 160 μm^3 mitochondrial volume per μm length of fiber. This is about one more capillary per fiber than in tuna red muscle with a similar mitochondrial volume per μm fiber length. The number of capillaries around a fiber is also linearly related to mitochondrial volume per μm fiber length in the muscles (Figure 8). Differences between Figures 7 and 8 reflect the variability in sharing factor values between muscles and muscle groups.

The size of the capillary-to-fiber interface (i.e. capillary surface per unit surface area of fiber) is unrelated to fiber size or maximal diffusion distance from sarcolemma to the center of the muscle fibers over the range of fiber cross-sectional areas (Figure 9) and shows striking features with respect to mitochondrial volume in the muscle fibers (Figure 10). In tuna red muscle, capillary surface per unit surface area of fiber is similar to that in rat M. soleus at the same mitochondrial volume per μm length of fiber. In hummingbird and bat flight muscles, where capillary-to-fiber ratio at a given mitochondrial volume per fiber μm length is similar to that in rat M. soleus (Figure 7), the smaller fiber size yields a greater capillary-to-fiber interface than in rat soleus and tuna red muscles, at the same volume of mitochondria per μm fiber length in the muscles (Figure 10).

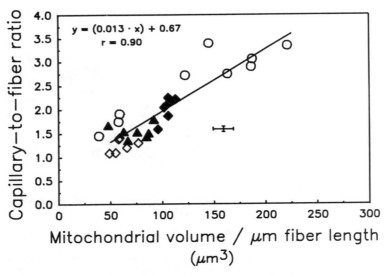

Figure 7 Correlation between capillary-to-fiber ratio and mitochondrial volume per μm fiber length in hummingbird flight muscles (*filled triangle*; 42), bat pectoralis (*filled diamond*), bat hindlimb (*open diamond*), and rat soleus muscle (*open circle*; 43). Group mean value (± SE) in tuna red muscle (37) is shown for comparison.

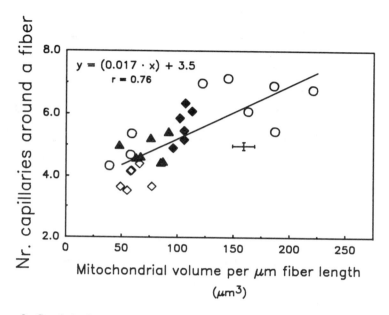

Figure 8 Correlation between capillary number around a fiber and mitochondrial volume per μm fiber length in hummingbird flight muscle (*filled triangle*; 42), bat pectoralis (*filled diamond*), bat hindlimb (*open diamond*), and rat M. soleus (*open circle*; 43). Group mean value (±SE) in red tuna muscle (37) is shown for comparison.

Comparison with Heart

Small fibers and high capillary densities (54, 55, 63), as well as high mitochondrial volume densities (23, 24, 28, 58), are typically found in the heart. In rat myocardium, fiber cross-sectional area at 2.1 μm sarcomere length (280±14 μm² (calculated from Reference 51) is very close to that in bat pectoralis muscle. However, capillary length per fiber volume is lower in the heart. It was ~ 6,000 mm⁻² in the left ventricular wall of rat hearts examined in diastole. This included a contribution of capillary tortuosity and branching of 350–1,300 mm⁻², i.e. 6–27% of capillary density in transverse sections (51). From diastole to systole, this contribution increases modestly to a maximum of 32 to 33% in calcium or barium-induced systolic hearts and capillary length per fiber volume decreases by about 20% (50). It is interesting that the effect of fiber shortening on capillary orientation is about the same in heart as in pigeon pectoralis muscle (Figure 5), with a different capillary arrangement. This may be the result of overall branching patterns, i.e. relative lengths and/or numbers of capillaries oriented at specific angles relative to

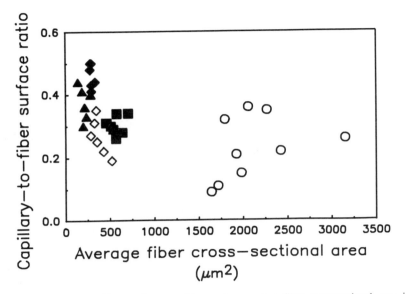

Figure 9 Plot of capillary surface per fiber surface against fiber cross-sectional area in hummingbird flight muscle (*filled triangle*; 42), bat pectoralis (*filled diamond*), bat hindlimb (*open diamond*), rat M. soleus (*open circle*; 43) and tuna red muscle (*filled square*; 37).

the muscle fiber axis in the muscles. The greater capillary length density in diastolic hearts suggests that capillary stretching occurs with fiber lengthening in the heart, as it does in skeletal muscle (9, 44, 50).

Capillary-to-fiber ratio averages 1.0 to 1.3 in rat heart (28, 51, 54, 63). Average mitochondrial volume density values of 28.5 and 33.5% (25, 58) and fiber cross-sectional areas of 280 and 310 μm^2 (28, 51) yield values for mitochondrial volume per μm fiber length of about 80 to 105 μm^3, which is remarkably close to those found in hummingbird and bat flight muscles. Calculated values of capillary-to-fiber perimeter ratio in the rat myocardium (42±2%; 51) suggest that the size of the capillary-to-fiber interface in that muscle is also very close to that in hummingbird and bat flight muscle.

Comparison with Less Aerobic Muscles

Large differences in capillary density between mixed skeletal muscles are mainly due to differences in the relative proportion of fiber types and in fiber size, while much smaller differences are found in capillary-to-fiber ratios (16). This is in keeping with the similarity in capillary-to-fiber ratio and number of capillaries around a fiber in red and white muscles with large differences in capillary density. In muscles with fiber cross-sectional area varying about

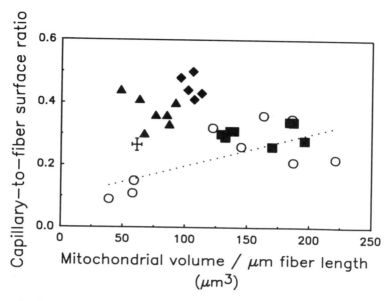

Figure 10 Plot of capillary surface per fiber surface against mitochondrial volume per μm fiber length in hummingbird flight muscle (*filled triangle*; 42), bat pectoralis (*filled diamond*), rat M. soleus (*open circle*; 43), and tuna red muscle (*filled square*; 37). Group mean value ± SE in bat hindlimb (43) is shown for comparison. The linear regression in rat soleus muscle (y = 0.0010 x + 0.1; r = 0.67) is from Reference 43.

fivefold (fibers/mm², 200–1,000), the mean number of capillaries around a fiber ranged from 3.2 to 4.0 (49). In hummingbird and bat flight muscles with fiber size < 300 μm², we find one and two additional capillaries around each fiber, respectively.

FUNCTIONAL IMPLICATIONS

Sullivan & Pittman (62) pointed out that matching O_2 demand and delivery in muscle can be achieved in nature via different strategies, i.e. by changing fiber size, or capillary-to-fiber contact area, or both. In hummingbird and bat flight muscle, we find both a small fiber size and a great capillary surface per fiber surface. Comparing these muscles with rat soleus muscle, we find that capillary-to-fiber surface ratio is unrelated to fiber size (Figure 9) and that there is a close correlation between capillary-to-fiber ratio and mitochondrial volume per μm fiber length (Figure 7). In rat soleus, mitochondrial volume density is smaller, but fiber cross-sectional area is much greater than in bat and hummingbird muscles. As a result, the product of mitochondrial density and fiber cross-sectional area (mitochondrial volume per μm length of fiber) is greater in several soleus muscles than in bat and hummingbird muscles. Interestingly, in those muscles, diffusion distances from capillary to fiber mitochondria is not reduced compared with muscles with lower mitochondrial volume, and fiber size is much greater than in hummingbird and bat flight muscles. Instead, one or two capillaries are added per fiber in soleus muscles with greater mitochondrial volume (Figure 7).

The finding of a greater capillary surface area per unit surface area of muscle fiber in hummingbird and bat flight muscle is consistent with the suggestion of an important role of the capillary-to-fiber interface in determining blood-tissue O_2 flux rates (12, 19). A greater capillary-to-fiber surface can allow flux rates to be maintained at a lower P_{O_2} at the surface of the red cell, or increased fluxes to be achieved at similar red blood cell P_{O_2} (see Reference 22 for review). The twofold greater capillary-to-fiber surface area in the hummingbird also remarkably matches the twofold greater respiratory rates of muscle mitochondria in flying hummingbirds compared with locomotory muscles of mammals running at $\dot{V}_{O_2}$ max (61). High values for capillary-to-fiber surface area at a given mitochondrial volume in the muscle fibers are also found in bat flight muscle. They suggest great capacities for O_2 fluxes. Mitochondrial respiratory rates at maximal activity in flying bats are not known, and the relationship between capillary-to-fiber geometry, O_2 delivery (e.g. blood rheology), and O_2 consumption (regulation of mitochondrial function) in bats compared with hummingbirds remain to be determined. Structural data suggest a similar structural capacity for high O_2 flux rates from capillary-to-fiber mitochondria in the flight muscle of both species.

Interestingly, calculated maximal mitochondrial respiratory rates in tuna red muscle yield substantially lower values (approximately one twentieth) than in muscles of mammals running at $\dot{V}_{O_2}$ max (37), while capillary-to-fiber surface in tuna red muscle is as large as in rat M. soleus (Figure 10). This could reflect a number of possible aspects of O_2 delivery or mitochondrial function between the muscles, including differences in operating temperature, mitochondrial regulation, and/or capillary function for tasks other than O_2 delivery per se, for example substrate or heat transfer.

CONCLUSION

The comparative study of the capillary supply of highly aerobic muscles shows that high capacities for O_2 fluxes can be achieved by different strategies, i.e. different capillary-to-fiber geometries in different muscles or animal groups. Examples are the bat and hummingbird flight muscles, where different capillary-to-fiber ratio, fiber size, and capillary arrangement yield remarkably similar length per fiber volume and mitochondrial density. Also, capillary-to-fiber surface area at a given mitochondrial volume per μm length of fiber is high and similar in the two muscles, consistent with the notion of an important role of the capillary-to-fiber interface in blood-tissue exchange kinetics. Similarly, different capillary geometry, fiber size, and capillary density yield similar capillary-to-fiber surface area per mitochondrial volume per μm fiber length in tuna and rat muscle with substantially different operational and metabolic characteristics. Combining comparative morphology with functional assessment of blood-tissue O_2 transport and mitochondrial function in muscles with different requirements should continue to provide insights into the structural design of the capillary network and its limiting aspects (or not) with respect to specific demands or constraints.

A number of histochemical assays have been developed in recent years to visualize capillaries in skeletal muscles. They include the specific staining of venular and arteriolar portions of capillaries with dipeptidyl peptidase IV and alkaline phosphatase reactions, respectively (46), the use of lectins to visualize capillary endothelium (20), and the determination of capillary filling patterns after injection of fluorescent dye (21, 60) in conjunction with fiber type histochemistry. These techniques combined with quantitative morphology and functional estimates of vascular kinematics should prove very useful in studying structure-function relationships in O_2 delivery to muscles.

Literature Cited

1. Andersen, P., Kroese, A. J. 1978. Capillary supply in soleus and gastrocnemius muscles of man. *Pflügers Arch.* 375:245–49

2. Appell, H.-J., Hammersen, F. 1978. Capillary density and patterns in skeletal muscle. II. The effect of the capillary patterns on capillary counts. *Pflügers Arch.* 373:R60

3. Armstrong, R. B., Ianuzzo, C. D., Kunz, T. H. 1977. Histochemical and biochemical properties of flight muscle fibers in the little brown bat, *Myotis lucifugus. J. Comp. Physiol. B.* 119: 141–54

4. Baddeley, A. J., Gundersen, H. J. G., Cruz-Orive, L. M. 1986. Estimation of surface area from vertical sections. *J. Microsc.* 142:259–76

5. Bone, Q. 1978. Myotomal muscle fiber types in *Scomber and Katsuwonus.* In *The Physiological Ecology of Tuna,* ed. G. D. Sharp, A. E. Dizon. pp. 183–205. New York/San Francisco/London: Academic

6. Cruz-Orive, L. M., Hoppeler, H., Mathieu, O., Weibel, E. R. 1985. Stereological analysis of anisotropic structures using directional statistics. *Appl. Stat.* 34:14–32

7. Dray, M. A., Poole, D. C., Mathieu-Costello, O. 1992. Muscle fiber cross-sectional area: comparison between fixed and frozen tissue. *Physiologist* 35:198

8. Egginton, S. 1990. Morphometric analysis of tissue capillary supply. In *Advances in Comparative and Environmental Physiology,* ed. R. G. Boutilier, 6:73–141. Berlin/Heidelberg: Springer-Verlag

9. Ellis, C. G., Mathieu-Costello, O., Potter, R. F., MacDonald, I. C., Groom, A. C. 1990. Effect of sarcomere length on total capillary length in skeletal muscle: in vivo evidence for longitudinal stretching of capillaries. *Microvasc. Res.* 40:63–72

10. Gaehtgens, P., Schmidt, F., Will, G. 1981. Comparative rheology of nucleated and non-nucleated red blood cells I: Microrheology of avian erythrocytes during capillary flow. *Pflügers Arch.* 390:278–82

11. Gaehtgens, P., Will, G., Schmidt, F. 1981. Comparative rheology of nucleated and non-nucleated red blood cells II: Rheological properties of avian red cell suspensions in narrow capillaries. *Pflügers Arch.* 390:283–87

12. Gayeski, T. E. J., Honig, C. R. 1986. O_2 gradients from sarcolemma to cell interior in red muscle at maximal V_{O_2}. *Am. J. Physiol.* 251:H789–99

13. George, J. C., Jyoti, D. 1955. Histological features of the breast and leg muscles of bird and bat and their physiological and evolutionary significance. *J. Anim. Morphol. Physiol.* 2:31–36

14. George, J. C., Stevens, E. D. 1978. Fine structure and metabolic adaptation of red and white muscles in tuna. *Env. Biol. Fish.* 3:185–91

15. Gokhale, A. M. 1990. Unbiased estimation of curve length in 3-D using vertical slices. *J. Microsc.* 159:133–41

16. Gray, S. D., Renkin, E. M. 1978. Microvascular supply in relation to fiber metabolic type in mixed skeletal muscles of rabbits. *Microvasc. Res.* 16:406–25

17. Grinyer, I., George, J. C. 1969. An electron microscopic study of the pigeon breast muscle. *Can. J. Zool.* 47:517–23

18. Grinyer, I., George, J. C. 1969. Some observations on the ultrastructure of the hummingbird pectoral muscles. *Can. J. Zool.* 47:771–74

19. Groebe, K., Thews, G. 1990. Role of geometry and anisotropic diffusion for modelling P_{O_2} profiles in working red muscle. *Respir. Physiol.* 79:255–78

20. Hansen-Smith, F. M., Watson, L., Lu, D. Y., Goldstein, I. 1988. *Griffonia simplicifolia* I: Fluorescent tracer for microcirculation vessels in nonperfused thin muscles and sectioned muscle. *Microvasc. Res.* 36:199–215

21. Hargreaves, D., Egginton, S., Hudlicka O. 1990. Changes in capillary perfusion induced by different patterns of activity in rat skeletal muscle. *Microvasc. Res.* 40:14–28

22. Honig, C. R., Gayeski, T. E. J., Groebe, K. 1991. Myoglobin and oxygen gradients. In *The Lung: Scientific Foundations,* ed. R. G. Crystal, J. B. West, P. J. Barnes, N. S. Cherniack, E. R. Weibel, pp. 1489–96. New York: Raven

23. Hoppeler, H., Kayar, S. R. 1988. Capillarity and oxidative capacity of muscles. *News Physiol. Sci.* 3:113–16

24. Hoppeler, H., Lindstedt, S. L. 1985. Malleability of skeletal muscle in overcoming limitations: Structural elements. *J. Exp. Biol.* 115:355–64

25. Hoppeler, H., Lindstedt, S. L., Claassen, H., Taylor, C. R., Mathieu, O., Weibel, E. R. 1984. Scaling mitochondrial volume in heart to body mass. *Respir. Physiol.* 55:131–37

26. Hudlicka, O., Hoppeler, H., Uhlmann, E. 1987. Relationship between the size of the capillary bed and oxidative capacity in various cat skeletal muscles. *Pflügers Arch.* 410:369–75

27. Hulbert, W. C., Guppy, M., Murphy, B., Hochachka, P. W. 1979. Metabolic sources of heat and power in tuna muscles. I. Muscle fine structure. *J. Exp. Biol.* 82:289–301

28. Kayar, S. R., Conley, K. E., Claassen, H., Hoppeler, H. 1986. Capillarity and mitochondrial distribution in rat myocardium following exercise training. *J. Exp. Biol.* 120:189–99

29. Krogh, A. 1918/19. The number and distribution of capillaries in muscles with calculations of the oxygen pressure head necessary for supplying the tissue. *J. Physiol.* 52:409–15

30. Lasiewski, R. C., Galey, F. R., Vasquez, C. 1965. Morphology and physiology of the pectoral muscles of hummingbirds. *Nature* 206:404–5

31. Mathieu, O., Cruz-Orive, L. M., Hoppeler, H., Weibel, E. R. 1983. Estimating length density and quantifying anisotropy in skeletal muscle capillaries. *J. Microsc.* 131:131–46

32. Mathieu-Costello, O. 1987. Capillary tortuosity and degree of contraction or extension of skeletal muscles. *Microvasc. Res.* 33:98–117

33. Mathieu-Costello, O. 1990. Histology of flight: Tissue and muscle gas exchange. In *Hypoxia: The Adaptations,* ed. J. R. Sutton, G. Coates, J. E. Remmers, pp. 13–19. Toronto/Philadelphia: Decker

34. Mathieu-Costello, O. 1991. Geometrical relationship between capillaries and muscle fibers in chronic hypoxia. In *Response and Adaptation to Hypoxia: Organ to Organelle,* ed. S. Lahiri, N. S., Cherniack, R. S. Fitzgerald, pp. 157–66. New York: Oxford Univ. Press

35. Mathieu-Costello, O. 1991. Morphometric analysis of capillary geometry in pigeon pectoralis muscle. *Am. J. Anat.* 191:74–84

36. Mathieu-Costello, O. 1993. Morphometry of the size of the capillary-to-fiber interface in muscles. *Adv. Exp. Med. Biol.* In press

37. Mathieu-Costello, O., Agey, P. J., Logemann, R. B., Brill, R. W., Hochachka, P. W. 1992. Capillary fiber geometrical relationships in tuna red muscle. *Can. J. Zool.* 70:1218–29

38. Mathieu-Costello, O., Ellis, C. G., Potter, R. F., MacDonald, I. C., Groom, A. C. 1991. Muscle capillary-to-fiber perimeter ratio: Morphometry. *Am. J. Physiol.* 261:H1617–25

39. Mathieu-Costello, O., Hoppeler, H., Weibel, E. R. 1989. Capillary tortuosity in skeletal muscles of mammals depends on muscle contraction. *J. Appl. Physiol.* 66:1436–42

40. Mathieu-Costello, O., Poole, D. C., Logemann, R. B. 1989. Muscle fiber size and chronic exposure to hypoxia. *Adv. Exp. Med. Biol.* 248:305–11

41. Mathieu-Costello, O., Potter, R. F., Ellis, C. G., Groom, A. C. 1988. Capillary configuration and fiber shortening in muscles of the rat hindlimb: Correlation between corrosion casts and stereological measurements. *Microvasc. Res.* 36:40–55

42. Mathieu-Costello, O., Suarez, R. K., Hochachka, P. W. 1992. Capillary-to-fiber geometry and mitochondrial density in hummingbird flight muscle. *Respir. Physiol.* 89:113–32

43. Mathieu-Costello, O., Szewczak, J. M., Logemann, R. B., Agey, P. J. 1992. Geometry of blood-tissue exchange in bat flight muscle compared with bat hindlimb and rat soleus muscle. *Am. J. Physiol.* 262:R955–65

44. Mermod, L., Hoppeler, H., Kayar, S. R., Straub, R., Weibel, E. R. 1988. Variability of fiber size, capillary density and capillary length related to horse muscle fixation procedures. *Acta Anat.* 133:89–95

45. Moyes, C. D., Mathieu-Costello, O., Brill, R. W., Hochachka, P. W. 1992. Mitochondrial metabolism of cardiac and skeletal muscles from a fast (*Katsuwonus pelamis*) and a slow (*Cyprinus carpio*) fish. *Can. J. Zool.* 70:1246–53

46. Mrazkova, O., Grim, M., Carlson, B. M. 1986. Enzymatic heterogeneity of the capillary bed of rat skeletal muscles. *Am. J. Anat.* 177:141–48

47. Ogilvie, R. W., Agey, P. J., Hansens, C., Mathieu-Costello, O. 1992. Comparison of fiber size and capillarity in perfusion fixed and frozen rat soleus muscle. *Physiologist* 35:198

48. Pietschmann, M., Bartels, H., Fons, R. 1982. Capillary supply of heart and skeletal muscle of small bats and non-flying mammals. *Respir. Physiol.* 50:267–82

49. Plyley, M. J., Groom, A. C. 1975. Geometrical distribution of capillaries in mammalian striated muscle. *Am. J. Physiol.* 228:1376–83

50. Poole, D. C., Batra, S., Mathieu-Costello, O., Rakusan, K. 1992. Capillary geometrical changes with fiber shortening in rat myocardium. *Circ. Res.* 70:697–706

51. Poole, D. C., Mathieu-Costello, O. 1990. Analysis of capillary geometry in rat subepicardium and subendocardium. *Am. J. Physiol.* 259:H204–10

52. Potter, R. F., Groom, A. C. 1983. Capillary diameter and geometry in cardiac and skeletal muscle studied by means of corrosion casts. *Microvasc. Res.* 25:68–84

53. Potter, R. F., Mathieu-Costello, O., Dietrich, H. H., Groom, A. C. 1991. Unusual capillary network geometry in a skeletal muscle, as seen in microcorrosion casts of M. pectoralis of pigeon. *Microvasc. Res.* 41:126–32

54. Rakusan, K., Moravec, J., Hatt, P.-Y. 1980. Regional capillary supply in the normal and hypertrophied rat heart. *Microvasc. Res.* 20:319–26

55. Rakusan, K., Poupa, O. 1963. Changes in the diffusion distance in the rat heart muscle during development. *Physiol. Bohemoslov.* 12:220–27

56. Ranvier, L. 1874. Note sur les vaisseaux sanguins et la circulation dans les muscles rouges. *Arch. Physiol.* Ser. 2 1:446–50

57. Romanul, F. C. A. 1965. Capillary supply and metabolism of muscle fibers. *Arch. Neurol.* 12:497–509

58. Schaper, J., Meiser, E., Stammler, G. 1985. Ultrastructural morphometric analysis of myocardium from dogs, rats, hamsters, mice and from human hearts. *Circ. Res.* 56:377–91

59. Schmidt-Nielsen, K., Pennycuik, P. 1961. Capillary density in mammals in relation to body size and oxygen consumption. *Am. J. Physiol.* 200:746–50

60. Snyder, G. K., Farrelly, C., Coelho, J. R. 1992. Capillary perfusion in skeletal muscle. *Am. J. Physiol.* 262:H828–32

61. Suarez, R. K., Lighton, J. R. B., Brown, G. S., Mathieu-Costello, O. 1991. Mitochondrial respiration in hummingbird flight muscles. *Proc. Natl. Acad. Sci. USA* 88:4870–73

62. Sullivan, S. M., Pittman, R. N. 1987. Relationship between mitochondrial volume density and capillarity in hamster muscles. *Am. J. Physiol.* 252:H149–55

63. Tomanek, R. J. 1970. Effects of age and exercise on the extent of the myocardial capillary bed. *Anat. Rec.* 167:55–62

Annu. Rev. Physiol. 1993. 55:527–46

CONTRACTION DYNAMICS AND POWER OUTPUT OF SKELETAL MUSCLE

R. K. Josephson

School of Biological Science, University of California, Irvine, California 92717

KEY WORDS: skeletal muscle, work, power, contraction kinetics, shortening velocity

INTRODUCTION

Skeletal muscles are used in several different ways. Often they form variable-length struts, stiffening joints and appendages for such tasks as standing or holding objects. During shivering muscles act as furnaces to produce heat; during nutritional stress they serve as energy reserves. But certainly the most important function of muscle is to shorten against a load and thus to do work. The rate at which work is done by a muscle, its mechanical power output, depends on the force that the muscle can develop, the rate at which it can shorten, and the rapidity with which it can be turned on at the beginning of a contraction and turned off at its end. The following review considers recent studies on the muscle dynamics that determine mechanical work and power, and measurements of the sustainable power available from skeletal muscle.

CONTRACTION DYNAMICS

Muscle Force and Shortening Velocity

The velocity (V) at which a muscle shortens varies inversely with the force (F) on the muscle. The relationship between muscle force and shortening velocity is generally expressed with the Hill equation (31), which is that of a rectangular hyperbola:

$$(F + a) \bullet (V + b) = (F_0 + a) \bullet b;$$

527

0066–4278/93/0315-0527$02.00

F_0 is the maximum isometric tension of the muscle (i.e. the intercept of the force-velocity curve with the force axis; see Figure 1), and a and b are constants whose values vary from muscle to muscle. The ratio a/F_0 is used to express the curvature of the force-velocity relationship. A typical value of a/F_0 might be 0.25; a low value indicates a strongly curved force-velocity plot, a high value indicates a plot approaching linearity. There are systematic deviations between the actual force-velocity relationship of a muscle and that predicted by the Hill equation at both high forces (17, 20, 50) and at low forces (10, 42), but the fit through intermediate force and velocity regions is usually good. Alternative expressions have been offered that are claimed to better express the force-velocity characteristics of a muscle over the full range of shortening velocities (e.g. 11, 60), but the Hill equation is still the model most widely used.

In some preparations, the shortening velocity during isotonic (= constant force) contraction is reasonably constant over some time and distance of shortening; or, conversely, the muscle force is reasonably constant during isovelocity shortening. In many muscles, however, shortening velocity declines during isotonic contraction and force declines during isovelocity

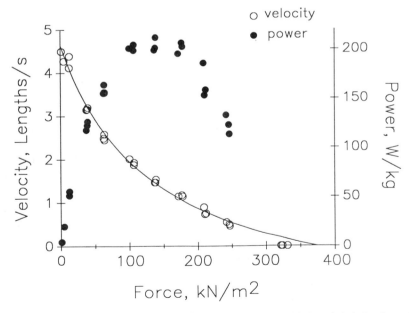

Figure 1   Shortening velocity (*open circles*) and power output (*filled circles*) during isotonic shortening of an insect flight muscle, 30°C. The data are from a tergocoxal muscle of the locust *Schistocerca americana* and were provided by Malamud (see 57).

shortening (e.g. 1, 8, 14, 27, 44, 50). The decline of force or velocity during shortening is attributed to shortening-induced deactivation of the contractile machinery (27, 50; see also 16, 21); or to the development of an internal load, possibly resulting from distortion of the cellular cytoskeleton (8). Published force-velocity relations generally apply to the initial velocity during isotonic contraction, or to the initial force during isovelocity shortening, either one being measured as soon as possible after the subsidence of any transient responses associated with transitions to isotonic or isovelocity shortening.

The maximum shortening velocity can be determined by extrapolating a force-velocity curve based on velocities at finite forces to the velocity axis (force = 0); or, often more conveniently, by using what is termed the slack test (15). In the slack test an isometrically-contracting muscle is quickly released a distance great enough to bring the force to zero. The muscle is then allowed to shorten at the new length so as to take up the imposed slack, and the time until the onset of force redevelopment (= slack time) is measured. This procedure is repeated using different release distances. The slope of the line relating release distance with slack time gives the shortening velocity under 0 load. The maximum shortening velocity determined with the slack test is sometimes referred to as V_0, that from a force-velocity curve as V_{max}. Values for V_0 tend to be higher than those of V_{max} measured from the same muscle or muscle fiber (Table 1). In whole muscles, the difference between V_0 and V_{max} is likely the result, at least in part, of heterogeneity among the fibers composing the muscle (10, 34, 42). The velocity of isotonic shortening at other than extremely light loads comes from contributions of all the participating muscle fibers, and thus V_{max}, which is based on extrapolation from measured isotonic shortening velocities to the predicted velocity at 0 force, should reflect properties of the population of fibers. On the other hand, the slack test should measure the shortening velocity of just the fastest fibers within the muscle. It has been suggested that the ratio of V_0 and V_{max} is a measure of the degree of heterogeneity among the fibers of a muscle (42). Although fiber heterogeneity probably contributes to differences between values of V_{max} and V_0 from whole muscles, V_{max} and V_0 have also been reported to be different in single fibers. In a thorough study, in which care was taken to collect force-velocity data at very low loads so as to reduce the distance of extrapolation to the zero-force axis, and in which slack time was measured both optically and mechanically, V_0 and V_{max} were found to be essentially identical (49), which suggests that the differences between V_0 and V_{max} reported for single fibers in some studies may be a consequence of measurement error.

Force-velocity relations are less well studied and are seemingly more complex for lengthening muscles than for shortening muscles. In general there is not a unique value for muscle force during isovelocity lengthening at a given constant velocity. Typically force during isovelocity stretch rises to a yield point, following which the force may continue to rise but at a different slope than initially, it may remain reasonably constant, or it may fall (18, 19, 26, 28, 48, 52, 66, 85). The force at which the yield point is reached and whether or not there is a drop in force after the yield vary with the rate of stretch (26, 66). Morgan (64) argues that much of the behavior of stretched muscles, including the trajectory of force during lengthening and the development of extra tension at the end of lengthening, is explicable on the basis of sarcomere instability, which leads to sudden elongation of individual sarcomeres throughout the muscle.

Maximum shortening velocity, maximum isometric tension, and a/F_o for a number of muscles are given by Woledge et al (91). Some values, which have appeared since the publication of this important source, selected with emphasis on taxonomic diversity, are included in Table 1. In general, maximum strain rates for muscles are strongly temperature-dependent and, for skeletal muscles, range from about 1 to 20 muscle lengths per second. Maximum stress tends to be about 100–300 kN m^{-2}. Stresses ranging from 400 to 2,000 kN m^{-2} have been reported for claw muscles of crustaceans (7, 24). Muscles that are particularly fast or that operate at high frequencies may produce only relatively low stress. The reduced force is in part a consequence of the great abundance of sarcoplasmic reticulum and mitochondria in fast high-frequency muscles, which reduces the volume occupied by myofibrils in a given muscle mass. Maximum force per area myofibril would be a better measure for making comparisons between muscle types than is maximum force per muscle area, but in only a few cases is the morphological data available to allow conversion of muscle stress to myofibrillar stress.

Power During Isotonic Contraction

The product of the shortening velocity of a muscle and the force under which it shortens has dimensions of force X distance (= work) per time and is the mechanical power output by the muscle. Thus each point on a force-velocity plot represents a power output. The power output is 0 at zero force and at F_o, where the shortening velocity is 0, and reaches a maximum at an intermediate force and associated velocity. The optimum force for mechanical power output (F_{opt}) for a muscle whose force-velocity relationships are those of the Hill equation is given by (69, 91)

$$F_{opt} = (a^2 + a \cdot F_o)^{1/2} - a.$$

The maximum power output is the product of F_{opt} and the optimum shortening velocity (V_{opt}), the latter being obtained by solving the Hill equation for that shortening velocity at $F = F_{opt}$. The maximum power output during isotonic shortening ranges from about 10 to 500 W kg^{-1}.

Table 1 Force-velocity characteristics of skeletal muscles

Muscle type	Temperature (°C)	V_{max} Ls^{-1}	V_o Ls^{-1}	F_o kN m^{-2}	a/F_o	P_{max} W kg^{-1}	Reference
Mammal							
Soleus							
mouse	20	3.4	6.1	148	0.15	36	5
rat	15	1.3			0.11		70
	25	3.6			0.21		70
	35	7.0		198	0.24	133	70
	20	2.0	4.2	168	0.33	37	5
	20	3.1	5.0	162	0.075	22	10
	30	2.8	4.3	212[2]	0.14	41	9
guinea-pig	20	1.5	1.7	147	0.10	12	5
Rat EDL	15	3.6			0.19		70
	25	7.3			0.37		70
	35	13.0		209	0.38	323	70
Rabbit psoas[1]	10	1.6	1.63	132	0.23	20	12
Reptile, amphibian							
Lizard (*Dipsosaurus dorsalis*)							
iliofibularis							
(FG portion)	15	3.0		157		52	60
	25	8.4		188		167	60
	35	14.6		208		325	60
	44	20.1		205		505	60
Turtle (*Pseudemys scripta*)							
iliofibularis							
SO fibers[1]	15	0.91	1.3	71	0.33	7.1	65
FOG fibers[1]	15		3.0	120			65
FG fibers[1]	15		5.5	183			65
Xenopus laevis							
iliofibularis							
1N fibers	20	8.9		396	0.32	431	51
2S	20	7.7		337	0.29	313	51
2F	20	6.6		312	0.26	242	51
2N	20	6.2		300	0.21	199	51
Salamander (*Ambystoma tigrinum*)							
leg muscle	10	1.6		305		60	25
	20	2.9		338		113	25
Fish							
Dogfish myotome, white fiber	12	3.8	3.8	241	0.24	91	13
Carp myotome, red fiber	10	3.6		109	0.49	51	75
	20	5.7		123	0.29	73	75

Table 1   *(Continued)*

Muscle type	Temperature (°C)	V_{max} Ls^{-1}	V_o Ls^{-1}	F_o kN m^{-2}	a/F_o	P_{max} W kg^{-1}	Reference
Scup *(Stenotomus chrysops)*							
red fiber	10	3.3		169[3]	0.25	71	77
	20	5.6		183[3]	0.25	134	77
Marlin *(Makaira nigricans)*							
red fibers[1]	15	1.8		55	0.24	9.7	37
	25	2.5		57	0.23	13	37
white fibers[1]	15	4.0		153	0.12	37	37
	25	5.3		176	0.12	57	37
Arthropod							
Crab *(Carcinus maenas)*							
scaphognathite							
levator	15	1.9	3.3	122	0.41	28	44
Locust *(Schistocerca)*							
flight muscle							
S. gregaria	30	5.8	8.0	295	0.30	163	58
S. americana	25	5.2		363	0.58	276	57
Katydid (Tettigoniid) wing muscle							
Neoconocephalus triops							
flight	25	10.2	11.6	118			38
	35	16.1	17.0	122	0.9	326	38
Singing/flight	25	8.3	11.1	52			38
	35	12.2	15.6	55	2.06	136	38
N. robustus							
flight	25	6.3		113			38
	35	11.1		137	1.02	262	38
Singing/flight	25	5.9		42			38
	35	10.1		48	1.75	96	38

Abbreviations: V_{max}—maximum shortening velocity from force-velocity curve; V_o—maximum shortening velocity from slack test; Ls^{-1}—muscle lengths per second; F_o—maximum tetanic stress; a—force asymptote of Hill equation; P_{max}—maximum power output during isotonic shortening. Values for P_{max}, when not given in the original paper, were calculated from values of V_{max}, F_o and a/F_o.
[1] From skinned or glycerinated muscle fibers. [2] Calculated using fiber length and pinnation data given in (78). [3] Compensation made for extracellular space in area and mass-specific values.

The mechanical power output of a muscle is maximal when it contracts at a shortening velocity of about 0.3 V_{max}, or against a load of about 0.3 F_o. Muscle efficiency during isotonic contraction, defined as $W/(H+W)$, where W is the work done and H the heat produced, is greatest at a velocity somewhat less than or a load somewhat greater than that at which mechanical power output is maximal (32, 33). In an influential paper on the relationships between animal size and muscle dynamics, Hill (32) proposed that, "Each muscle is

designed for maximal power and efficiency in its important range of speed."
For this to be true, the "important range of speed" of a muscle should be
about 0.3 V_{max}. This proposal has been investigated by Rome and his
colleagues in a series of studies on the swimming muscles of fish (72–77).
The trunk musculature of a fish is typically composed of a pair of lateral
bands of red muscle fibers and a large, central mass of white muscle fibers.
In Rome's studies, the tail stroke frequencies at which red fibers and white
fibers were active were determined with electromyographic recordings; the
extent and time course of muscle fiber shortening were determined by
combining cinematographic anlysis of trunk movements in swimming fish
with muscle histology. Muscle contraction kinetics were measured from
isolated fiber bundles. It was demonstrated that red muscle, which has a low
V_{max}, is used at low tail beat frequencies, whereas white muscle, which has
a high V_{max}, is used at high frequencies, and that the frequency of transition
from the use of red muscle to that of white muscle declines with declining
temperature. The arrangement of red and white muscles in the trunk of a fish,
and the tail-beat frequencies at which the two muscle types are used, are such
that both muscle types operate with the ratio V/V_{max} remaining in the rather
narrow range of about 0.2–0.4 predicted by Hill (72, 75, 77).

For several reasons the maximum power measured from a force-velocity
curve greatly overestimates the sustainable power available from a muscle
during repetitive contraction such as during running, swimming, or flying.
First, during repetitive contraction, a muscle shortens, doing work, for part
of the activity cycle, and then is lengthened, having work done upon it, for
the remainder of the cycle. If the shortening and lengthening hemicycles were
of equal duration, and if the work required to relengthen the muscle after
shortening were negligible, then the power output averaged over a full cycle
would be only half of that for the shortening phase alone. In practice the work
required to relengthen a muscle can be appreciable, and the net work done
over a full cycle can be substantially less than the work done during the
shortening phase. Second, it is probably rare for muscle shortening velocity
to be constant, and at the optimum velocity for power output, throughout the
shortening phase. For many repetitively-active muscles, the shortening
trajectory is probably sinusoidal or nearly so (30, 73, 74). The maximum
power available from a muscle shortening with a sinusoidal trajectory is
expected to be 10–20% less than would be obtained were the muscle to shorten
only at the optimum velocity (41). Finally, muscle activation and relaxation
are not instantaneous processes. A muscle does not become immediately and
fully active at the onset of shortening and instantaneously relaxed at the end
of the shortening. The extent to which muscle activation is incomplete during
parts of the shortening phase reduces the shortening work done by the muscle.
The extent to which the muscle remains active into the lengthening phase, or

becomes active during lengthening before the onset of shortening, increases the work required to re-extend the muscle and reduces the net work and power over a full cycle. Force-velocity curves are a good measure of the maximum instantaneous power output of a muscle but, because of the several limitations just listed, they are not a good measure of the sustainable power of a muscle, nor of the work available through a full contraction-relaxation cycle under conditions resembling those under which a muscle might normally operate. The work loop method, described below, is an approach for measuring mechanical power output that does include both positive work done during shortening and negative work during lengthening, and which allows for changing muscle velocity and degree of activation throughout a cycle. The work loop method permits evaluation of the sustainable mechanical power available from a muscle.

WORK LOOP STUDIES OF WORK AND POWER

In an innovative series of papers, Pringle, Machin, and colleagues examined the power output of insect flight muscle (54–56). A muscle was stimulated at a frequency sufficient to keep it continuously activated, and force was measured while sinusoidal length change was imposed on the muscle. Asynchronous muscles were used. A characteristic of asynchronous muscle is that there is pronounced, delayed change in muscle activation with change in muscle length; stretch leads to delayed activation and release to delayed inactivation. When the muscle is subjected to sinusoidal length change at an appropriate frequency, muscle force lags change in length. The result is that the muscle force at any length is higher during the shortening portion of the cycle than during lengthening. A plot of muscle force against length thus forms a loop, which is traversed counterclockwise. The area of this loop is equal to the work done per length cycle (see below).

By introducing phasic stimulation in the length cycle, the work loop technique can be used to measure work output from synchronous muscle of the sort found throughout the animal kingdom (39). The muscle is subjected to cyclic length change and stimulated with a single stimulus or with a burst of stimuli at a selected time in the length cycle. A plot of muscle force against length again forms a loop (Figure 2). The area beneath the lower limb of the loop, from minimal to maximal length, has dimensions of force X distance (= work) and is the work needed to stretch the muscle from its shortest to its longest length. The area beneath the upper limb of the loop, from longest to shortest length, is the work done by the muscle during its subsequent shortening. The loop area is the difference between the work put into the muscle to lengthen it and the work recovered from the muscle during its subsequent shortening, which is the net work done over the cycle. The net work per cycle (Joules) times the cycle frequency (s^{-1}) is the mechanical power output (J s^{-1} = W).

The work loop approach is well suited for estimating the muscle power available during activities involving repetitive movement such as running, swimming, or flying. During repetitive movements, the muscles that are attached directly or indirectly to moving skeletal structures must undergo repetitive length changes. The question that can be answered with the work loop approach is, How much work and power is available from a muscle given that it is undergoing cyclic length change?

The number of parameters that affect power output in work loop studies is a bit formidable. In addition to the muscle selected, the way it is prepared, and the solution with which it is bathed, factors affecting work output from a muscle include the cycle frequency; the average muscle length upon which the length change (strain) is superimposed; the strain trajectory (e.g. sinusoidal, triangular, etc.); the phase and pattern of stimulation in the cycle; the cycle in a series chosen for analysis; and muscle temperature. Some muscles normally operate with a single twitch contraction per cycle; for example, vertebrate heart muscle, some insect wing muscles (39, 40), and probably lizard leg

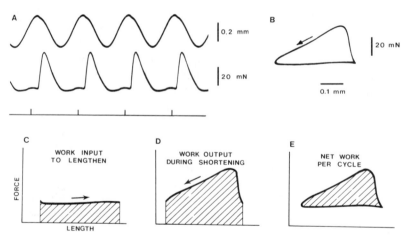

Figure 2   The work loop approach for measuring power output. The example is from a katydid flight muscle at 30°C. The muscle was subjected to sinusoidal length change at the normal wing stroke frequency (25 Hz) and stimulated with single shocks at a chosen phase in the length cycle. (*A*) Upper trace = muscle length change; middle trace = force; lower trace = stimulus marker. (*B*) A plot of muscle force against length forms a loop, which here is traversed counterclockwise. (*C-E*) The area of the loop is the difference between the work required to lengthen the muscle and the work done by the muscle during its subsequent shortening; thus the loop area is the net work per cycle. The position of the force trace in C-E has been artificially elevated to illustrate more clearly the lengthening work component of the cycle. Normally the force during lengthening and the lengthening work are quite small (from 39).

muscles during running at low temperature (60). For such muscles, a single stimulus per cycle is obviously appropriate for evaluating power output in vivo. However, most muscles probably operate with brief tetanic contractions on each cycle, and for these the number and pattern of stimuli per cycle are important determinants of work output. Muscle fatigue and limitations on experimenter time generally preclude complete characterization of the full parameter space. Typically some of the parameters are chosen to mimic, as closely as available information will allow, normal operating conditions in vivo, and the other parameters are either chosen arbitrarily, or are systematically varied so as to find the values that maximize mechanical power output.

The stimulus phase that is optimal for work output is that at which muscle activation and active force production are high throughout the shortening phase of a cycle, yet low during the lengthening phase, to minimize the work required to restretch the muscle. In general, the optimum stimulus phase for work output is such that muscle activation begins shortly before the end of the lengthening half cycle. It is widely found that there is an optimum strain for work output per cycle. The effects of strain on work output have been analyzed in some detail for a crustacean muscle (45). Here it was found that the work required to restretch a muscle after shortening increased nearly monotonically with increasing strain, while the work done during shortening increased with increasing strain to a plateau or to a peak beyond which shortening work fell with increasing strain. The decline in shortening work at high strain presumably is a consequence of the increase in muscle shortening velocity at high strain and the concomitant decrease in muscle force.

The effects of cycle frequency on work and power are complex. Work per cycle declines at high cycle frequencies (e.g. 2, 81, 87). The decrease in work per cycle at high cycle frequencies is a consequence of an increase in strain rate or a decrease in the amount of strain. If the distance of shortening is held constant, the strain rate increases in proportion to cycle frequency. Because of the inverse relationship between shortening velocity and muscle force (Figure 1), an increase in strain rate decreases muscle force and the work done during the shortening phase of the cycle. Alternatively, if strain rate is maintained constant, the distance of shortening must decline as cycle frequency increases, which likewise reduces the work per cycle. Further, as the frequency increases and cycle duration decreases, relaxation is likely to be less complete at the end of the shortening phase, which increases the force and work required to re-extend the muscle and thus reduces net work. In experiments in which muscles are activated with a single stimulus per cycle, work output declines at low cycle frequencies as well as at high frequencies (81). With decreasing cycle frequency, the twitch duration becomes an increasingly smaller fraction of the duration of the shortening half cycle and thus force is generated and work is done over increasingly less of the cycle.

Work per cycle need not decline with decreasing cycle frequency. If a muscle is activated with a burst of stimuli on each cycle, and if the length of the stimulus burst is increased as cycle frequency is decreased so that the duration of muscle activation remains consonant with that of shortening, work may continue to increase with decreasing cycle frequency to rather low frequencies (87).

Mechanical power output increases with increasing cycle frequency to an optimum frequency beyond which power output falls. Power is the product of work per cycle and cycle frequency, and the decline in power at high frequency indicates that the decrease in work per cycle at high frequency is disproportionate to the increase in cycle frequency. As expected, the optimum frequency for power output is greater than the frequency at which work per cycle is maximal (81). Increasing muscle temperature increases the optimum frequency for power output (35, 36, 81). The optimum frequency for power output is lower in equivalent muscles from large animals than from small animals, presumably reflecting a slowing in muscle contraction kinetics with increasing animal size (2, 3).

Work loops from an unstimulated muscle are traversed in a clockwise direction (force higher during lengthening than shortening). The loop area depends on the cycle frequency, the strain, and the passive visco-elastic properties of the muscle (29, 86). The absolute area of a passive work loop is generally quite small as compared to that from a stimulated muscle (45, 86).

Power output from work loop analysis is available for about 20 different skeletal muscles (Figure 3). Maximum power values range from less than 10 W kg^{-1} to slightly over 150 W kg^{-1}, the latter from a lizard leg muscle at 42°C (S. Swoap et al, unpublished). Most of the variability among the power values reported from different studies is attributable to differences in the temperatures at which the measurements were made. For the data displayed in Figure 3, the mean variance about the least-squares regression line for power as a function of temperature is only 39% of the mean variance of power output from the sample as a whole (for log-transformed values of power the variance about the least-squares regression line is 35% of the sample variance). Interestingly, the kind of animal providing the muscle does not seem to be an important determinant of power output. The maximum power is about the same for insect wing muscles and mammalian diaphragm muscles, for lizard leg muscle and fish trunk muscle (Figure 3). The datum in Figure 3 from a bird wing muscle is of particular interest because this is from work loops constructed with forces measured during normal flight from implanted strain gauges, and muscle lengths estimated from changing wing position (6). The similarity between this in vivo measurement and the other work loop values, which were obtained from muscles in vitro, is a validation of both approaches.

Some of the differences in power output from different muscles are explicable on anatomical grounds. For example, the two crab muscles in Figure 3, which were examined at 15°C, have power outputs that are distinctly lower than those of fish or lizard muscles at the same temperature. The fibers of these crab muscles are particularly richly endowed with mitochondria and with fields of glycogen granules. The myofibrils, those elements of a muscle fiber that actually do work, make up only about 30–40% of the muscle volume in the crab muscles (83). The fish muscles and the lizard muscle, which were measured at 15°C, were fast white muscles, presumably relying largely on anaerobic metabolism and having fewer mitochondria and more myofibrils per muscle volume than is true of the crab muscles. Similarly, the moth flight muscle (joined, filled circles, Figure 3) is an aerobic muscle with well-developed mitochondria and proportionally-reduced myofibrils, and on this basis, one assumes, with reduced potential for power output as compared to anaerobic muscles with little investment in mitochondria such as the lizard muscle (joined upright triangles, Figure 3). In general, aerobic muscles, with

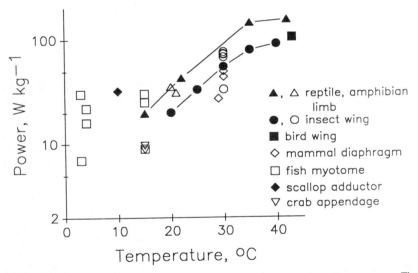

Figure 3 Maximum power output from different muscles as a function of temperature. The symbols joined by lines are from two studies in which power output was measured at several different temperatures. The value for the bird wing muscle is from work loops collected from an intact animal during normal flight; the other data are from work loops generated by muscles in vitro. Sources: reptile and amphibian (79, 80, and S. Swoap et al, unpublished); insect wing muscles (39, 40, 58, 61, 81); bird wing muscle (6), temperature assumed to be 43°C (88); mammalian diaphragm (3, 87); fish myotome (2, 35, 36, 63); scallop adductor (R. Marsh, personal communication); crab appendage (82, R. Josephson & D. Stokes, unpublished).

their abundant mitochondria, can be expected to have lower values for maximum, mass-specific power output than muscles that rely on anaerobic metabolism; however, power output from the latter should be more quickly limited by fatigue.

Most of the muscles from which power measurements have been made are fast muscles used in locomotion. It seems likely that myofibrillar efficiency rather than power output has been the major selective force in slow postural muscles and that such muscles may have lower power output per unit volume of myofibrils than do the fast locomotory muscles that have thus far been studied, but this assertion remains to be tested.

THEORETICAL PREDICTIONS OF SUSTAINABLE MUSCLE POWER

Three theoretical analyses of the sustainable mechanical power available from striated muscle appeared shortly before the recent wave of studies in which the work loop approach was used to obtain direct evidence on the topic. A primary motivation for the theoretical studies was to provide estimates of the muscle power available to drive flying or swimming for comparison with the estimates of power requirement derived from aerodynamic and hydrodynamic models of animal locomotion. With informed hindsight, it is of interest to consider the theoretical treatments in order to see how close their predictions came to the values of power output actually measured from muscles.

Weis-Fogh & Alexander (90) assumed that a muscle shortened during each contraction cycle at constant velocity over a length range that bracketed the optimal length for isometric force production. They further assumed that the relations between force and velocity during shortening were those of the Hill equation, and that muscle activation and inactivation were sufficiently rapid that the muscle was fully active during the whole of shortening and fully inactive, producing negligible force, during lengthening. By using generous estimates for the relevant parameters in the Hill equation ($V_{max} = 25$ L s^{-1}, $F_o = 400$ kN m^{-2}, $a/F_o = 0.3$), it was concluded that the maximum power output of myofibrils would be about 500 W kg^{-1} which is, not surprisingly, about half the peak instantaneous power during isotonic shortening (1053 W kg^{-1}) predicted from the dynamic parameters used (remember that during cyclic contraction, a muscle spends half its time shortening and half lengthening). Weis-Fogh & Alexander further pointed out that sustainable mechanical power in muscles relying on aerobic metabolism requires that the fiber's mitochondrial volume is sufficient to provide the metabolic power needed to support the mechanical power. They concluded that a given volume of myofibrils at maximum power output requires about an equal volume of mitochondria to provide metabolic support. Inclusion of mitochondria in the fiber reduces the relative volume occupied by myofibrils and accordingly reduces the power output per unit volume of muscle. Thus a muscle designed for maximal, sustainable power output would be equally made up of mitochondria and myofibrils and would deliver about 250 W kg^{-1}, a value substantially higher than any yet obtained in work loop studies.

The analysis of Weis-Fogh & Alexander probably overestimates the maximum power available from myofibrils for two reasons. First, it neglects the finite time course of muscle activation and inactivation, which reduces the work done during the shortening phase of a contraction and increases the work required to be done during the lengthening phase. Second, these authors were very generous in their selection of values for V_{max}, F_o and a/F_o (compare with Table 1). Partially offsetting the apparent overestimate of mass-specific power from myofibrils is an overestimate of the muscle volume occupied by mitochondria and hence an underestimate of the volume available for myofibrils. The volume density of mitochondria does not exceed about 40–45%, even in highly active muscles (47, 69, 84).

Pennycuick & Rezende (69), continuing the vein started by Weis-Fogh & Alexander, gave particular attention to relations between cycle frequency and power output of flight muscles and provided some direct measurements of mitochondrial volume density in flight muscle that were used to estimate the metabolic power output of mitochondria in vivo. In their model, they proposed that the flight muscles of an animal are adapted to work at a characteristic operating frequency, and that at the operating frequency the average myofibrillar stress and the fractional change in length (= strain) during shortening are constant from animal to animal and independent of the actual value of the operating frequency. Since stress and strain are constant, the myofibrillar work per contraction would also be constant and, therefore, the specific power output of the myofibrils should change in proportion to the characteristic operating frequency. The strain at the operating frequency was taken to be 15% for synchronous muscles and 2% for asynchronous ones; and the strain rates were assumed to be such that the muscle force during shortening was 0.5 F_o. Based on this model, and accounting for the relative volumes within the muscle appropriately occupied by myofibrils and mitochondria, it was concluded that power output should increase with increase in the normal operating frequency of the muscle to a limiting value of over 800 W kg^{-1}.

The Pennycuick & Rezende model, like that of Weis-Fogh & Alexander, can be faulted for its failure to allow for activation/inactivation time course and for unrealistic assumptions about muscle contractile parameters. For the strain at the characteristic operating frequency to be the same in muscles from different animals, the shortening velocity must be proportional to the frequency. If the stress is constant at the different operating frequencies and velocities, the shortening velocity at that stress must be greater in a muscle with a higher operating frequency than in one with a lower operating frequency. In fact, according to the model, V_{max} for a muscle should be directly proportional to the operating frequency of the muscle. In reality, maximum shortening velocities do not appear to get ever faster with higher normal operating frequency. There seems to be an upper limit in maximum shortening velocity of about 25 L s^{-1}, which is not exceeded even in muscles with very high operating frequencies (4, 11, 38, 53). That the assumed value for strain of 15% is unrealistic, at least for some muscles, is made clear by considering locust flight muscle, which is synchronous muscle. The normal wing-stroke frequency during locust flight is 20 Hz. The shortening velocity of locust muscle would have to be 6 L s^{-1} for the muscle to shorten 15% within the 25 ms duration of the shortening half-cycle. The required velocity is near to or somewhat greater than V_{max} for the muscle, so essentially no force would be developed nor work done while shortening at this velocity (Figure 1). Because of the limitation on maximum shortening velocity, it seems likely that all muscles working at high frequency will also prove to operate at relatively small strains.

In calculating the volume of a muscle fiber occupied by myofibrils, the Pennycuick & Rezende model, as does that of Weis-Fogh & Alexander, ignores the portion of muscle volume occupied by sarcoplasmic reticulum (SR). In synchronous muscles from various animals, the fractional volume of SR increases with operating frequency and can be appreciable, reaching 15–25% of the fiber volume in some insect wing muscles (62, 67, 68, 71), and about a third of the total fiber volume in a cicada muscle with an exceedingly high (550 Hz) operating frequency (46). The model also does not take into account the mitochondrial volume needed to support the metabolic costs of the SR in turning the muscle on and off, a cost that is likely to be rather great at high operating frequencies (for discussion, see 43). The volume occupied by SR, and that by the mitochondria needed to support the SR, reduces the volume available for myofibrils in a given muscle mass and reduces the mass-specific power output.

Ellington (22) borrowed a basic formula for calculating mechanical power output (power = strain per cycle X average stress X cycle frequency) from Pennycuick & Rezende and the assumption that average stress during cyclic contraction at normal operating frequency is about half the maximum isometric stress. Using empirically-determined values for maximum stress and cycle frequency, and estimates for total strain, Ellington predicted the work output to be about 80 W kg^{-1} for locust flight muscle and 97 W kg^{-1} for katydid wing muscle. These values are satisfactorily close to those actually measured in work loop studies [about 70 W kg^{-1} for locust muscle (58, 61); 68 W kg^{-1} for katydid muscle (39)], and also satisfactorily close to power output estimates based on aerodynamic performance (22, 23). The predicted power outputs are somewhat higher than those actually measured, again presumably in part because no allowance was made in the model for the finite time course of muscle activation and inactivation.

van Leeuwen et al (89) provide an imaginative analysis of the expected time course of muscle force and work output in fish swimming muscles. This analysis is based on assumed force-velocity and length-tension properties of the trunk muscle, an assumed time course for muscle activation, and measured values of muscle strain (from cinematography) and the phase of muscle activation (from EMG recordings). The approach does produce work loops that look rather like those from actual fish muscles, but the model is based on normalized parameters (e.g. F/F_{max}, work/maximal possible work, etc) so absolute values of work output and power are not available.

The preceding models have been useful in focusing attention on the problem of predicting muscle power from muscle contractile properties and in identifying the relevant parameters. They also illustrate the need to use realistic data to obtain realistic predictions. All the models suffer from a lack of direct information on the changing degree of muscle activation with time after stimulation. A recent study on locust flight muscle (57) provides information on the force-velocity characteristics of the muscle throughout a twitch contraction and provides a general approach for obtaining information on the time course of muscle activation.

CONCLUSIONS

The inverse relationship between muscle force and muscle shortening velocity is reasonably described by the Hill equation, although there are deviations between measured and predicted values of velocity both at high and at low muscle force. Recent values for the maximum shortening velocities of skeletal muscles range from less than 1 to over 20 lengths s^{-1}, and values for maximum isometric tension are from 40 to 2000 kN m^{-2}. Values for the maximum power output during isotonic contraction are 7–500 W kg^{-1}. The maximum power during isotonic contraction substantially overestimates the sustainable power available from muscle. The work-loop method provides an empirical approach for measuring the sustainable power available from muscle during repetitive contraction. Values of power output obtained with the work loop approach range from less than 5 to over 150 W kg^{-1}, varying largely with temperature. On the basis of a limited set of measurements, it now appears that the maximum power available from fast muscle relying largely on anaerobic metabolism is about 150 W kg^{-1}, that from fast aerobic muscle is about 100 W kg^{-1}.

ACKNOWLEDGMENTS

Preparation of this review was supported by National Science Foundation grant DCB-9104170. I thank D. Syme for helpful comments on the manuscript.

Literature Cited

1. Aidley, D. J. 1966. Transient changes in isotonic shortening velocity of frog rectus abdominis muscles in potassium contracture. *Proc. R. Soc. London Ser. B* 163:215–23

2. Altringham, J. D., Johnston, I. A. 1990. Modelling muscle power output in a swimming fish. *J. Exp. Biol.* 148:395–402

3. Altringham, J. D., Young, I. S. 1991. Power output and the frequency of oscillatory work in mammalian diaphragm muscle: the effects of animal size. *J. Exp. Biol.* 157:381–89

4. Asmussen, G., Beckers-Bleukx, G., Maréchal, G. 1992. Force-velocity relation of the rabbit inferior oblique muscle: influence of temperature. *J. Muscle Res. Cell Motil.* 13:221 (Abstr.)

5. Asmussen, G., Maréchal, G. 1989. Maximal shortening velocities, isomyosins and fibre types in soleus muscle of mice, rats and guinea-pigs. *J. Physiol.* 416:245–54

6. Biewener, A. A., Dial, K. P., Goslow, G. E. Jr. 1992. Pectoralis muscle force and power output during flight in the starling. *J. Exp. Biol.* 164:1–18

7. Blundon, J. A. 1988. Morphology and muscle stress of chelae of temperate and tropical stone crabs *Minippe mercenaria*. *J. Zool.* 215:663–73

8. Brenner, B. 1986. The necessity of using two parameters to describe isotonic shortening velocity of muscle tissues: the effect of various interventions upon initial shortening velocity (v_i) and curvature (b). *Basic Res. Cardiol.* 81:54–69

9. Caiozzo, V. J., Herrick, R. E., Baldwin, K. M. 1991. Influence of hyperthyroidism on maximal shortening velocity and myosin isoform distribution in skeletal muscles. *Am. J. Physiol.* 261:C285–95

10. Claflin, D. R., Faulkner, J. A. 1989. The force-velocity relationship at high shortening velocities in the soleus muscle of the rat. *J. Physiol.* 411:627–37

11. Close, R. I., Luff, A. R. 1974. Dynamic properties of inferior rectus muscle of the rat. *J. Physiol.* 236:259–70

12. Cooke, R., Franks, K., Luciani, G. B., Pate, E. 1988. The inhibition of rabbit skeletal muscle contraction by hydrogen ions and phosphate. *J. Physiol.* 395:77–97

13. Curtin, N. A., Woledge, R. C. 1988. Power output and force-velocity relationship of live fibres from white myotomal muscle of the dogfish, *Scyliorhinus canicula*. *J. Exp. Biol.* 140:187–97

14. Curtin, N. A., Woledge, R. C. 1991. Efficiency of energy conversion during shortening of muscle fibres from the dogfish *Scyliorhinus canicula*. *J. Exp. Biol.* 158:343–53

15. Edman, K. A. P. 1979. The velocity of unloaded shortening and its relation to sarcomere length and isometric force in vertebrate muscle fibres. *J. Physiol.* 291:143–59

16. Edman, K. A. P. 1980. Depression of mechanical performance by active shortening during twitch and tetanus of vertebrate muscle fibres. *Acta Physiol. Scand.* 109:15–26

17. Edman, K. A. P. 1988. Double-hyperbolic force-velocity relation in frog muscle fibres. *J. Physiol.* 404:301–21

18. Edman, K. A. P., Elzinga, G., Noble, M. I. M. 1978. Enhancement of mechanical performance by stretch during tetanic contractions of vertebrate skeletal muscle fibres. *J. Physiol.* 281:139–55

19. Edman, K. A. P., Elzinga, G., Noble, M. I. M. 1982. Residual force enhancement after stretch of contracting frog single muscle fibers. *J. Gen. Physiol.* 80:769–84

20. Edman, K. A. P., Mulieri, L. A., Scubon-Mulieri, B. 1976. Non-hyperbolic force-velocity relationship in single muscle fibres. *Acta Physiol. Scand.* 98:143–56

21. Ekelund, M. C., Edman, K. A. P. 1982. Shortening induced deactivation of skinned muscle fibres of frog and mouse striated muscle. *Acta Physiol. Scand.* 116:189–99

22. Ellington, C. P. 1985. Power and efficiency of insect flight muscle. *J. Exp. Biol.* 115:293–304

23. Ellington, C. P. 1991. Limitations on animal flight performance. *J. Exp. Biol.* 160:71–91

24. Elner, R. W., Campbell, A. 1981. Force, function and mechanical advantage in the chelae of the American lobster *Homarus americanus* (Decapoda: Crustacea). *J. Zool.* 193:269–86

25. Else, P. L., Bennett, A. F. 1987. The thermal dependence of locomotor performance and muscle contractile function in the salamander *Ambystoma tigrinum nebulosum*. *J. Exp. Biol.* 128:219–33

26. Flitney, F. W., Hirst, D. G. 1978.

Cross-bridge detachment and sarcomere 'give' during stretch of active frog's muscle. *J. Physiol.* 276:449–65

27. Floyd, K., Smith, I. C. H. 1971. The mechanical and thermal properties of frog slow muscle fibres. *J. Physiol.* 213:617–31

28. Harry, J. D., Ward, A. W., Heglund, N. C., Morgan, D. L., McMahon, T. A. 1990. Cross-bridge cycling theories cannot explain high-speed lengthening behavior in frog muscle. *Biophys. J.* 57:201–8

29. Heerkens, Y. F., Woittiez, R. D., Kiela, J., Huijing, P. A., Huson, A., et al. 1987. Mechanical properties of passive rat muscle during sinusoidal stretching. *Pflügers Arch.* 409:438–47

30. Hess, F., Videler, J. J. 1984. Fast continuous swimming of saithe (*Pollachius virens*): a dynamic analysis of bending moments and muscle power. *J. Exp. Biol.* 109:229–51

31. Hill, A. V. 1938. The heat of shortening and the dynamic constants of muscle. *Proc. R. Soc. London Ser. B* 126:136–95

32. Hill, A. V. 1950. The dimensions of animals and their muscular dynamics. *Sci. Prog.* 38:209–30

33. Hill, A. V. 1964. The efficiency of mechanical power development during muscular shortening and its relation to load. *Proc. R. Soc. London Ser. B* 159:319–24

34. Hill, A. V. 1970. *First and Last Experiments in Muscle Mechanics.* Cambridge: Cambridge Univ. Press. 141 pp.

35. Johnson, T. P., Johnston, I. A. 1991. Power output of fish muscle fibres performing oscillatory work: effects of acute and seasonal temperature change. *J. Exp. Biol.* 157:409–23

36. Johnson, T. P., Johnston, I. A., Moon, T. W. 1991. Temperature and the energy cost of oscillatory work in teleost fast muscle fibres. *Pflügers Arch.* 419:177–83

37. Johnston, I. A., Salamonski, J. 1984. Power output and force-velocity relationship of red and white muscle fibres from the Pacific blue marlin (*Makaira nigricans*). *J. Exp. Biol.* 111:171–77

38. Josephson, R. K. 1984. Contraction dynamics of flight and stridulatory muscles of tettigoniid insects. *J. Exp. Biol.* 108:77–96

39. Josephson, R. K. 1985. Mechanical power output from striated muscle during cyclic contraction. *J. Exp. Biol.* 114:493–512

40. Josephson, R. K. 1985. The mechanical power output of a tettigoniid wing muscle during singing and flight. *J. Exp. Biol.* 117:357–68

41. Josephson, R. K. 1989. Power output from skeletal muscle during linear and sinusoidal shortening. *J. Exp. Biol.* 147:533–37

42. Josephson, R. K., Edman, K. A. P. 1988. The consequences of heterogeneity on the force-velocity relation of skeletal muscle. *Acta Physiol. Scand.* 132:341–52

43. Josephson, R. K., Stevenson, R. D. 1991. The efficiency of a flight muscle from the locust *Schistocerca americana*. *J. Physiol.* 442:413–29

44. Josephson, R. K., Stokes, D. R. 1987. The contractile properties of a crab respiratory muscle. *J. Exp. Biol.* 131: 265–87

45. Josephson, R. K., Stokes, D. R. 1989. Strain, muscle length and work output in a crab muscle. *J. Exp. Biol.* 145:45–61

46. Josephson, R. K., Young, D. 1985. A synchronous muscle with an operating frequency greater than 500 Hz. *J. Exp. Biol.* 118:185–208

47. Josephson, R. K., Young, D. 1987. Fiber ultrastructure and contraction kinetics in insect fast muscles. *Am. Zool.* 27:991–1000

48. Joyce, G. C., Rack, P. M. H., Westbury, D. R. 1969. The mechanical properties of cat soleus muscle during controlled lengthening and shortening movements. *J. Physiol.* 204:461–74

49. Julian, F. J., Rome, L. C., Stephenson, D. G., Striz, S. 1986. The maximum speed of shortening in living and skinned muscle fibres. *J. Physiol.* 370:181–99

50. Lännergren, J. 1978. The force-velocity relation of isolated twitch and slow muscle fibres of *Xenopus laevis*. *J. Physiol.* 283:501–21

51. Lännergren, J. 1987. Contractile properties and myosin isoenzymes of various kinds of *Xenopus* twitch muscle fibres. *J. Muscle Res. Cell Motil.* 8:260–73

52. Lombardi, V., Piazzesi, G. 1990. The contractile response during steady lengthening of stimulated frog muscle fibres. *J. Physiol.* 431:141–71

53. Luff, A. R. 1981. Dynamic properties of the inferior rectus, extensor digitorum longus, diaphragm and soleus muscles of the mouse. *J. Physiol.* 313:161–71

54. Machin, K. E., Pringle, J. W. S. 1959. The physiology of insect fibrillar muscle. II. Mechanical properties of

beetle flight muscle. *Proc. R. Soc. London Ser. B* 151:204–25

55. Machin, K. E., Pringle, J. W. S. 1960. The physiology of insect fibrillar muscle. III. The effect of sinusoidal changes of length on a beetle flight muscle. *Proc. R. Soc. London Ser. B* 152:311–30

56. Machin, K. E., Pringle, J. W. S., Tamasige, M. 1962. The physiology of insect flight muscle. IV. The effect of temperature on a beetle flight muscle. *Proc. R. Soc. London Ser. B* 155:493–99

57. Malamud, J. G., Josephson, R. K. 1991. Force-velocity relationships of a locust flight muscle at different times during a twitch contraction. *J. Exp. Biol.* 159:65–87

58. Malamud, J. G., Mizisin, A. P., Josephson, R. K. 1988. The effects of octopamine on contraction kinetics and power output of a locust flight muscle. *J. Comp. Physiol. A* 162:827–35

59. Deleted in proof

60. Marsh, R. L., Bennett, A. F. 1985. Thermal dependence of isotonic contractile properties of the skeletal muscle and sprint performance of the lizard *Dipsosaurus dorsalis. J. Comp. Physiol. B* 155:541–55

61. Mizisin, A. P., Josephson, R. K. 1987. Mechanical power output of locust flight muscle. *J. Comp. Physiol. A* 160:413–19

62. Mizisin, A. P., Ready, N. R. 1986. Growth and development of flight muscle in the locust (*Schistocerca nitens,* Thünberg). *J. Exp. Zool.* 237:45–55

63. Moon, T. W., Altringham, J. D., Johnston, I. A. 1991. Energetics and power output of isolated fish fast muscle fibres performing oscillatory work. *J. Exp. Biol.* 158:261–73

64. Morgan, D. L. 1990. New insights into the behavior of muscle during active lengthening. *Biophys. J.* 57:209–21

65. Mutungi, G., Johnston, I. A. 1987. The effects of temperature and pH on the contractile properties of skinned muscle fibres from the terrapin, *Pseudemys scripta elegans. J. Exp. Biol.* 128:87–105

66. Nichols, T. R. 1984. Velocity sensitivity of yielding during stretch in the cat soleus muscle. In *Contractile Mechanisms in Muscle,* ed. G. H. Pollack, H. Sugi, pp. 753–55. New York: Plenum. 921 pp.

67. Novicki, A. 1989. Rapid postembryonic development of a cricket flight muscle. *J. Exp. Zool.* 250:253–62

68. Novicki, A. 1989. Neural activity is not necessary for the development of adult ultrastructure in katydid (*Neoconocephalus robustus*) singing muscles. *Cell Tissue Res.* 255:641–44

69. Pennycuick, C. J., Rezende, M. A. 1984. The specific power output of aerobic muscle, related to the power density of mitochondria. *J. Exp. Biol.* 108:377–92

70. Ranatunga, K. W. 1984. The force-velocity relation of rat fast- and slow-twitch muscles examined at different temperatures. *J. Physiol.* 351:517–29

71. Ready, N. E. 1986. Development of fast singing muscles in a katydid. *J. Exp. Zool.* 238:43–54

72. Rome, L. C. 1990. Influence of temperature on muscle recruitment and muscle function in vivo. *Am. J. Physiol.* 259:R210–22

73. Rome, L. C., Choi, I.-H., Lutz, G., Sosnicki, A. 1992. The influence of temperature on muscle function in the fast swimming scup. I. Shortening velocity and muscle recruitment during swimming. *J. Exp. Biol.* 163:259–79

74. Rome, L. C., Funke, R. P., Alexander, R. McN. 1990. The influence of temperature on muscle velocity and sustained performance in swimming carp. *J. Exp. Biol.* 154:163–78

75. Rome, L. C., Sosnicki, A. A. 1990. The influence of temperature on mechanics of red muscle in carp. *J. Physiol.* 427:151–69

76. Rome, L. C., Sosnicki, A. A. 1991. Myofilament overlap in swimming carp. II. Sarcomere length changes during swimming. *Am. J. Physiol.* 260:C289–96

77. Rome, L. C., Sosnicki, A., Choi, I.-H. 1992. The influence of temperature on muscle function in the fast swimming scup. II. The mechanics of red muscle. *J. Exp. Biol.* 163:281–95

78. Roy, R. R., Meadows, I. D., Baldwin, K. M., Edgerton, V. R. 1982. Functional significance of compensatory overloaded rat fast muscle. *J. Appl. Physiol.* 52:473–78

79. Stevens, E. D. 1988. Effect of pH and stimulus phase on work done by isolated frog sartorius muscle during cyclic contraction. *J. Muscle Res. Cell Motil.* 9:329–33

80. Stevens, E. D., Syme, D. A. 1989. The relative changes in isometric force and work during fatigue and recovery in isolated toad sartorius muscle. *Can. J. Physiol. Pharmacol.* 67:1544–48

81. Stevenson, R. D., Josephson, R. K. 1990. Effects of operating frequency

and temperature on mechanical power output from moth flight muscle. *J. Exp. Biol.* 149:61–78

82. Stokes, D. R., Josephson, R. K. 1988. The mechanical power output of a crab respiratory muscle. *J. Exp. Biol.* 140: 287–99

83. Stokes, D. R., Josephson, R. K. 1992. Structural organization of two fast, rhythmically active crustacean muscles. *Cell Tissue Res.* 267:571–82

84. Suarez, R. K., Lighton, J. R. B., Brown, G. S., Mathieu-Costello, O. 1991. Mitochondrial respiration in hummingbird flight muscles. *Proc. Natl. Acad. Sci. USA* 88:4870–73

85. Sugi, H., Tsuchiya, T. 1988. Stiffness changes during enhancement and deficit of isometric force by slow length changes in frog skeletal muscle fibres. *J. Physiol.* 407:215–29

86. Syme, D. A. 1990. Passive viscoelastic work of isolated rat, *Rattus norvegicus,* diaphragm muscle. *J. Physiol.* 424: 301–15

87. Syme, D. A., Stevens, E. D. 1989. Effect of cycle frequency and excursion amplitude on work done by rat diaphragm muscle. *Can. J. Physiol. Pharmacol.* 67:1294–99

88. Torre-Bueno, J. R. 1976. Temperature regulation and heat dissipation during flight in birds. *J. Exp. Biol.* 65:471–82

89. van Leeuwen, J. L., Lankheet, M. J. M., Akster, H. A., Osse, J. W. M. 1990. Function of red axial muscles of carp (*Cyprinus carpio*): recruitment and normalized power output during swimming in different modes. *J. Zool.* 220:123–45

90. Weis-Fogh, T., Alexander, R. Mc. N. 1977. The sustained power output from striated muscle. In *Scale Effects in Animal Locomotion,* ed. T. J. Pedley, pp. 511–25. London: Academic. 545 pp.

91. Woledge, R. C., Curtin, N. A., Homsher, E. 1985. *Energetic Aspects of Muscle Contraction.* London: Academic. 357 pp.

Annu. Rev. Physiol. 1993. 55:547–69

LIMITS TO MAXIMAL PERFORMANCE

James H. Jones

Department of Physiological Sciences, School of Veterinary Medicine, University of California, Davis, California 95616

Stan L. Lindstedt

Department of Biological Sciences, Northern Arizona University, Flagstaff, Arizona 86011

KEY WORDS: exercise, energetics, aerobic capacity, allometry, running

INTRODUCTION

Performance is defined as the "execution of an action" or "capacity to achieve a desired result" (36). Locomotor performance has been extensively studied and quantified in a variety of taxa, but is difficult to directly compare between them because of fundamental differences in the activities and media involved: running, hopping, crawling, brachiating, flying, gliding, soaring, swimming, diving, burrowing, etc. In addition, differences in body temperature dramatically affect the metabolic power available during locomotion for different taxa and individuals, further complicating physiological comparisons. This review is restricted to considering limits to terrestrial locomotor performance in mammals, a taxon that is relatively homeothermic.

HOW TO COMPARE LOCOMOTOR PERFORMANCE

Absolute vs Relative Variables: Maximum Running Speed

Body size affects nearly all physiological functions (90) and presents a basic problem in determining how to compare performance among animals. This difficulty is illustrated in Figure 1, which shows the maximum running speeds (*solid circles*, 32, 33) reported for 148 species of mammals ranging in size

547

0066–4278/93/0315–0547$02.00

from 9 g to 6 tons, plotted semi-logarithmically as a function of body mass. Figure 1 (*top*) shows the data in absolute terms, with speed measured in units of m s^{-1}. However, as the distance that an animal's muscles shorten varies directly with body length, a body length-dependent scale might be a more appropriate measure of the animals' performances. Figure 1 (*bottom*) shows the same data in relative terms, standardized to a calculated body length (see Figure 1 legend for equation), with speed measured as body length s^{-1}. Comparison of the maximum locomotor performances of a 55 kg cheetah and 35 g Merriam kangaroo rat gives different results if comparing in absolute terms, in which the cheetah is the fastest mammal at 30.6 m s^{-1}, three and one half times faster than the kangaroo rat at 8.9 m s^{-1}, as opposed to comparing in relative terms, in which the kangaroo rat is the fastest mammal at 110 body length s^{-1}, three and one half times faster than the cheetah at 32.4 body length s^{-1}. The curved lines in Figure 1 show the speeds (absolute, *top*; relative, *bottom*) that mammals of different sizes would have to run to perform identically to the fastest 70 kg human athlete in terms of relative performance (10.9 calculated body length s^{-1}, *top*) and absolute performance (11.1 m s^{-1}, *bottom*). In comparing locomotor performance of different sized animals, it is essential to consider whether absolute or relative measurements are more relevant for the comparison in providing insight into the role of body size in limiting performance.

Maximum Speed vs Endurance

Peak running speed during a sprint is not the only criterion by which maximal locomotor performance can be defined; the ability to maintain a high power output for an extended period of time, or endurance capacity, is an alternative measure of maximal performance. The physiological mechanisms that limit power output during exercise of increasing duration are similar for different species of mammals, vary with the duration of activity and fiber types recruited, and include factors such as increased intracellular H^+ and/or lactic acid concentrations for short duration/high intensity exercise, and skeletal muscle glycogen depletion for long duration/low intensity exercise (89).

Figure 2 shows a log-log plot of average speed as a function of running time during US indoor (<100 m) or world record performances for three species at various racing distances (68, 80): humans, greyhounds, and horses. For all three species, the time required to accelerate from a standing start to full speed significantly reduces the average speed in those races with shortest running times (<20 s). For each of the three species, the maximum average running speed is attained in a race lasting 18 to 21 s, after which there is a progressive decline in average speed as running time increases, a relationship long established for humans (65, 112).

Two patterns are apparent in the speed vs time relationship at distances

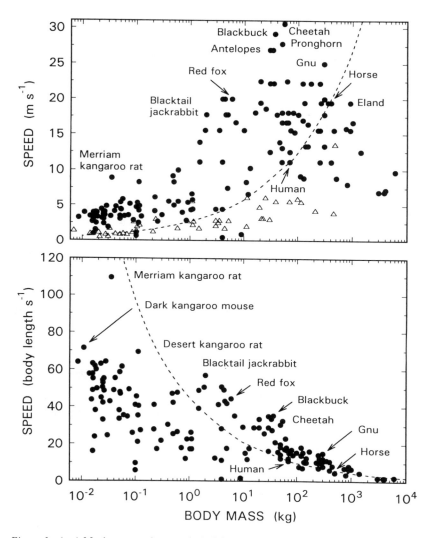

Figure 1 (*top*) Maximum running speeds (*solid circles*) reported for 148 species of mammals plotted as a function of log-body mass. The dashed curve represents the speeds that mammals of different sizes would have to run to have identical relative performance (body length s^{-1}) as a 70 kg human. Open triangles are maximum aerobic running speeds reported for 45 species of mammals. (*bottom*) Maximum running speeds for the same 148 species plotted in relative terms, in units of calculated body length s^{-1}. The dashed curve represents the relative speeds that mammals of different sizes would have to run to have identical absolute performance (m s^{-1}) as a 70 kg human. Body lengths (in cm) were calculated as 24.8 $M_b^{1/3}$, where M_b is body mass in kg, yielding values (exclusive of legs) of 183 cm and 102 cm for a 400 kg horse and 70 kg human, respectively. Data from 14, 32, 33, 57.

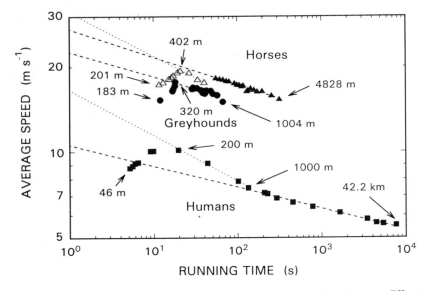

Figure 2   Log-log plot of average running speed as a function of running time over different distances for US indoor (humans < 100 m) and world record performances for humans (*squares*), greyhounds (*circles*) and horses (*open triangle*, quarterhorses; *closed triangle*, thoroughbreds). Dashed lines are linear regressions for longer distances over which aerobic metabolism provides the majority of metabolic power; dotted lines are linear regressions for shorter distances over which anaerobic metabolism provides the majority of metabolic power. Data from 68, 80.

greater than that at which the maximum speed is attained. In Figure 2 the dotted regressions represent race durations for horses and humans during which anaerobic glycolysis provides the majority of metabolic power (8, 14); they have indistinguishable slopes (−0.154 vs −0.161). The dashed regressions represent race durations during which aerobic metabolism provides the majority of metabolic power for humans and horses, and presumably greyhounds, the slopes of which are similar for all three species, −0.074, −0.098, and −0.087. Because running speed is directly related to metabolic power for a given sized mammal (96, 102), the slopes of these regressions represent the rates at which metabolic power (aerobic or anaerobic) diminishes with increased exercise duration. The closer the slope is to zero, the greater the ability to maintain power for longer durations, i.e. the relative endurance capacity. The similarities between species of the aerobic slopes and the anaerobic slopes indicate that the power output of their muscles decreases at similar rates and suggest that over these durations the relative anaerobic and aerobic endurance capacities of these animals are similar.

The regressions in Figure 2 also allow estimates to be made of the peak anaerobic (glycolytic) and aerobic power output of the animals. Extrapolation of the regressions to a short time interval (1 s shown here) indicates a theoretical maximum speed, corresponding to a peak power output, that each animal could produce for a brief period of time. Such a comparison could be made using an absolute time scale (e.g. 1 s), or more appropriately using a relative time scale [e.g. one actin-myosin cross-bridge cycling interval, proportional to $M_b^{0.25}$ (72), where M_b is body mass]. Reference 90 discusses the relationship between absolute and physiological time scales.

Endurance capacity can be compared in absolute terms as the speed that an animal can maintain for a given period of time, or it can be compared in relative terms as the flatness of the average speed vs time relationship. Because the specific cost of locomotion (J km^{-1} kg^{-1}) is proportional to $M_b^{-0.3}$ (96, 102), it is more energetically costly for a smaller mammal to move a given distance, and would more likely deplete its energy reserves sooner than a larger mammal, when travelling at an equivalent fraction of its maximal speed.

DETERMINANTS OF LOCOMOTOR PERFORMANCE

Locomotor performance is ultimately determined by the quantities of useful force and mechanical power that an animal can generate and sustain. It is the application of this force and mechanical power that accelerates the animal, supports its center of mass, and overcomes friction, inertia, and wind resistance while running (40, 96). The quantities of useful force and mechanical power that can be generated during locomotion are functions of at least four physiological variables: (*a*) neuromuscular coordination, (*b*) skeletal muscle mechanics and energetics, (*c*) the efficiency with which metabolic power is converted to mechanical power, and (*d*) skeletal muscle metabolic capacity, both anaerobic and aerobic.

Neuromuscular Coordination

Neuromuscular coordination and muscle recruitment patterns play a role in determining how metabolic power and force are generated by skeletal muscle and are translated into useful work in accelerating an animal and maintaining its velocity (38). Although differences in coordination during locomotion clearly exist in animals, they are exceptionally difficult to quantify in nonhuman species and are not considered in this review.

Skeletal Muscle Mechanics and Energetics

Vertebrate skeletal muscle is conservative in the structure of its force generating proteins, actin and myosin. As a result, the maximum stress (force/area, approximately 300 kPa) it can generate and its maximum strain (relative shortening, approximately 0.3) are nearly constant for all vertebrates (18, 44). Hill (44) recognized this similarity and calculated that, because the cross-sectional area of muscle ($\propto$ maximum force it can generate) changes in proportion to $M_b^{2/3}$, and the distance over which it contracts is proportional to $M_b^{1/3}$, the maximum specific muscular work (J kg^{-1}) per contraction should be constant for all mammalian muscle. He concluded that all mammals should be capable of nearly the same maximum running speed.

STRIDE FREQUENCY AND LENGTH   Figure 1 (*top*) indicates that maximum running speed in mammals is not independent of body size, and that maximum speeds are achieved at approximately 50 kg. A number of factors may explain this departure from Hill's prediction. Schmidt-Nielsen (90) calculated that since stride frequency scales as $M_b^{-0.17}$ (81), if mammals of different size had geometrically similar stride lengths ($\propto M_b^{1/3}$), their maximum speeds should scale as $M_b^{0.16}$, identical to the value calculated for the data in Figure 1 (32). However, mammals do not have geometrically similar stride lengths; the joints of large mammals move through smaller angular excursions than do those of smaller mammals (12, 79). Nevertheless, this general size-dependent pattern is highly variable. The limbs of very fast runners, e.g. the cheetah, move through much larger angles than predicted for their size, and the limbs of 32 kg pronghorn antelope (maximum speed 28 m s^{-1}) undergo much larger excursions than those of similar sized goats (maximum speed 12 m s^{-1}) (S. Lindstedt, unpublished observation). These basic mechanical considerations could explain the general ability of larger mammals to run faster (in absolute terms) than smaller mammals. The reason that maximal speeds decrease as body size increases above 50 kg may be related to postural and gait changes attendant with increases in size and concomitant reductions in safety factors for bone, muscle, and tendon stresses (11, 12).

ENERGETIC COST   Taylor and co-workers (40, 41, 94, 96, 97) have examined the relationship between body size, energy cost of running, and the work that is done by muscles while running. They determined that the metabolic cost of running is directly related to speed and to $M_b^{-0.3}$ and concluded that the energetic cost per stride per kg is independent of body size at similar gaits, and increases with increasing running speed. Stride frequencies at similar gaits are proportional to M_b raised to the -0.14 to -0.17 power (41, 42, 81). Therefore, small mammals take more strides per unit time than do large mammals, increasing their energetic cost for running at a similar gait, and increasing it even further when they run at identical speed. These considerations could permit larger mammals, in general, to attain higher maximal speeds than smaller mammals if their ratios of metabolic energy available to energetic cost of running were higher.

Efficiency

Taylor's and Alexander's groups have reported that efficiency during locomotion, defined as (mechanical power output)/(metabolic power input), which ranges from a few percent for small rodents to values > 70% for large species, e.g. humans, kangaroos and ponies (1, 2, 17, 40, 94), increases with body size and speed. These observations seem inconsistent with isolated muscle experiments that show that peak efficiency may only approach 25% (43, 77). However, efficiencies > 25% have been measured in rat muscles when they were stretched while stimulated before shortening (39), which suggests that elastic storage of energy while the muscle was stretched increased its efficiency. Nevertheless, measured efficiencies do not exceed 50%, and these findings would not explain the apparent size-dependence of efficiency during locomotion.

Recent work (87) has demonstrated that the maximum velocity of shortening (V_{max}) of slow oxidative fibers in mammals is proportional to $M_b^{-0.18}$. This value is similar to the scaling of stride frequency ($\propto M_b^{-0.16}$, 41), and the frequency of optimal power output in diaphragm muscle ($\propto M_b^{-0.16}$, 6), which is used synchronously with stride during high speed locomotion in many species (15). Matching of V_{max} with the frequencies at which the muscles are used during locomotion could allow skeletal muscles of both small and large mammals to shorten with velocities (V) such that V/V_{max} is constant and maximizes efficiency, as suggested by Rome et al (85, 86). Molecular evidence supports this hypothesis since mammals seem to have eight to ten different myosin isoforms available so that V/V_{max} can be tuned to demand (104). Kram & Taylor (66) have argued that V_{max} may directly set locomotor efficiency. They contend that V_{max} and ground contact time must be inversely related, which would account for much greater efficiencies in large mammals with their lower stride frequencies. Alexander (3) has reviewed this hypothesis.

Substantial evidence indicates that elastic strain energy is stored and released from muscles and connective tissues during locomotion (3, 4). Furthermore, it appears that large mammals may store more of this energy than do small mammals (5, 13), thus larger mammals may have relatively more elastic recoil energy available during locomotion than do small mammals. Elastic energy storage may not function as well in extremely large species because of differences in mechanical advantage and design, which may account for the decrease in maximal running speeds in mammals larger than 50 kg.

Metabolic Power

Because the metabolic cost of running is proportional to $M_b^{-0.3}$ (96), a smaller mammal requires greater metabolic power to run at the same speed as a larger mammal. Two major sources of metabolic power are available to working muscle cells during locomotion: anaerobic glycolysis and oxidative phosphorylation. In humans, exercise of short duration (1 to 6 s) is accomplished using high-energy phosphate supplied by the breakdown of ATP and PCr in the myocytes (23, 51). Following this interval, anaerobic glycolysis predominates as the source of high-energy phosphate until aerobic metabolism is elevated to meet the demand, or until it reaches its maximum rate. After 2 min of work eliciting maximum aerobic power in humans, the total metabolic power has been generated approximately half anaerobically and half aerobically (8). The kinetics of O_2 uptake are faster in smaller mammals because of their shorter physiological time scales (92); however, the kinetics may also be faster in larger species highly adapted to extremes of aerobic performance, e.g. racehorses (14). Once the maximum rate of O_2 uptake ($\dot{V}_{O_2max}$) is achieved, any additional increase in metabolic power must be achieved by recruiting fibers that utilize anaerobic pathways, which results in the accumulation of lactic acid/lactate in the muscle and plasma (8, 77, 92).

ANAEROBIC POWER   Maximal anaerobic power in humans has been estimated by several methods (20, 23); however, this measurement requires cooperation and maximal effort by the subject and is impractical for use with nonhuman animals. The most common means of estimating anaerobic capacity in mammals has been by evaluating muscle activities of glycolytic enzymes, e.g. glycogen phosphorylase, pyruvate kinase, and lactate dehydrogenase (27, 46). Although specific maximal aerobic power (W kg^{-1}) and the specific activities of aerobic enzymes (e.g. citrate synthase) scale with negative exponents, specific activities of the glycolytic enzymes scale in proportion to $Mb^{0.15}$. Therefore, it appears that larger mammals should have the capacity for greater specific anaerobic power than do smaller mammals. If such a difference in anaerobic capacity exists, it is presumably reflected in the data in Figure 1 (*solid circles*), which are primarily sprint data.

AEROBIC POWER   If an animal's exercise lasts sufficiently long, its muscles' metabolic demand for energy must be met largely or completely by oxidative phosphorylation. Maximum aerobic power is much lower than maximum anaerobic power, a fact illustrated by the lower speeds at which mammals run when they just reach their maximum aerobic capacities (Figure 1, *top, open triangles*) compared with anaerobic sprinting speeds (*solid circles*). Aerobic power can be maintained much longer than anaerobic power, however, as evidenced by the flatter slopes of the aerobic endurance capacity curves in Figure 2. As aerobic metabolic power is considered to be the primary limiting factor for many types of exercise, the remainder of the review focuses on factors that limit it.

LIMITATIONS TO AEROBIC PERFORMANCE

During exercise that elicits an animal's maximal rate of oxygen consumption, or $\dot{V}_{O_2max}$, the animal can transiently utilize anaerobic metabolic pathways and sprint, with the consequent accumulation of lactic acid/lactate in muscle and blood (8, 77, 92). This ability to generate mechanical power in excess of that sustained under fully aerobic conditions demonstrates that muscle is not mechanically limited at $\dot{V}_{O_2max}$, but rather that aerobic capacity is limited and is a fundamental determinant of maximal sustained performance. Factors limiting aerobic metabolism were reviewed six years ago (95) from a different perspective.

Body Size and Aerobic Capacity

It has long been recognized that body size and basal metabolism are allometrically related (90), with the standard rate of oxygen consumption ($\dot{V}_{O_2}$ std) proportional to $M_b^{0.7}$. Taylor and co-workers (10, 14, 57, 71, 75, 92, 98, 99, 101) have measured $\dot{V}_{O_2max}$ in a number of mammalian species using a modification of Margaria's treadmill technique (78, 92). The relationship between $\dot{V}_{O_2max}$ and body mass for 37 species of mammals is shown in Figure 3 (*top*). Least-squares linear regression of these data shows that $\dot{V}_{O_2max}$ is proportional to $M_b^{0.871}$, a significantly larger exponent than the scaling of $\dot{V}_{O_2}$std (0.7), which indicates that aerobic scope ($\dot{V}_{O_2max}/\dot{V}_{O_2}$std) increases with body size among mammals. The data for larger species show more variance around the regression line, which suggests that aerobic capacity may be more plastic among larger species. The slope calculated for the regression may be biased high from a general relationship for mammals since some of the larger species were selected for study because they were hypothesized to have unusually high aerobic capacities.

Figure 3 (*bottom*) shows the same data plotted as mass-specific $\dot{V}_{O_2max}$ (W kg^{-1}), which enables relative comparisons to be made between aerobic capacities of small and large mammals. In general, small mammals have higher specific aerobic capacities than larger mammals. However, great variability is possible within a size since the aerobic capacity of the 32 kg pronghorn antelope is nearly four times higher, and that of the 50 kg capybara three times lower, than those predicted for their sizes. Although the aerobic scope of a larger mammal on average exceeds that of a smaller species, the absolute increase in specific $\dot{V}_{O_2}$(W kg^{-1}) from $\dot{V}_{O_2}$std to $\dot{V}_{O_2max}$) is greater for a smaller mammal. Body size plays a fundamental role in limiting aerobic capacity; no mammal measured comes within 25% of the highest specific $\dot{V}_{O_2}$, that of the smallest mammal, the 2 g Etruscan shrew. Within any given

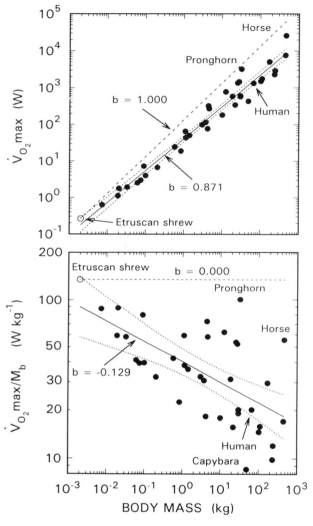

Figure 3   (*top*) Log-log plot of whole-body maximal rate of O₂ consumption ($\dot{V}_{O_2max}$, aerobic power calculated as 1 ml O₂ (STPD) s^{-1} = 20.1 W) as a function of body mass for 37 species of mammals. Etruscan shrew point is open because it is not a verified maximum for that species. Solid line is the least-squares linear regression fitted to the data points (slope = 0.871, dotted curves are 95% confidence limits). Dashed line (slope = 1) is the line of identity representing direct proportionality between $\dot{V}_{O_2max}$ and body size. (*bottom*) Maximum aerobic power for the 37 species above expressed in mass- specific terms. Solid and dotted lines as above; dashed line (b = 0) corresponds to the line of identity above, representing independence of specific $\dot{V}_{O_2max}$ and body size. Data from 10, 28, 56, 71.

body size, several different factors could structurally or functionally limit aerobic capacity, as discussed below.

Potential Mechanisms For Limiting $\dot{V}_{O_2}$ max

The respiratory system has been characterized by Dejours and others (21, 110) as a series of conductances and partial pressure differences of O_2 and CO_2. The ultimate driving force for O_2 flux through the system is the P_{O_2} difference between the mitochondria and the atmospheric air, subdivided into a series of transport steps as follows: (a) the P_{O_2} around the mitochondria is reduced as oxidative phosphorylation consumes O2 molecules; (b) the increased ΔP_{O_2} between the interior of the myocyte and erythrocytes in the muscle capillary increases the diffusive flux; (c) the decreased P_{O_2} in the venous blood exiting the muscle capillary lowers the mixed venous P_{O_2} and O_2 concentration, thereby increasing convective delivery by the circulation (the arterial-mixed venous O_2 concentration difference increases, and cardiac output, $\dot{Q}$, or hemoglobin concentration, [Hb], may increase as well); (d) the decreased P_{O_2} in the mixed venous blood increases the ΔP_{O_2} across the blood-gas barrier in the lung, increasing diffusive flux; and (e) increased PCO_2 (and other factors) stimulate increased alveolar ventilation, which raises the alveolar P_{O_2} so as to increase diffusive flux of O_2 into the pulmonary capillary blood. As mitochondrial consumption of O_2 increases, O_2 flux through the transport system increases to meet that demand, up to the limiting rate of $\dot{V}_{O_2max}$.

The maximum flux of O_2 through the respiratory system could be limited by either the demand for O_2, i.e. a limitation of mitochondrial oxidative capacity, or a limitation of O_2 transport capacity by the diffusive and convective components of the system. The hypothesis of convective limitation has deep historical roots (45, 105) and is still widely held (25, 89). Because of the interdependence of each of the transport steps, compensation may be made by one or more steps in the O_2 transport system for deficiencies in the capacity of any other single step in the system (54). Only one step in the entire respiratory system, mitochondrial oxidative phosphorylation, is truly independent of adjoining steps in affecting O_2 transport. Appreciation of this interdependence of function has led to recurring suggestions that limitations to aerobic capacity are likely determined by interactions of multiple components of the O_2 transport system (24, 53, 54, 73, 74, 103, 106, 108), rather than by any single step. The contribution of each step of the O_2 transport system to limiting $\dot{V}_{O_2max}$ in mammals is considered below.

Mitochondrial Oxidative Capacity

Because mitochondrial oxidative activity sets the demand for O_2 during aerobic exercise, skeletal muscle mitochondrial oxidative capacity would limit aerobic capacity of an animal if O_2 transport capacity were to exceed oxidative capacity, as it does during submaximal exercise. Skeletal muscle oxidative capacity can be assessed by measuring enzyme activities and reaction rates (27, 91), or by morphometric estimates of inner mitochondrial membrane surface area, which in most mammals is directly proportional to the volume of mitochondria in the muscle (50). For a variety of mammals, the relationship between maximum O_2 demand ($\dot{V}_{O_2max}$) and mitochondrial oxidative capacity (whole body skeletal muscle mitochondrial inner membrane surface area) has been found to be nearly constant, such that at $\dot{V}_{O_2max}$ the inner mitochondrial membrane consumes O_2 at a rate of approximately 2,000 molecules s^{-1} μm^{-2}, regardless of whether the mitochondria are in a large or small mammal, or an athletic or non-athletic species (49, 50, 64, 95, 98, 99). The upper limit to muscle oxidative capacity may be reached when approximately 35% of the muscle fibers are occupied by mitochondria, as this is the maximal mitochondrial volume density observed in either cardiac or skeletal muscles of highly aerobic species of mammals and hummingbirds (S. Lindstedt, unpublished observation).

Although maximum specific skeletal muscle mitochondrial $\dot{V}_{O_2}$ is nearly constant among mammals, it does not necessarily follow that mitochondrial oxidative capacity limits $\dot{V}_{O_2max}$. To test the hypothesis that the mitochondria are functioning at their aerobic maxima when an animal is at $\dot{V}_{O_2max}$, it is necessary to determine if the animal's $\dot{V}_{O_2max}$ increases when more O_2 is delivered to its mitochondria. Experiments in humans using one-legged exercise, thereby allowing the O_2 delivery system to supply a smaller volume of working mitochondria than when both legs were exercised, found that specific $\dot{V}_{O_2max}$ of the muscles recruited increased when a single leg was exercised maximally (7). Whole body $\dot{V}_{O_2max}$ increases in humans exercising in hyperoxia (83), although not as dramatically as in racehorses, in which breathing 25–30% O_2 while running increases $\dot{V}_{O_2max}$ by 11–19% (52, 53). These results definitively demonstrate that the muscles of these animals have the oxidative capacity to utilize more O_2 if it can be delivered by the O_2 transport system, and implicate O_2 delivery as their primary limitation for $\dot{V}_{O_2max}$.

In contrast to these findings, goats do not increase $\dot{V}_{O_2max}$ in hyperoxia (S. Lindstedt, unpublished observation) and can maintain their normoxic sea level $\dot{V}_{O_2max}$ while exercising in hypoxia as severe as 15% inspired O_2 (55, 61). In effect, 21% O_2 at sea level is a hyperoxic environment for the goat relative to the hypoxic conditions under which it can attain an equivalent $\dot{V}_{O_2max}$. Thus in contrast to humans and horses, $\dot{V}_{O_2max}$ in the goat appears to be limited by mitochondrial oxidative capacity. This fundamental difference in respiratory system design may reflect selective pressures that have acted on these species during their evolutionary histories (73).

Peripheral Diffusion

Evidence that peripheral tissue diffusion limitation occurs at $\dot{V}_{O_2max}$ is suggested by the observation that the P_{O_2} of neither mixed venous blood nor the blood draining any individual muscle ever reaches 0 torr (82). Decreases in mixed venous P_{O_2} in humans exercising near $\dot{V}_{O_2max}$ at simulated altitudes (106) and breathing hypoxic gases (84) are consistent with the hypothesis that peripheral tissue diffusion limitation plays a role in limiting O_2 delivery. Similar patterns of change occur in thoroughbred horses in which $\dot{V}_{O_2max}$ increases during exercise in hyperoxia (52, 53), and in isolated perfused canine limb preparations, in which flow and capacitance for O_2 are independently altered (48). The latter experiments must be interpreted carefully, however, as the specific $\dot{V}_{O_2max}$ attained by the canine skeletal muscle in the isolated limb preparation (approximately 10 ml O_2 min^{-1} 100 g^{-1}) is only one third the value calculated for skeletal muscle in an intact dog exercising at whole body $\dot{V}_{O_2max}$ (99), assuming 90% of the O_2 consumed at $\dot{V}_{O_2max}$ goes to skeletal muscle and dividing whole animal specific $\dot{V}_{O_2max}$ by the skeletal muscle's fraction of body mass, 0.44 (99). This discrepancy between isolated limb preparations and intact animals is universal and suggests that factors limiting $\dot{V}_{O_2max}$ in isolated preparations may be different from those operating in whole animals.

Diffusion limitation would occur if the tissue diffusing capacity were too small for the time available for diffusion as the erythrocytes pass through the muscle capillaries (transit time). Although insufficient transit time has been suggested as the cause of diffusion limitation in humans (88), humans and other large mammals have longer transit times than smaller mammals (63). Krogh (67) noted that muscles of small mammals with high specific $\dot{V}_{O_2}$ have higher capillary densities than those of larger mammals; this relationship would help to increase both diffusing capacities and transit times in small mammals with high specific Q.

Circulatory Convection

Perhaps the most avidly defended hypothesis of factors limiting $\dot{V}_{O_2max}$ in humans is that circulatory delivery of O_2, a function of Q and [Hb], constitutes a single limiting step in the system (25, 89). The rationale for this conclusion is the correlation between $\dot{V}_{O_2max}$ and changes in circulatory O_2 delivery, typically the result of infusion or withdrawal of erythrocytes (16, 26). Several analyses have demonstrated that changes in circulatory convection also affect adjacent diffusive gas exchangers in the lung and muscle (47, 54, 75, 100, 106); furthermore, it is impossible for $\dot{V}_{O_2max}$ to change unless the product of Q and the arterial-mixed venous O_2 concentration difference changes, which dictates, a priori, that changes in these variables must be correlated. Lindstedt et al (74) analyzed the results of all such experiments conducted to that time and concluded that no absolute correlation exists between [Hb] and $\dot{V}_{O_2max}$ in humans. Instead, it appears that a minimal [Hb] must exist to enable the individual to attain a particular $\dot{V}_{O_2max}$, but the [Hb] in itself is not limiting. Although induced erythrocythemia appears to be associated with increased $\dot{V}_{O_2max}$ in humans, this procedure is unlikely to be as significant in nonhuman mammals because, unlike humans, during exercise they mobilize erythrocytes stored in the spleen or capacitance vessels. Using this mechanism, nonhuman species increase [Hb] by 40–50% as they increase work intensity from rest to $\dot{V}_{O_2max}$ (53, 57, 62, 75), and highly selected aerobic species, e.g. racehorses, may have hematocrits > 65% when exercising at $\dot{V}_{O_2max}$. di Prampero's (24) analysis of the factors involved in limiting $\dot{V}_{O_2max}$ in normal humans indicated that all components of the O_2 transport system contribute to the limitation, but that the system is most sensitive to changes in circulatory function.

Goats maintained their normoxic $\dot{V}_{O_2max}$ at 15% inspired O_2 by increasing $\dot{Q}$ by 21% to compensate for decreased arterial O_2 saturation and concentration (55, 61); they clearly experience no $\dot{Q}$ limitation in normoxia. In contrast, horses increased normoxic $\dot{V}_{O_2max}$ by 11% when breathing 25% O_2 and 19% when breathing 30% O_2, which they achieved with no change in $\dot{Q}$ and a 10% increase in $\dot{Q}$, respectively (52, 53). Cardiac stroke volume (SV) increased in hyperoxia, but heart rate (HR) never exceeded its value at $\dot{V}_{O_2max}$ in normoxia. Horses were able to increase $\dot{V}_{O_2max}$ without increasing $\dot{Q}$ at 25% O_2 because their arterial O_2 saturation in normoxia is only 77% and hyperoxia increased saturation. Therefore, in this species, O_2 flux is limited in portions of the O_2 transport system other than the circulation, even though the cardiac pump may be operating at its maximal capacity at $\dot{V}_{O_2max}$ in normoxia. The relatively high $\dot{Q}$ that horses attain at $\dot{V}_{O_2max}$ is achieved at a high price: most racehorses experience exercise-induced pulmonary hemorrhage when they race. The hemorrhage appears to originate from pulmonary vessels that rupture because of high transmural pressures (60, 111). Mean pulmonary arterial pressures in horses at $\dot{V}_{O_2max}$ (120 torr) are three to four times higher than in other mammals and may be a consequence of their extremely high left atrial pressures (> 70 torr, 58), which in turn may be required for them to achieve high $\dot{Q}$. Catastrophic failure of structures in the equine respiratory system may result from humans' efforts to defy allometric constraints and select large mammals for extremely high $\dot{V}_{O_2max}$ and $\dot{Q}$.

Specific $\dot{Q}$ (ml s^{-1} kg^{-1}) at $\dot{V}_{O_2max}$ is close to the maximum value that can be recorded for a normoxic animal. It scales with $M_b^{-0.19}$ (100), identical to the scaling of maximal HR during locomotion (9, 14, 57, 62), and similar to the exponent of -0.13 for specific $\dot{V}_{O_2max}$. For mammals other than humans, SV remains constant as an animal increases its exercise intensity from rest to $\dot{V}_{O_2max}$ in normoxia, therefore, limits to $\dot{Q}$ appear to be set by maximal HR. Stroke volume is directly related to heart size (57, 62); cardiac hypertrophy following aerobic training leads to increased SV and $\dot{Q}$, and is associated with increased $\dot{V}_{O_2max}$ (8). The pericardium may play a role in limiting SV, since its removal from the hearts of untrained dogs led to significant increases in SV, $\dot{Q}$, and $\dot{V}_{O_2max}$ compared with sham-operated dogs (93).

Pulmonary Gas Exchange

Because the lungs of adult mammals do not alter their structural or functional capacities in response to functional demands, e.g. exercise, the lung has been viewed as a potential source of limitation for aerobic capacity (22, 110). Few data are available with which to assess limitations to $\dot{V}_{O_2max}$ that might be imposed by pulmonary diffusion limitation in mammals. Weibel and collaborators (19, 34, 53, 75) evaluated the relationship between morphometric estimates of pulmonary diffusing capacity for O_2 (DL_{O_2}) and body size. They found that DL_{O_2} varies in almost direct proportion to M_b (34, 103), whereas specific $\dot{V}_{O_2max}$ is proportional to M_b with a negative exponent. They interpreted this discrepancy in allometric exponents as evidence that large mammals have "excess lung" above what they need for O_2 flux at $\dot{V}_{O_2max}$, and small mammals have sufficient DL_{O_2} to meet their O_2 transport demands. If the transit time of erythrocytes flowing through pulmonary capillaries scales with a positive exponent, as has been suggested (70), then achieving diffusion equilibrium requires a larger functional pressure head in the lung for smaller mammals (75, 100).

The adequacy of the morphometric DL_{O_2} for gas exchange in different sized mammals at $\dot{V}_{O_2max}$ has been evaluated using a simple one-compartment homogeneous Bohr integration model of pulmonary gas exchange (19, 53, 61, 75). The results suggest that species with very high specific $\dot{V}_{O_2max}$, e.g. the 4 kg fox and 500 kg thoroughbred horse, may experience significant diffusion limitation at $\dot{V}_{O_2max}$, whereas less aerobic species do not. (Some studies evaluating pulmonary gas exchange during exercise have corrected blood gases to rectal temperature; because large temperature differences may exist between the rectum and arterial blood, arterial P_{O_2} values corrected to rectal temperature may be biased low by up to 20 torr (59), thus leading to erroneous conclusions.)

Imperfect pulmonary gas exchange may depress arterial O_2 saturation as low as 90% in highly aerobic human athletes (83). Contributing to this decrease are both ventilation-perfusion mismatch (31) and diffusion limitation (37); diffusion limitation becomes significant in humans during exercise at high altitudes (109). In exercising horses ventilation-perfusion mismatching is modest at all exercise intensities; however, diffusion limitation at near maximal exercise can decrease arterial P_{O_2} by 20 torr or more (107). Pulmonary diffusion limitation may become a significant factor in limiting $\dot{V}_{O_2max}$ in a species or an individual that develops the malleable elements of its O_2 transport system (e.g. heart, peripheral capillary beds) to capacities that approach the genetically programmed gas exchange potential of the animal's lungs.

Pulmonary Ventilation

Adequate pulmonary ventilation during exercise is essential for removing alveolar CO_2 and increasing alveolar P_{O_2}. Normal ventilation at rest is defined by matching alveolar ventilation to the body's rate of CO_2 production so that arterial P_{CO_2} remains unchanged from its regulated value (40 torr for most mammals, 21). During exercise at $\dot{V}_{O_2max}$, most mammals hyperventilate and maintain or increase arterial P_{O_2} (29, 61, 75); however, larger mammals hypoventilate and may become hypoxemic (52, 53, 57). The magnitude of hyperventilation appears to be related to body size, as arterial P_{CO_2} at $\dot{V}_{O_2max}$ is proportional to $M_b^{0.17}$, and arterial P_{O_2} is proportional to $M_b^{-0.06}$ (76, J. Jones, unpublished observations). These values range from a 4 kg fox with arterial P_{CO_2} and P_{O_2} of 19 torr and 121 torr (75) to a 500 kg thoroughbred horse with arterial P_{CO_2} and P_{O_2} of 56 torr and 69 torr, respectively (53).

Why body size should affect alveolar ventilation during exercise is unclear. Higher specific $\dot{V}_{O_2max}$ in smaller mammals (Figure 3, *bottom*) causes higher specific rates of CO_2 production and requires greater increases in specific alveolar ventilation than in larger mammals just to remain normocapnic, much less to hyperventilate. Many species of mammals synchronize ventilatory frequency with stride frequency when running (15); as stride frequency scales with $M_b^{-0.18}$ during galloping (41), small mammals with synchronized stride and breathing would have higher ventilatory frequencies than large mammals. However, synchronization of stride and ventilation might be a disadvantage in maintaining effective alveolar ventilation. For instance, a 500 kg thorough-bred horse runs with stride and ventilatory frequencies of 2.2 Hz, thereby having to move its tidal volume of 13–14 liters in < 220 ms, requiring mean flows of 60 liter s^{-1}, peak flows in excess of 120 liter s^{-1}, and high dead space ventilation (35, J. Jones, unpublished observations). These flows may reach values that produce airway closure, which would force the horse to hypoventilate at these ventilatory frequencies.

It has been suggested that mechanical linkage between stride and ventilatory maneuvers is responsible for their entrainment (15, 29). However, it is possible to disrupt the 1:1 ratio between stride and breathing in some horses by using high inspired concentrations of CO_2 and thereby improve alveolar ventilation (35). Pressure-flow analyses during galloping also argue against there being an obligatory mechanical link between stride and ventilation in the horse (30).

Although average humans hyperventilate during heavy exercise, elite athletes do not (29). These individuals may be operating near the upper limits of the ventilatory system's functional capacity. This interpretation is supported by the observation that increasing airway resistance by a fixed amount decreases aerobic performance because of the increased cost of ventilation only in individuals with extremely high specific $\dot{V}_{O_2max}$ (69); average athletes are unaffected.

Symmorphosis

In 1976 Taylor & Weibel undertook a series of combined physiologic and morphometric studies to test the hypothesis that a principle existed that they termed symmorphosis. Symmorphosis proposes that structural elements in an animal, and specifically the respiratory system, are designed so as to just meet the functional demand and avoid "wasted" excess structure (99, 103, 110). They tested the hypothesis by determining whether structural elements of the mammalian respiratory system varied quantitatively with the maximum functional demand of the system for O_2 transport, $\dot{V}_{O_2max}$, in mammals that varied greatly in specific $\dot{V}_{O_2max}$ because of allometric differences or adaptation through evolution (99, 110).

Their findings can be summarized by saying that some structures in the respiratory system do appear to change nearly stoichiometrically with $\dot{V}_{O_2max}$, e.g. inner mitochondrial membrane surface area (50, 95, 98), whereas others clearly do not, e.g. pulmonary diffusing capacity for O_2 (34). The latter observation indicates that symmorphosis, as originally stated, is not a general feature of animal design.

Because natural selection acts on an integrated mosaic of structural and functional features in an animal, it seems unlikely that the respiratory system would be designed to optimize respiratory structure-function matching unless selective pressures were strongly directed toward extreme aerobic performance (73). For most species, e.g. humans and goats, aerobic performance presumably plays a minor role in survival and selection, thus rendering matching of respiratory structure and function unimportant. In these species, any individual component of the respiratory system might appear as a "weakest link" that limits aerobic capacity. In contrast, selection of racehorses by humans for phenotypic traits directly dependent on aerobic capacity has occurred for hundreds to thousands of generations. This selective pressure may have led to the observed pattern of physiologic responses that suggests that all elements of the O_2 transport system contribute significantly to limiting $\dot{V}_{O_2max}$ in these animals (52, 53, 54). Similar patterns of limitation may exist in non-domestic species that have experienced strong selective pressures for aerobic performance, e.g. the pronghorn antelope (73).

SUMMARY

Body size fundamentally affects maximal locomotor performance in mammals. Comparisons of performances of different-sized animals yield different results if made using relative, rather than absolute scales. Absolute speed may be a reasonable way to evaluate the locomotor performance of an animal that must escape predators in real time. However, comparisons of metabolic power in animals of different size can only be made meaningfully on a mass-specific basis.

Numerous factors associated with the mechanics, energetics, and storage of elastic energy during locomotion change with body size, which results in allometric relationships that make the energetic cost of locomotion ($\propto M_b^{-0.3}$) more expensive for small mammals than for large mammals. Small mammals have lower enzymatic capacities for anaerobic glycolysis ($\propto M_b^{0.15}$) and higher specific aerobic capacities ($\propto M_b^{-0.13}$) than large mammals. However, the energetic cost of transport increases more than aerobic power as mammals get smaller. The higher ratio of cost to available power in small mammals may explain why they run more slowly than large mammals, as a rule.

Maximum aerobic capacity is allometrically related to body size. Limits to $\dot{V}_{O_2 max}$ can be imposed by mitochondrial oxidative capacity, as in goats, or by the O_2 transport system, as in humans and horses. No single step in the O_2 transport system can limit the flux of O_2 by itself; however, in an average non-athletic species of mammal, any of the steps in the system might appear to be the weakest link. In highly aerobic athletic species, and possibly elite athletic individuals of other species (e.g. humans), the malleable elements of the O_2 transport system may develop to the point that their O_2 transport capacities approach that of the least malleable element in the system, the lung. $\dot{V}_{O_2 max}$ is very high in such individuals, and appears to be limited by simultaneous failure of all components of the O_2 transport system.

ACKNOWLEDGMENTS

We thank K. E. Longworth for comments and suggestions regarding this manuscript. Work for this review was supported by the University of California, Davis Equine Research Laboratory with contributions from the California Satellite Wagering Fund, the Oak Tree Racing Foundation and private contributions, and by National Institutes of Health (RO1) HL4196.

Literature Cited

1. Alexander, R. M. 1977. Terrestrial locomotion. In *Mechanics and Energetics of Animal Locomotion*, ed. R. M. Alexander, G. Goldspink, pp. 168–203. London: Chapman & Hall

2. Alexander, R. M. 1980. Optimum walking techniques for quadrupeds and bipeds. *J. Zool.* 192:97–117

3. Alexander, R. M. 1991. Energy-saving mechanisms in walking and running. *J. Exp. Biol.* 160:55–69

4. Alexander, R. M., Dimery, N. J., Ker, R. F. 1985. Elastic structures in the back and their role in galloping in some mammals. *J. Zool.* A207:467–82

5. Alexander, R. M., Vernon, A. S. 1975. Mechanics of hopping by kangaroos (Macropodidae). *J. Zool.* 177:265–303

6. Altringham, J. D., Young, I. S. 1991. Power output and the frequency of oscillatory work in mammalian diaphragm muscle: the effects of animal size. *J. Exp. Biol.* 157:381–89

7. Andersen, P., Saltin, B. 1985. Maximal perfusion of skeletal muscle in man. *J. Physiol.* 366:233–49

8. Åastrand, P., Rodahl, K. 1986. *Textbook of Work Physiology*. New York: McGraw Hill. 681 pp. 3rd ed.

9. Baudinette, R. V. 1978. Scaling of heart rate during locomotion in mammals. *J. Comp. Physiol.* 127:337–42

10. Bicudo, J. E. P. W., Jones, J. H., Jackson, A., Wong, D. 1992. Allometry of aerobic metabolism in rodents: minimal, maximal and scope. *Physiologist.* 35:225

11. Biewener, A. A. 1982. Bone strength in small mammals and bipedal birds: do safety factors change with body size? *J. Exp. Biol.* 98:289–301

12. Biewener, A. A. 1989. Scaling body support in mammals: limb posture and muscle mechanics. *Science* 245:45–48

13. Biewener, A., Alexander, R. M., Heglund, N. C. 1981. Elastic energy storage in the hopping of kangaroo rats. *J. Zool.* 195:369–83

14. Birks, E. K., Jones, J. H., Berry, J. D. 1991. Plasma lactate kinetics in exercising horses. In *Equine Exercise Physiology 3*, ed. S. G. B. Persson, A. Lindholm, L. B. Jeffcott, pp. 179–87. Uppsala: Almqvist & Wiksell

15. Bramble, D. M., Carrier, D. R. 1983. Running and breathing in mammals. *Science* 219:251–56

16. Buick, F. J., Gledhill, N., Froese, A. B., Spriet, L., Meyers, E. C. 1980. Effect of induced erythrocythemia on aerobic work capacity. *J. Appl. Physiol.* 48:636–42

17. Cavagna, G. A., Heglund, N. C., Taylor, C. R. 1977. Mechanical work in terrestrial locomotion: two basic mechanisms for minimizing energy expenditure. *Am. J. Physiol.* 233:R243–61

18. Close R. I. 1972. Dynamic properties of mammalian skeletal muscle. *Physiol. Rev.* 52:129–97

19. Constantinopol, M., Jones, J. H., Weibel, E. R., Taylor, C. R., Lindholm, A. 1989. Oxygen transport during exercise in large mammals. II. Oxygen uptake by the pulmonary gas exchanger. *J. Appl. Physiol.* 67:871–78

20. Davies, C. T. M., Rennie, R. 1968. Human power output. *Nature* 217:770–71

21. Dejours, P. 1975. *Principles of Comparative Respiratory Physiology*. Amsterdam: Elsevier/North-Holland Biomedical. 253 pp.

22. Dempsey, J. A. 1986. Is the lung built for exercise? *Med. Sci. Sports Exerc.* 18:143–55

23. di Prampero, P. E. 1981. Energetics of muscular exercise. *Rev. Physiol. Biochem. Pharmacol.* 89:143–222

24. di Prampero, P. E. 1985. Metabolic and circulatory limitations to $\dot{V}_{O_2 max}$ at the whole animal level. *J. Exp. Biol.* 115:319–31

25. Ekblom, B. 1986. Factors determining maximal aerobic power. *Acta Physiol. Scand.* 128:15–19

26. Ekblom, B., Goldbarg, A. N., Gullbring, B. 1972. Response to exercise after blood loss and reinfusion. *J. Appl. Physiol.* 33:175–80

27. Emmett, B., Hochachka, P. W. 1981. Scaling of oxidative and glycolytic enzymes in mammals. *Respir. Physiol.* 45:261–72

28. Fons, R., Sicart, R. 1976. Contribution a la connaissance du metabolisme energetique chez deuz crocidurinae: *Suncus etruscus* (Savi, 1822) et *Crocidura russala* (Hermann, 1780) (Insectivora, Soricidae). *Mammalia* 40:299–311 (In French)

29. Forster, H. V., Pan, L. G. 1988. Breathing during exercise: demands, regulation, limitations. *Adv. Exp. Med. Biol.* 227:257–76

30. Frevert, C. W., Nations, C. S., Seeher-

man, H. J., Loring, F. H., Banzett, R. B. 1990. Airflow associated with stride in the horse. *Physiologist* 33:A83 (Abstr.)

31. Gale, G. E., Torre-Bueno, J., Saltzman, H. A., Wagner, P. D. 1985. V̇A/ Q̇ inequality in normal man during exercise at sea level and simulated altitude. *J. Appl. Physiol.* 58:978–88

32. Garland, T. 1983. The relation between maximal running speed and body mass in terrestrial mammals. *J. Zool.* 199:157–70

33. Garland, T., Geiser, F., Baudinette, R. V. 1988. Comparative locomotor performance of marsupial and placental mammals. *J. Zool.* 215:505–22

34. Gehr, P., Mwangi, D. K., Ammann, A., Maloiy, G. M. O., Taylor, C. R. 1981. Design of the mammalian respiratory system. V. Scaling morphometric diffusing capacity to body mass: wild and domestic mammals. *Respir. Physiol.* 44:61–86

35. Gillespie, J. R., Landgren, G. L., Leith, D. E. 1991. 1:2 ratio of breathing to stride frequencies in a galloping horse breathing 6% CO_2 See Ref. 14, pp. 66–70

36. Gove, P. B., ed. 1986. *Webster's Third New International Dictionary Unabridged.* Springfield, Mass: Merriam-Webster. 2662 pp.

37. Hammond, M. D., Gale, G. E., Kapitan, K. S., Ries, A., Wagner, P. D. 1986. Pulmonary gas exchange in humans during exercise at sea level. *J. Appl. Physiol.* 60:1590–98

38. Hasan, Z., Stuart, D. G. 1988. Animal solutions to problems of movement control: the role of proprioceptors. *Annu. Rev. Neuroscience* 11:199–223

39. Heglund, N. C., Cavagna, G. A. 1987. Mechanical work, oxygen consumption, and efficiency in isolated frog and rat muscle. *Am. J. Physiol.* 253:C22–29

40. Heglund, N. C., Fedak, M. A., Taylor, C. R., Cavagna, C. A. 1982. Energetics and mechanics of terrestrial locomotion. IV. Total mechanical energy changes as a function of speed and body size in birds and mammals. *J. Exp. Biol.* 97:57–66

41. Heglund, N. C., Taylor, C. R. 1988. Speed, stride frequency and energy cost per stride: how do they change with body size and gait? *J. Exp. Biol.* 138:301–18

42. Heglund, N. C., Taylor, C. R., McMahon, T. A. 1974. Scaling stride frequency and gait to animal size: mice to horses. *Science* 186:1112–13

43. Hill, A. V. 1938. The heat of shortening and dynamic constants of muscle. *Proc. R. Soc. London Ser. B* 126:136–95

44. Hill, A. V. 1950. The dimensions of animals and their muscular dynamics. *Sci. Prog.* 38:209–30

45. Hill, A. V., Lupton, H. 1923. Muscular exercise, lactic acid, and the supply and utilization of oxygen. *Q. J. Med.* 16:135–71

46. Hochachka, P. W., Emmett, B., Suarez, R. K. 1988. Limits and constraints in the scaling of oxidative and glycolytic enzymes in homeotherms. *Can. J. Zool.* 66:1128–38

47. Hogan, M. C., Bebout, D. E., West, J. B., Wagner, P. D. 1990. Effect of altered Hb concentration on maximal O_2 consumption in canine gastrocnemius in situ. *FASEB J.* 4:5499 (Abstr.)

48. Hogan, M. C., Roca, J., West, J. B., Wagner, P. D. 1989. Dissociation of maximal O_2 uptake from O_2 delivery in canine gastrocnemius in situ. *J. Appl. Physiol.* 66:1919–26

49. Hoppeler, H., Jones, J. H., Lindstedt, S. L., Claasen, H., Straub, R., et al. 1987. Relating $\dot{V}_{O_2max}$ to skeletal muscle mitochondria in horses. In *Equine Exercise Physiology II*, ed. J. R. Gillespie, N. E. Robinson, pp. 278–89. Davis, Calif: ICEEP Publ.

50. Hoppeler, H., Lindstedt, S. L. 1985. Malleability of skeletal muscle tissue in overcoming limitations: structural elements. *J. Exp. Biol.* 115:355–64

51. Hultman, E., Sjöholm, H. 1983. Energy metabolism and contraction force of human skeletal muscle in situ during electrical stimulation. *J. Physiol.* 345:525–32

52. Jones, J. H., Birks, E. K., Berry, J. D. 1989. Does oxygen transport limit $\dot{V}_{O_2max}$ in horses? *FASEB J.* 3:A234 (Abstr.)

53. Jones, J. H., Birks, E. K., Pascoe, J. R. 1992. Factors limiting aerobic performance. In *The Vertebrate Gas Transport Cascade: Adaptations to Environment and Mode of Life,* ed. J. E. P. W. Bicudo, pp. 169–78. Boca Raton: CRC Press. 376 pp.

54. Jones, J. H., Karas, R. H. 1988. Structural vs. functional limitations to oxygen transport: is there a difference? *Adv. Exp. Med. Biol.* 227:293–300

55. Jones, J. H., Lindstedt, S. L., Longworth, K. E., Karas, R. H., Taylor, C. R. 1985. Muscle respiration limits aerobic capacity in goats. *Physiologist* 28:342 (Abstr.)

56. Jones, J. H., Longworth, K. E. 1992.

Gas exchange at rest and during exercise in mammals. In *Comparative Biology of the Normal Lung*, ed. R. A. Parent, pp. 271–307. Boca Raton: CRC Press

57. Jones, J. H., Longworth, K. E., Lindholm, A., Conley, K. E., Karas, R. H. 1989. Oxygen transport during exercise in large mammals. I. Adaptive variation in oxygen demand. *J. Appl. Physiol.* 67:862–70

58. Jones, J. H., Smith, B. L., Birks, E. K., Pascoe, J. R., Hughes, T. R. 1992. Left atrial and pulmonary arterial pressures in exercising horses. *Fed. Proc.* 6:A2020 (Abstr.)

59. Jones, J. H., Taylor, C. R., Lindholm, A., Straub, R., Longworth, K. E. 1989. Blood gas measurements during exercise: errors due to temperature correction. *J. Appl. Physiol.* 67:879–84

60. Jones, J. H., Tyler, W. S., Pascoe, J. R., Smith, B. L., Birks, E. K. 1992. Origin of airway blood in exercise-induced pulmonary hemorrhage in race horses. *Physiologist.* 30:225 (Abstr.)

61. Karas, R. H., Taylor, C. R., Jones, J. H., Lindstedt, S. L., Reeves, R. B. 1987. Adaptive variation in the mammalian respiratory system in relation to energetic demand. VII. Flow of oxygen across the pulmonary gas exchanger. *Respir. Physiol.* 69:101–15

62. Karas, R. H., Taylor, C. R., Rosler, K., Hoppeler, H. 1987. Adaptive variation in the mammalian respiratory system in relation to energetic demand. V. Limits to oxygen transport by the circulation. *Respir. Physiol.* 69:65–80

63. Kayar, S. R., Hoppeler, H., Armstrong, R. B., Lindstedt, S. L., Jones, J. H. 1987. Minimal blood transit time in muscle capillaries. *Fed. Proc.* 46:352 (Abstr.)

64. Kayar, S. R., Hoppeler, H., Lindstedt, S. L., Claasen, H., Jones, J. H. 1989. Total muscle mitochondrial volume and capillary length in relation to aerobic capacity of horses and steers. *Pflügers Arch.* 413:343–47

65. Kennely, A. E. 1906. An approximate law of fatigue in the speeds of racing animals. *Proc. Am. Acad. Arts Sci.* 42:275–331

66. Kram, R., Taylor, C. R. 1990. Energetics of running: a new perspective. *Nature* 346:265–67

67. Krogh, A. 1919. The supply of oxygen to the tissues and the regulation of the capillary circulation. *J. Physiol.* 52:457–74

68. Lane, H. U., ed. 1985. *The World Almanac and Book of Facts 1986.* New York: Newspaper Enterprise Assoc. 928 pp.

69. Leith, D. E., Knuttgen, H. G., Cymerman, A., Fencl, V., Gabel, R. A. 1984. Inspiratory muscle endurance, exercise tolerance, and loaded breathing. *Fed. Proc.* 43:898 (Abstr.)

70. Lindstedt, S. L. 1984. Pulmonary transit time and diffusing capacity in mammals. *Am. J. Physiol.* 246:R384–88

71. Lindstedt, S. L., Hokanson, J. F., Wells, D. J., Swain, S. D., Hoppeler, H. 1991. Running energetics in the pronghorn antelope. *Nature* 353:748–50

72. Lindstedt, S. L., Hoppeler, H., Bard, K. M., Thronson, H. A. J. 1985. Estimate of muscle shortening rate during locomotion. *Am. J. Physiol.* 249: R699–703

73. Lindstedt, S. L., Jones, J. H. 1987. Symmorphosis: the concept of optimal design. In *New Directions in Ecological Physiology,* ed. M. E. Feder, A. F. Bennett, W. W. Burggren, R. B. Huey, pp. 289–309. Cambridge: Cambridge Univ. Press

74. Lindstedt, S. L., Wells, D. J., Jones, J. H., Hoppeler, H., Thronson, H. A. 1988. Limitations to aerobic performance in mammals: interaction of structure and demand. *Int. J. Sports Med.* 9:210–17

75. Longworth, K. E., Jones, J. H., Bicudo, J. E. P. W., Taylor, C. R., Weibel, E. R. 1989. High rate of O_2 consumption in exercising foxes: large P_{O_2} difference drives diffusion across the lung. *Respir. Physiol.* 77:263–76

76. Longworth, K. E., Jones, J. H., Karas, R. H., Bicudo, J. E. P. W. 1988. Scaling of blood gases in athletic mammals at $\dot{V}_{O_2max}$. *FASEB J.* 2:A499 (Abstr.)

77. Margaria, R. 1976. *Biomechanics and Energetics of Muscular Exercise.* Oxford: Clarendon. 146 pp.

78. Margaria, R., Edwards, H. T., Dill, D. B. 1933. The possible mechanism of contracting and paying the oxygen debt and the role of lactic acid in muscular contraction. *Am. J. Physiol.* 106:689–715

79. McMahon, T. A. 1975. Using body size to understand the structural design of animals: quadrupedal locomotion. *J. Appl. Physiol.* 39:619–27

80. McWhirter, N., ed. 1984. *1985 Guinness Book of World Records.* New York: Sterling Publ. 694 pp.

81. Pennycuick, C. J. 1975. On the running of the gnu, (*Connochaetes taurinus*) and other animals. *J. Exp. Biol.* 63: 775–99

82. Pirnay, F., Lamy, M., Dujardin, J., Deroanne, R., Petit, J. M. 1972. Analysis of femoral venous blood during maximal muscular exercise. *J. Appl. Physiol.* 33:289–92

83. Powers, S. K., Lawler, J., Dempsey, J. A., Dodd, S., Landry, G. 1989. Effects of incomplete pulmonary gas exchange on $\dot{V}_{O_2max}$. *J. Appl. Physiol.* 66:2491–95

84. Roca, J., Hogan, M. C., Story, D., Bebout, D. E., Haab, P. 1989. Evidence for tissue diffusion limitation of $\dot{V}_{O_2max}$ in normal humans. *J. Appl. Physiol.* 67:291–99

85. Rome, L. C. 1993. The mechanical design of the muscular system. In *Comparative Vertebrate Exercise Physiology*, ed. J. H. Jones. New York: Academic. In press

86. Rome, L. C., Funke, R. P., Alexander, R. M., Lutz, G., Aldridge, H. D. J. N. 1988. Why animals have different muscle fibre types. *Nature* 355:824–27

87. Rome, L. C., Sosnicki, A. A., Goble, D. O. 1990. Maximum velocity of shortening of three fibre types from the horse soleus: implications for scaling with body size. *J. Physiol.* 431:173–85

88. Saltin, B. 1985. Hemodynamic adaptations to exercise. *Am. J. Cardiol.* 55:42D-47D

89. Saltin, B., Gollnick, P. D. 1983. Skeletal muscle adaptability: significance for metabolism and performance. In *Handbook of Physiology. Skeletal Muscle*, ed. L. D. Peachy, R. H. Adrian, S. R. Geiger, pp. 555–631. Baltimore: Williams & Wilkins

90. Schmidt-Nielsen, K. 1984. *Scaling: Why Is Animal Size So Important?* New York: Cambridge Univ. Press. 241 pp.

91. Schwerzmann, K., Hoppeler, H., Kayar, S. R., Weibel, E. R. 1989. Oxidative capacity of muscle and mitochondria: correlation of physiological, biochemical and morphometric characteristics. *Proc. Natl. Acad. Sci. USA* 86:1583–87

92. Seeherman, H. J., Taylor, C. R., Maloiy, G. M. O., Armstrong, R. B. 1981. Design of the mammalian respiratory system. II. Measuring maximum aerobic capacity. *Respir. Physiol.* 44:11–23

93. Stray-Gundersen, J., Musch, T. I., Haidet, G. C., Swain, D. P., Ordway, G. A. 1986. The effect of pericardiectomy on maximal oxygen consumption and maximal cardiac output in untrained dogs. *Circ. Res.* 58:523–30

94. Taylor, C. R. 1985. Force development during sustained locomotion: a determinant of gait, speed and metabolic power. *J. Exp. Biol.* 115:253–62

95. Taylor, C. R. 1987. Structural and functional limits to oxidative metabolism: insights from scaling. *Annu. Rev. Physiol.* 49:135–46

96. Taylor, C. R., Heglund, N. C., Maloiy, G. M. O. 1982. Energetics and mechanics of terrestrial locomotion. I. Metabolic energy consumption as a function of speed and body size in birds and mammals. *J. Exp. Biol.* 97:1–21

97. Taylor, C. R., Heglund, N. C., McMahon, T. A., Looney, T. R. 1980. Energetic cost of generating muscular force during running. *J. Exp. Biol.* 86:9–18

98. Taylor, C. R., Jones, J. H. 1987. Maximal oxygen consumption in mammals. In *Comparative Physiology of Environmental Adaptations*, ed. P. Dejours, 2:188–95. Basel: Karger

99. Taylor, C. R., Karas, R. H., Weibel, E. R., Hoppeler, H. 1987. Adaptive variation in the mammalian respiratory system in relation to energetic demand. *Respir. Physiol.* 69:1–127

100. Taylor, C. R., Longworth, K. E., Hoppeler, H. 1988. Matching O_2 delivery to demand in muscle. II. Allometric variation in energy demand. *Adv. Exp. Med. Biol.* 227:171–81

101. Taylor, C. R., Maloiy, G. M. O., Weibel, E. R., Langman, V. A., Kamau, J. M. Z. 1981. Design of the mammalian respiratory system. III. Scaling maximum aerobic capacity to body mass: wild and domestic mammals. *Respir. Physiol.* 44:25–37

102. Taylor, C. R., Schmidt-Nielsen, K., Raab, J. L. 1970. Scaling of energetic cost of running to body size in mammals. *Am. J. Physiol.* 219:1104–7

103. Taylor, C. R., Weibel, E. R. 1991. Learning from comparative physiology. In *The Lung: Scientific Foundations*, ed. R. G. Crystal, J. B. West, 2:1595–1607. New York: Raven

104. Termin, A., Pette, D. 1991. Myosin heavy-chain-based isomyosins in developing, adult fast-twitch muscles. *Eur. J. Biochem.* 195:577–84

105. Verzar, F. 1912. The gaseous metabolism of striated muscle in warm-blooded animals. *J. Physiol.* 44:243–58

106. Wagner, P. D. 1988. An integrated view of the determinants of maximum oxygen uptake. *Adv. Exp. Med. Biol.* 227:245–56

107. Wagner, P. D., Gillespie, J. R.,

Landgren, G. L., Fedde, M. R., Jones, B. W. 1989. Mechanism of exercise-induced hypoxemia in horses. *J. Appl. Physiol.* 66:1227–33

108. Wagner, P. D., Hoppeler, H., Saltin, B. 1991. Determinants of maximal oxygen uptake. See Ref. 103, pp. 1585–93

109. Wagner, P. D., Sutton, J. R., Reeves, J. T., Cymerman, A., Groves, B. M. 1988. Operation Everest II. Pulmonary gas exchange during a simulated ascent of Mt. Everest. *J. Appl. Physiol.* 63:2348–59

110. Weibel, E. R., Taylor, C. R. 1981. Design of the mammalian respiratory system. *Respir. Physiol.* 44:1–164

111. West, J. B., Mathieu-Costello, O., Logemann, R. B., Jones, J. H., Pascoe, J. R. 1992. Stress failure of pulmonary capillaries in racehorses with exercise-induced pulmonary hemorrhage. *Fed. Proc.* 6:A2048 (Abstr.)

112. Wilkie, D. R. 1980. Equations describing power input by humans as a function of duration of exercise. In *Exercise Bioenergetics and Gas Exchange,* ed. P. Cerretelli, B. J. Whip, pp. 75–80. Amsterdam: Elsevier

GASTROINTESTINAL PHYSIOLOGY

THE MOLECULAR BASIS OF G.I. TRANSPORT

Introduction, David C. Dawson, *Section Editor*

To students of the epithelial transport processes that are so prominent in the G.I. tract, the words "molecular basis" have special meaning. One by one the individual elements that form the basis for transport models—scribbled on note pads or neatly drawn in review articles—are succumbing to molecular cloning, so that specific transport modalities can be identified with specific gene products. For several decades, the study of absorption and secretion has been based on a paradigm in which a particular transepithelial transport process was accounted for by a series arrangement of specific transport elements in the apical and basolateral membranes of a polar epithelial cell, and a substantial amount of effort was devoted to identifying individual transporters, e.g. pumps, channels, cotransporters, etc., on the basis of function. The widespread application of cloning strategies has led us to the present state of affairs in which many of these functional definitions can be attached to specific membrane proteins for which the exact primary structure is known. This collision of molecular biology and transport physiology has produced at least two results of general importance. First, it is clear that the broad families of transporters defined on the basis of function indeed have counterparts in molecular structure. The taxonomy of transporters based on amino acid sequences has largely confirmed that based on function, although the former

571

provides the opportunity to detect similarities of structure and evolutionary relationships not discernible from functional determinations alone. Second, and perhaps ironically to some, the identification of genes and gene families for transporters has, if anything, made the detailed determination of transport function even more important. The ability to manipulate protein structure, one amino acid at a time, must be complemented by high resolution functional measurements if the rewards of structure-function analysis are to be realized.

In the following collection of articles, we have several good examples of the impact of molecular cloning on transport physiology. Ernie Wright reviews the Na-glucose cotransporter that is expressed in the apical membranes of intestinal cells and is the molecular basis for the coupling of the free energy inherent in the Na electrochemical gradient to the transport of glucose. This is a particularly interesting protein, not only because it functions as an energy converter, but also because the catalytic cycle is accompanied by current flow so that electrophysiological strategies can be employed to gain insight into the role of charge movement in solute translocation.

In the next article, Bernard Thorens reviews the facilitated glucose carrier that serves as the basolateral route for passive glucose exit from the intestinal cell. Members of this family of glucose transporters inhabit virtually every cell and are important in the regulation of blood glucose. In these two proteins we have the elements required to account for the entry and exit steps in a model for transcellular transport, and the availability of amino acid sequences for these proteins has meant that the required, polarized expression can be demonstrated clearly.

In the third article, Jack Riordan reviews the rapidly increasing body of information pertaining to the cystic fibrosis transmembrane conductance regulator (CFTR), the product of the gene that is mutated in the genetic disease, cystic fibrosis. This transporter is of special significance, not only because of its relation to disease, but also because its unexpected membership in an ancient superfamily of transporters found from *E. coli* to humans means that an understanding of CFTR will probably substantially illuminate the fundamental relationships between carriers, pumps, and channels. In contrast to the Na-coupled glucose cotransporter that was cloned by expression, CFTR was cloned by genetic linkage analysis of CF patients so that understanding the function of the protein and how function is compromised by mutations has been a focus of recent research. The CFTR channel is likely to be the ubiquitous, cAMP-activated apical Cl secretory channel that appears to be nonfunctional in cystic fibrosis, but is chronically active in secretory diarrhea.[1]

---

[1]For the sake of completeness, it is noted that the basolateral partner of CFTR in Cl secretion, the loop-diuretic-sensitive, Na/K/2Cl cotransporter, has recently been cloned from shark rectal gland (Xu, J., et al. 1992. *J. Gen. Physiol.* 100:39A).

In the final article, Carol Semrad and Michael Field review the circumstances surrounding the opposite extreme of CFTR function. Their discussion of secretory diarrhea, e.g. cholera, brings this section full circle in as much as an important therapeutic approach to the potentially lethal salt and water loss is the application of oral rehydration therapy that relies on the ability of glucose to enhance salt and water absorption by activating the apical Na-glucose cotransporter.

As a group, these four articles provide an interesting glimpse into the state of the art in molecular transport physiology and into a future in which we can anticipate the molecular identification of more of the lines and squiggles in our transport diagrams, and the unravelling of the cellular mechanisms that enable apical and basolateral transporters to function in a coordinated fashion to achieve transepithelial absorption and secretion.

Annu. Rev. Physiol. 1993. 55:575–89

THE INTESTINAL Na$^+$/GLUCOSE COTRANSPORTER

Ernest M. Wright

Department of Physiology, UCLA School of Medicine, Los Angeles, California
90024–1751

KEY WORDS: brush border, sugar transport, glucose-galactose malabsorption, kinetics

INTRODUCTION

Dietary carbohydrates are absorbed from the small intestine as monosaccharides. Digestion of complex carbohydrate occurs in the gut through the action of pancreatic enzymes and the brush border hydrolases such as sucrase and maltase. The final products of digestion are mostly D-glucose, D-galactose, and D-fructose, which are absorbed into the body by the mature enterocytes lining the upper third of the intestinal villi. Absorption occurs in the duodenum and jejunum and is generally complete before the chyme reaches the ileum. The pyranoses are absorbed by a two-stage process (Figure 1). Glucose and galactose are first accumulated within the epithelium across the brush border membrane. The energy for this step is obtained by coupling sugar transport to the sodium and electrical gradients ($\Delta\mu_{Na} \sim -120$ mV) across the membrane. The integral membrane protein responsible for this coupling is the Na$^+$/glucose cotransporter (SGLT1). The second step is the downhill transport of sugar out of the enterocyte across the basolateral membrane into the blood. This facilitated sugar transporter (GLUT2) is considered in depth by B. Thorens in a companion review in this volume.

Fructose is absorbed by a completely independent mechanism that does not involve Na$^+$. It appears that fructose absorption is simply determined by its concentration gradient from gut to blood and facilitated transporters in the brush border and basolateral membranes. Evidence suggests that GLUT5 is the brush border fructose transporter and that GLUT2 handles fructose,

575

0066–4278/93/0315–0575$02.00

Lumen   Cell   Blood

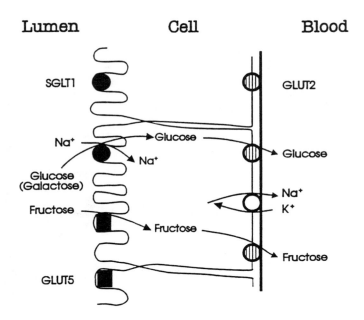

Figure 1   A model for sugar absorption across the enterocytes of the small intestine. The brush border Na$^+$/glucose cotransporter (SGLT1) accumulates glucose and galactose in the call, and the basolateral facilitated transporter (GLUT2) allows the intracellular sugars to exit to the cell down their concentration gradient. The basolateral Na$^+$/K$^+$ pump transports the Na$^+$ that enters via SGLT1 out of the cell.

glucose, and galactose at the basolateral membrane (4). The separate pathways for glucose and fructose across the brush border are consistent with normal fructose absorption in patients with glucose-galactose malabsorption (6, 38) and provide the rationale for clinical treatment of these patients.

In addition to the role of the brush border Na$^+$/glucose contransporter in the absorption of dietary glucose and galactose, the cotransporter plays an important role in salt and water absorption. Na$^+$ entering the cell from the gut lumen via this protein is pumped out into the lateral intercellular spaces by the basolateral Na$^+$/K$^+$ pump, and the resulting local osmotic gradient in turn drives fluid absorption. Thus the presence of luminal sugar stimulates salt and water absorption. This phenomenon is the scientific basis of oral rehydration therapy (ORT) used to such advantage in the treatment of cholera. According to the World Health Organization, about 4 million children under five succumb to acute diarrhea each year, and ORT saves more than one million small children annually. It is argued that no child, or adult would die of diarrhea if ORT were readily available (14). A genetic defect in the brush border Na$^+$/glucose cotransporter causes a rare disease called glucose-galactose malabsorption (6). Just over 100 cases have been reported in the literature. The defect produces severe diarrhea that is fatal unless glucose and galactose are removed from the diet. Recently a missense mutation was identified as being responsible for the defect in one pedigree (33).

This review of the brush border Na$^+$/glucose cotransporter emphasizes the progress since the transport protein was cloned in 1987. In particular, I discuss the structure and function of cloned protein, and the progress in intestinal physiology made possible by the development of SGLT1 DNA and protein probes.

STRUCTURE AND FUNCTION

The rabbit intestinal brush border Na$^+$/glucose cotransporter was cloned by a novel expression cloning technique (8), and the human clone was subsequently isolated from an intestinal λgt10 library using the rabbit cDNA (10). The amino acid sequence and secondary structure model of the human SGLT1 is shown in Figure 2. The 664 residue protein is predicted to wind through the plasma membrane 12 times. Each hydrophobic membrane span is composed of 21 residues arranged in an α-helix. The predicted mass of the primary transcript is 73 kd, but the hydrophobic protein runs with an apparent mass of 61,000 on SDS-PAGE (13).

There is N-linked glycosylation of SGLT1 at Asparagine 248 (9), between membrane spans (M) 5 and 6. Core glycosylation occurs in the endoplasmic reticulum (ER), and further processing between the ER and the brush border

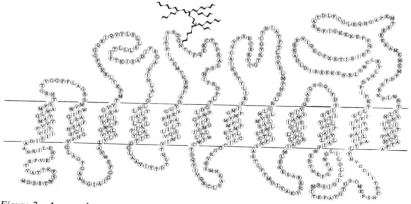

Figure 2   A secondary structure model of human SGLT1 in the plasma membrane. Fructose is transported across the epithelium down its concentration gradient by GLUT5 and GLUT2 in series (figure provided by E. Tuck).

membrane produces complex glycosylation of the tri or tetra-antennary type (13). Glycosylation increases the mass by about 15 kd, but the mature protein runs on SDS-PAGE with an apparent mass of $\sim$ 71,000. This is consistent with the size of the protein identified by biochemical techniques (36). There is no evidence of O-linked glycosylation. Neither the native nor the cloned protein require glycosylation for normal transport activity (9, 13). Finally, the site of N-linked glycosylation between M5 and M6 indicates that this hydrophilic loop is on the exterior face of the membrane. This places the NH_2 and COOH termini on the cytoplasmic side of the 12M model.

The orientation of the protein in the membrane has been examined by treating right-side-out brush border membrane vesicles with proteases (11). Fragments of SGLT1 were then identified by antipeptide antibodies on Western blots and purified for NH_2-terminal sequencing and amino acid analysis. One 14-kd chymotrypsin fragment recognized by an antibody to residues Arg602-Asp613 revealed that the cleavage site was at Try561 and that the peptide extended through the COOH terminus. This indicates that the large hydrophilic loop, Thr548-Arg640, between M11 and M12 is on the external face of the membrane.

Although there is no direct evidence that the activity of SGLT1 is regulated by phosphorylation, there are consensus sites (17) for phosphorylation at several putative cytoplasmic, hydrophilic domains (Ser 303 and 418).

The clone coding for SGLT1 has been functionally expressed in *Xenopus* oocytes (2, 8, 10, 16, 21, 23, 34), cultured renal (1), HeLa (3), and insect ovary (26) cells. The sugar specificity, ion specificity, phlorizin sensitivity, and kinetics appear to be quite similar to those reported for the native transporter in brush border membranes. For all systems, the apparent affinity for α-methyl-D-glucopyranose (αMeDGlc) and Na^+ was about 0.2 and 30 mM respectively, the phlorizin inhibitor constant was 5–10 μM, the Hill coefficient for Na^+ was $\sim$1.6, Na^+/glucose cotransport was electrogenic, and apparent sugar affinity increased as the external Na^+ concentration increased. Because post-translation processing and plasma membrane lipid composition are different in mammalian, amphibian, and insect cells, it is unlikely that such factors are important in the function of the cotransporter.

IS SGLT1 THE BRUSH BORDER Na^+/GLUCOSE COTRANSPORTER?

The close similarity between the kinetics of the cloned SGLT1 cotransporter and the brush border transporter provides circumstantial evidence that SGLT1 is indeed the intestinal brush border transporter. More direct evidence is that antipeptide antibodies to SGLT1 specifically immunoreacted with intestinal brush borders as determined by Western blot analysis (12) and immuno-cytochemistry (15, 29). Furthermore, these antibodies immunoprecipitated a proteolytic fragment from brush borders with an NH_2 terminal sequence and amino acid composition expected for SGLT1 (11). These results confirm that SGLT1 is present in brush borders; but is it the only brush border Na^+/glucose cotransporter? A recurring speculation in the literature, based on kinetic experiments using either the intact epithelium or brush border vesicles, is that there are multiple brush border Na^+/glucose cotransporters. Three recent observations seriously undermine this speculation: (a) careful re-examination of the kinetics of Na^+-dependent D-glucose uptake into vesicles using a rapid-uptake apparatus showed only a single saturable uptake (20); (b) patients with glucose-galactose malabsorption have a mutation on SGLT1 that accounts for the defect in sugar absorption (33); and (c) in sheep, where the rate of intestinal Na^+/glucose cotransport varies by as much as 500-fold, there was a good correlation between sugar transport and the amount of SGLT1 protein in brush border vesicles (25). We conclude that there is only one major Na^+-cotransporter for D-glucose in intestinal brush border membranes (SGLT1). SGLT1 is present in the kidney, but it is clear that there is also a second, as yet unidentified Na^+/glucose cotransporter in the renal cortex (22).

Is there a second brush border protein required for Na^+/glucose transport activity? So far, the evidence suggests that SGLT1 alone is fully capable of transporting sugar. The fact that SGLT1 can be expressed in oocytes, COS-7 cells, HeLa cells, and insect cells (see above) makes it rather unlikely that another protein (subunit) is required. Nevertheless, a preliminary abstract reported that the coexpression of SGLT1 and P20 (a clone isolated from pig kidney that codes for a 56-kd protein with one putative transmembrane segment near the COOH terminus) in oocytes dramatically altered the rate of αMDGlc transport (35): when low amounts of SGLT1 cRNA were injected, αMDGlc uptake was enhanced, but when optimal amounts of SGLT1 cRNA were injected, αMDGlc uptake was inhibited. The possibility of an interaction between SGLT1 and P20 needs further study.

There is one unconfirmed study suggesting that SGLT1 exists in brush border membranes as a homotetramer (28). Irradiation of brush border membrane vesicles gave a target size of 290 ± 5 kd for the functional cotransporter. Chemical cross-linking and/or immunoprecipitation experiments are needed to explore this issue further. Parenthetically, it should be noted that irradiation of vesicles did not inhibit Na^+-independent glucose uptake.

KINETICS

The general characteristics of the cloned cotransporter expressed in cells were examined using radioactive tracer and electrophysiological techniques (16, 34, 2, 23). Sugar uptake was Na^+-dependent ($Na^+ > Eu^{3+} \gg Li^+$, K^+, $Choline^+$ $> NMG^+$) with a Hill coefficient of 1.5 and K_m for Na^+ that was voltage dependent, ranging from 50 mM at 0 mV to 5 mM at -150 mV. Sugar uptake as a function of sugar concentration could be accounted for by a single, saturable system. In any given oocyte the maximal rate of transport was identical for D-glucose, D-galactose, α-methyl-D glucopyranose, 3-O-methyl-D-glucoside, and insensitive to the external Na^+ concentration between 10 and 100 mM. The D-glucose K_m at 100 mM Na^+ was $\sim$100 μM, and competition experiments indicate that sugar affinities were D-glucose, D-galactose, α-methyl-D-glucopyranose $>$ 3-O-methyl-D-glucoside $\gg$ D-allose $>$ D-xylose. Phlorizin inhibited sugar transport with a K_i of 5–10 μM. In the absence of sugar, phlorizin also inhibited a small Na^+ current through SGLT1; the leak current was about 10% of the maximum current in the presence of sugar. Finally, SGLT1 was demonstrated to transport sugar in both directions across the plasma membrane, i.e. in oocytes preloaded with αMeDGlc, there was a large phlorizin-sensitive outward current at positive membrane potentials (+25 mV).

The K_m for sugar transport was a function of the Na^+ concentration. At a membrane potential of –50 mV, the αMeDGlc K_m increased from 180 μM to greater than 10,000 μM as the external Na^+ was lowered from 100 to 2 mM. This is consistent with an ordered reaction mechanism in which the binding of two Na^+ ions to SGLT1 changes the conformation of the protein so as to increase its affinity for sugar. This laboratory has previously reported Na^+-dependent conformational changes in the brush border protein using fluorescent group-specific reagents (36).

Recently, our group conducted a detailed study of the kinetics of SGLT1 expressed in oocytes using an electrophysiological technique (23, 24). The approach measured SGLT1 steady-state and presteady-state currents as a function of external Na^+ and αMeDGlc concentrations and membrane potential. The goal was to measure transporter currents and the apparent K_ms and i_{max}s for αMeDGlc and Na^+ as a function of Na^+ and αMeDGlc concentrations over a wide range of membrane voltages. The results were then analyzed in terms of a simple six-state model (Figure 3). Computer-generated simulations were performed to determine a set of rate constants that would account for the global kinetic properties of SGLT1.

The model assumed that there were 5×10^{10} carriers per oocyte and that the valancy of the empty carrier was –2. We predicted that there were two voltage-dependent steps: (a) Na^+ binding, and (b) translocation of the empty carrier across the membrane. This latter step is equivalent to the conformation change in the protein that presents the binding sites to one and then the other side of the membrane.

One numerical solution was found for the 14 rate constants that satisfactorily accounts for six experimental observations; namely, (a) the sigmoid shape of the sugar-induced current-voltage curves, (b) the Na^+ and voltage dependence of the apparent K_m for αMeDGlc, (c) the sugar and voltage dependence of the apparent K_m for Na$^+$, (d) the voltage dependence of the current at saturating Na$^+$ and sugar concentrations, (e) presteady-state currents ($t_{1/2} \sim 13$ ms), and (f) the SGLT1 leak currents. The major voltage-dependent step is the reorientation of the empty carrier, which senses 70% of the membrane electrical field. In this non-rapid equilibrium model, the rate-limiting step for the normal sugar transport cycle depends on the membrane potential and the Na$^+$ and sugar concentrations. At physiological voltages and concentrations the rate-limiting step is the recycling of the unloaded carrier.

A subsequent more thorough study of the presteady-state currents (19) validated several of the previous assumptions and confirmed key aspects of our conclusions. Using a faster voltage-clamp (settling time 0.5 ms), signal averaging, and procedures to compensate for the oocyte capacitance (175–250 nF), we were able to monitor the gating currents arising from charge translocation by SGLT1 as a function of voltage, temperature, and the external Na$^+$ and sugar concentrations. The charge translocation was saturable, reversible, and could be fitted to the Boltzman equation ($Q_{max} \sim 20$ nC, $V_{0.5} = -40$ mV, and $Z = -1$). The maximum charge transfer (Q_{max}) was directly proportional to the number of functional SGLT1 proteins expressed in the membrane. Q_{max} values correspond to $\sim 10^{11}$ carriers/oocyte, close to that assumed in the model. Q_{max} was independent of holding potential and temperature, but was eliminated by saturating concentrations of sugar and phlorizin. These latter observations indicate that the charge transfer observed on rapidly depolarizing the membrane potential in the absence of sugar is due to Na$^+$ dissociation from SGLT1 and reorientation of the empty carrier in the field (k_{21} and k_{16}, Figure 3). Simulation of the voltage and Na$^+$ dependence of the time constant for the charge transfer to the three reaction steps, C'Na$_2$ $\leftrightarrow$ 2Na + C' $\leftrightarrow$ CÆ, indicates that the major charge translocation step is C' $\leftrightarrow$ CÆ ($\delta = 0.7$) and, in the case of the human clone, the slow step is the dissociation of Na$^+$ from C'Na$_2$. The apparent valence ($Z = -1$) obtained for the Boltzman equation, and a δ of 0.7 is consistent with the assumed valence of the cotransporter (–2). Finally, Q_{max} and the maximum rate of Na$^+$/glucose cotransport (i_{max}) for a given oocyte yield an estimate of the rate constant (57 ± 5 s^{-1}) for translocation of the fully loaded carrier (C'Na$_2$S $\leftrightarrow$ CÆNa$_2$S). This is virtually identical to that computed in Figure 3.

As a result of these kinetic studies, a fairly clear model for Na$^+$/glucose cotransport is beginning to emerge. This is represented in cartoon form in Figure 4. In the absence of Na$^+$, glucose is unable to bind to SGLT1 (glucose $K_m \gg 10$ mM), but in the presence of Na$^+$, there is a conformation change that allows sugar to bind (glucose $K_m \ll 0.5$ mM). The external Na$^+$-binding site is at the bottom of a well, 30% across the membrane electrical field. A tyrosine residue is thought to be close to, or at, the Na$^+$ active site, and a lysine residue is close to, or at, the sugar active site. On the basis of the sugar

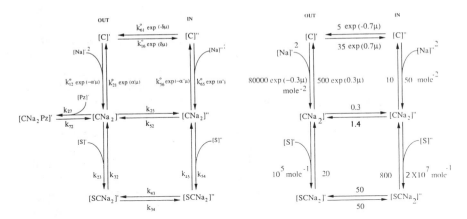

Figure 3   A kinetic model for Na$^+$/glucose cotransport by SGLT1. Included are the rate constants estimated from pre-steady state and steady-state kinetic data (redrawn from 24).

selectivity and the fact that phlorizin is a competitive inhibitor of sugar transport, it is reasonable to propose that the C_4 end of the sugar enters the active site first. Only sugars with bulky residues at C_1 are recognized by the protein. After substrate binding, a conformation change occurs ($\sim$50 s^{-1}) that orients the active sites to the cytoplasm. The nature of this conformation change in the protein is presently unknown. Since the internal Na$^+$ concentration is low ($\sim$10 mM), Na$^+$ dissociates, the affinity for glucose decreases, and the sugar is released to the cytoplasm. To complete the cycle, the protein undergoes a third transition where the binding sites reorient to the external surface. This transition is slow, but is enhanced by the negative membrane potential ($\sim$50 mV) and the negative charge on the protein (–2).

COMPARATIVE STUDIES

The involvement of the Na$^+$/glucose cotransporter in intestinal sugar absorption has been reported in animals from fish to man. Using Northern and Western blot analysis it has been confirmed that SGLT1 is the protein involved (21). Using two anti-peptide polyclonal antibodies (12) in Western blot experiments on brush border membrane vesicles, positive, specific reactions have been observed for mammals (human, rabbit, rat, mouse, cat, dog, sheep, cow, and pig), birds, amphibians, and an alligator. One epitope, residue 604–615, was conserved, but another epitope, residues 402–419, was not. SGLT1 mRNA was detected in the mucosa of human, rabbit, rat, mouse,

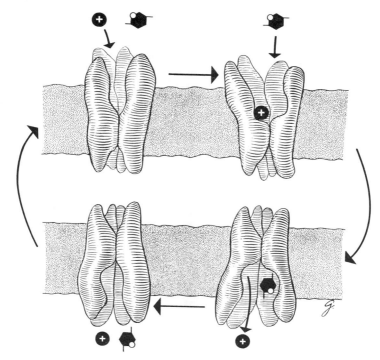

Figure 4 A cartoon representing Na$^+$/glucose cotransport. The brush border cotransporter is presented as a homotetramer of a 75-kD integral membrane protein. In the absence of Na$^+$, D-glucose is unable to bind (Km » 50 mM), but in the presence of Na$^+$, the ion binds to produce a conformation change that now permits the sugar to bind (Km « 1 mM). For simplicity only, one of the two Na$^+$ binding sites is shown. The fully loaded cotransporter undergoes another conformation change to present the substrates to the internal face of the membrane where the Na$^+$ and sugar dissociate and the active sites are then returned to face the outside of the cell. Under physiological conditions, the rate-limited steps are the membrane translocation steps and these exhibit high energies of activation (figure redrawn from reference 28).

sheep, and trout intestine (5, 18) when poly A$^+$ RNA isolated from the intestine was probed at high stringency with rabbit SGLT1 cDNA. These results indicate that the SGLT1 DNA and protein sequence have been highly conserved throughout evolution. This is perhaps not surprising in light of the existence of a Na$^+$/glucose cotransporter gene family, where highly homologous proteins transport very different substrates, e.g. proteins with 50–60% identity to SGLT1 transport myo-inositol and nucleosides (37). In the human and rabbit SGLT1 sequences, 84% of the residues are identical, and when conservative substitutions are considered, the homology increases to 94% (37).

CELL BIOLOGY

Sugars are absorbed by the mature enterocytes lining the upper region of the villus, and this together with the fact that enterocytes are continuously renewed with a half time of a few days, raises intriguing questions about the expression and regulation of SGLT1 and GLUT2 as cells migrate and differentiate along the crypt-villus axis. The cloning of the sugar transporters and the development of antibodies has led to a renewed interest in this problem. Immunocytochemical studies using SGLT1 antibodies showed that SGLT1 is found in the brush border membrane of mature enterocytes in the rabbit intestine, and all enterocytes lining the villus of the rat intestine (15, 29). Apart from a light staining in the supra-nuclear region of some enterocytes, there was no significant amount of SGLT1 in the cytoplasm. This indicates that there are no intracellular stores of SGLT1 in these cells. In rabbit intestine, in situ hybridization experiments with antisense SGLT1 RNA probes detected mRNA coding for SGLT1 in enterocytes lining the villus, but none in the cells of the crypt (15, 27). Overall, these results show that the SGLT1 gene is transcribed only as the enterocytes begin to differentiate and this continues throughout the life of the cell. There is some evidence that expression of SGLT1 is at the post-transcriptional level, and this also appears to be the case for the dietary regulation of sugar absorption (see below). The role of the putative phosphorylation sites on SGLT1 in the regulation of transport activity is not yet clear (see above), but it is unlikely that recycling of intracellular SGLT1 protein is involved.

As expected from the location of brush border Na^+/glucose activity on the villus, the basolateral facilitated glucose transporter is only found in the mature enterocytes (30). This ensures that sugars accumulated in enterocytes can reach the blood (see Figure 1).

REGULATION OF SUGAR ABSORPTION

The sheep provides an interesting model to study the regulation of sugar absorption (25). The diet of newborn lambs consists of milk and the rate of intestinal sugar absorption is high, but as the diet changes from milk to grass the development of the rumen ensures a virtual block in the delivery of carbohydrate to the small intestine. Weaning is accompanied by a huge drop in the ability of the gut to absorb sugar (100–500-fold). Maintaining lambs on a milk-replacer diet prevented rumen development and the loss of intestinal sugar transport. Infusing sugars (30 mM) directly into the adult sheep lumen increased the rate of sugar transport close to the level in newborn lambs. This suggests that the ontogenic change in intestinal sugar transport is due to the decrease in sugar reaching the intestine.

The molecular basis for these diet-induced changes in Na^+/glucose cotransport was examined by measuring the abundance of brush border SGLT1 protein Western blots and mucosal SGLT1 mRNA (Northern blots). The diet-induced changes in Na^+/glucose cotransport were proportional to the brush border SGLT1 protein levels (25), but were not matched by significant changes in tissue mRNA levels (18). It was, therefore, concluded that the principal level of SGLT1 regulation by intestinal sugar is translational or post-translational. Parenthetically, it is noteworthy that αMeDGlc, a non-metabolized substrate for SGLT1, was as effective as D-glucose in up-regulating SGLT1 activity in adult sheep, while a non-transported sugar (2 deoxy-D-glucose) was not. This suggests that the signal for up-regulation is the presence of sugar substrates for SGLT1 in the gut. It will be interesting to identify the site, signal, and mechanism of up-regulation.

THE GENE

The SGLT1 gene was mapped to human chromosome 22 by screening Southern blots of mouse-human somatic cell hybrids with a SGLT1 probe (7). Probing of hamster-human hybrids selectively retaining chromosome 22 or portions of it allowed assignments of the locus to the q11.2 → qter region. This was confirmed by autoradiography in human metaphase chromosome spreads, and the use of fluorescence in situ hybridization (FISH) techniques refined the locus to 22q13.1 (32). Unpublished data (E. Turk, personal communication) indicate a gene in excess of 100 kb coding for the 2.3 kb SGLT1 transcript.

GLUCOSE-GALACTOSE MALABSORPTION

This is an autosomal recessive disease that is characterized by a defect in intestinal glucose and galactose absorption. It appears as a neonatal onset of a severe, watery diarrhea that results in death unless fluid and electrolyte balance is restored, or glucose, galactose, and lactose are removed from the diet. The diarrhea ceases within one hour of removing the sugars from the food. Oral tolerance or hydrogen breath tests demonstrate that malabsorption is specific for glucose and galactose. Absorption of fructose and xylose is normal (33). Laboratory studies using mucosal biopsies further demonstrate that this disease is due to a defect in the ability of enterocytes to accumulate glucose or galactose (6). It was concluded that the defect is at the level of the brush border Na^+/glucose cotransporter.

When the SGLT1 clone was isolated, an RFLP analysis of genomic DNA from three pedigrees containing four patients was conducted (M. Hediger, personel communication). Negative results were obtained, but this is perhaps not surprising in view of the large size of the gene.

In a more direct approach, cDNA was obtained from intestinal biopsies of two sisters diagnosed with glucose-galactose malabsorption (33). Overlapping segments of the cDNA were amplified using PCR, and the entire coding region was sequenced for one child. A single base change (guanine to adenine) was found at position 92, and this was also detected in the sister. This mutation was also present in one chromosome of each parent as deduced by sequencing exon 1 of the gene. Since the base change removes a Eco RV restriction site, the mutation in the genomic DNA was confirmed by Southern blot analysis. This mutation resulted in an amino acid change at position 28 from an aspartate to an asparagine. Does this mutation account for the malabsorption syndrome? This was tested using the *Xenopus* oocyte expression system. cRNA from mutant and wild-type plasmids was injected into oocytes and transport was assayed by αMeDGlc uptake. Wild-type cRNA gave normal transport, but the mutant cRNA gave transport indistinguishable from water-injected controls. It was concluded that the $Asp_{28} \rightarrow Asn_{28}$ mutation was responsible for glucose-galactose malabsorption in these two children.

We have examined genomic DNA for the $Asp_{28} \rightarrow Asn_{28}$ mutation in seven other GGM patients using Eco RV restriction analysis. This mutation was not found, which suggests that there is at least one other defect in the SGLT1 gene in these patients. Sequence analysis of other Na^+ cotransporters (37) indicates that the aspartate residue implicated in glucose-galactose malabsorption exists at the boundary between the amino terminus and the first transmembrane segment in 10 transporters. It is reasonable to predict that this Asp residue is essential for transport activity in these 10 carriers.

FUTURE PERSPECTIVES

After the identification, cloning, and expression of the intestinal Na^+/glucose cotransporter, two large questions remain. One concerns the actual mechanism of Na^+/glucose cotransport across the plasma membrane. This requires structure/function studies to locate and map the active sites for Na^+ and sugar binding, and to describe the actual conformation changes responsible for Na^+-dependent sugar binding, translocation of substrates, and the return of the empty sites to the external face of the membrane. While molecular genetics offers a powerful tool, it will not necessarily solve the problems unless other biochemical and biophysical techniques are employed. A stumbling block lies in the fact that this hydrophobic, rare integral membrane protein has yet to be isolated in quantities sufficient for structural investigation. Thus far, expression systems such as *E. coli*, sf9 cells, oocytes, and cultured mammalian cells have not yielded the desired quantities of functional protein. The second question that is germane to intestinal physiology is how SGLT1 is regulated. This includes problems about tissue-specific gene expression, the signals and mechanisms involved in the up-regulation of the functional expression of SGLT1 in enterocytes, and the selective sorting of SGLT1 and GLUT2 to the brush border and basolateral membranes. These issues are not wholly unique to SGLT1 in the intestine, but the rapid cell turnover of epithelial cells in the intestine complicates practical experimental approaches. Some answers may be obtained through the development of cell culture models, but these cannot be expected to solve factors related to the beautiful dynamic architecture of the intestinal villus. Innovative experimental approaches are required to successfully address these remaining problems of intestinal absorption. Despite these difficulties, some comfort can be taken from the fact that as a focus for both molecular and biophysical techniques, the intestinal epithelium will continue to play a central role in our understanding of membrane transport biology.

ACKNOWLEDGMENTS

I can not overstate the contributions of my co-workers in both the intellectual and experimental advances underlying this review. In particular, it is a pleasure to acknowledge Bryndis Birnir, Michael Coady, Karl Hager, Akihiro Hazama, Mathias Hediger, Bruce Hirayama, Leslie Lescale-Matys, Don Loo, Ana Pajor, Lucie Parent, Soraya Shirazi-Beechey, Chari Smith, Stephane Supplisson, and Eric Turk. The research was largely supported by a grant from the National Institutes of Health (DK-19567).

Literature Cited

1. Birnir, B, Lee, H.-S., Hediger, M. A., Wright, E. M. 1990. Expression and characterization of the intestinal Na⁺/glucose cotransporter in COS-7 cells. *Biochim. Biophys. Acta* 1048: 100–4

2. Birnir, B., Loo, D. D. F., Wright, E. M. 1991. Voltage clamp studies of the Na⁺/glucose cotransporter cloned from rabbit small intestine. *Pflügers Arch.* 418:79–85

3. Blakely, R. D., Clark, J. A., Rudnick, G., Amara, S. G. 1991. Vaccina-T-7 RNA polymerase expression system. Evaluation for the expression cloning of plasma membrane transporters. *Anal. Biochem.* 194:302–8

4. Burant, C. F., Takeda, J., Brot-Laroche, E., Bell, G. I., Davidson, N. O. 1992. Fructose transporter in human spermatozoa and small intestine in GLUT5. *J. Biol. Chem.* 267:14523–26

5. Coady, M. J., Pajor, A. M., Wright, E. M. 1990. Sequence homologies among intestinal and renal Na⁺/glucose cotransporters. *Am. J. Physiol.* 259 (28):C605–10

6. Desjeux, J.-F. 1989. Congenital selective Na⁺-D-glucose cotransport defects leading to renal glycosuria and congenital selective intestinal malabsorption of glucose and galactose. In *The Metabolic Basis of Inherited Disease,* ed. C. Scriver, A. Beaudet, W. Sly, D. Valle, pp. 2463–78. New York: McGraw-Hill

7. Hediger, M. A., Budarf, M. L., Emanuel, B. S., Mohandas, T. K., Wright, E. M. 1989. Assignment of the human intestinal Na⁺/glucose cotransporter gene (SGLT1) to the q11.2 → qter region of chromosome 22. *Genomics* 4:297–300

8. Hediger, M. A., Coady, M. J., Ikeda, T. S., Wright, E. M. 1987. Expression

cloning and cDNA sequencing of the Na$^+$/glucose cotransporter. *Nature* 330: 379–81

9. Hediger, M. A., Mendlein, J., Lee, H.-S., Wright, E. M. 1991. Biosynthesis of the cloned Na$^+$/glucose. *Biochim. Biophys. Acta* 1064:360–64

10. Hediger, M. A., Turk, E., Wright, E. M. 1989. Homology of the human intestinal Na$^+$/glucose and *E. coli* Na/proline cotransporters. *Proc. Natl. Acad. Sci. USA* 86:5748–52

11. Hirayama, B. A., Smith, C. D., Wright, E. M. 1992. Secondary structure of the Na$^+$/glucose cotransporter. *J. Gen. Physiol.* 100:19a–20

12. Hirayama, B. A., Wong, H. C., Smith, C. D., Hagenbuch, B. A., Hediger, M. A., Wright, E. M. 1991. Intestinal and renal Na$^+$/glucose cotransporters share common structures. *Am. J. Physiol.* 261:C296–304

13. Hirayama, B. A., Wright, E. M. 1992. Glycosylation of the rabbit intestinal brush border Na$^+$/glucose cotransporter. *Biochim. Biophys. Acta* 1103:37–44

14. Hirschhorn, N., Greenough, W. B. III. 1991. Progress in oral rehydration therapy. *Sci. Am.* 264:50–56

15. Hwang, E.-S., Hirayama, B. A., Wright, E. M. 1991. Distribution of the SLGT1 Na$^+$/glucose cotransporter and mRNA along the crypt-villus axis of rabbit small intestine. *Biochem. Biophys. Res. Commun.* 181:1208–17

16. Ikeda, T. S., Hwang, E.-S., Coady, M. J., Hirayama, B. A., Hediger, M. A., Wright, E. M. 1989. Characterization of a Na$^+$/glucose cotransporter cloned from rabbit small intestine. *J. Membr. Biol.* 110:87–95

17. Kennelly, P. J., Krebs, E. G. 1991. Consensus sequences as substrate specificity determinants for protein kinases and protein phosphates. *J. Biol. Chem.* 266:15555–58

18. Lescale-Matys, L., Dyer, J., Scott, D., Wright, E. M., Shirazi-Beechey, S. P. 1992. Regulation of ovine intestinal Na$^+$/glucose cotransporter (SGLT1) by sugar is dissociated from mRNA abundance. *Biochem. J.* In press

19. Loo, D. D. F., Hazama, A., Supplisson, S., Turk, E., Wright, E. M. 1992. Charge translocation associated with conformational transitions of the Na$^+$/glucose cotransporter. *J. Gen. Physiol.* 100:19a

20. Malo, C., Berteloot, A. 1991. Analysis of kinetic data in transport studies: New insights from kinetic studies of Na$^+$-D-glucose cotransport in human intestinal brush- border membrane vesicles using a fast sampling, rapid filtration apparatus. *J. Membr. Biol.* 122: 127–41

21. Pajor, A. M., Hirayama, B. A., Wright, E. M. 1992. Molecular biology approaches to the comparative study of Na$^+$/glucose cotransport. *Am. J. Physiol.* 263:R489–95

22. Pajor, A. M., Hirayama, B. A., Wright, E. M. 1992. Molecular evidence for two renal Na$^+$/glucose cotransporters. *Biochim. Biophys. Acta* 1106:216–20

23. Parent, L., Supplisson, S., Loo, D. F., Wright, E. M. 1992. Electrogenic properties of the cloned Na$^+$/glucose cotransporter. Part I. Voltage-clamp studies. *J. Membr. Biol.* 125:49–62

24. Parent, L., Supplisson, S., Loo, D. F., Wright, E. M. 1992. Electrogenic properties of the cloned Na$^+$/glucose cotransporter: Part II. A transport model under non rapid equilibrium conditions. *J. Membr. Biol.* 125:63–79

25. Shirazi-Beechey, S. P., Hirayama, B. A., Wang, Y., Scott, D., Smith, M. W., et al. 1991. Ontogenic development of the lamb intestinal Na$^+$/glucose cotransporter is regulated by diet. *J. Physiol.* 437:699–708

26. Smith, C. D., Hirayama, B. A., Wright, E. M. 1992. Baculovirus mediated expression of the Na$^+$/ glucose cotransporter in Sf9 cells. *Biochim. Biophys. Acta* 1104:151–59

27. Smith, M. W., Turvey, A., Freeman, T. C. 1992. Appearance of phlorizin-sensitive glucose transport is not controlled at mRNA level in rabbit jejunal enterocytes. *Exp. Physiol.* 77: 525–28

28. Stevens, B. R., Fernandez, A., Hirayama, B., Wright, E. M., Kempner, E. S. 1990. Intestinal brush border membrane Na$^+$/glucose cotransporter functions in situ as a homotetramer. *Proc. Natl. Acad. Sci. USA* 87:1456–60

29. Takata, K., Kasahara, T., Kasahara, M., Ezaki, O., Hirano, H. 1992. Immunohistochemical localization of Na$^+$-dependent transporter in rat jejunum. *Cell Tissue Res.* 267:3–9

30. Thorens, B., Cheng, Z.-Q., Brown, D., Lodish, H. F. 1990. Liver glucose transporter: a basolateral protein in hepatocytes and intestine and kidney cells. *Am. J. Physiol.* 259:C279–85

31. Deleted in proof

32. Turk, E., Klisak, I., Bacallao, R., Sparkes, R. S., Wright, E. M. 1992. Assignment of the human Na$^+$/glucose

cotransporter gene SGLT1 to chromosome 22q13.1. *Genomics.* Submitted

33. Turk, E., Zabel, B., Mundlos, S., Dyer, J., Wright, E. M. 1991. Glucose/galactose malabsorption caused by a defect in the Na$^+$/glucose cotransporter. *Nature* 350:354–56

34. Umbach, J. A., Coady, M. J., Wright, E. M. 1990. The intestinal Na$^+$/glucose cotransporter expressed in *Xenopus* oocytes is electrogenic. *Biophys. J.* 57: 1217–24

35. Veyhl, M., Büschel, B., Spangenberg, J., Dekel, C., Koepsell, H. 1992.

Cloning of the β-subunit of the Na$^+$-D-glucose symporter. *FASEB J.* 6: A1459

36. Wright, E. M. 1989. Intestinal sugar transport. In *Textbook of Secretory Diarrhea*, ed. E. Lebenthal, M. Duffey, pp. 119–24. New York: Raven

37. Wright, E. M., Hager, K. M., Turk, E. 1992. Sodium cotransport proteins. *Curr. Biol.* 4:696–702

38. Wright, E. M., Turk, E., Zabel, B., Mundlos, S., Dyer, J. 1991. Molecular genetics of intestinal glucose transport. *J. Clin.Invest.* 88:1435–40

Annu. Rev. Physiol. 1993. 55:591–608

FACILITATED GLUCOSE TRANSPORTERS IN EPITHELIAL CELLS

Bernard Thorens

Institute of Pharmacology and Toxicology, University of Lausanne, 27, Bugnon 1005 Lausanne, Switzerland

KEY WORDS: membrane proteins, molecular cloning, cell polarity, intestine, kidney

INTRODUCTION

Glucose enters the organism through a transport system present in the epithelial cells lining the small intestine and is reabsorbed by a similar mechanism located in the epithelial cells forming the kidney proximal tubules. The simultaneous presence of three different membrane proteins, located at the apical and basolateral poles of the epithelial cells, is required for the transepithelial transport process to take place. The first step is the transport of glucose into the cells against its concentration gradient: this step is carried out by a Na^+-dependent glucose symporter located in the apical brush border (39, 62). This symporter transports Na^+ ions down their electrochemical gradient, a mechanism that provides the driving force to cotransport and concentrate glucose into the cells. A low intracellular concentration of Na^+ ions is maintained by the Na^+/K^+ ATPase localized in the basolateral membrane (41). The glucose accumulated in the cells is then released into the extracellular space adjacent to blood capillaries by a mechanism of facilitated diffusion also located on the basolateral membrane.

In other epithelial cells, such as those forming more distal parts of the kidney nephron or constituting the choroid plexus, no transepithelial glucose transport occurs. However, glucose uptake is of critical importance to provide the cells with a source of metabolic energy required to perform their various transport functions. Therefore, these cells need a basolateral membrane glucose uptake system designed for their specific needs.

Considerable progress has been made in the last few years in elucidating

591

0066–4278/93/0315–0591$02.00

the molecular structure and function of membrane proteins that catalyze sugar transport processes. The basolateral membrane glucose transporters are part of a family of facilitated glucose transporters of which there are five different isoforms. These molecules transport D-glucose and closely related sugars down their concentration gradient. Different isoforms are expressed by various epithelial cells and may perform specific functions in glucose transport and metabolism. Recently, an isoform of these facilitated diffusion transporters was shown to be primarily a fructose transporter and to be localized in the brush border of enterocytes. In this chapter we discuss the structure of the facilitated glucose transporters; in particular, those expressed in epithelial cells of the intestine and kidney. We consider their potential cell-specific functions, either in transepithelial glucose transport or in glucose uptake. The molecular structure of the apical Na^+-dependent glucose transporter (SGLT1) has been elucidated by analysis of cDNA clones obtained by expression cloning (39).

FACILITATED DIFFUSION GLUCOSE TRANSPORTERS: Molecular Structure and Function

GLUT1

MOLECULAR AND FUNCTIONAL CHARACTERIZATION   The human erythrocyte glucose transporter, now referred to as GLUT1, was the first transporter to be biochemically characterized. The ability to solubilize it from the erythrocyte membrane with non-ionic detergents and to reconstitute it in a functional form in liposomes provided a means to follow its purification (44, 46, 79). Glucose transport is efficiently blocked by many inhibitors, such as phloretin, mercuric chloride, and cytochalasin B. Binding of cytochalasin B to the transporter can be competitively inhibited by glucose (64). ^{3}H-cytochalasin B can be covalently bound to GLUT1 and other GLUT molecules by ultraviolet irradiation (15), thereby allowing quantitation of glucose transporter expression in different cell types. Monoclonal and polyclonal antibodies were raised against the purified human erythrocyte glucose transporter. By Western blotting of erythrocyte membranes, these antibodies recognized a protein of 55 kd that is heterogenously glycosylated. Treatment of this transporter with N-glycanase, which removes N-linked oligosaccharides, resolved the broad 55 kd species to a single 46 kd polypeptide (1, 11, 50, 65).

Polyclonal antibodies against the human erythrocyte transporter (50) were used to isolate a cDNA encoding GLUT1 by screening an expression library prepared from the human hepatoma cell line, HepG2 (56). The primary sequence of the protein encoded by the isolated cDNA was consistent with partial protein sequence information obtained from the erythrocyte transporter.

The fact that this cDNA encoded a glucose transporter was confirmed by expressing the protein in bacteria with an inducible system (60). In induced cells, GLUT1 was synthesized and inserted into the bacterial membrane. Glucose uptake transport was stereospecific for D-glucose and was inhibited by cytochalasin B and mercuric chloride, which confirmed that the encoded polypeptide was indeed a glucose transporter. GLUT1 molecules now have also been cloned from rat (10), mouse (45), pig (78), and rabbit (5), and they share 97–98% identity with human GLUT1.

Analysis of the deduced primary sequence of human GLUT1 (56) suggested that twelve transmembrane domains were connected by hydrophilic segments (Figure 1). Both the NH2- and COOH-terminals are on the cytoplasmic side of the plasma membrane. A large exoplasmic loop is present between the first and second transmembrane domains and contains one of two potential N-glycosylation sites, the other is in transmembrane domain 11. A large cytoplasmic loop is located in the middle of the molecule between the sixth and seventh transmembrane domains. Analysis of the topology of GLUT1 with anti-peptide antibodies directed against the NH2- or COOH-terminal of the protein, together with trypsin and glycosidase digestion studies, confirmed several features of the model. Specifically, the N-linked oligosaccharide is attached to an Asn in the first exoplasmic loop, and the large hydrophilic loop

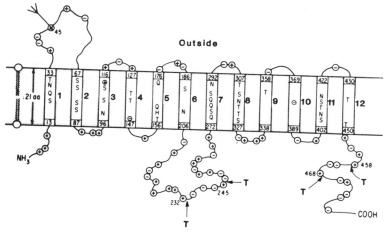

Figure 1 Model for orientation of GLUT1 in membrane. Twelve putative membrane-spanning domains are numbered and shown as rectangles. Positions of acidic (Glu, Asp) and basic (Lys, Arg) amino acid residues are indicated by circled + and −, respectively. Uncharged polar residues within membrane-spanning domains are indicated by S, serine; T, threonine; H, histidine; N, asparagine; Q, glutamine. Predicted position of N-linked oligosaccharide at Asn 45 is shown. Arrows indicate position of known tryptic cleavage sites in native membrane-bound erythrocyte glucose transporter. From Mueckler et al (56) (copyright 1985 by the AAAS).

present in the middle of the molecule and the COOH-terminal of the protein lie on the cytoplasmic side of the plasma membrane (4, 25, 38). Biophysical measurements showed that GLUT1 purified from human erythrocyte and reconstituted in liposomes is predominantly in α-helical configuration; thus the transmembrane segments form α-helices perpendicular to the plane of the lipid bilayer (2, 20).

The availability of a molecular probe for GLUT1 allowed a careful analysis of its tissue distribution. An mRNA corresponding to the 2.8 kb GLUT1 mRNA found in HepG2 cells was also detected in a number of tissues including brain, heart, kidney, fibroblasts, adipose cells, and every transformed cell line tested. Very little expression was found, however, in liver or skeletal muscle, tissues known to be important for the control of glucose homeostasis. These observations led to the search for other glucose transporter isoforms. Four additional isoforms (GLUT2 to GLUT5) have now been cloned by screening cDNA libraries with a GLUT1 cDNA probe using conditions that allow the hybridization of these probes to homologous cDNAs.

KINETIC PROPERTIES   Michaelis constants for glucose transport by human erythrocytes have been measured in a number of studies (14, 66). The K_m for D-glucose uptake was 1–2 mM, while K_m for glucose efflux was about an order of magnitude higher (20–30 mM), which indicates that the transport process is asymmetric. The kinetics of glucose transport in GLUT1 mRNA-injected Xenopus oocytes exhibit a similar asymmetry (33, 49) (Table 1).

Harrison et al (37, 36) presented evidence that the intrinsic activity of GLUT1 can be modulated. 3T3-L1 fibroblasts express a greater number of GLUT1 molecules at their cell surface than do CHO-K1 fibroblasts as measured by an exofacial GLUT1-specific antibody and by photoaffinity

Table 1   Michaelis constants (K_m) for sugar transport by GLUT molecules expressed in Xenopus oocytes in different conditions

	GLUT1	GLUT2	GLUT3	GLUT4	GLUT5
K_m for equilibrium exchange					
30MG [1,2]	17	42	10	—	—
30MG [3]	20	—	—	—	—
30MG [4]	21.3	—	—	1.8	—
K_m for glucose uptake					
2DOG [5,6]	5	7	—	—	—
2DOG[7]	—	—	1.8	4.6	—
Fructose [8]	—	—	—	—	6

The values of the K_m are expressed in mM. 1- 30MG: 3-0-methyl-glucose; 2- Human GLUTs, (32); 3- rat GLUT1, (30); 4- Human GLUT1, rat GLUT4, (49); 5- 2DOG: 2-deoxy-D-glucose; 6- Rat GLUT1 and GLUT2, (77); 7- Human GLUT3 and GLUT4, (58); 8- Human GLUT5, (12).

labeling with a ^{125}I-labeled derivative of forskolin. Yet the rate of glucose uptake is lower in 3T3-L1 cells than in CHO-K1 fibroblasts, which suggests that the intrinsic activity of this transporter may differ in these two cell types. Although the molecular basis for this difference in activity is not known, an altered turnover number of these transporters is an intriguing possibility and deserves to be further studied.

GLUT2

MOLECULAR AND FUNCTIONAL CHARACTERIZATION   The cloning of GLUT2 was achieved by screening rat (73) and human (28) liver cDNA libraries with a cDNA probe for GLUT1, using reduced stringency conditions. GLUT2 is 55% identical in amino acid sequence to GLUT-1. Its hydropathy plot is similar to GLUT1 and displays the same alternation of hydrophobic and hydrophilic segments, which predicts a protein with twelve putative trans-membrane domains. Both GLUT1 and GLUT2 sequences are colinear with the exception of the exoplasmic glycosylated loop connecting the first and second transmembrane domain: this loop is 64 amino acids long in GLUT2 vs 32 amino acid long in GLUT1 and other GLUT molecules (8, 28, 73).

Comparison of the amino acid sequence of the human (28), rat (73), and mouse (67) GLUT2 proteins shows a sequence identity of 82% between the human and the rat transporter and 95% between the mouse and rat forms. This level of conservation of the primary sequence between different species is lower than for GLUT1 as discussed above.

The characterization of GLUT2 as a glucose carrier was accomplished by functionally expressing the transporter in bacteria (73) and by injecting in vitro synthesized mRNA for GLUT2 into *Xenopus* oocytes, followed by measurement of glucose uptake (76, 77). Gould et al (33) further determined the sugar specificity for GLUT2 expressed in oocytes: GLUT2 transports

Table 2 Sugar specificity for GLUT molecules expressed in oocytes

	GLUT1	GLUT2	GLUT3	GLUT4	GLUT5
Glucose	+	+	+	+	−
Galactose	+	+	+	ND[1]	ND
Mannose	+	+	+	ND	ND
Fructose	−	+	−	ND	+
Xylose	−	−	+	ND	ND

Data are from Gould et al (32), except for GLUT5: Burant et al (12). +: sugar is transported; −: sugar is not transported; [1]- ND: not determined.

glucose, galactose, mannose, and fructose (Table 2). The ability to transport fructose is unique to GLUT2 and GLUT5, as discussed further below.

KINETIC PROPERTIES   GLUT2 is the predominant facilitated diffusion glucose transporter in hepatocytes and in the basolateral membrane of epithelial cells from the intestine, the kidney proximal tubules, and the pancreatic beta cells. Studies of glucose uptake by intact liver showed the presence of a stereospecific system for D-glucose with a high K_m for glucose (17 mM) (80). Further studies on isolated hepatocytes characterized the transport system in greater detail and showed that (*a*) the K_m for glucose was relatively high, about 15–20 mM (23); (*b*) the transporter was symmetric, i.e. the K_m for glucose was the same (about 20 mM) for influx or efflux in zero *trans* conditions or for equilibrium exchange entry or exit (21, 23); (*c*) the concentration of cytochalasin B producing half-maximum inhibition of glucose uptake (K_i) by isolated hepatocytes is 1.9 micromolar, a value about tenfold higher than the K_i for inhibition of the human erythrocyte glucose transporter (7).

Glucose transport by vesicles prepared from the basolateral membrane of intestinal epithelial cells has a K_m for glucose uptake of 48 mM and a similar value of 23 mM for efflux (51). The K_i for cytochalasin B inhibition of glucose transport is 0.11 μM, similar to that for the erythrocyte transporter, but lower than that of hepatocytes. Because GLUT2 has been localized to the basolateral membrane of intestinal absorptive cells (see below), the measured glucose transport kinetic most probably reflects GLUT2 activity.

Beta cells have an efficient stereoselective uptake system for glucose (40). Recently, using 3-O-methyl-glucose to measure kinetics of uptake by preparations of dispersed islet cells, Johnson et al (43) demonstrated the presence of a high K_m (17 mM), high V_{max} (32 mmole/min/l) component for glucose uptake that is thought to represent the activity of GLUT2. Indeed, in islet cells that no longer express GLUT2, as a result of a hyperinsulemic clamp, this high K_m component for glucose uptake disappears (19).

The kinetics of glucose uptake by GLUT2 has also been measured directly by expression of the transporter in *Xenopus* oocytes injected with GLUT2 mRNA (33, 77). These experiments showed a K_m for 2-deoxy-D-glucose uptake of 7 mM (77), a value lower than that measured in intact tissues and a value of 42 mM for 3-O-methyl glucose equilibrium exchange (33). In both conditions, the K_m values for glucose transport by GLUT2 were clearly greater than those for the other GLUT molecules measured in the same experiments. A high K_m for glucose is therefore a unique property of the GLUT2 isoform (Table 1).

The presence in the plasma membrane of transporting epithelial cells of a glucose transporter with a K_m of about 15–20 mM allows the rate of glucose transport through the basolateral membrane to increase in proportion to glucose concentrations varying over the normal value of about 5 mM up to values as high as 20 mM. A low K_m, high affinity transporter such as GLUT1 (K_m = 1.3 mM) is already functioning close to V_{max} at the normal blood glucose concentration and therefore would not permit an increase in the rate of glucose tranport when the glucose concentration increases above 5 mM. Therefore, the unique kinetic propert of GLUT2 is probably required for the efficient absorption or reabsorption of glucose through intestinal or kidney epithelial cells.

The structural basis for the low affinity for glucose of GLUT2 is not known. However, a unique structural feature of GLUT2 is the length of the glycosylated exoplasmic loop present between the first and second transmembrane domains. Is this long loop important for the low affinity for glucose? The ability to express glucose transporters in *Xenopus* oocytes (12, 32, 33, 49, 76, 77) and to measure the kinetics of glucose uptake using chimeric or mutated transporters may answer this question.

GLUT3

MOLECULAR AND FUNCTIONAL CHARACTERIZATION   GLUT3 was originally cloned from a human fetal muscle cDNA library (48) and was found to be almost ubiquitously expressed in human tissues; however, low level of expression was seen in adult muscle. Mouse GLUT3 is only 83% identical to human GLUT3 (57), a degree of homology similar to human and rodent GLUT2. In mouse and rat, the tissue distribution of GLUT3 is more restricted and its mRNA is detected only in the brain (31, 57, 81). By in situ hybridization (57), GLUT3 seems to be expressed principally in neurons. Kinetic measurement of glucose uptake by *Xenopus* oocytes injected with GLUT3 mRNA showed a K_m for equilibrium exchange of 10 mM, a value smaller than that for GLUT1 (17 mM) (Table 1).

GLUT4

MOLECULAR AND FUNCTIONAL CHARACTERIZATION   GLUT4 is the major glucose transporter of brown and white adipose tissues and of skeletal and cardiac muscles. In these tissues, insulin stimulates the rate of glucose uptake mainly by inducing the translocation of GLUT4 from intracellular vesicles to the cell surface. This transporter has been cloned from human (27), rat (9, 16, 42), and mouse (45). Its sequence is highly conserved between the different species, being 95 and 96% identical between human and rat or mouse. Kinetic properties and sugar specificities are shown in Tables 1 and Table 2.

GLUT5

MOLECULAR AND FUNCTIONAL CHARACTERIZATION   GLUT5 was isolated from a human intestinal epithelial cDNA library (47). It has the most divergent primary structure from the facilitated diffusion glucose transporter family and shows only 39 to 40% identity with the other glucose transporter isoforms. GLUT5 is expressed mostly in the jejunum, its mRNA, however, is also detected at low levels in human kidney, skeletal muscle, and adipocytes. Recently, using expression of GLUT5 in *Xenopus* oocytes, Burant et al (12) showed that GLUT5 is actually a fructose transporter rather than a glucose transporter (Table 2). Interestingly, fructose transport by GLUT5 could not be inhibited by D-glucose nor by cytochalasin B. In contrast, transport of fructose by GLUT2 (see above) could be inhibited by D-glucose and cytochalasin B. The K_m for fructose uptake in GLUT5 mRNA-injected cells was about 6 mM (Table 1). GLUT5 was also detected in spermatozoa at high levels, in agreement with the ability of these cells to utilize mostly fructose as a source of energy (12).

GLUCOSE TRANSPORTERS IN EPITHELIAL CELLS

Here we discuss the sugar transport processes taking place in intestine and kidney. Since GLUT1, GLUT2, and GLUT5 are the main transporters expressed in these cells, we concentrate our discussion on the possible specific functions of these transporters. We also show that GLUT1 expression in the choroid plexus may be important for the normal function of this tissue. Several recent reviews discuss various aspects of the structure and function of the facilitated glucose transporters (8, 30, 55, 58, 63, 69, 70).

Intestine

GLUT2 IN INTESTINAL ABSORPTIVE EPITHELIAL CELLS   In intestine, GLUT2 is expressed at a high level in the basolateral membrane of the absorptive epithelial cells (71), a location similar to that of the Na^+/K^+ ATPase (3). GLUT2 is not found in the brush border (Figure 2a). The expression of GLUT2 in the basolateral membrane of enterocytes suggests that it is responsible for the release of cellular glucose close to the blood capillaries. Because GLUT2 can also transport fructose, the export of this sugar across the basolateral membrane may also be mediated by GLUT2. Interestingly, GLUT2 is expressed only in enterocytes present on the tip and the sides of the villi, but not on the base of the villi nor in the crypts (71). Intestinal epithelial cells are produced from dividing stem cells present in the crypts of Lieberkuhn and differentiate into mature absorptive cells as they migrate towards the tip of the villi. Therefore, GLUT2 expression in intestine is a marker of the differentiated state of epithelial cells. In the rat, GLUT2 mRNA levels are low in the newborn, but increase progressively to reach adult level 25 days after birth (54).

REGULATED EXPRESSION OF GLUT2 IN INTESTINE   The rate of glucose transport across the intestinal mucosa is increased by hyperglycemia, either in streptozocin-induced diabetes or following perfusion with a glucose solution. In guinea pig, the increased transepithelial glucose absorption results from an increase in the rate of transport across the basolateral membrane, in addition to an increase across the brush border (26). In rat, hyperglycemia induced by glucose perfusion, leads within 2 hr to a three and one-half-fold increase in the V_{max} for glucose uptake by vesicles prepared from the basolateral membrane of jejunal epithelial cells (51). Interestingly, this increased rate of glucose uptake is not paralleled by an increase in the number of glucose-inhibitable cytochalasin B binding sites, a measure of the number of glucose transporters. Furthermore, cycloheximide injection prior to glucose perfusion decreased glucose uptake rates by 80% with no change in the number of cytochalasin B binding sites (18). In contrast, the increase in the glucose transport rate in basolateral membrane vesicles resulting from the chronic exposure of rats to a high carbohydrate diet also is accompanied by an increase in cytochalasin B binding sites (17). This increase in basolateral glucose transporters could be stimulated by dietary glucose or fructose, but not by other sugars. Together, these observations suggest that the rate of glucose transport through the basolateral membrane after an acute exposure to high glucose may result from changes in the intrinsic activity of the transporter, but chronic exposure to a high luminal glucose concentration may stimulate the production of new basolateral glucose transporters. Since GLUT2 is the main glucose transporter in the basolateral membrane of these cells, the measured glucose transport activity and its regulation by hyperglycemia should reflect changes in expression or in intrinsic activity of this transporter. Compatible with these data, GLUT2 mRNA in intestine of streptozocin-diabetic rats is increased three to fourfold starting 3 days after the onset of the diabetes (53). However, it is not yet known whether the increased expression of basolateral transporters reflects an increase in transporter number per cell, or whether additional enterocytes located closer to the base of the villi are recruited to express GLUT2.

GLUT5 IN INTESTINAL ABSORPTIVE CELLS   Antipeptide antibodies raised against the COOH-terminal domain of GLUT5 were used to study the localization of this transporter in human intestine (24) and in the Caco2 cell

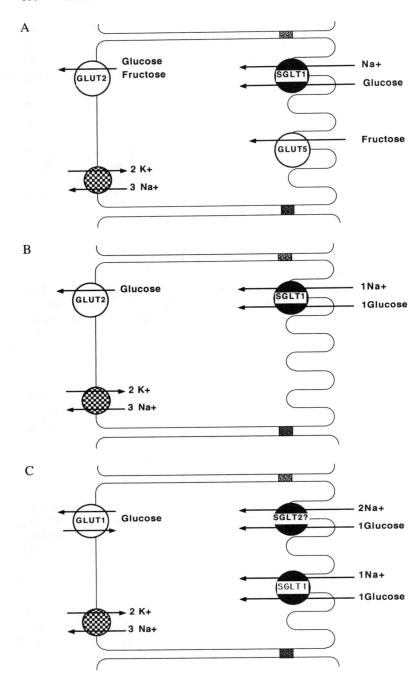

D

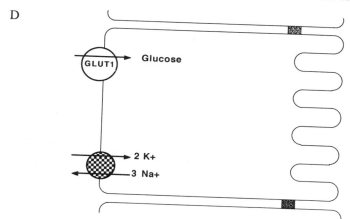

Figure 2   Schematic representation of the membrane molecules involved in sugar transport in different epithelial cells (see text for additional informations). (*A*) Transepithelial glucose and fructose transport across intestinal epithelial cells. The apical sodium-dependent symporter, SGLT1, concentrates glucose into the epithelial cells by transporting Na$^+$ ions down their electrochemical gradient. The low intracellular sodium concentration is maintained by the activity of the basolateral Na$^+$/K$^+$ ATPase. Glucose is then released close to blood capillaries by the activity of the Na$^+$-independent glucose transporter, GLUT2. Fructose enters the enterocytes by facilitated diffusion through the apically located GLUT5 molecule and is probably transported through the basolateral by GLUT2, which can transport both glucose and fructose. (*B*) Glucose reabsorption through epithelial cells forming the first part of the proximal convoluted tubule (S1) is similar to glucose absorption into the intestine. Glucose uptake into the cells is mediated by SGLT1, a symporter identical to the intestinal SGLT1. Glucose is then released through the basolateral membrane by facilitated diffusion through GLUT2. The driving force of the transport is also provided by the activity of the Na$^+$/K$^+$ ATPase. (*C*) Glucose reabsorption through the epithelial cells forming the straight part (S3) of the proximal tubule. Glucose reabsorption is thought to be carried out by a high-energy symporter (SGLT2 ?), which requires two Na$^+$ ions to transport one molecule of glucose. However, immunocytochemistry has also revealed the presence of SGLT1 in these cells. Glucose release close to blood capillaries is probably mediated by the the high affinity transporter GLUT1; GLUT2 is not detected in these cells. Since epithelial cells of S3 contain glycolytic enzymes, GLUT1 may also be required to provide these cells with a source of metabolic energy. (*D*) Glucose absorption into epithelial cells of Henle's loop, connecting tubule and collecting duct. These cells do not participate in transepithelial glucose transport, but express variable levels of GLUT1 in their basolateral membrane. These cells express different levels of glycolytic enzymes, and the level of GLUT1 expression correlates well with their known glycolytic activity. Therefore, GLUT1 expression is probably required for glucose uptake to provide cells with a source of metabolic energy. A similar situation occurs in epithelial cells forming the choroid plexus.

line (52). Immunoreactivity was mostly concentrated in the brush border of the intestinal epithelial cells and differentiated Caco2 cells. Therefore, rather than being a glucose transporter, GLUT5 appears to be the transport system carrying fructose through the brush border of intestinal epithelial cells (Figure 2a). The presence of a Na$^+$-independent, apical fructose transporter had been reported previously (34, 61).

REGULATED EXPRESSION OF GLUT5 IN INTESTINE   Detection of GLUT5 by immunofluorescence microscopy in intestinal epithelial cells revealed that it was present only in mature enterocytes present above the mid-part of the intestinal villi (24). During development in human, its expression reaches highest levels in the adult, while in the rat, highest expression is at 10 days after birth and decreases thereafter to reach the adult level at 20 days (54). The level of GLUT5 mRNA was unchanged in adult rats up to 10 days after induction of diabetes by streptozocin, but was decreased significantly 30 to 60 days after induction of diabetes. This regulation is in contrast to the increased expression of the mRNAs for GLUT2 and SGLT1 under the same metabolic conditions (48).

Kidney

GLUT2 IN KIDNEY ABSORPTIVE EPITHELIAL CELLS OF THE PROXIMAL CONVO-LUTED TUBULE   In kidney, GLUT2 is present only in the basolateral membrane of the cells forming the first (S1) part of the proximal convoluted tubule (72, 71) (Figure 2b). This segment of the kidney nephron is where the bulk of glucose reabsorption takes place, and glucose entry into the cells is probably mediated by the same Na^+-glucose symporter (SGLT1) present in intestine (22, 68). In kidney, GLUT2 mRNA and proteins levels are increased in streptozocin-diabetic rats, an effect completely prevented by insulin treatment (29).

GLUT1 IN KIDNEY EPITHELIAL CELLS OF THE PROXIMAL STRAIGHT TUBULE   Using antipeptide antibodies specific for GLUT1, this high affinity transporter isoform was localized in different segments of the kidney nephron (68, 72). It was found at a low level in the basolateral membrane of cells forming the straight part (S3) of the proximal convoluted tubule. In this region, glucose is reabsorbed from a low luminal concentration, and the transport across the brush border is thought to occur via a high-energy symporter, which requires two Na^+ ions to cotransport one molecule of glucose (13, 74). Therefore, glucose reabsorption in different segments of the kidney nephron is based on the presence of two different pairs of apical Na^+-dependent, and basolateral Na^+-independent, glucose transporters. A Na^+-dependent glucose symporter, probably identical to the intestinal one (SGLT1), and the low affinity GLUT2 are responsible for the bulk of glucose reabsorption in the S1 part of the proximal convoluted tubule (Figure 2b), while reabsorption of the remaining low concentrations of glucose present in the S3 segment of the proximal tubule requires an apical high-energy Na^+-dependent glucose symporter coupled to the basolateral high affinity GLUT1 (Figure 2c). However, the presence of SGLT1 in the brush border of epithelial cells forming the S3 segment has been reported (68), and this symporter was also detected in all three parts of the proximal tubule. It is thus possible that S3 cells possess two different glucose symporters in their brush borders, or that SGLT1 is regulated differently in S1 and S3 segments.

The cells in the S3 segment of the proximal tubule also have a low but detectable level of glycolytic enzymes, in contrast to cells of the S1 segment, which have no measurable levels of these enzymes (59, 75). Therefore, GLUT1 may also mediate glucose uptake into the cells for energy production through the glycolytic pathway.

GLUT1 IN EPITHELIAL CELLS OF THE DISTAL NEPHRON   In the more distal part of the kidney nephron, where reabsorption of glucose does not normally take place, GLUT1 is detected at variable levels. It is found at intermediate levels in the thin and thick ascending limbs, and at highest concentrations in the connecting segment and the collecting duct (Figure 2d). In the collecting duct, the highest expression of GLUT1 is in intercalated cells, and it is present at a lower level in the principal cells. In the papilla, only intercalated cells expressed this transporter isoform. This distribution of GLUT1 in different cells of the kidney nephron correlates well with the known glycolytic activity of these cells (59, 75). Therefore it is likely that this low K_m, high affinity glucose transporter is required primarily as an efficient glucose uptake system to facilitate energy production through aerobic or anaerobic glycolysis.

GLUT5 IN KIDNEY EPITHELIAL CELLS   In kidney, it is not yet known which segment of the nephron expresses GLUT5. However, if it functions primarily as a fructose transporter for transepithelial reabsorption of fructose, one can anticipate that GLUT5 will be coexpressed in GLUT2-containing cells, i.e. cells from the proximal convoluted tubule.

CHOROID PLEXUS

In the epithelial cells forming the choroid plexus, a situation similar to that present in the distal nephron cells is found. These cells, which transport a large number of solutes into and maintain the composition of the cerebrospinal fluid, express a high level of GLUT1 in their basolateral membrane (35). Because only little glucose reaches the cerebrospinal fluid, the uptake of glucose through GLUT1 is also most probably required for energy production within the cells.

SUMMARY

The molecular cloning of facilitated sugar transporters has led to the identification of a family of transport molecules having similar functions, but possessing specific kinetic and regulatory properties. These transporter isoforms are characterized by different primary structures, specific tissue localization, and polarized expression within the same epithelial cells. The use of *Xenopus* oocytes for the functional expression of different members of this transporter family has been of considerable value in defining the kinetic properties and sugar specificities of the different isoforms. The expression of chimeric or variously mutated transporters should, in the near future, permit the determination of the structural basis for their kinetic properties and sugar specificities. cDNA probes and antipeptide antibodies specific for each isoform are now being used to determine their specific regulation during development and in different states of altered glucose homeostasis. The variety of molecular forms implicated in the apparently simple task of sugar uptake or transepithelial transport has been surprising. With the available molecular tools now in hand, it will be possible to study these mechanisms in much greater detail.

ACKNOWLEDGMENTS

I want to thank Dr. Graeme Bell (Howard Hughes Medical Institute, University of Chicago) and Dr. Edith Brot-Laroche (INSERM, Villejuif) for communicating results before publication. The critical reading of this manuscript by Dr. Bernard Rossier and Dr. Henry Binder is gratefully acknowledged. The work of the author is supported by grant No. 31–30313.90 from the Swiss National Science Foundation and No. 191581 from Juvenile Diabetes Foundation International.

Literature Cited

1. Allard, W. J., Lienhard, G. E. 1985. Monoclonal antibodies to the glucose transporter from human erythrocytes. *J. Biol. Chem.* 260:8668–75
2. Alvarez, J., Lee, D. C., Baldwin, S. A., Chapman, D. 1987. Fournier transform infrared spectroscopic study of the structure and conformational changes of the human erythrocyte glucose transporter. *J. Biol. Chem.* 262: 3502–9
3. Amerongen, H. M., Mack, J. A., Wilson, J. M., Neutra, M. R. 1989. Membrane domains of intestinal epithelial cells: Distribution of Na$^+$, K$^+$-ATPase and the membrane skeleton in adult rat intestine during fetal development and after epithelial isolation. *J. Cell Biol.* 109:2129–38
4. Andersson, L., Lundahl, P. 1988. C-terminal-specific monoclonal antibodies against the human red cell glucose transporter. *J. Biol. Chem.* 263:11414–20
5. Asano, T., Shibasaki, Y., Kasuga, M., Kanazawa, Y., Takaku, F., et al. 1988. Cloning of a rabbit brain glucose transporter cDNA and alteration of glucose transporter mRNA during tissue development. *Biochem. Biophys. Res. Commun.* 154:1204–11
6. Asano, T., Shibasaki, Y., Lin, J.-L., Akanuma, Y., Takaku, F., Oka, Y. 1989. The nucleotide sequence of cDNA for a mouse liver-type glucose transport protein. *Nucleic Acids Res.* 17:6386
7. Axelrod, J. D., Pilch, P. F. 1983. Unique cytochalasin B binding characteristics of the hepatic glucose carrier. *Biochemistry* 22:2222–27
8. Bell, G. I., Kayano, T., Buse, J. B., Burant, C. F., Takeda, J., et al. 1990.

Molecular biology of mammalian glucose transporters. *Diabetes Care* 13: 198–208

9. Birnbaum, M.J. 1989. Identification of a novel gene encoding an insulin-responsive glucose transporter protein. *Cell* 57:305–15

10. Birnbaum, M. J., Haspel, H. C., Rosen, O. M. 1986. Cloning and characterization of a cDNA encoding the rat brain glucose-transporter protein. *Proc. Natl. Acad. Sci. USA*. 83:5784–88

11. Boyle, J. M., Whetton, A. D., Dexter, T. M., Meeran, K., Baldwin, S. A. 1985. Characterisation of monoclonal antibodies which specifically recognise the human erythrocyte glucose transport protein. *EMBO J*. 4:3093–98

12. Burant, C. F., Takeda, J., Brot-Laroche, E., Bell, G. I., Davidson, N. O. 1992. Fructose transporter in human spermatozoa and small intestine is GLUT5. *J. Biol Chem.* 267:14523–26

13. Burg, M. B. 1986. Renal handling of sodium, chloride, water amino acids, and glucose. In *The Kidney 3rd Ed.*, ed. B. M. Brenner, F.C. Rector, pp. 145–75. Philadelphia: Saunders

14. Carruthers, A. 1990. Facilitative diffusion of glucose. *Physiol. Rev.* 70: 1135–76

15. Carter-Su, C., Pessin, J. E., Mora, R., Gitomer, W., Czech, M. P. 1982. Photoaffinity labeling of the human erythrocyte D-glucose transporter. *J. Biol. Chem.* 257:5419–25

16. Charron, M. J., Brosius, F. C., Alper, S. L., Lodish, H. F. 1989. A glucose transport protein expressed predominantly in insulin-responsive tissues. *Proc. Natl. Acad. Sci USA* 86:2535–39

17. Cheeseman, C. I., Harley, B. 1991. Adaptation of glucose transport across rat enterocyte basolateral membrane in response to altered dietary carbohydrate intake. *J. Physiol.* 437:563–75

18. Cheeseman, C. I., Maenz, D. D. 1989. Rapid regulation of D-glucose transport in basolateral membrane of rat jejunum. *Am. J. Physiol.* 256:G878–83

19. Chen, L., Alam, T., Johnson, J. H., Hughes, S., Newgard, C. B., Unger, R. H. 1990. Regulation of β-cell glucose transporter gene expression. *Proc. Natl. Acad. Sci. USA*. 87:4088–92

20. Chin, J. J., Jung, E. K. Y., Jung, C. Y. 1986. Structural basis of human erythrocyte glucose transporter function in reconstituted vesicles. *J. Biol. Chem.* 261:7101–4

21. Ciaraldi, T. P., Horuk, R., Matthaei, S. 1986. Biochemical and functional characterization of the rat liver glucose-transport system. *Biochem. J.* 240: 115–23

22. Coady, M. J., Pajor, A. M., Wright, E. M. 1990. Sequence homologies among intestinal and renal Na$^+$/glucose cotransporters. *Am. J. Physiol.* 259: C605–10

23. Craik, J. D., Elliott, K. R. F. 1979. Kinetics of 3-O-methyl-D-glucose transport in isolated rat hepatocytes. *Biochem. J.* 182:503–8

24. Davidson, N. O., Hausman, A. M. L., Ifkovits, C. A., Buse, J. B., Gould, G. W., et al. 1992. Human intestinal glucose transporter expression and localization of GLUT5. *Am. J. Physiol.* 262:C795–800

25. Davies, A., Meeran, K., Cairns, M. T., Baldwin, S. A. 1987. Peptide-specific antibodies as probes of the orientation of the glucose transporter in the human erythrocyte membrane. *J. Biol. Chem.* 262:9347–52

26. Fischer, E., Lauterbach, F. 1984. Effect of hyperglycaemia on sugar transport in the isolated mucosa of Guinea-pig small intestine. *J. Physiol.* 355: 567–86

27. Fukumoto, H., Kayano, T., Buse, J. B., Edwards, Y., Pilch, P. F., et al. 1989 Cloning and characterization of the major insulin-responsive glucose transporter expressed in human skeletal muscle and other insulin-responsive tissues. *J. Biol. Chem.* 264:7776–79

28. Fukumoto, H., Seino, S., Imura, H., Seino, Y., Eddy, R. L., et al. 1988. Sequence tissue distribution and chromosomal localization of mRNA encoding a human glucose transporter-like protein. *Proc. Natl. Acad. Sci. USA* 85:5434–38

29. Garvey, W. T., Maianu, L., Camp, K., Dominguez, J. H. 1990. Diabetes alters glucose transporter gene expression in rat proximal tubule. *J. Am. Soc. Nephrol.* 1:718(Abstr.)

30. Gould, G. W., Bell, G. I. 1990. Facilitative glucose transporters: an expanding family. *Trends Biochem. Sci.* 15: 18–22

31. Gould, G. W., Brant, A. M., Kahn, B. B., Shepherd, P. R., McCoid, S. C., Gibbs, E. M. 1992 Expression of the brain-type glucose transporter is restricted to brain and neuronal cells in mice. *Diabetologia* 35:304–9

32. Gould, G. W., Lienhard, G. E. 1989. Expression of a functional glucose

transporter in *Xenopus* oocytes. *Biochemistry.* 28:9447–52

33. Gould, G. W., Thomas, H. M., Jess, T. J., Bell, G. I. 1991. Expression of human glucose transporters in *Xenopus* oocytes: kinetic characterization and substrate specificities of the erythrocyte (GLUT1), liver (GLUT2) and brain (GLUT3) isoforms. *Biochemistry.* 30:5139–45

34. Gracey, M., V. Birke, V., Oshin, A. 1972. Active intestinal transport of D-fructose. *Biochem. Biophys. Acta* 266:397–406

35. Hacker, H. J., Thorens, B., Grobholz, R. 1991. Expression of facilitative glucose transporter in rat liver and choroid plexus: A histochemical study in native cryostat sections. *Histochemistry.* 96:435–39

36. Harrison, S. A., Buxton, J. M., Clancy, B. M., Czech, M. P. 1991. Evidence that erythroid-type glucose transporter intrinsic activity is modulated by cadmium treatment of mouse 3T3-L1 cells. *J. Biol. Chem.* 266:19438–49

37. Harrison, S. A., Buxton, J. M., Czech, M. P. 1991. Suppressed intrinsic catalytic activity of GLUT1 glucose transporters in insulin-sensitive 3T3-L1 adipocytes. *Proc. Natl. Acad. Sci. USA* 88:7839–43

38. Haspel, H. C., Rosenfeld, M. G., Rosen, O. M. 1988. Characterization of antisera to a synthetic carboxyl-terminal peptide of the glucose transporter protein. *J. Biol. Chem.* 263:398–403

39. Hediger, M. A., Coady, M. J., Ikeda, T. S., Wright, E. M. 1987. Expression cloning and cDNA sequencing of the Na$^+$/glucose cotransporter. *Nature* 330:379–81

40. Hellman, B., Sehlin, J., Taljedal, I. 1971. Evidence for mediated transport of glucose in mammalian pancreatic beta cells. *Biochim. Biophys. Acta* 241:147–54

41. Horisberger, J.-D., Lemas, V., Kraehenbuhl, J.-P., Rossier, B. C. 1991. Structure-function relationship of Na,K-ATPase. *Annu. Rev. Physiol.* 53:565–84

42. James, D. E., Strube, M., Mueckler, M. 1989. Molecular cloning and characterization of an insulin-regulatable glucose transporter. *Nature* 338:83–87

43. Johnson, J. H., Newgard, C. B., Milburn, J. L., Lodish, H. F., Thorens, B. 1990. The high K_m glucose transporter of islets of Langerhans is functionally similar to the low affinity

transporter of liver and has an identical primary sequence. *J. Biol. Chem.* 265:6548–51

44. Jones, M. N., Nickson, J. K. 1981. Monosaccharide transport proteins of the human erythrocyte membrane. *Biochim. Biophys. Acta* 650:1–20

45. Kaestner, K. H., Christy, R. J., McLenithan, J. C., Braiterman, L. T., Cornelius, P., et al. 1989. Sequence, tissue distribution, and differential expression of mRNA for a putative insulin-responsive glucose transporter in mouse 3T3-L1 adipocytes. *Proc. Natl. Acad. Sci. USA* 86:3150–54

46. Kasahara, M., Hinkle, P. C. 1976. Reconstitution of D-glucose transport catalyzed by a protein fraction from human erythrocytes in sonicated liposomes. *Proc. Natl. Acad. Sci. USA* 73:396–400

47. Kayano, T., Burant, C. F., Fukumoto, H., Gould, G. W., Fan, Y.-S., et al. 1990. Human facilitative glucose transporters: Isolation, functional characterization, and gene localization of cDNAs encoding an isoform (GLUT5) expressed in small intestine, kidney, muscle and adipose tissue and an unusual glucose transporter pseudogene-like sequence (GLUT6). *J. Biol. Chem.* 265:13276–82

48. Kayano, T., Fukumoto, H., Eddy, R. L., Fan, Y.-S., Byers, M. G., et al. 1988 Evidence for a family of human glucose transporter-like proteins. Sequence and gene localization of a protein expressed in fetal skeletal muscle and other tissues. *J. Biol. Chem.* 263:15245–48

49. Keller, K., Strube, M., Mueckler, M. 1989. Functional expression of the human HepG2 and rat adipocyte glucose transporters in *Xenopus* oocytes. Comparison of kinetic parameters. *J. Biol. Chem.* 264:18884–89

50. Lienhard, G. E., Kim, H. H., Ransome, K. J., Gorga, J. C. 1982. Immunological identification of an insulin-responsive glucose transporter. *Biochem. Biophys. Res. Commun* 105:1150– 56

51. Maenz, D. D., Cheeseman, C. I. 1987. The Na$^+$ independent D-glucose transporter in the enterocyte basolateral membrane: orientation and cytochalasin B binding characteristics. *J. Membr. Biol.* 97:259–66

52. Mahraoui, L., Rousset, M., Dussaulx, E., Darmoul, D., Zweibaum, A., Brot-Laroche, E. 1993. Expression and localization of GLUT5 in Caco-2 cells

in human small intestine and colon. *Am. J. Physiol.* 263:G312–18

53. Miyamoto, K.-I., Hase, K., Taketani, Y., Minami, H., Oka, T., et al. 1991. Diabetes and glucose transporter gene expression in rat small intestine. *Biochem. Biophys. Res. Commun.* 181:1110–17

54. Miyamoto, K.-I., Hase, K., Taketani, Y., Minami, H., Oka, T., et al. 1992. Developmental changes in intestinal glucose transporter mRNA levels. *Biochem. Biophys. Res. Commun.* 183:626–31

55. Mueckler, M. 1990. Family of glucose transporter genes: Implications for glucose homeostasis and diabetes. *Diabetes* 39:6–11

56. Mueckler, M., Caruso, C., Baldwin, S. A., Panico, M., Blench, I., et al. 1985. Sequence and structure of a human glucose transporter. *Science* 229:941–45

57. Nagamatsu, S., Kornhauser, J. M., Burant, C. F., Seino, S., Mayo, K. E., Bell, G. I. 1992. Glucose transporter expression in brain. cDNA sequence of mouse GLUT3, the brain facilitative glucose transporter isoform, and identification of sites of expression by in situ hybridization. *J. Biol. Chem.* 267:467–72

58. Pessin, J. E., Bell, G. I. 1992. Mammalian facilitative glucose transporter family: Structure and molecular regulation. *Annu. Rev. Physiol.* 54:911–30

59. Ross, B. D., Espinal, J., Silva, P. 1986. Glucose metabolism in renal tubular function. *Kidney Int.* 29:54–67

60. Sarkar, H. K., Thorens, B., Lodish, H. F., Kaback, H. R. 1988. Expression of the human erythrocyte glucose transporter in *Escherichia coli. Proc. Natl. Acad. Sci. USA* 85:5463–67

61. Schultz, S. G., Strecker, C. K. 1970. Fructose influx across the brush border of rabbit ileum. *Biochem. Biophys. Acta* 211:586–88

62. Semenza, G., Kessler, M., Hosang, M., Weber, J., Schmidt, U. 1984. Biochemistry of the Na⁺ D-glucose cotransporter of the small-intestine brush-border membrane. *Biochim. Biophys. Acta* 779:343–79

63. Silverman, M. 1991. Structure and function of hexose transporters. *Annu. Rev. Biochem.* 60:757–94

64. Sogin, D. C., Hinkle, P. C. 1980. Binding of cytochalasin B to human erythrocyte glucose transporter. *Biochemistry* 19:5417–20

65. Sogin, D. C., Hinkle, P. C. 1980. Immunological identification of the human erythrocyte glucose transporter. *Proc. Natl. Acad. Sci. USA* 77:5725–29

66. Stein, W. D., ed. 1986. Facilitated diffusion: the simple carrier. In *Transport and Diffusion across Cell Membrane,* pp. 231–361. Orlando: Academic

67. Suzue, K., Lodish, H. F., Thorens, B. 1989. Sequence of the mouse liver glucose transporter. *Nucleic Acids Res.* 17:10099

68. Takata, K., Kasahara, T., Kasahara, M., Ezaki, O., Hirano, H. 1991. Localization of Na⁺-dependent active type and erythrocyte/HepG2-type glucose transporters in rat kidney: Immunofluorescence and immunogold study. *J. Histochem. Cytochem.* 39:287–98

69. Thorens, B. 1992. Molecular and cellular physiology of GLUT2: a high K_m glucose transporter. *Int. Rev. Cytol. Surv. Cell Biol.* 137A:209–38

70. Thorens, B., Charron, M., Lodish, H. F. 1990. Molecular physiology of glucose transporters. *Diabetes Care* 13:209–18

71. Thorens, B., Cheng, Z.-Q., Brown, D., Lodish, H. F. 1990. Liver glucose transporter: a basolateral protein in hepatocytes and intestine and kidney epithelial cells. *Am. J. Physiol.* 259:C279–85

72. Thorens, B., Lodish, H. F., Brown, D. 1990. Differential localization of two glucose transporter isoforms in kidney nephron. *Am. J. Physiol.* 259:C286–95

73. Thorens, B., Sarkar, H. K., Kaback, H. R., Lodish, H. F. 1988. Cloning and functional expression in bacteria of a novel glucose transporter present in liver, intestine, kidney, and pancreatic islets. *Cell* 55:281–90

74. Turner, R. J., Moran, A. 1982. Heterogeneity of sodium-dependent D-glucose transport sites along the proximal tubule: evidence from vesicle studies. *Am. J. Physiol.* 242:F406–14

75. Uchida, S., Endou, H. 1988. Substrate specificity to maintain cellular ATP along the mouse nephron. *Am. J. Physiol.* 255:F977–83

76. Vera, J. C., Rosen, O. M. 1989. Functional expression of mammalian glucose transporters in *Xenopus laevis* oocytes: evidence for cell-dependent insulin sensitivity. *Mol. Cell. Biol.* 9:4187–95

77. Vera, J. C., Rosen, O. M. 1990.

Reconstitution of an insulin signaling pathway in *Xenopus laevis* oocytes: coexpression of a mammalian insulin receptor and three different mammalian hexose transporters. *Mol. Cell. Biol.* 10:743–51

78. Weiler-Guttler, H., Zinke, H., Mockel, B., Frey, A., Gassen, H. G. 1989. cDNA cloning and sequencing analysis of the glucose transporter from porcine blood-brain barrier. *Biol. Chem. Hoppe-Sevler* 370:467–73

79. Wheeler, T. J., Hinkle, P. C. 1985. The glucose transporter of mammalian cells. *Annu. Rev. Physiol.* 47:503–17

80. Williams, T. F., Exton, J. H., Park, C. R., Regen, D. M. 1968. Stereo-specific transport of glucose in the perfused rat liver. *Am. J. Physiol.* 215:1200–9

81. Yano, H., Seino, Y., Inagaki, N., Hinokio, Y., Yamamoto, T., et al. 1991. Tissue distribution and species differences of the brain type glucose transporter (GLUT3). *Biochem. Biophys. Res. Comm.* 174:470–77

Annu. Rev. Physiol. 1993. 55:609–30

THE CYSTIC FIBROSIS TRANSMEMBRANE CONDUCTANCE REGULATOR

J. R. Riordan

Research Institute, The Hospital for Sick Children, Toronto, Ontario, Canada M5G 1X8 and Departments of Biochemistry and Clinical Biochemistry, University of Toronto

KEY WORDS: CFTR, chloride channel, ABC transporter, TM6-NBF transporter, CF mouse

INTRODUCTION

Cystic fibrosis (CF) is a fatal genetic disease with an especially high incidence in Caucasian populations, where it has a frequency of approximately one in 2500 live births (11). There is dysfunction at wet epithelial surfaces of a range of tissues, but most significantly those of the gastrointestinal and respiratory tracts. It is widely accepted that as a consequence of an aberrant control of salt and water movement across these surfaces, macromolecular secretions have an altered physical state and cannot be normally cleared (27). This results in blockage of small diameter tubes such as pancreatic ductules and small airways. In the pancreas, this leads to fibrosis and obliteration of the exocrine ductular system, which results in a reduction or absence of delivery of digestive enzymes to the small intestine. The ensuing malabsorption and malnutrition can be severe, although nowadays, the ingestion of capsules containing pancreatic enzymes is a reasonably effective therapy. In addition to the impact of the pancreatic deficiency, there is aberrant fluid balance in the intestine per se. In the lung, an inability to clear excessively viscous mucus has much more severe consequences. Recurrent infections with a variety of microorganisms, the establishment of encapsulated antibiotic-resistant strains, and repeated bouts of inflammation cause progressive tissue deterioration. This loss of lung function is almost always the cause of death.

Other tissues are also affected including the reproductive tracts in both

609

0066–4278/93/0315–0609$02.00

sexes and the sweat gland. The latter is most significant because it has provided the definitive diagnosis of the disease (26). Although defects in both sweat secretion (82) and the reabsorption (63) of salt from the secretory fluid are described, the latter is much more pronounced and results in a sodium chloride concentration that is approximately twice the normal level (26). Research into the transport defect that accounts for the diminished reabsorptive capacity of the sweat duct has played a central role in reaching our current interpretation of the basic biochemical defect in CF (64).

The principal aim of this review is to describe the present understanding of how dysfunction of the product of the gene mutated in CF patients results in the defective tissue function. To do this, the discovery of the gene in the context of other CF research at the time is outlined. The predicted properties of the gene product are also considered from this perspective and compared with the most recent information, derived largely from studies of the heterologous expression of normal and mutant versions of the gene. Other technical accomplishments such as the purification and functional reconstitution of the gene product and the implications are reviewed. In addition to the structure-function relationships of the molecule, its biosynthesis and intracellular trafficking is a focus of investigation because the most common disease-causing mutation results in a biosynthetic defect that causes the protein to be mislocalized (16, 25, 36, 43). Current progress and continuing efforts to understand this problem are discussed. Finally, because there is real hope that these molecular studies of CF will lead to new therapies, the prospects in this area are also considered.

CF GENE DISCOVERY

CF behaves as a simple autosomal recessive disease, but because of the wide variety of symptoms, the classical progression of elucidation that typically involves moving from an altered biochemical pathway to a defective or deficient protein (enzyme) within the pathway to the gene coding for it was not effective. No reproducible defect in a pathway, let alone a specific protein, was found (23). However, in the early 1980s, major progress was made in three different areas that later proved to be enabling in terms of the subsequent discovery of the CF gene. First, the realization that DNA sequence polymorphisms may be reflected as variant restriction endonuclease fragments detectable at any locus in the genome for which a hybridization probe is available (12) made it feasible to detect genetic linkage between a specific polymorphic locus and a particular phenotype such as CF as they segregate in families. The approach was applied to CF by several groups and resulted in the detection of linkage with DNA probes mapping to chromosome 7, first by Tsui et al (97) and then by Wainwright et al (98) and White et al (101). Linkage disequilibrium was established between CF and two loci separated by approximately 1.5×10^6 bp on chromosome 7 band q31 (96). The second important discovery was made earlier in the decade and finally established a reproducible phenotypic property of the disease. Electrophysiological studies of the sweat gland duct (65) and upper respiratory epithelia (47) revealed reproducible decreases in the transcellular conductance difference that could be best accounted for by a defective chloride permeation. These observations and interpretations were extremely important because they focused attention on anion permeability rather than cation transport pathways that had previously been studied in CF. The reports directed the attention of the burgeoning patch-clamp technology on chloride channels in epithelial cells affected in CF (39, 50, 83). These studies were possible because of the third development, which also turned out to play an important role in the gene identification, particularly the cloning of cDNAs from both normal subjects and CF patients. This development was the establishment of methods to culture the highly differentiated epithelial cells in which the defect is expressed. Available cell culture models, including skin fibroblasts and lymphoblasts that had been employed previously in CF research (15), were of no use because they express the CF gene minimally, if at all. Primary cultures of respiratory epithelial and sweat gland cells (20, 25, 48, 61, 68, 77, 102, 105) grown in defined media, which retained the anion conductance defect, were widely used to characterize the conductance and its regulation, especially by cAMP. Although the interpretation of some of these studies has been complicated by ambiguities regarding the identity of the channel underlying the conductance (99), the observation of a defect at the level of activation by a cAMP-mediated step became a central focus in subsequent attempts to understand the role of the gene product in this pathway.

The identification of the gene on the basis of its chromosomal localization approached the limits of resolution by genetic linkage analysis alone, and it became necessary to apply methods that could cover actual physical distances on the DNA in the region of chromosome 7 band q31. Tsui and co-workers (97) used a method termed saturation mapping in which clones selected randomly from a chromosome 7 library were localized using a battery of somatic cell hybrids with different segments of the chromosome deleted. Two clones were obtained that were situated closer than any of the previous markers, and they were employed to initiate chromosome walking and jumping. A distance of approximately 260 kb was covered containing at least four expressed sequences (46). Clues that these particular segments might be expressed came from their conservation among many different species ("zoo blots") and the presence of DNA sequences rich in dCTP and dGTP ("CpG islands," 79) known to be present at the beginning of many genes. However, concrete evidence of expression relied on the screening of messenger RNA and derived cDNA libraries (76).

Because the sweat gland is the tissue that most reproducibly exhibits a functional defect in patients, one could be assured that the gene mutated in the disease would be expressed there. Methods for the culture of sweat gland epithelial cells that retained many of the ion transport characteristics of the tissue (67) had been established earlier (20). RNA was isolated from cultures initiated with sweat glands of healthy individuals and CF patients and utilized to generate cDNA libraries, presumably representative of all the genes expressed in this tissue. Screening of the control non-CF libraries with genomic fragments from the walk that were positive in "zoo blots" eventually yielded a cDNA clone, 10-1, which had a long open reading frame and hybridized to a 6.5 kb mRNA in epithelial tissues affected in CF, but not other tissues (76). Rescreening of this and other cDNA libraries yielded a large set of overlapping cDNAs. Clones containing the same sequences were isolated from a library constructed from the sweat gland RNA of a CF patient. Sequencing revealed the absence of three nucleotides in the CF version of the sequence corresponding to the codon for a phenylalanine residue at amino acid position 508 (76).

The deletion (ΔF508) was subsequently discovered in approximately 70% of 200 CF chromosomes, but not in normal chromosomes; strong evidence that the gene responsible for CF had been identified (46).

PREDICTED PROPERTIES OF THE GENE PRODUCT

Primary Structure

The overlapping cDNAs had a large open reading frame predicting a polypeptide of 1480 amino acids. Its most obvious feature was the presence of several potential membrane-spanning hydrophobic helical sequences, which indicated that it was likely an integral membrane protein. Searches of protein sequence data bases revealed homology with a large group of active transport proteins (38). The primary sequence homology was restricted to regions of approximately 150 residues that constitute nucleotide-binding folds (NBFs; Figure 1). In addition there are potential secondary structure similarities in the arrangements of predicted transmembrane (TM) helices of which there may be six in each half of the molecule. The feature that is unique to a large and diverse class of prokaryotic and eukaryotic transporters is the apposition of these two domains, and hence the term TM6-NBF super family has been applied (74). Alternatively, they are also referred to as the adenine nucleotide-binding cassette (ABC) transporters (40) or traffic ATPases (1). In CFTR and several of the other eukaryotic membrane transporters, there are two of each of these domains. Hence, the initial deductions that the product of the

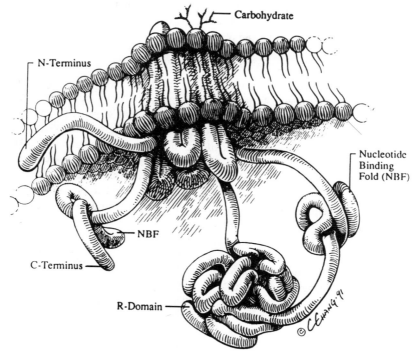

Figure 1   Schematic representation of CFTR indicating predicted major domains.

CF gene was a large membrane glycoprotein, apparently of an active transport genre, was both satisfying and puzzling.

The most obvious distinction between CFTR and the other known molecules sharing this structural motif was the presence of an additional highly charged hydrophilic region that was called the R domain. Since this product of exon 13 was an extra domain present in CFTR, it seemed likely that it might be responsible for an additional aspect of its function not exhibited by the other members of the super family. Since the R domain is rich in consensus phosphorylation sites for protein kinases A and C, it seemed reasonable to postulate that it might be responsible for the added functional attribute of regulation by these enzymes. However, it was not possible to predict if this regulation was of a separate chloride channel, such as the one that had been reported defective in CF epithelia (49), or if other CFTR domains might also constitute the channel itself. Hence, it was proposed that the gene product might be either a regulated chloride channel, or a regulator of a separate channel molecule. Charged amino acids within the putative transmembrane helices and a preponderance of residues with positive charges in the predicted cytoplasmic loops separating the TMs were features noted as consistent with the suggestion that it might be the channel (76).

Relationship to Cl^- Conductance Defect

The structural features were interpreted in the context of what had been reported of the Cl^- permeability defect in epithelial cells of airways and sweat glands from CF patients. Subsequent to the initial seminal papers (47, 63), studies mainly on cultured airway cells using the patch-clamp technique described the defect as one of a lack of activation of Cl^- currents by cAMP (reviewed in 100). It was suggested that the defect may not be in a chloride channel itself, rather in its regulation (33). Attention had become focused on an outwardly rectifying channel with a conductance of approximately 40 pS, which was claimed to be involved in Cl^- secretion and to be defective in its regulation by cAMP in primary cultures of airway cells from CF patients (39, 49, 50, 83). However, when more thorough studies of this channel had been completed, it appeared that it was neither normally activated by cAMP nor defective in CF (99). Although a recent report suggests that the larger channel may be secondarily affected by CFTR (31), it does not appear to be the channel responsible for secretagogue-stimulated secretion. Studies with cells of the pancreatic duct (34) and a colonic tumor cell line (89) indicated that this role was probably played by a low conductance (approximately 10 pS) cAMP-activated channel. However, the absence of a cAMP-dependent low conductance Cl^- channel from cells of CF patients was not actually demonstrated. The relationship between this channel and CFTR had to await the heterologous expression of the gene in cells not normally expressing it (see below).

HETEROLOGOUS EXPRESSION AND MUTAGENESIS

CFTR Produces Regulated Low Conductance Cl^- Channels

The most direct experimental means of gaining an understanding of the function of the protein was to introduce it into cells that did not contain it or where it was defective because of mutation, i.e. cells from CF patients. The latter feat was accomplished first (29, 69). However, it should be mentioned that the generation of an expressible full-length cDNA from the original overlapping cDNAs (76) was a formidable task that delayed expression studies for about one year. Because the protein is extremely toxic to the bacterial hosts used to propagate the cloned full-length cDNA, sequences in exon six, which could serve as a prokaryotic RNA polymerase promotor, had to be mutagenized (7, 35, 78). The effectiveness of the expression of the cDNA in restoring cAMP-mediated chloride conductance to epithelial cells derived from both the airway (69) and pancreatic duct (29) of CF patients was interpreted as confirmation that the CFTR gene was indeed (when mutated) responsible for the disease. However, no conclusions could be drawn about the mechanism whereby the Cl^- permeability was restored. As mentioned above, the favored interpretation was that CFTR had restored regulation of a separate channel that was not itself defective (29). However, soon after this, the expression of the normal CFTR cDNA in several different types of non-epithelial cells, without Cl^- channels of the type present in CFTR-containing cells, was found to cause the appearance of a cAMP-activated chloride conductance (4, 44). In one of these studies, the single channel events underlying this conductance in the recipient invertebrate cells were characterized and found to be identical to those of human epithelial cells in which CFTR was expressed endogenously (44). Furthermore, the magnitudes of the whole cell currents were proportional to the amounts of CFTR synthesized in these insect cells. These findings strongly supported the possibility that CFTR was itself the regulated Cl^- channel rather than only the regulator of a separate channel.

Properties of the Pore

The argument that CFTR was the channel was further strengthened by in vitro mutagenesis experiments in which two of the positively charged amino acids that were originally postulated to be among those within putative transmembrane sequences of CFTR giving it channel-like characteristics were replaced by ones of negative charge (3). This altered the anion selectivity from a preference for Cl^- to a preference for I^-. Interestingly the apparent anion selectivity of the wild-type channel exhibits an asymmetry that may involve either or both of these two positively charged residues (K95 and K335). The permeability of I^- relative to Cl^- is approximately 0.6 when iodide is present on the outside of the cell, but about 1.5 when iodide is on the inside (88). Reduction of iodide permeation from the outside by binding to charged sites within the pore may account for this difference. Cl^- on the outside can diminish this interaction and thereby increase iodide permeability. Because mutagenesis of K95 and K335, which were predicted to be towards the outer edge of the pore, changed the selectivity observed with iodide outside the cell to that observed with iodide on the inside with native channel (88), one or both of these residues could be involved in the iodide block. More extensive mutagenesis studies are being performed to further elucidate the constituents of the pore that may be formed by some as yet undefined arrangement of bundles of the putative transmembrane helices. Ultimately, three-dimensional structural information obtained with the pure protein will be required to test models evolving on the basis of in vitro mutagenesis. The protein has been purified to homogeneity and reconstituted in planar lipid bilayers, thus providing formal evidence that CFTR is the regulated low conductance chloride channel (9). This is discussed in detail below.

Regulation by Phosphorylation

Within regulatory aspects of the molecule, the predicted role of phosphorylation has been examined in several ways. The direct role of protein kinase A was demonstrated in several expression systems including *Xenopus* oocytes (7) into which the enzyme was injected, and excised patches from a variety of transfected cells, onto which the enzyme was applied (3, 10, 44, 10, 87). Tabcharani et al (87), applying the latter technique to permanent CHO cell lines expressing CFTR, first observed that phosphorylation and dephosphorylation by protein kinase A and a phosphatase, respectively, served as a molecular switch involved in gating of the channel. Similar findings were reported by Berger et al (10), and other important studies from the same group provided evidence in support of the hypothesis that sites of phosphorylation by PKA within the R domain are involved in regulation (70, 17). In one investigation, deletion of the C-terminal half of the R domain seemed to at least partly abolish the need for cAMP stimulation to activate the channel (70). In an other study, mutagenesis of four of the nine predicted PKA sites in the R domain was reported to abolish activation by cAMP (17) of whole cell Cl⁻ permeability in cells transiently expressing CFTR. These same four sites at serines 660, 737, 795, and 813 were also reported to account for all of the cAMP-stimulated phosphorylation of the protein in vivo. However, in more recent experiments that used stable CFTR-expressing cell lines in which the amounts of the protein present were matched and single channel characterization was performed in addition to the measurement of the permeability of the entire cell population, both phosphorylation and activation persisted after mutagenesis of these four sites (X.-B. Chang et al, unpublished). In fact, substantial activation occurred even after substitution of all nine R domain sites. The one remaining strict PKA consensus site, which is located outside of the R domain and just N-terminal of NBF1 at serine 422, accounted for some of the remaining activation. Furthermore, the effects of mutagenesis of the sites individually suggested that phosphorylation of some, such as serine 660, may be inhibitory to activation. Hence, the mechanism of regulation by PKA is more complex than initially thought and may involve unidentified regulatory sites. In addition, PKC was shown to potentiate activation by PKA (87). Picciotto et al (62), working with a recombinant R domain synthesized in bacteria, showed that it could be phosphorylated at serines 684 and 790 by PKC, but further details of the response of CFTR to this enzyme remain to be elucidated. The mechanisms mediating the channel activating effects of kinases are unknown, but we have recently found that PKA causes a large conformational change in purified recombinant R domain synthesized in bacteria (A. Dulhanty & J. R. Riordan, unpublished).

Regulation by ATP

Experiments similar to those mentioned above have been directed at elucidating the roles of the nucleotide binding domains in channel activation. Because ATP is the common substrate for both these domains and the kinases, the independent action of the former had been difficult to ascertain. However, Anderson et al (2) succeeded in maintaining CFTR in a phosphorylated state in excised patches so that the kinase-independent action of ATP could be assessed. Some other nucleotides such as GTP were able to substitute for ATP reasonably effectively, but non-hydrolyzable analogues were not. These authors cite this as evidence that ATP hydrolysis is required for activation. In constrast, studies with isolated intact ducts of the sweat gland, which were permeabilized on their basolateral sides, showed that chloride conductance, most probably mediated by CFTR, could be stimulated to maximal levels by non-hydrolyzable ATP analogues when a low concentration of ATP was present as a kinase substrate (66). This apparent discrepancy may be resolved in direct studies of the ATPase activity of purified CFTR. Although these investigations have not yet been reported, further recent mutagenesis studies have pointed to a lack of functional identity between the two nucleotide binding folds (5). For example, ADP was found to competitively inhibit activation by ATP by virtue of a specific interaction at NBF2. These findings suggest that CFTR responds acutely to the energy charge of the cell. Quinton & Reddy (66) have proposed that this response not only regulates CFTR, but also indirectly serves as a sensor that can spare epithelial cell ATP by shutting down transcellular ion transport when the energy charge of the cell is low. More detailed mutagenesis and structural studies on the CFTR domains involved in mediating the response to purine nucleotides are required to reveal the mechanism of this second switch involved in channel activation. Its connection with the phosphorylation switch is also not yet understood. As an entirely speculative model to reconcile the regulated channel activity of CFTR with the fact that all other known molecules sharing the same structural motif are active transporters (74), we have suggested that the R domain might be the substrate of this active transport function (44, 59, 73, 75). Consistent with the fact that all the higher eukaryotic transporters of this type pump substrate only outwardly, the R domain would be actively moved into the cytoplasmic mouth of the pore thereby causing a conformational change leading to pore opening; opening would be further promoted by the PKA-mediated phosphorylation of sites on the R domain surface. The possibility of some form of compensatory interaction between the two modes of activation was suggested by the important study of Drumm et al (30). They showed that some mutant versions of CFTR expected to compromise function of a nucleotide-binding domain could be compensated for by using increased amounts of a cyclic nucleotide phosphodiesterase inhibitor to increase cAMP-activated protein kinase activity. This fascinating apparent interaction between the two levels of regulation is now receiving intensive scrutiny. However, as with the nature of the conductance pore, real understanding of these regulatory mechanisms will require determinations of the three-dimensional structures of the domains involved and preferably the whole protein.

In addition to these studies of wild-type and engineered mutant forms of CFTR for the purpose of understanding structure and function, the first report of expression of the cDNA in non-epithelial cells described the effects of a number of disease-causing mutations not on function, but on the biosynthetic processing and intracellular transport of CFTR (16). Several of the mutations, especially ones in NBF1 including the most frequent (ΔF508), were found to prevent maturation and delivery to the cell surface. The same investigators later showed, not unexpectedly, that no regulated Cl$^-$ conductance could be detected at the surfaces of the cells in which this biosynthetic arrest had occurred. This has turned out to be an extremely significant finding and is discussed in more detail in a following section.

PURIFICATION AND RECONSTITUTION

Despite the enormous utility of the combination of the tools of molecular biology and patch clamping for the study of ion channels, purification of the polypeptide(s) forming the channel is still required before the channel structure can be determined. Furthermore, since the absence of the CFTR channel causes cystic fibrosis, its restoration by protein replacement therapy is one of the molecular means of therapy being envisaged. A more immediate aim is to determine definitively if CFTR is the Cl$^-$ channel, or if it functions by interacting with separate and independent channel molecules as had been proposed by some. Finally, because different disease-causing mutations have different effects, some influencing CFTR localization and stability and some its function, use of the purified and reconstituted protein may be necessary to study effects on function alone.

Purification

Because CFTR is a low abundance protein in tissues where it is normally expressed, there is no adequate natural source as a starting point for purification. Furthermore, it has proven difficult to generate large amounts of the protein in heterologous mammalian cell expression systems, presumably because of a stringent quality control of its biosynthesis (16). Two potentially large sources of CFTR for purification have been developed thus far. The first is the high capacity baculovirus-insect cell expression system in which synthesis of the protein is not limited (44), and the second is directed expression in the mammary gland of transgenic mice (28). The latter approach employing a casein promotor in the CFTR transgene results in the incorporation of the protein into milk fat globule membranes, but purification from this source has not been reported. In the baculovirus-insect cell expression system, CFTR had been found to be synthesized in large quantity in caterpillar cells and, despite incomplete glycosylation, to be fully active at the cell surface (44). The first step in the purification from this source involved detergent solubilization of the protein (9). This proved difficult but informative in terms of the state of the molecule in the cell membrane. Hence, the requirement for strong ionic detergents to effectively solubilize the protein from cell membranes suggests that it may be involved in strong protein-protein interactions in addition to its integration in the lipid bilayer. The nature of these interactions has not yet been investigated, but could involve the cytoskeleton and relate to the localization of the protein within the cell. Fortunately, the requirement for strong dissociating conditions to keep the protein in solution during conventional chromatography steps minimized the possibility of copurification of associated molecules that might contribute to channel function. The product obtained was homogeneous by rigorous criteria of purity including one- and two-dimensional electrophoresis, N-terminal sequence determination, and quantitative amino acid analysis.

Reconstitution

The protein was transferred from detergent to phospholipid vesicles at a ratio of less than one molecule per vesicle. Fusion of these proteoliposomes with a planar lipid resulted in single chloride channel activity with essentially the same properties as those present uniquely in CFTR-expressing cells. This activity required ATP and PKA; the channels exhibited characteristic flickering and wavelike activity, linear current-voltage relationships, and a unitary conductance of approximately 11 pS. Fusion of membrane vesicles from different cell types expressing CFTR, either endogenously or after transfection with CFTR cDNA, produced identical channels in the black films, although other types of channels were then also observed. This latter type of experiment incorporating crude CFTR-containing fractions into planar bilayers was also performed by Tilly et al (93) with similar results. The functional reconstitution of the purified protein provides strong evidence that it alone is sufficient to generate regulated low conductance chloride channel activity.

Activity of Purified ΔF508-CFTR

Purification and reconstitution has also been accomplished with several of the disease-causing mutant versions of CFTR. In the case of the major ΔF508 mutation, the results have been especially informative in that the channel properties in the bilayer did not differ from those of the wild-type protein.

The longer closed time reported by Dalemans et al (22) at the surface of mammalian cells in which most of the ΔF508 protein had been biosynthetically arrested were not observed with the purified protein in the bilayer. However, because Drumm et al (30) have shown that hyperphosphorylation of some mutant CFTRs can restore activity to a near normal level, the possibility exists that addition of excess PKA to the bilayer is responsible for overcoming the kinetic defect observed by Dalemans et al (22). It is also possible that this defect might be revealed in the bilayer at limiting ATP concentrations. Conversely, it is possible that the effect observed by Dalemans et al (22) was a secondary consequence of the aberrant processing and transport of the protein. Further work is required to distinguish between these possibilities. The fidelity of the planar bilayer measurement was reinforced by experiments with another severe mutation, G551D known to affect CFTR function, but not biosynthesis and transport (16). It was also capable of generating a channel with the same properties, but the open probability was greatly reduced.

LOCALIZATION AND MISLOCALIZATION

Localization of Wild-type CFTR

When the CFTR gene was cloned, mRNA was detected by Northern hybridization blot analysis primarily in those tissues affected by the disease including pancreas, lung, sweat gland, colon, parotid gland, and liver, and not in other tissues such as brain and adrenal gland (76). These observations served as one of the early pieces of evidence that the gene cloned was likely to be the one affected in CF. More detailed studies of the tissue specificity of expression have since been performed using RNA in situ hybridization (95) and immunocytochemistry (19, 21, 24, 43, 45, 56). These studies have for the most part confirmed the correlation between the presence of CFTR and CF tissue pathology and extended the original observations substantially. For example, regulated expression in both male and female reproductive tissues have provided interesting clues to the basis of the infertility of patients (95). The amount of CFTR detected varies substantially from tissue to tissue. The largest amount is present in the centroacinar cells constituting the smallest pancreatic ductules. In the lung, the other tissue suffering the most damage in the disease, the amount detected is less, especially in the epithelial cells lining the airways, which do exhibit elevated transcellular potentials in CF (103, 104). Recently, both RNA and protein have been detected in submucosal glands beneath the larger airways (32). The presence of CFTR has been reported in the proximal tubules of the kidney (21) and heart myocytes (57), tissues not grossly affected in the disease. The significance of these observations remains to be confirmed and evaluated. Evidence also has been reported of very low levels of CFTR mRNA detectable by PCR techniques in lymphoid cells (54).

Location of Mutant CFTR

In epithelial tissues expressing CFTR, the protein's primary location is in the apical plasma membrane (43) where it apparently serves as a tightly regulated chloride channel. The determinants of targeting to the apical surface are not yet known. When expressed in heterologous non-polarized cells, the wild-type CFTR protein follows the route of other integral plasma membrane glycoproteins from the endoplasmic reticulum through the Golgi apparatus to the cell surface. In the first heterologous expression experiments in which the fate of the protein was followed, its maturation, including the processing and extension of its oligosaccharide chains that required movement from the endoplasmic reticulum to the Golgi, appeared to occur inefficiently (16). That is, only a small proportion of the immature precursor turning over at the endoplasmic reticulum appeared to be successfully converted to the mature fully glycosylated product that would travel to the cell surface. In the case of some mutant versions of the protein, including ΔF508, which accounts for about 70% of CF mutations, the precursor was formed, but no conversion to the mature form occurred. This was interpreted as reflecting trapping of the precursor in the endoplasmic reticulum, possibly because of misfolding of the mutant protein caused by the deletion of phe 508. Although the details of this series of events have not been directly demonstrated, the basic failure of maturation and traffic to the cell surface has been confirmed in several different cell culture expression systems (22, 51).

It then became critical to determine if this consequence of the major mutation was an artifact of the heterologous expression systems, or if this biosynthetic arrest also occurred in patients' tissues in situ. Of the tissues in which the protein is readily detectable in apical membranes, only the sweat gland is not damaged by the secondary manifestations of the disease process. Specimens could be obtained from patients of defined genotypes by benign skin biopsy procedures. When this was done with patients homozygous for ΔF508-CFTR, the protein was undetectable in the apical membrane of the reabsorptive duct (43). Instead, only some granular intracellular staining could be seen. In contrast, strong apical staining was seen in ducts from individuals containing no mutant alleles. This study also confirmed the original observation in heterologous CFTR-expressing cells in culture that the product of some less frequent missense mutations such as G551D does reach the apical membrane (16, 36). A recent unpublished report of immunocytochemical studies of large airway specimens obtained from homozygous ΔF508 patients undergoing lung transplantation claims that CFTR does not reach the apical surface of epithelial cells in submucosal glands (32). Primary airway surface cell cultures from patients also indicates the absence of CFTR from the apical membrane (25). Thus it appears from the present state of knowledge that in the case of 70% of CF alleles (which contain the major mutant), and presumably those with nonsense mutations, the defect is an absence of the CFTR chloride channel from the apical membrane.

ΔF508-CFTR is Functionally Competent

It became obvious to ask whether the ΔF508 protein could function if it were able to reach the apical membrane. At least three different studies indicated that it could. When large amounts of the protein were expressed in cultured kidney cells using the *Vaccinia* virus T7 expression system, only a small amount reached the surface, but the cells did exhibit cAMP-activated low conductance Cl^- channel activity (22). Channel kinetics were reported to be altered, however, as reflected by a substantial increase in closed time. In a second study, injection of ΔF508 cRNA into *Xenopus* oocytes led to the expression of cAMP-dependent Cl^- currents, although these were reduced in magnitude compared to wild-type CFTR (30) and exhibited a substantially reduced sensitivity to activation by cAMP. The proportion of the ΔF508 protein reaching the oocyte surface was not monitored, nor were single channel kinetics. In the third study, when ΔF508-CFTR was expressed in insect cells, no biosynthetic arrest was found to occur (8). As with the wild-type protein (44), a large amount was synthesized and moved to the cell surface where it was functional. Open probabilities, open times, and closed times were computed from long patch-clamp recordings of channels in excised patches exposed to protein kinase A catalytic subunit (200 nM) and MgATP (1 mM) and were found not to differ significantly from those of the wild type (51). At this stage, it is not known why the small amount of ΔF508-CFTR that leaks past the biosynthetic block in mammalian cells (22) exhibits longer closed times, while in insect cells, where the biosynthetic block apparently does not occur, this kinetic change is not observed. However, the validity of the latter finding was confirmed using purified ΔF508-CFTR incorporated into planar lipid bilayers (51). Even if ΔF508-CFTR function is imperfect, the fact that it is active focuses attention on the search for ways to promote its maturation and intracellular transport.

The fact that the biosynthetic block does not occur in insect cells and probably not in *Xenopus* oocytes may at least partially reflect the lower temperatures at which the insect and amphibian cells are maintained. This is believed to be the case because the synthesis of other mutant membrane glycoproteins, which become trapped in the endoplasmic reticulum of mammalian cells because of misfolding, is promoted at reduced temperature (55). Another example of a membrane protein that is more efficiently assembled and transported to the surface of insect cells than mammalian cells is the MHC class I molecule (41). Recently it was shown that the processing and transport of ΔF508-CFTR is improved when mammalian cell hosts are grown at reduced temperature (23a).

To determine the nature of the misfolding that may occur because of the deletion of phe 508, both local and global three-dimensional structural information is necessary. Thomas et al (91, 92) compared the circular dichroism spectra and ATP-binding abilities of 67 and 66 residue synthetic peptides (corresponding to residues 450 to 516) with or without phe 508, respectively. Differences were not detected until the peptides were subjected to 4 M urea. Other investigators examined the binding of ATP to recombinant polypeptides corresponding to the entire NBF1 synthesized in bacteria, but could detect no influence of the presence or absence of phe 508 (37). It is possible, of course, that the absence of the residue compromises the propagation of the effect of the nucleotide interaction; however, the balance of the current evidence indicates that a substantial amount of function is retained. The other major effect of the phe 508 deletion is the biosynthetic arrest.

In addition to its principal location in the apical membrane, CFTR is known to have to pass through the endoplasmic reticulum and Golgi apparatus during synthesis, and its presence has been demonstrated in endosomes (53). At this latter site it provides a cAMP-activated pathway for the Cl^- counterion and thereby potentially influences the rate of endosomal acidification. However, at least when expressed heterologously in CHO cells, its presence does not influence the steady-state pH. In contrast to these findings, studies in cells from CF patients have been reported to have elevated pH in some intracellular membranous compartments including the *trans*-Golgi (6). These investigators suggest that this may cause altered activities of glycosyl transferases and consequently result in abnormal oligosaccharide compositions of glycoproteins synthesized in CF cells. Another study has reported that CFTR expression influences both endo- and exocytotic events, possibly reflecting the influence of endosomal CFTR (13, 14). The generality of these effects on glycoprotein synthesis and cycling of membrane vesicles to and from the cell surface will be determined in continuing investigations.

PROSPECTS: Understanding and Application

CFTR was the first epithelial ion channel for which the primary structure was determined. Initially the fact that its overall structure is distinctly different from known channels of excitable tissue was emphasized (40, 52, 71). However, it would appear that at least some fundamental features are common, i.e. the presence of multiple transmembrane helices containing residues with charged side chains contributing to ion selectivity and separated by hydrophilic loops with dense clusters of charged amino acids that may help distinguish between anions and cations (72). Certainly the regulatory elements involved in channel gating would seem to be very different. Whereas appropriate extracellular ligand-binding domains and voltage sensors are present in excitable tissue channels to account for the activation of the ligand- and voltage-gated families, respectively, CFTR possesses domains that mediate metabolic and hormonal regulation. Interestingly, epithelial chloride channels cloned since CFTR (42, 60, 85, 90), apparently have structural elements responsible for voltage activation that differ from the well-studied S4 helix motif with its regularly spaced positive charges in Na^+, Ca^{2+}, and K^+ channels of nerve and muscle (58). Whether any other epithelial channels participating in transcellular ion transport also utilize mechanisms of regulation by ATP and phosphorylation, like those employed by CFTR, remains to be determined. The Na-K-Cl cotransporter situated in the basolateral membrane of Cl^--secreting epithelial cells is also apparently activated when Cl secretion is stimulated (47a). Comparison of the mechanism of this regulation with that of CFTR will be useful in attempts to understand the coordinate activation.

In terms of the mechanism of action of the CFTR channel itself, only initial glimpses have been obtained thus far. One of the most fascinating challenges at this time is to understand the interactions between the two levels of regulation, i.e. that elicited by nucleotide binding and that caused by phosphorylation. Extension of the kinds of studies described employing in vitro mutagenesis, heterologous expression, and protein reconstitution will provide some of this understanding. Structural studies with the purified protein should provide more realistic models. Even though CFTR is one of the more recently discovered members of the TM6-NBF super family, the fact that its function is now readily assayed at the single molecule level means that elucidation of its structure-function relationships can proceed more rapidly than some of the others and hence may lead the way in elaborating features shared by all family members.

From the cystic fibrosis perspective, the discovery of the CFTR gene and the intensive research that has followed has already had a major impact. Although made somewhat complex by the large number of different CFTR mutations detected in patients, it is now possible to readily detect between 80 and 90% of mutant alleles. However, since there is no disease-specific treatment for CF that is aimed at the basic defect, research on CFTR has led to attempts to develop molecularly based therapies (81). These fall into at least three general categories including gene therapy, protein replacement therapy, and designed drug therapy. Initial studies with rodents not exhibiting any disease symptoms have demonstrated the feasibility of effectively delivering expressible CFTR using a virus vehicle (81). The possibility of stimulating alternative Cl⁻ channels to circumvent the CFTR block is also being explored (86). However, these efforts, which have only just begun, are not discussed here except to emphasize that the rapidly progressing basic research on CFTR is the basis of all three. For example, the finding that the major ΔF508 mutation and several others results in aberrant processing and intracellular transport of a protein that is otherwise functionally competent focuses attention on efforts to overcome the biosynthetic block. A drug that could accomplish this task would be expected to be highly effective in the treatment of the disease.

One of the main obstructions to the development of therapies as well as to basic CF research in general has been the lack of an animal model for the disease. Since the cloning of CFTR, several groups have been attempting to develop a "CF mouse" by interrupting the murine counterpart of CFTR using the homologous recombination-embryonic stem cell technology. This has recently been accomplished (18, 19a, 28a, 84) and should further accelerate progress towards completely understanding this disease.

Much of the research described here has been an excellent example of the interplay between curiosity-driven and mission-oriented science. At this juncture, it is difficult to judge which has benefited more, the understanding of CF or aspects of the many scientific disciplines employed to gain this understanding; e.g. the identification of human disease-causing genes, mechanisms of epithelial ion transport, membrane protein biosynthesis and transport, etc. Whatever the present balance of this ledger, it is very likely to change continually as studies of the molecular basis of cystic fibrosis continue.

Literature Cited

1. Ames, G. F., Mimura, C. S. Shyamala, V. 1990. Bacterial periplasmic permeases belong to a family of transport proteins operating from *Escherichia coli* to human: traffic ATPases. *FEMS Microbiol. Rev.* 6:429–46
2. Anderson, M. P., Berger, H. A., Rich, D. P., Gregory, R. J., Smith, A. E., Welsh, M. J. 1991. Nucleoside triphosphates are required to open the CFTR chloride channel. *Cell* 67:775–84
3. Anderson, M. P., Gregory, R. J., Thompson, S., Souza, D. W., Paul, S., et al. 1991. Demonstration that CFTR is a chloride channel by alteration of its anion selectivity. *Science* 253:202–5
4. Anderson, M. P., Rich, D. P., Gregory, R. J., Smith, A. E, Welsh, M. J. 1991. Generation of cAMP-activated chloride currents by expression of CFTR. *Science* 251:679–82
5. Anderson, M. P. Welsh, M. J. 1992. Regulation by ATP and ADP of CFTR chloride channels that contain mutant nucletoide binding domains. *Science* 257:1701–4
6. Barash, J., Kiss, B., Prince, A., Saiman, L., Gruenert, D., Al-Awqati, Q. 1991. Defective acidification of intracellular organelles in cystic fibrosis. *Nature* 352:70–73
7. Bear, C., Duguay, F., Naismith, A. L., Kartner, N., Hanrahan, J. W, Riordan, J. R. 1991. Cl⁻ channel activity in *Xenopus* oocytes expressing the cystic fibrosis gene. *J. Biol. Chem.* 266:19142–45
8. Bear, C. E., Jensen, T. J., Riordan, J. R. 1992. Functional capacity of the major mutant form of the cystic fibrosis transmembrane conductance regulator. *Biophys. J.* 61:A127
9. Bear, C. E., Li, C., Kartner, N.,

Bridges, R. J., Jensen, T. J., et al. 1992. Purification and functional reconstitution of the cystic fibrosis transmembrane conductance regulator (CFTR). *Cell* 68:809–18

10. Berger, H. B., Anderson, M. P., Gregory, R. J., Thompson, S., Howard, P. W., et al. 1991. Identification and regulation of the CFTR-generated chloride channel. *J. Clin. Invest.* 88:1422–31

11. Boat, T. F., Welsh, M. I., Beaudet, A. L. 1989. Cystic fibrosis. In *The Metabolic Basis of Inherited Disease*, ed. C. R. Scriver, A. L. Beaudet, W. S. Sly, D. Valle, pp. 2649–80. New York: McGraw-Hill

12. Botstein, D., White, R. L., Skolnick, M,, Davis, R. W. 1980. Construction of a genetic linkage map in man using restriction fragment length polymorphisms. *Am. J. Hum. Genet.* 32:314–31

13. Bradbury, N. A., Jilling, T., Berta, G., Sorscher, E. J., Bridges, R. J., Kirk, K. L. 1992. Regulation of plasma membrane recycling by CFTR. *Science* 256:530–32

14. Bradbury, N. A., Jilling, T., Kirk, K. L., Bridges, R. J. 1992. Regulated endocytosis in a chloride secretory epithelial cell line. *Am. J. Physiol.* 262: C752–59

15. Buchwald, M. 1987. Use of cultured human cells for biochemical analysis. *Clin. Biochem. Rev.* 1:1–20

16. Cheng, S. H., Gregory, R. J., Marshall, J., Paul, S., Souza, D. W., et al. 1990. Defective intracellular transport and processing of CFTR is the molecular basis of most cystic fibrosis. *Cell* 63:827–34

17. Cheng, S. H., Rich, D. P., Marshall, J., Gregory, R. J., Welsh, M. J., Smith, A. E. 1991. Phosphorylation of the R domain by cAMP-dependent protein kinase regulates the CFTR chloride channel. *Cell* 66:1027–36

18. Clarke, L. L., Grubb, B. R., Gabriel, S. E., Smithies, O., Koller, B. H., Boucher, R. C. 1992. Defective epithelial chloride transport in a gene-targeted mouse model of cystic fibrosis. *Science* 257:1125–28

19. Cohn, J. A., Melhus, O., Page, L. J., Dittrich, K. L., Vigna, S. R. 1991. CFTR: Development of high-affinity antibodies and localization in sweat gland. *Biochem. Biophys. Res. Commun.* 181:36–43

19a. Colledge, W. H., Ratcliff, R., Foster, D., Williamson, R., Evans, M. J. 1992. Cystic fibrosis mouse with intestinal obstruction. *Lancet* 340:680

20. Collie, G., Buchwald, M., Harper, P.,

Riordan, J. R. 1985. Culture of sweat gland epithelial cells from normal individuals and patients with cystic fibrosis. *In Vitro* 21:597–602

21. Crawford, I., Maloney, P. C., Zeitlin, P. L., Guggino, W. B., Hyde, S.-C., et al. 1991. Immunocytochemical localization of the cystic fibrosis gene product, CFTR. *Proc. Natl. Acad. Sci. USA* 88:962–66

22. Dalemans, W., Barbry, P., Champigny, G., Jallat, S., Dott, K., et al. 1991. Altered chloride ion channel kinetics associated with the ΔF508 cystic fibrosis mutation. *Nature* 354:526–28

23. Davis, P. B., di Sant'Agnese, P. A. 1980. A review. Cystic Fibrosis at forty—quo vadis? *Pediatr. Res.* 14:83–87

23a. Denning, G. M., Anderson, M. P., Amara, J. F., Marshall, J., Smith, A. E., Welsh, M. J. 1992. Processing of mutant cystic fibrosis transmembrane conductance regulator is temperature-sensitive. *Nature* 358:761–64

24. Denning, G. M., Ostedgaard, L. S., Chang, S. H., Smith, A. E., Welsh, M. J. 1992. Localization of cystic fibrosis transmembrane conductance regulator in chloride secretory epithelia. *J. Clin. Invest.* 89:339–49

25. Denning, G. M., Ostedgaard, L. S., Welsh, M. J. 1992. Abnormal localization of cystic fibrosis transmembrane conductance regulator in primary cultures of cystic fibrosis airway epithelia. *J. Cell. Biol.* 118:551–59

26. di Sant'Agnese, P. A., Powell, G. F. 1962. The eccrine sweat defect in cystic fibrosis of pancreas (mucoviscidosis). *Ann. NY Acad. Sci.* 93:555–59

27. di Sant'Agnese, P. A., Talamo, R. C. 1967. Pathogenesis and physiopathology of cystic fibrosis of the pancreas. *N. Engl. J. Med.* 277:1399–408

28. DiTullio, P., Cheng, S. H., Marshall, J., Gregory, R. J., Ebert, K. M., et al. 1992. Production of cystic fibrosis transmembrane conductance regulator in the milk of transgenic mice. *Bio-Technology* 10:74–77

28a. Dorin, J. R., Dickinson, P., Alton, E. W. F. W., Smith, S. N., Gedder, D. M., et al. 1992. Cystic fibrosis in the mouse by targeted insertional mutagenesis. *Nature* 359:211–15

29. Drumm, M. L., Pope, H. A., Cliff, W. H., Rommens, J. M., Marvin, S. A., et al. 1990. Correction of the cystic fibrosis defect in vitro by retrovirus-mediated gene transfer. *Cell* 62: 1227–33

30. Drumm, M. L., Wilkinson, D. S.,

Smit, L. S., Worrell, R. T., Strong, T. V., et al. 1991. Chloride conductance expressed by ΔF508 and other mutant CFTRs in *Xenopus* oocytes. *Science* 254:1797–99

31. Egan, M., Flotte, T., Atone, S., Jolow, R., Zeitlin, P. L., et al. 1992. Defective regulation of outwardly rectifying Cl⁻ channels by protein kinase A corrected by insertion of CFTR. *Nature* 358:581–84

32. Engelhardt, J. F., Wilson, J. M. 1992. *J. Cell Biol.* Submitted

33. Frizzell, R. A., Rechkemmer, G., Shoemaker, R. L. 1986. Altered regulation of airway epithelial cell chloride channels in cystic fibrosis. *Science* 233:558–60

34. Gray, M. A., Harris, A., Coleman, L., Greenwell, J. R., Argent, B. E. 1989. Two types of chloride channel on duct cells cultured from human fetal pancreas. *Am. J. Physiol.* 257:C240–51

35. Gregory, R. J., Cheng, S. H., Rich, D. P., Marshall, J., Paul, S., et al. 1990. Expression and characterization of the cystic fibrosis transmembrane conductance regulator. *Nature* 347:382–86

36. Gregory, R. J., Rich, D. P., Cheng, S. H., Souza, D. W., Paul, S., et al. 1991. Maturation and function of cystic fibrosis transmembrane conductance regulator variants bearing mutations in putative nucleotide-binding domains 1 and 2. *Mol. Cell. Biol.* 11:3886–93

37. Hartman, J., Huong, Z., Rado, T. A., Peng, S., Jilling, T., et al. 1992. Recombinant synthesis purification and nucleotide binding characteristics of the first nucleotide binding domains of the cystic fibrosis gene product. *J. Biol. Chem.* 267:6455–58

38. Higgins, C. F., Gallagher, M. P., Mimmack, M. L., Pearce, J. R. 1988. A family of closely related ATP-binding subunits from prokaryotic and eukaryotic cells. *BioEssays* 8:111–16

39. Hwang, T., Lu, L., Zeitlin, P. L., Gruenert, D. C., Huganir, R., Guggino, W. B. 1989. Cl⁻ channels in CF: Lack of activation by protein kinase C and cAMP-dependent protein kinase. *Reports* 244:1351–53

40. Hyde, S. C., Emsley, P., Hartshorn, M. J., Mimmack, M. M., Gileadi, H., et al. 1990. Structural model of ATP-binding proteins associated with cystic fibrosis, multidrug resistance and bacterial transport. *Nature* 346:362–65

41. Jackson, M. R., Song, E., Yang, Y.,

Peterson, P. A. 1992. Expression of empty MHC class I in insect cells. *J. Cell. Biochem. Suppl.* 15:15

42. Jentsch, T. J., Steinmeyer, K., Schwarz, G. 1990. Primary structure of *Torpedo marmorata* chloride channel isolated by expression cloning in *Xenopus* oocytes. *Nature* 348:510–14

43. Kartner, N., Augustinas, O., Jensen, T. J., Naismith, A. L., Riordan, J. R. 1992. Mislocalization of ΔF508 CFTR in cystic fibrosis sweat gland. *Nature Genetics* 1:321–26

44. Kartner, N., Hanrahan, J. W., Jensen, T. J., Naismith, A. L., Sun, S., et al. 1991. Expression of the cystic fibrosis gene in non-epithelial invertebrate cells produces a regulated anion conductance. *Cell* 64:681–91

45. Kartner, N., Jensen, T. J., Sun, S.-Z., Sapp, M. M., Collins, F. S., et al. 1990. The generation and use of antibodies to CFTR. *Ped. Pulmonol. Suppl.* 5:196

46. Kerem, B. S., Rommens, J. M., Buchanan, J. A., Markiewicz, D., Cox, T. K., et al. 1989. Identification of the cystic fibrosis gene: Genetic analysis. *Science* 245:1073–80

47. Knowles, M. R., Stutts, M. J., Spock, A., Fischer, N., Gatzy, J. T., Boucher, R. C. 1983. Abnormal ion permeation through cystic fibrosis respiratory epithelium. *Science* 221:1067–70

47a. Lauf, P. K., McManus, T. J., Haas, M., Forbush, B., Dunham, J., et al. 1987. Physiology and biophysics of chloride and cation cotransport across cell membranes. *Fed. Proc.* 46:2377–94

48. Lee, C. M., Carpenter, F., Coaker, T., Kealey, T. 1986. The primary culture of epithelia from the secretory coil and collecting duct of nominal human and cystic fibrosis eccrine sweat glands. *J. Cell Sci.* 83:103–18

49. Li, M., McCann, J. D., Anderson, M. P., Clancy, J. P., Liedtke, C. M., et al. 1989. Regulation of chloride channels by protein kinase C in normal and cystic fibrosis airway epithelia. *Science* 244:1353–56

50. Li, M., McCann, J. D., Liedtke, C. M., Nairn, A. C., Greengard P., Welsh, M. J. 1988. Cyclic AMP-dependent protein kinase opens chloride channels in normal but not cystic fibrosis airway epithelium. *Nature* 331:359–60

51. Li, C., Ramjeesingh, M., Reyes, E. F., Chang, X.-B., Riordan, J. R., et al. 1992. The major cystic fibrosis mutation does not influence the chloride

channel activity of CFTR. *Nature*. Submitted

52. Lodish, H. F. 1990 Revelations of a chloride channel. *Nature* 348:489–90

53. Lukacs, G. L., Chang, X.-B., Kartner, N., Rotstein, O. D., Riordan, J. R., Grinstein, S. 1992. The cystic fibrosis transmembrane regulator is present and functional in endosomes. Role as a determinant of endosomal pH. *J. Biol. Chem.* 267:14568–72

54. MacDonald, T. V., Nghiem, P. T., Gardner, P., Martens, C. L. 1992. Human lymphocytes transcribe the cystic fibrosis transmembrane conductance regulator gene and exhibit CF-defective cAMP-regulated chloride current. *J. Biol. Chem.* 267:3242–48

55. Machamer, C. E., Rose, J. K. 1988. Vesicular stomatitis virus G-proteins with altered glycosylation sites display temperature sensitive intracellular transport and are subject to aberrant intermolecular disulfide bonding. *J. Biol. Chem.* 263:5955–60

56. Marino, C. R., Matovcik, L. M., Gorelick, F. S., Cohn, J. A. 1991. Localization of the cystic fibrosis transmembrane conductance regulator in pancreas. *J. Clin. Invest.* 88:712–16

57. Nagel, G. A., Hwang, T.-C., Nairn, A. C., Gadsby, D. C. 1992. Regulation of PKA-activated Cl conductance in guinea pig ventricular myocytes: single channel studies. *J. Gen. Physiol.* 100:70a

58. Noda, M., Shimizu, S., Tanabe, T., Takai, T., Kayano, T., et al. 1994. Primary structure of *Electrophorus electricus* sodium channel deduced from cDNA sequence. *Nature* 312:121–27

59. Nowak, R. 1991. CFTR: it's a pump, it's a channel, it's a little of each. *J. NIH Res.* 3:30–31

60. Paulmicih, M., Li., Y., Wickman, K., Ackerman, M., Peralta, E., Clapham, D. 1992. New mammalian chloride channel identified by expression cloning. *Nature* 356:238–41

61. Pedersen, P. S. 1984. Primary culture of epithelial cells derived from the reabsorptive coiled duct of human sweat glands. *ICRS Med. Sci.* 12:752–53

62. Picciotto, M. R., Cohn, J. A., Bertuzzi, P., Greengard, P., Nairn, A. C. 1992. Phosphorylation of the cystic fibrosis transmembrane conductance regulator. *J. Biol. Chem.* 267:12742–52

63. Quinton, P. M. 1983. Chloride impermeability in cystic fibrosis. *Nature* 301:421–22

64. Quinton, P. M. 1990. Cystic fibrosis: a disease of electrolyte transport. *FASEB J.* 4:2709–17

65. Quinton, P. M., Bijman, J. 1983 Higher bioelectric potentials due to decreased chloride absorption in the sweat glands of patients with cystic fibrosis. *N. Engl. J. Med.* 308:1185–89

66. Quinton, P. M., Reddy, M. M. 1992. Energy sensitive passive Cl^- absorption in cystic fibrosis. *Nature*. Submitted

67. Reddy, M. M., Riordan, J. R., Quinton, P. M. 1988. Electrical properties of cultured reabsorptive sweat duct cells from normal and cystic fibrosis subjects: Intracellular microelectrode analysis. In *Cellular and Molecular Basis of Cystic Fibrosis*, ed. G. Mastella, P. M. Quinton, pp. 383–93. San Francisco: San Francisco Press

68. Reddy, M. M., Riordan, J. R., Quinton, P. M. 1988. The retention of basic electrophysiological properties by human sweat gland cells in primary culture. *In Vitro Cell. Dev. Biol.* 24:905–10

69. Rich, D. P., Anderson, M. P., Gregory, R. J., Cheng, S. H., Paul, S., et al. 1990. Expression of cystic fibrosis transmembrane conductance regulator corrects defective chloride channel regulation in cystic fibrosis airway epithelial cells. *Nature* 347:358–63

70. Rich, D. P., Gregory, R. J., Anderson, M. P., Manavalan, P., Smith, A. E., Welsh, M. J. 1991. Effects of deleting the R domain on CFTR-generated chloride channels. *Science* 253:205–7

71. Ringe, D., Petsko, G. A. 1990. Cystic fibrosis: a transport problem? *Nature* 347:358–63

72. Riordan, J. R. 1992. Molecular biology of chloride channels. *Curr. Opin. Nephrol. Hypertens.* 1:34–42

73. Riordan, J. R. 1992. CFTR function. In *Current Topics in Cystic Fibrosis*, Chpt. VI. Sussex: Wiley & Sons. In press

74. Riordan, J. R., Alon, N., Grzelczak, Z., Dubel, S., Sun, S. 1991. The CF gene product as a member of a membrane transporter (TM6-NBF) super family. *Adv. Exp. Med. Biol.* 290:19–29

75. Riordan, J. R., Chang, X.-B. 1992. CFTR, a channel with the structure of a transporter. *Biochim. Biophys. Acta* 1101:221–22

76. Riordan, J. R., Rommens, J. M., Kerem, B.-S., Alon, N., Rozmahel, R., et al. 1989. Identification of the cystic fibrosis gene: Cloning and characterization of complementary DNA. *Science* 245:1066–73

77. Riordan, J. R., Vokaty, C., Jensen, T., Bums, J. E., Tsui, L.-C., Buchwald, M. 1988. Molecular studies of cultured epithelial cells from the sweat gland. See Ref. 67, pp. 416–24

78. Rommens, J. M., Dho, S., Bear, C. E., Kartner, N., Kennedy, D., et al. 1991. cAMP-inducible chloride conductance in mouse fibroblast lines stably expressing human cystic fibrosis transmembrane conductance regulator. *Proc. Natl. Acad. Sci. USA* 88:7500–04

79. Rommens J. M., Iannuzzi, M. C., Kerem, B.-S., Drumm, M. L., Melmer, G., et al. 1989. Identification of the cystic fibrosis gene: Chromosome walking and jumping. *Science* 245:1059–65

80. Rommens, J. M., Zengerling, S., Bums, J., Melmer, G., Kerem, B., et al. 1988. Identification and regional localization of DNA markers on chromosome 7 for the cloning of the cystic fibrosis gene. *Am. J. Hum. Genet.* 43:645–63

81. Rosenfeld, M. A., Yoshimura, K., Trapnell, B. C., Yoneyama, K., Rosenthal, E. R., et al. 1992. In vivo transfer of the human cystic fibrosis transmembrane conductance regulator gene to the airway epithelium. *Cell* 68:143–55

82. Sato, K., Sato, F. 1984 Defective beta-adrenergic response of cystic fibrosis sweat glands in vivo and in vitro. *J. Clin. Invest.* 73:1763–71

83. Schoumacher, R. A., Shoemaker, R. L., Halm, D. R., Tallant, E. A., Wallace, R. W., Frizzell, R. A. 1987. Phosphorylation fails to activate chloride channels from cystic fibrosis airway cells. *Nature* 330:752–54

84. Snouwaert, J. N., Brigman, K. K., Latour, A. M., Malouf, N. N., Boucher, R. C., et al. 1992. An animal model for cystic fibrosis made by gene targeting. *Science* 257:1083–88

85. Steinmeyer, K., Orland, C., Jentsch, T. J. 1991. Primary structure and functional expression of a developmentally regulated skeletal muscle chloride channel. *Nature* 354:301–4

86. Stutts, M. J., Chinet, T. C., Mason, S. J., Fullton, J. M., Clarke, L. L., Boucher, R. C. 1992. Regulation of Cl⁻ channels in normal and cystic fibrosis airway epithelial cells by extracellular ATP. *Proc. Natl. Acad. Sci. USA* 89:1621–25

87. Tabcharani, J. A., Chang, X.-B., Riordan, J. R., Hanrahan, J. W. 1991. Phosphorylation-regulated Cl channel in CHO cells stably expressing the cystic fibrosis gene. *Nature* 352:628–31

88. Tabcharani, J. A., Chang, X.-B., Riordan, J. R., Hanrahan, J. W. 1992. The CFTR chloride channel: Iodide block and permeation. *Biophys. J.* 62:1–4

89. Tabcharani, J. A., Low, D., Elie, D., Hanrahan, J. W. 1990. Low-conductance chloride channel activated by cAMP in the epithelial cell line T84. *FEBS Lett.* 270:157–64

90. Thiemann, A., Grander, S., Pusch, M., Jentsch, T. J. 1992. A chloride channel widely expressed in epithelial and non-epithelial cells. *Nature* 356:57–60

91. Thomas, P. J., Shenbagamurthi, Sondek, J., Hulliben, J. M., Pedersen, P. L. 1992. The cystic fibrosis transmembrane conductance regulator - Effects of the most common cystic fibrosis-causing mutation on the secondary structure and stability of a synthetic peptide. *J. Biol. Chem.* 267:5727–30

92. Thomas, P. J., Shenbagamurthi, P., Ysern, X., Pedersen, P. 1991. The cystic fibrosis transmembrane conductance regulator: Nucleotide binding to a synthetic sixty-seven amino acid peptide. *Science* 251:555–57

93. Tilly, B. C., Winter, M., Ostegaard, L. S., O'Riordan, C., Smith, A. E., Welsh, M. J. 1992. cAMP dependent protein kinase activation of CFTR chloride channel in planar lipid bilayers. *J. Biol. Chem.* 267:9470–73

94. Deleted in proof

95. Trezise, A. E. 0, Buchwald, M. 1991. In vivo cell specific expression of the cystic fibrosis transmembrane conductance regulator. *Nature* 353:434–37

96. Tsui, L.-C. 1989. Tracing the mutations in cystic fibrosis with closely linked DNA markers (invited editorial). *Am. J. Hum. Genet.* 44:303–6

97. Tsui, L.-C., Buchwald, M., Barker, D., Braman, J. C., Knowlton, R. G., et al. 1985. Cystic fibrosis locus defined by a genetically linked polymorphic DNA marker. *Science* 230:1054–57

98. Wainwright, B. J., Scambler, P. J., Schmidtke, J., Watson, E. A., Law, H.-Y., et al. 1985. Localization cystic fibrosis locus to human chromosome 7een-q22. *Nature* 318:384–85

99. Ward, C. L., Krouse, M. E., Gruenert, D. C., Kopito, R. R., Wine, J. J. 1991. Cystic fibrosis gene expression is not correlated with rectifying Cl⁻ channels. *Proc. Natl. Acad. Sci. USA* 88:5277–81

100. Welsh, M. J. 1990. Abnormal regula-

tion of ion channels in cystic fibrosis epithelia. *FASEB J.* 4:2718–25

101. White, R., Woodward, S., Nakamura, Y., Leppert, M., O'Connell, P., et al. 1985. A closely linked genetic marker for cystic fibrosis. *Nature* 318:382–84

102. Widdicombe, J. R., Welsh, M. J. 1985. Cystic fibrosis (CF) alters the electrical properties of monolayers cultured from cells of human tracheal mucosa. *Fed. Proc.* 44:1365

103. Willumsen N. J., Boucher R. C. 1989. Shunt resistance and ion permeabilities in normal and cystic fibrosis airway epithelia. *Am. J. Physiol.* 256:C1054–63

104. Willumsen, N. J., Davis, C. W., Boucher, R. C. 1989. Cellular Cl⁻ transport in cultured cystic fibrosis airway epithelium. *Am. J. Physiol.* 256:C1045–53

105. Yankaskas, J. R., Knowles, M. R., Gatzy, J. T., Boucher, R. C. 1985. Persistence of abnormal chloride ion permeability in cystic fibrosis nasal epithelial cells in heterologous culture. *Lancet* 1:954–56

Annu. Rev. Physiol. 1993. 55:631–55

TOXIGENIC DIARRHEAS, CONGENITAL DIARRHEAS, AND CYSTIC FIBROSIS: Disorders of Intestinal Ion Transport

M. Field and C. E. Semrad

Departments of Medicine and of Physiology and of Cellular Biophysics, College of Physicians and Surgeons, Columbia University, New York, New York 10032

KEY WORDS: cholera toxin, heat-stable *Escherichia coli* enterotoxin, guanylin, congenital chloridorrhea, sodium secretory diarrhea, microvillus inclusion disease, chloride channel

INTESTINAL FLUID SECRETION: An Overview

The pathophysiology of enterotoxic diarrheas, congenital diarrheas, and cystic fibrosis (CF) are discussed in this review. The last provides an interesting contrast to diarrheal disorders in that the intestine of CF patients fails to secrete in response to the usual secretory stimuli. To provide a conceptual framework, we begin with a brief summary of the ion transport properties of intestine as they relate to the active secretion of electrolytes.

Fluid transport across a segment of intestine is the net result of both absorptive and secretory processes, which may well be spatially separate. There is a general consensus that this is so based on compelling, but not altogether unassailable, circumstantial evidence (112). Na and Cl are thought to be absorbed by the villus epithelium in the small intestine and by the surface epithelium of the colon; Cl secretion, on the other hand, is thought to be a crypt cell function in both the small intestine and colon. It is of interest in this regard that the mRNA for the CF gene product, the so-called CF transmembrane conductance regulator or CFTR, has been localized to small intestinal and colonic crypt cells, almost none being detected in more

631

0066–4278/93/0315–0631$02.00

superficial cells (119). As discussed below, intestinal Cl secretion is lost in CF, whereas intestinal absorptive capacity is unimpaired.

The ion transport abnormalities manifested in secretory diarrheas are the following: (*a*) Active Cl secretion is stimulated in the small intestine and/or the colon. Its cellular mechanism is shown in Figure 1 (see legend for description). (*b*) In the ileum and/or the colon, HCO_3 secretion is also stimulated, the mechanism for which has not been elucidated. (*c*) In the colon, K is also actively secreted in response to cAMP (60). (*d*) In the small intestine, secretory stimuli tend to inhibit Na and Cl absorption as well as stimulate Cl secretion (112). Thus they contribute to diarrhea through their antiabsorptive as well as their secretory effect. Na-coupled absorptive processes for organic solutes such as sugars, amino acids, and bile acids are unaffected, however,

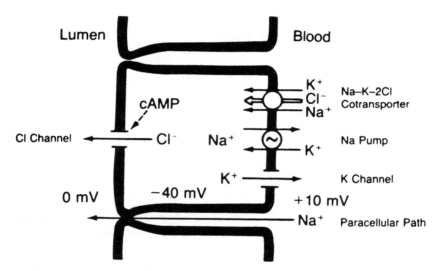

Figure 1   Cellular paradigm for active Cl secretion (from 47). In the basolateral (BL) membrane the inward movements of Na and Cl are coupled either by a Na-K-2Cl cotransporter (see figure), a K-independent Na-Cl cotransporter, which is present in a few tissues (89, 113), or by intracellular pH in conjunction with Na/H and Cl/HCO3 exchangers. Bumetanide-sensitive Na-K-2Cl cotransport has been demonstrated in the BL membrane of distal colonic enterocytes (126) and T84 colon cancer cells (81), but not yet in small intestine or proximal colon. The entering Na is recycled by Na,K-ATPase in the BL membrane. The K entering via the Na/K pump and the Na-K-Cl cotransporter is recycled through one or more K channels residing in the BL membrane and, in colon, also in the brush border (BB) membrane (60). Ca-activated, cAMP-activated, and ATP-inhibited K channels all have been described (104). They are activated when secretion is stimulated, thereby hyperpolarizing the cell and increasing the driving force for Cl secretion. The BB membrane possesses one or more anion channels, the opening of which initiates the secretory process. Cyclic AMP, cGMP, Ca, and protein kinase C have all be implicated in the activation of these channels. Finally, Na moves passively across the epithelium through the paracellular pathway.

which explains why oral rehydration therapy with glucose or amino acid-supplemented salt solutions is successful.

In the absence of organic solutes, the principal means for salt absorption across the intestinal brush border (BB) membrane appears to be Na/H exchange in the jejunum, a combination of Na/H and Cl/HCO$_3$ exchange in the ileum and proximal colon, and Na channel-mediated Na absorption in the distal colon (60, 112). Enterocyte brush border Na/H exchange is inhibited by increases in the concentrations of cAMP and calcium (Ca) (110), which explains, at least in part, the antiabsorptive effect of secretory stimuli.

CYSTIC FIBROSIS: An Antidiarrheal State

Since the physiology and biochemistry of CFTR are discussed elsewhere in this volume, we confine ourselves to its role in the intestine. Diarrhea is not uncommon in patients with CF, but this is because they develop pancreatic insufficiency with a consequent maldigestion of nutrients. The diarrhea can be overcome by ingesting pancreatic enzymes. Intestinal obstruction by abnormally viscous meconium occurs in 5 to 10% of newborns with CF (24). Meconium ileus may be due to abnormalities of the secreted mucopolysaccharides, or to their inadequate hydration, or both.

The ion transport properties of both the small intestine and colon of subjects with CF have been studied in vivo (6, 55–57, 93) and in vitro (8, 13, 62, 115). These studies have demonstrated the complete inability of CF intestine to secrete Cl in response to either cAMP-related agonists (PGE$_2$, theophylline) or Ca-related agonists (cholinergic stimuli, Ca ionophore). This has been shown for jejunum, ileum, distal colon, and rectum. Since theophylline increases cGMP as well as cAMP concentration, its failure to stimulate Cl secretion also suggests that CF intestine cannot respond to cGMP. This was more directly confirmed by an in vivo study in which CF intestine was shown not to respond to heat-stable *Escherichia coli* enterotoxin, a known stimulator of intestinal guanylate cyclase (see below) (55).

The Cl secretory defect in CF intestine appears to be an isolated ion transport abnormality. Electrogenic Na absorption in colon (56, 62, 93) and electrically neutral NaCl absorption in small intestine (8) operate normally in CF. Glucose-stimulated Na absorption is also normal (6, 8). Active K secretion in the colon is also unaffected by CF (13, 57). Whether CF affects ileal and colonic HCO$_3$ secretion has not been determined.

Intestinal Cl Channels and Their Regulation

The failure of both cAMP- and Ca-related secretagogues to stimulate Cl secretion in CF gut distinguishes this tissue from CF airway epithelia (3) and sweat glands (106), which can still respond normally to Ca-related agonists.

In airway epithelia, cytosolic cAMP and Ca appear to activate different anion channels in the apical membrane; the former but not the latter is abnormal in CF (3). The anion channels present in the apical membranes of normal intestinal cells have not been well characterized. In part this is due to the difficulty of accessing the apical membranes of crypt cells. Since neither cAMP nor Ca can stimulate secretion in CF intestine, it is possible that a single CFTR-related apical Cl channel is directly or indirectly the target for both intracellular mediators. In a recent study in HT29 colon cancer cells, whole cell patch-clamp experiments have identified a single Cl current activated by both Ca and cAMP (17).

The T84 colon cancer cell line has been extensively used for studies of Cl secretion and is thought to be a good model system for the intestinal secretory process (3, 33–35, 59, 61, 68, 78, 81, 127, 128). Both Ca and cAMP stimulate secretion in T84 cells, but appear to do so by somewhat different mechanisms. Ca activates K conductance in the basolateral (BL) membrane, thereby hyperpolarizing the apical membrane potential and increasing the electrochemical driving force for Cl secretion (33, 81). Since T84 cell monolayers exhibit some baseline Cl secretion (the short-circuit current ranges from 2 to 20 $\mu a/cm^2$), a baseline Cl conductance in the apical membrane is clearly present. Thus an increase in the electrochemical driving force for Cl secretion can by itself, without any change in apical Cl permeability, increase the rate of secretion. Whether or not agents that increase cell Ca in T84 cells also increase apical membrane Cl permeability is unclear. Two studies (3, 35) found no evidence for an apical Ca-activated Cl conductance, but a more recent study has found such a conductance, although smaller in magnitude than the cAMP-activated conductance (78). A protein kinase C-activated conductance was also demonstrated.

Synergism between agonists that increase cell Ca and those that increase cAMP occurs in T84 cells (78, 81), but not in normal mammalian intestine (15). In T84 cells, this synergism can be attributed to cAMP having its predominant effect on apical membrane Cl conductance and Ca having its predominant effect on BL membrane K conductance. The lack of synergism in normal intestine suggests that both agonists cause appreciable increases in both conductances. There are, therefore, significant differences in the secretory mechanism between T84 cells and normal intestine.

Do CF Heterozygotes Have Less Risk of Severe Secretory Diarrhea?

The extraordinary frequency of CF gene mutations in populations of Northern European descent [1 out of every 25 individuals is a heterozygote; the disease appears in 1 of every 2500 births (24)] has led to speculation about a possible survival advantage for the heterozygote. If heterozygotes have diminished capacity for intestinal Cl secretion, which has not been established, they may, in ages past, have been better protected against death from enterotoxic diarrheas such as cholera.

VIBRIO CHOLERAE ENTEROTOXINS:
Multiplicity and Mechanisms of Action

Multiplicity

This organism seems determined to elicit a diarrheal response in its animal hosts. In addition to producing cholera toxin (CT), it has recently been shown to produce two additional enterotoxins. One has been called Zona Occludens Toxin, or ZOT, because it increases the ionic permeability of intestinal tight junctions (43). ZOT increases conductance, but not short-circuit current, when added to rabbit ileal mucosa in vitro, but increases both permeability and fluid secretion when added to rabbit ileal loops in vivo (A. Fasano, personal communication). The difference in hydrostatic pressure present in vivo may be the driving force for the fluid secretion evoked by ZOT. Recently a second *V. cholerae* enterotoxin, which does stimulate secretion in vitro, has also been identified (42). Its mechanism of action is not known, but the peptide involved has no structural resemblance to CT. In addition to producing three enterotoxins, *V. cholerae* organisms also produce what may be termed a cofactor to CT, a neuraminidase that converts polysialogangliosides to monosialogangliosides, but is not able to hydrolyze the last sialic acid moiety. It thus effectively increases the number of monosialoganglioside receptors for CT present in the BB membrane, thereby potentiating the action of the toxin (41).

Biochemical Mechanism of Action of Cholera Toxin

CT's biochemical mechanism of action is familiar to most students of medicine and biology. It is well described in a recent review by Moss & Vaughan (86). Briefly, the CT molecule binds through its B subunits to monosialoganglioside m1 (G_{m1}) molecules in the plasma membrane. Its A subunit is next internalized and reduced, releasing its 24,000 dalton A_1 component. A_1 is an enzyme that catalyzes the covalent incorporation of ADPR, which it derives from cellular NAD onto an arginine residue in the α subunit of Gs, the G protein that activates the catalytic subunit of adenylate cyclase (ad-cy). The ADP ribosylase activity of A_1 must first be activated by a small G protein found in the cytoplasm of most cells. The α subunit of Gs, once covalenty modified, detaches from the membrane bound β and γ subunits, which permits it to bind to and persistently activate the catalytic component of ad-cy.

CT's biochemical mechanism of action has for the most part been elucidated by studies using cells from outside the gastrointestinal tract. The true in vivo site of action of CT, however, is the intestine and we focus here on two interesting aspects of its intestinal action: how does CT, after binding to receptors on the luminal surface of small intestinal enterocytes, activate ad-cy, which is present only on their contraluminal surface, i.e. how is the CT signal transmitted across the cell? and does CT produce some of its diarrheagenic effect by intoxicating cells other than the enterocytes directly engaged in electrolyte transport?

Transduction of the Cholera Toxin Signal from Brush Border to the Basolateral Membrane

There is no detectable ad-cy activity in the BB membrane. How does CT, after binding to BB membrane receptors, activate ad-cy in the BL membranes? Two possibilities have been suggested that are not mutually exclusive: the Gs_α altered by CT could be in the BB membrane, and its α subunit, once activated, could migrate through the cytoplasm to the BL membrane and activate ad-cy. Alternatively, CT, once internalized, could migrate to the BL membrane and interact with Gs_α there.

CHOLERA TOXIC ACTIVATION OF INTESTINAL BRUSH BORDER MEMBRANE G PROTEINS   Dominguez et al (36) reported in 1986 that CT ADP-ribosylates three BB membrane proteins of 40, 45, and 47 kd and subsequently demonstrated that one of the ADP-ribosylated proteins in the BB membrane is the α subunit of Gs (37). They speculated that the α subunit, once activated, dissociates from the BB membrane and somehow reaches the catalytic subunit of ad-cy in the BL membrane, and cited, in support of this idea, the reported release of Gs_α from rat liver plasma membranes as a consequence of the action of CT (80). De Jonge and his colleagues (123), using specific antisera, confirmed the presence of Gs (as well as of several other G proteins) in the BB membrane, but they failed to find specific release of Gs_α from the BB membrane following activation by CT. Release of activated Gs_α from plasma membranes has, however, been noted by others in experiments with intact mastocytoma and lymphoma cells (91, 97) and isolated hepatocyte and neural plasma membranes (80, 83).

Regardless of its role in CT activation of intestinal ad-cy, the presence of Gs_α and other G proteins in the BB membrane is of great interest. Recently, De Jonge and his colleagues (117) reported that BB membranes from both rat small intestine and human HT29 cells contain a unique, inwardly rectifying 20 pS Cl channel activated by guanosine 5'-O-(3-thiophosphate). Neither cAMP, ATP, nor Ca was required for this activation. Its physiological role remains to be established. Conceivably it could be directly activated by CT, thereby representing an ad-cy-independent effect on the toxin.

CHOLERA TOXIN INTERNALIZATION, REDUCTION, AND TRANSPORT   The other possible means proposed for transduction of the CT signal from the BB to the BL membrane is internalization of CT by receptor-mediated endocytosis, followed by its reduction and transport to the BL membrane. This second possible avenue to ad-cy activation could complement the first, completely substitute for the first, or interact with the first in the sense that receptor-mediated endocytosis is a necessary prerequisite for activation of Gs in the BB membrane. Both CT and tetanus toxin, which also has a glycolipid membrane receptor, are internalized by rat liver cells via non-coated plasma membrane microinvaginations to which they preferentially bind (84). They differ in this regard from ligands that bind to glycoprotein receptors, which are internalized via clathrin-coated pits. After endocytosis, coated and non-coated vesicles appear to merge into the same endosomal compartment— the Golgi-endoplasmic reticulum-lysosome system (71). Recently it was shown in rat liver that endosomal acidification is necessary for the liberation of the A_1 subunit from CT and for its insertion into the endosomal membrane with its catalytic site exposed (70). In the same study it was shown that plasma membranes per se are unable to reduce CT, i.e. that internalization into acidifiable endosomes is a necessary prerequisite for generation of free, enzymicly active A_1 peptide. The requirement for endosomal acidification in CT action again raises the evolutionary question of a survival advantage for CF heterozygotes. Abnormal Cl channel regulation in CF cells has been shown to produce a defect in acidification of intracellular organelles (5). Does this render them relatively resistant to intoxication by CT?

Most studies of CT internalization and activation have employed non-intestinal cells, but Lencer et al (77) recently undertook an investigation of CT translocation from BB to BL membrane in the T84 intestinal cell line, the results of which may be more directly germane to intact small intestine. They have shown two temperature-sensitive steps for CT activation of ad-cy: one is internalization and reduction, which is necessary for ad-cy activation whether CT is added on the BB or the BL membrane side of the epithelial monolayer. A second temperature-sensitive step is also required for activation of ad-cy upon addition of CT to the BB side, but not upon addition of CT to the BL membrane side. Presumably this second step consists of transfer to the BL membrane of endosome-bound toxin, although endosomal transfer of Gs_α cannot be excluded.

Cholera Toxin and the Enteric Nervous System: Differences Between in Vitro and in Vivo Effects

Except for their slower time course, the in vitro effects of CT, as studied in experiments with rabbit ileal mucosa mounted in Ussing chambers, are indistinguishable from those of cAMP and theophylline (44, 45). It is reasonable to conclude that these effects are mediated by CT-induced increases in the cAMP concentration of intestinal epithelial cells, both villus and crypt. The in vivo effects of CT cannot, however, be described in such a simple fashion. In pioneering studies, Lundgren and his colleagues (21, 22), using the small intestine of cat and rat, showed that inhibitors of neuronal function (tetrodotoxin, hexamethonium, lidocaine) can block most of CT's secretory effect. This is not the case in vitro. Tetrodotoxin, when added to rabbit ileal mucosa in vitro, does not diminish the secretory effect of CT (85).

That inhibitors of neural function can inhibit CT-induced secretion in vivo but not in vitro is at first thought puzzling. CT presumably activates neural mechanisms in vivo by first activating ad-cy in neuroendocrine cells dispersed thoughout the intestinal epithelium. But how do these neural effects produce secretion above and beyond that directly elicited by CT in enterocytes? Some of the neural effects may be mediated by Ca-related neurotransmitters. In normal intestine in vitro, however, the effects of cAMP and Ca-related agonists are not additive (15). It seems likely, therefore, that under the conditions of the in vivo experiments done by Lundgren and others, CT failed to directly activate the ad-cy activity of some enterocytes, most likely those recessed in crypts; whereas under the conditions of in vitro experiments in which well stretched pieces of ileal mucosa are clamped in Ussing chambers, CT activates ad-cy in all of the enterocytes. In fact, Lundgren and his colleagues showed that in cat small intestine in vivo, luminal CT causes detectable increases of cAMP content in villus cells, but not in crypt cells (38). Without adequate stirring and some luminal distension to stretch the epithelium, a CT-containing luminal solution may simply not gain access to crypt lumina. Prolonged in vivo exposure of rat small intestinal mucosa to CT was found by others to increase cAMP in both cell populations (31). In the human disease, selective exposure of only villus cells to CT does not occur since the *V. cholerae* organisms grow on the luminal surface of both villus and crypt cells (96) and may transfer the toxin directly to surface receptors.

In vivo experiments in which CT is added to bulk luminal solutions may not accurately reflect the situation in human disease or in Ussing chambers, but they underscore the central role played by the enteric neuroendocrine axis in the regulation of intestinal electrolyte transport. CT appears to activate ad-cy in endocrine cells located in the villus epithelium, caused by the release of serotonin (5-HT) and neurotensin (NT) (10, 11, 18, 40, 92). Both activate receptors on enteric neurons and evoke the release of secretory neurotransmitters, the principal one being vasoactive intestinal polypeptide (VIP) (20, 39, 109). VIP directly stimulates ad-cy in enterocytes (109); its secretory effect is not blocked by tetrodotoxin or hexamethonium (118). 5-HT also causes leukocytes and fibroblasts in the lamina propria to synthesize and release PGE$_2$ (4, 10, 11) which, in turn, also appears to stimulate the release of secretory neurotransmitters (9, 11). Higher concentrations of PGE$_2$ also directly stimulate enterocytes (90).

HEAT-STABLE *ESCHERICHIA COLI* ENTEROTOXIN (STA) AND GUANYLIN: Ligands for an Intestinal Brush Border Receptor-Guanylate Cyclase

STa Mechanism of Action

Toxigenic *Escherichia coli* produces one or more heat-stable enterotoxins (STs), which appear to be responsible for a large portion of cases of diarrhea in developing countries (53). *E. coli* STa (STa is distinguished from STb, another heat-stable *E. coli* enterotoxin whose mechanism of action is not known) represents a family of 18–19 amino acid peptides containing six cysteines and sharing a highly conserved carboxy terminus (23, 107, 111, 116). These peptides activate guanylate cyclase in the intestinal brush border, thereby increasing cGMP concentration in the intestinal mucosa (46, 67). STa-like peptides are also produced by a number of other enteric organisms (107).

STa activates guanylate cyclase and stimulates short-circuit current rapidly and persistently when added to rabbit ileal mucosa in vitro (46). Its effects are also readily reversed by removing the toxin. Cyclic GMP is a known cell mediator for intestinal Cl secretion; its effect on short-circuit current in rabbit ileum is about two-thirds that of cAMP (58). Both nucleotides also have an anti-absorptive effect, manifest as a decrease in the uptake of ^{22}Na and ^{36}Cl across the brush border (58). The magnitudes of their anti-absorptive effects are identical. The reason for the difference in magnitudes of the secretory effect and, in general, the differences in mechanisms of secretory stimulation by the two nucleotides are not well understood.

Unlike CT, which can activate ad-cy in almost all cells, STa's action is confined in most mammals to intestine (107). Saturable, high affinity binding sites for STa have been demonstrated in small intestinal and colonic brush borders (49, 54, 98), which is where most of the intestinal guanylate cyclase activity is found (32). Receptors for STa are not found in a variety of other tissues. The opossum is unique among mammals thus far tested in having more widespread epithelial STa receptors which, in addition to being present in intestine (villi and crypts in small intestine and crypts in colon), have been found in kidney (proximal tubule), testis (seminiferous tubules), liver, gall bladder, and trachea (48, 75). The highest densities of receptors are found in intestine and kidney.

The STa Receptor

The intestinal STa receptor was recently cloned by Schulz et al (108). They used the polymerase chain reaction in conjunction with an oligonucleotide primer derived from a conserved sequence of already cloned guanylate cyclases to amplify intestinal mucosal cDNAs. A novel sequence was identified and used to screen a rat small intestinal cDNA library. The longest of the several clones isolated was transfected into Cos 7 cells. Sta, but not natriuretic peptides, elicted a marked increase in the cGMP content of the transfected cells. Specific binding of STa also developed. This cloned STa receptor is a unique guanylate cyclase with some homology to but substantial differences from the two guanylate cyclases that are receptors for the natriuretic peptides. Northern blot analysis detected this clone in RNA from small intestine, but not from kidney, heart, lung, adrenal gland, liver, or testis. The demonstration that receptor and enzymic activity reside in the same molecule is consistent with the natriuretic peptide-guanylate cyclase story and is clearly different from receptor-enzyme relationships for ad-cy.

Guanylin, the GI Hormone that Resembles STa

Once the cloning and expression of the small intestinal STa receptor-cyclase was reported, the search intensified for an endogenous ligand that normally acts through that receptor. Recently a 15-amino acid peptide containing four cysteines was isolated from rat jejunum by Currie and his colleagues (26) and shown to be a natural ligand for the STa receptor-cyclase. Using isoelectric focusing and reverse-phase HPLC, they fractionated extracts of rat jejunum and assayed each fraction by measuring cGMP responses in T84 cells. These cells were previously shown to respond to *E. coli* STa with Cl secretion and a marked increase in cGMP (59, 68). They eventually obtained a single active peptide, which they purified to homogeneity. The structure of this peptide, which has been named guanylin, is compared to that of STa in Figure 2. It can be seen that there is considerable structural homology, one notable difference being that guanylin has four cysteines, whereas STa has six. Synthesis of the guanylin peptide sequence followed by oxidation in air resulted in three HPLC fractions with identical molecular weights, only one of which raised cGMP levels in T84 cells, thus indicating that only one of guanylin's three possible folded S-S bond structures is active. By analogy with the known biologically active S-S bond structure of STa (52, 66), S-S bond alignments in active guanylin are likely to be between positions 4 and 12 and between positions 7 and 15. Bioactive synthetic guanylin raised cGMP levels in T84 cells at concentrations as low as 10^{-10}m and also displaced radiolabeled STa from its binding sites. Guanylin's effect on Na and Cl-dependent short-circuit current was recently examined in rat colon and

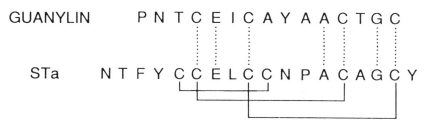

Figure 2 Comparison of the structures of guanylin and STa. Identical amino acids are indicated by the dotted lines. The reported disulfide alignment for ST (66) is represented by the solid lines (reproduced with permission from 26).

shown to be identical to that of STa (72). The physiologic effects of guanylin on intestine (which may not be confined to ion transport), its cellular localization, and the stimuli causing its release are now beginning to be investigated. Recently, Wiegand et al (125) identified a 115-amino acid preprohormone encoded by a 600 base mRNA in rat jejunum. This mRNA was found predominantly in intestine, the most in the colon, and the least in the duodenum. None was detected in stomach or esophagus.

CONGENITAL DEFECTS OF INTESTINAL ELECTROLYTE TRANSPORT

Rare congenital autosomal recessive defects of electrolyte transport in the intestine have brought to light the importance of two BB membrane transport proteins, the Na/H exchanger and the Cl/HCO$_3$ exchanger (see Figure 3). As might be predicted, congenital defects in the operation of these exchangers result in diarrhea because the capacity of the intestine to absorb fluid and electrolytes is diminished, and not because active secretion has been stimulated.

In both congenital choridorrhea and congenital sodium secretory diarrhea, which are discussed below, abnormal intestinal fluid absorption begins in utero and initially manifests itself as maternal hydramnios in the late second trimester (65, 82). By the third trimester of pregnancy, distended fluid-filled loops of fetal intestine can be seen on ultrasonographic examination of the maternal abdomen (82). Fetal intestinal fluid originates from two sources: swallowed amniotic fluid and endogenous gastrointestinal secretions. Normal fetal intestine does not contain appreciable fluid and can concentrate nonabsorbable radiopaque substances (25), which indicates that it absorbs fluid and electrolytes from these sources. Structural studies on developing human intestine support an early role of the fetal intestine in fluid reabsorption. By

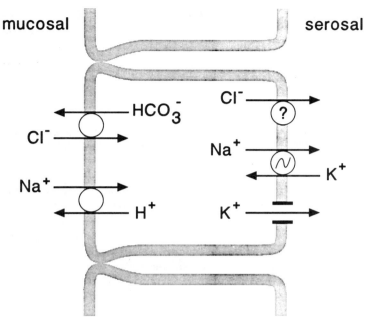

Figure 3 Model for coupled NaCl absorption in the ileum and proximal colon (reproduced with permission from 60). In the jejunum only the Na/H exchanger is present in the brush border membrane.

the twelfth week of development, intestinal villi (with well-defined microvilli on the absorptive cells), crypts, and specialized epithelial cells (goblet, enterochromaffin, Paneth) are present (87). Absorptive intestinal epithelial cells closely resemble those of the adult by twenty-two weeks of development (88).

There have been few studies of electrolyte transport in fetal human intestine. Active glucose uptake has been demonstrated in vitro in everted sacs of eleven-week-old fetal intestine (73) and in BB membrane vesicles from mid-gestational fetal intestine (69). Other ion transport processes of developing intestine have not been examined, but it is clear from these congenital defects that intestinal ion transport proteins are operative very early in fetal development and that their malfunction can lead to the accumulation of fluid in the fetal intestine. It is not certain that failure of the fetal intestine to reabsorb swallowed amniotic fluid leads to the observed increases in amniotic fluid volume, but it seems likely. Hydramnios also develops, for example, in esophageal atresia (25).

Congenital Chloridorrhea

Congenital chloridorrhea was first described in 1945 by Gamble et al (51) and Darrow (29), who noted high concentrations of Cl in the stool of an infant with severe watery diarrhea. Since then about 60 cases have been reported with clusters of cases in Finland (65) and most recently in Kuwait (79). These infants characteristically have diarrhea at birth and develop metabolic alkalosis. The intestine is morphologically normal.

In vivo ion transport studies in children and adults with congenital chloridorrhea have shown that these individuals absorb fluid normally in the jejunum, but are unable to actively absorb Cl in the ileum and colon (82). Na and Cl are thought to be absorbed in normal ileum and proximal colon by the coupling of Na/H exchange and Cl/HCO_3 exchange, which results in net absorption of Na and Cl and formation of CO_2 and water in the intestinal lumen (60, 112). There are two lines of evidence that provide support for a defect in the intestinal Cl/HCO_3 exchanger in individuals with congenital chloridorrhea: Cl cannot be absorbed against an electrochemical potential difference in the ileum or colon (12, 64, 94, 99, 122); and stool pH is acidic (65).

The intestinal Na/H exchanger appears to operate normally in individuals with congenital chloridorrhea. When the ileum or colon of these individuals is perfused with a HCO_3-containing balanced electrolyte solution, Na and HCO_3 are absorbed and luminal contents are acidified (12, 64). This is accompanied by an increase in luminal pCO_2 as would be expected for luminal acidification by Na/H exchange. In contrast, normal subjects, under the same conditions, absorb Na and Cl and do not acidify their luminal contents. These findings suggest that individuals with congenital chloridorrhea absorb Na at these sites by Na/H exchange operating in the absence of Cl/HCO_3 exchange. Eventually, the acidity of their luminal contents inhibits Na/H exchange, and Na absorption is then impaired.

There is one further line of evidence to suggest that a defect in Cl/HCO_3 exchange can explain the abnormalities found in the ileum of individuals with congenital chloridorrhea. The ion movements that ordinarily occur in the ileum of individuals with this disorder can be simulated in normal subjects by perfusing their ileum with a Cl-free, sulfate-containing balanced electrolyte solution (12). Under these conditions, the normal ileum absorbs Na and HCO_3, which is exactly what is observed when a Cl and HCO_3-containing electrolyte solution is perfused into the ileum of individuals with congenital chloridorrhea.

Although intestinal perfusion studies suggest a defect in Cl/HCO_3 exchange in both the ileum and colon in this disorder, there are no in vitro studies on intestine from these individuals to confirm this. It is not clear whether the molecular defect in congenital chloridorrhea is in the Cl/HCO_3 exchanger per se or in another pH regulatory mechanism. Could the exchanger be present but functioning in reverse? In a study of an individual with congenital chloridorrhea, Bieberdorf et al (12) found Cl to be secreted and HCO_3 absorbed when they perfused this individual's ileum with an electrolyte solution containing a high HCO_3 concentration. Therefore, a functional Cl/HCO_3 exchanger appears to have been present in this individual. For an otherwise normal Cl/HCO_3 exchanger to operate in reverse at the low luminal HCO_3 concentrations seen in these individuals, either cell pH must be abnormally low or cell Cl abnormally high. Conceivably, in congenital chloridorrhea, the pH of ileal enterocytes is abnormally low because of a defect in another cell pH regulatory mechanism. Intracellular pH measurements are needed to evaluate this possibility. A defective brush border Cl/CHO_3 exchanger would likely result in a higher than normal ileal cell pH. On the other hand, if the exchanger is operating in reverse because of another pH regulatory defect resulting in cell acidification, then an abnormally low ileal cell pH should be demonstrable.

Congenital Sodium Secretory Diarrhea

The clinical presentation of individuals with congenital sodium secretory diarrhea resembles that of congenital chloridorrhea except that these children have elevated stool Na and HCO_3 concentrations and metabolic acidosis (16, 63). Only a few cases have been reported to date. In vivo and in vitro intestinal ion transport studies point to a defect of the Na/H exchanger in the jejunum. Luminal perfusion studies done in the jejunum of one child with this disorder showed net secretion of Na and Cl, but normal glucose absorption (16). Perfusion of this child's jejunum with an alkaline, HCO_3-containing solution led to Na secretion rather than Na absorption, which would be the normal expectation. BB membrane vesicles made from jejunal biopsies taken from this child confirmed the presence of a defect in BB membrane Na/H exchange. In the presence of an outwardly directed proton gradient, the initial Na uptake into BB vesicles from the affected child was only 12% of that seen in BB vesicles from normal children. In contrast, sodium-stimulated glucose uptake was not appreciably different from control.

Ion transport studies have not been carried out in the ileum and colon of children with this disorder, but it is likely that the Na/H exchanger is also defective in these sites. If the Na/H exchanger were operating normally in the ileum and proximal colon, jejunal fluid delivered to these sites would be avidly reabsorbed by the combined action of the Na/H and Cl/HCO_3 exchangers, and diarrhea would be averted. However, if the Na/H exchanger is defective in these sites, Na absorption will be inhibited and the normally functioning Cl/HCO$_3$ exchanger, as well as any other HCO$_3$ secretory mechanisms, will lead to alkalinization of the stool.

It is interesting that individuals with a presumed congenital defect in Cl/HCO$_3$ or Na/H exchange in the intestine do not have widespread abnormalities in other organs. Several Na/H and Cl/HCO$_3$ exchanger isoforms have already been cloned (2, 74, 105, 120, 121), the most recent being an intestine and kidney-specific Na/H exchanger (NHE-3), which is speculated to be the Na/H exchanger located in the intestinal brush border (120). The mRNA for this gene has been detected in highest abundance in kidney cortex, ileum, and ascending colon, with lesser amounts found in the jejunum and kidney medulla. While a mutation in this gene could account for congenital sodium secretory diarrhea, renal manifestations, which would also be expected, are not seen. Furthermore only a trace amount of this mRNA was found in the jejunum, which suggests that yet another Na/H exchanger might be responsible for most jejunal Na absorption. The gene mutation responsible for congenital sodium secretory diarrhea may well reside in another, as yet uncloned, Na/H exchanger.

Microvillus Inclusion Disease: A Congenital Defect in Brush Border Membrane Placement

Recently an interesting subset of infants with intractable diarrhea was identified by Davidson et al (30). These infants were found to have severe villar atrophy and crypt hypoplasia in their jejunum. Electron microscopic studies showed absent, or shortened and disorganized, microvilli on their absorptive epithelial cells. In some of these cells, well-formed microvilli were contained within the cell cytoplasm, hence the name microvillus inclusion disease (27). Alkaline phosphatase and brush border hydrolases were found to be localized internally in the apical portion of the absorptive epithelial cells of these infants rather than in their usual brush border location (76). Microvilli on the surface of crypt cells and the other small intestinal epithelial cells (goblet, Paneth, and enteroendocrine) appeared normal.

The small intestinal absorptive epithelial cells are not the only epithelial cells affected. In most infants, microvillus inclusions were identified in the surface colonic epithelial cells (27). In two case, one in the small intestine (95) and the other in the gallbladder (102), well-formed microvilli were found misplaced in the BL membrane.

Microvillus inclusion disease is an autosomally recessive inherited disorder that is almost always fatal (27). Diarrhea in these infants starts shortly after birth, often after their first feed, and is choleraic in magnitude. These infants are dependent on total parenteral nutrition throughout their life.

In vivo intestinal perfusion studies done on infants with microvillus inclusion disease show severely reduced or absent glucose absorption and net secretion of Na, Cl, and water into the lumen (30). In vitro ion transport studies performed on the jejunum of one infant with this disorder has confirmed these findings (102). A marked decrease in unidirectional fluxes of Na and Cl and tissue conductance were observed in the intestine of this infant when compared to values measured in intestine from control infants, but this decrease in permeability may be accounted for by the loss of intestinal surface area resulting from villus atrophy. Under short-circuit conditions, net Cl and Na fluxes across this infant's intestinal epithelium were found to be secretory rather than absorptive as normally seen. Resting jejunal Cl secretion in this infant was close to the maximal rate of Cl secretion observed in control jejunum after theophylline addition. Theophylline only slightly increased Cl secretion when added to the jejunal mucosa of the affected infant. The reason for the secretory state is not apparent. Intestinal crypts in this infant were not hypertrophied. Although this infant's jejunal biopsy showed mild inflammation, which might have led to release of intestinal secretory stimuli, two other infants with this disorder had no intestinal inflammation and yet were found to have increased intestinal fluid secretion (30). It may be germane that there is an increased density of secretory granules in the apical portion of crypt cells in infants with this disorder (19, 30).

SIGNIFICANCE OF INTRACELLULAR MICROVILLUS INCLUSIONS   The genetic defect that leads to microvillus inclusion disease is unknown. It appears from ultrastructural studies that intact BB membranes are being formed de novo in abnormal locations within the absorptive epithelial cells, although the possibility of invagination of the apical BB membrane cannot be excluded. A better understanding of this disorder might be gained by considering the circumstances under which microvillus inclusion-like structures are seen in epithelial cells. These structures have been referred to by various names, i.e. intracellular lumen (100), brush border vacuole (1), vacuolar apical compartment (VAC) (124), and microvillus inclusion (27). Ultrastructurally all of the above look identical and are characterized by an intracellular lumen lined by inwardly facing microvilli.

There are two experimental conditions under which microvillus inclusions form in epithelial cells. Achler and co-workers (1) have shown that the microtubule inhibitor, colchicine, causes the development of such inclusions in the adult rat intestine. One hr after rats were treated with colchicine, microvillus-like projections were observed along the BL surface of intestinal epithelial cells, which by 6 hr had the appearance of brush borders. As the colchicine effect wore off, BBs disappeared from the BL membrane and appeared instead in cytoplasmic vacuoles. These BB vacuoles then fused with each other and with the cell membrane, at its apical or possibly lateral surface. Pretreatment of the rats with cycloheximide prevented the formation of BBs in the BL membrane, which suggests that they were formed from newly synthesized proteins rather than from the redistribution of pre-existing apical membrane proteins to the BL domain. Colchicine did not affect the localization of the Na/K ATPase to the BL membrane. These studies show that correct orientation of microtubules at the apical end of these cells appears to be necessary for delivery of Golgi-derived membrane proteins destined for the apical cell surface. It is doubtful that microtubules themselves are defective in microvillus inclusion disease, but perhaps a protein in the terminal web zone, which organizes apical microtubules or binds to Golgi-derived vesicles, for instance myosin, or a motor protein, which moves vesicles along microtubules, such as kinesin, is defective or produced in low amount. In one infant with microvillus inclusion disease, BB membrane-associated myosin was reported to be decreased (19).

It is hard to explain why individuals with this disorder have normal appearing microvillar membranes on their crypt epithelial cells if their gene defect results in the misplacement of apical membrane proteins. Villin alone may be capable of organizing actin into the microvilli seen in crypt epithelial cells. This is supported by experiments that show that cultured fibroblasts, when transfected with the villin gene, develop microvillus-like projections on their cell surface (50). However, additional proteins may be required to stabilize the apical microvillar membrane of absorptive epithelial cells and to direct BB enzymes and other components of the mature BB membrane to their apical surface locale. Alternatively, an ingested substance may trigger expression of the gene defect. It is of interest in this regard that abnormalities of intestinal absorption in these infants do not appear until after birth (see below). The toxic substance might only have access to villus and not crypt cells.

The second experimental condition under which microvillus inclusions develop involves the loss of epithelial cell-cell contacts. Such structures have been reported in Madin-Darby canine kidney (MDCK) epithelial cells in subconfluent culture and in confluent culture when grown in low calcium medium (124). Under low Ca growth conditions, which prevent complete cell-cell contacts, the apical microvillus membrane of these cells appears immature, and large VACs are observed inside the cell. When Ca is added back to the medium, these structures rapidly fuse with the lateral cell membrane at areas of cell-cell contact to form lateral intercellular microvilli. The microvilli lining the lateral space ultimately move onto the apical cell surface as the lateral domain becomes sealed by tight junctions. These studies show that cell adhesion proteins are important in maintaining and establishing apical membrane domains in MDCK cells.

Microvillus inclusions have not been reported in normal adult or fetal mammalian intestinal epithelial cells, which suggests that they are not involved in the normal assembly of the BB membrane during development of the intestinal epithelium. However, such structures are found in epithelial neoplasias and in intestinal epithelial tumor cell lines (100, 101); tumor cells are known to be less adhesive than normal cells. Conceivably, maintenance of a normal apical microvillar membrane on intestinal epithelial cells requires close cell-cell contact. If for some reason cell-cell adherence is decreased, then the apical domain of the cell may be lost and microvillus inclusions appear. Microvillus inclusion disease could be a consequence of a defective cell adhesion gene.

WHY DO THESE INFANTS HAVE INTESTINAL CL SECRETION?   A genetic defect leading to a loss of intestinal absorptive surface area does not explain the active Cl secretion observed in the intestine of infants with this disease. It is interesting that infants with this disorder were all born following a normal pregnancy. Since maternal hydramnios did not develop, the intestine of these infants must have functioned well enough to handle fluids ingested in utero. It is only after birth, usually after the first feeding, that these infants develop diarrhea. There appears to be some factor, either in the feedings or indigenous to the infant, i.e. nervous or hormonal, that stimulates the intestine and perhaps other organs of the gastrointestinal tract to secrete fluid after birth. Could a single gene defect result in both a partial loss of epithelial cell polarity and a persistent secretory state?

DIRECTIONS FOR FUTURE RESEARCH

Studies of disease processes that affect intestinal ion transport afford wonderful opportunities not only to discover potential new therapies, but to gain insight into the physiology of the intestine at organ, cellular, and molecular levels. A number of questions raised in this review merit further investigation.

The intestinal secretory mechanism needs to be more fully defined. The relative contributions of villus and crypt cells to the secretory process is an issue not wholly settled. The apical anion channels present in normal intestine, especially those present in crypt cells, have barely been studied. This can perhaps best be done on cells in primary culture. An immortalized CF intestinal cell line would provide the opportunity to systematically search for latent anion channels that can still be activated.

The intestinal effects of cholera toxin need to be further explored. Precisely how the CT signal gets from the BB membrane to the BL membrane remains to be resolved. The discovery that CT ADP ribosylates G proteins in the intestinal BB membrane raises the question of whether CT can have ad-cy-independent effects in intestine. For instance, could the intestinal CF defect be partially overcome through use of CT? If the enteric nervous system plays a role in the in vivo action of CT, 5-HT receptor antagonists could prove therapeutically useful in enteric infections with enterotoxin-producing organisms.

The recent discovery of guanylin and the cloning of its and STa's receptor opens up new and potentially exciting avenues of investigation. Are there receptors on crypt cells as well as villus cells? What are the physiologic stimuli to guanylin release? In which intestinal cells is it abundant? Does cGMP have a role in intestinal cell differentiation?

Existing studies of the congenital diarrheas, of which there is a paucity, also raise interesting questions. What are the precise gene defects involved? Is there a relation between secretion and the development or maintenance of villus epithelial cell polarity? Why does the severe defect in microvillus inclusion disease not become apparent until after birth when the defects in congenital chloridorrhea and sodium secretory diarrhea are already evident in utero? Immortalization of intestinal cells from infants with congenital diarrheas would allow further study of these unique defects.

ACKNOWLEDGMENTS

We wish to thank Drs. James Madara (77), Mark Currie (125), and Herbert Chase (78) for providing copies of their manuscripts in press, and also Dr. Alessio Fasano for discussing with us his work in progress. This work was supported in part by grant DK35183 from the National Institutes of Health and an American Gastrointestinal Association/Industry Research Scholar Award to C. E. S.

NOTE ADDED IN PROOF

In our survey of reports on intestinal ion transport abnormalities in cystic fibrosis, we overlooked a paper by OLoughlin et al (1991. *Am. J. Physiol.* 260:G758–63), which demonstrated that affected jejunal mucosa mounted in Ussing chambers fails to secrete Cl in response to either dibutyryl cGMP or phorbol ester and does not respond to dibutytyl cAMP and Ca ionophore.

Literature Cited

1. Achler, C., Filmer, D., Merte, C., Drenckhahn, D. 1989. Role of microtubules in polarized delivery of apical membrane proteins to the brush border of the intestinal epithelium. *J. Cell Biol.* 109:179–89

2. Alper, S. L., Kopito, R. R., Libresco, S. M., Lodish, H. F. 1988. Cloning and characterization of a murine band 3- cDNA from kidney and from a lymphoid cell line. *J. Biol. Chem.* 263:17092–99

3. Anderson, M. P., Welsh, M. J. 1991. Calcium and cAMP activate different Cl channels in the apical membrane of normal and cystic fibrosis epithelia. *Proc. Nat. Acad. Sci. USA* 88:6003–7

4. Autore, G., Capasso, F., Di Carlo, G., Mascolo, N. 1987. Effect of cholera toxin on the production of eicosanoids by rat jejunum. *Brit. J. Pharmacol.* 92:149–52

5. Barasch, J., Kiss, B., Prince, A., Saiman, L., Gruenert, D., Al-Awqati,

Q. 1991. Defective acidification of intracellular organelles in cystic fibrosis. *Nature* 352:70–73

6. Baxter, P. S., Wilson, A. J., Read, N. W., Hardcastle, J., Hardcastle, P. T., et al. 1989. Abnormal jejunal potential difference in cystic fibrosis. *Lancet* 1:464–66

7. Bear, C. E., Li, C., Kartner, N., Bridges, R. J., Jensen, T. J. et al. 1992. Purification and functional reconstitution of the cystic fibrosis transmembrane conductance regulator (CFTR). *Cell* 68:809–18

8. Berschneider, H. M., Knowles, M. R., Azizkhan, R. G., Boucher, R. C., Tobey, N. A. et al. 1988. Altered intestinal chloride transport in cystic fibrosis. *FASEB J.* 2:2625–29

9. Beubler, E., Bukhave, K., Rask-Madsen, J. 1986. Significance of calcium for the prostaglandin E2-mediated secretory response to 5-hydroxytryptamine in the small intestine of the rat in vivo. *Gastroenterology* 90:1972–77

10. Deleted in proof

11. Beubler, E., Kollar, G., Saria, A., Bukhave, K., Rask-Madsen, J. 1989. Involvement of 5-hydroxytryptamine, prostaglandin E2 and cyclic adenosine monophosphate in cholera toxin-induced fluid secretion in the small intestine of the rat in vivo. *Gastroenterology* 96:368–76

12. Bieberdorf, F. A., Gorden, P., Fordtran, J. S. 1972. Pathogenesis of congenital alkalosis with diarrhea: implications for the physiology of normal ileal electrolyte absorption and secretion. *J. Clin. Invest.* 51:1958–68

13. Bijman, J., Veeze, H., Kansen, M., Tilly, B., Scholte, B. et al. 1991. Chloride transport in the cystic fibrosis enterocyte. *Adv. Exp. Med. Biol.* 290:287–94

14. Deleted in proof

15. Bolton, J. E., Field, M. 1977. Caionophore stimulated ion secretion in rabbit ileal mucosa: relation to actions of cyclic 3′, 5′-AMP and carbamylcholine. *J. Membr. Biol.* 35:159–73

16. Booth, I. W., Stange, G., Murer, H., Fenton, T. R. Milla, P . J. 1985. Defective jejunal brush-border Na$^+$/H$^+$ exchange: a cause of congenital secretory diarrhoea. *Lancet* 1:1066–69

17. Breitweiser, G. E., Montrose, M. H. 1991. Neurotensin-activated Cl$^-$ currents in HT29 cells. *Biophysical J.* 59:27a

18. Bucheit, K. H. 1989. Inhibition of cholera toxin-induced intestinal secretion by the 5-HT3 receptor antagonist ICS 205–930. *Naunyn Schmiedebergs Arch. Pharmacol.* 339:704–5

19. Carruthers, L., Phillips, A. D., Dourmashkin, R., Walker-Smith J. A. 1985. Biochemical abnormality in brush border membrane protein of a patient with congenital microvillus atrophy. *J. Pediatr. Gastroenterol. Nutr.* 4:902–7

20. Cassuto, J., Fahrenkrug, J., Jodal, M., Tuttle, R., Lundgren, 0. 1981. Release of vasoactive intestinal peptide from the cat small intestine exposed to cholera toxin. *Gut* 22:958–63

21. Cassuto, J., Jodal, M., Lundgren, 0. 1982. The effect of nicotinic and muscarinic receptor blockade on cholera toxin induced intestinal secretion in cats and rats. *Acta Phsiol. Scand.* 114:573–77

22. Cassuto, J., Siewert, A., Jodal, M., Lundgren, 0. 1983. The involvement of intramural nerves in cholera toxin induced intestinal secretion. *Acta Physiol. Scand.* 117:195–202

23. Chan, S. K., Gianella, R. A. 1981. Amino acid sequence of heat-stable enterotoxin produced by *Escherichia coli* pathogenic for man. *J. Biol. Chem.* 256:7744–46

24. Collins, F. S. 1992. Cystic fibrosis: molecular biology and therapeutic implications. *Science* 256:774–79

25. Cunningham, F. G., MacDonald, P. C., Gant, N. F. 1989. In *Williams Obstetrics*, pp. 103–04, 554–55. East Norwalk, Conn./Calif.: Appleton & Lange. 18th ed.

26. Currie, M. G., Fok, K. F., Kato, J., Moore, R. J., Hamra, F. K. et al. 1992. Guanylin: an endogenous activator of intestinal guanylate cyclase. *Proc. Natl. Acad. Sci. USA* 89:947–51

27. Cutz, E., Rhoads, J. M., Drumm, B., Sherman, P. M., Durie, P. R., et al. 1989. Microvillus inclusion disease: an inherited defect of brush-border assembly and differentiation. *N. Engl. J. Med.* 320:646–51

28. Cutz, E., Thorner, P., Sherman, P. 1988. Microvillous inclusion disease (MID) - ? generalized defect of brush border membranes. *Lab. Invest.* 58:3P

29. Darrow, D. C. 1945. Congenital alkalosis with diarrhea. *J. Pediatr.* 26:519–32

30. Davidson, G. P., Cutz, E., Hamilton, J. R., Gall, D. G. 1978. Familial enteropathy: a syndrome of protracted diarrhea from birth, failure to thrive,

and hypoplastic villus atrophy. *Gastroenterology* 75:783–90

31. De Jonge, H.R. 1975. The response of small intestinal villous and crypt epithelium to choleratoxin in rat and guinea pig. Evidence against a specific role of the crypt cells in choleragen-induced secretion. *Biochim. Biophys. Acta* 381:128–43

32. De Jonge, H.R. 1975. The localization of guanylate cyclase in rat small intestinal epithelium. *FEBS Lett.* 53:237–42

33. Devor, D. C., Simasko, S. M., Duffey, M. E. 1990. Carbachol induces oscillations of membrane potassium conductance in a colonic cell line, T84. *Am. J. Physiol.* 258:C318–26

34. Dharmsathaphorn, K., McRoberts, J. A., Mandel, K. G., Tisdale, L. D., Masui, H. 1984. A human colonic tumor cell line that maintains vectorial electrolyte transport. *Am. J. Physiol.* 246:G204–8

35. Dharmsathaphorn, K., Pandol, S. J. 1986. Mechanism of chloride secretion induced by carbachol in a colonic epithelial cell line. *J. Clin. Invest.* 77:348–54

36. Dominguez, P., Barros, F., Lazo, P.S. 1985. The activation of adenylate cyclase from small intestinal epithelium by cholera toxin. *Eur. J. Biochem.* 146:533–38

37. Dominguez, P., Velasco, G., Barros, F., Lazo, P.S. 1987. Intestinal brush border membranes contain regulatory subunits of adenylyl cyclase. *Proc. Natl. Acad. Sci. USA* 84:6965–69

38. Eklund, S., Brunsson, I., Jodal, M., Lundgren, 0. 1987. Changes in cyclic 3′,5′-adenosine monophosphate tissue concentration and net fluid transport in the cat's small intestine elicited by cholera toxin, arachidonic acid, vasoactive intestinal peptide and 5-hydroxytryptamine. *Acta Physiol. Scand.* 129:115–25

39. Eklund, S., Fahrenkrug, J., Jodal, M., Lundgren, O., Sjoqvist, A. 1987. Mechanisms of neurotensin-induced fluid secretion in the cat ileum in vivo. *Acta Physiol. Scand.* 129:203–10

40. Eklund, S., Karlstrom, L., Rokaeus, A., Theodorsson, E., Jodal, M., et al. 1989. Effects of cholera toxin, *Escherichia coli* heat stable toxin, sodium deoxycholate on neurotensin release from the ileum in vivo. *Regul. Pept.* 26:241–52

41. Fasano, A., Baudry, B., Galen, J., Ketley, J., Ferraro, L., et al. 1992.

Role of vibrio cholerae neuraminidase in the function of cholera toxin. *Infect. Immunol.* 60:406–15

42. Fasano, A., Baudry, B., Galen, J., Ketley, J., Ferraro, L., et al. 1992. Further insights into vibrio cholerae diarrheal disease. *Gastroenterology* 102:A209

43. Fasano, A., Baudry, B., Pumplin, D. W., Wassermann, S. S., Tall, B. D., et al. 1991. Vibrio cholerae produces a second enterotoxin, which affects tight junctions. *Proc. Natl. Acad. Sci. USA* 88:5242–46

44. Field, M. 1971. Ion transport in rabbit ileal mucosa. II. Effects of cyclic 3′,5′-AMP. *Am. J. Physiol.* 221:992–97

45. Field, M., Fromm, D., Al-Awqati, Q., Greenough, W. B. III. 1972. Effect of cholera enterotoxin on ion transport across isolated ileal mucosa. *J. Clin. Invest.* 51:796–804

46. Field, M., Graff, L. H. Jr., Laird, W. J., Smith, P. L. 1978. Heat stable enterotoxin of *Escherichia coli*: in vitro effects on guanylate cyclase activity, cyclic GMP concentration and ion transport in small intestine. *Proc. Natl. Acad. Sci. USA* 75:2800–4

47. Field, M., Rao, M. C., Chang, E. B. 1989. Intestinal electrolyte transport and diarrheal disease, part I. *N. Engl. J. Med.* 321:879–83

48. Forte, L. R., Krause, W. J., Freeman, R. H. 1989. *Escherichia coli* enterotoxin receptors: localization in opossum kidney, intestine and testis. *Am. J. Physiol.* 257:F874–81

49. Frantz, J. C., Jaso-Friedman, L., Robertson, D.C. 1984. Binding of *Escherichia coli* heat-stable enterotoxin to rat intestinal cells and brush border membranes. *Infect. Immunol.* 43:622–30

50. Friederich, E., Huet, C., Arpin, M., Louvard, D. 1989. Villin induces microvilli growth and actin redistribution in transfected fibroblasts. *Cell* 59:461–75

51. Gamble, J. L., Gahey, K. R., Appelton, J., Machachlan, E. 1945. Congenital alkalosis with diarrhea. *J. Pediatr.* 26:509–18

52. Gariepy, J., Lane, A., Frayman, F., Wilbur, D., Robien, W., et al. 1986. Structure of the toxic domain of the *Escherichia coli* heat-stable enterotoxin ST I. *Biochemistry* 25:7854–66

53. Gianella, R. A. 1981. Pathogenesis of acute bacterial diarrheal disorders. *Annu. Rev. Med.* 32:341–57

54. Gianella, R. A., Luttrell, M., Thomp-

son, M. 1983. Binding of *Escherichia coli* heat-stable enterotoxin to receptors on rat intestinal cells. *Am. J. Physiol.* 245:G492–98

55. Goldstein, J. L., Bhuva, M. B., Layden, T. J., Rao, M. C. 1991. *E. coli* heat stable enterotoxin stimulated chloride secretion is abnormal in cystic fibrosis (CF) rectal mucosa in vivo. *Pediatr. Pulmonol. Suppl.* 6:260 (Abstr.)

56. Goldstein, J. L., Nash, N. T., Al-Bazzaz, F., Layden, T. J., Rao, M. C. 1988. Rectum has abnormal ion transport but normal cAMP-binding proteins in cystic fibrosis. *Am. J. Physiol.* 254:C719–24

57. Goldstein, J. L., Shapiro, A. B., Rao, M. C., Layden, T. J. 1991. In vivo evidence of altered chloride but not potassium secretion in cystic fibrosis rectal mucosa. *Gastroenterology* 101: 1012–19

58. Guandolini, S., Rao, M. C., Smith, P. L., Field, M. 1982. Cyclic GMP modulation of ion transport in rabbit ileum: studies with heat-stable *Escherichia coli* enterotoxin. *Am. J. Physiol.* 243:G36–41

59. Guarino, A., Cohen, M., Thompson, M., Dharmsathaphorn, K., Giannella, R. 1987. T84 cell receptor binding and guanyl cyclase activation by *Escherichia coli* heat-stable toxin. *Am. J. Physiol.* 253:G775–80

60. Halm, D. R., Frizzell, R. A. 1991. Ion transport across the large intestine. In *Handbook of Physiology, Sect. 6, The Gastrointestinal System, Vol. 4. Intestinal Absorption and Secretion,* ed. M. Field, R. A. Frizzell, pp. 257–74. Bethesda: Am. Physiol. Soc.

61. Halm, D. R., Rechkemmer, G. R., Schoumacher, R. A., Frizzell, R. A. 1988. Apical membrane chloride channels in a colonic cell line activated by secretory agonists. *Am. J. Physiol.* 254:C505–11

62. Hardcastle, J., Hardcastle, P. T. Taylor, C. J., Goldhill, J. 1991. Failure of cholinergic stimulation to induce a secretory response from the rectal mucosa in cystic fibrosis. *Gut* 32:1035–39

63. Holmberg, C., Perheentupa, J. 1985. Congenital Na$^+$ diarrhea: a new type of secretory diarrhea. *J. Pediatr.* 106:56–61

64. Holmberg, C., Perheentupa, J., Launiala, K. 1975. Colonic electrolyte transport in health and in congenital chloride diarrhea. *J. Clin. Invest.* 56: 302–10

65. Holmberg, C., Perheentupa, J., Launiala, K., Hallman, N. 1977. Congenital chloride diarrhoea. *Arch. Dis. Child.* 52:255–67

66. Houghten, R. A., Ostresh, J. M., Klipstein, F. A. 1984. Chemical synthesis of an octadecapeptide with the biological and immunological properties of human heat-stable *Escherichia coli* enterotoxin. *Eur. J. Biochem.* 145:157–62

67. Hughes, J. M., Murad, F., Chang, B., Guerrant, R. L. 1978. Role of cyclic GMP in the action of heat-stable enterotoxin of *Escherichia coli. Nature* 271:755–56

68. Huott, P. A., Liu, W., McRoberts, J. A., Giannella, R. A., Dharmsathaphorn, K. 1988. Mechanism of action of *Escherichia coli* heat stable enterotoxin in a human colonic cell line. *J. Clin. Invest.* 82:514–23

69. Iioka, H., Moriyama, I. S., Hino, K., Itani, Y., Ichijo, M. 1987. The absorption of d-glucose in small intestine of human fetus (using brush border membrane vesicles of jejunum). *Acta Obst. Gynaec. Jpn.* 39:347–51

70. Janicot, M., Fouque, F., Desbuquois, B. 1991. Activation of rat liver adenylate cyclase by cholera toxin requires toxin internalization and processing in endosomes. *J. Biol. Chem.* 266:12858–65

71. Joseph, K. C., Stieber, A., Gonatas, N. K. 1979. Endocytosis of cholera toxin in GERL-like structures of murine neuroblastoma cells pretreated with GM1 ganglioside. Cholera toxin internalization into neuroblastoma GERL. *J. Cell Biol.* 81:543–54

72. Kachur, J. F., Won-Kim, S., Moummi, C., Fok, K., Currie, M. G. 1002. Guanylyn, a newly discovered activator of intestinal guanylate cyclase, stimulates ion secretion across rat colon. *Gastroenterology* 102:A738 (Abstr.)

73. Koldovsky, O., Heringova, A., Jirsova, V., Jirasek, J. E., Uher, J. 1965. Transport of glucose against a concentration gradient in everted sacs of jejunum and ileum of human fetuses. *Gastroenterology* 48:185–87

74. Kopito, R. R., Lodish, H. F. 1985. Primary structure and transmembrane orientation of the murine anion exchange protein. *Nature* 316:234–38

75. Krause, W. J., Freeman, R. H., Forte, L. R. 1990. Autoradiographic demonstration of specific binding sites for *E. coli* enterotoxin in various epithelia of

the North American opossum. *Cell Tissue Res.* 260:387–94

76. Lake, B. D. 1988. Microvillus inclusion disease: specific diagnostic features shown by alkaline phosphatase histochemistry. *J. Clin. Pathol.* 41:880–82

77. Lencer, W. I., Delp, C., Neutra, M. R., Madara, J. L. 1992. Mechanism of cholera toxin action on a polarized human intestinal epithelial cell line: role of vesicular traffic. *J. Cell Biol.* 117:1197–1209

78. Lindeman, R. P., Chase, H. S. Jr. 1992. Protein kinase C does not participate in carbachol's secretory action in T84 cells. *Am. J. Physiol.* 263:140–46

79. Lubani, M. M., Doudin, K. I., Sharda, D. C., Shaltout, A. A., Al-Shab, T. S., et al. 1989. Congenital chloride diarrhoea in Kuwaiti children. *Eur. J. Pediatr.* 148:333–36

80. Lynch, C. J., Morbach, L., Blackmore, P. F., Exton, J.H. 1986. α-subunits of Ns are released from the plasma membrane following cholera toxin activation. *FEBS Lett.* 200:333–36

81. McRoberts, J. A., Beuerlein, G., Dharmsathaphorn, K. 1985. Cyclic AMP and Ca^{2+}-activated K^+ transport in a human colonic epithelial cell line. *J. Biol. Chem.* 260:14163–72

82. Milla, P. J. 1991. Congenital diarrhea. In *Diarrheal Diseases*, ed. M. Field, pp. 373–96. New York: Elsevier

83. Milligan, G., Unson, C. G. 1989. Persistent activation of the alpha subunit of Gs promotes its removal from the plasma membrane. *Biochem J.* 260:837–41

84. Montessano, R., Roth, J., Robert, A., Orci, L. 1982. Non-coated membrane invaginations are involved in binding and internalization of cholera and tetanus toxins. *Nature* 296:651–53

85. Moriarty, K. J., Higgs, N. B., Woodford, M., Turnberg, L. A. 1989. An investigation of the role of possible neural mechanisms in cholera toxin-induced secretion in rabbit ileal mucosa in vitro. *Clin. Sci.* 77:161–66

86. Moss, J., Vaughan, M. 1989. Guanine-nucleotide-binding proteins (G-proteins) in activation of adenylyl cyclase: lessons learned from cholera and "travelers' diarrhea." *J. Lab. Clin. Med.* 113:258–68

87. Moxey, P. C. , Trier, J. S. 1978. Specialized cell types in the human fetal small intestine. *Anat. Rec.* 191:269–86

88. Moxey, P. C., Trier, J. S. 1979. Development of villus absorptive cells in the human fetal small intestine: A morphological and morphometric study. *Anat. Rec.* 195:463–82

89. Musch, M. W., Field, M. 1989. K-independent NaCl cotransport in bovine tracheal cells: effects of secretory stimuli and hyperosmolarity. *Am. J. Physiol.* 256:C658–65

90. Musch, M. W., Field, M., Miller, R. J., Stoff, J. S. 1987. Prostaglandin induced desensitization to prostaglandins in rabbit ileum. *Am. J. Physiol.* 252:G120–27

91. Negishi, M., Hashimoto, H., Ichikawa, A. 1992. Translocation of (α subunits of stimulatory guanine nucleotide-binding proteins through stimulation of the prostacyclin receptor in mouse mastocytoma cells. *J. Biol. Chem.* 267:2364–69

92. Nilsson, O., Cassuto, J., Larsson, P. A., Jodal, M., Lidberg, P. et al 1983. 5-Hydroxytryptamine and cholera secretion: a histochemical and physiological study in cats. *Gut* 24:542–48

93. Orlando, R. C., Powell, D. W., Croom, R. D., Berschneider, H. M., Boucher, R. C., et al. 1989. Colonic and esophageal transepithelial potential difference in cystic fibrosis. *Gastroenterology* 96:1041–48

94. Pearson, A. J. G., Sladen, G. E., Edmonds, C. J., Tavill, A. S., Wills, M. R. et al. 1973. The pathophysiology of congenital chloridorrhoea. *Q. J. Med.* 167:453–66

95. Perez-Atayde, A. R., Katz, A., Flores, A. Madara, J. 1987. A diarrheal syndrome characterized by defective assembly of absorptive cell brush borders. *Lab. Invest.* 56:59A

96. Peterson, J. W., Molina, N. C., Houston, C. W., Fader, R. C. 1983. Elevated cAMP in intestinal epithelial cells during experimental cholera and salmonellosis. *Toxicon* 21:761–75

97. Ransnas, L. A., Svoboda, P., Jaspaer, J. R., Insel, P. A. 1989. Stimulation of β-adrenergic receptors of S49 lymphoma cells redistributes the (α subunit of the stimulatory G protein between cytosol and membranes. *Proc. Natl. Acad. Sci. USA* 86:7900–3

98. Rao, M. C., Guandalini, S., Smith, P. L., Field, M. 1980. Mode of action of heat-stable *Escherichia coli* enterotoxin: Tissue and subcellular specificity and role of cyclic GMP. *Biochem. Biophys. Acta* 632:35–46

99. Rask-Madsen, J., Kamper, J., Oddsson, E., Krag, E. 1976. Congenital

chloridorrhoea: a question of reversed brush border transport processes and varying junctional tightness. *Scand. J. Gastroenterol.* 11:377–83

100. Remy, L. 1986. The intracellular lumen: origin, role and implications of a cytoplasmic neostructure. *Biol. Cell* 56:97–106

101. Remy, L., Marvaldi, J., Rua, S., Secchi, J., Lechene de la Porte, P. 1984. The role of intracellular lumina in the repolarization process of a colonic adenocarcinoma cell line. *Virchows Arch.* 46:297–305

102. Rhoads, J. M., Vogler, R. C., Lacey, S. R., Reddick, R. L., Keku. E.O., et al. 1991. Microvillus inclusion disease: in vitro jejunal electrolyte transport. *Gastroenterology* 100:811–17

103. Deleted in proof

104. Rudy, B. 1988. Diversity and ubiquity of K channels. *Neuroscience* 25:729–49

105. Sardet, C., Franchi, A., Pouysségur, J. 1989. Molecular cloning, primary structure, and expression of the human growth factor-activatable Na^+/H^+ antiporter. *Cell* 56:271–80

106. Sato, K., Sato, F. 1984. Defective beta adrenergic response of cystic fibrosis sweat glands in vivo and in vitro. *J. Clin. Invest.* 73:1763–71

107. Schron, C. M., Gianella, R. A. 1991. Bacterial enterotoxins. See Ref. 82., pp. 115–38

108. Schulz, S., Green, C. K., Yuen, P. S. T., Garbers, D. L. 1990. Guanylyl cyclase is a heat-stable enterotoxin receptor. *Cell* 63:941–48

109. Schwartz, C. J., Kimberg, D. V., Sheerine, H. E., Field, M., Said, S. I. 1974. Vasoactive intestinal peptide stimulation of adenylate cyclase and active electrolyte secretion in intestinal mucosa. *J. Clin. Invest.* 54:536–44

110. Semrad, C. E., Chang, E. B. 1987. Calcium-mediated cyclic AMP inhibition of Na-H exchange in small intestine. *Am. J. Physiol.* 252:C315–22

111. Staples, S. J., Asher, S. E., Gianella, R. A. 1980. Purification and characterization of heat-stable enterotoxin produced by a strain of *E. coli* pathogenic for man. *J. Biol. Chem.* 255:4716–21

112. Sullivan, S. K., Field, M. 1991. Ion transport in mammalian small intestine. See Ref. 60, pp. 287–302

113. Sun, A., Grossman, E. B., Lombardi, M., Hebert, S. C. 1991. Vasopressin alters the mechanism of apical Cl^- entry from $Na^+:Cl^-$ to $Na^+:K^+:2Cl^-$ cotransport in mouse medullary thick

ascending limb. *J. Membr. Biol.* 120:83–94

114. Deleted in proof

115. Taylor, C. J., Baxter, P. S., Hardcastle, J., Hardcastle, P. T. 1987. Absence of secretory response in jejunal biopsy samples from children with cystic fibrosis. *Lancet* 2:107–8

116. Thomson, M. R., Gianella, R. A. 1985. Revised amino acid sequence for a heat-stable enterotoxin produced by *E. coli* pathogenic for man. *Infect. Immunol.* 47:834–36

117. Tilly, B. C., Kansen, M., van Gageldonk, P. G., van den Berghe, N, Galjaard, H., et al. 1991. G-proteins mediate intestinal chloride channel activation. *J. Biol. Chem.* 266:2036–40

118. Traynor, T. R., Brown, D. R., OGrady, S. M. 1991. Regulation of ion transport in porcine distal colon: effects of putative neurotransmitters. *Gastroenterology* 100:703–10

119. Tresize, A. E. O., Buchwald, M. 1991. In vivo cell-specific expression of the cystic fibrosis transmembrane conductance regulator. *Nature* 353:434–37

120. Tse, C.-M., Brant, S. R., Walker, M. S., Pouysségur, J., Donowitz, M. 1992. Cloning and sequencing of a rabbit cDNA encoding an intestinal and kidney-specific Na^+/H^+ exchanger isoform (NHE-3)*. *J. Biol. Chem.* 267:9340–46

121. Tse, C.-M., Ma, A. I., Yang, V. W., Watson, A. J. M., Levine, S., et al. 1991. Molecular cloning and expression of a cDNA encoding the rabbit ileal villus cell basolateral membrane Na^+/H^+ exchanger. *EMBO J.* 10:1957–67

122. Turnberg, L. A. 1971. Abnormalities in intestinal electrolyte transport in congenital chloridorrhoea. *Gut* 12:544–51

123. van den Berghe, N., Nieuwkoop, N. J., Vaandrager, A. B., De Jonge, H. 1991. Asymmetrical distribution of G-proteins among the apical and basolateral membranes of rat enterocytes. *Biochem. J.* 278:565–71

124. Vega-Salas, D. E., Salas, P. J. I., Rodriguez-Boulan, E. 1988. Exocytosis of vacuolar apical compartment (VAC): a cell-cell contact controlled mechanism for the establishment of the apical plasma membrane domain in epithelial cells. *J. Cell Biol.* 107:1717–28

125. Wiegand, R. C., Kato, J., Currie, M. G. 1992. Rat guanylin cDNA: charcterization of the precursor of an

endogenous activator of intestinal guanylate cyclase. *Biochem. Biophys. Res. Commun.* 185:812–17

126. Wiener, H., van Os, C. H. 1989. Rabbit distal colon epithelium: II. Characterization of (Na$^+$,K$^+$,Cl$^-$) cotransport and [3H]- bumetanide binding. *J. Membr. Biol.* 110:163–74

127. Worrell, R. T., Butt, A. G., Cliff, W. H., Frizzell, R. A. 1989. A volume sensitive chloride conductance in human colonic cell line T84. *Am. J. Physiol.* 256:C1111–19

128. Worrell, R. T., Frizzell, R. A. 1991. CAMKII mediates stimulation of chloride conductance by calcium in T84 cells. *Am. J. Physiol.* 260:C877–82

Annu. Rev. Physiol. 1993. 55:657–59

SPECIAL TOPIC:
CIRCADIAN RHYTHMS

Michael Menaker, Section Editor
Department of Biology, University of Virginia, Charlottesville,
Virginia 22903

Since its modern inception in about 1950, the development of the field of circadian biology has been remarkably analogous to the earlier development of the science of genetics. The parallels between them are close, yet genetics is far enough in the lead that it may be worth exploring the relationship in order to see where circadian biology may be heading. Both fields began with the observation of surprisingly discreet and precise regularities in nature and proceeded to describe these regularities and to probe them experimentally for some time without an inkling of the mechanisms that underlay them. The information developed by this approach (in modern shorthand termed black box analysis) was absolutely essential to further progress. In genetics, it led directly to the chromosome theory of heredity, which in turn provided the foundation of modern molecular genetics. In circadian biology, it revealed the great scope and general importance of the phenomena of biological oscillations and generated a theoretical framework based on the fruitful analogy with physical oscillations, without which it would not have been possible to identify and analyze the concrete components of the biological oscillators (a task well begun but by no means completed). The black box approach has been useful in these (and many other) fields because, if it is intelligently practiced, it defines the properties of the underlying mechanisms,

657

0066–4278/93/0315–0657$02.00

thus enabling their identification, and leads naturally to further reductionist analysis. It continues to be useful as long as new phenomena or new aspects of old phenomena are discovered for which there is not yet an adequate mechanistic explanation. Although black box analysis often deals with whole organisms or with complex, multifaceted end points, it is the first step in a reductionist analysis and should not be confused with attempts at synthesis.

On a scale defined by the history of genetics, circadian biology has gotten a bit past the chromosome theory; that is, we have localized several circadian oscillators and have made a good start at understanding how they work in cellular and molecular terms. We have not yet uncovered a common mechanism underlying them all, indeed we do not know if such a mechanism exists, although most of us proceed as if it does. If it does, and when it is discovered, this mechanism is likely to produce, on a small scale, the kind of change in outlook among circadian biologists that was produced among geneticists by the elucidation of the structure of DNA.

The three chapters that follow describe three different approaches directed toward this goal. In the first, the formal approach has been extended to apply to the cellular and molecular level, and the way is shown for the construction of explicit mathematical models that will guide the search for concrete mechanisms at these levels. The second chapter describes what is known about several such mechanisms and future directions are indicated that may lead to discovery of the specific feedback loops that are involved in the generation of circadian oscillations. In the third chapter, the ways in which genetic approaches can be used to uncover circadian mechanisms are described in principle, and some notable successes produced by them are reviewed. Over the past several years, the pace of progress in understanding circadian mechanisms at the cellular and molecular levels has been increasing steadily, and recent developments such as the finding of a circadian mutation in mice (J. Takahashi, personal communication) indicate that the pace will continue to accelerate. At the moment, the outlines of the shape such understanding will take are barely visible, but they are there, and will rapidly become clearer.

What then? It is instructive to recall that period in the history of genetics when it was widely believed that all the interesting and important problems could be solved by studying the genetics of bacteria and viruses. The (still) incredible commonality of basic mechanisms lulled many scientists into the naive view that nothing of great interest was to be learned by studying more complex organisms, and those geneticists who continued to study creatures such as flies and worms were often classified, with a kindly nod, as old-fashioned. How the *C. elegans* has turned!

The message is clear. It is the task of biologists to understand biological organization, and that task is far from over when the simplest version of a process has been reduced to its component parts, and their mutual interactions have been analyzed and used to define the underlying mechanism. Just as eukaryotic molecular genetics is now being used to solve longstanding problems in developmental biology and in neuroscience, so we are entitled to hope that knowledge of circadian molecular mechanisms will help to clarify the related but much more complex processes of hibernation and sleep, and will guide future investigations of the several temporal frameworks upon which much of biological organization hangs. Molecular explanations are often truly wonderful, but the phenomena that require them are the stuff of Biology. Circadian rhythmicity is one of the most fascinating of these phenomena and much remains to be learned about it on many different levels of organization.

Annu. Rev. Physiol. 1993. 55:661–81

FORMAL APPROACHES TO UNDERSTANDING BIOLOGICAL OSCILLATORS

W. Otto Friesen, Gene D. Block, and Craig G. Hocker

Department of Biology and NSF Center for Biological Timing, University of Virginia, Charlottesville, Virginia 22903–2477

KEY WORDS: circadian oscillators, calcium oscillators, neuronal circuit-reciprocal inhibition oscillators

INTRODUCTION

Scope of this Review

Arguably, biological oscillations are a fundamental property of living systems. From the rudimentary ciliary waves in protozoans to the complex chronometry required of birds navigating by the position of the sun, repetitive biological activities are ubiquitous through the plant and animal kingdoms. Biological oscillations differ markedly both in the nature of their expression and in their cycle period; however, in fundamental respects all biological oscillations enjoy common features, both in the mechanisms underlying their genesis and in the experimental and theoretical tools employed to study such systems. Our aim in presenting this review is to detail the methodology employed in the analysis of biological oscillators, from the development of qualitative functional diagrams to the formulation of adequate mathematical descriptions.

The approach for analyzing biological rhythmicity described in this review can be applied to any type of biological oscillator. To illustrate the general utility of these methods, this review considers three disparate types of oscillations that encompass a broad time domain. These illustrative biological oscillations are expressed in (*a*) circadian clocks with a cycle period of approximately 86,400 sec, (*b*) network neuronal oscillators with periods of about 1 sec, and (*c*) cellular oscillations in calcium concentrations $[Ca^{2+}]$ with cycle periods near 10 sec. With these examples we attempt to demonstrate

661

0066–4278/93/0315–0661$02.00

that common techniques may be applied productively to a wide range of systems independent of their cycle period.

The body of this review is divided into a discussion of the nature of biological oscillations, review of a qualitative scheme for describing neuronal oscillations, which is then applied to the three biological oscillators, an introduction to mathematical equations for linear and nonlinear physical oscillating systems, and a presentation of differential equations describing the three biological oscillators. In a final section we provide examples of how to proceed from qualitative models to a descriptive set of differential equations.

The term oscillator is well-defined for ideal systems. For such systems the oscillator activity is characterized by the repeated and unvarying occurrence of waveforms of arbitrary amplitude and shape. The outputs of these oscillators are described by their cycle period (or frequency), the phase relationships between oscillator variables, the amplitude, and the waveforms of these variables (including the first and higher derivatives). Cyclic (periodic) behaviors in real physical and biological systems only approximate these ideal characteristics. Of the three types of oscillatory systems described below, only the circadian clock closely approximates an ideal oscillator. One challenge awaiting those who wish to undertake the quantitative analysis of these non-stationary oscillators is how to rigorously apply techniques developed for ideal oscillators to these clearly non-ideal systems. Nevertheless, as physiologists and behaviorists have amply demonstrated, the methods for analyzing oscillators can be usefully applied to a wide variety of periodic biological systems (see below). To avoid cumbersome phrases such as quasi-oscillators, we refer to non-stationary, nearly periodic biological systems as biological oscillators. To explain the origins of any biological oscillation a specific question to be answered is, What is the nature of the central oscillator that generates the rhythmic signals? This review is intended to provide an approach that can answer the question.

How are Biological Oscillators Characterized?

CYCLE PERIOD   Oscillating systems are particularly amenable for analysis because their activity can be characterized by a few easily measured observables, the most important of which are cycle period and the phase relationships between oscillator elements. The primary observable is cycle period, the interval between the repetition of some arbitrary reference point in the activity cycle. Because the waveforms of repeated activity differ for each particular oscillator and because the particular choice for the reference point is immaterial for determining cycle period, this phase reference point should be chosen on the basis of convenience. Because the waveforms of biological oscillators usually vary from cycle to cycle, phase reference points are sometimes chosen by averaging techniques thus reducing the effects of small changes in waveform on the computed cycle period (24, 43). It should be noted that indicator variables, such as activity records, need not be state variables (see below); that is, the measured quantities are representative of the output of the system, but not part of the causal loop that generates the oscillations. In circadian studies, particularly, no state variables have been identified to date. On the other hand, measurements obtained from cellular Ca^{2+} oscillators and from neuronal circuit oscillators, for example intracellular Ca^{2+} concentration and neuronal membrane potential, respectively, appear to describe state variables. Hence for these latter two types of oscillators, physiological measurements are more likely to lead to insights into the mechanisms that generate the oscillations.

PHASE RELATIONSHIPS   The second observable factor for biological oscillators is phase (or phase angle). One use of the term phase is to designate subsequent points on the cycle with respect to some reference point. By this definition, the cycle period can be divided into 360, 2π radians, or 24 circadian hours. Another use of the term is to designate the normalized interval between the activity in two system variables (again measured as a fraction of the cycle period, in degrees or in normalized circadian hours). Two examples of phase relationships are the phase difference between the Zeitgeber (external timing cue) and an indicator variable in circadian systems, and the relationship between the membrane potential oscillations of two oscillatory neurons in neuronal circuit systems. Inasmuch as phase reference points are assigned arbitrarily in biological oscillators, the absolute value of phases also are arbitrary. For waveforms of differing shapes, or for quantities that are unrelated, absolute phase values are not meaningful, only changes in phase have meaning. However, insofar as the waveforms of two oscillating variables are similar, the absolute phase value does have meaning. For example, it is meaningful to describe the activity of two neurons as being 180 degrees out of phase. It is not meaningful, on the other hand, to characterize a rodent activity rhythm to be 180 degrees out of phase with the circadian day-night cycle. Also, because many biological oscillations have no rigidly fixed waveform, small changes in system states can alter computed phase relationships substantially.

WAVEFORM OF OUTPUT   A third measurable characteristic of biological oscillations is the waveform of the cycle activity. This characteristic is actually a constellation of attributes of measurable variables. The primary attribute of waveform is amplitude (often not constant for any of the three systems under consideration here). The remaining attributes can be described as shape, or more analytically as the first and higher derivatives of the observed variable with respect to time. For state variables, but not indicator variables, all aspects of the oscillator function can be determined from a complete description of the waveform. Thus a close analysis of the state variable waveforms can provide useful insights into oscillator mechanisms (43a). If the transformation between a state variable and an indicator variable is known, then the indicator variable can also be used to deduce the nature of the system.

QUALITATIVE DESCRIPTIONS OF BIOLOGICAL OSCILLATORS

A Formal Scheme for Characterizing Biological Oscillators

Many biological oscillators can be usefully described as systems incorporating negative feedback with delay. Several years ago, in order to assist physiologists in the analyses of such systems, we proposed a graphical conceptual scheme for describing the qualitative structures of biological oscillators (27). In this scheme (Figure 1), for which we appropriated the graphical approach used to depict neuronal circuits, the values of state variables (there are two, V_1 and V_2, in this illustration) are depicted as rectangles; the interactions between variables are shown as lines connecting the variable rectangles with T terminations to indicate positive effects and • terminals to indicate negative effects; and triangles interposed on the connecting lines to indicate suspected important delays. One benefit of this scheme is that it encourages researchers to be explicit in their modeling of system structure; not only are candidate state variables shown explicitly, but the postulated interactions are depicted. Under this scheme, valid diagrams that describe oscillating systems must include at least one inhibitory loop (defined as any closed loop that includes an odd number of negative interactions). Also, these explicit diagrams demand that the modeler propose plausible delays (in the form of system dynamics)

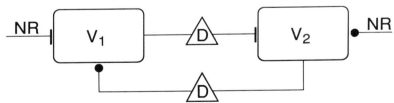

Figure 1 General qualitative model for biological oscillators. The fundamental requirement for generating oscillations is negative feedback with delay. The two rectangles represent the magnitudes of variables V_1 and V_2. Lines showing the interactions between elements terminate to designate an inhibitory (or negative) interactions, those ending with filled rectangles designate excitatory (positive) interactions. Triangles with D represent system delays. Interactions labeled NR represent tonic (nonrhythmic) inputs to the variables. In this example, the two variables are linked by a loop with an odd number of inhibitory elements, i.e. by one inhibitory and one excitatory interaction.

in the interactions between state variables. This graphical scheme does not provide quantitative information, rather it informs the researcher about the number of potential oscillatory loops found in the system, encodes the sign of the interactions, and shows where quantitative analysis is required. These considerations serve as a guide to the form of the differential equations that drive the system. Finally, the graphical depiction of inhibitory feedback with delay is remarkably heuristic for explaining the origins of biological oscillations, from the nerve impulses (or Hodgkin-Huxley equations) to Ca^{2+} oscillator models. Below we develop such schematics for circadian, Ca^{2+}, and neuronal reciprocal inhibition (RI) models.

Circadian Oscillators

While biological oscillations range in period from milliseconds to days, months, and even years, a subset of biological oscillations has evolved with period lengths that match significant external environmental cycles. These biological oscillations, commonly referred to as biological clocks, play a critical role in timing a myriad of behaviors and physiological processes in both terrestrial and marine environments. The most intensively studied of these chronometers are circadian clocks (from the Latin circa- about, dian - a day) although annual, lunar, and tidal clocks have also been identified. Circadian clocks have been implicated in the control of a wide range of behaviors and physiological processes, some of them obvious, such as the human circadian rhythm of sleep and wakefulness and the daily leaf movements of some plants. Circadian clocks also play more covert roles in many sophisticated animal behaviors including solar orientation and navigation, time sense, and photoperiodically controlled seasonal dormancy and reproductive cycles. It is becoming increasingly evident that few behaviors escape some form of modulation by biological clocks.

Efforts to localize circadian pacemakers within multicellular organisms have revealed that restricted portions of the nervous and endocrine systems of higher animals can generate circadian periodicities. Several brain structures have been identified as circadian pacemakers including the avian pineal organ (31, 61), the optic lobes of several insects (22, 43c, 47a, 48), the retinae of several opisthobranch mollusks (8, 10, 21, 39, 46) and some amphibia (7), and the suprachiasmatic nuclei of the rodent hypothalamus (47, 55). In many cases these pacemakers survive well in vitro, expressing several circadian cycles as isolated tissues or even as cells dispersed in cell culture (for reviews see 9, 57).

There is relatively little known about the specific cellular and molecular mechanisms underlying circadian rhythm generation. At present, research on the molluskan retina provides the most detailed information about processes and pathways involved in synchronization and expression of circadian rhythms. These studies have permitted the construction of preliminary models of the retinal pacemaker system (9, 40, 42, 44). While these models are largely speculative and developed primarily for didactic purposes, they have been useful in focusing research on specific cellular processes such as protein synthesis and ionic fluxes. Figure 2 depicts a model for rhythm generation and synchronization in the molluskan retina adapted from earlier, more detailed schemes (9, 44). The model is based on data implicating protein synthesis in rhythm generation and membrane potential and a transmembrane Ca^{2+} flux in synchronization of the rhythm by light cycles.

Briefly, the pacemaker system consists of two loops. The primary loop generating the circadian rhythm (which exhibits negative feedback with delay) consists of two state variables, cytosolic Ca^{2+} concentration and the concentration of a Ca^{2+}-regulated protein. In this scheme, cytosolic Ca^{2+} levels rise because of a persistent passive flux from intracellular storage sites. The increase in intracellular $[Ca^{2+}]$ leads to the synthesis of proteins that then act to reduce Ca^{2+} levels. The synthesized proteins could regulate a transport process that removes cytosolic $[Ca^{2+}]$ or act as Ca^{2+}-binding proteins.

In addition to the intracellular feedback loop involving protein synthesis, a transmembrane loop incorporating positive feedback is formed by two state variables, membrane potential and cytosolic $[Ca^{2+}]$. The transmembrane loop provides an output in the form of a spontaneous action potential rhythm and also provides the input pathway for synchronization. One source of regulation

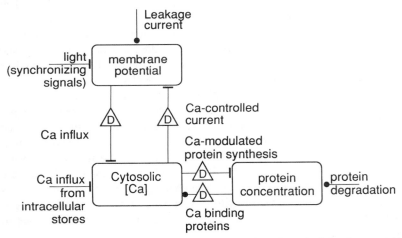

Figure 2   Qualitative scheme for a circadian oscillator. The scheme includes three variables; membrane potential, cytosolic calcium concentration, and the concentration of calcium-regulated protein. Interactions between variables include calcium currents, calcium-regulated concentration. Nonrhythmic inputs include light, calcium influx from intracellular stores, and protein degradation.

of this oscillation occurs via membrane depolarization by light, which then leads to Ca^{2+} influx, thereby shifting the phase of the rhythm.

Neuronal - Reciprocal Inhibition Oscillators

Rhythmic movements are expressed in many types of animal behaviors including flying, walking, swimming, eating, and visceral processes. These repetitive movements are, almost without exception, generated by neuronal circuits that lie within the central nervous system (17) where they form central oscillators. Neuronal circuit oscillators function to generate the activity cycles of motor neuron output, and thereby act to coordinate the often complex, multiphasic movements of limbs or body segments. The oscillatory networks that control animal locomotion express their rhythmicity in the form of membrane potential oscillations and nerve impulse bursts. Because of their relationships to a wide range of movements, cycle periods of these oscillations range from as low as 0.1 s (tadpole swimming movements, 51) up to 10 to 20 s (marine slug swimming, 32). Moreover such movements vary in complexity from a single phase oscillator (lobster heart, 23) to the coordinated multiphasic rhythms observed in animal locomotion (leech, 26, 28; lamprey, 36).

Surprisingly, given this diversity of outputs, similar mechanisms appear to generate the oscillations in all of the neuronal circuits that give rise to these movement rhythms (2, 14, 25, 29, 52–54). The specific model most commonly invoked for generating oscillations in neuronal circuits is reciprocal inhibition between neuron pairs, first proposed at the turn of the century (11). This model includes mutually inhibitory synapses with some dynamic process whereby the strength of the inhibition that one neuron exerts on the other decreases with time. One variant of this model (Figure 3), in which the dynamic, inhibition-limiting process is an h current, an excitatory current turned on by hyperpolarzation, is described for the cardiac oscillator in leech (1, 12). This simple model includes four variables, two for each neuron (60). These are the membrane potential and the conductance for the h channels. The membrane potential of each neuron is determined by leakage current, by the h current, and by the synaptic current. The value of the h conductance is determined by an activation factor and by a deactivation factor that depends on the membrane potential.

The main inhibitory interactions in this model, the mutual synaptic inhibition between the two neurons, form a loop with an even number of inhibitory elements. Hence this loop alone cannot function to generate oscillations. The model includes two additional loops, however, with an odd number (one) of inhibitory elements: loops formed by the membrane potential and the h-current conductance, for each neuron. These latter inhibitory loops, therefore form the oscillator core. Based on the schematic of Figure 1, we

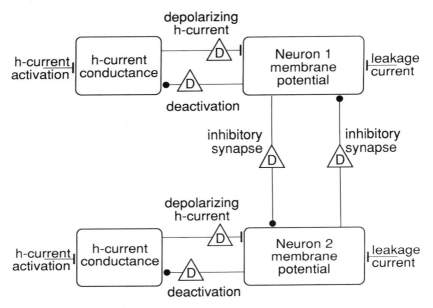

Figure 3 Qualitative scheme for a neuronal oscillator with reciprocal inhibition. The four variables are the membrane potential and the conductance for the h channels for each of the two neurons. Interactions between membrane potentials arise from synaptic currents. Membrane potential is also controlled by the h currents and by the nonrhythmic leakage current. The value of h conductances are formally determined by a deactivation factor that depends on membrane potential and nonrhythmic activation factors. Negative feedback with delay is present in the interactions between membrane potentials and h currents.

can state that each of these inhibitory loops can form competent oscillations for some set of model parameters and interaction terms. Thus the reciprocal inhibition could function primarily to ensure that the two neurons oscillate in antiphase.

Calcium Oscillators

Alterations in the concentration of free Ca^{2+} ions inside cells is a critical factor in the regulation of a variety of cellular activities. Such cellular functions range from the control of events following fertilization (or artificial activation) in eggs to the secretion of neurotransmitters at the synaptic terminals of neurons (58). Given the critical role of intracellular Ca^{2+} ions in controlling cell function, it is not surprising that Ca^{2+} concentrations are under the control of multiple regulatory mechanisms, including Ca^{2+} pumps and an array of Ca^{2+} sequestration mechanisms.

These mechanisms tend to maintain homeostasis in Ca^{2+} concentration via negative feedback loops. Given the presence of such negative feedback loops and the possibility of delays in these loops, one might expect as noted above, at least in retrospect, that the Ca^{2+} concentrations may not be stable, and that the intracellular concentration of Ca^{2+} ions will sometimes undergo oscillations (27). In fact, a curious observation was described a few years ago, that in response to appropriate stimulation, many types of cells (e.g. gonadotropes, hepatocytes, acinar cells, and eggs, 13, 16, 35, 41, 43b) exhibit periodic phenomena, including sinusoidal oscillations and regular, repetitive spiking in the intracellular concentration of Ca^{2+} ions (5, 58). These oscillations encompasses a broad range of periodicities, depending on the specific system, from near 1 s to as much as 100 s for each cycle. Perhaps because these oscillations were first detected recently, their specific function is not yet certain.

Several models have been proposed to account for oscillations in the intracellular Ca^{2+} concentration (15, 18, 45). One source of alterations for cytososlic Ca^{2+} is through cell membrane channels, which can regulate intracellular Ca^{2+} concentration by controlling Ca^{2+} ion currents passing through the cell plasma membrane (58). More recently, it has become apparent that release of Ca^{2+} from intracellular stores, long known for its critical function in muscle contraction, also serves as a source of Ca^{2+} ions in many cell types. Two primary mechanisms are thought to be responsible for release of Ca^{2+} from such intracellular stores: receptor-mediated release via the intracellular second messenger inositol 1,4,5 trisphosphate ($InsP_3$) (3, 6) and by Ca^{2+}-induced calcium release (30, 50a).

A two-pool model for generating oscillations in Ca^{2+} concentration (4) is depicted in Figure 4. The model describes two variables: the concentration of cytosolic Ca^{2+} and the concentration of Ca^{2+} in an $InsP_3$-insensitive pool. The qualitative schematic of Figure 4 illustrates that the concentration of Ca^{2+} in the cytosol is determined by six factors: the rate of Ca^{2+} flux into cytosol from outside the cell, the rate of Ca^{2+} flux into cytosol from an $InsP_3$-sensitive pool, the rate at which Ca^{2+} is pumped from the cytosol into the $InsP_3$-insensitive pool, the rate of Ca^{2+} efflux from the $InsP_3$-insensitive pool into the cytosol through Ca^{2+}-controlled Ca^{2+} (CICR) channels, the leakage rate of Ca^{2+} into the cytosol from the $InsP_3$-insensitive pool, and the rate at which Ca^{2+} is pumped from cytosol to the extracellular space. Similarly, the Ca^{2+} concentration of the $InsP_3$-insensitive pool is determined by three factors that link this pool to cytosolic Ca^{2+}: the rate at which Ca^{2+} is pumped into the $InsP_3$-insensitive pool from the cytosol, the rate of Ca^{2+} efflux from the $InsP_3$-insensitive pool into cytosol through CICR channels, and the leakage rate of Ca^{2+} from the $InsP_3$-insensitive pool into the cytosol. In this qualitative model, cytosolic Ca^{2+} oscillations arise if Ca^{2+} influx into the cytosol either from an extracellular source or from the InsP₃-sensitive Ca²⁺ pool is sufficiently large. Under these conditions, the InsP₃-insensitive Ca²⁺ concentration rises until CICR channels open to rapidly empty the InsP₃-insensitive pool, which causes a spike-like increase in cytosolic Ca²⁺ concentration. Membrane pumps are subsequently activated to quickly reduce cytosolic Ca²⁺ concentration. Although this qualitative description makes Ca²⁺ concentration oscillations plausible, verification that such oscillations are indeed generated by this model require the translation of the schematic diagram into explicit differential equations (see below).

MATHEMATICAL DESCRIPTIONS OF BIOLOGICAL OSCILLATIONS

One critical aim in the study of any oscillatory system is to understand the underlying mechanism in sufficient detail so that the system can be described by a set of differential equations that incorporates both qualitative and quantitative system features. Because of the complexity of identified biolog-

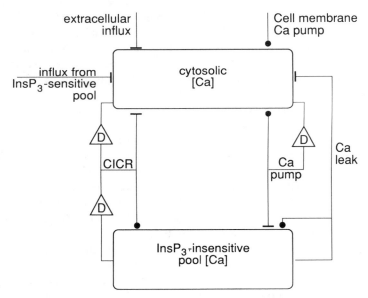

Figure 4   Qualitative scheme for a calcium concentration oscillator. The variables are free Ca²⁺ in cytosol and the free Ca²⁺ in an InsP₃-insensitive pool. Interactions between the variables are via calcium-induced calcium release (CICR), leakage of calcium from the InsP₃-insensitive pool into the cytoplasm, and a calcium pump in the membrane bounding the InsP₃-insensitive pool. Nonrhythmic inputs to the variables are Ca²⁺ flux into the cytosol from the InsP₃-sensitive pool and the cell membrane Ca²⁺ pump.

ical oscillators, we first illustrate the mathematical description of such systems by discussing two physical oscillators: the linear mass-spring oscillator and the nonlinear, electrical oscillator described by van der Pol. We then show that similar differential equations can be deduced for the three biological oscillators from the qualitative diagrams. A general introduction to the mathematics of biological oscillators can be found in the monograph by Pavlidis (49).

Comparison of Physical and Biological Oscillators

The linear mass-spring system is a well-characterized physical oscillator that serves as a starting point for describing more complex, nonlinear systems. The displacements of the mass about an equilibrium point in this system is described by a sine wave with a period that is determined by the two system parameters: the mass and the spring constant. Brief perturbations of the system lead to sustained changes in amplitude but not period. For any actual, physical representation of this system, the oscillations are damped by friction; only in the ideal case are the oscillations sustained. The biological oscillators discussed here generate both transient and protracted oscillations; they are all nonlinear. In most instances, perturbations transiently alter both cycle period and amplitude; given sufficient time, the cycle period and activity waveform return to the pre-perturbed values, provided that system parameters remain unchanged. Such systems are described as limit cycle oscillators, wherein the unperturbed activity is stable for all time, and where small perturbations vanish by exponential decay (i.e. the difference between the stable solution and the perturbation decreases as e^{-t}).

Equations that Describe the Linear Mass-Spring System

Recalling Newton's second law (F = m a), a linear, frictionless mass-spring system can be described by a second order, linear differential equation of the form:

$$-b\,x = m\,[d(dx/dt)/dt], \text{ or} \qquad\qquad 1a.$$

$$m\,[d(dx/dt)/dt] + b\,x = 0, \qquad\qquad 1b.$$

where x is distance (displacement from the equilibrium point), t is time, and b is the spring constant. This equation can be expanded to a system of two first-order linear equations if we set $dx/dt = y$:

$$dx/dt = y, \text{ and} \qquad\qquad 2a.$$

$$dy/dt = -(b/m)\,x. \qquad\qquad 2b.$$

The terms x and y, whose derivatives are given to the left, are the two state variables of this system. These equations can be solved analytically with a solution that describes the displacement and velocity of the mass,

$$x = x_0 \cos(w\,t) + y_0 \sin(w\,t) \text{ and} \qquad\qquad 3a.$$

$$y = w\,y_0 \cos(w\,t) - w\,x_0 \sin(w\,t), \qquad\qquad 3b.$$

where x_0 is the amplitude of the oscillation if the initial velocity, y_0, is zero. The angular frequency, w, is defined as $(b/m)^{1/2}$. In this ideal system, no limit cycle exists. For each mass and spring, the oscillatory solution is uniquely determined by the initial conditions (x_0,y_0 - displacement and velocity at time zero). A perturbation of the system is equivalent to invoking a new set of initial conditions and thus creating a new solution of the system. When the values of the state variables x and y are plotted as coordinates on a plane at chosen intervals of time, the resulting graph is called a phase plane diagram. In this linear example, the plot of y vs x is a graph of velocity vs displacement. The set of solutions (3) forms an infinite series of concentric ellipses about the origin $(0,0)$. The qualitative nature of the solution is completely independent of the frequency, w. We can recognize this formally through a linear transformation of all the differently shaped sets of concentric ellipses to one set of concentric circles. This is done by scaling the time axis, $\tau = wt$, in equation 1 and rewriting equations 1–3 without the terms b, m, or w.

Model Nonlinear Differential Equations (van der Pol)

The differential equations that describe biological oscillators differ in several ways from the linear system described above. First, the equations include nonlinear terms. Second, in general these equations cannot be solved in closed form, instead they are graphed via numerical procedures on computers. As an illustrative example of the close similarity in linear and nonlinear systems of some qualitative biological models often discussed, we will slightly alter the form of the linear system above to

$$dx/d\tau = y, \qquad\qquad 4a.$$

$$dy/d\tau = -x - \beta y. \qquad\qquad 4b.$$

If β is non-zero, the solution of the system is fundamentally changed, and there are no longer periodic solutions, instead there is but a single nonperiodic solution for long intervals. (The $-\beta y$ term describes the linear viscous damping of a dashpot.) If β is a positive value (a less than perfect spring), then the system is the damped harmonic oscillator, and the system, once displaced from the equilibrium, spirals to a stable constant state at the origin (in phase space). The system is said to be attracted to this singular solution. If β is negative, which might seem unrealistic but simply implies that energy is injected into the system at a constant rate, the system has the same, singular solution at the origin. However, when perturbed from this singularity, the system generates oscillations that grow in amplitude without bound. A real system into which energy is injected and from which energy is dissipated acts in a self-limiting manner; that is, the oscillation amplitude is bounded. (The spring during high stress becomes nonlinear.) To model this nonlinear behavior, we might propose that β be some nonlinear function of x. We could expect, for example, that for large x, the value of β would become positive and thus prevent the system from breaking as long as the constant energy influx is less than the tensile strength of the spring. One nonlinear function that meets this criteria with a linear restoring force and nonlinear damping is

$$\beta(x) = -\nu(1 - x^2), \qquad\qquad 5.$$

where ν is a positive constant. For small x, the system diverges away from the singular solution at the origin. For large x, the system converges toward the origin. Phase plane analysis can show that the result is qualitatively different from the harmonic oscillator or the damped form. The stable solution is a unique trajectory in the phase plane with intermediate values of x and y. This is a stable limit cycle because in the limit as time goes to infinity, any trajectory starting at some point (x_0, y_0) finds its way onto the set of x and y values that describes the closed loop of the limit cycle. This nonlinear extension of the damped harmonic oscillator in equations 4a and 4b is known as the van der Pol oscillator after the person who used these equations (59) to describe an electronic vacuum tube circuit:

$$dx/d\tau = y, \qquad\qquad 6a.$$

$$dy/d\tau = -x + \nu(1 - x^2)\, y. \qquad\qquad 6b.$$

The energy source is a battery. The state variable x is the fraction of the saturation voltage of the vacuum tube grid. The parameter ν is a ratio of proportionality constants related to the two inductors, one capacitor, one resistor, and one vacuum tube in the system. Two extreme forms of oscillation are represented in this model. If ν is close to zero, the waveform of x is nearly sinusoidal; if ν is large, then the oscillation of x is nearly a square waveform. In the latter case, the system has become a relaxation oscillator that is characterized by the fast switching between two nearly constant states.

RELEVANCE OF THE VAN DER POL TO BIOLOGICAL SYSTEMS   It was noted in the introduction that biological oscillators have a wide range of periods and that the period varies greatly for some while other oscillators act as clocks. The van der Pol oscillator provides a simple example of an oscillator in which the variation of one parameter alters the system from being relatively insensitive to noise to one that is very sensitive.

At large v, random fluctuation of x can cause the system to prematurely switch to the other nearly constant state that defines the square waveform. If v is decreased to a value where the x waveform becomes more sinusoidal in character, the same noise level has a much reduced effect on the period. For a biological clock, the value of v could not be zero since nonlinearity is needed to stably entrain the oscillator to external timing cues. The van der Pol oscillator is used as a qualitative description of the slave oscillator to the circadian pacemaker to which it is readily entrained (50). The van der Pol at large v is a paradigm of the behavior observed for chemical (20) and biochemical (37) oscillators. A two-dimensional reduced form of the Hodgkin-Huxley equations formulated by Fitzhugh to qualitatively describe the behavior of neuronal action potentials is essentially a van der Pol oscillator under special conditions with a nonlinear forcing term added (19, 34). In this form, a third typical waveform is exhibited, the spike of an excitable system, of which heart muscle, neurons, and intracellular Ca^{2+} oscillations are examples. This is a special case of the relaxation oscillator where one of the two states is visited briefly relative to the other and the sensitivity to noise remains.

Differential Equations that Describe Specific Biological Models

In order to determine the validity of a given qualitative oscillator model, it is necessary to obtain a set of differential equations that correspond to the qualitative model. We illustrate below how the form of the differential equations describing an oscillating system can be deduced from the qualitative model diagrams. Although specific, realistic differential equations have been established for only a few biological oscillator models, primarily those describing individual neurons and Ca^{2+} oscillators, the general form of the differential equations are useful for suggesting further experiments.

CIRCADIAN OSCILLATOR   The schematic diagram for the circadian system of the mollusk illustrated in Figure 2, leads easily to a set of differential equations. Each of the interactions and inputs shown in this figure can be given a name (Figure 5a), each then becomes a term in a differential equation. Because this model for the circadian pacemaker has three state variables, three differential equations are required. These equations have the form:

$$C \, dV_m/dt = I_{Ca} \, ([Ca^{2+}], V_m) - I_1 + I_L, \qquad\qquad 7a.$$

$$d[Ca^{2+}]/dt = J_{Ca}(V_m) + v_0 - v_2([P]), \text{ and} \qquad\qquad 7b.$$

$$d[P]/dt = v_1([Ca^{2+}]) - v_3, \qquad\qquad 7c.$$

where C is the capacitance of the receptor neuron, V_m is the membrane potential, I_{Ca} $([Ca^{2+}], V_m)$ is the cell membrane Ca^{2+} current (a function of both $[Ca^{2+}]$ and V_m), I_1 is a leakage current that maintains the resting potential and I_L is a current turned on by light. In the second equation, $[Ca^{2+}]$ is the cytosolic Ca^{2+} concentration, $J_{Ca}(V_m)$ is the rate of Ca^{2+} influx through the cell membrane, v_0 is leakage of Ca^{2+} from intracellular stores into the cytosol, and $v_2([P])$ is the rate at which cytosolic Ca^{2+} is decreased (indirectly) as a function of $[P]$. Finally, in the third equation $[P]$ is the concentration of a protein that controls cytosolic Ca^{2+} concentrations, $v_1([Ca^{2+}])$ is the rate of synthesis of this protein as a function of $[Ca^{2+}]$, and v_3 is the rate for protein degradation. The model equations for *Bulla* are speculative and no doubt will be substantially revised as more information becomes available; it appears unlikely that the oscillator period is set by the simple loop envisioned here. However, because of the experimental demonstration that Ca^{2+} influx is one factor in the control of the ocular oscillator in this animal, a set of equations like 7 will be part of any more complex description of this system. Equations 7 have not been simulated to test their validity.

NEURONAL CIRCUIT OSCILLATOR   The equations employed to describe neuronal network oscillators are often based on the parallel conductance model of nerve membrane formulated by Hodgkin and Huxley (38). State variables in these equations include the membrane potential for individual neurons in the circuits and time-dependent conductances that underlie impulses, synaptic transmission, and cellular processes such as postinhibitory rebound and synaptic fatigue. Parameter values include such quantities as the voltage sensitivity of conductance changes, resting conductance values, and membrane capacitance among others. Again, although these equations, and their evaluation by computer simulation provide only approximations to the observed cycle period, phases, and waveform, they provide the substrate for further quantitative evaluation of neuronal oscillator circuits. Such further evaluation might increase or decrease the number of state variables, alter the form of the equations or lead to a better measure of system parameters.

For parallel conductance models, the neuronal circuits are described by a series of equations of the form:

$$C_i \, dV_i/dt = I_{i1} + I_{i2} + \ldots + I_{in}, \qquad\qquad 8.$$

where C_i is the membrane capacitance of the ith neuron, V_i is the membrane potential. The term to the left of the equal sign is the capacitative current, whereas those to the right of the equal sign are the amplitudes of ionic currents through the membrane. The current terms are of the form:

A. Circadian model

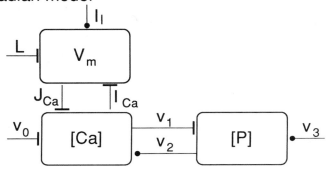

B. Neuronal RI model

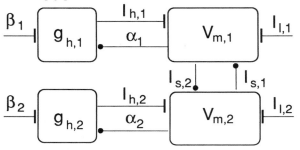

C. Calcium model

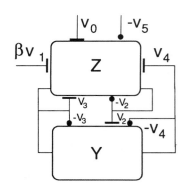

$$I_{ij} = g_{ij} \ (V_i - E_j),\tag{9.}$$

where I_{ij} is a specific current (j) in neuron (i) g_{ij} is the macroscopic membrane conductance for the specific ion, and E_j is the equilibrium potential for the ionic conductance. The conductances in equation 9 may be voltage-dependent, dependent on transmitter release from a presynaptic neuron (for synaptic transmission), and modulated by drugs. Moreover, the conductance terms may themselves be expressed via differential equations.

The depiction in Figure 3 of the simplified model for the leech heart oscillator again suggests the form of the differential equations that describe this system. The equations are

$$C_1 \ [dV_{m,1}/dt] = I_{l,1}(V_{m,1}) + I_{s,1}(V_{m,1},V_{m,2}) + I_{h,1}(V_{m,1}),\tag{10a.}$$

$$dg_{h,1}/dt = \beta_1 - \alpha_1(V_{m,1}),\tag{10b.}$$

$$C_2 \ [dV_{m,2}/dt] = I_{l,2}(V_{m,2}) + I_{s,2}(V_{m,2},V_{m,1}) + I_{h,2}(V_{m,2}), \text{ and}\tag{10c.}$$

$$dg_{h,2}/dt = \beta_2 - \alpha_2(V_{m,2}),\tag{10d.}$$

where C is the membrane capacitance, V_m is the membrane potential, $I_l(V_m)$ is the leakage current (a function of membrane potential), $I_s(V_{m,1},V_{m,2})$ is the synaptic current (a function of both pre- and postsynaptic membrane potentials), and $I_h(V_m)$ is the h current (a function of membrane potential). Also, g_h is the h conductance, β describes activation of this conductance with hyperpolarization, $\alpha(V_{m,1})$ describes the deactivation of the h conductance with membrane depolarization. Note that many and perhaps all of these terms

←———————————————————————————————

Figure 5 Summary of qualitative schemes for three biological oscillator models. (*A*) Circadian model. The state variables are V_m, the membrane potential; $[Ca^{2+}]$, the cytosolic Ca^{2+} concentration; and $[P]$, the concentration of a protein that controls cytosolic Ca^{2+}. The amplitude of these variables is controlled by the following parameters: I_{Ca}, the cell membrane Ca^{2+} current; I_l, a leakage current; I_L, a light-sensitive current; J_{Ca}, the transmembrane Ca^{2+} influx; v_0, leakage rate for Ca^{2+} from intracellular stores; v_2, the rate at which cytosolic Ca^{2+} is decreased by protein P; v_1, the rate of synthesis of P; and v_3, the rate for protein degradation. (*B*) Neuronal-reciprocal inhibition model. The state variables are the two neuronal membrane potentials, V_m, and the two h current conductances, g_h. Variables values are controlled by leakage current, I_1; synaptic currents, I_s; h currents, $I_h (V_m)$; h conductance activation, β; and h conductance deactivation, α. (*C*) Calcium oscillator model. The variables are Z, the free Ca^{2+} in cytosol, and Y, the free Ca^{2+} in the InsP3-insensitive pool. Model parameters that control the values of Z and Y are: v_0, rate of Ca^{2+} flux into cytosol from outside the cell; v_1, maximal rate of Ca^{2+} flux into cytosol from InsP3-sensitive pool; β, the fraction of maximal activation by $[InsP_3]$ in cytosol; v_3, rate of Ca^{2+} efflux from InsP3-insensitive pool into cytosol; v_4, leakage rate of Ca^{2+} from InsP3-insensitive pool to the cytosol; and v_5, rate of Ca^{2+} leakage from cytosol out of the cell.

may be nonlinear. This system of equations is a simplified description of the known interactions that control cardiac oscillations in the leech heart; missing elements include postinhibitory rebound and synaptic fatigue. These elements can be easily incorporated into Figure 4 and into the equation set 10. The specific form of the terms on the right side of these equations, many of which are nonlinear, must be determined through experimentation on physiological preparations. Computer simulations of these and similar equations incorporating reciprocal inhibition and an h current demonstrate that this model can generate oscillations with realistic cycle period (60, O. H. Olsen & W. O. Friesen, unpublished results.)

CALCIUM OSCILLATOR   The analysis is much further advanced for cellular calcium oscillators than for their circadian counterparts. Here explicit equations have been formulated, state variables assigned, and parameter values abstracted from experimental results. Although these equations are only capable of providing a rough approximation of the physiological Ca^{2+} oscillations, they do provide the basis for further research and refinement. Further experiments can be guided in an effort to revise the model and, in the process, add new rates or change the nonlinear form of the current rates.

We give here an example of the system of nonlinear equations employed to model biological oscillations that does not naturally appear as a nonlinear distortion of the harmonic oscillator described for the van der Pol system, but is more commonly written as a sum of the kinetic rates of several physiological or cellular processes. The form of the following pair of equations can be deduced directly from the qualitative description of the two-pool Ca^{2+} oscillator model depicted in Figure 4. The specific terms in this equation are from Goldbeter et al (33):

$$dZ/dt = v_0 + v_1\,\beta - v_2(Z) + v_3(Y,Z) + v_4(Y) - v_5(Z) \text{ and} \qquad 11a.$$

$$dY/dt = v_2(Z) - v_3(Y,Z) - v_4(Y), \qquad 11b.$$

where Z and Y are state variables that describe the time courses of the cytosolic free Ca^{2+} concentrations and the concentration of free Ca^{2+} of an intravesicular pool, respectively. In these equations, the v_i terms are rates that are functions of the state variables. Only v_2 and v_3 are nonlinear rate processes, while the terms v_0 and v_1 are zero order (constants), and v_4 and v_5 are first order rates (see Figure 5c). Only one parameter is explicitly shown here (β, the one varied by the authors, the saturation function of the receptor for InsP3). A limit cycle exists for a range of values of β. The nonlinear functions are the form of Hill functions to take into account the cooperative nature supposed for these rate processes. Even so, it was found that explicit cooperativity was not necessary for this model to oscillate. Given that differential equations, like 11, can approximate physiological oscillations, the task of the investigator is (*a*) to specify the form of the equations, that is to specify the general form of the equations (number of state variables, nonlinearities, and cross terms), (*b*) to determine the values of system parameters, and (*c*) to determine which of the parameters are most important for setting cycle period and phase relationships. Although none of these tasks is simple for circadian, Ca^{2+}, or neuronal network oscillators, a full understanding of biological oscillators requires the development of such explicit equations and the fixing of system parameter values.

SUMMARY

In this brief review, we have attempted to illustrate the utility of our qualitative scheme proposed in 1984 (27). This scheme provides a means of summarizing information concerning oscillating systems by identifying system variables and parameters and the interactions between variables. Moreover, the qualitative scheme can be employed to deduce the form of system differential equations. This second step then clearly shows the rate constants that must be deduced through experimentation for the construction of explicit mathematical models.

ACKNOWLEDGMENTS

This work is supported by grants from the National Science Foundation (BNS84014988) and National Institutes of Health (NS21778) to WOF. GDB was supported by National Institutes of Health grant NS15264. Further support was provided by the National Science Foundation Center for Biological Timing (NSF grant DIR8920162). CGH is a fellow of the National Science Foundation Center for Biological Timing.

Literature Cited

1. Angstadt, J. D., Calabrese, R. L. 1989. A hyperpolarization-activated inward current in heart interneurons of the medicinal leech. *J. Neurosci.* 9:2846–57
2. Arshavsky, Y. I., Beloozerova, I. N., Orlovsky, G. N., Panchin, Y. V., Pavlova, G. A. 1985. Control of locomotion in marine mollusc *Clione limacina*. III On the origin of locomotory rhythm. *Exp. Brain. Res.* 58:273–84
3. Berridge, M. J. 1988. Inositol trisphos-
phate-induced membrane potential oscillations in *Xenopus* oocytes. *J. Physiol.* 403:589–99
4. Berridge, M. J. 1991. Cytoplasmic calcium oscillations: A two pool model. *Cell Calcium* 12:63–72
5. Berridge, M. J., Galione, A. 1988. Cytosolic calcium oscillators. *FASEB J.* 2:3074–82
6. Berridge, M. J., Irvine, R. F. 1984. Inositol triphosphate, a novel second messenger in cellular signal transduction. *Nature* 312:315–21

7. Besharse, J. C., Iuvone, P. M. 1983. Circadian clock in *Xenopus* eye controlling retinal serotonin N-acetyltransferase. *Nature* 305:133–35

8. Block, G. D., Roberts, M. H. 1981. Circadian pacemaker in the *Bursatella* eye: Properties of the rhythm and its effect on locomotor behavior. *J. Comp. Physiol.* 142:403–10

9. Block, G. D., Khalsa, S. B., McMahon, D. G., Michel, S., Geusz, M. 1992. Cellular mechanisms of biological timekeeping. *Int. Rev. Cytol.* In press

10. Block, G. D., Wallace, S. F. 1982. Localization of a circadian pacemaker in the eye of the mollusc, *Bulla. Science* 217:155–57

11. Brown, T. G. 1911. The intrinsic factors in the act of progression in the mammal. *Proc. R. Soc. London Ser. B* 84:308–19

12. Calabrese, R. L., Arbas, E. A. 1989. Central and peripheral oscillators generating heartbeat in the leech *Hirudo medicinalis*. In *Neuronal and Cellular Oscillators*, ed. J. W. Jacklet, pp. 237–67. New York: Marcel Dekker

13. Cobbold, P. H., Sanchez-Bueno, A., Dixon, C. J. 1991. The hepatocyte calcium oscillator. *Cell Calcium* 12:87–95

14. Cohen, A. H., Rossignol, S., Grillner, S. 1988. *Neural Control of Rhythmic Movements in Vertebrates.* New York: Wiley-Interscience. 500 pp.

15. Cuthbertson, K. S. R., Chay, T. R. 1991. Modelling receptor-controlled intracellular calcium oscillators. *Cell Calcium* 12:97–109

16. Cuthbertson, K. S. R., Cobbold, P. H. 1985. Phorbol ester and sperm activate mouse oocytes by inducing sustained oscillations in cell Ca^{2+}. *Nature* 316:541–42

17. Delcomyn, F. 1980. Neural basis of rhythmic behavior in animals. *Science* 210:492–98

18. Dupont, G., Berridge, M. J., Goldbeter, A. 1991. Signal-induced Ca^{2+} oscillations: Properties of a model based on Ca^{2+}-induced Ca^{2+} release. *Cell Calcium* 12:73–85

19. Edelstein-Keshet, L. 1988. Limit cycles, oscillations, and excitable systems. In *Mathematical Models in Biology*, Chpt. 8. New York: Random House

20. Epstein, I. R., Kustin, K., De Kepper, P., Orban, M. 1983. Oscillating chemical reactions. *Sci. Am.* 248:112–23

21. Eskin, A., Harcombe, E. 1977. Eye of *Navanax*: Optic activity, circadian rhythm and morphology. *Comp. Biochem. Physiol.* 57A:443–49

22. Fleissner, G. 1982. Isolation of an insect circadian clock. *J. Comp. Physiol.* 149:311–16

23. Friesen, W. O. 1975. Physiological anatomy and burst pattern in the cardiac ganglion of the spiny lobster *Panulirus interruptus*. *J. Comp. Physiol. A* 101:173–89

24. Friesen, W. O. 1989. Neuronal control of leech swimming movements. I. Inhibitory interactions between motor neurons. *J. Comp. Physiol. A* 166:195–203

25. Friesen, W. O. 1989. Neuronal control of leech swimming movements. II. Motor neuron feedback to oscillator cells 115 and 28. *J. Comp. Physiol. A* 166:205–15

26. Friesen, W. O. 1989. Neuronal control of leech swimming movements. See Ref. 12, pp. 269–316

27. Friesen, W. O., Block, G. D. 1984. What is a biological oscillator? *Am. J. Physiol.* 246:R847–51

28. Friesen, W. O., Poon, M., Stent, G. S. 1976. An oscillatory neuronal circuit generating a locomotory rhythm. *Proc. Natl. Acad. Sci. USA* 73:3734–38

29. Friesen, W. O., Stent, G. S. 1978. Neural circuits for generating rhythmic movements. *Annu. Rev. Biophys. Bioeng.* 7:37–61

30. Galione, A., Lee, H. C., Busa, W. B. 1991. Ca^{2+}-induced Ca^{2+} release in sea urchin egg homogenates: Modulation by cyclic ADP-ribose. *Science* 253:1143–46

31. Gaston, S., Menaker, M. 1968. The biological clock in sparrows. *Science* 160:1125–27

32. Getting, P. 1989. A network oscillator underlying swimming in *Tritonia*. See Ref. 12, pp. 215–36

33. Goldbeter, A., Dupont, G., Berridge, M. J. 1990. Minimal model for signal-induced Ca^{2+} oscillations and for their frequency encoding through protein phosphorylation. *Proc. Natl. Acad. Sci. USA* 87:1461–65

34. Grassman, J. 1987. Asymptotic methods for relaxation oscillations and applications. In *Applied Mathematical Sciences*, Vol. 63. New York: Springer-Verlag

35. Gray, P. T. A. 1988. Oscillations of free cytosolic calcium evoked by cholinergic and catecholaminergic agonists in rat parotid acinar cells. *J. Physiol.* 406:35–53

36. Grillner, S., Wallen, P., Brodin, L., Lansner, A. 1991. Neuronal network

generating locomotor behavior in lamprey: Circuitry, transmitters, membrane properties and simulation. *Annu. Rev. Neurosci.* 14:169–99

37. Hahn, H.-S., Nitzan, A., Ortoleva, P., Ross J. 1974. Threshold excitations, relaxation oscillations, and effect of noise in an enzyme reaction. *Proc. Natl. Acad. Sci. USA* 71:4067–71

38. Hodgkin, A. L., Huxley, A. F. 1952. A quantitative description of membrane current and its application to conduction and excitation in nerve. *J. Physiol.* 117:500–44

39. Jacklet, J. W. 1969. Circadian rhythm of optic nerve impulses recorded in darkness from isolated eye of *Aplysia. Science* 164:562–63

40. Jacklet, J. W., ed. 1989. Circadian neuronal oscillators. See Ref. 12, pp. 483–527

41. Kline, D., Kline, J. T. 1992. Repetitive calcium transients and the role of calcium in exocytosis and cell cycle activation in the mouse egg. *Dev. Biol.* 149:80–89

42. Koumenis, C., Eskin, A. 1992. The hunt for mechanisms of circadian timing in the eye of *Aplysia. Chronobiology Int.* 9:201–21

43. Kristan, W. B. Jr., Calabrese, R. L. 1976. Rhythmic swimming activity in neurons of the isolated nerve cord of the leech. *J. Exp. Biol.* 65:643–68

43a. Ku, Y. H. 1958. Analysis and control of nonlinear systems. New York: Ronald Press. 360 pp.

43b. Leong, D. A. 1991. A model for intracellular calcium signaling and the coordinate regulation of hormone biosynthesis, receptors and secretion. *Cell Calcium* 12:255–68

43c. Loher, W. 1972. Circadian control of stridulation in the cricket, *Teleogryllus commodus* walker. *J. Comp. Physiol.* 79:179–90

44. McMahon, D. G. 1986. *Circadian Pacemaker Entrainment.* PhD thesis. Univ. Virginia. 274 pp.

45. Meyer, T., Stryer, L. 1988. Molecular model for receptor-stimulated calcium spiking. *Proc. Natl. Acad. Sci. USA* 85:5051–55

46. Michel, S., Geusz, M., Zaritsky, J., Block, G. 1992. Dissociated pacemaker cells of *Bulla* express circadian rhythms in membrane conductance. *Soc. Neurosci Abstr.* 18:1

47. Moore, R. Y., Eichler, V. B. 1972. Loss of a circadian adrenal corticosterone rhythm following suprachiasmatic lesions in the rat. *Brain Res.* 42:201–6

47a. Nishiitsutsuji-Uwo, J., Pittendrigh, C. S. 1968. Central nervous system control of circadian rhythmicity in the cockroach. *Z. Vergl. Physiol.* 58:1–13

48. Page, T. 1982. Transplantation of the cockroach circadian pacemaker. *Science* 216:73–75

49. Pavlidis, T. 1973. *Biological Oscillations: Their Mathematical Analysis.* New York: Academic. 207 pp.

50. Pittendrigh, C. S., Kyner, W. T., Takamura, T. 1991. The amplitude of circadian oscillations: Temperature dependence, latitudinal clines, and the photoperiodic time measurement. *J. Biol. Rhythms* 6:299–313

50a. Rink, T. J., Merritt, J. E. 1990. Calcium signalling. *Curr. Opin. Cell Biol* 2:198–205

51. Roberts, A. 1990. How does a nervous system produce behavior? A case study in neurobiology. *Sci. Progress Oxford* 74:31–51

52. Roberts, A., Roberts, B. L. 1983. *Neural Origins of Rhythmic Movements.* London: Cambridge Univ. Press. 501 pp.

53. Satterlie, R. A., Spencer, A. N. 1985. Swimming in the pteropod mollusc *clione limacina.* II. Physiology. *J. Exp. Physiol.* 116:205–22

54. Selverston, A. I. 1985. *Model Neural Networks and Behavior.* New York: Plenum 548 pp.

55. Stephan, F. K., Zucker, I. 1972. Circadian rhythms in drinking behavior and locomotor activity of rats are eliminated by hypothalamic lesions. *Proc. Natl. Acad. Sci. USA* 69:1583–86

56. Deleted in proof

57. Takahashi, J. S., Murkami, N., Nikaido, S., Pratt, B., Robertson, L. 1989. The avian pineal, a vertebrate model system of the circadian oscillator: cellular regulation of circadian rhythms by light, second messengers and macromolecular synthesis. *Recent Prog. Horm. Res.* 45:279–352

58. Tsien, R. W., Tsien, R. Y. 1990. Calcium channels, stores and oscillations. *Annu. Rev. Cell Biol.* 6:715–60

59. van der Pol, B. 1926. On relaxation oscillation. *Philos. Mag.* 2:978–92

60. Wang, X.-J., Rinzel, J. 1992. Alternating and synchronous rhythms in reciprocally inhibitory model neurons. *Neural Comp.* 4:84–97

61. Zimmerman, N., Menaker M. 1979. The pineal gland: a pacemaker within the circadian system of the house sparrow. *Proc. Natl. Acad. Sci. USA* 76:999–1003

Annu. Rev. Physiol. 1993. 55:683–728

GENETIC ANALYSIS OF CIRCADIAN CLOCKS

Jay C. Dunlap

Department of Biochemistry, Dartmouth Medical School, Hanover, New Hampshire 03755–3844

KEY WORDS: circadian clock, *Neurospora, Drosophila,* mutants, *frq, per*

INTRODUCTION

The goals of this review are twofold. The opening section introduces the tools and concepts of the genetic approach to understanding circadian rhythms. The following sections review the pertinent literature with an emphasis on those studies and approaches that appear most likely to lead to new answers to old questions concerning the mechanism(s) of circadian rhythmicity.

This survey has been made somewhat simpler due the series of excellent reviews on clocks that have appeared over the past five years (35, 36, 38, 39, 42, 63, 64, 65, 66, 67, 68, 84, 96, 107, 118, 153, 183, 184, 189). The length of this list reflects, in part, both a maturing of the genetics and molecular genetics of circadian clocks as a field, and an increasing interest and appreciation of the strengths of genetics in offering a different set of tools and a different way of thinking about the problems that circadian biologists have been considering for several decades.

GENETIC APPROACHES TO RHYTHMICITY

The Ground Rules for Genetics

Genetics and physiology share several attributes that lend themselves well to the early stages of the development of any field, clocks included. Both disciplines are inherently descriptive in approach and seek to identify and characterize at the simplest level the components that define the organism. Both deal with the characteristics of an ensemble of parts—a whole system (be it a cell or an organism)—rather than just one part of a system as does biochemistry. Mutational analysis, then, can be viewed as a fine tool for

683

0066–4278/93/0315–0683$02.00

altering just one component of a complex system while keeping all of the other parts constant; the phenotype, however, is still the result of the interaction of all of the parts. The goal of each approach is to understand the behavior of the ensemble; both physiology and genetics can begin with a scientifically untouched and inherently biological problem and each can ultimately serve as an entrée to biochemical approaches. Finally, because the process of problem solving using either physiology or genetics involves inference of the characteristics of component parts from the characteristics of the system, modeling plays an important role.

Genetics can be defined as the systematic study of the heritability of phenotypic variation. Because the Central Dogma (DNA encodes RNA, which encodes proteins) underlies the expression of all organismal characteristics, it follows that any characteristic can be studied through the identification of strains mutant in that characteristic. This implied assumption can be restated more explicitly in the context of circadian rhythms: clocks are built using proteins, the products of genes, and therefore the molecular gears and cogs of the biological clock can be isolated and studied through the identification of genetically altered strains with altered clocks. Thus if queried using the appropriate tools and genetic craftsmanship, the organism will identify the genes it needs to assemble and operate the clock. The strength of such an approach is that, to begin with, one needs to know almost nothing about the phenomenon (a molecular clock); all that is required is a description of the phenotype being studied (a rhythm in some parameter), and sex (or the ability to exchange genetic information and pass it on to progeny). The organism, and the screen for mutants, do the rest. The spectrum of genetic variants identified from such a screen has the virtue of being unbiased by the investigator; one gets just what one asks for, no more and no less. For example, if you ask for altered circadian locomoter behavior, you may get only that and not, for instance, mutations in the clock mechanism (e.g. 41) or even altered circadian photoperiodic response (e.g. 159, 160). This is also an inherent weakness of a genetic approach in that, just because a mutation in a gene turns up in a screen for clock mutations, it does not follow that the gene encodes a protein used in the assembly and operation of the clock. It might be involved in something else that somehow changes the milieu of the cell (e.g. subtle alteration of an ion channel) or the organism (e.g. nonspecific alteration of development that changes the neuroanatomy of a part of the brain) and thereby pleiotropically affects the clock.

This problem of sorting out the wheat from the chaff (the informative mutations from the uninformative ones) is commonly faced in genetic screens. Hartwell resolved a similar dichotomy in the early days of cell cycle genetics by limiting further studies to those temperature-sensitive genetic lesions that stopped cell cycle progression both at a unique phase in the cell cycle and within just a few cycles after the shift to nonpermissive conditions (77, 78). Without the benefit of circadian clock-phase specific markers, clock geneticists have used other criteria to classify mutants. Feldman, recognizing the distinction between "the clock and the hands of the clock" and that mutations that simply uncoupled the hands from the oscillator would yield an arrhythmic phenotype, specifically targeted his early studies on *Neurospora* clock mutants to those strains in which clock expression remained strong, but in which the periodicity was altered rather than altogether lost (55). Generally, one would like at least some alleles of a clock gene to affect only the period length of the oscillation (i.e. to leave the events downstream from the oscillator, the hands of the clock, unaffected) and not to grossly affect the viability of the organism. Since it appears that many of the canonical characteristics of circadian rhythms (period length, temperature compensation, entrainment) may be interconnected, it is comforting to find more than one basic clock property simultaneously affected in clock mutants; this has been the case with salient clock genes in both *Drosophila* and *Neurospora* (35, 64). However, regardless of the criteria used, uncertainty as to the specificity of a mutation is one of the caveats of a genetic approach. With this caveat in mind, it is understood that genes are typically named for the context in which they are isolated, not for what they actually are or do. Thus genes isolated in the context of the cell cycle are called *cell division cycle* (*cdc*) genes; genes that affect development are called developmental genes; and genes isolated in the context of circadian clocks are typically called clock genes. Some mutations identify genes that are informative about the process in question. For instance, mutations in the *CDC28* and *cdc2* genes of *S. cerevisiae* and *S. pombe,* respectively, led to the identification of the kinases that drive the mitotic engine in all eukaryotic cells (135). Other mutations have not been informative. For instance, one of the earliest *Drosophila* genes shown to affect development was the *rudimentary* locus, wherein mutations resulted in the development of truncated (rudimentary) wings. Subsequent biochemical analysis showed the product of this gene encodes enzymes of intermediary metabolism (a multifunctional polypeptide catalyzing the first three steps of pyrimidine biosynthesis), the mutation of which apparently exerts a developmental effect in some relatively uninterpretable and probably obscure manner (120). In the aggregate the same will be true of clock mutations: some will be informative and some will not.

Genetics tends only to be done in systems where people do genetics, a fact that has less to do with the perversity of scientists than the perversity of biological systems. First, while eukaryotes generally have sex and produce offspring, many do not do so in a laboratory context, either because the biology of the organism is too cumbersome (such as *Aplysia*) or too poorly understood (such as *Gonyaulax*). Secondly, the practice of genetics consists of following the segregation of genes (identified by phenotypes) and comparing that segregation to the assortment of other characteristics (the process of assigning genetic linkage of groups of genes to particular chromosomes). It is clear that it is easiest to classify the segregation of a novel gene if there are many markers available for comparison. In this way genetic systems are bootstrap operations; the more that is known, the easier it is to get additional information. These realities, combined with the need for a visible clock phenotype, have limited the serious use of classical genetics in the context of clocks to just a few organisms.

The strength of a genetic approach, however, remains in the fact that identification of genes is directly tied to a heritable change in phenotype. In this regard, classical genetics still has something to recommend it over a reverse genetic approach in which mutations can be engineered in candidate clock genes (for instance by constructing gene knockouts in transgenic organisms), and then the organisms bearing these candidate gene-mutations subsequently examined for changes in the clock. This can now be routinely done in the fungi including *Neurospora* (3) and even in mice (e.g. 87, 175). However, in all species where this technology is applicable, there exist precedents in which disruption of genes deemed to be important (based on time and place of expression or suspected activity) has not infrequently resulted in either a subtle unexpected phenotype or no obvious phenotypic defect (29, 170). This lack-of-phenotype-upon-inactivation could be in part due to redundancy of genes within the genome, in part to redundancy in function within the complex processes being studied, and in part to the complexity of biological systems. In any case, these negative results are congruent with, and were in fact anticipated by, similar findings in invertebrates (e.g. 186) and microorganisms (e.g. 1) and are likely to be true in all organisms.

How Genetics Has Been Used for the Study of Clocks

The primary use has been in studies aimed at identifying the components involved in the assembly or operation of the clock. Deliberate screens for such mutant strains have been carried out in *Chlamydomonas, Neurospora,* and *Drosophila,* although clock mutant strains are additionally available now in the hamster and blowfly. In each case, these mutations identify genes whose alteration is known to affect the function of the clock. The hope of this work is that eventually these genetic studies will provide, via molecular genetics, insight into the actual rhythmic biochemistry of the clock, a goal that is now in sight as a result of the study of the *period* gene in *Drosophila* and the *frequency* gene in *Neurospora* (see below).

Strains bearing known (i.e. biochemically understood) mutations have been used in *Drosophila* and extensively in *Neurospora* to begin to limit the number of different biochemical processes or pathways that might be required for the execution of rhythmicity. For instance, in the fruit fly and the mouse, mutations known to disrupt or destroy the visual system have been used to determine the role of vision in both entrainment and pacemaker function (41, 80, 132).

Genetics has been used as a fine dissecting tool, and as a specific tag for tissues, to determine what tissues are required for rhythmicity. Mosaic analysis as carried out in the fly (44, 101) has much in common with transplantation studies such as those carried out in the hamster (34, 147, 161).

Genetics has been used to begin to determine the complexity of the clock process. As genetic units, all clock genes have at least two distinct identifying characteristics, one being their phenotype (the effect on the clock), and the other their map position within the genome (i.e. chromosome number and arm, etc). In this way, two separate mutations having similar effects on the clock can be distinguished (e.g. the short period mutants *prd-4* and *frq* [2,4,6] in *Neurospora*), and a series of mutations having quite different characteristics can be shown to be due to different alterations in the just one gene (as in the case of the multiple long- and short-period alleles of both *per* in flies and *frq* in the fungi). On the assumption that all clock genes are equally accessible to mutation, one can estimate how many additional unidentified genes there are by how many times the same clock genes have appeared in screens so far. In untargeted screens, only *frq* and *per* have appeared more than once, which suggests that there are many more clock genes yet to be identified. Overall we have only begun to scratch the surface with respect to identification of genes involved with circadian rhythmicity, and the relative paucity of mutants makes it difficult even to draw meaningful generalizations.

Finally, genetics serves as a substrate for more and better genetics. This can be through the execution of suppressor screens (in which one starts with a mutant phenotype, isolates secondary mutations that counteract the phenotypic effects of the primary mutation and, subsequently, unmasks the secondary mutant by crossing out the primary mutation) (90), or through the design of better screens. For instance, through the use of molecular genetics, existing cloned clock genes or clock-controlled genes can be used to restrict the activity of selectable or screenable reporter genes to specific times of day and thereby drive the isolation of new mutants (see 35, 115 for rationale).

An Overview of the Clock, and Why It Is Hard to Generalize About Clock Genetics

A consensus is emerging that the fundamental feedback loop comprising the clock may be found at the level of intracellular regulation rather than intercellular communication (35, 172). This being the case, consider the clock within the cell. Many readers will be familiar with the ubiquitous symbolic statement of the clock problem coined by Eskin (43) in which INPUT is followed by a squiggle (the clock!) followed by OUTPUT. Figure 1 shows a similarly oversimplified picture that might represent a view of the cellular clock. The problems of circadian rhythmicity at the cellular level reduce to filling in the arrows, both within the clock and leading from the clock. As the complexity of the system increases, there may be a few more arrows per cell, and there are likely to be many more cells and additionally some arrows connecting the cells, and even feedback from the output back into the oscillator (e.g. 130). The application of genetics in the context of clocks has largely been targeted to filling in the arrows within the feedback cycle itself; the output arrows, even within the cell, have been approached only via molecular genetics and biochemistry. However, both for questions concerning how the clock works and how time information is transduced within the cell, there is the hope that the problem will not need to be independently solved for each different clock system.

Generally, aspects of biochemistry or regulation that all cells do they tend to do in similar ways. This is not only true for enzyme mechanisms and metabolic pathways, but probably can be applied to "cellular characteristics." For instance, the mechanisms whereby cells protect themselves from heat shock are known to be widely conserved (109), and both yeasts and vertebrates use DNA-binding homeodomain type proteins to specify cell type (181), heterotrimeric G proteins to mediate cell signaling (121), and similar

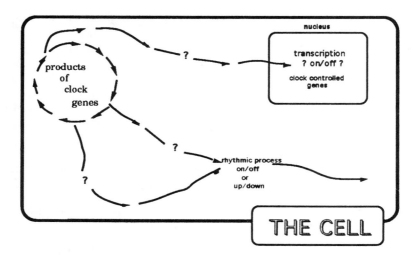

cyclin-modified kinases to supply the mitotic engines that execute the cell cycle (136). Clock molecular biology, however, has not yet reached this level; our view of the clock through genetic analysis is inextricably bound up in the biology of each system so that the data are always recast by the peculiar biology of each organism. Thus while there is reason to be optimistic about the possibility of general conservation of at least the general algorithm describing the clock's feedback loop(s), there is little real molecular data to buttress the optimism. There are simply not many organisms in which clocks have been examined genetically, and there are too few cases in which clock genes have been examined to be able to draw valid generalizations. This being the case, what if any common threads can be found?

Some Generalizations About Clock Genetics

A surprising observation is that there are genuine genetic hotspots for clock mutations, in *Drosophila,* the *period* locus, and in *Neurospora,* the *frequency* locus. In each organism, most of the independently isolated clock gene alleles have mapped to these two loci. In flies, the genetic tools utilized in most of the screens targeted only the X-chromosome (comprising about 40% of the fly's genome and containing *per*) and not the autosomes, while the *Neurospora* screens should have turned up clock loci anywhere; yet in each organism one locus predominates. There is a caveat to this statement, however, in that all screens carried out to date required that the organism bearing the mutation remain healthy enough to display the altered rhythm; a screen for conditional clock mutations might turn up additional genes in droves.

Secondly, most of the independently isolated mutations are semidominant (i.e. a heterozygote shows the phenotypic effects of both the mutant and wild-type allele equally) rather than recessive (in which a heterozygote is phenotypically normal, the mutant allele having been complemented by a copy of the wild-type gene). This is unexpected, since the easiest way to mutate a gene is simply to make it not work, thereby generating a null mutation. Null mutations are nearly always recessive. There are in fact null alleles mapping to both *per* and *frq* (see Table 1), so we know that it is possible to knock these genes out with a characteristic result, yet in most of the rhythm mutations mapping to these genes, their function has been modified rather than knocked out.

In the case of *Neurospora,* although *frq* null mutations still can express a banding pattern under appropriate conditions, the easiest interpretation might be that recessive null mutations (with their inherently poor circadian behavior) were discarded during the early screens in which arrhythmic mutations were not sought (54). In the case of flies, even this ad hoc explanation does not hold since the screens used were in no way biased against arrhythmic mutations. To paraphrase a recent review, this (preponderance of semidomin-

Table 1 Nuclear clock genes and clock affecting genes

Organism	Rhythm, wild type period length (hr)	Gene	Abbreviation; allele name	Period length (hr)	Dominance	Other clock properties affected	Comments on the strain	Reference
Golden hamster (*Mesocricetus auratus*)	Locomoter activity, 24	*tau* (τ)	—	$\tau/+ = 22$ $\tau/\tau = 20$	Semidominant	—	Identified in a shipment of animals from a commercial supplier	(127, 147, 148)
Chlamydomonas reinhardtii	Phototaxis, stickiness to glass, 24	*w-c₁*	—	21	—	—	Arose spontaneously from a wild-type strain	(15)
		90-	—	21	—	—	Naturally occurring wild strains	(15)
		s-	—	18	—	—	Spontaneously occurring	(128)
		period-1	*per-1*	26–28	Dominant	—	From nitrosoguanidine mutagenesis	(16, 17)
		period-2	*per-2*	26–28	Recessive	—	From nitrosoguanidine mutagenesis	(16, 17)
		period-3	*per-3*	26–28	—	—	From nitrosoguanidine mutagenesis	(16, 17)
		period-4	*per-4*	26–28	Semidominant	—	From nitrosoguanidine mutagenesis	(16,17)

Neurospora crassa						
Conidiation, 21.5						
arginine-13	arg-13	$19^{a,b}$	Recessive	—		
chain elongation	cel	Variable^c	Recessive	Temperature compensation	—	
chrono	chr	23.5	Semidominant	Temperature compensation	From nitroso-guanidine mutagenesis	(48, 53, 58)
clock affecting-1	cla-1	27	Semidominant	—	Spontaneous, associated with chromosomal translocation	(14)
cytochrome a-5	cya-5	19^b	—	—	Cytochrome aa3-deficient	(12)
cytochrome b-2	cyb-2	18^b	—	—	Cytochrome b-deficient	(12)
cytochrome b-3	cyb-3	20^b	—	—	Cytochrome b-deficient	(107)
cysteine-4	cys-4	$19^{a,b}$	Recessive	—	—	(53, 56)
cysteine-12	cys-12	$19^{a,b}$	Recessive	—	—	(53, 56)
cytochrome-4	cyt-4	20^b	—	—	Cytochromes-aa$_3$ and b deficient	(107)
female fertility-1 (allelic to glycerol phosphate-3)	ff-1 (glp-3)	19^b	—	—	—	(12, 142)
frequency	frq^1	16	Semidominant	—	From nitroso-guanidine mutagenesis	(54)
	$frq^2 = frq^4 = frq^{6d}$	19	Semidominant	—	From nitroso-guanidine mutagenesis	(54, 57)

Table 1 (Continued)

Organism	Rhythm, wild type period length (hr)	Gene	Abbreviation; allele name	Period length (hr)	Dominance	Other clock properties affected	Comments on the strain	Reference
			frq^3	24	Semidominant	Temperature compensation	From nitrosoguanidine mutagenesis	(54, 58)
			$frq^7 = frq^8$	29	Semidominant	Temperature compensation	From nitrosoguanidine mutagenesis	(54, 57, 58)
			frq^9	Variable	Recessive	Temperature and nutritional compensation, entrainment	From ultraviolet light mutagenesis	(117, 119)
			frq^{10}	Variable	Recessive	Temperature and nutritional compensation	Targeted gene disruption via DNA transformation	B. Aronson, J. Dunlap, in preparation
		maternally inherited	mi (mi-2, mi-3, mi-5)	18–19[b]	—	—	Mitochondrial gene: cytochrome oxidase subunit 1-deficient	(12)
		oligomycin-resistant	oli	18–19	Semidominant	—	Mitochondrial ATPase, subunit 9	(28)
		phenylalanine-1	phe-1	19[b]	—	—	Ergosterol synthesis-deficient	(107)

Organism	Function	Gene name	Allele	Period length	Dominance	Property	Comments	Ref.
		period-1	prd-1	26	Recessive	Temperature compensation	From nitroso-guanidine mutagenesis	(51, 53)
		period-2	prd-2	25.5	Recessive	—	From ultraviolet light mutagenesis	(48, 53, 58)
		period-3	prd-3	25	Recessive	Temperature compensation	From ultraviolet light mutagenesis	(48, 53, 58)
		period-4	prd-4	18	Semidominant[e]	Temperature compensation	From ultraviolet light mutagenesis	(48, 53, 58)
Drosophila melanogaster	Eclosion, locomoter activity (24)[f]	*Andante*	*And* (allelic to dusky (*dy*) gene)	24–26 (depending on allele)	Semidominant	—	Also affects wing color and morphology	(96, 133)
		Disconnected[g]	*disco¹* = *disco²* = *disco³*	Arrhythmic	Recessive	Entrainment	*Disco* flies typically display arrhythmic locomotor activity	(41)
				—	—	—		
				—	—	—		
			disco¹⁶⁵⁶	Arrhythmic	Recessive	Entrainment	Rhythmic eclosion	(75)
		gate	*gat*	24	—	—	Eclosion gating is disturbed; could be allelic to *psi-2* (below)	(85)
		no-receptor-potential A	*norp A^{P24}*	23	—	—	*norp A* is a visual mutant	
			norp A^{P41}	23.3	—	—		

Table 1 *(Continued)*

Organism	Rhythm, wild type period length (hr)	Gene	Abbreviation; allele name	Period length (hr)	Dominance	Other clock properties affected	Comments on the strain	Reference
		period[h]	$per^{D1} =$ $per^{D2} =$ per^{D3}	Arrhythmic	Recessive for rhythmicity, semidominant for period	Phase early (evening eclosion peak in LD)	—	(7, 70, 71, 97, 188)
			per^{D4}	Arrhythmic	Recessive for rhythmicity, semidominant for period	Phase early (evening eclosion peak in LD)	—	(71)
			per^{l}	16	Semidominant	Very early evening eclosion peak in LD	—	R. Konopka, personal communication in (63)
			per^{s}	18–20	Semidominant with per^+	Very early evening eclosion peak in LD	—	(97)
		Clock	per^{Clk}	22.5	Semidominant	Early evening eclosion peak in LD	Formerly thought to be separate from per	(40, 95)
			$per^{L1} =$ per^{L2}	28–30	Dominant to per^0, semidominant with per^+	Early evening eclosion peak in LD	per^L appears to interfere with per^+ function	(97)
		phase angle-2	per^{Lvar} psi-2	28–30	—	Early phase of eclosion	—	(70) (85)

	phase angle-3			Early phase of eclosion	(85)
	soiree[i]			Dark active in LD cycle	(182)
Drosophila pseudoobscura Eclosion, locomotor activity	psi-3	sre	Arrhythmic	—	(63, 144)
	(Not named)-A	$cl^7 = cl^9$	Arrhythmic	Incomplete complementation with other gene	—
	(Not named)-B	$cl^8 = cl^{10}$	Arrhythmic	—	(63, 144)
Lucilia cuprina (blowfly) Eclosion and activity	(Not named)		Arrhythmic	Natural variant encountered in screening	(168)

[a] This strain was originally isolated as an auxotroph. Period length is gradually reduced by increasing degrees of starvation for the required supplement. [b] While the period lengths in these strains are measurably shorter than wild-type under the same experimental conditions, the small magnitude of the differences, combined with the degree of variation obtainable in wild-type strains just from manipulation of growth conditions, raises questions about the biological significance of these period differences. [c] Mutation of this locus renders the period length of the clock manipulable by changes in the fatty acid composition of the medium. [d] Although isolated independently, these alleles are genotypically identical (i.e. have the same DNA sequence) and therefore are completely redundant [*frq*, B. D. Aronson & J. Dunlap, unpublished; *per* (63)]. [e] While *prd-4* is formally semidominant, it is more strongly dominant than, e.g., the *frq* alleles 1 through 8, which are equally dominant with wild type (Q. Liu & J. Dunlap, in preparation). [f] Period length is approximately 24 hr in male flies and 24.5 hr in female flies. [g] *Disco* flies have reduced viability and severely disrupted rhythms in locomoter activity, but several alleles result in detectable alterations in the eclosion rhythm. [h] Listed here are all of the *per* alleles identified through genetic screens. A number of additional alleles have been recently constructed by in vitro mutagenesis of the region of *per* containing the original *per*[s] mutation; most but not all of these are also short (8, 154). These new mutations are described in the text. [i] The phenotypes initially associated with the *sre* are now understood to be attributable to separate linked mutation causing arrhythmia and, separately, an inversion of the normal pattern of activity only in the light. Not included in this listing were genes like *ebony* (132) in *Drosophila* that display clock alterations or arrhythmicity in one clock output, but appear to have a normal pacemaker when a different output is monitored. It seems most likely that only a hand of the clock or the coupling of the clock to the pacemaker is altered in these strains.

Compiling this table was not altogether satisfying. While a desire for completeness compels the listing of all mutations that have been described as having period length effects, it is highly likely that some of these have little to do with the assembly or operation of the clock, their clock affects being due to subtle changes in the metabolic state (e.g. the mitochondrial mutants and amino acid auxotrophs in *Neurospora*) or tissue milieu (e.g. the pigmentation and morphological alleles of *Drosophila*) of important cells.

ance) is probably trying to tell us something (64). Along with the fact that most of the alleles are semidominant goes the observation that the semidominant mutations occur in several types, having both long and short period lengths. Furthermore, even the period lengths of the homozygous strains are similar: 16 hr (frq^1 and per^s), 19 hr ($frq^{2,4,6}$ and per^s), 24 hr (fly and hamster wild-type, frq^3), 28–29 hr ($frq^{7,8}$ and per^1) (see Table 1). While the similarity of these periods is most likely to be coincidental, the spectrum of these periods remains nonrandom, as has been noted before (48).

It is worth considering what semidominance could mean in terms of gene products. There are just a few classes of genes that give rise to semidominant mutations. One class includes genes that give rise to products involved in multisubunit complexes. For instance, in the nematode *C. elegans,* various mutations affecting behavior and morphology are known to be semidominant (138). These results were interpreted as follows: the mutant genes give rise to an altered subunit that is capable of conferring on the entire multisubunit complex an altered behavior since the whole complex must work together as a unit. Another common class of genes identified only via semidominant mutations are genes of multigene families in which each member of the family is functionally redundant. However, in such a scenario, a null mutation in any member of the family is phenotypically wild-type (i.e. the mutation is invisible because of redundancy); clearly in the case of the known clock mutations, null mutants do not have normal clocks, so there is no reason to believe that the clock genes are members of redundant multigene families. It is possible, however, that the clock genes could represent members of a multigene family in which the different members are distinctly regulated, or are similar but not identical. A third explanation of semidominant mutations relates to genes encoding enzymes of poorly (or non-feedback) regulated metabolic pathways. Enzymes that play the major role in determining the rate of passage of substrates through such pathways can be mutated to semidominance; see (92) for a thorough discussion of this topic. Fourthly, semidominant mutations are widely recognized among regulatory genes, especially among the genes involved in the regulatory loops and cascades that govern utilization of different carbon, nitrogen, and phosphorous sources in microbial systems. For instance, one of the best understood positive-acting transcription factors known, the product of the GAL4 gene of *Saccharomyces,* is known to give rise to semidominant mutations (91), as are a variety of other well-defined genetic regulatory factors including the *qa-1S* gene of *Neurospora* (60) and the PHO and GCD genes of yeast (81, 137, see 91 for a list of such regulators). The molecular basis of regulation is well understood with many of these genes, so that the meaning of semidominance in this last context can be at least partly discerned. Regarding clocks, one can easily imagine a feedback loop that incorporates aspects of a genetic regulatory cascade. A null mutation eliminates a part of the loop and stops the oscillation (yielding arrhythmicity), and an altered gene product still participates in the feedback loop but gives it different kinetics leading to a stable, yet identifiably different, characteristic periodicity.

A third generalization about clocks is that the diverse characteristics associated with the clock (e.g. period, temperature compensation, phase) appear to be highly interconnected at the molecular level since in all systems examined so far, single gene semidominant clock mutations are known to affect more than one clock property. Long period mutants of both *per* and *frq* also are altered in their temperature compensation (58, 98). Phase response curve (PRC) amplitude is altered from type 1 to type 0 in the short period hamster mutant *tau* and the short period alleles of *per* (94, 127). [A PRC plots the resetting response of the clock to short duration pulses of agents such as light or temperature that act to entrain the clock. Type 0 represents strong resetting and type 1, weak resetting (179).] Gradual enrichment for eclosion phase variants in *Drosophila pseudoobscura* resulted in the identification of strains that were simultaneously altered in period length (143), a finding qualitatively replicated with single gene mutations in *D. melanogaster* (85). In a recent systematic screen (162) of 12 inbred strains of mice showing minor period length differences, the period effects were correlated with altered PRCs qualitatively similar to the effects seen in the fly; i.e. shortening of period length appearing along with reduced phase advances in the night. In each of these examples, there is no reason why selection for strains altered in one clock property had to yield strains altered in more than one property; the fact that it happened is thus of genuine interest. It is worth noting, however, that such covariation of rhythm parameters is not always the case. For instance, the extensive screens for single gene mutations in *Neurospora* never resulted in the identification of phase variants, and normal temperature compensation is seen in the short period *Neurospora* mutants, the *And* and *per*^Clk mutants in *D. melanogaster,* and the rhythm variants in *C. reinhardtii*.

Finally, there are two documented cases where genetic alterations in the circadian clock are known to affect the periodicity of very short ultradian rhythms having time constants differing from the circadian rhythm by three orders of magnitude. The first of these was that of the male courtship song in the fruit fly, normally having an interpulse interval oscillation of about 55 sec. It is shortened to 35–40 sec in *per*^s and lengthened to 75–90 sec in *per*^l (reviewed in 65). [While these technically demanding observations were the center of some controversy, both retrospective (105) and independent (176) analyses of the data have confirmed the original observations of Kyriacou & Hall (103) and suggest that a published inability to reproduce the data (47) was due to incomplete analysis and technical aspects of the experimental detail.] The other more recent observation (A. Loudon & M.

Menaker, personal communication) is that the timing of LH (luteinizing hormone) pulses, normally arising from the pituitary in the hamster with an approximate periodicity of once every 30 min, is lengthened to once every 35 min in the short period hamster mutant *tau*. In each organism, the anatomical focus of the ultradian rhythm, the thorax for the fly courtship song (62) and the pituitary for the LH surges, is clearly distinct from the anatomical locus of the circadian oscillators, the head for the fly clock and the SCN for the hamster clock. Thus compelling data suggest that the self-same gene product (or alternative products arising from the same gene) is influencing oscillations with time constants different by several orders of magnitude in two distinct tissues. A caveat for the latter part of this generalization (two distinct tissues), however, was raised in the initial discussion about the use of genetics: the answers one gets from genetic analysis are directly tied to the questions that are asked. In the case of both flies and hamsters, the clock mutations were identified through screens for alterations in rhythmic behavior, as distinct from rhythmic hormone levels, or vision, or enzyme activities, etc. Thus the possibility exists (and in fact has been raised before, M. Menaker, personal communication, J. Hall personal communication) that if different rhythms were used as the basis of screens (for instance, visual perception instead of locomoter behavior), then different mutants might be isolated that could turn out to have different anatomical foci (the eyes rather than the brain). In other words, it may be the case that there are more cell and tissue autonomous clocks than we now recognize since most of our whole organism analyses, both physiological and genetic, have really targeted specialized aspects of behavior or growth (chiefly locomoter activity) and thus may not be providing information about the rest of the system. Consistent with this conjecture, there is now good evidence for tissue autonomous circadian rhythms in *per* protein immunoreactivity in the *Drosophila* eye [a rhythm whose autonomous nature could only be observed in a genetic background (*disco*) that eliminates the locomoter activity rhythm by eliminating connections between the fly eye and brain] (191), and in sperm release in the moth testis (59).

MUTANT STRAINS AND INDIVIDUALS

Several brief organism-specific overviews follow, which refer where possible to more comprehensive reviews that have appeared elsewhere. The only attempt at synopticity appears in Table 1, where a list of all of the known rhythm mutants has been attempted since there is now a considerable amount of unpublished data surrounding the existence, identity, and even redundancy of these genes.

Plants, Macro and Micro

Early studies of phenotypic variation among natural or selected populations suggested polygenic control of period length (18), and were used to suggest that single gene mutants affecting rhythmicity might never be attainable. However, subsequent identification of single gene mutants in *Chlamydomonas* (Table 1) showed this not to be the case. These mutants are a mixed lot. One of the rhythm variants, *90-*, is simply a naturally occurring wild-type strain and probably differs from other standard laboratory stocks at a variety of genetic loci. Such genetic background effects can contribute to a clock effect that is in fact due to the summation of a number of minor effects arising from different genes (see also similar studies with mice, discussed below). Of the *Chlamydomonas* clock genes, only the *per* alleles (all yielding long clocks) are likely to be biologically meaningful in terms of potentially identifying genes important for the assembly or operation of the clock, since they arose as apparently single gene mutants in an otherwise constant genetic background. The genes identified by these mutations are unlinked (no clustering as was the case for *frq* in *Neurospora* and *per* in *Drosophila*); temperature compensation in these strains is normal; and in multiply mutant strains, the mutations show cumulative effects such that double, triple, and quadruple mutants bearing different numbers of mutant clock genes display successively longer period lengths (16). Qualitatively the same result obtains when multiple mutants are made among the *Neurospora* mutants (57).

HIGHER PLANTS   Progress in genetics has often been tied to the identification and domestication of appropriate model systems and, in higher plants, the system of choice is the crucifer *Arabidopsis thaliana*. Currently, independent efforts are under way in two different laboratories (S. Kay & A. Millar, personal communication; R. McClung, personal communication) to identify rhythm mutants, so it will not be long before there are single gene variants in this species.

Mammals

Studies of natural and selected populations suggest multigenic control (e.g. 146, 162). Explicitly, limited screening of existing mouse mutants has so far failed to reveal any single gene mutations that have significant affects on period length, phase, or rhythm expression. There are currently two separate efforts underway to screen chemically induced mouse mutants for rhythm defects (J. Takahashi, personal communication; G. E. Pickard & M. Bucan, personal communication) so the paucity of single gene effects may soon disappear. This optimism concerning the possibility of obtaining mouse mutants comes from the recent appearance of a single gene mutation (in the gene known as *tau*) affecting the clock in a closely related species, the golden hamster.

The serendipitous origin of this amazing creature in a routine shipment of hamsters from the Charles River supply house has been recounted elsewhere (127, 148) and is now solidly ensconced in the lore of circadiana. *tau* appears to be equally expressed in both males and females, and it is (not surprisingly) semidominant, with heterozygotes having a period length of 22 hr and homozygotes 20 hr. Additionally, the amplitude of the light PRC is dramatically increased (discussed above in the context of covariance of clock characteristics), although despite this increased resetting ability, neither heterozygotes nor homozygotes entrain normally to 24 hr light cycles. It almost seems as if the pacemaker has become too responsive to light in the mutant strain. This distinctly heightened sensitivity is recapitulated in the context of the rodent's photoperiodic reproductive response. Normally hamsters require more than 12 hr of light per 24 hr to maintain reproductive competence, but in the mutant hamster, this requirement is reduced to less than 1 hr. This hypersensitive response to light may reflect both the greater amplitude of the light PRC and the attendant abnormal phase relationship that the hamster's clock adopts with respect to the light/dark cycle (127). In the general realm of pleiotropy, *tau* mutant hamsters are reported to be generally smaller than normal in size, more irritable, and perhaps more short lived (127).

Despite the fact that the *tau* mutation arose in a strain lacking formal genetic underpinnings, it has already proven to be immensely useful and may well prove to be a paradigmatic example of what a good tool a useful mutation can be in the context of physiology. First, the mutation has been useful as a marker for donor suprachiasmatic nucleus (SCN) tissue in transplantation protocols. These experiments, in which donor fetal hypothalamic tissue containing the SCN from an animal of one *tau* genotype is placed into the third ventricle of an SCN-lesioned (arrhythmic) recipient animal of a different *tau* genotype thereby restoring rhythmicity, established conclusively that the donor tissue did in fact contain a pacemaker of its own rather than simply being effective in recoupling existing oscillators (147). These results then paved the way for analyses aimed at determining the nature and identity of the neural and hormonal connections that must be re-established to couple the transplanted clock to the rodent's overt behavior. In fact, some progress toward these answers has been made by studying the rhythmic behavior of partially lesioned hamsters that are the recipients of SCN transplants (M. Vogelbaum & M. Menaker, submitted). Surprisingly, such temporal chimeras generally simultaneously express the rhythms of both tissues, with no hint of interaction or period averaging. This result suggests that there is less coupling between the paired SCN than would have been guessed a priori and that each individual nucleus must establish and maintain its own highly specific output pathway connections. A third use of the *tau* mutation has been to elucidate the nature of the circadian involvement in measuring the period of estrus: briefly, the estrus clock does not count circadian days, but rather the circadian clock acts to gate estrus at an appropriate time of day after an appropriate amount of developmental time (about 96 to 100 hr) is passed. Here then, the clock's involvement in gating estrus is formally identical to its involvement in gating fly eclosion (144). Finally, as mentioned above, the single gene *tau* mutation has been used to show the inter-relatedness of a circadian and an ultradian clock.

Despite the interest in the *tau* mutation, cloning this particular gene could be a molecular geneticist's nightmare. With a paucity of existing genetic markers, chromosome walking, such as was used to obtain *frq* (126) and *per* (6, 151), will be difficult until these markers, in forms such as RAPD markers or microsatellite DNAs, are first identified. Once a putative piece of *tau* is cloned, it may also be difficult to prove that it is in fact *tau* and not a gene that affects the action of *tau*. Methods for the generation of transgenic hamsters are in their infancy, but it is likely that DNAs could be transduced into mice and assayed for semidominant period shortening in the hope that a transgenic *tau* gene could be expressed at something approaching a normal level. Since hamsters are not isogenic (that is, they do not all have the same DNA sequence for each gene), there are undoubtedly a number of undescribed genetic variants silently assorting out among the progeny of any cross. Some of these naturally variant alleles will result in changes in the electrophoretic mobility of proteins on gels, so that efforts aimed at comparing protein gels from normal and mutant hamsters would not appear likely to be fruitful either. Still, since good fortune (and a well prepared mind) had a great deal to do with finding *tau* in the first place, it may be that trying to clone it now will be worth the effort.

Neurospora

BACKGROUND It all started with Feldman who, as a postdoc, abandoned what could have been a comfortable (if ultimately uninformative) career of using inhibitors on *Euglena* (50), followed Konopka's example (see below) in ignoring the sage counsel of a few more senior colleagues, and went to Cal Tech to a non-clock lab to pioneer the genetics of the *Neurospora* clock. For historical context, *Neurospora* was already a well developed genetic and biochemical system, following the 1940s work of Beadle & Tatum, who established the discipline of biochemical genetics using this system (for review see 141). A circadian clock governing the developmental potential of this ascomycete fungus had been described more than a decade before (145), and Sargent, Briggs, and colleagues had done much to begin to tame the clock system (e.g. 156, 157, 158). The *Neurospora* clock exhibited itself as a time-dependent change in the morphology of the culture. At some times of day (the late subjective night and early morning), aerial hyphae would emerge from the surface growth and elaborate asexual spores called conidia. At other times of day, mycelia laid down would permanently remain as undifferentiated surface growth. The periodicity of this rhythmic change in growth habit is about 21.6 hr at 25°C. Feldman spent several unsuccessful years designing and executing clever screens for clock mutants that took advantage of this daily change in morphology. Ultimately, using a brute force screen of the survivors of a mutagenesis, he isolated the first *Neurospora* clock mutants (54) among the first 100 or so survivors screened, and thus provided the second experimental verification of Konopka's rule (see below). The first *Neurospora* clock mutants all mapped to the same region of linkage group VII, at a locus called *frequency*. Thus as had been the case with the *Drosophila* mutants identified a few years earlier (97), these mutants were clustered. The genetic, physiological, and more recently molecular characterization of these and other clock mutant strains in *Neurospora* has generated a wealth of information concerning the physiology of this circadian oscillator. The *Neurospora* clock is of compelling interest because it represents a minimal system that still retains all of the axiomatic circadian characteristics by which clocks are known. Readers desiring more depth are referred to one of a series of excellent reviews on the clock of this organism (35, 36, 39, 48, 49, 52, 107).

THE CLOCK MUTANTS   There are presently 15 independently isolated alleles identifying seven different genes that, when mutated, display effects on the period length of the *Neurospora* clock. The genes are *frequency* (*frq*), *period-1* (*prd-1*), *period-2* (*prd-2*), *period-3* (*prd-3*), *period-4* (*prd-4*), *chrono* (*chr*), and *clock-affecting-1* (*cla-1*) (Table 1). Nine of the 15 alleles map to *frq*, and the additional genes are each identified by single alleles. No attempt has been made to isolate anonymous conditional (e.g. temperature-sensitive or nonsense suppressible) mutants of the clock. Thus this assemblage does not represent a complete or even a representative sampling of the possible clock mutants in *Neurospora*.

frq   Of the alleles mapping to *frq*, all show incomplete dominance except frq^9 and frq^{10} (Table 1). There exist different short period variants ranging from quite short (frq^1, period length 16 hr) to not as short ($frq^2 = frq^4 = frq^6$, period length 19.3 hr) and two different long variants ranging from slightly long (frq^3, period length 24 hr) to quite long ($frq^7 = frq^8$, period length 29 hr) (48). The short period alleles display normal temperature and nutritional compensation, while the long period alleles are altered in several ways reflecting effects on more than one basic clock property. Both frq^7 (and frq^8) and frq^3 have lost their temperature compensation to varying degrees (58), and frq^7 (and therefore also frq^8) has to a large extent lost its ability to be reset by short pulses of the protein synthesis inhibitor cycloheximide (37). Light and chemical PRCs done on the *frq* mutants suggest that the period length changes are not due to a uniform effect over the entire cycle, but rather that a specific part of the cycle in the late subjective day to early subjective night is uniquely lengthened or shortened (27, 131). Qualitatively the same effect is seen in PRCs using the short period *Drosophila* mutant per^s (94, 180).

One of the interesting aspects of the biology of *Neurospora* is the fact that the organism grows as a syncytium (i.e. like a muscle cell rather than a fibroblast), thus it is possible to generate heterokaryons in which nuclei of different genotype are mixed together in different proportions in the same cytoplasm. When such nuclear mixtures are made using the allelic clock mutants mapping to *frq*, there is a strict proportionality of period length that reflects the nuclear ratio of the syncytium. For instance, at 70% long (29 hr), 30% wild-type (21 hr), the period length of the heterokaryon is 70% long (or about 26.5 hr) (57). This is true for any mixture of the semidominant alleles tried so far (119). This suggests that *frq* may be acting at or near the heart of the pacemaker (49).

There are two recessive alleles of *frq*, one identified in a mutant screen (frq^9; 119) and one generated in vitro through the use of molecular genetics and transformation (frq^{10}; B. D. Aronson & J. Dunlap, unpublished; see below). While the former has been examined in greater detail, both appear to be null mutants and are therefore expected to have identical phenotypes. Interestingly, *frq* null alleles are not altogether devoid of rhythmicity, but rather display on the appropriate growth medium a ragged rhythm that entrains poorly to light and has completely lost the capacity for both nutritional and temperature compensation. Under some growth conditions, conidial bands fail to form altogether, and the production of conidia is dramatically reduced (117, 119). Pigmentation of mycelia and conidia, and the light inducibility of carotenoid synthesis, appears to be normal in these strains (K. A. Johnson & J. Dunlap, unpublished).

OTHER CLOCK GENES   Of the six mutations mapping to genes other than *frq*, three are semidominant (*chr, prd-4,* and *cla-1*) and three are recessive (*prd-1, prd-2,* and *prd-3*). Two of these display altered temperature compensation patterns, with *prd-3* being overcompensated such that the period actually increases with increasing temperature, and *chr* retains strong temperature compensation even at temperatures above 30°C, the point where compensation typically breaks down in *Neurospora*. These genes, combined with the long period *frq* alleles mentioned above, represent a large collection of genetic variants affecting the capacity for temperature compensation and may speak to the origin of this axiomatic circadian characteristic.

Several models have been advanced to explain temperature compensation, but they can be placed into two classes: those that postulate temperature compensation to be a property inherent to the feedback loop that generates the rhythm (e.g. 134, 140, 163) and those that imagine compensation to be a useful property appended onto a separate feedback loop constituting the oscillator itself (e.g. 79, 171). A prediction of the latter class of models is that mutations affecting the oscillator itself need not affect compensation. Yet, compensation is altered in some way in fully half of the clock mutant strains identified in *Neurospora* (it has not yet been examined in *cla-1*). While one must be cautious in drawing conclusions from the absence of mutants, the existence of so many period-affecting mutations that additionally affect compensation suggests that temperature compensation may in fact be an inherent property of the oscillator. An alternative and equally supportable interpretation is that only a few of the existing period-affecting mutations (not *frq, chr,* or *prd-1* at least) have actually altered the oscillator, but that instead, their period effects are due to lesions in temperature compensation (strengthening or weakening it) which, in turn, affects the period length of the clock (37).

Do different clock genes interact? The availability of multiple genes characterized by mutations having both lengthened and shortened period lengths has created the possibility of generating multiply mutant strains in which to search for possible interactive effects. Interestingly, the effects of multiple mutations in the same nucleus are cumulative, such that the combination of two short period mutations yields an even shorter double mutant, the combination of two longs an even longer double mutant, and the combination of a long and a shortened tend to cancel each other out (53, 57). Periods as short as 13.5 hr and as long as 58 hr have in this way been described (48). In the combinations of single mutations, each yielding period lengths within a few hours of wild-type, the period of the multiple mutants are well described by either additive or multiplicative effects, while in the combination of more deviant strains, a multiplicative model tends to describe the data somewhat better (106). In multiply mutant strains, the effects on period length must in some combinations of strains be further compounded by effects on temperature compensation. In general, the interaction is most generally described simply as interactive and cumulative; attempts at more mathematical descriptions anoint the data with more precision than the experiments allow. The most important point here, however, is that there have been no cases of genuine epistasis (masking of the phenotypic effects of one allele by the presence of a mutation in a different gene) among any combinations of the canonical clock mutants. This appears not to be the case among combinations of some other clock-affecting genes (see below).

DIRECT VS INDIRECT CLOCK EFFECTS   A point made above is that not every gene identified by mutations affecting the period length will necessarily encode a gear in the clock mechanism. All three of the recessive clock mutant strains display pleiotropic effects on morphology, growth rate, and fertility, which suggests that the period lengthening seen in these strains may represent yet another indirect effect of the lesion. The most extreme example of this is *prd-1*, and it may represent a good case for pleiotropic effects on the clock. In addition to having a longer than normal period length (25.8 hr), *prd-1* has an altered fatty acid composition (23), and cultures barely grow at all for some days after inoculation, prior to assuming a slower than normal growth rate (51). Although temperature compensation appears to be relatively unchanged in this strain, the amplitude of the PRC to light pulses shows a marked temperature dependence, with a nearly normal amplitude at 20°C but one that is greatly reduced at 25°C. The admixture of so many effects of a single mutation, several of which appear to be somewhat pleiotropic, suggests that the clock effects seen in *prd-1* may not be a direct result of the lesion, but rather a side effect of the strain's altered metabolism (51). *prd-1* has recently been cloned (H. Nakashima, personal communication), and it should soon be possible to determine the identity of the altered gene product in this strain and thereby approach the question of direct vs indirect clock effects.

Of all of the *Neurospora* clock mutants, only *cla-1* is known to be the result of something other than a point mutation. This strain was identified in a screen for clock effects among translocation-bearing strains, and is known to bear a reciprocal translocation exchanging parts of linkage group I R and VII R (14). Although the actual break points of the translocation have not been mapped, the mutation is semidominant and has a period length of about 27 hr, so the possibility exists that one end of the translocation may be within the *frq* gene (also located on VII R). Efforts to test this possibility are currently planned.

The *prd-4* gene has recently been intensely studied by Liu (111). The single known allele of this gene displays both altered temperature compensation and a 3.5 hr shortening of the clock to about 18 hr. It was mapped to a small interval on linkage group I R between *arg-13* and *os-1*. Subsequent cloning of *arg-13* (see below) allowed the cloning of *prd-4* by a chromosome walk (2, 39, 111); however, no molecular details are yet available concerning this gene. In heterokaryons, *prd-4* behaves as a strong allele; 50:50 (*prd-4* mutant:*prd-4*[+]) heterokaryons are still substantially mutant (111).

Other Mutations Affecting Rhythmicity

Nearly 100 biochemical, developmental, or morphological mutants have been screened for effects on rhythmicity, either directly or in the course of other analyses. The great preponderance of these (resulting in no clock effects) are listed and caveats discussed elsewhere (52, 107). Generally when effects are seen, they are small and result in a clock that runs an hour or two fast. Thus there is a distinct possibility that the clock changes are pleiotropic effects. However, three potentially important results have emerged from these screens.

FATTY ACIDS AND LIPID METABOLISM   Rhythmicity is altered in strains bearing either of two different mutations known to affect cellular lipids. The *phe-1* strain is deficient in ergosterol synthesis and has a period length of 19 hr (107). The *cel* strain (defective in fatty acid chain elongation) has been extensively studied by Brody and colleagues (reviewed in 107). This mutation is reported to render the period length of the clock manipulable by the addition of exogenous fatty acids (13, 124) and to result in a substantial temperature- and nutrition-dependent loss in the capacity for temperature compensation (125). Fatty acids apparently do not exert their period lengthening effects through alterations in the bulk fluidity of membranes (122–124). The fatty acid effects on period length are reversible by certain environmental or nutritional conditions that implicate mitochondrial metabolism (22) and also by genetic lesions at *prd-1* (106), *oli*^{r}, and a mitochondrially inherited locus (*mi*) (107). These three genes are known to affect mitochondrial function (see below), which suggests that the fatty acid effects may be acting through effects upon mitochondrial metabolism. An excellent review of this complicated and potentially important topic has recently been published (107).

MUTATIONS AFFECTING MITOCHONDRIAL FUNCTION   A number of mutations displaying slightly shortened period lengths (Table 1) are known to affect mitochondrial function. These include the cytochrome-a and -b genes (*cya-5, cyb-2, cyb-3*), the *cyt-4* gene required for processing mitochondrial rRNA, several maternally inherited (*mi*) alleles encoding cytochrome oxidase, and *oli*^{r} encoding subunit 9 of the mitochondrial ATPase (142). These strains often have slow growth rates, and perhaps as a compensatory mechanism, contain about twice as much mitochondrial protein as is typical for *Neurospora* extracts (11). Interestingly, only shortened periods have been seen to arise in this class of lesions. Reflecting on the relatively small magnitude of these period changes, it remains an open question whether these effects are specific for the clock or are pleiotropic results of global alterations in mitochondrial function.

MUTATIONS AFFECTING AMINO ACID METABOLISM   Several mutations listed in Table 1 occur in genes encoding products involved in the biosynthesis or metabolism of amino acids. It is likely that these clock effects, while real, may be indirect effects resulting from more global changes in pool sizes or pathway fluxes. Again, the clock alterations are seen as a slight shortening of the period. *phe-1* strains require phenylalanine for growth, but are also deficient in ergosterol biosynthesis, apparently because the two pathways share common intermediates early in the pathway (107). Three other strains, *arg-13, cys-4,* and *cys-12* only display the period effects when starved for either arginine (173) or cysteine, respectively (56). The *arg-13* gene has recently been cloned and sequenced and its product tentatively identified (111). The gene bears significant similarity to several other genes encoding mitochondrial transmembrane carriers (93) and, based on its physiology and nutritional requirements, apparently encodes a mitochondrial amino acid (perhaps citrulline) carrier. The arginine requirement of the strain would be consistent with the arginine metabolism of *Neurospora* in which the mitochondrion plays an essential role (26). Presumably, something about starvation for arginine in this strain brings about a change in mitochondrial metabolism (reminiscent of the clock affecting alterations in mitochondrial metabolism discussed above) that, possibly indirectly, affects the clock.

Molecular Biology of the Neurospora Clock

Three genes affecting the *Neurospora* clock have been cloned. Two of these have already been discussed above: *prd-4,* about which there is not yet any molecular information, and *arg-13,* which appears to encode a mitochondrial amino acid transporter. In the absence of sequence information, it would have been difficult to make the connection between *arg-13* and the mitochondrion, and yet the sequence similarities and physiology of the strain fit well with the effects of mitochondrial lesions previously identified by Brody and colleagues.

One of the major surprises of the era of DNA sequencing has been how conservative evolution has been. We now take it for granted that an enzyme performing an identical biochemical function in *E. coli* and humans will have a recognizably similar protein sequence. Similarly, a part of a protein (a domain) performing a function (such as binding to DNA or serving to localize the protein to the nucleus) is likely to be conserved among the proteins doing this. While there is often more than one sequence capable of conferring this ability, there are only a small number of different sequences associated with any capability. As a result, a strong sequence similarity between a gene or protein of unknown function and one of known function allows strong predictions about the biochemical function of the unknown gene. The unexpected elucidation of *arg-13* as a mitochondrial carrier is a good example of the value of a molecular genetic approach, and serves as a lead in to the molecular analysis of the first of the two clock genes that have been cloned and extensively studied at the molecular level.

THE MOLECULAR BIOLOGY OF *FREQUENCY*   *frq* was cloned by virtue of its well known genetic location on linkage group VII R (about 2.5 map units distal from *oli* and 2.5 map units proximal to *for*) (119). Since *oli* had been cloned elsewhere, a chromosome walk across the region containing the gene provided a logical approach (126). The actual *frq* gene was identified by transforming DNA from the vicinity of *frq* into *Neurospora* strains bearing the recessive frq^9 mutation, first selecting primary transformants that had taken up and were expressing the transforming DNA, and then screening the primary transformants for rescue of the frq^9 phenotype, signaled by a return to wild-type circadian rhythmicity. Four overlapping cosmid clones rescued frq^9, and their correct origin (from VII R) was confirmed by RFLP mapping and by continuing the walk to identify *for*.

What does *frq* encode? Analysis by transformation of smaller DNA pieces contained within the region of overlap of the cosmids showed *frq* to be contained within an approximately 8 kb piece of DNA that encodes two transcripts, one about 1500 nucleotides and the other about 5,000 nucleotides in length.

Each of the transcripts (Figure 2, modified from 36, with permission) is transcribed separately and divergently, each is polyadenylated, and the small

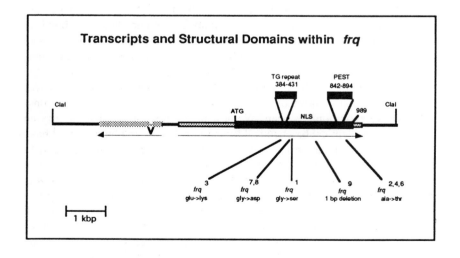

transcript contains a single intron that is removed. Neither of transcripts arising from *frq* is abundant, and little is known regarding their regulation. Importantly, however, recent data show that the amount of the large *frq* transcript is regulated by the clock (J. Loros & J. Dunlap, unpublished), with a maximum in the early morning. Since mutations in *frq* affect the clock, the finding that the clock, in turn, affects the level of *frq* product strongly suggests that *frq* is in the heart of the feedback loop describing the pacemaker itself. Thus FRQ can be used with confidence to replace one of the arrows describing the clock cycle in Figure 1. (Instead of developing a model for *frq* here, however, the feedback model for an oscillator will be presented with the discussion of *per*.) Partial genomic DNA sequences are available for portions of the large *frq* region from several species of *Neurospora* in addition to *N. crassa* (M. Merrow & J. Dunlap, in preparation; 108); these sequences are virtually identical to the *N. crassa* sequence. Additionally, the sequence of the entire large *frq* region from a more distantly related fungus, *Sordaria fimicola,* has recently been completed and shows regions of conservation interspersed with regions of divergence (M. Merrow & J. Dunlap, in preparation). cDNAs corresponding to both transcripts from *N. crassa* have been sequenced, thus allowing a prediction of the potential protein product(s) of *frq*.

Recent and unexpected data from both cDNA sequencing and PCR now strongly suggest the presence of an intron-containing third transcript that overlaps the central portion of the large *frq* transcript. Because of the length of large *frq*, no full length cDNAs from large *frq* have been isolated; this is not unusual for a long transcript. As a result, the separate nature of the long *frq* transcript and this novel intron-containing overlapping transcript remained obscure for some time. cDNA fragments deleted in a small distinct region were thought to have arisen from the large *frq* transcript, but sequence analysis from *Sordaria* unexpectedly showed this "intron" region to be among the most highly conserved regions of the protein. This prompted a reanalysis and the suggestion of the *frq*-antisense third transcript. Presently, little is known about this third transcript; however, no long open reading frames run through it in the region containing the intron.

Sequence analysis of the genomic region encoding the short transcript and cDNAs corresponding to the region suggests that this transcript may not encode a protein; there are no extended open reading frames in any of the potential reading frames, and STOP codons (over 35) are relatively evenly spaced throughout (K. A. Johnson & J. Dunlap, in preparation). Other reports note the existence of spliced, polyadenylated but nontranslated and nonprotein coding RNAs in both *Drosophila* (110) and the mammalian liver (10). However, these unusual and unexpected results regarding *frq* must be considered preliminary pending mutational studies and analysis of additional cDNAs.

The long transcript contains an open reading frame of 989 amino acids beginning with a good consensus (102) initiating methionine start site and preceded by a very long (nearly 1500 nucleotides) untranslated region. The open reading frame would encode a protein of approximately 108 kd without posttranslational modifications (K. A. Johnson & J. Dunlap, in preparation). Several structural features of this potential protein coding region include a mixed repeat of threonine/glycine and serine/glycine (marked TG, Figure 2) containing and surrounded by several potential sites for either N- or O-linked glycosylation; a potential nuclear localization signal (RKKRK, marked nls, Figure 2); a hyperacidic tail characteristic of transcription factors; a number of potential serine and threonine phosphorylation sites; and several PEST sequences (the strongest marked in Figure 2) (149, 152) associated with proteins that are rapidly turned over. These regions all show conservation between *Neurospora* and *Sordaria*.

FRQ is thus far unique. There are no sequences corresponding to any known proteins that bear strong and extended similarity to the predicted protein product of *frq* (FRQ). Interestingly, however, several of the potential protein modification sites found in FRQ are shared with the PER protein of *Drosophila,* and there is a short region of 48 amino acids including and surrounding the TG/SG repeat that shows some similarity (44% identity and 23% highly conservative substitutions) to the TG repeat and surrounding regions of PER (126). While it is remotely possible that FRQ and PER could be evolutionarily related, perhaps with each protein representing separate members of a multigene family, several independent pieces of data suggest that this similarity is simply fortuitous. First, the entire direct canonical TG repeat of PER can be deleted from PER without the protein losing the ability to, mostly, complement the defects in a *per⁻* mutant fly (187). Secondly, there is only limited sequence conservation among *Drosophila* species in this region of DNA (20, 174). Despite the lack of strict sequence conservation, however, all flies show some type of repeat in this domain of the protein, and the predicted structural properties of the repeat region of PER from all *Drosophila* species thus far analyzed (21) (and of the similar region of FRQ; K. A. Johnson & J. Dunlap in preparation) are quite similar and would consist of a series of helical turns of the type that might link functional domains (21). Recent work by Ishida et al (83) has demonstrated the existence of several diurnally regulated mRNA species found in several parts of the rodent brain (including the SCN) that show sequence similarity to *per* and less strongly to *frq*.

The Nature of the frq Mutations and the Nature of frq

Extensive Southern analyses have shown that none of the eight *frq* mutations arose because of gross DNA rearrangements. Similarly, all of the alleles including *frq*[9] appear to produce all of the messages and at approximately the same levels (J. Dunlap, unpublished). This suggests that the *frq* alleles arose as a result of point mutations or quite small local insertions or deletions. Based on the genetic fine structure analysis of the alleles (119), one would expect that these mutations would all be clustered in one part of the region. Single nucleotide changes associated with each of the period alterations in the *frq* allelic series have now been determined by sequencing DNA from the appropriate mutant strains (B. D. Aronson & J. Dunlap, in preparation). That these changes are in fact causative of the period alterations was confirmed in most cases by re-inserting a copy of *frq* bearing the nucleotide change back into *frq*[9] and demonstrating the appropriate period length. The data show a high degree of consistency in that all of the mutations except *frq*[9] were the result of nitrosoguanidine mutagenesis, a treatment generally resulting in G to A transitions. In fact, by sequence analysis, all the mutations are G to A changes. *frq*[9] was identified following UV mutagenesis and bears a single base pair deletion, again consistent with the mutagen. All of the mutations occur at nucleotides that are conserved between the *N. crassa* and *Sordaria frq* homologues. Although the different mutations were isolated independently of one another (54, 55, 57), all of the alleles sharing the same phenotype (e.g. *frq*[2], frq[4], and *frq*[6]) also bear the identically altered amino acid and nucleotide; phenotypically identical strains are also genotypically identical. This is a surprising finding. The short period mutations result from very conservative amino acid substitutions (Ala to Thr for *frq*[2], frq[4], and *frq*[6]; Gly to Ser for *frq*[1]) whereas the mutations resulting in long period lengths (Glu to Lys for *frq*[3]; Gly to Asp for *frq*[7] and *frq*[8]) might be expected to be more disruptive since they result in charge changes. Thus a G to A transition just downstream from the TG repeat and the region of *frq/per* similarity results in a Gly to Asp change. The introduction of a negative charge in this region is apparently sufficient to change the period length from 21.5 to 29 hr and to severely attenuate the capacity of the clock for temperature compensation. In general, then, sequence analysis of the different *frq* mutant alleles suggests that all are due to point mutations within the region of the large transcript open reading frame.

How does a cell with no FRQ behave? The mutation in *frq*[9] results in the generation of a truncated protein. This suggests, but does not confirm, that the phenotype associated with *frq*[9] is the null phenotype for *frq,* since such a strain might well still be producing a normal small transcript at the normal level. To confirm the identity of the null phenotype, the entire *frq* locus has been disrupted by replacing the front third of both the large and small transcripts, along with the intergenic promoter region, with a foreign DNA fragment encoding a dominant selectable marker (B. D. Aronson & J. Dunlap, in preparation). This allele, called *frq*[10], shows a phenotype identical to that of frq^9. Thus the varied effects of frq^9, including the reduced number of conidia, the poor entrainment, the lack of compensation, and the rudimentary rhythmicity, are all characteristics of *Neurospora* lacking *frq*. This sets one of the boundary conditions for understanding the role of *frq* in the operation of the pacemaker.

The other boundary condition is knowledge of the characteristics of the clock in a strain having too much FRQ. To create such a strain, the entire protein coding region of the large transcript was placed under the control of a highly regulated *Neurospora* promoter from the *qa-2* gene (60). When this construct is transformed back into a wild-type (frq^+) strain, in the absence the inducer (quinic acid), the clock operates normally. When inducer is added, the strain becomes arrhythmic (B. D. Aronson & J. Dunlap, in preparation). Thus the presence of FRQ under inducible control generates a conditional clock mutant. Apparently, whatever it is that FRQ is doing within the pacemaker must be saturable, with the result of saturation being arrhythmicity. It should be noted that although overexpression can be confirmed at the transcript level, nothing yet is known about the actual protein product of *frq*. Additionally, this inducible construct contains only the coding region of *frq* and none of the extremely long 5' untranslated (putative regulatory) region. Nonetheless, given this conditional arrhythmic phenotype, it should be possible to begin to identify genes encoding the proteins with which FRQ interacts in the operation of the clock, by isolating mutations in genes other than *frq* that suppress the conditional arrhythmia. This promises to become an important tool for dissection of the *Neurospora* pacemaker.

Drosophila

BACKGROUND   It all started with Konopka, who as a graduate student at Cal Tech, disregarded the prevailing wisdom (which cited polygenic control of phase and period, suggested that single gene clock mutants would be dead, and generally argued that single gene clock mutants could never be found) and found the first single gene clock mutants (97). These were isolated in a brute force screen in which mutations lying specifically on the X-chromosome were targeted. In this way recessive alleles could be seen (male flies are genetically XY, females XX). In fact, the first mutant turned up after screening just 200 mutagenic survivors, thus giving rise to another bit of circadiana that has coalesced as Konopka's Rule: "If you don't find it in the first 200, quit." Konopka's rhythm variants were all allelic, mapping to a locus he called *period* or *per* that has subsequently become quite well known. While it has been stated that this topic has been reviewed ad nauseam (63), this can only reflect the undeniable fact that it is a wonderful story with something in it for everyone. The general topic of the genetics and molecular genetics of the

Drosophila clock has been reviewed recently (63, 64) and readers whose interest is piqued are referred there.

THE GENETICS AND PHYSIOLOGY OF *PER*   The spectrum of *per* alleles is seen in Table 1. The original surprise from Konopka was that there were both long and short period mutants that arose from the same gene (later also seen with the *Neurospora frq* alleles), and subsequent work showed that temperature compensation was also altered in at least the long period mutants (45, 98), as was seen with the *frq* alleles (58). Similar to the *tau* mutant hamster, the period length changes associated with the *per* alleles drive predictable phase changes in both the locomoter activity and eclosion rhythms (72), with the evening peaks occurring early (during the day) in *per*^{s}and late (into the night) in *per*^{l}. Despite the dramatic changes in period length brought about by the *per* mutations, all strains bearing these can entrain to 24 hr LD cycles, a feat unattainable (see above) by the *tau* mutant hamsters. Developmentally, *per* has been shown to have reproducible effects on developmental timing, with *per*^{l} lengthening and *per*^{s}shortening both the larval and pupal stages (104), but it appears to have no significant effect on the life span of the fly (45). Recently, the *Clk* mutation, known previously to map genetically in the vicinity of *per,* has been shown to be an allele of *per* (40).

While the *per*^{0} mutants are generally believed to display arrhythmic behavior, it is by no means clear that they are entirely devoid of rhythmicity. This is reminiscent of *Neurospora (frq*^{9}). Two laboratories have suggested that there may be residual rhythmicity in *per*^{0} (30, 80), and using spectral analyses to analyze the activity records of *per*^{0} flies, Dowse and colleagues (30, 32, 33, reviewed in 31) identified statistically robust ultradian rhythms with period lengths ranging from about 5 to 15 hr. The implication is that these ultradian rhythms, and more importantly the oscillators that drive them, are normally also present in wild-type flies. Based on these findings, the possibility has been raised that the circadian clock as commonly observed is actually the result of a coupling, mediated by the product of the per locus, of these ultradian oscillators into a robust circadian oscillator. The mathematical underpinnings for such a model have been well established for some time and were a major focus of effort during the pre-molecular era of clocks research 25 to 30 years ago (e.g. 139). Pertinent to this discussion is the finding that a previous observation suggesting *per* effects on intercellular coupling in the larval salivary gland (5) has been found by the senior author (who performed the original coupling analysis) to be in error. This re-evaluation has involved and been corroborated by work in other laboratories (165). The issue of whether this coupling might occur intracellularly or intercellularly, however irrelevant to the mathematical basis of the model, has important consequences for visualizing the clock.

Considerable effort has gone into determining when and where in the fly the product(s) of this gene are found. The transcript and protein are found in the embryo (88, 112, 164, 185) in the midline region of the developing CNS. Reports of *per's* expression outside of the developing CNS, in particular in the developing salivary gland (5), have been disputed (88, 112, 164). Similarly during development in the larval salivary gland, *per* transcript and protein expression are either there (5, 9, 155) or not there (88, 112, 164), depending on who is reporting the work. At the protein level, these differences in results could reflect the use of different reagents (i.e. different antibodies, made in some cases to different antigens, different tissue preparations, etc) and to differences of opinion over what constitutes background staining (e.g. 112, 164) vs a specific signal (155). At the physiological level, a clock must be running then since both LD transitions and 15 min light pulses experienced anytime during the first, second, or third larval instar are capable of resetting the clock gating adult eclosion (192). Of course, finding that there is a clock may not mean that there must exist the products of *per* expression (e.g. 154, 160). After pupation, once again there is a consensus that *per* is expressed (88, 112, 155, 164) in a variety of places. And last of all, in the adult, there is an embarrassment of riches, as the products of *per* have been reported at specific sites all over the fly, in the photoreceptor cells of the eye and the ocelli, in the optic lobes and central brain (in both glia cells and the lateral neurons) (44), in the thoracic ganglion, the gut, antennae, esophagous, proboscis, rectal papillae, testes, the ovaries and ovarian follicle cells, and in the Malpighian tubules (88, 112, 113, 155, 164). At the cellular level, with the exception of the pupal and adult ovaries, the PER protein generally appears to be predominantly nuclear (113, 155, 164).

Is PER only required to set up the appropriate neuronal connections for the clock? To answer this question, *per* transcription has been driven from a putatively constitutive promoter (46) and used to show that when *per* is not expressed at normal levels there is no behavioral rhythmicity, but that when it is turned on, the rhythmicity returns. These experiments suggest that PER is not required to determine the "wiring diagram" for the oscillator, but rather it must be there as an active participant, with the caveat that there was insignificant basal level expression from the heat shock promoter used in this study compared to the amount needed to wire the clock developmentally (see, for instance, 9). A developmental role for *per* in establishing the cell-cell communications required for rhythmicity thus appears improbable but not impossible. The developmental question aside, however, these experiments establish that in the *per*[0]-arrhythmic adult, everything is poised for rhythmicity, awaiting only the appearance of enough PER protein.

Why is expression found in so many different places? A good possibility, favored by Liu et al (112) is that many of these tissues may contain intrinsic tissue autonomous circadian oscillators, each of which uses *per* in a similar manner. This possibility has gained additional credence by the identification of apparently tissue-autonomous oscillators in both the fly eye and the moth testes (59, 191). Additionally, *per* has been implicated in a wide variety of other cellular and organismal processes at least some of which may have little or nothing to do with the circadian clock. These include the courtship song and rate of developmental timing (see above), fluctuations in salivary gland membrane potentials (177), placement of neurosecretory cells (100), and synthesis of some neurotransmitters (114). A thorough listing and analysis of the issue of *per* pleiotropy is found elsewhere (64).

The issue of pleiotropy aside, it is clear both from mosaic (101) and transplantation (73) studies that the clock governing adult locomoter activity resides in the fly brain. In order to determine which and how many cells are actually required to constitute a/the clock, Ewer et al (44) carried out a heroic mosaic analysis, screening over 200 genetically mosaic flies for rhythmicity and then sectioning their brains and histologically mapping the mosaic borders and the *per* containing cells therein. In the central brain, *per* is expressed in a group of large dorsal lateral neurons (previously proposed as the site of the pacemaker) (164, 191) and a small group of neurons in the dorsal-most cortex of the central brain; it is also found in small cells (at the border of the cortex and central brain near the optic lobes, and within the neuropile and cortex of the central brain) that do not express a well characterized neuronal-specific marker and that therefore, by histological and anatomical criteria, appear to be glia (44). Surprisingly, the mosaic studies suggest that expression in any subset of the normal lateral neurons or glial cells was sufficient to support weak rhythmicity, although rhythmicity was stronger when expression was in more cells. Specifically, it appears that expression in any subset of these cells, including only glial expression, is sufficient to support true, albeit weak circadian rhythmicity (44). (Neuronal chauvinists take note.) Thus by this analysis, there does not appear to be one specific seat of the circadian pacemaker in the fly. It should be noted that studies such as this are in many ways more compelling than ablation/transplantation studies since they do not involve surgery and, more importantly, retain the normal neuroanatomy (and glial anatomy) of the brain (with the caveat that local loss of *per*-expression could locally affect the anatomy). The same antibody used in these studies also recognizes epitopes in the pacemaker neurons of *Aplysia* and *Bulla* (167) and in the rat suprachiasmatic nuclei (166).

THE MOLECULAR BIOLOGY OF *PER*   The cloning of *per* in 1984 by both the Young lab (6) and the Hall & Rosbash collaborative group (151) was a seminal event. It ushered in the molecular era of clocks research in the same way that the original identification of *per* by Konopka began the era of genetic approaches. *per* is interesting in its own right because it appears to be an almost prototypic example of a gene whose function is to govern and regulate behavior rather than development or metabolism. The arrival at the same gene by two different groups by two different routes initiated an extended and ultimately enormously productive competition that was the first of several steps (including but not limited to the identification of *tau* and its use in SCN transplantations, the cloning of *frq,* and the observation of light-inducible immediate early genes in the SCN) in the transformation of the entire field of rhythms from a comfortable phenomenologically-based scientific backwater into the well recognized fast-lane research problem that it is today.

What does *per* encode? *per* was cloned by a chromosome walk from a translocation break point (6), and by a chromosome walk within a series of phage clones corresponding to a micro-excised salivary chromosome band (151). A region about 7 kb in length encoding at least one approximately 4500 nucleotide transcript (6, 19) was shown by transformation to be capable of rescuing the arrhythmicity associated with either per^0 or per^- mutants (4, 70, 190). The complete sequence of *per* has been obtained from two different strains of *Drosophila melanogaster* (19, 86), and from three other different species of *Drosophila* [*D. virilis* and *D. pseudoobscura* (20) and *D. yakuba* (174)]. Partial sequence data are available from *D. simulans* (178, 187) and a number of wild isolates of *D. melanogaster* (21). The major transcript from the *D. melanogaster* gene is the result of splicing together eight exons, the first of which contains no protein coding information. Altogether the protein contains ca 1200 amino acids and includes six highly conserved regions among all of the strains sequenced, within the conserved regions are a nuclear localization signal, a number of potential sites for phosphorylation, N- and O-linked glycosylation, and PEST sequences associated with proteins that turnover quickly (152). One of the conserved regions contains an extended region (over 200 amino acids) showing similarity to three other proteins suspected or known to be nucleus-localized transcription factors: the products of the *single-minded* gene (25), the *aryl hydrocarbon nuclear translocator* ARNT (82), and the *aryl hydrocarbon receptor* (see below). These highly conserved regions are interspersed with regions that share little if any sequence similarities among species (20).

PER has proven to be an extremely difficult protein with which to work. It is present at extremely low levels, and until recently a good antibody proved difficult to raise. Based on both DNA sequence predictions and biochemical evidence, early reports predicted that the product(s) of *per* would be glycosylated and that PER would be a proteoglycan (5, 86, 150); however, no additional and complementary data confirming this has been produced. Given the widespread occurrence of PER, it may be that it is glycosylated in some but not all tissues. The core of the sequence suggesting that PER might be a proteoglycan is a repeat of threonine-glycine that falls within one of the regions that is poorly if at all conserved within species of *Drosophila*. The protein is composed chiefly of just four amino acids (47% Ser, Gly, Ala, Pro) and contains no major structural motifs such as acid blobs of the type associated with transcription factors, or hydrophobic amino acid stretches characteristic of signal sequences or membrane spanning domains.

Often the correlation of altered phenotype with altered protein sequence in mutant strains is helpful in understanding what a protein does and how it acts, and this is true with *per*. The entire canonical TG repeat region can be removed from PER, for instance, and the resulting internally deleted protein is still capable of functioning adequately, if not perfectly, in rescuing rhythmicity in per^0 recipient flies (187). Dosage analyses of *per* have been carried out genetically (169) and through transformation (7), and in each case suggest that more copies of *per* tend to shorten the period length of the oscillation, while decreased expression is associated with longer period lengths. Although this prompted the hypothesis that the per^smutation must result in extreme hyperactivity of the protein product (24), this turns out not to be the case. Repeated mutation of the same codon identified by the original per^smutation results in a short period length (154), and in an extensive set of in vitro-derived missense mutants constructed in the vicinity of the canonical per^smutant, most (10/16) resulted in a short period length (8). As these authors noted, this suggests that the original per^smutation was not unusual in producing a short period length, but rather was a typical reduction-of-function mutation. Thus there is a short-period-mutable domain in *per* whose function must somehow be to slow down the clock; when this is mutated, the clock speeds up (8). Insertion of an 11 amino acid tag into the N-terminal region of PER has a similar period shortening effect (154), although this region has not been nearly so well studied. The identification of the short-mutable domain suggests either that PER might interact with or be acted upon by another protein via this region. This could be something relatively nonspecific such as a determination of protein stability, or it could signal a quite specific protein-protein interaction critical to controlling PER activity and setting period length.

A critical question concerning the product(s) of any putative clock gene is whether or not the products of the gene cycle in amount or activity. Although an activity has yet to be definitively assigned to *per,* it is clear that the amount of both the major *per*-derived transcript(s) (74) and the PER protein (193) do oscillate just as has more recently been seen with the large transcript of *frq.* This was first suggested by the observation that PER-immunoreactive material appeared to oscillate in the eye and CNS (164, 191). Perhaps, the transcript and protein oscillate out of phase, with the peak of *per* transcript occurring after the time of the LD transition (or about CT 18 under constant conditions) and the peak of the protein occurring about 6 hr later in the end of the night (74, 164, 191, 193). Significantly, the timing of this oscillation is out of phase with the *frq* transcript oscillation mentioned above. *per* cycling is predictably altered in the *per* mutants, with the peaks in *per*[s] and *per*[l] occurring earlier or later, respectively, than the corresponding wild-type peak. Cycling is always seen in rescued transformants. The transcript cycling here does not, in itself, drive the protein cycling; this is no surprise, since protein cycling must reflect in part the stability characteristics of the protein. Specifically, although beta-galactosidase protein production driven rhythmically from the *per* promoter is not rhythmic in activity, fusion of the N-terminal part of the PER protein onto beta-galactosidase can confer cycling onto that protein (193). At the transcript level, rhythmicity appears to be controlled at the level of transcript production (rather than turnover) (76). The determinants for this transcriptional rhythmicity are apparently redundant, being found within 1.3 kb 5′ from the start of the gene and also either within or downstream of the gene (76).

What is *per* doing? Dosage and mutational analysis (above) can be interpreted to mean that PER interacts either with itself or with something else, via the *per*[s] region, to slow the clock, and that if this interaction is disturbed, the clock runs faster. Additionally, we know from mutational analysis (i.e. *per*[l]) and transformation studies, that too little PER or a mutated PER can interfere with normal PER function and make the clock run slower (*per*[l]/*per*[+] is slower than *per*[0]/*per*[+]) (97). The first solid clue to a potential biochemical role for this interesting molecule came in the discovery of other proteins of known function that bear sequence similarities to PER (SIM, ARNT, and ARH; see above). These are predominantly nuclear proteins that may act as transcription factors. All three are DNA-binding proteins, but probably bind to DNA by virtue of a region of each protein (a basic-helix-loop-helix motif) that they share among themselves, but not with PER. Still, there are numerous precedents for interaction between DNA-binding proteins and specific non-DNA-binding proteins in such a way as to affect the amount or activity of a transcriptional complex (reviewed in 89). It may be that PER interacts either with itself or other proteins to regulate transcription. This guilt-by-association argument for the function of PER in regulating transcription may not be compelling to all, but it is clear that PER (as *frq*) can affect its own transcript level at least indirectly (via affecting the clock that in turn dictates the timing of *per* transcription) and therefore might equally be expected to regulate the expression of other genes. This model of *per* and PER function, which given the cycling of *frq* transcript may equally well relate to the role of *frq* and FRQ in the clock mechanism, is shown in Figure 3.

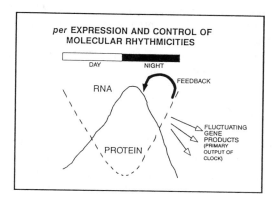

Figure 3   Description of PER expression and how it might act to regulate the fly's rhythms. *per* is transcribed with a time course reflected by the solid line (74, 193), and its translation product PER increases some time later (191) following a delay owing to undescribed translational control. As PER builds up, it negatively feeds back on the transcription of *per* (see text). In order for PER to cycle, something must finally act to reduce its level via proteolysis. This could be a non-specific effect reflecting the labile nature of the PER protein (193). Since PER affects its own transcription, it could also affect the transcription of other genes, thereby affecting rhythmic behavior (modified from 69 with permission).

MUTATIONS IN GENES OTHER THAN *PER*   As can be seen in Table 1, about half of the clock-mutant alleles in *Drosophila* have arisen at genes other than the *period* locus. However, in comparison to what is known about *per,* we know almost nothing about these other genes and their products beyond the descriptions of their phenotypes, several of which have been discussed above. An exception to this general dearth of information is the *Andante (And)* locus. *And* was first identified in 1982 by Smith working with Konopka (99). Although the mutant had a dusky wing phenotype (the result of reduced cell size in the developing wing) and mapped to the same small region of the X-chromosome containing the *miniature-dusky* locus, the possibility that *And* was an allele of *dy* was obscured by the fact that other known alleles of *dy* had normal clocks. This issue was recently resolved by Jackson and colleagues and Dowse and colleagues (133) who isolated additional *dy* alleles and found that a third of them displayed period lengthening similar to the original *And* allele. *And* is thus a part of the *miniature-dusky* complex locus. This region has recently been isolated as a series of overlapping clones (F. R. Jackson, personal communication), and new information on the molecular aspects of this gene should be forthcoming.

A second set of new mutations has been identified by Young and colleagues. Originally isolated together and thought to result from a single gene mutation (called *soiree* or *sre,* 182), these lesions have now been shown to be the result of separate mutations, one resulting in an inversion of the normal activity phase of the fly (from day active to night active), and the other resulting in arrhythmicity. The homozygote mutant in a normal per^+ genetic background has been suggested to display effects on the cycling of per transcript (A. Sehgal et al, personal communication).

CONCLUSION

It has been just over 20 years since Konopka's first publication (97). While growth in clock genetics was slow in the first decade, it has been explosive in the second, largely propelled by the awesome power of molecular genetics (to coin a phrase). Landmarks in the past decades have been the identification and eventual cloning of salient single gene mutants affecting the clock. The first definitive elucidation of the biochemical role of a clock macromolecule seems likely to be the next milestone.

The past decade has also seen the emergence of a second focus for molecular clocks research, that of the molecular biology of regulation by the clock. Twenty years ago, the dominant question was, how does the clock work? Now an equally dominant question revolves around, what is the molecular nature of time information within the cell?, or more simply, how do clocks control things? Recently great progress has been made in identifying genes controlled by the clock (e.g. 115) and in beginning to understand the mechanisms through which they are controlled (e.g. 61, 116, 129). In some systems, it is now possible to measure the progress of the clock at the molecular level, thereby blurring the distinction between the clock and the hands of the clock. Such clock-controlled genes will also be harnessed to drive the selection of new clock genes. This information will impact in major ways on how we view the molecular biology of time.

Reflecting the maxim that an honest approach wins its own friends, the final trend of the next decade will be the extension of genetic analyses to more complex systems. The first mouse circadian mutant is probably now in existence (J. Takahashi, personal communication), and efforts can now profitably focus on a system as complex as this. We have, in a real way, finally learned how to use genetics as a tool to dissect the clock.

ACKNOWLEDGMENTS

The author thanks Jeff Hall, Mike Young, Jennifer Loros, and the members of our lab for feedback on the manuscript, and several individuals cited in the manuscript for permission to report unpublished findings. The work was supported by grants GM 34985, MH 44651, and the core grant of the Norris Cotton Cancer Center at Dartmouth Medical School.

Literature Cited

1. Aramayo, R., Adams, T., Timberlake, W. E. 1989. A large cluster of highly expressed genes is dispensible for growth and development in *Aspergillus nidulans*. *Genetics* 122:65–71
2. Aronson, B. D., Johnson, A. K., Lui, Q., Dunlap, J. C. 1992. Molecular analysis of the *Neurospora* clock. *Chronobiol. Int.* 9:231–39
3. Aronson, B. D., Lindgren, K. M., Dunlap, J. C., Loros, J. J. 1992. An efficient method of gene disruption in *Neurospora crassa* and with potential for other filamentous fungi. *Mol. Gen. Genet.* Submitted
4. Bargiello, T. A., Jackson, F. R., Young, M. W. 1984. Restoration of circadian behavioral rhythms by gene transfer in *Drosophila*. *Nature* 312:752–54
5. Bargiello, T. A., Saez, L., Baylies, M. K., Gasic, G., Young, M. W., Spray, D. C. 1987. The *Drosophila* clock gene per affects intercellular junctional communication. *Nature* 328:686–91
6. Bargiello, T. A., Young, M. W. 1984. Molecular genetics of a biological clock in *Drosophila*. *Proc. Natl. Acad. Sci. USA* 81:2142–46
7. Baylies, M. K., Bargiello, T. A., Jackson, F. R., Young, M. W. 1987. Changes in abundance and structure of the *per* gene product can alter periodicity of the *Drosophila* clock. *Nature* 326:390–92
8. Baylies, M. K., Vosshall, L. B., Sehgal, A., Young, M. W. 1992. New short period mutations of the *Drosophila* clock gene *period*. *Neuron* 9:575–81
9. Baylies, M. K., Weiner, L., Vosshall, L. B., Saez, L., Young, M. W. 1992. Genetic, molecular and cellular studies of the *period* locus and its products in *Drosophila melanogaster*. In *Molecular Genetics of Biological Rhythms*, ed. M. W. Young, pp. 123–53. New York: Dekker
10. Brennan, C. I., Dees, R. S., Ingram, R. S., Tilghman, S. M. 1990. The product of the H19 gene may function as an RNA. *Mol. Cell. Biol.* 10:28–36
11. Brody, S., Coté, G., Germain, J. 1989. Circadian rhythms in *Neurospora crassa*: the effects of increased mitochondrial amounts and metabolism. *J. Cell Biol.* 107:348a (Abstr.)
12. Brody, S., MacKensie, L., Chuman, L. 1987. Circadian rhythms in *Neurospora crassa*: the effects of mitochondrial mutations and inhibitors. *Genetics* 116:S30
13. Brody, S., Martins, S. A. 1979. Circadian rhythms in *Neurospora crassa*: Effects of unsaturated fatty acids. *J. Bacteriol.* 137:912–15
14. Brody, S., Willert, K., Chuman, L. 1988. Circadian rhythms in *Neurospora crassa*: the effects of mutations at the *ufa* and *cla-1* loci. *Genome* 30:299 (Suppl.)
15. Bruce, V. G. 1972. Mutants of the biological clock in *Chlamydomonas reinhardtii*. *Genetics* 77:221–30
16. Bruce, V. G. 1974. Recombinants between clock mutants of *Chlamydomonas reinhardtii*. *Genetics* 77:221–30
17. Bruce, V. G., Bruce, N. C. 1978. Diploids of clock mutants of *Chlamydomonas reinhardtii*. *Genetics* 89:225–33
18. Bunning, E. 1935. Zur Kenntis der erblichen Tagesperiodizitat bei den Primarblattern von *Phaseolus multiflorus*. *Jahr. Wiss. Botan.* 81:411–18
19. Citri, Y., Colot, H. V., Jacquier, A. C., Yu, Q., Hall, J. C., et al. 1987. A family of unusually spliced and biologically active transcripts encoded by a *Drosophila* clock gene. *Nature* 326:42–47
20. Colot, H. V., Hall, J. C., Rosbash, M. 1988. Interspecific comparison of the *period* gene of *Drosophila* reveals large blocks of non-conserved coding DNA. *EMBO J.* 7:3929–37
21. Costa, R., Piexoto, A. A., Thackeray, J. R., Dalgleish, R., Kyriacou, C. P. 1991. Length polymorphism in the threonine-glycine encoding repeat region of the *period* gene in *Drosophila*. *J. Mol. Evol.* 32:238–46
22. Coté, G. G. 1986. *Circadian rhythms in Neurospora crassa: Studies on fatty acid metabolism*. PhD thesis. Univ. Calif., San Diego
23. Coté, G., Brody, S. 1987. Circadian rhythms in *Neurospora crassa*: membrane composition of a mutant defective in temperature composition. *Biochim. Biophys. Acta.* 898:23–36
24. Coté, G. G., Brody, S. 1986. Circadian rhythms in *Drosophila melanogaster*: Analysis of *period* as a function of gene dosage at the *per* (period) locus. *J. Theoret. Biol.* 121:487–503
25. Crews, S. T., Thomas, J. B., Goodman, C. S. 1988. The Drosophila *single-minded* gene encodes a nuclear

protein with sequence similarity to the *per* gene product. *Cell* 52:143–52

26. Davis, R. H. 1986. Compartmental and regulatory mechanismsin the arginine pathways of *Neurospora crassa* and *Saccharomyces cerevisiae*. *Microbiol. Rev.* 50:280 - 313

27. Dharmananda, S. 1980. *Studies of the Circadian Clock of Neurospora crassa: Light-induced Phase Shifting*. PhD thesis. Univ. Calif., Santa Cruz

28. Dieckmann, C., Brody, S. 1980. Circadian rhythms in *Neurospora crassa*: Oligomycin-resistant mutations affect periodicity. *Science* 207:896–98

29. Donehower, L., Harvey, M., Slagle, B., McArthur, J., Montgomery, C. Jr., et al. 1992. Mice deficient for p53 are developmentally normal but susceptible to spontaneous tumours. *Nature* 356:215–21

30. Dowse, H. B., Ringo, J. 1992. Is the circadian clock a "metaoscillator"? Evidence from studies of circadian rhythms in *Drosophila*. In *The Molecular Biology of Circadian Rhythms*, ed. M. Young. New York: Dekker. pp. 195–220

31. Dowse, H. B., Hall, J. C., Ringo, J. M. 1987. Circadian and ultradian rhythms in period mutants of *Drosophila melanogaster*. *Behav. Genet.* 17:19–35

32. Dowse, H. B., Ringo, J. M. 1987. Further evidence that the circadian clock in *Drosophila* is a population of coupled oscillators. *J. Biol. Rhythms.* 2:65–76

33. Dowse, H. B., Ringo, J. M. 1989. The search for hidden periodicities in biological time series revisited. *J. Theor. Biol.* 139:487–515

34. Drucker-Colin, R., Aguilar-Roblero, R., Garcia-Hernandez, F., Fernandez-Cancino, F., Bermudez-Rattoni, F. 1984. Fetal suprachiasmatic nucleus transplants diurnal rhythm recovery of lesioned rats. *Brain Res.* 311:353–57

35. Dunlap, J. C. 1990. Closely watched clocks: Molecular analysis of circadian rhythms in *Neurospora* and *Drosophila*. *Trends Genet.* 6(5):159–65

36. Dunlap, J. C. 1992. Genetic and molecular dissection of the *Neurospora* clock. In *Biological Clocks—from Cell to Human*, ed. T. Hiroshige, K. Honma, Sapporo: Hokkaido Univ. Press. pp. 3–18

37. Dunlap, J. C., Feldman, J. F. 1988. On the role of protein synthesis in the circadian clock of *Neurospora crassa*. *Proc. Natl. Acad. Sci. USA* 85:1096–100

38. Dunlap, J. C., Liu, Q., Johnson, K. A., Loros, J. J. 1992. Genetic and molecular dissection of the *Neurospora* clock. See Ref. 183, pp. 37–54

39. Dunlap, J. C., Loros, J. J. 1990. Genetics and molecular genetics of the circadian biological clock in *Neurospora*. *Sem. Dev. Biol.* 1:221–32

40. Dushay, M., Rosbash, M., Hall, J. C. 1992. *Clock* is an allele of *period*. *J. Neurogenet.* 8:713–19

41. Dushay, M. S., Rosbash, M., Hall, J. C. 1989. The disconnected visual system mutations in *Drosophila melanogaster* drastically disrupt circadian rhythms. *J. Biol. Rhythms* 4:1–27

42. Edmunds, L. E. Jr. 1988. *Cellular and Molecular Bases of Biological Clocks*. New York: Springer-Verlag. 497 pp.

43. Eskin, A. 1979. Identification and physiology of circadian pacemakers. *Fed. Proc.* 38:2570–72

44. Ewer, J., Frisch, B., Rosbash, M., Hall, J. C. 1992. Expression of the *period* clock gene in different cell types within the adult brain of *Drosophila melanogaster*. *J. Neurosci.* 12:3321–49

45. Ewer, J., Hamblen-Coyle, M., Rosbash, M., Hall, J. 1990. Requirement for *period* gene expression in the adult and not during development for locomoter activity rhythms of imaginal *Drosophila melanogaster*. *J. Neurogenet.* 7:31–73

46. Ewer, J., Rosbash, M., Hall, J. C. 1988. An inducible promoter fused to the *period* gene of *Drosophila* conditionally rescues adult per-mutant arrythmicity. *Nature* 333:82–84

47. Ewing, A. W. 1988. Cycles in the courtship song of male *Drosophila melanogaster* have not been detected. *Anim. Behav.* 36:1091–97

48. Feldman, J. F. 1967. Lengthening the period of a biological clock in *Euglena* by cycloheximide, an inhibitor of protein synthesis. *Proc. Natl. Acad. Sci. USA* 57:1080–87

49. Feldman, J. F. 1982. Genetic approaches to circadian clocks. *Annu. Rev. Plant Physiol.* 33:583–608

50. Feldman, J. F. 1983. Genetics of circadian clocks. *BioScience.* 33:426–31

51. Feldman, J. F., Atkinson, C. A. 1978. Genetic and physiological characterization of a slow growing circadian clock mutant of *Neurospora crassa*. *Genetics* 88:255–65

52. Feldman, J. F., Dunlap, J. C. 1983. *Neurospora crassa*: A unique system for studying circadian rhythms. *Photochem. Photobiol. Rev.* 7:319–68

53. Feldman, J. F., Gardner, G. F., Dennison, R. A. 1979. Genetic analysis of the circadian clock of *Neurospora*. In *Biological Rhythms and their Central Mechanism*, ed. M. Suda, pp. 57–66. Amsterdam: Elsevier

54. Feldman, J. F., Hoyle, M. 1973. Isolation of circadian clock mutants of *Neurospora crassa*. *Genetics* 75:605–13

55. Feldman, J. F., Hoyle, M. N. 1976. Complementation analysis of linked circadian clock mutants of *Neurospora crassa*. *Genetics* 82:9–17

56. Feldman, J. F., Widelitz, R. 1977. Manipulation of circadian periodicity in cysteine auxotrophs of *Neurospora crassa*. *Am. Soc. Microbiol. Abstr.* 158

57. Gardner, G. F., Feldman, J. F. 1980. The *frq* locus in *Neurospora crassa*: a key element in circadian clock organization. *Genetics* 96:877–86

58. Gardner, G. F., Feldman, J. F. 1981. Temperature compensation of circadian periodicity in clock mutants of *Neurospora crassa*. *Plant Physiol.* 68:1244–48

59. Giebultowicz, J. M., Riemann, J. G., Raina, A. K., Ridgway, R. L. 1989. Circadian system controlling release of sperm in the insect testis. *Science* 245:1098–100

60. Giles, N. H., Case, M. E., Baum, J., Geever, R., Huiet, L., et al. 1985. Gene organization and regulation in the *qa* (quinic acid) gene cluster of *Neurospora crassa*. *Microbiol. Rev.* 49:338–58

61. Giuliano, G., Hoffman, N. E., Ko, K., Scolnik, P. A., Cashmere, A. R. 1988. A light-entrained circadian clock controls transcription of several plant genes. *EMBO J.* 7:3635–42

62. Hall, J. C. 1984. Complex brain and behavior functions disrupted by mutations in *Drosophila*. *Dev. Genet.* 4:355–78

63. Hall, J. C. 1990. Genetics of circadian rhythms. *Annu. Rev. Genetics.* 24:659–97

64. Hall, J. C., Kyriacou, C. P. 1990. Genetics of biological rhythms in *Drosophila*. *Adv. Insect Physiol.* 22:221–98

65. Hall, J. C., Rosbash, M. 1987. Genes and biological rhythms. *Trends Genet.* 3:185–91

66. Hall, J. C., Rosbash, M. 1987. Genetic and molecular analysis of biological rhythms. *J. Biol. Rhythms.* 3:153–78

67. Hall, J. C., Rosbash, M. 1987. Genetics and molecular biology of rhythms. *Bioessays.* 7:108–12

68. Hall, J. C., Rosbash, M. 1988. Mutations and molecules influencing biological rhythms. *Annu. Rev. Neurosci.* 11:373–93

69. Hall, J. C., Rosbash, M. 1992. Spatial and temporal elements of a gene whose expression influences *Drosophila's* biological rhythms. *Discuss. Neurosci.* 8:88–93

70. Hamblen, M., Zehring, W. A., Kyriacou, C. P., Reddy, P., Yu, Q., et al. 1986. Germ-line transformation involving DNA from the *period* locus in *Drosophila melanogaster*: Overlapping genomic fragments that restore circadian and ultradian rhythmicity to *per*⁰ and *per* mutants. *J. Neurogenet.* 3:249–91

71. Hamblen-Coyle, M., Konopka, R. J., Zwiebel, L. J., Colot, H. V., Dowse, H. B., et al. 1989. A new mutation at the *period* locus with some novel effects on circadian rhythms. *J. Neurogenet.* 5:229–56

72. Hamblen-Coyle, M., Wheeler, D. A., Rutila, J. E., Rosbash, M., Hall, J. C. 1992. Behavior of period-altered circadian rhythm mutants of *Drosophila* in light:dark cycles. *J. Insect Biol.* 5:417–46

73. Handler, A. M., Konopka, R. J. 1979. Transplantation of a circadian pacemaker in *Drosophila*. *Nature* 279:236–38

74. Hardin, P. E., J. C. Hall, M. Rosbash, 1990. Feedback of the *Drosophila period* gene product on circadian cycling of its messenger RNA levels. *Nature* 343:536–40

75. Hardin, P. E., Hall, J. C., Rosbash, M. R. 1992. Molecular and behavioral analyses reveal that disconnected mutants affect the output pathway from the circadian clock in the fruit fly *Drosophila melanogaster* (Meigen). *EMBO J.* 12:1–11

76. Hardin, P. E., Hall, J. C., Rosbash, M. 1992. Circadian oscillations in *period* gene mRNA levels are transcriptionally regulated. *Proc. Natl. Acad. Sci. USA* In press

77. Hartwell, L. H. 1971. Genetic control of the cell division cycle in yeast II. Genes controlling DNA replication and its initiation. *J. Mol. Biol.* 59:183–94

78. Hartwell, L. H., Culotti, J., Reid, B. 1970. Genetic control of the cell di-

vision cycle in yeast 1. Detection of mutants. *Proc. Natl. Acad. Sci. USA* 66:352–59

79. Hastings, J. W., Sweeney, B. M. 1957. On the mechanism of temperature independence in a biological clock. *Proc. Natl. Acad. Sci. USA* 43:804–9

80. Helfrich, C., Engelmann, W. 1987. Evidences for circadian rhythmicity in the *per*^{O} mutant of *Drosophila melanogaster. Z. Naturforsch.* 42C:1335–38

81. Hinnebush, A. 1988. Mechanisms of gene regulation in the general control of amino acid biosynthesis in *Saccharomyces cerevisiae. Microbiol. Rev.* 52:248–73

82. Hoffman, E., Reyes, H., Chu, F., Sander, F., Conley, L. H., et al. 1991. Cloning of a factor required for activity of the Ah (dioxin) receptor. *Science* 252:954–58

83. Ishida, N., Noji, S., Katsuhiko, O., Koyama, E., Nohno, T., et al. 1991. Diurnal regulation of *per* repeat mRNA in the suprachiasmatic nucleus in rat brain. *Neurosci. Letts.* 122:113–16

84. Jacklet, J. 1989. *Neuronal and Cellular Oscillators.* pp. 482–527. New York: Dekker

85. Jackson, F. R. 1983. The isolation of biological rhythm mutations on the autosomes of *Drosophila melanogaster. J. Neurogenet.* 1:3–15

86. Jackson, F. R., Bargiello, T. A., Yun, S.-H., Young, M. W. 1986. Product of *per* locus of *Drosophila* shares homology with proteoglycans. *Nature* 320:185–88

87. Jaenisch, R. 1988. Transgenic animals. *Science* 240:1468–74

88. James, A. A., Ewer, J., Reddy, P., Hall, J. C., Rosbash, M. 1986. Embryonic expression of the *period* clock gene of *Drosophila melanogaster. EMBO J.* 5:2313–20

89. Jan, Y. N., Jan, L. Y. 1990. Genes required for specifying cell fates in the *Drosophila* embryonic nervous system. *Trends Neurosci.* 13:493–98

90. Jarvak, J., Botstein, D. 1975. Conditional-lethal mutations that suppress genetic defects in morphogenesis by altering proteins. *Proc. Natl. Acad. Sci. USA* 72:2738–42

91. Johnston, M. 1987. A model fungal gene regulatory mechanism: the GAL genes of *Saccharomyces cerevisiae. Microbiol. Rev.* 51:458–76

92. Kacser, H., Burns, J. A. 1981. The molecular basis of dominance. *Genetics* 97:639–66

93. Klingenberg, M. 1990. Mechanism and evolution of the uncoupling protein of brown adipose tissue. *Trends Biochem. Sci.* 15:108–12

94. Konopka, R. 1979. Genetic dissection of the *Drosophila* circadian system. *Fed. Proc.* 38:2602–5

95. Konopka, R. 1987. Neurogenetics of *Drosophila* circadian rhythms. In *Evolutionary Genetics of Invertebrate Behavior*, ed. M. D. Huettel, pp. 215–21. New York: Plenum

96. Konopka, R. J. 1987. Genetics of biological rhythms in *Drosophila. Annu. Rev. Genet.* 21:227–36

97. Konopka, R. J., Benzer, S. 1971. Clock mutants of *Drosophila melanogaster. Proc. Natl. Acad. Sci. USA* 68:2112–16

98. Konopka, R. J., Pittendrigh, C., Orr, D. 1989. Reciprocal behavior associated with altered homeostasis and photosensitivity of *Drosophila* clock mutants. *J. Neurogenet.* 6:1–10

99. Konopka, R., Smith, R. F., Orr, D. 1991. Characterization of *Andante*, a new *Drosophila* clock mutant, and its interaction with other clock mutants. *J. Neurogenet.* 7:103–14

100. Konopka, R. J., Wells, S. 1980. *Drosophila* clock mutations affect the morphology of a brain neurosecretory cell group. *J. Neurobiol.* 11:411–15

101. Konopka, R. J., Wells, S. 1983. Mosaic analysis of a *Drosophila* clock mutant. *Mol. Gen. Genet,* 190:284–88

102. Kozak, M. 1987. A consensus sequence for initiation of translation in eukaryotes. *Nucleic Acids Res.* 15:8125–47

103. Kyriacou, C. P., Hall, J. C. 1980. Circadian rhythm mutations in *Drosophila* affect short-term fluctuations in the male's courtship song. *Proc. Natl. Acad. Sci. USA* 77:6929–33

104. Kyriacou, C., Oldroyd, M., Wood, J., Sharp, M., Hill, M. 1990. Clock mutations alter developmental timing in *Drosophila. Heredity* 64:395–401

105. Kyriacou, C. P., van den Berg, M. J., Hall, J. C. 1990. *Drosophila* courtship song cycles in normal and *period* mutant males revisited. *Behav. Genet.* 20:631–58

106. Lakin-Thomas, P., Brody, S. 1985. Circadian rhythms in *Neurospora crassa*: interactions between clock mutations. *Genetics* 109:49–66

107. Lakin-Thomas, P., Coteacute, G., Brody, S. 1990. Circadian rhythms in *Neurospora. CRC Crit. Rev. Microbiol.* 17:365–416

108. Lewis, M., Feldman, J. F. 1992. Cloning, restriction analysis, and sequencing

of the *Neurospora sitophila* and *Neurospora tetrasperma frequency (frq)* clock gene homologs. *Soc. Res. Biol. Rhythms* 110 (Abstr.)

109. Lindquist, S. 1986. Heat shock. *Annu. Rev. Biochem.* 55:1151–91

110. Lipshitz, H. D., Beattie, D. A., Hogness, D. S. 1987. Untranslated transcripts in the Ultrabithorax region of *Drosophila*. *Genes Dev.* 1:307–22

111. Liu, Q. 1991. *Molecular cloning and analysis of arg-13, os-1, and prd-4 in Neurospora crassa*. PhD thesis. Dartmouth Coll. NH

112. Liu, X., Lorenz, L., Yu, Q., Hall, J. C., Rosbash, M. 1988. Spatial and temporal expression of the *period* gene in *Drosophila melanogaster*. *Genes Dev.* 2:228–38

113. Liu, X., Zweibel, L. J., Hinton, D., Benzer, S., Hall, J. C., Rosbash, M. R. 1992. The *period* gene encodes a predominantly nuclear protein in adult *Drosophila*. *J. Neurosci.* 12:2735–44

114. Livingstone, M. 1981. Two mutations in *Drosophila* affect the synthesis of octopamine, dopamine, and serotonin by altering the activities of two amino acid decarboxylases. *Neurosci. Abstr.* 7:351

115. Loros, J. J., Denome, S. A., Dunlap, J. C. 1989. Molecular cloning of genes under the control of the circadian clock in *Neurospora*. *Science* 243:385–88

116. Loros, J., Dunlap, J. C. 1991. *Neurospora crassa* clock-controlled genes are regulated at the level of transcription. *Mol. Cell. Biol.* 11(1):558–63

117. Loros, J. J., Feldman, J. F. 1986. Loss of temperature compensation of circadian *period* length in the *frq-9* mutant of *Neurospora crassa*. *J. Biol. Rhythms* 1:187–98

118. Loros, J., Lichens-Park, A., Lindgren, K., Dunlap, J. 1992. Molecular genetics of genes under circadian temporal control in *Neurospora*. See Ref. 183, pp.55–72

119. Loros, J. J., Richman, A., Feldman, J. F. 1986. A recessive circadian clock mutant at the *frq* locus in *Neurospora crassa*. *Genetics* 114:1095–110

120. Mahowald, A., Hardy, P. A. 1985. Genes involved in *Drosophila* development. *Annu. Rev. Genet.* 19:149–77

121. Marsh, L., Neiman, A. M., Herskowitz, I. 1991. Signal transduction during pheromone response in yeast. *Annu. Rev. Cell Biol.* 7:699–728

122. Mattern, D. L. 1985. Unsaturated fatty acid isomers: effects on the circadian rhythm of a fatty-acid- deficient *Neurospora crassa* mutant. *Arch. Biochem. Biophys.* 237:402–10

123. Mattern, D. L. 1985. Preparation of functional group analogs of unsaturated fatty acids and their effects on the circadian rhythm of a fatty-acid-deficient strain of *Neurospora crassa*. *Chem. Phys. Lipids.* 37:297–307

124. Mattern, D., Brody, S. 1979. Circadian rhythms in *Neurospora crassa*: effects of unsaturated fatty acids. *J. Bacteriol.* 139:977–88

125. Mattern, D. L., Forman, L. R., Brody, S. 1982. Circadian rhythms in *Neurospora crassa*: A mutation affecting temperature compensation. *Proc. Natl. Acad. Sci. USA* 79:825–29

126. McClung, C. R., Fox, B. A., Dunlap, J. C. 1989. The *Neurospora* clock gene frequency shares a sequence element with the *Drosophila* clock gene *period*. *Nature* 339:558–62

127. Menaker, M. 1992. The use of mutants in the analysis of mammalian circadian organization. *Discuss. Neurosci.* 8(2,3): 34–38

128. Mergenhagen, D. 1984. Circadian clock: Genetic characterization of a short-*period* mutant of *Chlamydomonas reinhardtii*. *Eur. J. Cell Biol.* 33:13–18

129. Millar, A., Kay, S. 1991. Circadian control of cab gene transcription and mRNA accumulation in *Arabidopsis*. *Plant Cell.* 3:541–50

130. Mrosovsky, N., Reebs, S. G., Honrado, G. I., Salmon, P. A. 1989. Behavioral entrainment of circadian rhythms. *Experientia* 45:696–702

131. Nakashima, H. 1985. Biochemical and genetic aspects of the conidiation rhythm in *Neurospora crassa*: phase shifting by metabolic inhibitors. In *Circadian Clocks and Zeitgebers*, ed. T. Hiroshige, K. Honma, pp. 35–43. Sapporo: Hokkaido Univ. Press

132. Newby, L., Jackson, F. R. 1990. *Drosophila ebony* mutants have altered circadian activity but normal eclosion. *J. Neurogenet.* 6:41–49

133. Newby, L., White, L., diBartolomeis, S., Walker, B., Dowse, H. B., et al. 1991. Mutational analysis of the *Drosophila* miniature- dusky (*m-dy*) locus: Effects on cell size and circadian rhythms. *Genetics* 128:571–82

134. Njus, D., Sulzman, F., Hastings, J. W. 1974. A membrane model for the circadian clock. *Nature* 248:116–22

135. North, G. 1989. A cycle is a cycle is a cycle. *Nature* 339:97–98

136. Nurse, P. 1990. Universal control

mechanism regulating onset of M-phase. *Nature* 344:503–8

137. Oshima, Y. 1991. Perspectives: Impact of the Douglass-Hawthorne model as a paradigm for elucidating cellular regulatory mechanisms in fungi. *Genetics* 128:195–201

138. Park, E., Horvitz, H. R. 1986. Mutations with dominant effects on the behavior and morphology of the nematode *Caenorhabditis elegans*. *Genetics* 113:821–52

139. Pavlidis, T. 1969. Populations of interacting oscillators and circadian rhythms. *J. Theor. Biol.* 22:418–36

140. Pavlidis, T., Kauzman, W. 1969. Toward a quantitative biochemical model for circadian oscillators. *Arch. Biochem. Biophys.* 132:338–48

141. Perkins, D. D. 1992. *Neurospora*: the organism behind the molecular revolution. *Genetics* 130:687–701

142. Perkins, D. D., Radford, A., Newmeyer, D., Bjorkman, M. 1982. Chromosomal loci of *Neurospora crassa*. *Microbiol. Rev.* 46:426–570

143. Pittendrigh, C. S. 1974. Circadian oscillations in cells and the circadian organization of multiculler systems. In *The Neurosciences Third Study Program*, ed. F. O. Schmitt, F. G. Worden, pp. 437–58. Cambridge: MIT Press

144. Pittendrigh, C. S. 1981. Circadian organization and the photoperiodic phenomena. In *Biological Clocks in Seasonal Reproductive Cycles*, ed. B. K. Follett, pp. 1–35. Bristol, England: Wright & Sons

145. Pittendrigh, C. S., Bruce, V. G., Rosenzweig, N. S., Rubin. M. L. 1959. A biological clock in *Neurospora*. *Nature* 184:169–70

146. Possidente, B., Hegmann, J. P. 1980. Circadian complexes: Circadian rhythms under common gene control. *J. Comp. Physiol.* 139:121–25

147. Ralph, M. R., Foster, R. G., Davis, F. C., Menaker, M. 1990. Transplanted suprachiasmatic nucleus determines circadian period. *Science* 247:975–78

148. Ralph, M. R., Menaker, M. 1988. A mutation of the circadian system in golden hamsters. *Science* 241:1225–27

149. Rechsteiner, M. 1988. Regulation of enzyme levels by proteolysis: the role of PEST regions. *Adv. Enzyme Regul.* 27:135–51

150. Reddy, P., Jacquier, A. C., Abovich, N., Petersen, G., Rosbash, M. 1986. The *period* clock locus of D.

melanogaster codes for a proteoglycan. *Cell* 46:53–61

151. Reddy, P., Zehring, W. A., Wheeler, D. A., Pirrotta, V., Hadfield, C., et al. 1984. Molecular analysis of the *period* locus in *Drosophila melanogaster* and identification of a transcript involved in biological rhythms. *Cell* 38:701–10

152. Rogers, S., Wells, R., Rechsteiner, M. 1986. The PEST hypothesis. *Science* 234:364–68

153. Rosbash, M., Hall, J. C. 1989. The molecular biology of circadian rhythms. *Neuron* 3:387–98

154. Rutila, J., Edery, I., Hall, J. C., Rosbash, M. 1992. The analysis of new short-period circadian mutants suggests features of *D. melanogaster period* gene function. *J. Neurogenet.* In press

155. Saez, L., Young, M. W. 1988. In situ localization of the *per* clock protein during development of *Drosophila melanogaster*. *Mol. Cell. Biol.* 8:5378–85

156. Sargent, M. L., Briggs, W. R. 1967. The effect of light on a circadian rhythm of conidiation in *Neurospora*. *Plant Physiol.* 42:1504–10

157. Sargent, M. L., Briggs, W. R., Woodward, D. O. 1966. The circadian nature of a rhythm expressed by an invertase-less strain of *Neurospora crassa*. *Plant Physiol.* 41:1343–49

158. Sargent, M. L., Kaltenborn, S. H. 1972. Effects of medium composition and carbon dioxide on circadian conidiation in *Neurospora*. *Plant Physiol.* 50:171–75

159. Saunders, D. S. 1990. The circadian basis of ovarian diapause in *Drosophila melanogaster*. Is the *period* gene causally involved in photoperiodic time measurement? *J. Biol. Rhythms* 5:315–32

160. Saunders, D. S., Henrich, V. C., Gilbert, L. I. 1989. Induction of diapause in *Drosophila melanogaster*. photoperiodic regulation and the impact of arrhythmic clock mutations on time measurement. *Proc. Natl. Acad. Sci.* 86:3748–52

161. Sawaki, Y., Nihonmatsu, I., Kawamura, H. 1984. Transplantation of the neonatal suprachiasmatic nucleus into rats with complete bilateral SCN lesion. *Neurosci. Res.* 1:67–72

162. Schwartz, W., Zimmerman, P. 1990. Circadian timekeeping in BALB/C and C57BL/6 inbred mouse strains. *J. Neurosci.* 10:3685–94

163. Schweiger, H.-G., Schweiger, M. 1977. Circadian rhythms in unicellular organisms: an endeavour to explain the molecular mechanism. *Int. Rev. Cytol.* 51:315–42

164. Siwicki, K. K., Eastman, C., Petersen, G., Rosbash, M., Hall, J. C. 1988. Antibodies to the *period* gene product of *Drosophila* reveal diverse tissue distribution and rhythmic changes in the visual system. *Neuron* 1:141–50

165. Siwicki, K., Flint, K. F., Hall, J. C., Rosbash, M., Spray, D. A. 1992. Dye coupling among salivary gland cells of *Drosophila* larvae as influenced by the *period* gene: A re-evaluation. *Biol. Bull.* 183:340–41

166. Siwicki, K. K., Schwartz, W. J., Hall, J. C. 1992. An antibody to the *Drosophila period* protein labels antigens in the suprachiasmatic nucleus of the rat. *J. Neurogenet.* 8:33–42

167. Siwicki, K. K., Strack, S., Rosbash, M., Hall, J. C. Jacklet, J. W. 1989. An antibody to the *Drosophila period* protein recognizes circadian pacemaker neurons in *Aplysia* and *Bulla. Neuron* 3:51–58d

168. Smith, P. H. 1987. Naturally occurring arrhythmicity in eclosion and activity in *Lucilia cuprina:* Its genetic basis. *Physiol. Entomol.* 12:99–107

169. Smith, R. F., Konopka, R. J. 1982. Effects of dosage alterations at the *per* locus on the period of the circadian clock of *Drosophila. Mol. Gen. Genet.* 185:30–36

170. Soriano, P., Montgomery, C., Geske, R., Bradley, A. 1991. Targeted disruption of the c-src proto- oncogene leads to osteoporosis in mice. *Cell* 64:693–702

171. Sweeney, B. M. 1974. A physiological model for circadian rhythms derived from the *Acetabularia* rhythm paradoxes. *Int. J. Chronobiol.* 2:25–34

172. Takahashi, J. 1991. Circadian rhythms: from gene expression to behavior. *Curr. Opin. Neurosci.* 1:21–26

173. Taylor, W. R., Feldman, J. F. 1982. Nutritional manipulation of circadian period length of auxotrophic mutants. *Neurospora News* 29:12

174. Thackeray, J. R., Kyriacou, C. P. 1990. Molecular evolution in the *Drosophila yakuba period* locus. *J. Mol. Evol.* 31:389–401

175. Travis, J. 1992. Scoring a technical knockout in mice. *Science* 256:1392–94

176. von Schilcher, F. 1989. Have cycles in the courtship song of *Drosophila* been detected? *Trends Neurosci.* 12:311–13

177. Weitzel, G., Rensing, L. 1981. Evidence for cellular circadian rhythms in isolated fluorescent dye-labelled salivary glands of wild type and an arrhythmic mutant of *Drosophila melanogaster. J. Comp. Physiol.* 143:229–35

178. Wheeler, D. A., Kyriacou, C. P., Greenacre, M. L., Yu, Q., Rutila, J. E., et al. 1991. Molecular transfer of a species specific behavior from *Drosophila simulans* to *Drosophila melanogaster. Science* 251:1082–85

179. Winfree, A. T. 1980. *The Geometry of Biological Time.* New York: Springer-Verlag. 530 pp.

180. Winfree, A., Gordon, H. 1977. The photosensitivity of a mutant circadian clock. *J. Comp. Physiol.* 122:87–109

181. Wolberger, C., Vershon, A. K., Liu, B., Johnson, A. D., Pabo, C. O. 1991. Homeodomain proteins specify cell type in yeast. *Cell* 67:517–28

182. Young, M. W. 1992. *Drosophila's* biological clocks. *Discuss. Neurosci.* 8:93–98

183. Young, M. W. 1992. *Molecular Genetics of Biological Rhythms.* New York: Dekker. 525 pp.

184. Young, M. W., Bargiello, T. A., Baylies, M. K., Saez, L., Spray, D. C. 1989. Molecular biology of the *Drosophila* clock. In *Neuronal and Cellular Oscillators,* ed. J. W. Jacklet, pp. 529–42. New York: Dekker

185. Young, M. W., Jackson, F. R., Shin, H. S., Bargiello, T. A. 1985. A biological clock in *Drosophila. Cold Spring Harbor Symp. Quant. Biol.* 50:865–75

186. Young, M. W., Judd, B. H. 1978. Nonessential sequences, genes, and the polytene chromosome bands of *Drosophila. Genetics* 88:723–42

187. Yu, Q., Colot, H. V., Hyriacou, C. P., Hall, J. C., Rosbash, M. 1987. Behaviour modification by in vitro mutagenesis of a variable region within the *period* gene of *Drosophila. Nature* 326:765–69

188. Yu, Q., Jacquier, A. C., Citri, Y., Hamblen, M., Hall, J. C., Rosbash, M. 1987. Molecular mapping of point mutations in the *period* gene that stop or speed up biological clocks in *Drosophila melanogaster. Proc. Natl. Acad. Sci. USA* 84:784–88

189. Zatz, M. 1992. *Circadian Rhythms.* Amsterdam: Elsevier. 124 pp.

190. Zehring, W. A., Wheeler, D. A., Reddy, P., Konolka, R. J., Kyriacou, C. P., et al. 1984. P-element trans-

formation with *period* locus DNA restores rhythmicity to mutant, arrhythmic *Drosophila melanogaster. Cell* 39:369–76

191. Zerr, D. M., Hall, J. C., Rosbash, M., Siwicki, K. K. 1990. Circadian fluctuations of *period* protein immunoreactivity in the CNS and the visual system of *Drosophila. J. Neurosci.* 10:2749–62

192. Zimmerman, W. F., Ives, D. 1971. Some photophysiological aspects of circadian rhythmicity in *Drosophila*. In *Biochronometry,* ed. M. Menaker, pp. 381–91. Washington, DC: Natl. Acad. Sci.

193. Zweibel, L. J., Liu, X., Hall, J. C., Rosbash, M. 1991. A post-transcriptional mechanism contributes to circadian cycling of a per-β-galactosidase fusion protein. *Proc. Natl. Acad. Sci. USA* 88:3882–86

Annu. Rev. Physiol. 1993. 55:729–53

MOLECULAR APPROACHES TO UNDERSTANDING CIRCADIAN OSCILLATIONS

Joseph S. Takahashi and Jon M. Kornhauser

NSF Center for Biological Timing, Department of Neurobiology and Physiology, Northwestern University, Evanston, Illinois 60208

Constantinos Koumenis and Arnold Eskin

Department of Biochemical and Biophysical Sciences, University of Houston, Houston, Texas 77204

KEY WORDS: suprachiasmatic nucleus, *Aplysia* eye, immediate-early gene, entrainment pathways, gene expression

INTRODUCTION

A fundamental question in the field of circadian rhythms concerns the molecular mechanism of circadian pacemakers: How are circadian oscillations generated? Answering this question will entail discovery of the molecules that comprise the circadian oscillator and the determination of how these molecules interact with one another to generate a circadian oscillation. On the basis of a wide variety of information, the mechanism of the circadian clock appears to be cell autonomous and to involve periodic gene expression. In addition, signal transduction pathways into the clock mechanism must exist for conveying environmental signals for entrainment. Furthermore, the clock mechanism must have output pathways for exerting rhythmic control at the physiological level.

Two major approaches have been used to study the cellular and molecular mechanisms generating and regulating circadian rhythms: (*a*) perturbation analysis using pharmacological agents and biochemical assays, and (*b*) genetic analysis using circadian clock mutants. Because most organisms used in circadian rhythm research have not always been amenable to genetic analysis, most work in the field has used nongenetic approaches. With the exception of *Drosophila, Neurospora* and perhaps a few other systems (see J. Dunlap, this volume), most work at the behavioral, physiological, biochemical, and

729

0066–4278/93/0315-0729$02.00

molecular level has not taken advantage of genetics. Among higher invertebrates and vertebrates, the predominant strategy for studying circadian clocks has been to localize circadian pacemakers at the organismal level and then to isolate the pacemaker-containing tissues in vitro for more mechanistic analysis (83). The success of this latter approach is exemplified best by the analysis of circadian oscillators in molluscan eyes (7, 45, 53), avian pineal cells (85, 96), and mammalian suprachiasmatic nucleus tissue (50, 57).

In this review we focus on cellular and molecular approaches to understanding circadian oscillations in animals. Although genetic approaches are crucial for a molecular understanding of the circadian clock, we limit our discussion of genetic approaches here because these issues are covered in depth in this volume (see J. Dunlap). A number of recent reviews have addressed various aspects of circadian rhythms at the cellular and molecular level (7, 20, 25, 40, 45, 53, 62, 74, 83, 85, 95) and we refer the reader to these reviews for more extensive coverage.

COMPONENTS OF CIRCADIAN OSCILLATOR SYSTEMS

All circadian systems contain at least three elements: (*a*) an input pathway or set of input pathways that convey environmental information to the circadian pacemaker for entrainment; (*b*) a circadian pacemaker that generates the oscillation; and (*c*) an output pathway or set of output pathways through which the pacemaker drives its various output rhythms. In most circadian systems, a photic entrainment pathway is present as an input. In some systems, other input pathways that convey either additional photic inputs or other types of inputs may exist. It is clear from the diversity of photopigments, phototransduction mechanisms, and types of photoreceptor cells that photic entrainment pathways differ markedly in different organisms. At the receptor level, the diversity stretches from phytochrome in plants, to "blue light flavoproteins" in microorganisms, to various members of the rhodopsin visual pigment receptor family in vertebrates. There appears to be comparable diversity at the second messenger level in the photic signal transduction pathways. At the output level, diversity is even more extreme. Because circadian control is so pervasive at the physiological level, it is likely that literally hundreds of different clock-regulated output pathways exist. Again this type of regulation spans clock control of photosynthesis in plants, to conidiation in *Neurospora*, to endocrine and behavioral rhythms in vertebrates. Clearly, the input and output pathways of the circadian clock within each organism appear to be specific to each system. It is important to keep this in mind when attempting to propose consensus models of the circadian oscillator.

Thus we are left with the circadian pacemaker itself. Is the "core mechanism" of the circadian clock, when stripped of its inputs and outputs, fundamentally similar or different in diverse organisms? At this time we can only speculate, but it is our belief that, as in the case of the cell cycle, a unified mechanism for the circadian clock is likely. We would argue that the effects of a few selective agents that affect all circadian systems are likely to be exerting their effects at the core mechanism; whereas, those agents that affect components of input pathways will have variable effects on circadian systems perhaps correlated with the nature of the input.

STRATEGIES FOR IDENTIFYING CLOCK COMPONENTS

The search for components of the clock (i.e. its core mechanism) is fraught with difficulties. First, we must infer properties of the oscillator indirectly by measuring an overt rhythm. Given that we cannot assay the state of the oscillator directly, how is it possible to distinguish the oscillator from its various inputs and outputs? Assuming a simple serial pathway, it is, in principle, easy to distinguish the output pathway from the oscillator and its inputs by determining whether a property of the oscillator can be perturbed. There are only two pacemaker properties upon which we can rely: the steady-state period and the steady-state phase of the oscillator. Step or pulse perturbations of the system that result in changes in either steady-state period or phase can be interpreted as having influenced the oscillator directly or indirectly through one of its inputs. Two types of input pathways may exist: one is the physiological entrainment pathway and the other could be pathways over which elements of the entrainment pathway or oscillator components are constitutively maintained. Discriminating between a direct effect on a component of the oscillator and an effect on an input pathway to the oscillator is difficult and sometimes impossible. The perturbation criterion is not sufficient to conclude an effect is direct because perturbations of input pathways would also lead to phase-dependent phase shifts. However, it is possible to distinguish among various input pathways if the phase-response curves for the inputs are qualitatively different. The shape of the phase-response curve (assuming short pulse duration and saturation dose) can be used as a signature of a particular input pathway. In other words, it should be possible to classify response curves as belonging to a family representing a specific physiological entraining signal (53, 73).

Logically there are two methods for finding the circadian oscillator: tracing the physiological entrainment pathways downstream toward the oscillator, and tracing the output pathways upstream toward the oscillator. Systems with multiple pathways should be advantageous because one could then attempt to identify their convergence. Logic dictates that all input and output pathways ultimately converge at the level of the circadian oscillator. Therefore, tactics that probe the nodal points should be especially fruitful. An example of such an approach would be to compare two different entrainment pathways to search for points of convergence (10, 53).

In this review, we have chosen to describe approaches to understanding oscillator mechanisms by reviewing progress obtained from three different systems. The first two case studies exemplify the downstream strategy of tracing input pathways to the circadian oscillator. The third case study provides an example of clock genetics to trace the oscillator. Descriptions of the upstream strategy of tracing output pathways may be found in several other reviews and papers (7, 85, 92).

CASE STUDY 1: The *Aplysia* Eye

The isolated eye of *Aplysia* contains a circadian oscillator that modulates the frequency of spontaneous nerve impulses generated by electrically coupled retinal neurons (29, 42). These afferent optic nerve impulses are recorded in the form of compound action potentials. This circadian rhythm of nerve impulses is routinely exhibited in vitro for 7 days, and it is possible to record rhythms for even longer periods of time (26).

The phase of the circadian oscillator in the eye is regulated through two distinct entrainment pathways (Figure 1). One pathway carries photic infor-

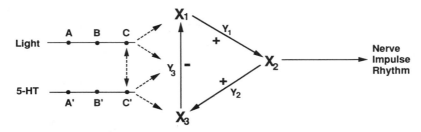

Figure 1 Model of the circadian system in the eye of *Aplysia*. The circadian oscillator consists of oscillating components (X_1, X_2, and X_3) and transducing components (Y_1, Y_2, and Y_3), which do not necessarily oscillate. The transduction processes mediate the effects of the oscillating elements upon each other. The eye circadian oscillator is regulated by at least two entrainment pathways: a photic entrainment pathway in the eye, and an efferent pathway bringing information from the CNS to the eye. The effect of the efferent pathway on the rhythm is mediated by 5-HT release in the eye. Initial portions of the two entrainment pathways are independent of one another, but they may converge at various levels of the entrainment pathway. Not shown in this figure are at least two other processes that are required for the system to operate. There must be another set of input pathways over which elements of the entrainment pathways are constitutively maintained and some oscillator components are synthesized. In addition, there must be pathways starting from elements of the system by which the levels of individual elements are reduced or degraded as they turn-over.

mation from the environment rather directly to the eye oscillator. Transmitter release does not appear to be involved in the photic entrainment pathway (28). The second entrainment pathway is an efferent one and carries neural information from the central nervous system to the oscillator in the eye (26). The effect of this efferent entrainment pathway on the oscillator is mediated through release of serotonin (5-HT) in the eye (17).

Photic Entrainment Pathway in Aplysia

The photic input pathway is capable of entraining the isolated eye to light-dark cycles (26). Light-induced depolarization appears to be involved in the phase-shifting process since a Na^+-dependent process is required for light to phase shift the rhythm (28). In addition, treatments that cause depolarization mimic the effects of light on the rhythm (27, 46). Cyclic GMP appears to link the effects of light with depolarization (34). Cyclic GMP is elevated by light pulses and treatments of a cGMP analogue, 8-bromo-cGMP, mimic the phase-shifting effects of light on the rhythm. 8-Bromo-cGMP produces a phase-response curve (PRC) that is indistinguishable from that produced by light (Figure 2). The effects of 8-bromo-cGMP are specific, as neither 8-bromo-5'-GMP nor 8-bromo-cAMP mimic the effects of 8-bromo-cGMP on the rhythm. The effects of light and 8-bromo-cGMP on the rhythm are

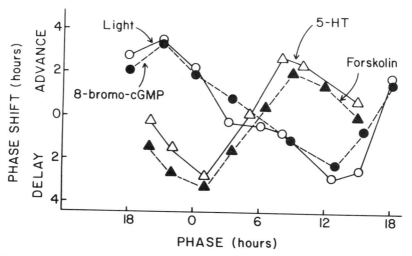

Figure 2 Comparison between phase-response curves (PRCs) for light, 8-bromo-cGMP, 5-HT, and forskolin. The duration of all treatments used to obtain the PRCs was 6 hr and the magnitudes of the treatments were 1,200 lux for light, 2×10^{-3} M for 8-bromo-cGMP, 10^{-5} M for 5-HT and 10^{-6} M for forskolin. The graphs show phase shifts produced in eye rhythms vs the phase of exposure of the eyes to the various agents (data for this figure were taken from references 33 and 34).

nonadditive, which indicates that these two agents act on the oscillator through the same pathway. Finally, low Na⁺ treatments that block the effects of light on the rhythm also block the effects of 8-bromo-cGMP on the rhythm. These findings indicate that light phase shifts the rhythm through changes in cGMP levels that then cause depolarization (Figure 3).

Another mediator of the effects of light on the rhythm may be Ca^{2+}. Treatments that lower extracellular Ca^{2+} concentrations or inhibit Ca^{2+} influx into the cell block the phase-shifting effects of light on the rhythm (28). At least some portion of the photic entrainment pathway of the *Aplysia* eye is similar to that in the eye of another mollusk, *Bulla gouldiana*, in which depolarization and Ca^{2+} fluxes are involved in mediating the effects of light on its circadian rhythm (49, 56). Protein synthesis also appears to be involved in the *Aplysia* eye photic entrainment pathway (Figure 3). The translation inhibitors, anisomycin and cycloheximide (CHX), block advance phase shifts produced by light (71). Blockade of light-induced phase shifts by translation inhibitors is emerging as a general phenomenon since experiments with translation inhibitors in *Bulla* (8), *Neurospora* (47), and the chick pineal gland (N. Murakami & J. S. Takahashi, unpublished) have yielded results similar to those obtained from *Aplysia*.

Serotonin Entrainment Pathway in Aplysia

Serotonin appears to play a neurotransmitter-like role in phase shifting the rhythm in the *Aplysia* eye (15, 16). Immunocytochemical studies have shown that the eye receives two types of efferent serotonergic innervation (39, 86). In one pathway, efferent serotonergic fibers travel through the optic nerve and invade the retina. In the other pathway, terminals of accessory optic nerves form a basket-like network around the eye, and some of these fibers also invade the retina. The ability of the eye to synthesize 5-HT, as well as the high affinity and specificity of receptors that mediate the 5-HT effect,

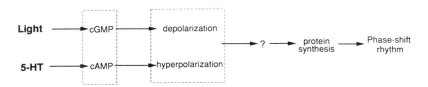

Figure 3 Model of entrainment pathways. Entrainment information appears to converge on membrane potential. The steps after changes in membrane potential are not as clear. Membrane potential, perhaps acting through Ca^{2+} or other second messengers, is believed to alter protein synthesis. Since light and 5-HT appear to have opposite effects on membrane potential, they also are predicted to have opposite effects on protein synthesis. Such a prediction is consistent with the out-of-phase PRCs for light and 5-HT shown in Figure 2.

also support a neurotransmitter role for 5-HT in the eye. Moreover, treatments that block neurotransmitter release do not block phase shifts produced by exogenous 5-HT, which indicates that 5-HT does not produce its phase-shifting effects on the rhythm by inducing the release of other neurotransmitters (15).

Elevation of cAMP acts as a second messenger for the phase-shifting effects of 5-HT. Analogues of cAMP such as 8-benzylthio-cAMP produce both advance and delay phase shifts of the rhythm similar to those produced by 5-HT (32). Furthermore, elevation of cAMP levels by forskolin (an activator of adenylate cyclase) or by phosphodiesterase inhibitors induces phase shifts similar to those produced by 5-HT. A PRC obtained using forskolin is indistinguishable from the PRC to 5-HT (Figure 2) (33). The effects of 5-HT and analogues of cAMP or phosphodiesterase inhibitors on the eye rhythm are nonadditive. The conclusion that 5-HT phase shifts the rhythm through the activation of adenylate cyclase and an increase in cAMP seems inescapable. In addition, high-K^+ solutions block the effects of 5-HT on the rhythm and solutions containing zero K^+ ($0\ K^+$) produce phase shifts with a PRC similar to that of 5-HT indicating that 5-HT phase shifts the rhythm through hyperpolarization (30). Therefore, the serotonin entrainment pathway appears to involve activation of adenylate cyclase, increase in cAMP, and then hyperpolarization (Figure 3). Protein synthesis has also been implicated in the serotonin entrainment pathway. Anisomycin blocks the advance phase shifts produced by 5-HT, while its inactive analogue, deacetylanisomycin, has no effect on such phase-shifts (35). Anisomycin also blocks phase shifts produced by analogues of cAMP. This last result demonstrates that protein synthesis is required after the cAMP step in the serotonin entrainment pathway (Figure 3).

It is not surprising that second messengers such as cyclic nucleotides are involved in the entrainment pathways of light and serotonin for it is through these messengers that environmental information must perturb the biochemistry of the cell that comprises the circadian oscillator mechanism. However, the identification of specific messengers that mediate effects of physiological entraining agents greatly aids the search for oscillator components because they provide additional experimental tools to help identify these components (see below). It is likely that different second messengers will be found to mediate entrainment in different organisms and in different cell types within the same organism. However, as the entrainment pathway approaches the oscillator, common elements of these pathways may emerge. Thus a particularly interesting result emerging in these studies is the requirement for protein synthesis in both the photic and serotonergic entrainment pathways.

The Role of Two Entrainment Pathways

The PRCs for the two entraining agents, light and serotonin, are of particular interest because they provide additional evidence that portions of the two pathways are distinct. Although the two PRCs are similar in shape, they are displaced by 180° on the phase axis (Figure 2). This fact, together with different second messengers being involved in the pathways and the morphology of the 5-HT pathway, demonstrate that at least portions of the light and 5-HT entrainment pathways in the eye are independent of one another. In all probability, the two agents used to generate opposite PRCs, light and 5-HT, phase shift by having opposite effects on some common element of the oscillator. The point of convergence of the two entrainment pathways may occur at the level of the membrane potential because depolarization and hyperpolarization appear to be involved in the two pathways (Figure 3). In this model, light and 5-HT would have opposite effects on components of the oscillator through events occurring after depolarization and hyperpolarization. The ability to perturb two separate physiological entrainment pathways has been used for identifying cellular processes that might be involved in the regulation of the oscillator.

The *Aplysia* eye has served as an important model system for analyzing entrainment pathways. In view of our caution concerning the diversity of input pathways, one should ask how general are the results obtained from *Aplysia*? Comparison with similar experiments using cultured chick pineals is illuminating because of the differences in the two systems, the most striking of which concerns the role of second messengers. In contrast to the molluskan systems, cyclic nucleotides, membrane depolarization, and calcium appear to play minor roles in the regulation of the circadian oscillator in the chick pineal cells (83, 85). Interestingly, the same second messengers are involved in both systems. However, in the case of molluskan eyes, the second messengers are primarily involved in input pathways to the circadian oscillator, whereas in the chick pineal the second messengers are primarily involved in output regulation.

In *Aplysia* and *Bulla*, input pathways to the circadian oscillator appear to depend strongly on changes in membrane potential (7), whereas in the chick pineal, this dependence is not obvious (96). However, it is interesting to note that experiments using the mammalian suprachiasmatic nucleus in vitro suggest that both membrane depolarization and cyclic nucleotides can phase shift rhythms in a neuronal circadian oscillator (24, 68). Perhaps neuronal circadian oscillators that depend on electrical signaling to couple inputs to the oscillator are more susceptible to perturbations of second messengers. One would expect that cyclic nucleotides and calcium would have profound effects on the electrophysiological properties of neurons. The differences between molluskan eyes and chick pineal cells may be due to differences in the coupling pathways of the oscillator rather than to fundamental differences in oscillator mechanisms.

CIRCADIAN OSCILLATIONS INVOLVE MACROMOLECULAR SYNTHESIS

In a wide variety of systems, the mechanism of the circadian clock appears to involve transcriptional and translational processes (20, 25, 40, 62, 74, 83, 85). For example, the existence of single-gene mutations that affect circadian period in *Chlamydomonas, Neurospora, Drosophila,* and *Mesocricetus* (hamster) demonstrates that gene products regulate the mechanism of the oscillator (20, 40, 74). In addition to the isolation of clock mutants, protein synthesis inhibitors have been shown to phase shift circadian rhythms in every microorganism, invertebrate, and vertebrate preparation that has been studied (25, 62, 74, 85). Among vertebrates, protein synthesis inhibitors phase shift circadian melatonin rhythms in chick pineal cells (85), and circadian activity rhythms in hamsters (87). Among invertebrates, translation inhibitors cause large phase shifts and change the period of the *Aplysia* eye rhythm (43, 44, 76). An accurate description of the phase of sensitivity to inhibitors of protein synthesis has been complicated in previous studies by the long recovery time of protein synthesis after removal of the drugs. Yeung & Eskin (94) tried to overcome this problem by using brief treatments of cycloheximide (CHX) as a translation inhibitor. The CHX-sensitive and -insensitive phases of the *Aplysia* eye rhythm are between circadian time (CT) CT20 and CT8, and CT8 and CT20, respectively. Furthermore, the differential effect of CHX on the rhythm at different phases is not due to differences in the effects of CHX on protein synthesis at different phases. CHX has similar effects on the inhibition of protein synthesis during the sensitive and insensitive phases of the rhythm (94).

Despite the involvement of translation in almost every known circadian system, its precise role in timing has not been revealed. Two roles of translation are consistent with the available data. Translation may play a role in the feedback loop of the oscillator, or it may play a role outside the loop, affecting the oscillator through a constitutive requirement of one or more important proteins. However, the facts that (*a*) brief treatments of translation inhibitors phase shift the rhythm, (*b*) continuous treatments alter the period of the rhythm, and (*c*) treatments during entraining stimuli block phase shifting suggest that translation is a component of the oscillator mechanism. Figure 4 contains a model of the circadian oscillator in *Aplysia* in which translation

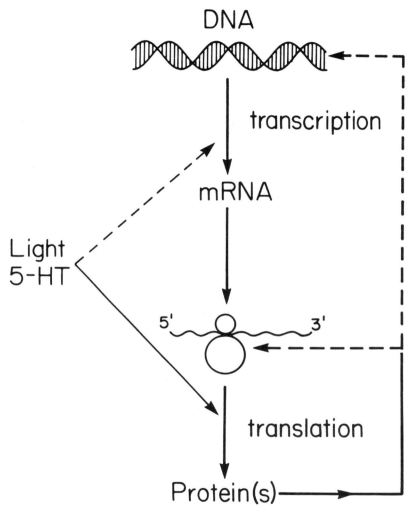

Figure 4 Model of the involvement of transcription and translation in the eye circadian system. Results obtained using inhibitors of transcription and translation on free-running rhythms as well as on rhythms exposed to entraining agents are consistent with this model. The model suggests that a gene is transcribed into mRNA and soon thereafter translated into a protein. The feedback loop is completed when this protein directly, or through its effect on other proteins, suppresses its transcription and/or translation. Light and 5-HT are proposed to perturb the rhythm through an effect on transcription or translation. The close phase relationship between the PRCs for transcription and translation inhibitors and the rapid appearance of phase shifts produced by transcription inhibitors indicate that transcription and translation are closely coupled processes in the *Aplysia* eye circadian system.

plays a key role in the oscillation. In this model, light and 5-HT regulate the phase of the oscillator through their effects on translation of proteins. Determining the precise role of protein synthesis in the circadian system will first require the identification of the proteins whose synthesis is important for the normal functioning of the circadian oscillator. Then the specific roles of these proteins in the circadian system can be determined.

Although a requirement for new RNA synthesis has been inferred from genetic experiments (20, 40, 74), this issue has only recently been addressed with the use of the reversible RNA synthesis inhibitor, 5,6-dichloro-1-b-D-ribofuranosylbenzimidazole (DRB), in the *Aplysia* eye (69). Pulses of DRB cause phase-dependent delays at phases between CT20 and CT10, and have no effect from CT10 to CT20. Continuous treatment with DRB caused a dose-dependent lengthening of the circadian period. Similar effects of DRB on phase and period have been found in chick pineal cells (64). The DRB experiments suggest that a critical period for transcription of specific genes involved in the generation of circadian rhythms occurs from CT20 to CT10 in *Aplysia* and from CT18 to CT9 in chick pineal cells. Thus a common feature of both circadian systems is a phase-dependent requirement for macromolecular synthesis. Importantly, the signal transduction processes for entrainment, as well as for the generation of circadian oscillations, involve macromolecular synthesis.

These DRB experiments suggest that transcription may be involved in the functioning of circadian oscillations in *Aplysia* and chick pineal cells (Figure 4). As in the case of translation, however, the precise role of transcription in the generation of the rhythm is still not clear. Transcription could reside either outside the oscillator loop, or be a part of the oscillator mechanism, or both as shown in Figure 4. The latter, if true, would result in oscillating message levels as are found in the *per* gene in *Drosophila* (41). The determination of the precise role of transcription in circadian timing (as of that of translation) will require the identification and study of the mRNAs important in the timing of the oscillator.

Identification of Candidate Protein Components of the Oscillator in Aplysia

Proteins are involved in nearly all mechanisms of cell regulation and cell signaling. The issue at hand is whether specific proteins play central roles in the mechanism of the circadian oscillator as indicated, for example, by the proteins shown in the model of Figure 4. How can one identify protein components of the oscillator? The model of Figure 4 can be used to generate a strategy for identification of such proteins. The model predicts that light and 5-HT regulate the synthesis of some protein components of the oscillator.

In addition, since light and 5-HT appear to regulate some components of the oscillator in opposite ways, the model predicts that light and 5-HT should have opposite effects on the synthesis of certain proteins. The same must also be true for agents that mimic the effects of light and 5-HT on the rhythm, such as analogues of cGMP and cAMP. Based on these predictions, a search was initiated for proteins as candidates for clock components (putative oscillator proteins, POPs) whose synthesis was altered in opposite ways by light and 5-HT. The experimental procedures used to identify protein candidates of the entrainment pathways or the oscillator mechanism involve treatment of a group of eyes with light, 5-HT, or other phase-shifting agents in the presence of labeled amino acid followed by two-dimensional polyacrylamide gel electrophoresis of the proteins from the eyes (35, 71, 93, 98).

Effects of Light, Serotonin, and Second Messengers on the Synthesis of Individual Proteins in Aplysia

In *Aplysia,* the effects of light on the synthesis of individual proteins has been examined at three phases: CT18–24, when light advances the rhythm; CT6–12, when light has no effect; and CT9–15, when light delays the rhythm (71). Incorporation of radiolabeled amino acids into 11 proteins was altered during the 6 hr light treatments. The effects of light on nine of these proteins were phase-dependent. The effect of 8-bromo-cGMP during CT18–24 on the synthesis of proteins was also examined. 8-Bromo-cGMP altered amino acid incorporation into five proteins. These five proteins were affected in similar ways by both light and 8-bromo-cGMP.

The results of experiments using entraining agents and inhibitors of protein synthesis can be interpreted as showing that critical synthesis occurred either during the treatments or shortly thereafter. To examine the possibility that critical synthesis occurred after the light treatment, the effect of light on the synthesis of proteins was examined 1 and 3 hr after a light pulse given at CT18–24. In these experiments, the synthesis of seven proteins was found to be altered after the light treatment. Two of these proteins were new proteins that were altered only in a delayed fashion by the light pulse.

The effects of 5-HT and 8-benzylthio-cAMP on the synthesis of proteins was examined at CT6–12, a phase during which 5-HT advances the rhythm (35, 93). When proteins were labeled during the 5-HT treatment, the synthesis of four proteins was altered by 5-HT. Three of these proteins were altered in the same way by 8-benzylthio-cAMP. When proteins were labeled 1 and 3 hr after the 5-HT treatment, the synthesis of four additional proteins was altered by 5-HT.

As mentioned above, proteins altered in opposite ways by light and 5-HT are of particular interest. So far six proteins have been found that were altered in opposite ways by light and 5-HT (53). These six proteins are particularly good candidates for clock components.

Identification of the Functions of the Putative Oscillator Proteins in Aplysia

What additional evidence can be obtained to determine whether a candidate protein is a molecular component of the oscillator? It is possible to determine a number of other properties of these proteins such as whether they oscillate or not, their cell location, etc. Although some additional evidence of this kind may be useful, we believe the next important step in this research is to determine the cellular functions of the candidate oscillator proteins. Only after the cellular functions of these proteins are known can more realistic oscillator models be proposed and tested. To investigate the cellular functions of these proteins, we have begun to obtain their amino acid sequences following techniques developed by Aebersold et al (1) and Kennedy et al (48).

The first protein selected for sequencing was a 40 kd/pI 5.6 protein (POP-1), one of the more abundant proteins of those altered by light and 5-HT. A peptide derived from POP-1 yielded a sequence of 38 amino acids (70). A significant sequence similarity exists between the 38 amino acid sequence obtained from POP-1 and a family of proteins collectively known as lipocortins or annexins. A 62% sequence identity exists in a 32 amino acid overlap region between POP-1 and lipocortin I from human and rat (88, 90). To confirm that POP-1 was a lipocortin, the 40-kd protein was isolated from two-dimensional gels and tested against several different antibodies raised against lipocortins. Several antibodies reacted with POP-1, which indicated that it indeed was a lipocortin protein. Furthermore, immunocytochemical studies using some of these antibodies demonstrated a widespread presence of these proteins in the eye (12).

What is the function of POP-1, and what is its role in the timing mechanism in the eye? Although lipocortins have been identified in a variety of cells and tissues, their precise physiological roles remain unknown. Lipocortins are a family of proteins (66). Members of this family are all Ca^{2+}/phospholipid-binding proteins, and they share close sequence similarities. Although all of these proteins are probably involved in mediating effects of Ca^{2+}, the different lipocortins may have somewhat different functions (18). Some lipocortins may function by inhibiting phospholipase A2 (PLA2) activity (19, 65), and Calignano et al (11) have shown that a 40-kd protein obtained from Aplysia central nervous tissue does modulate PLA2 activity. Since PLA2 regulates the metabolism of arachidonic acid, lipocortins could play a role in regulating this pathway by means of their phospholipid/PLA2 modulatory properties. Other roles of lipocortins are as Ca^{2+} channels (synexin) (67) and as mediators of exocytosis and membrane-cytoskeletal linkages (9). Also, the regulation of the metabolism of second messengers such as cyclic nucleotides and inositol phosphates has been postulated to be a function of some lipocortins (38, 75). In view of this information, lipocortins may mediate effects of Ca^{2+} on circadian rhythms. Ca^{2+} has been implicated in the regulation of the circadian oscillator in the *Aplysia* eye as well as several other systems (31, 49, 63, 91).

Elucidation of the role of lipocortins in the *Aplysia* eye circadian system will require examination of arachidonic acid as well as other possible functions of lipocortins. In addition, the study of the regulation of the expression of the lipocortin gene may provide valuable information on the possible involvement of lipocortins in the generation of the rhythm. For example, it would be interesting to see whether message levels of lipocortin oscillate during the cycle, or whether they are altered by entraining agents. Finally, antibodies are available to study localization and should allow more precise studies on the distribution and abundance of lipocortins.

Characterization of additional candidate oscillator proteins is essential for progress towards understanding the nature of the circadian oscillator. Recently, amino acid sequences of three other POPs have been obtained (54). As the functions of these and other candidate proteins become known, a critical issue will be whether any of the proteins are functionally related to one another. It is through functional relationships among candidate proteins that a model of the structure of the pacemaker will emerge. The next stage in this research would then entail testing specific predictions of the molecular model.

There are a number of pitfalls and potential problems with the approach described utilizing the eye of *Aplysia* or other similar systems. The eye contains several different types of cells. Thus it is important to associate changes in protein level or activity with those occurring in the pacemaker cells. Using two-dimensional gels to search for proteins has limitations. Certain proteins do not enter the gels, and it is difficult to study proteins that are present in small quantities. Finally, it is difficult, in preparations such as the *Aplysia* eye, to perturb or eliminate specific proteins. However, promising techniques are being developed in which it is possible to knock out the induction and/or synthesis of specific proteins in intact cells using nongenetic approaches (6).

CASE STUDY 2: Photic Entrainment and Regulation of Immediate Early Genes (IEGs) in Mammals

Photic entrainment in mammals is mediated by retinal photoreceptors that project to the hypothalamic suprachiasmatic nucleus (SCN) via the retinohypothalamic tract (RHT) (57). Recent interest has focused on the molecular level from the discovery that light exposure strongly induces the expression of the proto-oncogene, c-*fos*, in the SCN of rodents (5, 23, 51,

72, 78). There are several interesting characteristics of the photic induction of Fos in rodents. First, the induction of Fos in the brain is quite limited and appears to be restricted to neural elements thought to be involved in the photic entrainment of circadian rhythms. Second, the time course of c-*fos* mRNA induction is rapid and transient with peak levels occurring 30 min after light onset, and high levels of Fos-like immunoreactivity (Fos-lir) occurring 1–2 hr after the onset of light. These time courses for mRNA and protein increases are consistent with Fos induction by other stimuli in vitro and the CNS (61). Third, effectiveness of light stimuli in inducing phase shifting of locomotor activity rhythms and inducing c-*fos* mRNA in the SCN are quantitatively correlated. Fourth, photic induction of Fos in the SCN is gated by the circadian clock. This last result was the most surprising and perhaps the most significant.

Light has distinct effects on the hamster's circadian system at different circadian times. Light exposure during the subjective night, or active period, of the hamster's circadian cycle causes a phase shift in the activity rhythm of the animal (84), and these phase shifts result in entrainment of the circadian pacemaker. By contrast, light exposure during the subjective day produces no effect on the phase of the rhythm of locomotor activity. The induction of c-*fos* mRNA by light also depends on the circadian time when the light is presented (51). Light at CT14, which causes a phase delay in the circadian activity rhythm, greatly increases c-*fos* mRNA levels in the SCN; photic stimulation at CT19 or at CT21, which induces a phase advance, also elevates c-*fos* mRNA levels. Remarkably, light pulses during the subjective day at CT3, CT6, and CT9, which produce no behavioral phase shifts, do not cause a detectable increase in c-*fos* mRNA in the SCN. Hamsters receiving no light, examined at all circadian times, displayed no specific c-*fos* hybridization in the area of the SCN. The expression of c-*fos*, then, is not simply regulated by light but is controlled by circadian phase as well. The ability of light to induce expression of this immediate-early gene (IEG), like its ability to phase shift the pacemaker, is regulated by the circadian pacemaker itself.

Because Fos interacts with members of the Jun family to form the transcription factor, AP-1 (61), important issues concern whether members of the Jun family are regulated by light and whether light ultimately regulates AP-1 activity. We have found that light selectively stimulated *jun*-B mRNA levels in the hamster SCN and that the induction of *jun*-B was also phase-dependent (52). Furthermore, measurement of AP-1 activity using gel mobility shift assays has shown that light increased AP-1 activity in the hamster SCN following light pulses during the subjective night, but not during the subjective day (52). Taken together, these experiments suggest that photic entrainment in mammals may involve transcriptionally regulated signal transduction processes and that AP-1 may play a role in conveying photic information within the circadian system.

Most attention has focused on photic regulation of AP-1 transcription factor family genes, but at least two unrelated putative transcriptional regulators have also been shown to be induced in the SCN following light exposure. Levels of mRNA for *zif*/268 [also known as NGFI-A; (58)], encoding a zinc finger motif DNA-binding protein, are increased by light in the hamster and rat SCN during the subjective night (78; J. Kornhauser et al, unpublished results), as are mRNA levels of *nur*/77 [also known as NGFI-B; (59)], a member of the steroid receptor superfamily of nuclear receptors, in rat SCN (77). The photic induction of both of these genes appears to be phase-dependent; they are not induced during the subjective day (77). This suggests that the genomic response to entraining light stimuli is varied and complex and that there are likely to be other light-regulated transcription factors. The molecular events triggered by light in the SCN may be the result of coordinated transcriptional regulation by a specific set of factors.

Significance of Immediate-Early Genes to the Circadian Clock

The key issues still to be addressed concern the role, if any, of transcription in the entrainment of the circadian pacemaker and, perhaps, in the pacemaker mechanism itself. The relationship between IEGs and the clock may be conveniently placed in two categories: those involving the control of IEG expression by the clock, and the potential actions of IEG transcription factors on the clock. There is clear evidence that the circadian pacemaker affects IEG expression. How this circadian control is exerted remains to be determined. More difficult to assess are the potential regulatory roles of IEG transcription factors for entrainment of the pacemaker.

CIRCADIAN GATING OF IEG EXPRESSION   The signal transduction pathways mediating the photic induction of Fos and Jun-B are of obvious interest and importance to our understanding of both the biochemistry of the light input pathway and the mechanism of circadian pacemaker gating of IEG expression. Two well-characterized regulatory elements within the promoter region of the c-*fos* gene are known to mediate second messenger effects on c-*fos* transcription. Both calcium and cAMP pathways converge on the calcium/cAMP response element (Ca/CRE) located 60 bp upstream of the transcription start site (14, 60, 79, 81). Serum and growth factors act through a serum response element (SRE) at 300 bp upstream of the c-*fos* start site (61, 79, 80, 89). It is plausible that photic signals that activate SCN neurons lead to elevated intracellular Ca^{2+}; phosphorylation of the cAMP response element-binding protein (CREB) is regulated by Ca^{2+} levels (81). Therefore, the CRE is a prime candidate to mediate c-*fos* transcriptional activation. There is no evidence yet of the actual signal transduction events leading to increased transcription of c-*fos*, however, and other regulatory mechanisms may be important in addition to, or instead of, calcium regulation of CREB.

In the future, transgenic mice should be useful for elucidating the regulatory pathways involved in the photic regulation of c-*fos* gene expression (82). Expression of a c-*fos* promoter-*LacZ* transgene is light-regulated in the SCN in a similar way to the endogenous c-*fos* gene. The establishment of mouse lines containing mutations or deletions of specific *cis*-acting elements in the c-*fos* promoter regions of the transgene (work currently underway in the Curran and Morgan groups) will allow assessment of the role(s) of each regulatory element in c-*fos* induction by light. Understanding photic signal transduction regulating c-*fos* is a first step, and a complementary one, to approaching the problem of circadian regulation of c-*fos* expression.

The circadian clock gates the photic induction of the IEGs c-*fos* and *jun*-B in the SCN. That is, the ability of light to induce their expression is controlled by the pacemaker, so that light has differential effects on c-*fos* and *jun*-B expression during subjective day and night times. However, c-*fos* and *jun*-B mRNA levels do not appear to oscillate in a circadian manner in the absence of light. Therefore, the clock probably acts at some step upstream of c-*fos* and *jun*-B gene transcription. This regulation could occur at a number of different levels. First, the pacemaker could exert control on the photic input pathway to the SCN: retinal photoreceptor cells or other retinal neurons, ganglion cells comprising the RHT input to the SCN, or SCN neurons themselves might be targets of this regulation. The electrical excitability of cells in this neural pathway could be regulated, or synaptic transmission could be regulated, e.g. the amounts or activity of neurotransmitter receptors at RHT fiber synapses on SCN cells might be controlled. Second, signal transduction pathways leading to IEG activation within retino-recipient SCN cells might be gated. Second messengers, protein kinases, or other molecules involved in a signal transduction cascade could be modified as a result of clock regulation. Third, the pacemaker could act on the transcription of c-*fos* and *jun*-B through either positive or negative regulatory *trans*-acting factors. This last possibility is especially intriguing because it suggests that some transcriptional regulator may be clock-controlled and would exhibit a circadian rhythm in either its expression or in its activity. Molecular studies of the levels, posttranslational modifications, and activities of transcription factors known to regulate the Fos promoter might allow us to identify such putative circadian fluctuations in transcription factor activities. The transgenic mouse model (82) may be useful in solving this issue. One might hope to identify Fos promoter mutations that block circadian gating of photic Fos induction, thus identifying the *cis*-acting element(s) mediating the circadian control. Of course, even if one finds a transcription factor that regulates the c-*fos* promoter and that oscillates, this would still not explain how the pacemaker controls levels of this factor. One would then need to work back upstream to elucidate the mechanisms of pacemaker control of this factor's expression or activity. More detailed information about this particular system, circadian regulation of c-*fos* and *jun*-B, may provide insight into how gene expression is controlled by a circadian pacemaker.

EVIDENCE THAT AP-1 IS RELATED TO ENTRAINMENT   The most interesting issue, that of how AP-1 (as well as *zif*/268 and *nur*/77) regulation of target genes is related to circadian entrainment, is also likely to be the most complex and difficult to address. Eventually, we should be able to test whether AP-1 is functionally involved in photic phase shifting and to identify AP-1 target genes in the SCN that may be related to clock function. In the absence of this information, what reasons do we currently have to believe that expression of AP-1 may contribute to entrainment of the clock? A putative role of transcription in the entrainment of the pacemaker is consistent with previous studies demonstrating a requirement for macromolecular synthesis in the entrainment and expression of circadian rhythms (69, 87). All of the current information about IEG expression in the SCN, along with the roles proposed for transcription factors elsewhere in the brain, argues that AP-1 is an excellent candidate for a component of the photic input pathway to the clock.

Future Prospects: Defining the Role of IEGs in the SCN

Two approaches that may be useful for discovering how transcription factors act on the SCN clock are to manipulate AP-1 gene expression, in order to determine the consequences on entrainment and rhythmicity, and to identify target genes for AP-1 that may be integral to the entrainment mechanism. Neither of these approaches is easily realized in the intact nervous system. Various strategies for transfection of DNA or RNA into the SCN, with the aim of either overexpressing or blocking the expression of IEGs, may be possible. For example, measurement of the behavioral consequences of altering Fos expression on circadian entrainment and rhythmicity might demonstrate whether AP-1 is indeed necessary for entrainment of the pacemaker and what its effects on rhythms may be. This technique may be feasible in vivo, but the technical difficulties and variability seem formidable. Transfection approaches in an in vitro system, such as an SCN slice preparation, should be easier. This will, however, require a preparation in which one can both mimic light stimulation and measure a reliable circadian rhythmic output.

Another possible experimental approach to addressing whether AP-1 is necessary for entrainment by light involves the use of transgenic animals.

Photic induction of Fos expression has been demonstrated in the SCN of mouse (13, 82). Transgenic mice that over- or under-express Fos or Jun-B in the SCN might be an ideal model system for determining the role of AP-1 in entrainment and rhythmicity. However, the alteration of AP-1 expression throughout the entire animal is likely to have drastic effects on development and physiology; one would want to direct expression of the transgene specifically to the SCN and to the specific cells that normally express light-induced AP-1. To accomplish this, a promoter for a gene whose expression is reasonably specific to the appropriate SCN cells could be used to direct the expression of a Fos transgene. No genes exclusively expressed in these neurons have yet been identified. Eventually, the colocalization of neuropeptides in cells exhibiting photic Fos expression may provide a suitable tissue-specific promoter for such experiments. Until then, this strategy also remains problematic.

The identification of target genes for light-regulated transcription factors such as AP-1 may allow us to determine how these factors are related to entrainment and rhythmicity and may also help in understanding the molecular mechanisms of entrainment. A number of genes are probably regulated by AP-1, but candidate target genes that are known to be expressed in neurons of the ventrolateral SCN are scarce. The VIP/PHI gene has been shown to be transcriptionally activated by AP-1 complex binding to a CRE-like sequence in its promoter (37). However, Fos-lir and VIP do not appear to be predominantly colocalized in the SCN, which makes VIP/PHI less likely as a target gene. The GRP promoter contains a CRE site (55), but there is no evidence as yet for AP-1 regulation of this neuropeptide. A limited codistribution of Fos-lir and GRP immunoreactivity is seen in the SCN (22). It is interesting that co-injection of VIP, PHI, and GRP can mimic some of the phase-shifting effects of light in rats (2). If these peptides were indeed all regulated by light via AP-1, they might mediate phase shifting by light. While this idea is intriguing, there is no consistent evidence for VIP or GRP elevation by AP-1 in the SCN. In fact, VIP/PHI mRNA is lower during the day than during the night (4) and is lower in constant light than in constant darkness (3). Taken together, the current data do not clearly suggest any good potential AP-1-regulated genes in the retino-recipient SCN.

As the regulatory elements of other genes expressed in the SCN become characterized, potential AP-1 target genes may be revealed. Until then, other approaches are needed in order to identify light-regulated genes downstream of the transcription factors. Unfortunately, no direct strategy is available to identify SCN-specific genes containing, for example, AP-1-binding sites. Screening strategies to identify light-regulated genes may be useful. Subtractive hybridization, for example, may be used to select for genes expressed at higher levels after light stimulation. These would presumably include genes that are regulated by AP-1 and other light-induced IEGs. Such an approach, while technically difficult and laborious, may be the most straightforward method for finding potential target genes of light-induced transcription factors.

Additional IEGs that are induced by light may also be characterized using the subtractive hybridization strategy. Novel IEGs may even be identified, expanding our knowledge of molecular regulation in the SCN. It has been estimated that there are on the order of 100 IEGs, most of which have not been characterized (80). A subset of these IEGs may be selectively regulated by light, and the isolation of these unique IEGs might significantly enhance our understanding of this photic pathway.

Fos expression has already proven to be a useful functional marker for the study of photic signal transduction by the SCN. The strict correlation now apparent between photic phase shifting of behavioral circadian rhythms and light-induced Fos expression suggests that a great deal more about the physiological effects of light on the SCN may be learned using this approach. Phase-shifting light stimuli induce *jun*-B mRNA expression and levels of AP-1 transcription factor binding activity in the SCN, and genes encoding other transcription factors are also photically regulated. The specificity of the photic regulation of these genes suggests that transcriptional events may be closely linked to circadian entrainment. Obviously, we are only beginning to understand transcriptional regulation by light in the SCN. In continuing studies, more should be learned about the biochemical mechanisms of IEG regulation by light and by the circadian clock. Insight also may be gained into the molecular events involved in entrainment, and perhaps the character- ization of light-regulated genes can lead us closer to the identification of biochemical components of the clock.

CASE STUDY 3: Circadian Cycling of *Drosophila* Period Gene mRNA and Protein

Both of our examples of entrainment pathway analysis in *Aplysia* eye and mammalian SCN have led to the idea that these pathways appear to be converging at a level of macromolecular synthesis. Are these pathways converging upon macromolecular steps that are part of the core mechanism of the circadian clock? The inference that a critical period for macromolecular synthesis exists for the progression of the circadian clock through its cycle is based primarily upon indirect pharmacological experiments (69, 85). In *Drosophila,* however, direct measurements of Per protein immunoreactivity (97) and mRNA levels (41) show that both the Per protein and mRNA levels oscillate. Because *per* mutations regulate the period length of the *per* mRNA oscillation, and because germline transformation of arrhythmic *per*[01] mRNA with wild-type *per* DNA can rescue both circadian behavior and cycling of *per*[01] mRNA, it is thought that the Per protein level or activity affects the *per* mRNA oscillation. Hardin et al (41) have proposed that there is a feedback loop with the *per* gene product regulating its own mRNA levels and have suggested that this loop may be an important component of the circadian pacemaker. Interestingly, the *per* mRNA peak precedes the Per protein peak by 6–8 hr. Although the mechanism is unknown, the time lag nicely allows a negative feedback loop to operate and control a low frequency oscillation (J. Hall, personal communication). Zwiebel et al (99) have shown that 5′ noncoding sequences from *per* are sufficient to drive mRNA cycles from β-galactosidase fusion gene in a wild-type background. The Per protein cycling requires additional sequences derived from the *per* coding region, however. These results suggest that a transcriptional mechanism accounts for the *per* mRNA cycle, but that a posttranscriptional mechanism, under circadian clock control is required for the Per protein cycle (99). Combined with experiments using conditional *per* mutants, these results show that ongoing *per* expression is necessary for pacemaker function (36) and strongly suggest that *per* is a critical component of the circadian oscillator mechanism.

PERSPECTIVE

The similarities in the mechanisms involved in circadian clock function based upon diverse approaches using both invertebrate and vertebrate systems suggest that the field is converging upon the identification of clock components and the description of how they function. It is clear, however, that new approaches and systems will have to be developed. Research involving the elucidation of the circadian oscillator is an attractive molecular biological challenge because, at least conceptually, we are dealing with a discrete entity. The problem may be relatively simple if the circadian oscillator is comprised of relatively few elements and processes. On the other hand, the problem could be quite difficult if a large number of biochemical reactions in the cell are coupled together to make the oscillator. Our task for the future is to develop systems and strategies for determining which molecules and processes are critical components of the core mechanism of the circadian oscillator. From work in *Drosophila* and *Neurospora* it is obvious that genetics has been an effective approach in identifying genes and gene products that appear to be uniquely associated with oscillator function. Together with the approaches described here, an integrated analysis of circadian oscillators should ultimately define the mechanisms involved.

Literature Cited

1. Aebersold, R. H., Leavitt, J., Saavedra, R. A., Hood, L., Kent, S. B. 1987. Internal amino acid sequence analysis of proteins separated by one- or two-dimensional gel electrophoresis after in situ protease digestion on nitrocellulose. *Proc. Natl. Acad. Sci USA* 84:6970–74
2. Albers, H. E., Liou, S. Y., Stopa, E. G., Zoeller, R. T. 1991. Interaction of colocalized neuropeptides: Functional significance in the circadian timing system. *J. Neurosci.* 11:846–51
3. Albers, H. E., Minamitani, N., Stopa, E., Ferris, C. F. 1987. Light selectively alters vasoactive intestinal peptide and peptide histidine isoleucine immunoractivity within the rat suprachiasmatic nucleus. *Brain Res.* 437:189–92
4. Albers, H. E., Stopa, E. G., Zoeller, R. R., Kauer, J. S., King, J. C., et al. 1990. Day-night variation in prepro vasoactive intestinal peptide/peptide histidine isoleucine mRNA within the rat suprachiasmatic nucleus. *Mol. Brain Res.* 7:85–89
5. Aronin, N., Sagar, S. M., Sharp, F. R., Schwartz, W. J. 1990. Light regulates expression of a Fos-related protein in rat suprachiasmatic nuclei. *Proc. Natl. Acad. Sci. USA* 87:5959–62
6. Bielinska, A., Shivdasani, R. A., Zhang, L. 1990. Regulation of gene expression with double-stranded phosphorothioate oligonucleotides. *Science* 250:997–1000
7. Block, G., Khalsa, S. B. S., McMahon, D. G., Michel, S., Geusz, M. E. 1992. Cellular mechanisms of biological timekeeping. *Int. Rev. Cytol.* In press
8. Bogart, B. L., Block, G. D. 1988. Light induced phase shifts of the *Bulla* eye in the presence of protein synthesis inhibitors. *Soc. Neurosci. Abstr.* 14:386
9. Burgoyne, R. D., Geisow, M. J. 1989. The annexin family of calcium-binding proteins. *Cell Calcium* 10:1–10
10. Cahill, G. M., Besharse, J. C. 1991. Resetting the circadian clock in cultured *Xenopus* eyecups: regulation of retinal melatonin rhythms by light and D2 dopamine receptors. *J. Neurosci.* 11:2959–71
11. Calignano, A., Piomelli, D., Wallner, B., Schwartz, J. H. 1988. *Aplysia* nervous tissue contains proteins that inhibit or activate phospholipase A2 (PLA2). *Soc. Neurosci. Abstr.* 14:131
12. Cleary, L. J., Eskin, A., Byrne, J. H. 1991. Annexins are differentially expressed in CNS, including sensory neurons, and eye of *Aplysia*. *Soc. Neurosci. Abstr.* 17:1592
13. Colwell, C. S., Foster, R. 1991. The NMDA receptor antagonist MK-801 inhibits light-induced changes in fos-like immunoreactivity in the mouse suprachiasmatic nucleus. *Soc. Neurosci. Abstr.* 17:668
14. Comb, M., Birnberg, N. C., Seasholtz, A., Herbert, E., Goodman, H. M. 1986. A cyclic AMP-and phorbol ester-inducible DNA element. *Nature* 323: 353–56
15. Corrent, G., Eskin, A. 1982. Transmitterlike action of serotonin in phase shifting a rhythm from the *Aplysia* eye. *Am. J. Physiol.* 242:R333–38
16. Corrent, G., Eskin, A., Kay, I. 1982. Entrainment of the circadian rhythm from the eye of *Aplysia*: role of serotonin. *Am. J. Physiol.* 242:R326–32
17. Corrent, G., McAdoo, D. J., Eskin, A. 1978. Serotonin shifts the phase of the circadian rhythm from the *Aplysia* eye. *Science* 202:977–79
18. Crompton, M. R., Owens, R. J., Totty, N. F., Moss, S. E., Waterfield, M. D. et al. 1988. Primary structure of the human, membrane-associated Ca^{2+} binding protein p68: a novel member of a protein family. *EMBO J.* 7:21–27
19. Davidson, F. F., Dennis, E. A., Powell, M., Glenney., J. R. Jr. 1987 Inhibition of phospholipase A2 by "lipocortins" and calpactins. An effect of binding to substrate phospholipids. *J. Biol. Chem.* 262:1698–705
20. Dunlap, J. C. 1990. Closely watched clocks: molecular analysis of circadian rhythms in *Neurospora* and *Drosophila*. *Trends Genet.* 6:159–65
21. Deleted in proof
22. Earnest, D. J., Di Giorgio, S. M., Trojanczyk, L. A., Olschowka, J. A. 1991. Light induces proto-oncogene expression in gastrin releasing peptide neurons within the suprachiasmatic nucleus. *Soc. Neurosci. Abstr.* 17:24
23. Earnest, D. J., Iadarola, M., Yeh, H. H., Olschowka, J. A. 1990. Photic regulation of c-*fos* expression in neural components governing the etrainment of circadian rhythms. *Exp. Neurol.* 109:353–61
24. Earnest, D. J., Sladek, C. D. 1987. Circadian vasopressin release from perifused rat suprachiasmatic explants in

vitro: effects of acute stimulation. *Brain Res.* 422:398–402

25. Edmunds, L. E. 1988. *Cellular and Molecular Basis of Biological Clocks.* New York: Springer-Verlag. 337 pp.

26. Eskin, A. 1971. Properties of the *Aplysia* visual system: in vitro entrainment of the circadian rhythm and centrifugal regulation of the eye. *Z. Vgl. Physiol.* 74:353–71

27. Eskin, A. 1972. Phase shifting a circadian rhythm in the eye of *Aplysia* by high potassium pulses *J. Comp. Physiol.* 80:353–76

28. Eskin, A. 1977. Neurophysiological mechanisms involved in photo-entrainment of the circadian rhythm from the *Aplysia* eye. *J. Neurobiol.* 8:273–99

29. Eskin, A. 1979. Circadian system of the *Aplysia* eye: properties of the pacemaker and mechanisms of its entrainment. *Fed. Proc.* 38:2573–79

30. Eskin, A. 1982. Increasing external K^+ blocks phase shifts in a circadian rhythm produced by serotonin or 8-benzylthio-cAMP. *J. Neurobiol.* 13: 241–49

31. Eskin, A., Corrent, G. 1977. Effects of divalent cations and metabolic poisons on the circadian rhythm from the *Aplysia* eye. *J. Comp. Physiol.* 117:1–21

32. Eskin, A., Corrent, G., Lin, C.-Y., McAdoo, D. J. 1982. Mechanism of shifting the phase of a circadian oscillator by serotonin: involvement of cAMP. *Proc. Natl. Acad. Sci. USA* 79:660–64

33. Eskin, A., Takahashi, J. S. 1983. Adenylate cyclase activation shifts the phase of a circadian pacemaker. *Science* 220:82–84

34. Eskin, A., Takahashi, J. S., Zatz, M., Block, G. D. 1984. Cyclic guanosine $3':5'$-monophosphate mimics the effects of light on a circadian pacemaker in the eye of *Aplysia*. *J. Neurosci.* 10: 2466–71

35. Eskin, A., Yeung, S. J., Klass, M. R. 1984. Requirement for protein synthesis in the regulation of a circadian oscillator by serotonin. *Proc. Natl. Acad. Sci. USA* 81:7637–41

36. Ewer, J., Hamblin-Coyle, M., Rosbash, M., Hall, J. C. 1990. Requirement for period gene expression in the adult and not during development for locomotor activity rhythms of imaginal *Drosophila melanogaster*. *J. Neurogenet.* 7:31–73

37. Fink, J. S., Verhave, M., Walton, K., Mandel, G., Goodman, R. H. 1991. Cyclic AMP- and phorbol ester-induced transcriptional activation are mediated by the same enhancer element in the human vasoactive intestinal peptide gene. *J. Biol. Chem.* 266:3882–87

38. Gerzer, R., Brash, A. R., Hordman, J. G. 1986. Activation of soluble guanylate cyclase by arachidonic acid and 15-lipoxygenase products. *Biochim. Biophys. Acta* 886:383–89

39. Goldstein, R., Kistler, H. B., Steinbusch, H. W. M., Schwartz, J. H. 1984. Distribution of serotonin-immunoreactivity in juvenile *Aplysia*. *Neuroscience* 11:535–47

40. Hall, J. C. 1990. Genetics of circadian rhythms. *Annu. Rev. Genet.* 24:659–97

41. Hardin, P. E., Hall, J. C., Rosbash, M. 1990. Feedback of the *Drosophila* period gene product on circadian cycling of its messenger RNA levels. *Nature* 343:536–40

42. Jacklet, J. W. 1969. Circadian rhythm of optic nerve impulses recorded in darkness from isolated eye of *Aplysia*. *Science* 164:562–63

43. Jacklet, J. W. 1977. Neuronal circadian rhythm: phase shifting by a protein synthesis inhibitor. *Science* 198:69–71

44. Jacklet, J. W. 1980. Circadian rhythm from the eye of *Aplysia*: Temperature compensation of the effects of protein synthesis inhibitors. *J. Exp. Biol.* 84:1–75

45. Jacklet, J. W. 1984 Neural organization and cellular mechanisms of circadian pacemakers. *Int. Rev. Cytol.* 89:251–94

46. Jacklet, J. W., Lothsaw, D. P. 1981. Light and high potassium cause similar phase shifts of the *Aplysia* eye circadian rhythm. *J. Exp. Biol.* 94:345–49

47. Johnson, C. H. 1990. Cycloheximide inhibits light-induced phase-shifting of the circadian clock in *Neurospora*. *J. Biol. Rhythms* 5:159–67

48. Kennedy, T. E., Gawinowicz, M. A., Barzilai, A., Kandel, E. R., Sweatt, J. D. 1988. Sequencing of proteins from two-dimensional gels by using in situ digestion and transfer of peptides to polyvinylidene difluoride membranes: Application to proteins associated with sensitization in *Aplysia*. *Proc. Natl. Acad. Sci. USA* 85:7008–12

49. Khalsa, S. B. S., Block, G. D. 1988. Calcium channels mediate phase-shifts of the *Bulla* circadian pacemaker. *J. Comp. Physiol.* 164:195–206

50. Klein, D. C., Moore, R. Y., Reppert, S. M., eds. 1991. *Suprachiasmatic Nucleus. The Mind's Clock.* New York: Oxford Univ. Press. 467 pp.

51. Kornhauser, J. M., Nelson, D. E.,

Mayo, K. E., Takahashi, J. S. 1990. Photic and circadian regulation of c-*fos* gene expression in the hamster suprachiasmatic nucleus. *Neuron* 5:127–34

52. Kornhauser, J. M., Nelson, D. E., Mayo, K. E., Takahashi, J. S. 1992. Regulation of *jun*-B messenger RNA and AP-1 activity by light and a circadian clock. *Science* 255:1581–84

53. Koumenis, C., Eskin, A. 1992. The hunt for mechanisms of circadian timing in the eye of *Aplysia*. *Chronobiol. Int.* 9:201–21

54. Koumenis, C., Nunez-Regueiro, J., Eskin, A. 1992. Identification of three additional putative oscillator proteins (POPs) from the eye of *Aplysia* as stress related proteins. *Soc. Neurosci. Abstr.* 18:881

55. Lebacq-Verheyden, A.-M., Way, J., Battey, J. 1990. Structural characterization of a brain-specific promoter region directing transcription of the rat prepro-gastrin-releasing peptide gene. *Mol. Brain Res.* 7:235–41

56. McMahon, D. G., Block, G. D. 1987. The *Bulla* ocular circadian pacemaker. II. Chronic changes in membrane potential lengthen free running period. *J. Comp. Physiol.* 161:347–54

57. Meijer, J. H., Rietveld, W. J. 1989. Neurophysiology of the suprachiasmatic circadian pacemaker in rodents. *Physiol. Rev.* 69:671–707

58. Milbrandt, J. 1987. A nerve growth factor-induced gene encodes a possible transcriptional regulatory factor. *Science* 238:797–99

59. Milbrandt, J. 1988. Nerve growth factor induces a gene homologous to the glucocorticoid receptor gene. *Neuron* 1:183–88

60. Montminy, M. R., Sevarino, K. A., Wagner, J. A., Mandel, G., Goodman, R. H. 1986. Identification of a cyclic-AMP-responsive element within the rat somatostatin gene. *Proc. Natl. Acad. Sci. USA* 83:6682–86

61. Morgan, J. I., Curran, T. 1991. Stimulus-transcription coupling in the nervous system: involvement of the inducible proto-oncogenes *fos* and *jun*. *Annu. Rev. Neurosci.* 14:421–51

62. Morse, D. S., Fritz, L., Hastings, J. W. 1990. What is the clock? Translational regulation of of circadian bioluminescence. *Trends Biochem. Sci.* 15:262–65

63. Nakashima, H. 1984. Calcium inhibits phase shifting of the circadian conidation rhythm of *Neurospora crassa* by the calcium ionophore A23187. *Plant Physiol.* 74:268–71

64. Ohi, K., Takahashi, J. S. 1991. Effects of the transcriptional inhibitor, 5,6-dichloro-1-b-D-ribofuranosylbenzimidazole (DRB), on the circadian melatonin rhythm of cultured chick pineal cells. *Soc. Neurosc. Abstr.* 17:675

65. Pepinsky, R. B., Sinclair, L. K., Browning, J. L., Mattalino, R. J., Wallner, B. P. 1986. Purification and partial sequence analysis of a 37-kDa protein that inhibits phospholipase A2 activity from rat peritoneal exudates. *J. Biol. Chem.* 261:4239–46

66. Pepinsky, R. B., Tizard, R., Mattallino, R. J., Sinclair, L. K., Miller, G. T., et al. 1988. Five distinct calcium and phospholipid binding proteins share homology with lipocortin I. *J. Biol. Chem.* 63:10799–811

67. Pollard, H. B., Burns, A. L., Rojas, E. 1990. Synexin (Annexin VII): a cytosolic calcium-binding protein which promotes membrane fusion and forms calcium channels in artificial bilayer and natural membranes. *J. Memb. Biol.* 117:101–12

68. Prosser, R. A., Gillette, M. U. 1989. The mammalian circadian clock in the suprachiasmatic nuclei is reset in vitro by cAMP. *J. Neurosci.* 9:1073–81

69. Raju, U., Koumenis, C., Nunez-Regueiro, M., Eskin, A. 1991. Alteration of the phase and period of a circadian oscillator by a reversible transcription inhibitor. *Science* 253: 673–75

70. Raju, U., Nunez-Regueiro, M., Cook, R., Eskin, A. 1990. Characterization of a putative circadian oscillator protein in the eye of *Aplysia*. *Soc. Neurosci. Abstr.* 16:1322

71. Raju, U., Yeung, S. J., Eskin, A. 1990. Involvement of proteins in light resetting ocular circadian oscillators in *Aplysia*. *Am. J. Physiol.* 258:R256–62

72. Rea, M. A. 1989. Light increases fos-related protein immunoreactivity in the rat suprachiasmatic nuclei. *Brain Res. Bull.* 23:577–81

73. Rensing, L., Hardeland, R. 1990. The cellular mechanism of circadian rhythms—a view on evidence, hypotheses and problems. *Chronobiol. Int.* 7:353–70

74. Rosbash, M., Hall, J. C. 1989. The molecular biology of circadian rhythms. *Neuron* 3:387–98

75. Ross, T. S., Tait, J. F., Majerus, P. W. 1990. Identity of inositol 1,2-cyclic phosphate 2-phosphohydrolase with lipocortin III. *Science* 248:605–7

76. Rothman, B. S., Strumwasser, F. 1976. Phase shifting the circadian rhythm of

neuronal activity in the isolated *Aplysia* eye with puromycin and cycloheximide. *J. Gen. Physiol.* 68:359–84

77. Rusak, B., McNaughton, L., Robertson, H. A., Hunt, S. P. 1992. Circadian variation in photic regulation of immediate-early gene mRNA in rat suprachiasmatic nucleus cells. *Mol. Brain Res.* 14:124–30

78. Rusak, B., Robertson, H. A., Wisden, W., Hunt, S. P. 1990. Light pulses that shift rhythms induce gene expression in the suprachiasmatic nucleus. *Science* 248:1237–40

79. Sheng, M., Dougan, S. T., McGadden, G., Greenberg, M. E. 1988. Calcium and growth factor pathways of c-*fos* transcriptional activation require distinct upstream regulatory sequences. *Mol. Cell. Biol.* 8:2787–96

80. Sheng, M., Greenberg, M. E. 1990. The regulation and function of c-*fos* and other immediate early genes in the nervous system. *Neuron* 4:477–85

81. Sheng, M., McFadden, G., Greenberg, M. E. 1990. Membrane depolarization and calcium induce c-*fos* transcription via phosphorylation of transcription factor CREB. *Neuron* 4:571–82

82. Smeyne, R. J., Schilling, K., Robertson, L., Luk, D., Oberdick, J., et al. 1992. Fos-lacZ transgenic mice: mapping sites of gene induction in the central nervous system. *Neuron* 8:13–23

83. Takahashi, J. S. 1991. Circadian rhythms: from gene expression to behavior. *Curr. Opin. Neurobiol.* 1:556–61

84. Takahashi, J. S., DeCoursey, P. J., Bauman, L., Menaker, M. 1984. Spectral sensitivity of a novel photoreceptive system mediating entrainment of mammalian circadian rhythms. *Nature* 308:186–88

85. Takahashi, J. S., Murakami, N., Nikaido, S. S., Pratt, B. L., Robertson, L. M. 1989. The avian pineal, a vertebrate model system of the circadian oscillator: cellular regulation of circadian rhythms by light, second messengers, and macromolecular synthesis. *Recent Prog. Horm. Res.* 45:279–352

86. Takahashi, J. S., Nelson, D. E., Eskin, A. 1989. Immunocytochemical localization of serotonergic fibers innervating the ocular circadian system of *Aplysia. Neuroscience* 28:139–47

87. Takahashi, J. S., Turek, F. W. 1987 Anisomycin, an inhibitor of protein synthesis, perturbs the phase of a mammalian circadian pacemaker. *Brain Res.* 405:199–203

88. Tamaki, M., Nakamura, E., Nishikubo, C., Sakata, T., Shin, M., et al. 1987. Rat lipocortin I cDNA. *Nucleic Acids Res.* 15:7637

89. Treisman, R. 1985. Transient accumulation of c-*fos* RNA following serum stimulation requires a conserved 5′ element and c-*fos* 3′ sequences. *Cell* 42:889–902

90. Wallner, B. P., Mattalino, R. J., Hession, C., Cate, R. L., Tizard, R., et al. 1986. Cloning and expression of human lipocortin, a phospholipase A2 inhibitor with potential anti-inflammatory activity. *Nature* 320:77–81

91. Woolum, J. C., Strumwasser, F. 1983. Is the period of the circadian oscillator in the eye of *Aplysia* directly homeostatically regulated? *J. Comp. Physiol.* 151:253–59

92. Wuarin, J., Schibler, U. 1990. Expression of the liver-enriched transcriptional activator protein DBP follows a stringent circadian rhythm. *Cell* 63:1257–66

93. Yeung, S. J., Eskin, A. 1987. Involvement of a specific protein in the regulation of a circadian rhythm in the *Aplysia* eye. *Proc. Natl. Acad. Sci. USA* 84:279–83

94. Yeung, S. J., Eskin, A. 1988. Responses of the circadian system in the *Aplysia* eye to inhibitors of protein synthesis. *J. Biol. Rhythms* 3:225–36

95. Young, M. W., ed. 1992. *Molecular Genetics of Biological Rhythms.* New York: Dekker. In press

96. Zatz, M., Mullen, D. A., Moskal, J. R. 1988. Photoendocrine transduction in cultured chick pineal cells: effects of light, dark and potassium on the melatonin rhythm. *Brain Res.* 438:199–215

97. Zerr, D. M., Hall, J. C., Rosbash, M., Siwicki, K. K. 1990. Circadian fluctuations of period protein immunoreactivity in the CNS and the visual system of *Drosophila. J. Neurosci.* 10:2749–62

98. Zwartjes, R. E., Eskin, A. 1989. Changes in protein phosphorylation in the eye of *Aplysia* associated with circadian rhythm regulation by serotonin. *J. Neurobiol.* 21:376–83

99. Zweibel, L. J., Hardin, P. E., Liu, X., Hall, J. C., Rosbash, M. 1991. A post-transcriptional mechanism contributes to circadian cycling of a Per-β-galactosidase fusion protein. *Proc. Natl. Acad. Sci. USA* 88:3882–86

Annu. Rev. Physiol. 1993. 55:755–84

CONTROLLING CELL CHEMISTRY WITH CAGED COMPOUNDS

Stephen R. Adams and Roger Y. Tsien

Howard Hughes Medical Institute and Department of Pharmacology, University of California, San Diego, La Jolla, California 92093-0647

KEY WORDS: photolabile groups, calcium chelator, flash photolysis, enzymes and peptides, two-photon excitation

INTRODUCTION

"Caged" compounds are artificial molecules whose biological activity is controlled by light, usually by photolytic conversion from an inactive to an active form. The term caged has become popular because it is brief and pictorial, not because it is accurate. It is based on an early concept that small biologically active species might in general be trapped inside a large framework that would be opened or dismembered upon illumination, thus uncaging the contents. In fact, total imprisonment of one molecule by another so that the contents cannot exchange with the outside world has only recently been accomplished (19, 29), and controlled photochemical disruption of the cage is difficult or impossible. In nearly all successful caged molecules so far, simple covalent bond formation masks some feature important for biological recognition. Photochemical cleavage of that single bond releases the active species.

Caged compounds are biologically useful because illumination can be so easily controlled in timing, location, and amplitude. Therefore abrupt or localized changes in concentration of active species can be generated with controlled amplitudes. This capability is particularly valuable when rapid mechanical mixing is impractical, for example inside a more-or-less intact cell, tissue, or protein crystal, or when microscopic spatial gradients are desired. Photolysis of caged compounds is one of the best techniques to examine the fast kinetics or spatial heterogeneity of biochemical responses in

755

0066–4278/93/0315–0755$02.00

such systems. Their application in cell biology and biochemistry has burgeoned over the last decade and has been the subject of many reviews (15, 37, 38, 46, 50, 53, 56, 64, 74, 85, 113, 132, 134). To avoid duplication, this review focuses on selected novel or controversial areas such as development of new photosensitive masking groups, extension of photochemical activation to species such as Ca^{2+}, neurotransmitters, fluorochromes, peptides, and enzymes, and prospects and goals for further development.

CAGING GROUPS

Caged compounds are most commonly designed by modifying the desired biomolecule with a suitable photoremovable protecting group or caging group. To be useful in biological experiments this group must satisfy (at least partially) several criteria: (*a*) It should render the biomolecule inert to the biological system used. (*b*) It should release the biomolecule in high yield at sufficient speed by photolysis at wavelengths of light that are non-detrimental to the biological preparation. (*c*) Any photoproducts other than the desired biomolecule should not interact or interfere with the biological system.

Since the introduction of caged compounds in 1978 (28, 55), several different caging groups have been described that have resulted in the almost bewildering choice available today (Figure 1). In this section we discuss the relative merits of these caging groups and potential alternatives.

2-Nitrobenzyl Groups

Caging groups based on the photoisomerization of 2-nitrobenzyl substituents are by far the most prevalent in present caged compounds. Their advantages include compatibility with a wide variety of functional groups (e.g. phosphates, carboxylates, hydroxyl groups, amines and amides), ease of synthesis, and reasonable light sensitivity and kinetics (74).

A major problem of the unsubstituted 2-nitrobenzyl (NB) group (Figure 1, number 1) is the photoproduct, 2-nitrosobenzaldehyde, which may react with the released compound or other components of the preparation (55). The 1-(2-nitrophenyl)ethyl (NPE) group (Figure 1, number 2) generates the less-reactive acetophenone and is less toxic particularly in the presence of scavengers such as thiols and semicarbazide (55). However, both NB and NPE groups only absorb weakly at wavelengths greater than 340 nm ($\in_{347}$ 500 $M^{-1}cm^{-1}$) greatly limiting photolysis in the more convenient range of 350 to 400 nm. The 4, 5-dimethoxy-2-nitrobenzyl (DMNB) cage (Figure 1, number 5) has much higher absorbance in this region ($\in_{360}$ 5000 $M^{-1}cm^{-1}$), but it also has lower quantum yields, so the sensitivity to longwave UV improves by less than tenfold (141). Another advantage of DMNB, at least

1. **2-nitrobenzyl (NB) (R^1 = H)**
2. **2-(2-nitrophenyl)ethyl (NPE) (R^1 = Me)**
3. **α-carboxy-2-nitrobenzyl (CNB) (R^1 = COO⁻)**

4. **2,2'-dinitrobenzhydryl (DNB)**

5. **4,5-dimethoxy-2-nitrobenzyl (DMNB) (R^1=H)**
6. **2-(4,5-dimethoxynitrophenyl)ethyl (DMNPE) (R^1 = Me)**

7. **bis(2-nitro-4,5-dimethoxyphenyl)methyl**

8. **α-benzoyl-3,5-dimethoxybenzyl**

9. **3,5-dinitrophenyl**

10. **(4-methoxy-8-azido-1-naphthyl)methyl**

11. **5,7-dinitroindolinyl**

12. **4-methoxyphenacyl**

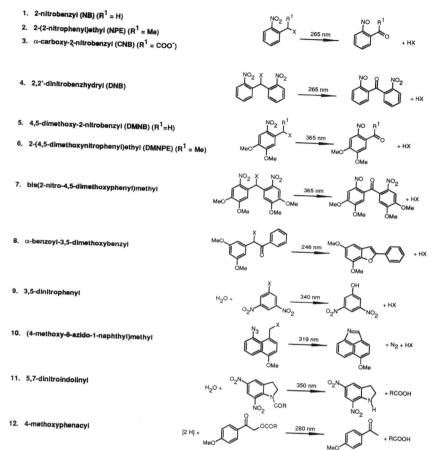

Figure 1 Structures of photolabile protecting groups discussed in this article. The wavelengths given above each reaction arrow are approximate estimates of the absorption maxima; often photolysis can be accomplished at substantially longer wavelengths. HX can in principle represent any alcohol, amine, phenol, carboxylic acid, or phosphoric acid, but individual compounds may vary considerably in their compatibility with each caging group.

for caging cyclic nucleotides (cyclic AMP and GMP), is that the kinetics of release are much faster than for the corresponding NPE-caged versions (141). Recently, the 1-(4, 5-dimethoxy-2-nitrophenyl)ethyl (DMNPE) cage (Figure 1, number 6), which combines both modifications of the NPE and DMNB groups, has been investigated, but failed to show fast release kinetics with ATP (141) or amino acids (138). The NPE and DMNPE groups are chiral, a property that is disadvantageous because coupling to chiral biomolecules produces diastereomers. These pairs of compounds may have different biological and photochemical properties, yet may be difficult to separate preparatively. A synthetic route to each of the diastereomers of NPE-caged ATP has recently been described (16). Although considerable biological success has been achieved in the use of NPE and DMNB caged compounds, especially with phosphate ester and anhydrides, improvement in the speed of release of the compound and the ability to photolyze efficiently at longer wavelengths are still desirable. For example, although NPE-caged ATP has been used extensively to probe the kinetics of muscle contraction (46), it is not completely inert before photolysis, its release rate is modest, its photoproducts are protein-reactive and release protons, and costly, powerful laser systems are required to photolyze sufficient nucleotide. Interaction of NPE-caged carbamoylcholine (133) with the nicotinic acetylcholine receptor before photolysis was prevented by introducing a negatively-charged carboxylate group into the cage (the α-carboxy-2-nitrobenzyl or CNB) (Figure 1, number 3) with the added bonus of faster release kinetics (78). This new protecting group has also proven useful with caged glycine derivatives (12). The 2, 2'-dinitrobenzhydryl (DNB) group (Figure 1, number 4), which essentially incorporates two 2-nitrobenzyl substituents, was one of the first reported nitrobenzyl-related photoremovable protecting groups (92). It merits fresh attention as a caging group for phosphates, carboxylates, and hydroxyls following recent reports hinting of favorable properties (8). The related bis(2-nitro-4,5-dimethoxyphenyl)methyl group (Figure 1, number 7) was the most photosensitive group used to protect one of the carboxylates of BAPTA (2, 30).

New Protecting Groups

A number of photoremovable protecting groups for functional groups such as carboxylates and amines have been devised by organic chemists, in particular for use in peptide and nucleotide synthesis (95, 96). Many of these require photolysis with short wavelength ultraviolet (< 300 nm) and would be impractical for complex biological systems because of considerable absorbance by proteins and nucleic acids at these wavelengths. However, some (Figure 1) have been designed to work at longer wavelengths to prevent photodestruction of amino acids such as tryptophan and tyrosine. Application of several of these for improved caged compounds is in progress.

Substituted benzoin esters (for example containing the α-benzoyl-3,5-dimethoxybenzyl group, Figure 1, number 8) were introduced by Sheehan over 25 years ago as potential photosensitive protecting groups for carboxylates (110). These have recently been reinvestigated as a replacement for the NPE group for protecting phosphate groups (8, 18, 96). α-Benzoyl-3,5-dimethoxybenzyl phosphate appears to show the most favorable properties with a high quantum yield (0.78) and fast release kinetics ($>10^5$ s^{-1}). However, it only absorbs modestly between 340–360 nm ($\in_{347}$ 170 M^{-1} cm^{-1}), its synthesis is non-trivial, and the caging group is converted into an unreactive (although more absorbent and probably fluorescent) photoproduct, a phenylbenzofuran (15, 18). α-Benzoyl-3,5-dimethoxybenzyl-caged ATP has similar release kinetics about two orders of magnitude faster than NPE-caged ATP at pH 7 (15, 121).

Other potential phosphate cages are the 3-nitrophenyl ester and its derivatives such as 3,5-dinitrophenyl (Figure 1, number 9), which undergo photosolvolysis, thus releasing the phosphate and the nitrophenol (43, 58). 3,5-Dinitrophenyl (DNP) phosphate has been used to photorelease phosphate in crystals of glycogen phosphorylase b to permit monitoring of the catalytic cycle by Laue X-ray diffraction (25). The DNP-caged phosphate is converted by irradiation at 300–360 nm ($\in_{340}$ about 3000 M^{-1}cm^{-1}) with reasonable quantum efficiency (0.67) and releases phosphate at $>10^4$s^{-1} (15) at pH 7. Unfortunately, DNP-caged ATP is at least 100-fold less photosensitive than DNP-phosphate (15), as reported for other phosphate diesters (58). Other potential problems with this protecting group include the danger of other nucleophiles (such as lysine side chains) competing in the photosolvolysis and leading to protein modification. Also, 3,5-dinitrophenol might have some ability to uncouple mitochondria, which would be undesirable in living cells.

Other protecting groups suggested for photogeneration of carboxylates include (azidonaphthyl)methyl esters (Figure 1, number 10), in which photolysis generates a nitrene that inserts in a peri-methylene group and triggers elimination of the molecule being caged (10). One problem with using this group as a protecting group for carboxylate or phosphate is the danger of nitrene insertion at other sites, which would result in no release and potential biomolecule or protein modification such as was described for a caged BAPTA using this group (2). Another group that utilizes photosolvolysis for the release of carboxylates is the 5,7-dinitroindolinylamide (Figure 1, number 11) (5). This can be irradiated at wavelengths beyond 400 nm and is much more photosensitive than the DMNB group for the release of acetate (S. Adams & R. Tsien, unpublished observations).

Methoxyphenacyl groups (Figure 1, number 12) have been proposed as carboxyl-photosensitive protecting groups that can be photolyzed by irradiation of greater than 330 nm (109). In a recent comparison, this group compared favorably with the NPE group for blocking inorganic phosphate although no details of quantum efficiency, absorbance coefficient, or kinetics of release were described (8).

Most of the groups described above are mainly suitable for protection of carboxylates or phosphates. Although this covers many of the desired applications, there is still a need for photorelease of amines such as amino acid neurotransmitters and protein side chains of lysine. In traditional organic synthesis, oxycarbonyl (OCO) linkers have generally been inserted to permit the use of such protecting groups as the 2-nitrobenzyl (92) and 3-nitrophenyl groups (95) (and potentially the benzoin, phenacyl and dinitroindolinyl groups). This introduces a further dark reaction in the photorelease mechanism because CO_2 release is now required and could conceivably become rate-limiting. NPE-oxycarbonyl glutamate and serine do show relatively slow kinetics for release of glutamate and serine, 50 ms and 40 ms respectively (57, 76), although an analysis of the rate-determining step has not yet been given. Such a linker has been used with a DMNB group for the caging of the amino group of a lysine residue in phage T4 lysozyme (75). Photolysis regenerated the catalytic activity of the caged protein although the kinetics were not determined. This linker is avoided with the CNB group used for protecting the amide of carbamoylcholine (78) and the amine of glycine (12).

One question commonly asked is why all the standard photosensitive groups require ultraviolet wavelengths for photolysis, rather than visible wavelengths that would be more convenient optically, better able to penetrate biological tissues, and possibly less injurious. Is the restriction to UV a fundamental limitation in photochemistry, based perhaps on the minimum energy needed to break a covalent bond? Momentary reflection on photobiology shows that such is not the case. Vision, ion-pumping by bacteriorhodopsin, photosynthesis, and phytochrome signaling use visible or far red photons to accomplish profoundly important photochemistry. These reactions are all the more impressive because their chromophores can be rapidly recycled and do not use high energy bonds such as nitrogen-nitrogen or nitrogen-oxygen as used in nearly all the synthetic caging groups. Whereas biological light-harvesting systems have been under strong selection pressure to use the visible and near-infrared wavelengths most abundant in sunshine, organic chemists have usually had the opposite incentive. Molecules highly sensitive to visible light tend to have more complex, extended chromophores and are experimentally more difficult to work with than UV-sensing molecules because darkrooms are required. However, the need for longer-wavelength caging groups has probably been supplanted by the advent of excitation of UV chromophores by two photon pulsed IR (see below).

CAGED NEUROTRANSMITTERS AND AMINO ACIDS

One of the first applications of light-sensitive compounds to physiology actually preceded the invention of traditional caged compounds. Erlanger & Wasserman described a series of photoactivatable and photoreversible acetylcholine agonists and antagonists that incorporated a photochromic azobenzene (9). The best known member is Bis-Q, a reversible agonist only in the *trans* form. It was used in combination with electrophysiological techniques for pioneering mechanistic studies of the nicotinic acetylcholine receptor (AChR) of *Torpedo* and *Electrophorus* species (reviewed in 38, 64). Its limited applicability to other AChR and side-effects of desensitization and inactivation have restricted its widespread use (23).

An alternative to Bis-Q was caged carbamoylcholine, introduced by Hess and co-workers in 1986 (133). They exploited established 2-nitrobenzyl group chemistry in a novel way to protect the carbamate nitrogen of this acetylcholine agonist as the NPE or NB derivative. Although the NPE-carbamoylcholine showed favorable quantum yield and release kinetics, biological use was limited partly by its weak inhibition and inactivation of the acetylcholine receptor before photolysis. However, replacement of the methyl group on the benzylic carbon with a carboxylic acid (the CNB group) gave a physiologically inert caged carbamoylcholine with increased light-sensitivity and speed of release ($t_{\frac{1}{2}}$ 95 µs) (78). Laser pulse photolysis of patch-clamped BC$_3$H1 muscle cells perfused with this compound caused activation of the whole cell current through the nicotinic acetylcholine receptors after a lag of 200 µs (72, 78). Desensitization of the receptor began after 1.5 ms and the current returned to baseline after 300 ms. Using this data, Matsubara et al (72) calculated values for the rate constants for the opening and closing of the channel and the dissociation constant for the ligand-binding site that causes this opening. The opening rate obtained agrees with one of the values obtained from single-channel current analysis of the same cells (112), although this was originally thought to be incorrect. It is of interest because it determines an upper limit on the rate at which ACh-mediated signals can pass between cells and, with the other constants determined, it permits calculation of the fraction of channels open at any given concentration of agonist. In the long term, knowledge of such values for any neurotransmitter receptor may allow prediction of the combined actions of a mixture of these in a single neuron and help explain signal transduction at the single cell level. The faster time resolution of this flash photolysis method has significant advantage over traditional rapid-mixing procedures, which have a 10-ms dead time (44). Single-channel current analysis is carried out under assumed equilibrium conditions in which desensitization may occur and determining the rate of channel opening is complex (47, 67). Using caged compounds offers an alternative and independent method for this measurement.

Further steps towards this approach have been the synthesis of caged derivatives of other neurotransmitters such as glycine, glutamate, GABA, and aspartate. Although initial attempts to use the DMNPE group to mask the carboxylate of glycine (138) allowed only slow release of the neurotransmitter (time constant about 1 s^{-1}), protecting the amine with the CNB group was much more successful (12). CNB-caged glycine releases glycine upon photolysis at a rate of 600 s^{-1} at pH 7.5 and activates channels in cultured mouse spinal cord cells. Fortunately, the channel opening rate is considerably slower than that of the acetylcholine receptor with carbamoylcholine and is not limited by release of glycine ($t_{\frac{1}{2}}$ 1 ms). A number of other caged amino acids have been reported although these all use the DMNB or DMNPE group to mask the carboxylate (138). With glycine they gave slow release (see above), and no release kinetics are reported. Glycine caged with NPE on the amine releases glycine upon photolysis at a similar rate to the CNB derivative described above (12). A NPE-caged phenylephrine has been described in which the protecting group is attached to one of the phenolic positions (135). Although its kinetics are slow (3 s^{-1} at pH 7), it has been used successfully to activate force generation in smooth muscle (114). The more recently synthesized CNB-caged L-phenylephrine has much more favorable release kinetics of 1980 s^{-1} (J. Walker et al, submitted).

CAGED FLUOROPHORES

The active or diffusional movement of molecules in biological systems under steady-state conditions is conventionally measured using the "fluorescence recovery after photobleaching" (FRAP) technique (48). Thus, fluorescently-labeled proteins or phospholipids are incorporated into biological membranes or cells, allowed to equilibrate, photobleached in a spatially defined region of interest, and the movement of unbleached label into this area is then measured. Photoactivation of fluorescence (PAF) achieved by the photolysis of caged fluorophores attached to biomolecules and measurement of its dissipation has recently been proposed (60, 79) as a complementary method with some potential advantages:

1. With FRAP, fluorescence recovery entails the measurement of a small decrease in signal (photobleached) against a high background of unbleached dye. Contrastingly, PAF generates a positive signal against a negative background and will have a more favorable signal to noise ratio, especially with the low levels of fluorescent labeling required to prevent perturbation of the properties of the biomolecule.

2. With PAF, photolysis of the caging groups usually requires ultraviolet irradiation, and the released fluorophore is then monitored at a longer, non-photoactivating wavelength. However with FRAP, light of the same wavelength is used to photobleach the fluorophore and monitor the subsequent fluorescence recovery (although at a reduced intensity). Further photobleaching during monitoring is therefore inherent in this technique.

3. A final disadvantage of FRAP is the requirement for high light intensity to photobleach these relatively photostable fluorophores. PAF requires much

less irradiation for photoactivation (although usually at shorter and more energetic wavelengths) and therefore might reduce side-effects of irradiation on the biological system. In addition, the photoproducts of PAF, stable fluorophores and nitrosobenzaldehydes, are relatively innocuous, whereas the usually unknown bleaching mechanisms of fluorophores, often involving reactive oxygen species, may be more pernicious.

Krafft and co-workers devised several strategies (60) for caging fluorophores for use in the PAF method that included fluorescent amine dyes (e.g. coumarins, naphthalenes, anthracenes) quenched by fluorescence resonant energy transfer (FRET) to photoremovable 2-nitrobenzyl oxycarbonyl groups (21). Photolysis of these groups eliminates FRET and restores fluorescence. However, this method is limited to fluorophores whose emission, when protected, overlaps the absorption of the methoxy-substituted 2-nitrobenzyl groups used (λ_{max} 360 nm). A furyl-chromone derivative, which upon photolysis at 350 nm becomes fluorescent (emitting at 517 nm), was also described, but the excitation wavelength used to monitor fluorescence also causes further photolysis (20). A more successful approach was to protect the phenolic position of a fluorescein monoether with a photoremovable 2-nitrobenzyl group (17, 61). The fluorescein is forced into the non-fluorescent colorless lactone form, but on photolysis tautomerises to the fluorescent quinonoid structure. By using the monoether of fluorescein, rather than the familiar diphenol, only one 2-nitrobenzyl group has to be photolyzed to generate fluorescence and the other masked phenolic position can be used to improve solubility or attach the caged fluorophore to the macromolecule via a linker. Mitchison described a carboxyfluorescein protected with 2-nitrobenzyl groups on both phenolic positions with attachment through the carboxyl group to amines of the macromolecule (79). Although requiring photocleavage of both protecting groups, the product is the more fluorescent carboxyfluorescein rather than fluorescein monoether. More recently, Theriot & Mitchison described a thiol-reactive caged resorufin that requires photolysis of only one 2-nitrobenzyl group to generate fluorescence (119). The caged fluorophores of Mitchison are the only compounds to be used for biological studies; the bis-caged fluorescein is commercially available.

Mitchison examined the dynamics of the microtubules forming the mitotic spindle in tissue culture cells by microinjecting tubulin labeled with the bis-caged fluorescein and using the PAF technique (79). The modified tubulin successfully incorporated into functional spindles, and fluorescent bars generated by photolysis migrated polewards at 0.3-0.7 μm/min. Analogous experiments using FRAP (35, 102) failed to detect such movement possibly because the much faster dissolution of a subset of microtubules (Mitchison observed 50–75% of the initial fluorescence rapidly dissipated) obscured the slower directed motion of the kinetochore (chromosome-carrying) microtubules. In these circumstances, for the signal-to-noise reason described above, PAF should be more sensitive than FRAP. Mitchison suggests microtubules polymerize at the kinetochore (point of attachment to the chromosome) and depolymerize near the poles throughout metaphase (79). Still unanswered is the source of force generation and why the rate of microtubular movement was only ~25% that of chromosome movement in anaphase. Subsequent studies using mitotic spindles assembled in vitro from cell-free extracts of *Xenopus* eggs confirmed polewards movement of non-kinetochore microtubules, this time at a similar rate to chromosomal movement (105).

Two recent studies have used bis-caged fluorescein modified tubulin and PAF to examine microtubule assembly and transport during axonal growth (88, 100). New tubulin (for microtubules) is required for axonal elongation but is synthesized in the cell body and must therefore be transported to the growth cone either as monomers or microtubules. Reinsch et al followed the movement of photoactivated fluorescent marks along the axons of cultured *Xenopus* neurons (100). Their results suggest that the transport of coherent, polymerized microtubules occurs continuously from the cell body to the growth cone and at a rate faster at the growth cone. Photobleaching experiments failed to detect such vectorial movement and concluded that monomers were the transport form of tubulin (65, 87). Although these studies used cell types whose axons elongate more slowly, Reinsch et al found no such evidence for monomer transport (100). Okabe & Hirokawa, using the same PAF method, found similar evidence for translocation of microtubules en bloc in similar *Xenopus* neurons (88). However, no such movement of microtubules or tubulin monomers could be measured in elongating cultured mouse sensory neurons, which suggests that different tubulin transport mechanisms exist in mammalian and *Xenopus* neurons (88). The transport form of tubulin in mouse sensory neurons remains unknown.

Theriot & Mitchison recently applied the PAF method to follow the movement of actin labeled with caged resorufin in the actively-extending veil-like regions (lamellipodia) of motile goldfish epithelial keratocytes (119). Similar lamellipodia are found in other motile cells such as fibroblasts, leucocytes, epithelial cells, and neurite growth cones. Fluorescent marks photogenerated in the lamellipodia of keratocytes remained coherent and fixed relative to the substrate as the cell moved over them, regardless of cell speed, until their rapid dissipation ($t_{\frac{1}{2}}$ 23 s). A model (called nucleation-release) to explain these observations involves a network of randomly orientated, rapidly exchanging actin filaments spread uniformly throughout the lamellipodia. Fresh polymerization of actin must occur in extending regions. How this mesh of actin is coupled to generate force transduction or what constitutes the molecular motor involved are unknown. Whether actin microfilaments behave similarly in other motile cells is unclear as the PAF experiments failed to reveal the centripetal flow reported in fibroblasts and growth cones using FRAP (136).

This technique has also been used to examine the motion of the pathogenic bacterium, *Listeria monocytogenes* in the cytoplasm of infected PtK2 epithelial cells (120). Moving bacteria generate "comet tails" of actin filaments in their wake that may be marked by photoactivation of incorporated actin modified with caged resorufin. These marks stay stationary relative to the substrate, rather than to the bacteria, and decay rapidly ($t\frac{1}{2}$ 33 s). These findings are consistent with polymerization of actin filaments at or near the bacterium surface (103), crosslinking by actin-binding proteins thus forming the tail, and subsequent exponential depolymerization. A prediction of the model that the length of the tail would increase with the speed of the bacteria was found to hold. The molecular nature of the coupling of actin polymerization to movement may be deciphered more readily in this system by the ability to genetically manipulate the bacteria and may shed light on general mechanisms of cell motility involving actin.

CAGED ENZYMES AND PEPTIDES

The photochemical control of the catalytic activity of enzymes has been the focus of considerable research in the last 25 years [for early work see references in Turner et al (128) and review by Martinek & Berezin (71)]. In general two approaches have been studied: the reversible control of enzymic activity by light, and the photoactivation of catalytically inactive enzymes.

Reversible Photoregulation

Research in this area has involved the modification of enzymes with photochromic compounds, which results in some degree of photocontrol of the catalytic activity. Appending five azobenzene units (per molecule) to the exposed lysine groups of papain gave an almost threefold change in activity on interconversion of the *trans* and *cis* forms (139). Similarly binding of α-D-mannopyranose to concanavalin A modified with a fulgide was photoregulated (140). Such unspecific modifications, with no clear or predictable mechanism of action, appear to produce only modest changes in activity and are not generally applicable to other proteins.

Photoactivation

Porter and co-workers have devised a series of *trans*-cinnamoyl esters that bind to and acylate the catalytic serine residue in the active site of a number of serine proteases such as thrombin, Factor Xa, trypsin, and chymotrypsin (116, 117, 128, 129). The resulting stable and inactive acyl-enzymes can be re-activated by photoisomerization of the *trans*-cinnamoyl ester to the *cis* isomer, which spontaneously cyclises to a coumarin, thus deacylating the enzyme and restoring catalytic activity. Introduction of a diethylamino substituent in the cinnamoyl group greatly increased the absorbance of the acyl-enzyme at 350 to 400 nm, increased the dark stability, and permitted the photocontrol of coagulation of serum by regulation of thrombin activity (98). The release rate of active enzyme was complete in a few milliseconds (98).

Photoactivation of enzymes has recently been exploited to investigate the precise structural changes occurring at an enzyme's active site during catalysis. Conventional X-ray diffraction techniques are far too slow as hours to weeks are often required to accumulate sufficient data. However, Laue X-ray crystallography using high intensity synchrotron X-rays sources has reduced the exposure time to the millisecond timescale or less (39). If an ordinary substrate were just applied to the solution bathing the crystal, long diffusional delays and spatial non-uniformities would result. The use of rapid photorelease from caged compounds already present in the crystal seems to offer a solution to this problem (15, 39). For example, caged GTP was photolyzed in crystals of *ras* p21 to generate the GTP-enzyme complex (half-life about 20 min) and observe the protein structural changes upon hydrolysis (106, 107). Acylated inactive chymotrypsin crystals (prepared as described above) were photolyzed and the free active enzyme detected after 1 min (with a 100 msec exposure), as diffusion of the coumarin photo-by-product out of the active site had occurred by this time (117, 118). The slow subsequent reaction of the enzyme with the inhibitor, 3-benzyl-6-chloro-2-py-rone, previously loaded into the crystal by diffusion, could then be followed over the next 24 hr. The formation of inhibited enzyme-pyrone complex could be detected after 3 hr, although no earlier intermediate was resolvable. More recently, photolysis of a caged phosphate in crystals of glycogen phosphoryl-ase *b* containing bound substrate failed to give catalysis as detected in a time-resolved Laue diffraction experiment, but catalysis was detected when data were collected on a slower time scale with conventional methods (25). The full potential of this marriage between caged compound technology and Laue X-ray diffraction has yet to be realized but offers exciting prospects for understanding how enzymes work.

Another recent development that will expand the use of caged enzymes and proteins is the incorporation of unnatural amino acids at specific sites into proteins. Schultz and co-workers describe the synthesis of a photoactivatable lysozyme containing a 2-nitrobenzyl-caged aspartyl residue at the active site (75). This group was incorporated into the polypeptide in an in vitro-coupled transcription-translation system, in which the gene sequence was mutated to the nonsense amber codon TAG at the appropriate position, and a comple-mentary tRNA acylated with aspartyl β-nitrobenzyl ester was supplied as a suppressor. The caged lysozyme was catalytically inactive, but upon photolysis regained the activity of the native enzyme (75). The ability to target a caged group to a specific site in a protein should allow a large number of processes such as protein-folding, protein-protein interactions, and catalytic mechanisms to be studied with high time resolution in a precise and controlled manner. The incorporation and photolysis of caged proteins or peptides into living cells could help delineate the control and kinetics of intracellular signaling pathways. Short peptides should be more easily prepared by conventional chemical synthesis with suitable amino acid derivatives.

Fodor et al used DMNB oxycarbonyl protected amino acids to construct arrays of peptides of defined and controllable sequence in a innovative technique that combines solid-phase peptide chemistry, photosensitive protecting groups, and photolithography (31). The peptides are synthesized by stepwise addition of the amino acids at sites that had been activated by photoremoval of a 2-nitrobenzyl protecting group by irradiation through masks that leave other areas unphotolyzed. By altering this photolysis pattern at each cycle, the sequence of each peptide at each site can be easily controlled. For example, an array of 1024 peptides was synthesized in ten steps and measured 400 by 400-μm square. Such arrays of peptides or oligonucleotides could be used to screen potential ligands for biological molecules.

CAGED CALCIUM CHELATORS

Caged Calcium: Nitr and DM-Nitrophen

The photochemical release of the important second messenger, Ca^{2+} has recently been made possible by the introduction of the nitr series of compounds and DM-nitrophen (1, 54, 127). Because Ca^{2+} does not form covalent bonds in aqueous solution, it cannot be caged by simple derivatization as in most other caged species. Instead Ca^{2+} is sequestered by a chelator that changes from high (but not infinite) affinity to a much lower affinity upon photolysis. Therefore at least four species are involved, the free and Ca^{2+}-bound forms before and after photolysis. Additional species may have to be considered if Mg^{2+} or H^+ complexes are formed to significant extents, or if more than one photolabile group is contained in each molecule. Depending on the complexity of these equilibria and the presence of other buffers and Ca^{2+}-transporting systems, pulsed photolysis can generate step increases or pulses, or more complicated waveforms of $[Ca^{2+}]$ change (142a). Both nitr and DM-nitrophen utilize the 2-nitrobenzyl photorearrangement that has been exploited in most other caged compounds (74).

The nitr series (1, 127) is based upon BAPTA (123), a highly selective chelator for Ca^{2+}, whereas DM-nitrophen uses the metal coordinating site of

EDTA (Figure 2) (54). Nitr chelators have the high selectivity for Ca^{2+} over Mg^{2+}, pH-insensitivity, and fast buffering kinetics of BAPTA (123) while DM-nitrophen has the Mg^{2+} interference, pH-sensitivity, but higher Ca^{2+} affinity of EDTA. A further major difference is the mechanism by which photolysis results in a decrease in the Ca^{2+} affinity of the chelator. Nitr relies on photochemical conversion of a 2-nitrobenzyl substituent on one or more of the benzene rings to a more electron-withdrawing group, which steals electron density from one or both of the metal coordinating nitrogens. These remote electronic effects cause a 40-fold decrease in Ca^{2+} affinity for nitr-5 upon photolysis (1). Contrastingly, photolysis of DM-nitrophen results in the chemical disintegration of the Ca^{2+}-binding site and therefore yields a much larger decrease in affinity.

The structures of the most popular members of the nitr chelators are shown in Figure 2. Nitr-5, the most well-known member, increases its dissociation constant Ca^{2+} from 150 nM to about 6.5 μM upon photolysis at 360 nm and releases Ca^{2+} at a rate of 3000 s^{-1} (1). Nitr-7, also commercially available, has tighter Ca^{2+} binding resulting from incorporation of a *cis*-cyclopentane ring into the backbone of the metal coordinating site. Under typical levels of $[Ca^{2+}]_i$, more Ca^{2+} is bound and therefore releasable by photolysis with nitr-7 compared to nitr-5; less free chelator also decreases any buffering of $[Ca^{2+}]_i$ before photolysis. However, the $[Ca^{2+}]_i$ level achievable after photolysis is also lowered and the rate of release is slightly slower (1). Nitr-8 was designed for studies requiring larger changes in $[Ca^{2+}]_i$ such as might occur in the vicinity of ion channels. A 1600-fold decrease in Ca^{2+} affinity is achieved by incorporating two nitrobenzyl substituents into BAPTA; however they must both undergo photolysis to produce this change in $[Ca^{2+}]_i$ (S. Adams & R. Tsien, unpublished observations). Nitr-9 is an important control for side-effects of the photolysis flash and any toxicity from the photoproducts of nitr chelators in biological experiments, since it should undergo the same photochemical events but cause no change in $[Ca^{2+}]_i$ (51). Both nitr-5 (as the free chelator and membrane permeant AM form) and nitr-7 are commercially available.

DM-nitrophen, introduced by Ellis-Davies & Kaplan in 1988, changes dissociation constant for Ca^{2+} from about 5 nM to several mM upon photolysis at pH 7.2, 0.15 M ionic strength (54). A recent detailed examination of the kinetics of Ca^{2+} release as detected by the metallochromic indicator anti-pyrylazo III showed a half time of 180 μs, which could well have been limited by the indicator rather than the DM-nitrophen (73). DM-nitrophen also has tight binding ($K_d = 2.5$ μM) for Mg^{2+}, which likewise weakens to 3 mM on photolysis. Therefore if DM-nitrophen were incorporated into cells, intracellular free $[Mg^{2+}]$ would probably be depleted, then photoreleased along with the $[Ca^{2+}]_i$ jump. Alternatively, if free Mg^{2+} were initially maintained at

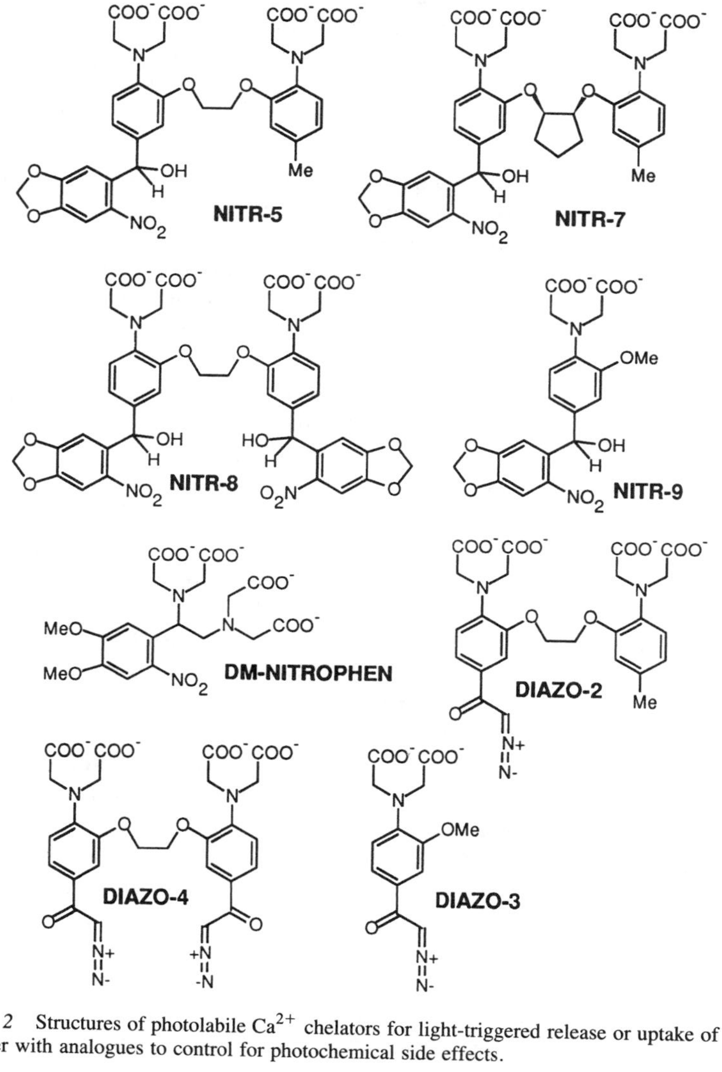

Figure 2 Structures of photolabile Ca^{2+} chelators for light-triggered release or uptake of Ca^{2+} together with analogues to control for photochemical side effects.

quasi-normal intracellular levels, for example 1 mM, the Mg^{2+} competition would raise the apparent Ca^{2+} dissociation constant of DM-nitrophen to 2 μM, an uncomfortably high value. This problem, together with the lack so far of a permeant ester, has tended to restrict DM-nitrophen to microinjected, perfused, or permeabilized systems in which the precise concentrations of

DM-nitrophen, Ca^{2+}, and Mg^{2+} can be set to achieve the desired photo-release of Ca^{2+}. Ellis-Davies & Kaplan also synthesized an analogue based on the more Ca^{2+}-selective chelator EGTA, but unfortunately its affinity for Ca^{2+} before photolysis was too low (27). However, DM-nitrophen can be used as a caged-Mg^{2+}, for example in studying enzymes utilizing MgATP as a substrate (7).

The kinetics of the Ca^{2+} change after the initial release are complicated because unphotolyzed DM-nitrophen rebinds Ca^{2+} relatively slowly, while the Mg^{2+}-complex probably (26) dissociates Mg^{2+} and exchanges it for Ca^{2+} even more slowly. Therefore, if Ca^{2+}-DM-nitrophen is flash photolyzed in the presence of residual unphotolyzed free or Mg^{2+}-bound DM-nitrophen, the initial spike of high Ca^{2+} decays back to a much lower plateau level as the Ca^{2+} gradually rebinds to and displaces Mg^{2+} from the unphotolyzed species (22, 53, 73). Analogous complications with the nitr series are unlikely to be kinetically detectable (53) because Mg^{2+} complexes are hardly significant, and all the cation equilibria are nearly diffusion-limited. Another minor caution with DM-nitrophen is that its photolysis products pick up protons at pH 7, so careful pH buffering is desirable, particularly since the dissociation constant of DM-nitrophen is itself pH-sensitive.

An important part of any biological experiment involving a caged Ca^{2+} is determining the extent of concentration jump achieved upon photolysis. The preferable method is to measure the $[Ca^{2+}]$ concurrently through use of a Ca^{2+} indicator such as fluo-3 or fura-2. Fluo-3 has the advantage of being excited at wavelengths that do not photolyze the caged Ca^{2+} (all of which require light in the 340–370 nm range), but precise calibration of this non-ratiometric dye is difficult (52). Fura-2 is a ratiometric indicator and is usually alternately excited at 340 and 385 nm (36), wavelengths that can cause some photolysis of the caged Ca^{2+}. The large increases of $[Ca^{2+}]_i$ to tens of micromolar obtainable with DM-nitrophen fall outside the accuracy range of these indicators, so that older metallochromic indicators such as tetramethyl-murexide and antipyrylazo III may be preferable (73) even though they are difficult to calibrate in intact cells. Other potential problems include severe inner-filtering in thick cells or tissues by the high concentrations (a few millimolar) of caged Ca^{2+} often used to control $[Ca^{2+}]_i$ (142). This effect increases after photolysis, since both DM-nitrophen and particularly the nitr series increase in extinction upon photolysis. The magnitude of this problem should be calculated in each case from the optical pathlength, chelator concentration, and extinction coefficients before and after photolysis. Recalibrating the indicator in the presence of typical concentrations and pathlengths of caged Ca^{2+} before and after photolysis may therefore be required for accurate measurements of any Ca^{2+} jumps produced (142). Other reported problems include contaminating fluorescence from nitr-5 and DM-nitrophen preparations (with nitr-5, this must come largely from impurities since purer samples have lower levels of fluorescence) and partial quenching of fluo-3 by DM-nitrophen (142).

An alternative to direct measurement of photoreleased Ca^{2+} is to estimate the changes by computer modeling. Landò & Zucker predicted Ca^{2+} jumps in giant *Aplysia* neurons based on the flash intensity, the cell diameter, the concentration of nitr and Ca^{2+}, the Ca^{2+}-pump rate, and the period between subsequent flashes (63). Similar calculations for DM-nitrophen were complicated by Mg^{2+} interference and were considered only partly accurate for the initial $[Ca^{2+}]_i$ after photolysis and unsafe for subsequent changes (22).

Caged calciums have been used to examine aspects of Ca^{2+} control in muscle contraction (for reviews see 6, 46), Ca^{2+} regulation of ion channels (33, 38a, 70a, 80a), Ca^{2+} oscillations in REF52 fibroblasts (41, 42), Ca^{2+}-induced Ca^{2+} release in muscle (56a, 63a, 83, 131), and mitosis (51). They have also been much used to analyze neurotransmitter release at nerve synapses and to answer the controversial question of whether exocytosis has a direct dependence on membrane potential in addition to its accepted dependence on $[Ca^{2+}]_i$. An important and direct test is to eliminate the normal voltage-gated Ca^{2+} influx by pharmacological blockade or removal of external Ca^{2+} or both, then to raise $[Ca^{2+}]_i$ using caged Ca^{2+} and see whether depolarization additionally enhances transmitter release. Haydon & Zucker (144) were the first to report such an experiment done on an inhibitory synapse formed between two *Helisoma* neurons in culture. Elevations in pre-synaptic $[Ca^{2+}]_i$ produced by photolysis of nitr-5 caused neurotransmitter release in the absence of external Ca^{2+} (144). Simultaneous depolarization of the presynaptic cell did not enhance that release, which argues against a direct effect of voltage and suggests that depolarization under normal conditions works only by opening Ca^{2+} channels (143). However, the transmitter release was already fatiguing during the voltage ramps, and the synapse may not be representative of the fast synapses for which direct voltage modulation was proposed. Next, Hochner et al (45) reaffirmed the importance of membrane potential using the more classical fast synapse of the crayfish neuromuscular junction. To block Ca^{2+} influx, they decreased extracellular Ca^{2+} to 0.2 mM and added 2 mM Mn^{2+}, 12.5 mM Mg^{2+}. In some experiments the mitochondrial poison CCCP was added to weaken mitochondrial Ca^{2+} buffering. Photolysis of presynaptic nitr-5 caused only a little transmitter release itself, but permitted action potentials to elicit quantal events with the normal latency. These findings would seem to be strong evidence that depolarization per se and $[Ca^{2+}]_i$ elevation are necessary for transmitter release in this preparation (91). However, Mulkey & Zucker (82) counterattacked by using fura-2 imaging of Ca^{2+} to show that action potentials still evoked sizable Ca^{2+} influxes under the blocking conditions used by Hochner et al (45), whereas

13.5 mM Co^{2+} and 30 mM Mg^{2+} in the absence of added Ca^{2+} were sufficient to prevent significant Ca^{2+} entry. Under these conditions, photolysis of DM-nitrophen gave transmitter release, which was not modulated by presynaptic action potentials (82). Similar results were reported from the squid giant synapse (22). However, it is unclear whether the controversy has been definitively settled. Quantification of the Ca^{2+}-sensitivity and kinetics of neurotransmitter release in fast synapses await further study, but would seem to be more tractable in slower-secreting systems such as bovine chromaffin cells (84).

Caged Calcium Buffer: Diazo

Following the introduction of the nitr series, it seemed desirable to be able to produce a decrease in $[Ca^{2+}]_i$ following a light flash. Such a caged calcium-buffer could be used to prevent or ablate rises or transients in $[Ca^{2+}]_i$, which are suspected to control subsequent biological events. A more frequently used approach is continuous rather than transient buffering of $[Ca^{2+}]_i$ with chelators such as BAPTA (126). However, continuous passive buffering, in principle, only diminishes, but does not eliminate, the change in free $[Ca^{2+}]_i$ caused by Ca^{2+} movements and has potential long-term side effects such as chelation of heavy metals and increase of Ca^{2+} diffusibility. It also cannot reveal the kinetics of response to a sudden fall in $[Ca^{2+}]_i$. A more powerful method is to quickly or continuously photorelease a chelator just when Ca^{2+} is to be lowered. Producing a rapid decrease in $[Ca^{2+}]_i$ from elevated levels in cells is obviously difficult using conventional BAPTA buffering.

Two approaches to designing a caged Ca^{2+} buffer have been described (2, 30). Firstly, masking one of the carboxyl groups of a Ca^{2+} chelator such as EGTA or BAPTA with a photosensitive protecting group would greatly decrease its Ca^{2+} affinity and photolysis would restore it. Considerable efforts with a wide variety of protecting groups were made to achieve this, but only very low quantum efficiencies were obtained, perhaps because the excited states were quenched by the aromatic amino groups in BAPTA (2, 30). A more successful strategy was the diazo series of chelators, which use photochemical changes of remote substituents to achieve the required increase in Ca^{2+} affinity (Figure 2). Thus an electron-withdrawing diazoketone substituent is photochemically converted to a electron-donating carboxymethyl group. The resulting increased electron density at the coordinating nitrogen atoms increases the Ca^{2+} affinity.

Diazo-2 (Figure 2) tightens Ca^{2+} binding from dissociation constants of 2.2 μM to 80 nM upon photolysis and is capable of binding Ca^{2+} in fractions of milliseconds (2). Diazo-3 is a control compound for the photochemistry and the released H^+, which are by-products of diazo photolysis without the Ca^{2+} sensitivity. Diazo-4 undergoes a much greater change in affinity from

89 μM to 55 nM, but requires photolysis of the two diazoketone substituents. All the diazo chelators have been derivatized as acetoxymethyl (AM) esters. They seem to load as well or better than BAPTA/AM into intact living cells, reaching millimolar intracellular concentrations of released chelators, probably because of their low molecular weight and non-excessive hydrophobicity.

Diazo-2 has been useful in studies of muscle relaxation (for review, see 6) and the mechanism of Ca^{2+} oscillations in REF52 fibroblasts (42). Very recently, diazo-4 proved useful in delineating the role of Ca^{2+} in long-term potentiation (LTP) in the hippocampus, a frequently used model system for neuronal plasticity. Malenka et al, using the whole-cell patch-clamp technique, incorporated diazo-4 into hippocampal CA1 pyramidal neurons (69). Photolysis at varying times after tetanus revealed that post-synaptic $[Ca^{2+}]_i$ had to be elevated for 1.5–2 s after stimulation to induce LTP. Release of Ca^{2+} buffer before 1.5–2 s prevented LTP, but left short-term potentiation intact. Interestingly, a similar timecourse has been reported for the neural activation of smooth muscle by increased $[Ca^{2+}]_i$, activation of calmodulin-dependent kinase, phosphorylation of myosin light chain, and subsequent contraction. There is substantial evidence that calmodulin-dependent kinase II and protein kinase C are involved in the initiation of LTP (68, 70).

Diazo-4 has also proven helpful in studies of the control by $[Ca^{2+}]_i$ of hyperpolarizations in rat hippocampal pyramidal cells (62) and Ca^{2+}-dependent inactivation of Ca^{2+} currents in *Aplysia* neurons (33).

Outlook

The optimal caged Ca^{2+} has yet to be made; it would include the large change in affinity and light-sensitivity of DM-nitrophen with the Ca^{2+} selectivity and pH insensitivity of the nitr chelators. One step in this direction is a recently prepared derivative of fura-2, which changes Ca^{2+} dissociation constant from 200 nM to over 110 μM with a high quantum efficiency (S. Adams & R. Tsien, unpublished observations). Another major need is a photoreversible Ca^{2+} chelator, or a chelator that can repetitively cycle between high and low Ca^{2+} affinities. Reversion to the tight-binding form would occur either spontaneously (i.e. thermally), or better yet upon illumination with a different wavelength. The ability to artificially generate reproducible repetitive transients of Ca^{2+} without exhausting the photolabile chelator would greatly facilitate controlled experiments and dose-response curves. Imposition of Ca^{2+} pulses of controlled frequency and amplitude could reveal the elusive function of $[Ca^{2+}]_i$ oscillations (77, 122). Gradients of $[Ca^{2+}]_i$, which have been observed in many cell types (122), could be created to examine their biological role. Devising photoreversible chelators will probably require the adaption of photochromic materials such as azo dyes (101), spiropyrans (11), or fulgides (137). Cleaving the Ca^{2+}-binding site into two unlinked pieces is unlikely to be reversible. Ironically, some of the first attempts to make caged Ca^{2+} were based on the photoreversible isomerization of azo compounds (64). Thioindigo and azo linkages have also been incorporated into a variety of polyethers and macrocyclic crown ethers in attempts to photocontrol ion-binding and transport of alkali, alkaline earth, and heavy metals (reviewed in 111). These pioneering chemical studies have been little noticed in the biological community, perhaps because they were largely conducted in organic solvents or involved heavy metals of lesser biological importance. All these classes of photochromic compounds have been used more extensively in the control of enzyme activity by photochemistry (see above).

INCORPORATION OF CAGED COMPOUNDS INTO CELLS

Most applications of caged compounds in physiology require their introduction into the cytoplasm of the cells or tissue to be studied. However, the majority of caged compounds are phosphate or polyphosphate esters and bear one or several negative charges, which prevent free diffusion across cell membranes. When caged compounds have been used with whole-cell patch-clamping, internal dialysis of the cell permits reasonable control of the intracellular concentration, but may lead to washout of important regulatory molecules. The latter is avoided with microinjection or iontophoresis, but the cell must be sufficiently large and the control of introduced compound is less precise. These methods work well for single-cell studies, but methods for use with large numbers of cells or in intact tissue are also required. Several approaches have been used to overcome this obstacle, including permeabilization of the cell and transient masking of the negative charges of caged compounds as acetoxymethyl esters. It should be noted that some caged compounds, such as caged cAMP, cGMP (86), and diacylglycerol (40), are uncharged at physiological pH values and readily cross biological membranes.

Cell permeabilization is used routinely in studies of the control of force generation in skeletal muscle. Glycerol-treated muscle permits ready diffusion of caged ATP and caged Ca^{2+} into muscle fibers (46). Saponin-treated smooth muscle has been used similarly (113). Disadvantages include the potential loss of soluble regulatory molecules and proteins, and the physical and permanent disruption of the plasma membrane (and often internal membranes) prevents an understanding of how these cellular components might be involved in controlling the biological process being studied. More recently, selective or reversible permeabilization has been used to circumvent such problems (for reviews, see 3, 4). Somlyo and co-workers used staphylococcal α-toxin to introduce caged ATP, GTPγS, GDPβS, and IP$_3$ into smooth muscle cells. This toxin permits entry of compounds with molecular weights less than 1000

(113, 115). β-escin, a saponin ester, allows introduction of compounds with molecular weights up to 17000 although some loss of small proteins may occur (59).

A less invasive approach is the use of acetoxymethyl ester derivatives of the caged compound to permit passive diffusion across the cell membrane. Hydrolysis of these groups by intracellular esterases liberates the membrane impermeant caged compound that accumulates inside the cell. This technique has proven useful with the fluorescent Ca^{2+} indicators such as fura 2 and fluo-3 on a wide variety of cell types and tissues (124, 125). The nitr and diazo series of Ca^{2+} chelators have been readily adaptable to caged calciums and calcium buffers (1, 2). For example, nitr-5 AM has been successfully loaded into REF52 (41, 42, 52) and Swiss 3T3 (51) fibroblasts, rat ventricular myocytes (131), and strips of gastric smooth muscle (14). Diazo-2/AM and diazo-3/AM load very efficiently into REF52 fibroblasts probably because of its low molecular weight and low hydrophobicity (A. Harootunian, personal communication). To produce a Ca^{2+} jump in such cells, nitr-5 has to overcome to some extent the intrinsic Ca^{2+} buffer and probably requires loading levels of hundreds of micromolar to millimolar chelator. In analogy to loading with quin-2 or BAPTA, homeostatic mechanisms probably titrate the buffer to normal resting $[Ca^{2+}]_i$ levels during the loading process, providing that extracellular Ca^{2+} is available (126). High levels of free nitr-5 chelator were found to buffer Ca^{2+} oscillations in REF52 fibroblasts before photolysis (A. Harootunian, personal communication). Such effects were less noticeable when nitr-7 was used, presumably because of its tighter Ca^{2+} binding so that less free chelator is present at typical resting levels of $[Ca^{2+}]_i$ (41). The lack of direct control over the Ca^{2+} loading level of nitr-5 or -7 and the general difficulties with any AM ester (125) are the major problems with using this method.

It should be possible to make a membrane-permeant AM ester from DM-nitrophen (54) although experimental confirmation has not been presented. Additional problems to those described for nitr-5 include significant binding of intracellular Mg^{2+} upon liberation of the free chelator inside the cell, which results in a jump in Mg^{2+} as well as Ca^{2+} upon photolysis. The more basic amines of DM-nitrophen might hinder the diffusion of the AM ester across cell membranes.

Until recently, AM esters have been applied almost exclusively to carboxyl groups. They have now been shown to work on phosphates (104, 108, 130), so they may be useful with many other caged compounds such as nucleotides and inositol phosphates. The synthesis of membrane permeant AM esters of dibutyryl cAMP, dibutyryl cGMP, tributyryl IP$_3$, and dibutyryl IP$_4$ has now been described (108, 130). Although cAMP is already slightly cell permeant as their dibutyryl derivatives, the additional AM ester to mask the charge permits its use at a few micromolar extracellular concentration rather than the customary hundreds of micromolar or even millimolar (130). The tributyryl IP$_3$-AM ester causes release of intracellular Ca^{2+} stores from REF52 fibroblasts within a few minutes when applied extracellularly (108). With this derivative, hydrolysis of some of the butyryl esters (on the free hydroxyl groups) in addition to the AM esters must occur before generation of the physiologically active agent. Application of this method to caged IP$_3$ could permit more controlled release of this important second messenger. Surprisingly, it has been reported that incubation of bovine pulmonary microvascular endothelial cells with high concentrations (100 μM) of caged IP$_3$ resulted in sufficient incorporation to provoke their contraction upon photolysis (81, 93). AM esters of any caged compounds other than the caged Ca^{2+} have yet to be synthesized.

SPATIAL CONTROL OF PHOTORELEASE

Most applications of caged compounds have emphasized sudden temporal jumps in concentration without any particular spatial control. However, by focusing the illumination, it is possible to affect cell biochemistry in a spatially restricted pattern. Aside from photoactivation of fluorophores (PAF) already discussed, relatively few examples (89, 90) of localized photorelease have been reported. One reason for this comparative neglect may be the need to adapt a microscope to provide UV illumination through the objective using an image-plane mask or focused laser spot. Localized illumination can not only reveal the spatial spread or response heterogeneity of a cell or tissue, but also has the advantage that exhaustion of the caged compound is much slower, since the latter can be replenished by diffusion from nonilluminated zones. It should be remembered that conventional illumination through a microscope objective travels as a double cone of light through the specimen. Although the photon density is highest at the plane of focus, and techniques such as confocal microscopy or three-dimensional deconvolution can restrict fluorescence readout to that plane, nevertheless the planes above and below the focus also receive similar total photon dosages. If one desires to confine the photolysis to the plane of focus as closely as possible, the photolysis should be made to require absorption of more than one photon in rapid succession, thus discriminating in favor of the zone with the highest local flux. The most elegant and general method uses two-photon absorption, a quantum effect in which two red or infrared photons are simultaneously absorbed by a chromophore and simulate a single UV photon of half the wavelength (24, 97). The energy densities required for this effect are so high that they require tight focusing of a pulsed laser operating with a temporal duty cycle of about 1 in 10^5, for example pulses of 10^{-13} s width repeating every 10^{-8} s. The low duty cycle allows high peak power without much average power or thermal effect. An additional advantage is that absorption and scattering are very much less at infrared than at ultraviolet wavelengths, so that localized photolysis could be performed much deeper inside a complex tissue. The main problem here is the cost and delicacy of such pulsed lasers, which are at the leading edge of current laser technology. In fact, the basic concept of two-photon excitation is not new (34), but its practical application to biology is. A possible alternative of lesser generality, but retaining traditional wavelengths and light sources, might be to put two or more caging groups on each molecule such that all of them have to photolyze to regenerate biological activity. If the starting molecule has more than one reactive functionality, saturating all of them with caging groups may be synthetically easier than specifically reacting one. Also, multiple caging should help insure that the product is biologically inactive before photolysis. Assuming that the overall percentage of photoconversion is kept low, either by limiting the total incident photons or by allowing diffusion or perfusion to wash away partially uncaged species, the formation of active molecules will be largely confined to the zone of highest instantaneous photon flux where the beam is focused.

PROSPECTS AND GOALS FOR FUTURE DEVELOPMENT

Because the present authors are deeply involved in the design and synthesis of new molecules, the areas that seem to us to offer the greatest scope for fundamental improvements mostly require construction of new compounds. Some examples are as follows: (*a*) An obvious extension of caged neurotransmitters would be to cage receptor-specific agonists and antagonists such as the glutamate analogues α-amino-3-hydroxy-5-methyl-4-isoxazolepropionate (AMPA) and N-methyl-D-aspartate (NMDA), the NMDA antagonist 2-amino-5-phosphonovalerate (APV), or the γ-aminobutyrate agonist muscimol. (*b*) Now that entire enzymes have been caged, it is surprising that few or no caged peptides have been synthesized. [The Affymax process (31) for combinatorial generation of multiple peptides uses caging groups in the synthesis; however, the caging groups are photolyzed away from the peptides before they are released from the support, whereas we envisage isolation of homogeneous caged peptides, microinjection into cells or tissues and photolysis in situ.] A particularly fertile area of application might be caged pseudosubstrate inhibitors for protein kinases, where the known requirements for recognition of pseudosubstrates (94) should make it easy to mask their activity by appropriate caging of a side chain or the N-terminus. Such molecules would fill a particular need in dissecting the spatial and temporal requirements for intracellular signaling, since methods for cleanly and controllably inhibiting kinases are much fewer than those for activating kinases. (c) Some exciting prospects in developmental biology might be opened up by the use of caged fluorophores as lineage tracers, which would permit considerably more complicated initial patterns of labeling than can currently be achieved by direct localized microinjection of the tracer. A remote but more novel application would be the use of caged inducers and repressors of genes to activate or suppress gene expression in specific loci within transgenic embryos. Already analogous photochemical techniques such as chromophore-assisted laser inactivation (66) are having an impact on developmental biology (49). In this method, laser irradiation of malachite-green labeled antibodies causes inactivation of the protein to which the antibody is bound. (d) Photochemical control of Ca^{2+} would be greatly improved by development of a chelator that can reversibly cycle between two states, high and low affinity for Ca^{2+}, as mentioned above. (e) The recent surge of interest in paracrine messengers that are inherently unstable in normal media, for example nitric oxide (NO) (13, 80) and certain oxygenated metabolites of arachidonic acid, suggests that caged precursors of greater physicochemical stability would be quite useful.

In most cases (e.g. a-c above), new photosensitive protecting groups radically different from those already described should not be necessary, especially because many of the present groups seem to have the right wavelengths to work with two-photon IR excitation. As described above, this exciting new technique should greatly improve penetration into living tissue, minimize photodynamic damage, and optimize three-dimensional spatial localization (24). Now that titanium-sapphire crystals have made the necessary pulsed IR lasers so much cheaper, better tunable (720–900 nm, corresponding to 360–450 nm effective excitation) and easier to use, an increasing number of laboratories may acquire the capability. Even with more mundane forms of excitation, which have been well described in the literature, e.g. shuttered arc lamps, flashlamps (99), or UV lasers, turnkey commercial systems are not yet widely available, especially when versatile spatial control through a microscope is required. Perhaps manufacturers do not offer them because the market seems small, which in turn is because few biologists are willing to do the engineering and integration themselves. If this review helps demystify caged compounds and disseminate their wider use, it will have served a useful function.

ACKNOWLEDGMENTS

We wish to thank Drs. C. Ashley, G. Hess, L. Johnson, J. Kaplan, P. Schultz, D. Trentham, J. Walker, W. Webb, and R. Zucker for sending reprints and preprints prior to publication. Financial support from the Howard Hughes Medical Institute and the National Institutes of Health (NS 27177) is gratefully acknowledged.

Literature Cited

1. Adams, S. R., Kao, J. P. Y., Grynkiewicz, G., Minta, A., Tsien, R. Y. 1988. Biologically useful chelators that release Ca^{2+} upon illumination. *J. Am. Chem. Soc.* 110:3212–20

2. Adams, S. R., Kao, J. P. Y., Tsien, R. Y. 1989. Biologically useful chelators that take up Ca^{2+} upon illumination. *J. Am. Chem. Soc.* 111:7957–68

3. Ahnert-Hilger, G., Gratzl, M. 1988. Controlled manipulation of the cell interior by pore-forming proteins. *Trends Pharmacol. Sci.* 9:195–97

4. Ahnert-Hilger, G., Mach, W., Föhr, K. J., Gratzl, M. 1989. Poration by α-toxin and streptolysin O: an approach to analyze intracellular processes. *Methods Cell Biol.* 31:63–90

5. Amit, B., Ben-Efraim, D. A., Patchornik, A. 1976. Light-sensitive amides. The photosolvolysis of substituted 1-acyl-7-nitroindolines. *J. Am. Chem. Soc.* 98:843–44

6. Ashley, C. C., Mulligan, I. P., Lea, T. J. 1991. Ca^{2+} and activation mechanisms in skeletal muscle. *Q. Rev. Biophys.* 24:1–73

7. Backx, P. H., O'Rourke, B., Marban, E. 1991. Flash photolysis of magnesium-DM-nitrophen in heart cells. A novel approach to probe magnesium- and ATP-dependent regulation of calcium channels. *Am. J. Hypertension* 4:416S–21

8. Baldwin, J. E., McConnaughie, A. W., Moloney, M. G., Pratt, A. J., Shim, S. B. 1990. New photolabile phosphate protecting groups. *Tetrahedron* 46:6879–84

9. Bartels, E., Wassermann, N. H., Erlanger, B. F. 1971. Photochromic activators of the acetylcholine receptor. *Proc. Natl. Acad. Sci. USA* 68:1820–23

10. Barton, D. H. R., Sammes, P. G., Weingarten, G. G.1971. Photochemical transformations. Part XXVIII. Aryl azides as potential photosensitive protecting groups. *J. Chem. Soc. (C)* pp. 721–28

11. Bertelson, R. C. 1971. Photochromic processes involving heterolytic cleavage. In *Photochromism,* ed. G. Brown, pp. 45–431. New York: Wiley-Interscience

12. Billington, A. P., Walstrom, K. M., Ramesh, D., Guzikowski, A. P., Carpenter, B. K., et al. 1992. Synthesis and photochemistry of photolabile N-glycine derivatives and effects of one on the glycine receptor. *Biochemistry* 31:5500–7

13. Bredt, D. S., Snyder, S. H. 1992. Nitric oxide, a novel neuronal messenger. *Neuron* 8:3–11

14. Carl, A., McHale, N. G., Publicover, N. G., Sanders, K. M. 1990. Participation of Ca^{2+}-activated K^+ channels in electrical activity of canine gastric smooth muscle. *J. Physiol.* 429:205–21

15. Corrie, J. E. T., Katayama, Y., Reid, G. P., Anson, M., Trentham, D. R. 1992. The development and application of photosensitive caged compounds to aid time-resolved structure determination of macromolecules. *Philos. Trans. R. Soc. London Ser. A* 340:233–43

16. Corrie, J. E. T., Reid, G. P., Trentham, D. R., Hursthouse, M. B., Mazid, M. A. 1992. Synthesis and absolute stereochemistry of the two diastereoisomers of P^3-1-(2-nitrophenyl)ethyl adenosine triphosphate ("caged" ATP). *J. Chem. Soc. Perkin Trans.* 1:1015–19

17. Corrie, J. E. T., Trentham, D. R. 1991. The development of photosensitive "caged" fluorophores for cellular physiology. *J. Physiol.* 434:7P (Abstr.)

18. Corrie, J. E. T., Trentham, D. R. 1992. Synthetic, mechanistic and photochemical studies of phosphate esters of substituted benzoins. *J. Chem. Soc. Perkin Trans. 1* pp. 1015–19

19. Cram, D. J. 1992. Molecular container compounds. *Nature* 356:29–36

20. Cummings, R. T., DiZio, J. P., Krafft, G. A. 1988. Photoactivable fluorophores. 2. Synthesis and photoactivation of functionalized 3-aroyl-2- (2-furyl)-chromones. *Tetrahedron Lett.* 29:69–72

21. Cummings, R. T., Krafft, G. A. 1988. Photoactivable fluorophores. 1. Synthesis and photoactivation of o-nitrobenzyl-quenched fluorescent carbamates. *Tetrahedron Lett.* 29:65–68

22. Delaney, K. R., Zucker, R. S. 1990. Calcium released by photolysis of DM-nitrophen stimulates transmitter release at squid giant synapse. *J. Physiol.* 426:473–98

23. Delcour, A. H., Hess, G. P. 1986. Chemical kinetic measurements of the effect of *trans*- and *cis*-3,3'-Bis[(trimethylammonio)methyl]azobenzene bromide on acetylcholine receptor mediated ion translocation in *Electrophorus electricus* and *Torpedo californica*. *Biochemistry* 25:1793–98

24. Denk, W., Strickler, J. H., Webb, W. W. 1990. Two-photon laser scanning fluorescence microscopy. *Science* 248: 73–76

25. Duke, E. M. H., Hadfield, A., Walters, S., Wakatsuki, S., Bryan, R., et al. 1992. Time resolved diffraction studies on glycogen phosphorylase b. *Philos. Trans. R. Soc. London Ser. A* 340:245–61

26. Eigen, M., Hammes, G. G. 1963. Elementary steps in enzyme reactions. *Adv. Enzymol.* 25:1–38

27. Ellis-Davies, G. C. R., Kaplan, J. H. 1988. A new class of photolabile chelators for the rapid release of divalent cations: generation of caged Ca and caged Mg. *J. Org. Chem.* 53:1966–69

28. Engels, J., Schlaeger, E.-J. 1977. Synthesis, structure, and reactivity of adenosine cyclic 3',5'-phosphate benzyl triesters. *J. Med. Chem.* 20:907–11

29. Fagan, P. J., Calabrese, J. C., Malone, B. 1992. Metal complexes of buckminsterfullerene (C_{60}). *Acc. Chem. Res.* 25:134–42

30. Ferenczi, M. A., Goldman, Y. E., Trentham, D. R. 1989. Relaxation of permeabilized, isolated muscle fibres of the rabbit by rapid chelation of Ca^{2+}-ions through laser-pulse photolysis of "caged-BAPTA". *J. Physiol.* 418:155P (Abstr.)

31. Fodor, S. P. A., Read, J. L., Pirrung, M. C., Stryer, L., Lu, A. T., et al. 1991. Light-directed, spatially addressable parallel chemical synthesis. *Science* 251:767–73

32. Deleted in proof

33. Fryer, M. W., Zucker, R. S. 1992. Ca^{2+}-dependent inactivation of Ca^{2+} current in *Aplysia* neurons: kinetic studies using photolabile Ca^{2+} chelators. *J. Physiol.* In press

34. Göppert-Mayer, M. 1931. Über elementarakte mit zwei quantensprüngen. *Annu. Phyz.* 9:273–94

35. Gorbsky, G. J., Borisy, G. G. 1989. Microtubules of the kinetochore fiber turn over in metaphase but not in anaphase. *J. Cell Biol.* 109:653–62

36. Grynkiewicz, G., Poenie, M., Tsien, R. Y. 1985. A new generation of Ca^{2+} indicators with greatly improved fluorescence properties. *J. Biol. Chem.* 260:3440–50

37. Gurney, A. M. 1991. Photolabile calcium buffers to selectively activate calcium-dependent processes. In *Cellular Neurobiology: a practical approach*, ed. J. Chad, H. Wheal, pp. 153–77. New York: IRL Press

38. Gurney, A. M., Lester, H. A. 1987. Light-flash physiology with synthetic photosensitive compounds. *Physiol. Rev.* 67:583–617

38a. Gurney, A. M., Tsien, R. Y., Lester, H. A. 1987. Activation of a potassium current by rapid photochemically generated step increases of intracellular calcium in rat sympathetic neurons. *Proc. Natl. Acad. Sci. USA* 84:3496–500

39. Hajdu, J., Johnson, L. N. 1990. Progress with Laue diffraction studies on protein and virus crystals. *Biochemistry* 29:1669–78

40. Harootunian, A. T., Kao, J. P. Y., Paranjape, S., Adams, S. R., Potter, B. V. L., et al. 1991. Cytosolic Ca^{2+} oscillations in REF52 fibroblasts: Ca^{2+}-stimulated IP_3 production or voltage-dependent Ca^{2+} channels as key positive feedback elements. *Cell Calcium* 12:153–64

41. Harootunian, A. T., Kao, J. P. Y., Paranjape, S., Tsien, R. Y. 1991. Generation of calcium oscillations in fibroblasts by positive feedback between calcium and IP_3. *Science* 251:75–78

42. Harootunian, A. T., Kao, J. P. Y., Tsien, R. Y. 1988. Agonist-induced calcium oscillations in depolarized fibroblasts and their manipulation by photoreleased Ins(1,4,5)P_3, Ca^{2+}, and Ca^{2+} buffer. *Cold Spring Harb. Symp. Quant. Biol.* 53:935–43

43. Havinga, E., De Jongh, R. O. 1962. Photochemical reactions of nitrophenylesters and -ethers. *Bull. Soc. Chim. Belg.* 71:803–10

44. Hess, G. P., Udgaonkar, J. B., Olbricht, W. L. 1987. Chemical kinetic measurements of transmembrane processes using rapid reaction techniques: acetylcholine receptor. *Annu. Rev. Biophys. Biophys. Chem.* 16:507–34

45. Hochner, B., Parnas, H., Parnas, I. 1989. Membrane depolarization evokes neurotransmitter release in the absence of calcium entry. *Nature* 342:433–35

46. Homsher, E., Millar, N. C. 1990. Caged compounds and striated muscle contraction. *Annu. Rev. Physiol.* 52:875–96

47. Jackson, M. B. 1988. Dependence of acetylcholine receptor channel kinetics on agonist concentration in cultured mouse muscle fibres. *J. Physiol.* 397:555–83

48. Jacobson, K., Elson, E., Koppel, D., Webb, W. 1989. International workshop on the application of fluorescence photobleaching techniques to problems in cell biology. *Fed. Proc.* 42:72–79

49. Jay, D. G., Keshishian, H. 1990. Laser inactivation of fasciclin I disrupts axon adhesion of grasshopper pioneer neurons. *Nature* 348:548–50

50. Kao, J. P. Y., Adams, S. R. 1992. Photosensitive caged compounds: design, properties, and biological applications. In *Optical Microscopy: New Technologies and Applications,* ed. B. Herman, J. L. Lemasters, pp. 27–85. New York: Academic. In press

51. Kao, J. P. Y., Alderton, J. M., Tsien, R. Y., Steinhardt, R. A. 1990. Active involvement of Ca^{2+} in mitotic progression of Swiss 3T3 fibroblasts. *J. Cell Biol.* 111:183–96

52. Kao, J. P. Y., Harootunian, A. T., Tsien, R. Y. 1989. Photochemically generated cytosolic calcium pulses and their detection by fluo-3. *J. Biol. Chem.* 264:8179–84

53. Kaplan, J. H. 1990. Photochemical manipulation of divalent cation levels. *Annu. Rev. Physiol.* 52:897–914

54. Kaplan, J. H., Ellis-Davies, G. C. R. 1988. Photolabile chelators for the rapid photorelease of divalent cations. *Proc. Natl. Acad. Sci. USA* 85:6571–75

55. Kaplan, J. H., Forbush, B. III, Hoffman, J. F. 1978. Rapid photolytic release of adenosine 5'-triphosphate from a protected analogue: utilization by the Na:K pump of human red blood cell ghosts. *Biochemistry* 17: 1929–35

56. Kaplan, J. H., Somlyo, A. P. 1989. Flash photolysis of caged compounds: new tools for cellular physiology. *Trends Neurosci.* 12:54–59

56a. Kentish, J. C., Barsotti, R. J., Lea, T. J., Mulligan, I. P., Patel, J. R., et al. 1990. Calcium release from cardiac sacroplasmic reticulum induced by photorelease of calcium or Ins(1,4,5)P3. *Am. J. Physiol.* 258:H610–15

57. Khan, S., Amoyaw, K., Spudich, J. L., Reid, G. P., Trentham, D. R. 1992. Bacterial chemoreceptor signaling probed by flash photorelease of a caged serine. *Biophys. J.* 62:67–68

58. Kirby, A. J., Varvoglis, A. G. 1967. A photosensitive protecting group for phosphate esters. *Chem. Comm.* p. 406

59. Kobayashi, S., Kitazawa, T., Somlyo, A. V., Somlyo, A. P. 1989. Cytosolic heparin inhibits muscarinic and α-adrenergic Ca^{2+} release in smooth muscle. *J. Biol. Chem.* 264:17997–8004

60. Krafft, G. A., Cummings, R. T., DiZio, J. P., Furukawa, R. H., Brvenik, L. J., et al. 1986. Fluorescence photoactivation and dissipation (FPD). In *Nucleocytoplasmic Transport,* ed. R. Peters, M. Trendelenburg, pp. 35–52. Berlin: Springer-Verlag

61. Krafft, G. A., Sutton, W. R., Cummings, R. T. 1988. Photoactivable

fluorophores. 3. Synthesis and photoactivation of fluorogenic difunctionalized fluoresceins. *J. Am. Chem. Soc.* 110:301–3

62. Lancaster, B., Zucker, R. S. 1991. Photolytic manipulation of $[Ca^{2+}]_i$ controls hyperpolarizations in hippocampal pyramidal cells. *Soc. Neurosci. Abstr.* 60:1114

63. Landò, L., Zucker, R. S. 1989. "Caged calcium" in *Aplysia* pacemaker neurons. *J. Gen. Physiol.* 93:1017–60

63a. Lea, T. J., Ashley, C. C. 1990. Ca^{2+} release from the sarcoplasmic reticulum of barnacle myofibrillar bundles initiated by photolysis of caged Ca^{2+}. *J. Physiol.* 427:435–53

64. Lester, H. A., Nerbonne, J. M. 1982. Physiological and pharmacological manipulations with light flashes. *Annu. Rev. Biophys. Bioeng.* 11:151–75

65. Lim, S.-S., Sammak, P. J., Borisy, G. G. 1989. Progressive and spatially differentiated stability of microtubules in developing neuronal cells. *J. Cell Biol.* 109:253–63

66. Linden, K. G., Liao, J. C., Jay, D. G. 1992. Spatial specificity of chromophore assisted laser inactivation of protein function. *Biophys. J.* 61:956–62

67. Madsen, B. W., Edeson, R. O. 1988. Nicotinic receptors and the elusive β. *Trends Pharmacol. Sci.* 9:315–16

68. Malenka, R. C., Kauer, J. A., Perkel, D. J., Mauk, M. D., Kelly, P. T., et al. 1989. An essential role for postsynaptic calmodulin and protein kinase activity in long-term potentiation. *Nature* 340:554–57

69. Malenka, R. C., Lancaster, B., Zucker, R. S. 1992. Temporal limits on the rise in postsynaptic calcium required for the induction of long-term potentiation. *Neuron* 9:121–28

70. Malinow, R., Schulman, H., Tsien, R. W. 1989. Inhibition of postsynaptic PKC or CaMKII blocks induction but not expression of LTP. *Science* 245: 862–66

70a. Marrion, N. V., Zucker, R. S., Marsh, S. J., Adams, P. R. 1991. Modulation of M-current by intracellular Ca^{2+}. *Neuron* 6:533–45

71. Martinek, K., Berezin, I. V. 1979. Artificial light-sensitive enzymatic systems as chemical amplifiers of weak light signals. *Photochem. Photobiol.* 29:637–49

72. Matsubara, N., Billington, A. P., Hess, G. P. 1992. How fast does an acetylcholine receptor channel open? Laser-pulse photolysis of an inactive precursor of carbamoylcholine in the microsecond

time region with BC3H1 cells. *Biochemistry* 31:5507–14

73. McCray, J. A., Fidler-Lim, N., Ellis-Davies, G. C. R., Kaplan, J. H. 1992. Rate of release of Ca^{2+} following laser photolysis of the DM-nitrophen Ca^{2+} complex. *Biochemistry*. In press

74. McCray, J. A., Trentham, D. R. 1989. Properties and uses of photoreactive caged compounds. *Annu. Rev. Biophys. Biophys. Chem.* 18:239–70

75. Mendel, D., Ellman, J. A., Schultz, P. G. 1991. Construction of a light-activated protein by unnatural amino acid mutagenesis. *J. Am. Chem. Soc.* 113:2758–60

76. Messenger, J. B., Katayama, Y., Ogden, D. C., Corrie, J. E. T., Trentham, D. R. 1991. Photolytic release of glutamate from "caged" glutamate expands squid chromatophores. *J. Physiol.* 438:293P (Abstr.)

77. Meyer, T., Hanson, P. I., Stryer, L., Schulman, H. 1992. Calmodulin trapping by calcium-calmodulin-dependent protein kinase. *Science* 256:1199–202

78. Milburn, T., Matsubara, N., Billington, A. P., Udgaonkar, J. B., Walker, J. W., et al. 1989. Synthesis, photochemistry, and biological activity of a caged photolabile acetylcholine receptor ligand. *Biochemistry* 28:49–55

79. Mitchison, T. J. 1989. Polewards microtubule flux in the mitotic spindle: evidence from photoactivation of fluorescence. *J. Cell Biol.* 109: 637–52

80. Moncada, S., Palmer, R. M. J., Higgs, E. A. 1991. Nitric oxide: physiology, pathophysiology, and pharmacology. *Pharmacol. Rev.* 43:109–42

80a. Morad, M., Davies, N. W., Kaplan, J. H., Lux, H. D. 1988. Inactivation and block of calcium channels by photoreleased Ca^{2+} in dorsal root ganglion neurons. *Science* 241:842–44

81. Morel, N. M. L., Dodge, A. B., Patton, W. F., Herman, I. M., Hechtman, H. B., et al. 1989. Pulmonary microvascular endothelial cell contractility on silicone rubber substrate. *J. Cell. Physiol.* 141:653–59

82. Mulkey, R. M., Zucker, R. S. 1991. Action potentials must admit calcium to evoke transmitter release. *Nature* 350:153–55

83. Näbauer, M., Morad, M. 1990. Ca^{2+}-induced Ca^{2+} release as examined by photolysis of caged Ca^{2+} in single ventricular myocytes. *Am. J. Physiol.* 258: C189–93

84. Neher, E., Augustine, G. J. 1992. Calcium requirements for secretion in bovine chromaffin cells. *J. Physiol.* 450:273–301

85. Nerbonne, J. M. 1986. Design and application of photolabile intracellular probes. In *Optical Methods in Cell Physiology (Soc. Gen. Physiol. Ser.)*, ed. P. de Weer, B. M. Salzburg, 40:417–45. New York: Wiley

86. Nerbonne, J. M., Richard, S., Nargeot, J., Lester, H. A. 1984. New photoactivatable cyclic nucleotides produce intracellular jumps in cyclic AMP and cyclic GMP concentrations. *Nature* 310:74–76

87. Okabe, S., Hirokawa, N. 1990. Turnover of fluorescently labelled tubulin and actin in the axon. *Nature* 343:479–82

88. Okabe, S., Hirokawa, N. 1992. Differential behavior of photoactivated microtubules in growing axons of mouse and frog neurons. *J. Cell Biol.* 117:105–20

89. O'Neill, S. C., Mill, J. G., Eisner, D. A. 1990. Local activation of contraction in isolated rat ventricular myocytes. *Am. J. Physiol.* C1165–68

90. Parker, I., Yao, Y. 1991. Regenerative release of calcium from functionally discrete subcellular stores by inositol trisphosphate. *Proc. R. Soc. London Ser. B* 246:269–74

91. Parnas, I., Parnas, H., Hochner, B. 1991. Amount and time-course of release. The calcium hypothesis and the calcium-voltage hypothesis. *Ann. NY Acad. Sci.* 635:177–90

92. Patchornik, A., Amit, B., Woodward, R. B. 1970. Photosensitive protecting groups. *J. Am. Chem. Soc.* 92:6333–35

93. Patton, W. F., Alexander, J. S., Dodge, A. B., Patton, R. J., Hechtman, H. B., et al. 1991. Mercury-arc photolysis: a method for examining second messenger regulation of endothelial cell monolayer integrity. *Anal. Biochem.* 196:31–38

94. Pearson, R. B., Kemp, B. E. 1991. Protein kinase phosphorylation site sequences and consensus specificity motifs: tabulations. *Methods Enzymol.* 200: 62–81

95. Pillai, V. N. R. 1980. Photoremovable protecting groups in organic synthesis. *Synthesis* pp. 1–26

96. Pillai, V. N. R. 1987. Photolytic deprotection and activation of functional groups. *Org. Photochem.* 9:225–323

97. Piston, D. W., Wu, E.-S., Webb, W. W. 1992. Three dimensional diffusion measurements in cells by two-photon excitation fluorescence photobleaching recovery. *Biophys. J.* 61:A34 (Abstr.)

98. Porter, N. A., Bruhnke, J. D. 1989. Acyl thrombin photochemistry: kinetics for deacylation of enzyme cinnamate geometric isomers. *J. Am. Chem. Soc.* 111:7616–18

99. Rapp, G., Güth, K. 1988. A low cost high intensity flash device for photolysis experiments. *Pflügers Arch.* 411:200–3

100. Reinsch, S. S., Mitchison, T. J., Kirschner, M. 1991. Microtubule polymer assembly and transport during axonal elongation. *J. Cell Biol.* 115: 365–79

101. Ross, D. L., Blanc, J. 1971. Photochromism by *cis-trans* isomerization. In *Photochromism*, ed. G. H. Brown, pp. 471–556. New York: Wiley-Interscience

102. Salmon, E. D., Leslie, R. J., Saxton, W. M., Karow, M. L., McIntosh, J. R. 1984. Spindle microtubule dynamics in sea urchin embryos: analysis using a fluorescein-labeled tubulin and measurements of fluorescence redistribution after laser photobleaching. *J. Cell Biol.* 99:2165–74

103. Sanger, J. M., Mittal, B., Southwick, F. S., Sanger, J. W. 1990. Analysis of intracellular motility and actin polymerization induced by *Listeria monocytogenes* in PtK2 cells. *J. Cell Biol.* 111:415a (Abstr.)

104. Sastry, J. K., Nehete, P. N., Khan, S., Nowak, B. J., Plunkett, W., et al. 1992. Membrane-permeable dideoxyuridine 5'-monophosphate analogue inhibits human immunodeficiency virus infection. *Mol. Pharmacol.* 41: 441–45

105. Sawin, K. E., Mitchison, T. J. 1991. Poleward microtubule flux in mitotic spindles assembled in vitro. *J. Cell Biol.* 112:941–54

106. Schlichting, I., Almo, S. C., Rapp, G., Wilson, K., Petratos, K., et al. 1990. Time-resolved X-ray crystallographic study of the conformational change in Ha-*ras* p21 protein on GTP hydrolysis. *Nature* 345:309–15

107. Schlichting, I., Rapp, G., John, J., Wittinghofer, A., Pai, E. F., et al. 1989. Biochemical and crystallographic characterization of a complex of c-Ha-*ras* p21 and caged GTP with flash photolysis. *Proc. Natl. Acad. Sci. USA* 86:7687–90

108. Schultz, C., Tsien, R. Y. 1992. Membrane-permeant derivatives of inositol polyphosphates applied to REF-52 fibroblasts. *FASEB J.* 6(5):A1924 (Abstr.)

109. Sheehan, J. C., Umezawa, K. 1973. Phenacyl photosensitive blocking groups. *J. Org. Chem.* 38:3771–74

110. Sheehan, J. C., Wilson, R. M., Oxford, A. W. 1971. The photolysis of methoxy-substituted benzoin esters. A photosensitive protecting group for carboxylic acids. *J. Am. Chem. Soc.* 93:7222–28

111. Shinkai, S., Manabe, O. 1984. Photocontrol of ion extraction and ion transport by photofunctional crown ethers. *Top. Curr. Chem.* 121:67–104

112. Sine, S. M., Steinbach, J. H. 1986. Activation of acetylcholine receptors on clonal mammalian BC3H-1 cells by low concentrations of agonist. *J. Physiol.* 373:129–62

113. Somlyo, A. P., Somlyo, A. V. 1990. Flash photolysis studies of excitation-contraction coupling, regulation, and contraction in smooth muscle. *Annu. Rev. Physiol.* 52:857–74

114. Somlyo, A. P., Walker, J. W., Goldman, Y. E., Trentham, D. R., Kobayashi, S., et al. 1988. Inositol trisphosphate, calcium and muscle contraction. *Philos. Trans. R. Soc. London Ser. B* 320:399–414

115. Somlyo, A. V., Kitazawa, T., Horiuti, K., Kobayashi, S., Trentham, D., et al. 1990. Heparin-sensitive inositol trisphosphate signaling and the role of G-proteins in Ca^{2+}-release and contractile regulation in smooth muscle. *Prog. Clin. Biol. Res.* 327:167–82

116. Stoddard, B. L., Bruhnke, J., Koenigs, P., Porter, N., Ringe, D., et al. 1990. Photolysis and deacylation of inhibited chymotrypsin. *Biochemistry* 29:8042–51

117. Stoddard, B. L., Bruhnke, J., Porter, N., Ringe, D., Petsko, G. A. 1990. Structure and activity of two photoreversible cinnamates bound to chymotrypsin. *Biochemistry* 29:4871–79

118. Stoddard, B. L., Koenigs, P., Porter, N., Petratos, K., Petsko, G. A., et al. 1991. Observation of the light-triggered binding of pyrone to chymotrypsin by Laue x-ray crystallography. *Proc. Natl. Acad. Sci. USA* 88:5503–7

119. Theriot, J. A., Mitchison, T. J. 1991. Actin microfilament dynamics in locomoting cells. *Nature* 352:126–31

120. Theriot, J. A., Mitchison, T. J., Tilney, L. G., Portnoy, D. A. 1992. The rate of actin-based motility of intracellular *Listeria monocytogenes* equals the rate of actin polymerization. *Nature* 357: 257–60

121. Trentham, D. R., Corrie, J. E. T., Reid, G. P. 1992. A new caged ATP with rapid photolysis kinetics. *Biophys. J.* 61:A295 (Abstr.)

122. Tsien, R. W., Tsien, R. Y. 1990.

Calcium channels, stores, and oscillations. *Annu. Rev. Cell Biol.* 6:715–60

123. Tsien, R. Y. 1980. New calcium indicators and buffers with high selectivity against magnesium and protons: design, synthesis, and properties of prototype structures. *Biochemistry* 19: 2396–404

124. Tsien, R. Y. 1981. A non-disruptive technique for loading calcium buffers and indicators into cells. *Nature* 290: 527–28

125. Tsien, R. Y. 1989. Fluorescent probes of cell signaling. *Annu. Rev. Neurosci.* 12:227–53

126. Tsien, R. Y., Pozzan, T., Rink, T. J. 1984. Measuring and manipulating cytosolic Ca^{2+} with trapped indicators. *Trends Biochem. Sci.* 9:263–66

127. Tsien, R. Y., Zucker, R. S. 1986. Control of cytoplasmic calcium with photolabile tetracarboxylate 2-nitrobenzhydrol chelators. *Biophys. J.* 50: 843–53

128. Turner, A. D., Pizzo, S. V., Rozakis, G. W., Porter, N. A. 1988. Photoreactivation of irreversibly inhibited serine proteinases. *J. Am. Chem. Soc.* 110:244–50

129. Turner, A. D., Pizzo, S. V., Rozakis, G. W., Porter, N. A. 1987. Photochemical activation of acylated α-thrombin. *J. Am. Chem. Soc.* 109: 1274–75

130. Vajanapanich, M., Schultz, C., Buranawuti, T., Tsien, R. Y., Pandol, S., et al. 1992. Synergistic epithelial chloride secretion via cAMP and calcium pathways - a re-examination. *Gastroenterology* 102:A249 (Abstr.)

131. Valdeolmillos, M., O'Neill, S. C., Smith, G. L., Eisner, D. A. 1989. Calcium-induced calcium release activates contraction in intact cardiac cells. *Pflügers Arch.* 413:676–78

132. Walker, J. W. 1991. Caged molecules activated by light. In *Cellular Neurobiology: a practical approach,* ed. J. Chad, H. Wheal, pp. 179–203. New York: IRL Press

133. Walker, J. W., McCray, J. A., Hess, G. P. 1986. Photolabile protecting groups for an acetylcholine receptor ligand. Synthesis and photochemistry of a new class of *o*-nitrobenzyl derivatives and their effects on receptor function. *Biochemistry* 25:1799–805

134. Walker, J. W., Reid, G. P., Trentham,

D. R. 1989. Synthesis and properties of caged nucleotides. *Methods Enzymol.* 172:288–301

135. Walker, J. W., Trentham, D. R. 1988. Caged phenylephrine: synthesis and photochemical properties. *Biophys. J.* 53:596a (Abstr.)

136. Wang, Y.-L. 1985. Exchange of actin subunits at the leading edge of living fibroblasts: possible role of treadmilling. *J. Cell Biol.* 101:597–602

137. Whittal, J. 1990. 4n+2 Systems: Fulgides. In *Photochromism. Molecules and Systems,* ed. H. Dürr, H. Bouas-Laurent, pp. 467–92. New York: Elsevier

138. Wilcox, M., Viola, R. W., Johnson, K. W., Billington, A. P., Carpenter, B. K., et al. 1990. Synthesis of photolabile "precursors" of amino acid neurotransmitters. *J. Org. Chem.* 55: 1585–89

139. Willner, I., Rubin, S., Riklin, A. 1991. Photoregulation of papain activity through anchoring photochromic azo groups to the enzyme backbone. *J. Am. Chem. Soc.* 113:3321–25

140. Willner, I., Rubin, S., Wonner, J., Effenberger, F., Bäuerle, P. 1992. Photoswitchable binding of substrates to proteins: photoregulated binding of α-D-mannopyranose to concanavalin A modified by a thiophenefulgide dye. *J. Am. Chem. Soc.* 114:3150–51

141. Wootton, J. F., Trentham, D. R. 1989. "Caged" compounds to probe the dynamics of cellular processes: synthesis and properties of some novel photosensitive P-2-nitrobenzyl esters of nucleotides. *NATO ASI Ser. C* 272:277–96

142. Zucker, R. S. 1992. Effects of photolabile calcium chelators on fluorescent calcium indicators. *Cell Calcium* 13:29–40

142a. Zucker, R. S. 1992. The calcium concentration clamp: spikes and reversible pulses using the photolabile chelator DM-nitrophen. *Cell Calcium.* In press

143. Zucker, R. S., Delaney, K. R., Mulkey, R., Tank, D. W. 1991. Presynaptic calcium in transmitter release and posttetanic potentiation. *Ann. NY Acad. Sci.* 635:191–207

144. Zucker, R. S., Haydon, P. G. 1988. Membrane potential has no direct role in evoking neurotransmitter release. *Nature* 335:360–62

Annu. Rev. Physiol. 1993. 55:785–817

MULTIMODE LIGHT MICROSCOPY AND THE DYNAMICS OF MOLECULES, CELLS, AND TISSUES

Daniel L. Farkas[1], *George Baxter*[1], *Robbin L. DeBiasio*[1,2], *Albert Gough*[1,2], *Michel A. Nederlof*[3], *David Pane*[1], *John Pane*[1], *David R. Patek*[1], *Kevin W. Ryan*[3], *D. Lansing Taylor*[1,2]

[1]Center for Light Microscope Imaging and Biotechnology, and [2]Department of Biological Sciences, Carnegie Mellon University, 4400 Fifth Ave., Pittsburgh, Pennsylvania 15213, and [3]Biological Detection Systems, Inc., 4617 Winthrop St., Pittsburgh, Pennsylvania 15213

KEY WORDS: fluorescence, light microscopy, live cells, image processing, machine vision, three-dimensional imaging

INTRODUCTION

There is a renaissance and revolution in light microscopy and its use in biological research, biotechnology, and clinical diagnostics (139, 163). This renaissance has been driven primarily by the need to define the interplay of ions, metabolites, and macromolecules in time and space in living cells and tissues. The goal is to understand fundamental biological functions by temporal-spatial mapping of chemical and molecular events in vivo. The revolution has been fueled by the integration of advances in the heretofore distinct fields of biology, chemistry, physical optics, robotics, and computer science. Powerful new reagents are being used in conjunction with automated light microscope imaging workstations to investigate the contents, activity, and dynamics of living cells and tissues.

There are also great challenges. Some challenges involve instrumental

785

0066–4278/93/0315–0785$02.00

limitations (speed and accuracy of image detectors, image processing performance) and are met by the pace of technical developments typically outside the field of microscopy. However, some challenges are more inherent (resolution limits for each technique, trade-offs between speed and resolution, complexity and narrow range of optimal conditions for biological samples) and are addressed by bringing into play new elements (novel fluorescent probes, lasers, acousto-optical filters, environmental chambers) and techniques (photo-activation chemistry, confocal microscopy, optical trapping).

One of the promising new developments is multimode light microscopy (53). It is based on applying several techniques (modes) of light-microscopic investigation to a biological specimen and doing so within a single, automated instrument (workstation). Significant problems of sample variability are thus eliminated, and the modes being combined achieve complementarity, and often synergism, in providing structural and functional information, down to the molecular level. A multimode workstation is a highly automated instrument, with tight motion, timing, and sample controls that utilizes advanced processing, analysis, and display software. We present here a description of this new generation of workstations and review their current and future uses. It should be noted that, while additions to or advances in the specific modes should clearly ensure progress in this field, the emphasis of this review is on the combination rather than the functional details of individual modes, which are covered in excellent review volumes (1, 35, 62, 69, 75, 106, 120, 145, 159, 161, 165), and on live cell applications, which most clearly differentiate light microscopy from other types of microscopic investigation.

MODES OF LIGHT MICROSCOPY

Most of the traditional modes of light microscopy involve continuous illumination of the sample for a certain time period, while recording images. Although this is a useful way of data acquisition, the special challenges posed by the typical biological samples (low contrast, structural and chemical complexity, movement) require higher levels of sophistication for extracting truly useful information (see Table 1).

Transmitted light microscopy, typically yielding morphological information, has evolved towards increasing the contrast and resolution of the images obtained by either optical modifications to the microscope components (phase contrast, Hoffmann modulation contrast), use of additional light properties such as polarization and interference (differential interference contrast, DIC), or a combination of optical and electronic enhancements (video-enhanced contrast, VEC). Further refinements can be obtained by contrast-enhancing reagents that extend detection capabilities into the nanometer range (nanovid microscopy; 33, 132, 165).

Table 1 Modes of light microscopy

Mode of microscopy	Main features	Information derived
a Brightfield	Densitometric measurement	Morphology, absorbance
b Polarized light	Optical anisotropy	Molecular orientation, structural arrangement
c Phase contrast	Refractive index-based contrast	Morphology, refractive index
Differential interference contrast/video-enhanced contrast	Polarization and interference-based high contrast	Two- and three-dimensional dynamics of cells, organelles and molecules
Reflection interference contrast	Imaging thin refractive layers	Cell attachment points
d Real-time fluorescence	High temporal resolution, specificity	Temporal and spatial dynamics of labeled entities, physiological parameters
Time-resolved fluorescence	Based on molecular fluorescence lifetimes, volume-independent	Size, mobility, assembly, binding of molecules, ion concentrations
Steady-state fluorescence anisotropy	Polarized excitation	Rotational diffusion, viscosity, binding
Fluorescence ratio imaging	Sample-based image normalization	Ion and analogue concentrations, anisotropy, intermolecular distances
Fluorescence photobleaching	Molecular tracking	Molecular size, transport and diffusion
Multi-color fluorescence	Independent labeling/imaging of selected components	Simultaneous mapping/correlated distribution of components
Microspectrofluorometry	Spatially resolved spectral analysis	Changes in chemical environment
Microtomography	Accurate optical slicing by selective excitation/detection	Three-dimensional analysis of structure and chemistry, in-focus fluorescence quantitation
Total internal reflection	Shallow axial excitation depth	Physico-chemical interactions at an interface
e Luminescence/phosphorescence	Delayed emission	Signals without auto-fluorescence, scatter
Uncaging/photoactivation	Light-induced spatio-temporally localized chemical change	Biochemical kinetics within cells
Optical traps	Fine manipulation of small structures	Initiating interactions selectively by physical placement

Modes of light microscopy are defined as complete techniques of investigation/imaging based on light microscopy. This is a partial list, the main selection criterion being frequency of use (current or projected). Thus a number of interesting, quantitative techniques such as Jamin-Lebedeff, as well as some contrast methods (darkfield, Hoffman modulation, etc) are not included. The organization is based on the physical feature/principle for image generation and contrast achievement: (a) direct microscopy; (b) polarization; (c) refractive index; (d) fluorescence; (e) special/accessories.

Fluorescence microscopy is progressing particularly fast because of the intrinsic appeal of its high specificity, sensitivity, and signal-to-noise ratio (9, 141, 145). Its evolution has also been greatly helped by the availability of and improvements in low light image detectors (5, 66, 72, 125, 135, 149). By combining techniques of synthetic chemistry, biochemistry, and molecular biology, custom-designed fluorescent probes (65, 154, 156) can be attached to selected components of living cells and tissues, thus allowing fluorescence microscopy to become an irreplaceable tool in investigating the detailed workings of cells and tissues (63, 139, 141, 161). Furthermore, other properties of light and the molecules that absorb it can be used to increase the usefulness of light microscopy techniques; fluorescence lifetimes, polarization, photobleaching, and photoactivation as well as luminescence emission are just a few examples (9, 10, 12, 80, 84, 85, 88, 90, 100, 148, 162, 163, S. Adams, R. Y. Tsien, this volume).

Light microscopes have been traditionally designed for static, two-dimensional observations and image recording. Therefore, more recent attempts at extracting three-dimensional information through them have been beset with numerous problems. The main difficulty is that an image viewed through a microscope is defined by the optical resolution limitations in the plane of focus, in addition to the blur from out-of-focus portions of the object. This attenuation of high spatial frequencies yields significantly poorer resolution axially than in the plane of focus (4, 75, 76, 126). Typical ways of dealing with this limitation are either optical (as implemented in confocal microscopes) or computational (removal of out-of-focus blur).

We define a microscopy mode as a method of acquiring image data that includes specific optical configurations of the microscope (like epifluorescence, DIC, reflection interference), the optimal light source, the use and settings of a suitably matched detector, and the digital processing required to yield a particular image representation.

In reviewing the modes of light microscopy that can be considered for implementation on a multimode workstation, it is not our aim to give an exhaustive survey, to classify by importance, or to reiterate the considerations for performing high-quality microscopy; rather, we focus on the most promising modes and on the best way they can combine to deal with the central challenges of biological light microscopy: contrast maximization, spatial resolution (in all three spatial dimensions), time resolution, and reliable quantitation.

Transmitted Light Microscopy Modes

Brightfield microscopy (43, 75) is based on the absorbing characteristics, either intrinsic or staining-induced, of the sample under investigation. It can be used for microdensitometry and other morphometric applications, but for live cells, contrast is generally too low, unless used with light scattering reagents (33, 131, 132, 165). However, no other optical components are required.

Phase contrast (54, 75, 176, 180) is a technique in which the influence of specimen thickness and refractive index on the phase of light passing through it is used for contrast enhancement by manipulating the phase and amplitude of the undiffracted light relative to the diffracted light. This mode yields excellent contrast and axial resolution when used with video enhancement (75, 76, 78). However, the fixed phase plate in the objective reduces light; this could affect low level fluorescence detection when these two modes are combined.

Differential interference contrast (DIC) (8, 45, 134) and video-enhanced contrast (VEC) (67, 78, 130, 133, 164, 165) are based on a combination of light polarization and interference techniques (DIC) coupled with electronic contrast amplification and noise reduction (VEC). VEC-DIC described by Allen (6, 7) is characterized by high geometrical resolution, about 100 nm for VEC under certain conditions, both in the plane of focus (based on the Sparrow rather than the Rayleigh criterion; 8, 165) and axially (75, 76, 120). Moreover, the detection capabilities extend to objects as small as 10 nm (8, 33, 78, 132, 158). The outstanding axial resolution is due to the negligible contributions from out-of-focus regions to the resulting microscope images, as the stringent phase criteria for contrast-generating interference are not met in those sample areas. Image quality can be further improved by special accessories (38). Fine structures can be detected and tracked in living cells. These modes can be combined with fluorescence, but require the removal (manually or robotically) of optical components such as the upper Wollaston prism analyzer.

Other transmitted light contrast modes (43, 73, 75, 86, 165) have been described that use sample optical properties as well as spatial manipulation of the light to generate contrast.

In a multimode environment, consideration should be given to the compatibility of each mode with other implemented modes, both in terms of hardware and in terms of complementarity of the types of information derived.

Fluorescence Microscopy Modes

The attributes, advantages, and uses of fluorescence microscopy are well documented (4, 9, 11, 12, 17, 19, 65, 84, 120, 141, 142, 145, 152, 161). Advances in fluorescent probe design and synthesis (65, 106, 152, 154, 156), and molecular biology and protein chemistry (63, 161), coupled with technological improvements in microscopes and detectors have further enhanced the advantages and extended applications and performance.

REAL-TIME FLUORESCENCE   With specific fluorescent labeling, one can identify and detect the distribution, quantity, motion, and interactions of any selected entity in cells and tissues. The main constraint is the need for light exposure and fluorescence detection for intervals sufficient for acceptable signal-to-noise image formation. This time resolution has reached nanoseconds for certain cases (90, 99), but even the micro- and milli-second range can prove extremely valuable for new applications (70, 107, 159). The sensitivity of fluorescence detection has greatly improved through recent years, allowing detection, for example, of single DNA molecules (74, 117). Quantitative information can be derived not only on the amount and dynamics of labeled material, but also on physiologically important cell parameters, from membrane potentials (39, 107) to gene expression (102). There is some variation in the use of the term real-time fluorescence, with the most conservative description referring to the relative time scales of monitoring and the changes under study (i.e. the time-sampling must make continuous event monitoring possible) (171). A more widespread definition includes any fluorescence imaging at video frame rates (or faster).

MULTICOLOR FLUORESCENCE/MICROSPECTROFLUOROMETRY   The spectral range available for light microscopy was traditionally limited to the visible region, but solid state imaging devices (5, 71) have extended it into the near infrared (other types of microscopy such as thermal and acoustic are using still other spectral regions). The fact that up to six or seven fluorophores can be unambiguously differentiated in both excitation and emission in this spectral range has made it possible to label and image independently a corresponding number of components within the same sample (124, 157). This was even achieved for five fluorophores in living, locomoting cells (31), and it constitutes a unique way of mapping not only the location and interrelationships of cellular components, but also their dynamic reorganization and interactions upon performing a certain physiological function.

The wavelength separation can be achieved either discretely, by optical filter combinations (multicolor or multiparameter fluorescence; 48, 157), or continuously (microspectrofluorometry; 160) by monochromators. Acousto-optic modulators (135) could extend the flexibility of the former and the speed of the latter. While microspectrofluorometry has the advantage of being able to detect spectral changes of the fluorophores, the multicolor imaging approach is easier to translate into a multimode environment. For optimal extraction of information, the spectral channels for imaging must be well differentiated, and images obtained at different wavelengths have to be carefully corrected and registered (47, 48).

FLUORESCENCE RATIO IMAGING   Fluorescence ratio imaging microscopy was developed in order to normalize fluorescence signals for sample path-length, accessible volume, and local probe concentration (137). In the resulting ratio image, areas of changed intensity (concentration, activity) have been normalized by an unchanged or oppositely changed image originating from the same sample, thus eliminating a host of potential imaging artifacts. The original paper (137) suggested several applications of ratio imaging beyond ion quantitation. Some of the applications are as follows:

- Ion concentrations—dyes whose fluorescence is sensitive to local free calcium, protons, sodium, magnesium, chloride, and other ions have been synthesized for measuring the concentrations of these ions by ratio imaging microscopy and used with great success (19, 65, 151–153, 170, 177) in investigating their role in cellular processes. Clearly, the ability to perform this type of experiment simultaneously for two or more ratiometric indicators on the same sample could help clarify mechanistic details and the interplay of different ions.

- Relative concentrations of analogues—fluorescently labeled proteins have been shown to possess full functionality (143, 144). This finding has engendered a new approach for elucidating the role of individual molecular species in cell physiology (161). For proper quantitation of analogue concentrations by imaging, it is important to normalize their fluorescence emission, typically by ratioing with a volume indicator image of the same sample, obtained at a different wavelength (32, see also below). Since shape changes are characteristic of live cells, this procedure must be accomplished with good time resolution in order to provide the true dynamics of analogue fluorescence. This can only be achieved with a robotic microscope approach.

- Cytoplasmic structure—the attachment of dye molecules suitable for ratio imaging to carrier molecules has the advantage of typically reporting on structural and functional features determined by the carrier, rather than the reporting molecules. A typical application is the investigation of cytoplasm structure and compartmentalization by ratio imaging of labeled dextrans and ficolls of known hydrodynamic radii (20, 108, 161).

- Optical biosensors (63, 65)—fluorescent analogues based on environmentally sensitive fluorophores can help gain insights into the role of the labeled protein in conformational changes, ligand binding, posttranslational modifications, and other chemical interactions. Volumetric normalization by ratio imaging is necessary for quantitation in this case as well.

- Membrane electrical potential measurements using fluorescent probes (58, 65) can also benefit from a ratiometric approach. The complicated, relatively small changes in the fluorescence of fast-responding voltage-sensitive dyes can be enhanced and internally standardized by ratioing images obtained at two wavelength of excitation that induce opposite fluorescence intensity shifts (107, 116).

- Resonance energy transfer (69, 136)—in the presence of two species of fluorophores, light excitation energy can be transmitted non-radiatively from one (donor) to the other (acceptor). The fluorescence of the acceptor increases upon excitation of the donor, at the expense of donor fluorescence. The efficiency of transfer depends, inter alia, on relative molecular orientations, but even more strongly on donor-acceptor distances. This is the basis for mapping these distances (as low as a few nanometers) between two species by fluorescence ratioing: upon excitation of the donor, images of acceptor and donor fluorescence emission are recorded, which provides an absorption-normalized representation of resonance energy transfer. While in principle applicable to a number of cellular components, the approach has proven particularly useful in vitro (19, 63, 140) and for cell membrane components (69).

- Steady-state fluorescence anisotropy (SSFA)—fluorescence anisotropy (FA) has been extensively used to study molecular interactions in vitro. It can be easily incorporated into the multimode microscope and used to map the dynamics of one or more interactions, in both time and space, in living cells. The FA measures the degree of polarization of fluorescence emission resulting from excitation with polarized light and is an indicator of the rotational mobility of the fluorophore (14, 96, 101). FA can be detected by either steady-state or time-resolved methods. The steady-state FA (SSFA) requires illumination with a fixed polarizer in the excitation path and a rotatable polarizer or a pair of polarizers, oriented 90° to each other, in the emission path (10, 12, 36, 55, 90). Its value depends on the relative magnitudes of the fluorescence lifetime and the rotational correlation time. Since the rotational correlation time depends linearly on the viscosity and hydrodynamic volume of the molecule (as described by the Einstein equation), the SSFA can be used to extract information about one of three variables: the hydrodynamic volume, the viscosity, or the fluorescence lifetime (36, 56, 97) of the labeled molecule. FA has been widely used in assays of molecular interactions, conformational changes, and viscosity (36, 56, 90, 97), with recent applications of fluorescence anisotropy including measurement of membrane fluidity (109), membrane protein mobility (23, 89), protein-DNA interactions (27, 28), protein-protein interactions (41, 56, 113, 114, 129), protein-membrane interactions (82), and protein conformation and dynamics (13, 60). FA is powerful method for assaying molecular interactions in vivo by allowing the dynamic spatial mapping of anisotropies. Time-resolved FA measurements inherently contain more information, but the present generation of time-resolved fluorescence microscopes is limited to measuring single spots sequentially, or averaging over regions (44, 56, 90), and require expensive and complex instrumentation.

- Time-resolved fluorescence is a potentially information-rich approach that until recently was applied only to selected, spatially averaged areas of the samples under microscopic observation. Improvements in light sources, detector speed, and experimental design allow the extension of this technique to full two-dimensional lifetime imaging (99, 100), with many applications in cell and tissue physiology. Although experimentally demanding, the method has the advantage of high specificity since the contrast is created by local-molecular properties (analogously to magnetic resonance imaging).

- Fluorescence recovery after photobleaching (FRAP) is based on a time and space-selective bleaching of fluorescence, usually by a laser beam focused to a few microns through the microscope optics, in a region of interest of a biological sample (70, 80, 127, 173). The recovery of fluorescence in the bleached area is indicative of the motility of the fluorescently labeled species in cellular membranes and cytoplasm. This information can be collected photometrically, but quantitation by imaging can add to the picture by following the motion of the bleached spot itself (139) or by Fourier analysis (150). Polarized photobleaching extends the time resolution into the microsecond range (155). A related mode, the photoactivation of fluorescence (PAF), is a reverse technique to FRAP in that the laser beam creates a local fluorescence increase by uncaging (162). This mode is even more quantitative than FRAP at tracking labeled macromolecules (147).

- Total internal reflection fluorescence (TIRF)—the shallow region immediately adjacent to the coverslips used in light microscopy can be illuminated with very high selectivity using the evanescent wave created by total internal reflection of light at the glass/aqueous medium interface (11, 104, 118). The resulting fluorescence image provides specific information on the amount, morphology, dynamics, and interactions of labeled components at the cell-substrate contact region; contributions from other regions of the sample are minimized by the exponential decay of the evanescent wave intensity with distance from the interface. The importance of illumination symmetry has been recently recognized, and a simple optical solution for implementation was described (96).

Three-dimensional Fluorescence Modes

CONFOCAL MICROSCOPY   The confocal microscope (17, 18, 50, 77, 92, 120, 126, 128, 166, 168, 172, 174) is a physical-optical solution to the problems of three-dimensional imaging. In a confocal microscope, the object is viewed through a pinhole (or slit), which is at a point in the optical path where the object is in focus. Light from objects that are not in focus is widely spread at the pinhole and mostly blocked; thus defocused objects contribute very little to the image. The pinhole or slit is mechanically or electronically scanned to cover the entire field of view. Fluorescent objects in confocal microscopy are usually illuminated with a laser, also focused on the point imaged by the pinhole. This further improves the rejection of defocused blur by optimally exciting only the point of interest.

The confocal microscope generates an image with a greatly reduced depth of field, which allows direct imaging of the three-dimensional object a slice at a time. No post-processing is required, which allows immediate viewing of individual two-dimensional slices with negligible out-of-focus blurring (18, 24, 120, 126). Drawbacks to this technique are fluorescence bleaching from the high illumination intensities required, slow acquisition, the limited choice of excitation wavelengths, and the high instrumentation cost. Real-time confocal instruments and their applications have recently been described (120, 175).

MICROTOMOGRAPHY/COMPUTATIONAL THREE DIMENSIONS   Methods for reconstructing three-dimensional objects in the presence of out-of-focus blur range from simple high pass filtering of each image, to nearest neighbor approximations (26), above-below plane deconvolution (3), matrix inversion (4), and various iterative inverse (25), regularized non-iterative (122), and convergence methods (1). Adjacent plane deconvolution represents a compromise between accuracy and computational complexity. While not as accurate as iterative inverse filtering, it provides a definite improvement in axial resolution at a computational cost at least two orders of magnitude lower than iterative convergence schemes. In addition, little of the data set need be in memory at any one time, which greatly reduces disk access compared to full volume techniques. However, improvements in computer performance allow application of the more accurate, but computationally demanding, algorithms.

Special Modes

UNCAGING/PHOTOACTIVATION   The controlled change in the chemical concentration of a compound in biological microscopy can often provide mechanistic information. While simple mixing in a flow set-up can provide such a change, a more elegant and precise method is photoactivation ("uncaging"). In this approach, an inactive, custom-synthesized chemical species is converted to an active one of interest by the action of light, usually in the UV range, which induces photolytic conversion (87, S. Adams, R. Y. Tsien, this volume). The newly created species range from ions such as calcium (61, S. Adams, R. Y. Tsien, this volume) to other biological molecules made biologically recognizable by this photolysis/photoactivation (88, 110). The appeal of the technique lies in its optical nature, high temporal and spatial resolution, and controllable activation.

REFLECTION INTERFERENCE MICROSCOPY (RIM)   With appropriate choice of illumination angles, apertures, wavelength, and other parameters, epi-illumination microscope interferometry can be used to selectively investigate the cell-substrate region (51, 79), similar to the case of TIRF.

OPTICAL TRAPS   A laser beam focused through the microscope optics is capable of influencing the motion of small particles in a biological sample. These optical traps (or tweezers) open the way to micromanipulate subcellular components in living cells (30, 57) and create exciting possibilities for combining micromanipulation with detecting structural, chemical, and molecular changes.

What Defines a Multimode Microscopy Workstation

The variety of light microscopy modes that have evolved over the years has provided large amounts of information, but has given rise to an even larger array of questions about living cells, their chemical and biological properties, their spatial structure in two and three dimensions, and about the dynamics of those properties. Although dedicated equipment was available to study living specimens in most of these individual modes of microscopy, and clever optical ways of combining typically two modes have been described (42, 134), there was no instrument that could be used in a more flexible way to study multiple properties in parallel in order to gain insight into the complex processes that occur in biological systems. If one were not limited to one image acquisition mode during an experiment, the interrelated information derived from multiple modes should be greater than the simple sum. With this goal, we developed a multimode microscope system capable of acquiring two- and three-dimensional image data in several integrated modes. Typically, we use one "morphometric" (transmitted light) mode, several fluorescence modes, and one special mode. For example, a VEC mode consists of transmitted light illumination with the DIC optical components, optimal gain and offset settings on a high resolution camera (like a Newvicon), and ratio-based digital mottle image correction with a few frames averaged for noise reduction; a fluorescence mode includes an epifluorescence illumination path with filter sets (excitation, dichroic, emission) for a particular fluorophore, the use of a low light level camera with suitable exposure or integration time, and a digital background subtraction or other correction method. The modes can also be more complex: a mode to investigate changes in calcium concentration includes two excitation or emission filter configurations to acquire images at two different wavelengths and the digital processing to compute the corrected, calibrated image ratio between the two signals in order to show the calcium distribution.

A mode of microscopy also assumes appropriate preparation and maintenance of the specimen (e.g. the fluorescent labeling of constituents, sample environment control). In addition, during the experiment certain perturbations can be made like spot photobleaching, or photoactivation of caged compounds (as described above), or manipulation with optical tweezers, in order to study the responses to those changes.

To achieve these objectives, a multimode workstation is typically a highly modified and automated (robotic) microscope with a wide choice of software tools controlling the image acquisition, storage, processing, analysis, and display steps for optimal performance. The optical, mechanical, electronic, and digital components (as well as sample chemistry and biology) must be individually optimized and then brought together and integrated into a versatile workstation. This is conceptually somewhat different from multimodality imaging (81, 112), where three-dimensional images obtained by medical diagnostic techniques such as computed tomography, magnetic resonance, positron emission tomography, and ultrasound, obtained at different times and locations, are brought together for co-display.

PRESENT GENERATION SYSTEMS

Multimode Workstation Design Considerations

The design considerations for the multimode microscope refer to the choice of the microscope, its optical modification and automation, the integration of peripherals, the image detectors, and the computer hardware and software.

Microscopes have been designed for human vision with manual interactions and usually require a significant number of adjustments and exchanging of parts in order to switch between optical configurations (modes). This can become cumbersome in a time-critical experiment combining several modes of light microscopy. It is obvious that significant automation of the microscope is crucial, covering—for every mode—the choice of wavelengths, light intensity, optical path, and appropriate image detector. We have chosen a Zeiss Axiovert (Carl Zeiss, New York) inverted microscope as a base, for its optimal light throughput and infinity-corrected (91) optics. In order to mount three electronic cameras and add the various motorized components, the mechanical robustness of this microscope was also an advantage. One major modification to the microscope consisted of the replacement of the two-position slider, containing the excitation, dichroic and emission filters in "filter cubes," with a more versatile arrangement of three decoupled and independently controlled sliders for the aforementioned filters. Each slider has six positions, which yield a large number of spectral choices as well as simple dual wavelength excitation and/or emission configuration options. An additional slider was motorized to select optical modifiers like polarizers, needed to automatically switch between fluorescence and DIC, or to perform steady-state fluorescence anisotropy measurements.

Accurate positioning of the sample in the (xy) plane is necessary to enable studies on multiple preselected regions in parallel. This is achieved using a scanning stage of 0.25 μm accuracy. Since three-dimensional imaging is an integral part of the system, the axial (z) positioning of the sample was automated as well. The stepping motor controlling this function has been independently calibrated using a capacitance gauge, and actual step sizes (as low as 19.75 nm) are integrated into the software control. This allows for precise microtomography (acquiring stacks of multiple images through different z levels, thus yielding three-dimensional data sets). By logging cell positions (in x, y, and z) as coordinates in the computer and revisiting those positions during the time lapse acquisition, three-dimensional multimode imaging of any pre-selected volume of the sample is possible.

It is a fact that the quality of biological imaging data is not solely dependent on the microscope optics used. Some of the peripheral devices can play a major role in determining the ultimate outcome of an experiment. We found the choice of optical filters (31, 47, 48, 157) and the design of an environmental chamber (111, 121, 157) to be particularly important. The filters must be optimized not only for the particular fluorophores used, but also take into account the combination of fluorophores in the sample. The filters must be made from optical flats to avoid image shifts (157). The environmental chamber must be optimized for Koehler illumination, laminar liquid exchange, and tight temperature control.

There is a wide range of image detectors suitable for use in light microscope imaging. Typically, these detectors have not been developed for quantitative imaging, and one should choose and characterize them carefully for light sensitivity, gamma correction, geometric distortion, shading, response lag and linearity, pixel defects, and resolution (16, 21, 47, 48, 75, 178). Each camera has its inherent trade-offs in speed, resolution, and precision. Given the wide range of light levels that need to be covered in transmitted and low light level fluorescence, it is not possible presently to use a single image detector on the system for all modes of microscopy . We use three image sensors to fully optimize all modes: in terms of image quality, the best-performance camera is a cooled CCD (charge-coupled device; 5, 71), which yields high dynamic range (12 to 16 bit) image data with a truly linear response in both intensities and exposure times, across a large range of conditions. Its major drawback is in the present readout speed limitation of 500 kHz, which yields full readout times (for a typical high-resolution image) of around 0.5 sec. However, rapid improvements in cooled CCD performance are expected. For time-critical uses like focusing or locating microinjected fluorescent cells, or for real-time imaging experiments, this camera is not suitable. Therefore, two video cameras were added, one (ICCD) with an image intensifier to give "live" images of low light level fluorescence, and another (Newvicon) for high spatial resolution transmitted light imaging. Both were needed, however, since the normal video cameras are not sensitive enough for the fluorescence, and the intensified cameras do not give satisfactory image quality and resolution at high light levels (16, 135, 149, 178). The cameras are mounted on three parfocal microscope ports that output the images in the same magnification and orientation. Port switching is automated through a mechanism inside the microscope body, since the requirement for maximum throughput of light at the fluorescence detection ports precludes partial beam splitting in most applications, although it is possible.

Multimode microscopy requires not only significant optical-mechanical modifications to a conventional light microscope and advanced detectors, but also a well-planned control of the automation, in a user-interactive way. This is achieved via computer control, and the platform needed to acquire, process, and display digital image data needs to be of sufficient quality to handle video data at high throughput rates. In addition, it needs fast general purpose computing power to perform the image analysis. We chose the Apple Macintosh Quadra as an initial platform with a number of special boards for image acquisition and an accelerator card to boost its performance for a variety of complex imaging tasks. The Macintosh is user friendly, is affordable, offers many utilities for digital imaging in hardware and system software and, with the added accelerator, competes very well with much higher priced workstations.

The software used to run the complete system was developed at Carnegie Mellon University and is now part of a package called BDS-Image from Biological Detection Systems, Inc. It offers central control of all microscope automation and image acquisition as well as over 400 image processing and analysis functions. It is important not to be limited to the functionality of separate programs for either acquisition, control, or analysis: an experiment almost always involves a combination of those seemingly different functional groups. Going back and forth between different programs would be limiting in live cell experiments. Since the video acquisition and accelerator cards and the microscope automation hardware are all part of the same package, it becomes possible to design application modules for the system dedicated to performing particular kinds of experiments. Using these special application packages, it is possible to set up complicated multimode experiments with simple (point and click) mouse operations.

As an example of the implementation details, and in view of our focus on live cell imaging applications of multimode, the video acquisition and display options of the multimode workstation are discussed below.

The live video acquisition and display window provides a tool to grab a live image from a video camera and display it onto a Macintosh screen via direct display memory access. Taking advantage of the digitizer's arithmetic-logic unit (ALU) and secondary buffer, various noise correction operations such as background subtraction, geometric averaging, arithmetic averaging, and mottle division can also be easily applied to incoming images at video rates (46).

A tool palette incorporated in the live video window was designed using the standard Macintosh interface and provides an intuitive environment for user interaction with the live video acquisition. Changes between modes can be effected either interactively or in a pre-set sequence. The tool palette also features an interactive contrast and brightness control that alters the displayed image (through look-up tables), but preserves the output data, a small window displaying the correcting background or mottle image, and a live image intensity histogram. From this live video window, the user has the ability to monitor and acquire a real-time or delayed series of monochromatic, 8-bit video images of up to 640 × 480 pixel resolution. These data can be saved at video rates to a sister NuBus memory board and later displayed in the movie playback utility or saved to disk. The current implementation is memory limited to a few hundred images at full sampling resolution. A movie playback window provides a tool with an intuitive interface to review captured image sequences. Designed to have the look and feel of a VCR, it offers playback speeds adjustable from 0.1 to 30 frames/sec. The movie can be played once, continuously, or oscillating back-and-forth, which provides the user with a way to discern details that could not be recognized by reviewing the movie sequence in real time. Different movies can be loaded onto the board simultaneously, and the images in these movies, or parts thereof, can be combined (e.g. in a split-screen) to create new, easier to analyze sequences.

Multimode System for Live Cell Experiments

The selection of the microscopy modes we included in our multimode workstation described here was determined by the type of application most typical in our research: the monitoring of structural and functional changes in live, motile cells.

VEC   Of the transmitted modes of light microscopy, we chose video-enhanced differential interference contrast (VEC-DIC) for several reasons. It offers the highest spatial detection/discrimination capability (5, 6, 59, 61, 106, 107), excellent contrast for submicron structures, and a very shallow depth of field. Moreover, the optical components it requires can be removed upon switching to another mode such as fluorescence. This is not true for the phase rings inside phase objectives, which ultimately reduce the total number of photons reaching the detector, thus potentially decreasing performance in a low light fluorescence experiment. In our implementation, the DIC analyzer is on a motorized slider and is automatically inserted and removed upon switching from VEC to fluorescence. For most applications, in order to prevent excitation of the fluorophores in the sample by the transmitted light imaging, an optical filter (typically red long-pass) is inserted into the light path. Illumination intensity control is achieved by a filter wheel/shutter combination, with neutral density filters. This allows automation and does not change the spectral distribution of the light. The electronic enhancement necessary for VEC can be obtained either through the analogue electronics of the camera controller (which also has a shading correction option), or through the settings of the frame-capture board. The images obtained can be further improved by video-rate mottle division with a background image, which eliminates the effect of camera imperfections, uneven field illumination, or impurities in the optics. Due to the speed of automation and the ease of mode switching, VEC-DIC is often used for identifying cells suitable for observation in the fluorescence-based modes and (re-)focusing before fluorescence acquisition (in order not to bleach the sample by the additional exposure) and analysis of cell and subcellular movements.

RIM   In our current implementation, reflection interference microscopy (RIM) is used to provide information on cell attachment areas to the glass coverslip substrate. High resolution images obtained using 540 nm excitation and detection interference filters and a half-silvered mirror or a suitable wavelength dichroic filter can be further improved by a ratiometric operation aimed at removing reflections caused by the objective lens elements. In this case, the background image must be acquired at the focal plane under investigation because the reflections are extremely sensitive to focus; stage automation makes this possible.

GENERAL RATIO/ION CONCENTRATION QUANTITATION   Ratio imaging methods for ion concentration measurements can be performed using the standard system options. The availability of six different automated excitation, dichroic, and emission filters permits several different ratiometric measurements to be performed in the same experiment. This allows the investigation of several parameters, as long as the spectral selection characteristics avoid overlap of illumination or emission. A fast filter wheel on the epi-illumination path is used in higher time-resolution dual excitation ratioing experiments.

RESONANCE ENERGY TRANSFER RATIOING   This is a multimode option since all the necessary optical components are already available and automated. The challenge is to select an optimal pair of probes (68).

MULTICOLOR FLUORESCENCE   The optical filter sliders described above allow the choice of up to six fluorophores to be imaged independently in a sample of interest. In our implementation, the switching between the corresponding conditions (with neutral density control of light intensities, exposure times, and other conditions) is made flexible through the use of various software. The filters used are custom designed for the particular combination of fluorescent probes. Extensive image correction, registration, and display options allow the quantitative monitoring of any fluorophore combinations, while use of dual and triple dichroics in conjunction with a fast excitation filter wheel can increase the time resolution for acquisition.

FRAP   This option uses an optical adaptor guiding a (shuttered) beam from a 300 mW Ar ion laser to the sample on the automated stage, which can position the bleaching beam accurately.

CAGED COMPOUND ILLUMINATION/RELEASE   The addition of an uncaging option to multimode capabilities is relatively simple on a microscope equipped with UV-transmitting optics. A 75 W mercury arc lamp is placed in the position usually occupied by the transmitted light source to provide the required light pulse. Software control of timing, wavelength, and localization is achieved by an automated shutter and filter wheel, the x-y stage described above, and a variable aperture. Switching to a monitoring configuration of the microscope after uncaging can be as fast as a few milliseconds. Existing caged compounds such as caged calcium (S. Adams, R. Y. Tsien, this volume) can be used to create step-increases in chemical activity. In a different implementation, the UV lines of an Ar ion laser (that we use for FRAP studies) can be used for uncaging, with even better temporal and spatial resolution.

STEADY STATE FLUORESCENCE ANISOTROPY RATIOING   The steady-state FA approach (as described above) is more amenable to incorporation into a multimode microscopy workstation than its time-resolved counterparts because of the relative simplicity of implementation. There are several features of SSFA that make it a powerful tool in multimode microscopy for assaying molecular interactions in cells. First, the data can be acquired in parallel, which allows the mapping of anisotropies in two or three dimensions. Second, for molecules $> \sim 150$ kd, the rotational correlation time will generally be less than 100 ns. In this short time frame, even very small proteins will diffuse only a few nanometers on average, thus minimizing the effect of surrounding cytoplasmic structures on the measured mobility (108). Third, because of the linear dependence of the rotational correlation time on molecular size (approximately 0.6 ns/kd), the FA is a highly sensitive assay of changes in molecular size, e.g the change in size that results from an interaction with another molecule, or a conformational change induced by ligand binding. Finally, the SSFA is normalized to the total fluorescence emission, which gives a measurement that is independent of intensity.

THREE-DIMENSIONAL ACQUISITION AND ANALYSIS   Microtomography is a complete application on our multimode system, designed for a precise time and illumination-efficient means of acquiring three-dimensional data sets at selectable time intervals, wavelengths, and section spacing in an automated, computer-controlled way. In one of our systems, the confocal scanning and cooled CCD-based implementations coexist, but for live cell applications, currently available laser scanning is too slow. Deconvolution of out-of-focus blur is usually carried out using the nearest neighbor algorithm, with a theoretical point spread function (PSF). For better results, a measured PSF can be substituted, with more sophisticated processing algorithms. For fast deconvolution a "no-neighbors" option could be useful (115). Three-dimensional data analysis is perhaps the most difficult part of the three-dimensional imaging problem and the one with the least established methodology. Automated three-dimensional analysis is less mature as a field than its two-dimensional counterpart. Problems of thresholding, segmentation, object morphology, and other aspects of analysis all increase in difficulty with the addition of another dimension of information. While there are several research groups performing automated three-dimensional analysis of specific data types on various platforms (4, 40, 128, 169), there are few comprehensive commercial offerings.

Multimode Image Processing and Display

BATCH PROCESSING AND MOVIE DISPLAY   The ultimate aim of a multimode live cell experiment is a set of images that contains all of the information acquired, corrected for instrumental and other limitations and artifacts, in an easily comprehensible, dynamic form.

The sheer volume of data generated by an automated microscope leads to interesting challenges in achieving this goal. In order to view a large data set as a coherent unit, it is necessary to process each part of the data set identically, otherwise it becomes impossible to separate changes in the data from differences in processing. Performing contrast enhancement, sharpening, and zooming (for example) on a data set of 100 images or more would be very tedious by manual processing.

We have developed a feature called movie processing in order to overcome this problem and to answer the need for consistent, visually-oriented treatment of the data. Given a data set named and numbered in a consistent fashion (usually by automatic convention, upon acquisition), up to 15 different image operations can be applied to the entire image series, identically. These operations include contrast adjustment, smoothing, sharpening, zooming, and background subtraction. In addition, the user can specify any transformation of one image set into another and include those commands in the processing sequence. Once specified and begun, the movie processing application will cycle through the entire data set performing these operations. Particular operation settings can be saved to disk, which allows the user to specify processing for any number of 'movies' and run them in a batch mode, with no need for intervention. After processing, the user can load the series of images produced by the movie processing application and view and combine them using the controls and display options described above.

THREE-DIMENSIONAL DISPLAY   After the three-dimensional data set has been acquired and deconvolved, the next step is to display it (29). Currently most systems are limited to volumetric displays, which allow the user to view the three-dimensional object from various angles while manipulating the illumination, contrast, and other parameters. Three-dimensional information is conveyed through the use of motion cues, stereo displacement, intensity depth cues, and perspective. In order of increasing complexity and flexibility, our direct display options are through-focus, shear stack, and volumetric rendering. These are discussed below, along with an indirect approach called geometric model display. Any of these methods involves the transformation of three-dimensional information into a two-dimensional view of the data set, but various schemes can be employed to enhance the three-dimensional perception.

Through-focus display involves putting together the processed images (acquired by optical slicing) into a movie loop, equivalent to focusing through the sample. This simple method typically precedes more substantial processing of the same set for other types of display.

Shear stack is an exaggerated three-dimensional presentation, usually called upon when the thickness of the specimen imaged is significantly less than the other two dimensions. It can be computed quickly by introducing linear shifts to each image in the stack, with the amount of shift proportional to the depth in the image. Displayed in succession, usually in a back-and-forth motion, it results in a convincing three-dimensional effect.

The most flexible and complex method of direct three-dimensional display of data is called volume rendering. Volume rendering allows the user to view the three-dimensional data set from an arbitrary point of view (including the inside of the specimen), by computing how each voxel of the data set should appear on the screen if viewed from that point of view. Apparent data quality declines when looking perpendicular to the z axis because of out-of-focus information. To assist the user in deriving three-dimensional information from what is essentially a two-dimensional view, motion, perspective, and stereo representations can be used.

When multicolor fluorescence data sets are acquired in three dimensions, we have the ability to simultaneously display up to three of the parameters in colored images. Each data set is assigned a channel in the RGB spectrum, and the traditional rendering technique, combining the color information, is done on each data set. This results in images that correctly place three-dimensional structures into their relative positions in the multiple data sets. In some cases, however, the resulting output is confusing because of the way the disjoint color spaces interact to form other colors. Multicolor three-dimensional display methods need to be improved.

Geometric display describes a method in which the structure of the specimen is extracted from the data, and a model is built that describes the structure. The result is a very clear image, at the expense of some loss of information. This type of display is particularly suitable for presentation and publication, in cases where the spatial features of the sample are more important than the local quantitative details.

KNOWLEDGE-BASED IMAGE ANALYSIS   The multimode microscope system can yield large numbers of images from which the challenge of extracting quantitative data involves image analysis on the time series, which usually requires the separation of particular objects from their background before actually measuring their features. To achieve the identification of objects (by what is usually referred to as scene segmentation), one can not rely completely on user interaction, which limits the analysis to small numbers of two-dimensional images and can carry an arbitrary element. Image analysis operations like thresholding, in order to obtain a binary mask, followed by cellular logics to assess morphological features can be used to automatically distinguish different kinds of objects. These methods work well on images of simple, predictable scenes with high contrast, but not on more complex data, where reliability is strongly dependent on image quality and is seldom better than 80%.

Performance can be greatly improved by giving the system some knowledge about the kind of objects it should recognize and a few of their salient features. Conventional imaging algorithms have little or no way to make use of this object-specific knowledge. Our goal was to build a software system that circumvents current limitations of image analysis by offering a way of analyzing complex imaging data from the light microscope quantitatively without the need of extensive manual interaction. This was based on a knowledge-driven scene segmentation module that finds objects in an image based on a basic description of their properties.

In addition, even though it seems intuitively obvious that the added information of e.g. a second labeled parameter should help a machine vision system in distinguishing a particular object, there is no available method for current state-of-the-art equipment to make use of this added information. The same argument can be made for the added information available from multiple optical contrast yielding modes and from time lapse image series. In the design of the software architecture, we try to take advantage of this added information even at the low level scene segmentation phase.

Recently, we proposed the details of an architecture for the computational model that is needed to realize this goal (119). Clearly, this architecture is designed to be expanded towards multiple parameter, multimode, time lapse and three-dimensional data analysis, which will provide a framework that can make quantitative use of the wealth of information obtained by multimode data acquisition.

SELECTED BIOLOGICAL EXPERIMENTS

Multimode microscope technology is currently being used to advance biological research by investigating complex interrelated processes that cannot be studied separately. In live cell experiments, specimen preparation can become more complicated when cells are labeled with several fluorescent probes. Specific cell components must be labeled without alteration of normal cell function. The optimal method of entry of the fluorescent probe into the cell (i.e. pinocytosis, microinjection, diffusion, scrape-loading) must be determined for each probe to ensure specific labeling and minimize interactions between probes. Fluorescent probes (analogues, free dyes, biosensors, antibodies) should be tested in the cell separately and then in combination to determine the best sequence of labeling compatible with preserving cell function. Despite technical challenges, the wealth of biological information from live cell research gives a strong impetus to the growth of multimode microscopy (22, 53, 105). The following are a few examples of experiments designed for a multiparameter study on a multimode microscope system. Other applications are described elsewhere (19, 32, 52, 53, 55, 56, 63, 64, 94, 95, 139, 157).

Biological Model: Wound-Healing

Parameters/modes: VEC/RIM/Vinculin/Myosin-II. Experiment: Studying cell motility by examining the temporal and spatial dynamics of focal contacts, vinculin, and myosin-II-based fibers during active contraction and locomotion of polarized cells.

Fibroblast cell movement involves a complex sequence of mechano-chemical steps including cell interaction with the substrate, changes in multiple cytoskeletal proteins, and internal chemical signaling systems. Fibroblasts are induced to migrate in a single direction (polarization) by removing an area of cells (wounding) from a densely confluent monolayer of cells. The contact-inhibited fibroblasts immediately begin to uniformly migrate out onto the free substrate (glass coverslip). This method of polarizing fibroblasts is termed wound-healing. Cell movement involves the formation, contraction, and elongation of actin and myosin-II-based fibers that are found throughout the cell. When myosin-II-based fibers contract during cell migration, the cell shape changes significantly, and the cell elongates as it moves across the glass coverslip. Bundles of fibers in the cell bind to the cell membrane through attachment proteins, one of which is vinculin. Many of these bundles terminate at or close to regions of the cell that are in close contact with the coverslip. These regions are called focal contacts, and their positions change as myosin-II-based fibers contract and elongate during cell migration. To detect the focal contacts in living cells, reflection interference microscopy (RIM) is used, in which light is reflected from the lower surface of the cell, and the contacts appear as dark patches. Examining cell migration, myosin-II-based fibers, focal contacts, and the attachment protein vinculin, provides a comprehensive way to study contractile mechanisms during fibroblast locomotion.

Polarized Swiss 3T3 fibroblasts migrating along the wound edge are microinjected with a solution of fluorescein-labeled vinculin and rhodamine-labeled myosin-II. After a recovery period, the cells are mounted in the environmental chamber, placed on the microscope's scanning stage, and maintained at 37°C by a feedback controlled temperature system. The x,y,z coordinates of fluorescent cells are logged into the timelapse program, and the system is set to acquire a sequence of four images (VEC, RIM, vinculin, myosin-II). Optimal light levels for each parameter are predetermined by using a test image feature that displays image statistics. The correct filters, shutters, and cameras for each parameter are set in the configuration mode. For this experiment, the timelapse mode is set for 10 min intervals over a 3 hr period, and a cooled CCD detector is used for three of the four modes (the Newvicon camera is used for VEC).

After acquisition, a series of images for each parameter is processed for display purposes (background subtraction, contrast stretching, sharpening, and registration are the most widely used steps). Movie loops of the VEC images show changes in the shape of the motile cell, contraction and elongation of the leading lamella, and tail retraction. The sequence of myosin-II images can be shown in split screen together with the VEC sequence in order to correlate myosin-II-based fiber contraction to activity of the cell during different stages of locomotion. Movie loops of RIM images follow the translocation of focal contacts and the formation of new contacts as the cell undergoes force-generating processes during polarized cell movements. Changes in the cell contact with the substrate during migration can be correlated with the location and distribution of vinculin and myosin-II-based fibers. Multicolor overlay images of myosin-II, vinculin, and RIM can be generated to easily identify the position of each parameter in the same cell and detect areas of colocalization, or a multicolor movie loop can be made to determine the movement of the three parameters in relationship to each other over time. Measurements can be made using programs that calculate the distance and direction of movements made by the myosin-II-based fibers and/or the focal contacts. Changes in the sarcomeric distribution along myosin-II-based fibers during contraction and elongation can also be measured. The distribution of vinculin along a specific myosin fiber, as identified by the knowledge-based image analysis approach described above, can also be obtained; this type of result is nearly impossible by traditional image processing (139).

Biological Model: Serum Stimulation

Parameters/modes: VEC/Calcium Green/Myosin-II/Volume Indicator/Uncaging. Experiment: A study of intracellular calcium signaling using ratio imaging to examine myosin-II-based fiber contraction and spatial changes in intracellular calcium induced by serum stimulation of quiescent cells.

When fibroblasts are serum-deprived, the cells become well spread and a state of metabolic quiescence is induced. Adding medium containing serum stimulates the cells and activates many signaling systems. Intracellular calcium levels rise, myosin-II-based fibers contract, the cytosol condenses, and a dramatic change in the cell shape occurs. Using the serum stimulation model, the localized areas of high calcium are detected within the cell and the spatial changes over time are correlated to areas of increased myosin-II concentration and myosin-II fiber contraction.

Quiescent Swiss 3T3 fibroblasts are microinjected with rhodamine-labeled myosin-II. After a recovery period, the same cells are microinjected with a solution of calcium green dextran (10 kd), and the volume indicator Cy5 dextran (10 kd), which distributes evenly throughout the cell. Ratio imaging using a volume indicator eliminates effects of intracellular probe concentration and cellular optical pathlength variations.

Fluorescent cells are identified, logged in, and optical parameters set as described above. The multimode program is set to acquire a sequence of four images (VEC, calcium green, volume indicator, myosin-II) using the rapid acquisition mode necessary for ratio imaging. Images are collected in rapid sequence, held in computer RAM, and saved only after all images in the series have been acquired. This procedure minimizes changes occurring within the cell between acquisition modes.

A series of images is taken during the quiescent state to determine the baseline level and spatial distribution of myosin-II and free calcium. A peristaltic pump apparatus perfuses equilibrated medium containing a high concentration of serum into the environmental chamber. The timelapse mode begins immediately and takes the series of four images at each stage position using rapid acquisition. The cycle repeats at the selected 2 min intervals for 30 min.

After background subtraction and image registration, ratios are made by dividing the calcium green image by the volume indicator image, as well as the myosin-II image by the volume image at each time point. The resulting ratios show areas of elevated calcium and local concentrations of myosin-II in the same cell. Image analysis provides data on the rise in calcium seen after serum stimulation and the changes in spatial distribution over time.

Calibration of the calcium green fluorescence yields measurements of the concentration of intracellular calcium at different locations in the cell. Pseudocolor analysis enhances the display of the spatial changes of intracellular calcium levels within the cell. Movie loop split screen and color overlay studies provide information on the relationship of cellular changes and contraction of fibers induced by serum stimulation (VEC images) with areas of local calcium elevation (calcium green ratios) and contraction of myosin-II-based fibers and/or areas of elevated myosin-II (myosin-II images and ratios). Caged calcium can be used to explore the necessary and sufficient role of calcium in the induction of a myosin-II-based contraction.

VISION FOR THE FUTURE

Performance Improvements

Current acquisition techniques have severe temporal constraints, in particular for the three-dimensional case. Under normal fluorescence labeling, a single confocal image can require thirty or more seconds of sampling to obtain a reasonable signal-to-noise ratio. Full field imaging is faster, but current systems are for the most part limited to an image every few seconds, again depending on sample characteristics. These limitations prevent the application of three-dimensional imaging to thick living samples because they move too quickly to allow acquisition of an accurate three-dimensional image set. Nevertheless, this remains a most desirable goal. One of the obvious developmental directions is to construct a fast acquisition system that will allow three-dimensional and other modal imaging of live samples. The time requirements are stringent: recording an image at typical magnifications before the specimen moves laterally by one pixel requires an acquisition time of a fraction of a second. This can be achieved by simultaneously addressing the current limiting factors: photometric efficiency, axial sampling, and camera readout times. A high-intensity (pulsed) illuminator with a feedback-stabilized fast focal plane controller (a stage driven by piezoelectric or electrostrictive devices to precise locations) can increase current yields of three-dimensional stack acquisition by at least an order of magnitude (F. Lanni, personal communication).

New Modes for Multimode

Some emerging modes of light microscopy, such as luminescence (49, 84, 138) and lifetime (98–100) imaging, as well as innovative approaches to three-dimensional imaging such as standing wave microscopy (103) could provide new types of information. Also, a method similar to FA, polarized fluorescence depletion (83, 179), takes advantage of long lifetime phosphorescent probes to measure rotational diffusion coefficients that extend into the microsecond range (37, 123), further enhancing the utility of polarized light microscopy. These approaches could prove particularly useful if used in conjunction with more established techniques. Thus a multimode implementation should be investigated.

Ratio imaging has evolved impressively in sophistication and applications in recent years. One of its significant shortcomings, namely the need for wavelength (or polarization) switching and separate recording, affects the maximal time-resolution attainable. A new technique, termed W (dual view video) imaging (93), based on polarization splitting with a crystal (146) could alleviate the problem, by simultaneously recording the two images to be ratioed onto the same imaging chip, side-by-side. Acquisition times could then be set dynamically, depending on conditions and application.

The elegant technique of two-photon absorption laser scanning fluorescence microscopy (34) delivers confocal performance with less photobleaching. Although now requiring expensive lasers, this technique could constitute an important mode for three-dimensional applications of imaging and uncaging.

The continuous quest for higher resolution has received a significant boost in recent years from an unexpected source: lensless (near field) microscopy (15, 167), which allows improvements of more than an order of magnitude in resolution. The implications for a multimode implementation are self-evident, but the technique is still in its infancy in terms of biological applications.

Advanced Analysis and Processing Options

Future multimode microscopy systems require more advanced image analysis options than those currently available. In particular it appears that some of the key information is not used optimally in the complex image scene segmentation. Next generation instruments should take advantage of the biochemical specificity of labeling techniques and of the variety of optical contrast generating methods in a more objective-oriented and robust way and make proper use of all the information that is available in setting the algorithmic paths. Rule-based processing paths, fuzzy logic and neural nets for vague problems, and learning and artificial intelligence algorithms are only some of the other exciting options to investigate.

Real-time Processing Interactive Workstation

Processes of interest do not happen spontaneously. In the world of biological experimentation, they are induced (triggered, facilitated) by interacting with the system. When such a (physical, chemical or biological) perturbation is applied, the current goal of microscope imaging has been to start recording with the highest spatial and temporal accuracy (sampling rate) feasible. This usually means recording of raw data (images), with subsequent post-processing to ensure that what we see is quantitative and close to what we would have seen if our devices were perfect. Automated image acquisition, triggering of perturbations, and image analysis should improve performance.

A related alternative approach presumes that if the acquisition of images and their processing and analysis were fast enough to yield the results while the experiment is going on, it would allow interacting with the experiment (perturbations, decisional tree) in a cogent, time-critical way. Assuming that the extent and location of the events to be quantitated are not known, fast processing would allow "zooming into" the right volume, at the right time, and set the appropriate temporal sampling rate and other acquisition parameters. This would also facilitate simultaneous monitoring of other relevant sample regions, with significant methodological advantages. The processing speeds needed to make such an approach a reality are only available today on supercomputers and massively parallel processors. Using heterogeneous distributed computing approaches on these, all of the above could be achieved via an Automated Interactive Microscope (AIM). While current multimode workstations automate simple, repetitive operations with great success, the AIM would permit the experimenter to alter biological processes while they are occurring.

ACKNOWLEDGMENTS

We would like to thank our colleagues at the Center for Light Microscope Imaging and Biotechnology for stimulating discussions and many other forms of help. Support from the National Science Foundation (through a Science and Technology Center grant, NSF-DIR 8920118) is gratefully acknowledged.

Literature Cited

1. Acharya, R. S., Cogswell, C. J., Gold-gof, D. B. eds. 1992. *Biomedical Image Processing and Three-Dimensional Microscopy.* Proc. SPIE Vol. 1660 (pt 1, 2)
2. Deleted in proof
3. Agard, D.A. 1984. Optical sectioning microscopy: Cellular architecture in three dimensions. *Annu. Rev. Biophys. Bioeng.* 13:191–219
4. Agard, D. A., Hiraoka, Y., Shaw, P., Sedat, J. W. 1989. Fluorescence microscopy in three dimensions. See Ref. 145, pp. 353–77
5. Aikens, R. S., Agard, D. A., Sedat, J. W. 1989. Solid-state imagers for microscopy. See Ref. 161, pp. 291–313
6. Allen, R. D. 1985. New observations on cell architecture and dynamics by video-enhanced contrast optical microscopy. *Annu. Rev. Biophys. Biophys. Chem.* 14:265–90
7. Allen, R. D., Allen, N. S. 1983. Video-enhanced microscopy with a computer frame memory. *J. Microsc.* 129:3–17
8. Allen, R. D., David, G. B., Nomarski, G. 1969. The Zeiss-Nomarski differential interference equipment for transmitted-light microscopy. *Z. Wiss. Mikrosk.* 69:193–221
9. Arndt-Jovin, D. J., Robert-Nicoud, M., Kaufman, S. J., Jovin, T. M. 1985. Fluorescence digital microscopy in cell biology. *Science* 230:247–56
10. Axelrod, D. 1979. Carbocyanine dye orientation in red cell membrane studied by microscopic fluorescence polarization. *Biophys. J.* 26:557–74
11. Axelrod, D. 1989. Total internal reflection fluorescence microscopy. See Ref. 145, pp. 246–70
12. Axelrod, D. 1989. Fluorescence polarization microscopy. See Ref. 145, pp. 333–52
13. Axelsen, P. H., Gratton, E., Prendergast, F. G. 1991. Experimentally verifying molecular dynamics simulations through fluorescence anisotropy measurements. *Biochemistry* 30:1173–79
14. Bentley, K. L., Thompson, L. K., Klebe, R. J., Horowitz, P. M. 1985. Fluorescent polarization: a general method for measuring ligand binding and membrane microviscosity. *Bio Techniques* 3:356–66
15. Betzig, E., Trautman, J. K., Harris, T. D., Weiner, S. J., Kostelak, R. L. 1991. Breaking the diffraction barrier: optical microscopy on a nanometric scale. *Science* 251:1468–70
16. Bookman, R. J. 1990. Temporal response characterization of video cameras. See Ref. 69, pp. 235–50
17. Brakenhoff, G. J., van der Voort, H. T. M., Oud, J. L., Mans, A. 1990. Potentialities and limitations of confocal microscopy for the study of 3-dimensional biological structures. See Ref. 69, pp. 19–28
18. Brakenhoff, G. J., van Spronsen, E. A., van der Voort, H. T. M., Nannings, N. 1989. Three-dimensional confocal fluorescence microscopy. See Ref. 145, pp. 379–98
19. Bright, G. R., Fisher, G. W., Rogowska, J., Taylor, D. L. 1989. Fluorescence ratio imaging microscopy. See Ref. 145, pp. 157–92
20. Bright, G. R., Rogowska, J., Fisher, G. W., Taylor, D. L. 1987. Fluorescence ratio imaging spectroscopy: temporal and spatial measurements in single living cells. *BioTechniques* 5:556–63
21. Bright, G. R., Taylor, D. L. 1986. Imaging at low light level in fluorescence microscopy. See Ref. 143, pp. 257–88
22. Brundage, R. A., Fogarty, K. E., Tuft, R. A., Fay, F. S. 1991. Calcium gradients underlying polarization and chemotaxis of eosinophils. *Science* 254:703–6
23. Burgun, C., Waksman, A., Cremel, G. 1991. pH-induced reorganization of synaptic membrane as revealed by fluorescence anisotropy and energy transfer. *Arch. Biochem. Biophys.* 286:394–401
24. Carlsson, K., Mossberg, K. 1992. Reduction of cross-talk between fluorescent labels in scanning laser microscopy. *J. Microsc.* 167:23–37
25. Carrington, W. A., Fogarty, K. E., Fay, F. S. 1989. Three-dimensional imaging on confocal and wide-field microscopes. See Ref. 120, pp. 137–46
26. Castleman, K. R. 1979. *Digital Image Processing.* Englewood Cliffs, NJ: Prentice Hall. 429 pp.
27. Chabbert, M., Hillen, W., Hansen, D., Takahashi, M., Bousquet, J. A. 1992. Structural analysis of the operator binding domain of Tn10-encoded tet repressor — A time-resolved fluorescence and anisotropy study. *Biochemistry* 31:1951–60
28. Chabbert, M., Lami, H., Takahashi, M. 1991. Cofactor-induced orientation

of the DNA bases in single-stranded DNA complexed with RecA protein—a fluorescence anisotropy and time-decay study. *J. Biol. Chem.* 266:5395–400

29. Chen, H., Sedat, J. W., Agard, D. A. 1989. Manipulation, display and analysis of three-dimensional biological images. See Ref. 120, pp. 127–35

30. Chu, S. 1991. Laser manipulation of atoms and particles. *Science* 253:861–66

31. DeBiasio, R., Bright, G. R., Ernst, L. A., Waggoner, A. S., Taylor, D. L. 1987. Five parameter fluorescence imaging: wound healing of living Swiss 3T3 cells. *J. Cell Biol.* 105:1613–22

32. DeBiasio, R. L., Wang, L.-L., Fisher, G. W., Taylor, D. L. 1988. The dynamic distribution of fluorescent analogues of actin and myosin in protrusions at the leading edge of migrating Swiss 3T3 fibroblasts. *J. Cell Biol.* 107:2631–45

33. DeBrabander, M., Nuydens, R., Geerts, H., Nuyens, R., Leunissen, J., Jacobson, K. 1990. Using nanovid microscopy to analyse the movement of cell membrane components in living cells. See Ref. 69, pp. 345–56

34. Denk, W., Strickler, J. H., Webb, W. W. 1990. Two-photon laser scanning fluorescence microscopy. *Science* 248:73–75

35. DeWeer, P., Salzberg, B. M. 1986. *Optical Methods in Cell Physiology.* New York: Wiley

36. Dix, J. A., Verkman, A. S. 1990. Mapping of fluorescence anisotropy in living cells by ratio imaging: Application to cytoplasmic viscosity. *Biophys. J.* 57:231–40

37. Eads, T. M., Thomas, D. D. 1984. Microsecond rotational motions of eosin-labeled myosin measured by time-resolved anisotropy of absorption and phosphorescence. *J. Mol. Biology* 179:55–81

38. Ellis, G. W. 1985. Microscope illuminator with fiber optic source integrator. *J. Cell Biol.* 101:83a

39. Farkas, D. L., Wei, M.-D., Febbroriello, P., Carson, J. H., Loew, L. M. 1989. Simultaneous imaging of cell and mitochondrial membrane potential. *Biophys. J.* 56:1053–69

40. Fay, F. S., Carrington, W., Fogarty, K. E. 1989. Three-dimensional molecular distribution in single cells analyzed using the digital imaging microscope. *J. Microsc.* 153:133–49

41. First, E. A., Taylor, S. S. 1989. Selective modification of the catalytic subunit of cAMP-dependent protein ki-

nase with sulfhydryl-specific fluorescent probes. *Biochemistry* 28:3598–605

42. Foskett, J. K. 1988. Simultaneous Nomarski and fluorescence imaging during video microscopy of cells. *Am. J. Physiol.* 255:C566–71

43. Francon, M. 1961. *Progress in Microscopy.* Evanston: Row Peterson. 295 pp.

44. Fushimi, K., Verkman, A. S. 1991. Low viscosity in the aqueous domain of cell cytoplasm measured by picosecond polarization microfluorimetry. *J. Cell Biol.* 112:719–25

45. Galbraith, W., David, G. B. 1976. An aid to understanding differential interference contrast microscopy: computer simulation. *J. Microsc.* 108:147–76

46. Galbraith, W., Farkas, D. L. 1992. Remapping disparate images for coincidence. *J. Microsc.* Submitted

47. Galbraith, W., Ryan, K. W., Gliksman, N., Taylor, D. L., Waggoner, A. S. 1989. Multiple spectral parameter imaging in quantitative fluorescence microscopy. 1: quantitation of bead standards. *Comput. Med. Imag. Graph.* 13:47–60

48. Galbraith, W., Wagner, C. E., Chao, J., Abaza, M., Ernst, L. A., et al. 1991. Imaging cytometry by multiparameter fluorescence. *Cytometry* 12:579–96

49. Garland, P. B., Moore, C. H. 1979. Phosphorescence of protein-bound eosin and erythrosin: a possible probe for measurements of slow rotational mobility. *Biochem. J.* 183:561–72

50. Gautier, T., Robert-Nicoud, M., Gouilly, M.-N., Hernandez-Verdun, D. 1992. Relocation of nucleolar proteins around chromosomes at mitosis—a study by confocal laser scanning microscopy. *J. Cell Sci.* 102:729–37

51. Gingell, D., Todd, I. 1979. Interference reflection microscopy. A quantitative theory for image interpretation and its application to cell-substratum separation measurement. *Biophys. J.* 26:507–26

52. Giuliano, K. A., Kolega, J., DeBiasio, R., Taylor, D. L. 1992. Myosin II phosphorylation and the dynamics of stress fibers in serum-deprived and stimulated fibroblasts. *Mol. Biol. Cell.* 3:1037–48

53. Giuliano, K. A., Nederlof, M. A., DeBiasio, R., Lanni, F., Waggoner, A. S., Taylor, D. L. 1990 Multimode light microscopy. See Ref. 69, pp. 543–57

54. Goldstein, D. J. 1982. A simple quan-

titative analysis of phase contrast microscopy, not restricted to objects of very low retardation. *J. Microsc.* 128:33–47

55. Gough, A. H., DeBiasio, R. L., Taylor, D. L. 1992. Mapping calmodulin binding in living cells by fluorescence anisotropy ratio imaging. *J. Cell Biol.* Submitted

56. Gough, A. H., Taylor, D. L. 1993. Fluorescence anisotropy imaging of protein mobility. *Biophys. J.* Submitted

57. Greulich, K. O., Weber, G. 1992. The light microscope on its way from an analytical to a preparative tool. *J. Microsc.* 167:127–51

58. Gross, D., Loew, L. M. 1989. Fluorescent indicators of membrane potential: microspectrofluorometry and imaging. See Ref. 145, pp. 193–218

59. Grynkiewicz, G., Poenie, M., Tsien, R. Y. 1985. A new generation of Ca^{2+} indicators with greatly improved fluorescence properties. *J. Biol. Chem.* 260:3440–50

60. Gryczynski, I., Steiner, R. F., Lakowicz, J. R. 1991. Intensity and anisotropy decays of the tyrosine calmodulin proteolytic fragments, as studied by GHz frequency-domain fluorescence. *Biophys. Chem.* 39:69–78

61. Gurney, A. M. 1991. Photolabile calcium buffers to selectively activate calcium-dependent processes. In *Cellular Neurobiology: A Practical Approach*, ed. J. Chad, H. Wheal, pp. 153–77. New York: IRL Press

62. Hader, D.-P. 1991. *Image Analysis in Biology.* Boca Raton: CRC Press 363 pp.

63. Hahn, K., DeBiasio, R., Taylor, D. L. 1993. Fluorescent analogs: optical biosensors of the chemical and molecular dynamics of macromolecules in living cells. In *Fluorescent Probes for Biological Function of Living Cells: A Practical Guide,* ed. W. T. Mason. London: Academic. In press

64. Hahn, K., DeBiasio, R., Taylor, D. L. 1992. Patterns of elevated free calcium and calmodulin activation in living cells. *Nature.* 359:736–38

65. Haugland, R. P. 1992. *Handbook of Fluorescent Probes and Research Chemicals.* Eugene, OR: Molecular Probes, Inc. 421 pp.

66. Hayakawa, T. 1991. Single photon imaging. See Ref. 62, pp. 75–86

67. Hayden, J. H., Allen, R. D. 1984. Detection of single microtubules in living cells: particle transport can occur in both directions along the same microtubule. *J. Cell Biol.* 99:1785–93

68. Herman, B. 1989. Resonance energy transfer microscopy. See Ref. 145, pp. 219–43

69. Herman, B., Jacobson, K. eds. 1990. *Optical Microscopy for Biology.* New York: Wiley-Liss. 658 pp.

70. Hibino, M., Shigemori, M., Itoh, H., Nagayama, K., Kinosita, K. Jr. 1991. Membrane conductance of an electroporated cell analyzed by submicrosecond imaging of transmembrane potential. *Biophys. J.* 59:209–20

71. Hiraoka, Y., Sedat, J. W., Agard, D. A. 1987. The use of a charge-coupled device for quantitative optical microscopy of biological structures. *Science* 238:36–41

72. Hiraoka, Y., Sedat, J. W., Agard, D. A. 1990. Determination of three-dimensional imaging properties of a light microscope system. Partial confocal behavior in epifluorescence microscopy. *Biophys. J.* 57:325–33

73. Hoffman, R. 1977. The modulation contrast microscope: principles and performance. *J. Microsc.* 110:205–22

74. Houseal, T. W., Bustamante, C., Stump, R. F., Maestre, M. F. 1989. Real-time imaging of single DNA molecules with fluorescence microscopy. *Biophys. J.* 56:507–16

75. Inoue, S. 1986. *Video Microscopy.* New York/London: Plenum

76. Inoue, S. 1989. Imaging of unresolved objects, superresolution, and precision of distance measurement with video microscopy. See Ref. 145, pp. 85–112

77. Inoue, S. 1989. Foundations of confocal scanned imaging light microscopy. See Ref. 120, pp. 1–13

78. Inoue, S. 1990. Whither video microscopy? Towards 4-D imaging at the highest resolution of the light microscope. See Ref. 69, pp. 497–511

79. Izzard, C. S., Lochner, L. R. 1976. Cell-to-substrate contacts in living fibroblasts: an interference-reflection study with an evaluation of the technique. *J. Cell Sci.* 21:129–59

80. Jacobson, K., Elson, E., Koppel, D., Webb, W. 1983. International workshop on the application of fluorescence photobleaching techniques to problems in cell biology. *Fed. Proc.* 42:72–79

81. Jiang, H., Holton, K., Robb, R. 1992. Image registration of multimodality 3-D medical images by chamfer matching. *Proc. SPIE* 1660:356–66

82. John, E., Jähnig, F. 1988. Dynamics of melittin in water and membranes as determined by fluorescence anisotropy decay. *Biophys. J.* 54:817–27

83. Johnson, P., Garland, P. B. 1981.

Depolarization of fluorescence depletion: A microscopic method for measuring rotational diffusion of membrane proteins on the surface of a single cell. *FEBS Lett.* 132:252–56

84. Jovin, T. M., Arndt-Jovin, D. J. 1989. Luminescence digital imaging microscopy. *Annu. Rev. Biophys. Biophys. Chem.* 18:271–308

85. Jovin, T. M., Bartholdi, M., Vaz, W. 1981. Rotational diffusion of biological macromolecules by time-resolved delayed luminescence (phosphorescence, fluorescence) anisotropy. *Ann. NY Acad. Sci.* 366:176–96

86. Kachar, B. 1985. Asymmetric illumination contrast: a method for image formation for video light microscopy. *Science* 227:766–68

87. Kao, J. P. Y., Adams, S. R. 1992. Photosensitive caged compounds: design, properties and biological applications. In *Optical Microscopy: New Technologies and Applications,* ed. B. Herman, J. J. Lemasters. New York: Academic. In press

88. Kaplan, J. H., Somlyo, A. P. 1989. Flash photolysis of caged compounds: new tools for cellular physiology. *Trends Neurosci.* 12:54–59

89. Kawato, S., Ashikawa, I., Iwase, T., Hara, E. 1991. Drug-induction decreases the mobility of cytochrome-P-450 in rat liver microsomes—protein rotation study. *J. Biochem.* 109:587–93

90. Keating, S. M., Wensel, T. G. 1991. Nanosecond fluorescence microscopy: Emission kinetics of Fura-2 in single cells. *Biophys. J.* 59:186–202

91. Keller, H. E. 1989. Objective lenses for confocal microscopy. See Ref. 120, pp. 69–77

92. Kett, P., Geiger, B., Ehemann, V., Komitowski, D. 1992. Three-dimensional analysis of cell nucleus structures visualized by confocal scanning laser microscopy. *J. Microsc.* 167:169–79

93. Kinosita, K. Jr., Itoh, H., Ishiwata, S., Hirano, K., Nishizaka, T., Hayakawa, T. 1991. Dual-view microscopy with a single camera: real-time imaging of molecular orientations and calcium. *J. Cell Biol.* 115:67–73

94. Kolega, J., Janson, L. W., Taylor, D. L. 1991. The role of solation-contraction coupling in regulating stress fiber dynamics in nonmuscle cells. *J. Cell Biol.* 114:993–1003

95. Kolega, J., Taylor, D. L. 1991. Regulation of actin and myosin II dynamics in living cells. In *Ordering the Membrane-Cytoskeleton Trilayer,* ed. J. S.

Morrow, M. S. Mooseker, pp. 187–206. New York: Academic

96. Lakowicz, J. R. 1980. Fluorescence spectroscopic investigations of the dynamic properties of proteins, membranes and nucleic acids. *J. Biochem. Biophys. Methods* 2:91–119

97. Lakowicz, J. R. 1983. *Principles of Fluorescence Spectroscopy.* New York: Plenum. 436 pp.

98. Lakowicz, J. R. 1986. Biochemical applications of frequency-domain fluorometry. See Ref. 159, pp. 225–44

99. Lakowicz, J. R., Berndt, K. W. 1991. Lifetime-selective fluorescence imaging using an rf phase-sensitive camera. *Rev. Sci. Inst.* 62:1727–34

100. Lakowicz, J. R., Szmacinski, H., Nowaczyk, K., Johnson, M. L. 1992. Fluorescence lifetime imaging of free and protein-bound NADH. *Proc. Natl. Acad. Sci. USA* 89:1271–75

101. Lambooy, P. K., Steiner, R. F., Sternberg, H. 1982. Molecular dynamics of calmodulin as monitored by fluorescence anisotropy. *Arch. Biochem. Biophys.* 217:517–28

102. Langridge, W. H. R., Escher, A., Baga, M., O'Kane, D., Wampler, J., et al. 1989. Use of low light image microscopy to monitor genetically engineered bacterial luciferase gene expression in living cells and gene activation throughout the development of a transgenic organism. See Ref. 159, pp. 216–26

103. Lanni, F. 1986. Standing-wave fluorescence microscopy. See Ref. 142, pp. 505–21

104. Lanni, F., Waggoner, A. S., Taylor, D. L. 1985. Structural organization of interphase 3T3 fibroblasts studied by total internal reflection fluorescence microscopy. *J. Cell Biol.* 100:1091–102

105. Lemasters, J. J., Nieminen, A.-L., Gores, G. J., Dawson, T. L., Wray, B. E., et al. 1990. Multiparameter digitized video microscopy (MDVM) of hypoxic cell injury. See Ref. 69, pp. 523–41

106. Loew, L. M. ed. 1988. *Spectroscopic Membrane Probes.* Boca Raton: CRC Press. Vol. I, 227 pp.; Vol. II, 206 pp.; Vol. III, 228 pp.

107. Loew, L. M., Farkas, D. L., Wei, M.-D. 1990. Membrane potential imaging: ratios, templates, and quantitative confocal microscopy. See Ref. 69, pp. 131–42

108. Luby-Phelps, K., Taylor, D. L., Lanni, F. 1986. Probing the structure of cytoplasm. *J. Cell Biol.* 102:2015–22

109. Mazzanti, L., Faloia, E., Rabini, R.

A., Staffolani, R., Kantar, A., et al. 1992. Diabetes-mellitus induces red blood cell plasma membrane alterations possibly affecting the aging process. *Clin. Biochem.* 25:41–46

110. McCray, J. A., Trentham, D. R. 1989. Properties and uses of photoreactive caged compounds. *Annu. Rev. Biophys. Biophys. Chem.* 18:239–70

111. McKenna, N. M., Wang, Y.-L. 1989. Culturing cells on the microscope stage. See Ref. 161, pp. 195–205

112. Mealha, O., Pereira, A. S., Santos, B. S. 1992. Data structures for multimodality imaging: concepts and implementation. *Proc. SPIE* 1660: 367–74

113. Mejillano, M. R.. Himes, R. H. 1989. Tubulin dimer dissociation detected by fluorescence anisotropy. *Biochemistry* 28:6518–24

114. Mills, J., Walsh, M., Nemcek, K., Johnson, J. 1988. Biologically active fluorescent derivatives of spinach calmodulin that report calmodulin target protein binding. *Biochemistry* 27:991–96

115. Monck, J. R., Oberhauser, A. F., Keating, T. J., Fernandez, J. M. 1992. Thin-section ratiometric Ca images obtained by optical sectioning of Fura-2 loaded mast cells. *J. Cell Biol.* 116:745–59

116. Montana, V., Farkas, D. L., Loew, L. M. 1989. Dual-wavelength ratiometric fluorescence measurement of membrane potential. *Biochemistry* 28:4536–39

117. Morikawa, K., Yanagida, M. 1981. Visualization of individual DNA molecules in solution by light microscopy: DAPI staining method. *J. Biochem* 89:693–96

118. Murray, J. M., Eshel, D. 1992. Evanescent-wave microscopy: a simple optical configuration. *J. Microsc.* 167: 49–62

119. Nederlof, M. A., Witkin, A., Taylor, D. L. 1991. Knowledge-driven image analysis of cell structures. *Proc. SPIE* 1428:233–41

120. Pawley, J., ed. 1989. *The Handbook of Biological Confocal Microscopy.* Madison, Wl: IMR Press. 201 pp.

121. Pentz, S., Horler, H. 1992. A variable cell culture chamber for 'open' and 'closed' cultivation, perfusion and high microscopic resolution of living cells. *J. Microsc.* 167:97–103

122. Preza, C., Miller, M. I., Thomas, L. J. Jr., McNally, J. G. 1992. Regularized linear method for reconstruction of three-dimensional microscopic objects from optical sections. *J. Opt. Soc. Am. A* 9:219–28

123. Rahman, N. A., Pecht, I., Roess, D. A., Barisas, B. G. 1992. Rotational dynamics of type-I Fc epsilon receptors on individually-selected rat mast cells studied by polarized fluorescence depletion. *Biophys. J.*61:334–46

124. Reed, T., Baldini, A., Rand, T. C., Ward, D. C. 1992. Simultaneous visualization of seven different DNA probes by in situ hybridization using combinatorial fluorescence and digital imaging microscopy. *Proc. Natl. Acad. Sci. USA* 89:1388–92

125. Reynolds, G. T., Taylor, D. L. 1980. Image intensification applied to light microscopy. *BioSci.* 30:586–92

126. Rigaut, J. P., Carvajal-Gonzalez, S., Vassy, J. 1991. Confocal image cytometry—quantitative analysis of three-dimensional images obtained by confocal scanning microscopy. See Ref. 62, pp. 109–33

127. Rigler, R., Ehrenberg, M. 1973. Molecular interactions and structure as analysed by fluorescence relaxation spectroscopy. *Q. Rev. Biophys.* 6:139–99

128. Robert-Nicoud, M., Arndt-Jovin, D., Schormann, T., Jovin, T. M. 1989. 3-D imaging of cells and tissues using confocal laser scanning microscopy and digital processing. *Eur. J. Cell Biol.* 48:49–52

129. Royer, C. A., Rusch, R. M., Scarlata, S. F. 1989. Salt effects on histone subunit interactions as studied by fluorescence spectroscopy. *Biochemistry* 28:6631–37

130. Salmon, E. D., Walker, R. A., Pryer, N. K. 1989. Video-enhanced differential interference contrast light microscopy. *BioTechniques* 7:624–33

131. Schnapp, B. J. 1987. Viewing single microtubules by video light microscopy. *Methods Enzym.* 134:561–73

132. Sheetz, M. P., Turney, S., Qian, H., Elson, E. L. 1989. Nanometre-level analysis demonstrates that lipid flow does not drive membrane glycoprotein movements. *Nature* 340:284–88

133. Shotton, D. M. 1988. Video-enhanced light microscopy and its applications in cell biology. *J. Cell Sci.* 89:129–50

134. Spring, K. R. 1990. Quantitative imaging at low light level: differential interference contrast and fluorescence microscopy without significant light loss. See Ref. 69, pp. 513–22

135. Spring, K. R., Smith, P. D. 1987. Illumination and detection systems for

quantitative fluorescence microscopy. *J. Microsc.* 147:265–78

136. Stryer, L. 1978. Fluorescence energy transfer as a spectroscopic ruler. *Annu. Rev. Biochem.* 47:819–46

137. Tanasugarn, L., McNeil, P., Reynolds, G. T., Taylor, D. L. 1984. Microspectrofluorometry by digital image processing: measurement of cytoplasmic pH. *J. Cell Biol.* 98:717–24

138. Tao, T. 1969. Time-dependent fluorescence depolarization and brownian rotational diffusion coefficients of macromolecules. *Biopolymers* 8:609–32

139. Taylor, D. L., Nederlof, M. A., Lanni, F., Waggoner, A. S. 1992. A new vision of light microscopy. *Am. Sci.* 80:322–35

140. Taylor, D. L., Reidler, J., Spudich, J., Stryer, L. 1981. Detection of actin assembly by fluorescence energy transfer. *J. Cell Biol.* 89:362–67

141. Taylor, D. L., Salmon, E. D. 1989. Basic fluorescence microscopy. See Ref. 161, pp. 208–37

142. Taylor, D. L., Waggoner, A. S., Murphy, R. F., Lanni, F., Birge, R. R., ed. 1986. *Applications of Fluorescence in the Biomedical Sciences.* New York: Liss. 639 pp.

143. Taylor, D. L., Wang, Y.-L. 1978. Molecular cytochemistry: incorporation of fluorescently labeled actin into living cells. *Proc. Natl. Acad. Sci. USA* 75:857–61

144. Taylor, D. L., Wang, Y.-L. 1980. Fluorescently labeled molecules as probes of the structure and function of living cells. *Nature* 284:405–10

145. Taylor, D. L., Wang, Y.-L. 1989. *Fluorescence Microscopy of Living Cells in Culture, Part B: Quantitative Fluorescence Microscopy -Imaging and Spectroscopy; Methods in Cell Biology,* Vol. 30, New York: Academic. 503 pp.

146. Taylor, D. L., Zeh, R. M. 1976. Methods for measurement of polarization optical properties 1. Birefringence. *J. Microsc.* 108:251–59

147. Theriot, J. A., Mitchison, T. J. 1991. Actin microfilament dynamics in locomoting cells. *Nature* 352:126–31

148. Tinoco, I., Mickols, W., Maestre, M. F., Bustamante, C. 1987. Absorption, scattering, and imaging of biomolecular structures with polarized light. *Annu. Rev. Biophys. Biophys. Chem.* 16:319–49

149. Tsay, T.-T., Inman, R., Wray, B. E., Herman, B., Jacobson, K. 1990. Characterization of low light level video cameras for fluorescence microscopy. See Ref. 69, pp. 219–33

150. Tsay, T.-T., Jacobson, K. A. 1991. Spatial Fourier analysis of video photobleaching measurements. Principles and optimization. *Biophys. J.* 59:360–68

151. Tsien, R. Y. 1983. Intracellular measurements of ion activities. *Annu. Rev. Biophys. Bioeng.* 12:91–116

152. Tsien, R. Y. 1989. Fluorescent probes of cell signaling. *Annu. Rev. Neurosci.* 12:227–53

153. Tsien, R. Y., Poenie, M. 1986. Fluorescence ratio imaging: a new window into intracellular ionic signalling. *Trends Biochem. Sci.* 11:450–55

154. Tsien, R. Y., Waggoner, A. S. 1990. Fluorophores for confocal microscopy: photophysics and photochemistry. See Ref. 120, pp. 169–78

155. Velez, M., Axelrod, D. 1988. Polarized fluorescence photobleaching recovery for measuring rotational diffusion in solutions and membranes. *Biophys. J.* 53:575–91

156. Waggoner, A. S. 1990. Fluorescent probes for cytometry. In *Flow Cytometry and Sorting,* ed. M. R. Melamed, T. Lindmo, M. L. Mendelsohn, pp. 209–225. New York: Wiley-Liss

157. Waggoner, A. S., DeBiasio, R., Conrad, P., Bright, G. R., Ernst, L., et al. 1989. Multiple spectral parameter imaging. See Ref. 145, pp. 449–78

158. Walker, R. A., Gliksman, N. R., Salmon, E. D. 1990. Using video-enhanced differential interference contrast microscopy to analyze the assembly dynamics of individual microtubules in real time. See Ref. 55, pp. 395–407

159. Wampler, J. E., ed. 1989. *New Methods in Microscopy and Low Light Imaging.* Proc. SPIE, Vol. 1161

160. Wampler, J. E., Furukawa, R., Fechheimer, M. 1990. Microspectrofluorometry for measuring intracellular pH of single cells. See Ref. 69, pp. 269–82

161. Wang, Y.-L., Taylor, D. L. 1989. *Fluorescence Microscopy of Living Cells in Culture, Part A: Fluorescent Analogs, Labeling Cells and Basic Microscopy; Methods in Cell Biology,* Vol. 29. New York: Academic. 333 pp.

162. Ware, B. R., Brvenik, L. J., Cummings, R. T., Furukawa, R. H., Krafft, G. A. 1986. Fluorescence photoactivation and dissipation. See Ref. 143, pp. 141–57

163. Webb, W. W. 1986. Light microscopy

- A modern renaissance. *Ann. NY Acad. Sci.* 483:387–91

164. Weiss, D. G. 1986. Visualization of the living cytoskeleton by video-enhanced microscopy and digital image processing. *J. Cell Sci. Suppl.* 5:1–15

165. Weiss, D. G., Galfe, G. 1991. Video-microscopic techniques to study the living cytoplasm. See Ref. 62, pp. 135–58

166. Wells, K. S., Sandison, D. R., Strickler, J., Webb, W. W. 1989. Quantitative fluorescence imaging with laser scanning confocal microscopy. See Ref. 120, pp. 23–35

167. Wessel, J. 1985. Surface-enhanced optical microscopy. *J. Opt. Soc. Am. B.* 2:1538–41

168. White, J. G., Amos, W. B., Fordham, M. 1987. An evaluation of confocal versus conventional imaging of biological structures by fluorescence light microscopy. *J. Cell Biol.* 105:41–48

169. Wijnaendts van Resandt, R. W., Marsman, H. J. B., Kaplan, R., Davoust, J., Stelzer, E. H. K., Stricker, R. 1985. Optical fluorescence microscopy in three dimensions: microtomoscopy. *J. Microsc.* 138:29–34

170. Williams, D. A., Fogarty, K. E., Tsien, R. Y., Fay, F. S. 1985. Calcium gradients in single smooth muscle cells revealed by the digital image microscope using Fura-2. *Nature* 318:558–60

171. Willingham, M. C., Pastan, I. H. 1978. The visualization of fluorescent proteins in living cells by video intensification microscopy (VIM). *Cell* 13:501–7

172. Wilson, T., Sheppard, C. 1984. *Theory and Practice of Scanning Optical Microscopy.* New York: Academic. 213 pp.

173. Wolf, D. E. 1989. Designing, building, and using a fluorescence recovery after photobleaching instrument. See Ref. 145, pp. 271–306

174. Wright, S. J., Walker, J. S., Schatten, H., Simerly, C., McCarthy. J. J., Schatten. G. 1989. Confocal fluorescence microscopy with the tandem scanning light microscope. *Cell Sci.* 94: 617–24

175. Xiao, G. Q., Corle, T. R., Kino, G. S. 1988. Real-time confocal scanning optical microscope. *Appl. Phys. Lett.* 53:716–18

176. Yamamoto, K., Taira, A. 1983. Some improvements in the phase contrast microscope. *J. Microsc.* 129:49–62

177. Yelamarti, R. V., Cheung, J. Y. 1992. Measurement of intracellular calcium gradients in single cells using optical sectioning microscopy. See Ref. 1, pp. 606–16

178. Young, I. T. 1989. Image fidelity: characterizing the imaging transfer function. See Ref. 143, pp. 1–45

179. Yoshida, T. M., Zarrin, F., Barisas, B. G. 1988. Measurement of protein rotational motion using frequency domain polarized fluorescence depletion. *Biophys. J.* 54:277–88

180. Zemike, F. 1958. The wave theory of microscopic image formation. In *Concepts of Classical Optics,* ed. J. Strong, pp. 525–36. San Francisco: Freeman

SUBJECT INDEX

CUMULATIVE INDEXES

CONTRIBUTING AUTHORS, VOLUMES 51–55

CHAPTER TITLES, VOLUMES 51–55

ANNUAL REVIEWS INC.

a nonprofit scientific publisher
4139 El Camino Way
P. O. Box 10139
Palo Alto, CA 94303-0897 • USA

Annual Reviews Inc. publications may be ordered directly from our office; through booksellers and subscription agents, worldwide; and through participating professional societies. **Prices are subject to change without notice.** California Corp. #161041 • ARI Federal I.D. #94-1156476

- **Individual Buyers:** Prepayment required on new accounts by check or money order (in U.S. dollars, check drawn on U.S. bank) or charge to MasterCard, VISA, or American Express.

- **Institutional Buyers:** Please include purchase order.

- **Students/Recent Graduates:** $10.00 discount from retail price, per volume. Discount does not apply to Special Publications, standing orders, or institutional buyers. **Requirements:** [1] be a degree candidate at, or a graduate within the past three years from, an accredited institution; [2] present proof of status (photocopy of your student I.D. or proof of date of graduation); [3] Order direct from Annual Reviews; [4] prepay.

- **Professional Society Members:** Societies that have a contractual arrangement with Annual Reviews offer our books to members at reduced rates. Check your society for information.

- **California orders** must add applicable sales tax.

- **Canadian orders** must add 7% General Sales Tax. GST Registration #R 121 449-029. Now you can also telephone orders Toll Free from anywhere in Canada (see below).

- **Telephone orders,** paid by credit card, welcomed. **Call Toll Free 1-800-523-8635** from anywhere in USA or Canada. From elsewhere call 415-493-4400, Ext. 1 (not toll free). Monday – Friday, 8:00 am – 4:00 pm, Pacific Time. Students or recent graduates ordering by telephone must supply (by FAX or mail) proof of status if current proof is not on file at Annual Reviews. Written confirmation required on purchase orders from universities before shipment.

- **FAX: 415-855-9815 – 24 hours a day.**

- **Postage paid** by Annual Reviews (4th class bookrate). UPS ground service (within continental U.S.) available at $2.00 extra per book. UPS air service or Airmail also available at cost. UPS requires a street address. P.O. Box, APO, FPO, not acceptable.

- **Regular Orders:** Please list below the volumes you wish to order by volume number.

- **Standing Orders:** New volume in series is sent automatically each year upon publication. Please indicate volume number to begin the standing order. Each year you can save 10% by prepayment of standing-order invoices sent 90 days prior to the publication date. Cancellation may be made at any time.

- **Prepublication Orders:** Volumes not yet published will be shipped in month and year indicated

- **We do not ship on approval.**

ANNUAL REVIEWS SERIES *Volumes not listed are no longer in print*	Prices, postpaid, per volume. USA / other countries (incl. Canada)	Regular Order Please send Volume(s):	Standing Order Begin with Volume:
Annual Review of **ANTHROPOLOGY**			
Vols. 1-20 (1972-1991)	$41.00/$46.00		
Vol. 21 (1992)	$44.00/$49.00		
Vol. 22 (avail. Oct. 1993)	$44.00/$49.00	Vol(s). _____	Vol._____
Annual Review of **ASTRONOMY AND ASTROPHYSICS**			
Vols. 1, 5-14 (1963, 1967-1976)			
16-29 (1978-1991)	$53.00/$58.00		
Vol. 30 (1992)	$57.00/$62.00		
Vol. 31 (avail. Sept. 1993)	$57.00/$62.00	Vol(s). _____	Vol._____
Annual Review of **BIOCHEMISTRY**			
Vols. 30-34, 36-60 (1961-1965, 1967-1991)	$41.00/$47.00		
Vol. 61 (1992)	$46.00/$52.00		
Vol. 62 (avail. July 1993)	$46.00/$52.00	Vol(s). _____	Vol._____

ANNUAL REVIEWS SERIES *Volumes not listed are no longer in print*	Prices, postpaid, per volume. USA / other countries (incl. Canada)	Regular Order Please send Volume(s):	Standing Order Begin with Volume:

Annual Review of **BIOPHYSICS AND BIOMOLECULAR STRUCTURE**

Vols. 1-20	(1972-1991)............................ $55.00/$60.00		
Vol. 21	(1992)..................................... $59.00/$64.00		
Vol. 22	(avail. June 1993)................... $59.00/$64.00	Vol(s). _____	Vol._____

Annual Review of **CELL BIOLOGY**

Vols. 1-7	(1985-1991)............................ $41.00/$46.00		
Vol. 8	(1992)..................................... $46.00/$51.00		
Vol. 9	(avail. Nov. 1993)................... $46.00/$51.00	Vol(s). _____	Vol._____

Annual Review of **COMPUTER SCIENCE**

Vols. 1-2	(1986-1987)............................ $41.00/$46.00		
Vols. 3-4	(1998-1989/1990)................... $47.00/$52.00	Vol(s). _____	Vol._____

Series suspended until further notice. Purchase the complete set for the special promotional price of $100.00 USA / $115.00 other countries, when all four volumes are ordered at the same time. Orders at the special price must be prepaid.

Annual Review of **EARTH AND PLANETARY SCIENCES**

Vols. 1-19	(1973-1991)............................ $55.00/$60.00		
Vol. 20	(1992)..................................... $59.00/$64.00		
Vol. 21	(avail. May 1993)................... $59.00/$64.00	Vol(s). _____	Vol._____

Annual Review of **ECOLOGY AND SYSTEMATICS**

Vols. 2-12, 14-22	(1971-1981, 1983-1991)......... $40.00/$45.00		
Vol. 23	(1992)..................................... $44.00/$49.00		
Vol. 24	(avail. Nov. 1993)................... $44.00/$49.00	Vol(s). _____	Vol._____

Annual Review of **ENERGY AND THE ENVIRONMENT**

Vols. 1-16	(1976-1991)............................ $64.00/$69.00		
Vol. 17	(1992)..................................... $68.00/$73.00		
Vol. 18	(avail. Oct. 1993)................... $68.00/$73.00	Vol(s). _____	Vol._____

Annual Review of **ENTOMOLOGY**

Vols. 10-16, 18	(1965-1971, 1973)		
20-36	(1975-1991)............................ $40.00/$45.00		
Vol. 37	(1992) .... $44.00/$49.00		
Vol. 38	(avail. Jan. 1993) .... $44.00/$49.00	Vol(s). _____	Vol._____

Annual Review of **FLUID MECHANICS**

Vols. 2-4, 7, 9-11	(1970-1972, 1975, 1977-1979)		
14-23	(1982-1991) .... $40.00/$45.00		
Vol. 24	(1992) .... $44.00/$49.00		
Vol. 25	(avail. Jan. 1993) .... $44.00/$49.00	Vol(s). _____	Vol._____

Annual Review of **GENETICS**

Vols. 1-12, 14-25	(1967-1978, 1980-1991) .... $40.00/$45.00		
Vol. 26	(1992)..................................... $44.00/$49.00		
Vol. 27	(avail. Dec. 1993).................... $44.00/$49.00	Vol(s). _____	Vol._____

Annual Review of **IMMUNOLOGY**

Vols. 1-9	(1983-1991) .... $41.00/$46.00		
Vol. 10	(1992) .... $45.00/$50.00		
Vol. 11	(avail. April 1993) .... $45.00/$50.00	Vol(s). _____	Vol._____

Annual Review of **MATERIALS SCIENCE**

Vols. 1, 3-19	(1971, 1973-1989)................... $68.00/$73.00		
Vols. 20-22	(1990-1992) .... $72.00/$77.00		
Vol. 23	(avail. Aug. 1993) .... $72.00/$77.00	Vol(s). _____	Vol._____